G000139145

*Dear Reader*

*I was born in 1898. During my hundred years as Bibendum I have accompanied you all over the world, attentive to your safety while travelling and your comfort and enjoyment on and off the road.*

*The knowledge and experience I acquire each year is summarised for you in the Red Guide.*

*In this, the 17 th edition, I offer some advice to help you find good food at moderate prices: look for the many restaurants identified by my red face,* **"Bib Gourmand"***!*

*I look forward to receiving your comments...*

*I remain at your service for a new century of discoveries.*

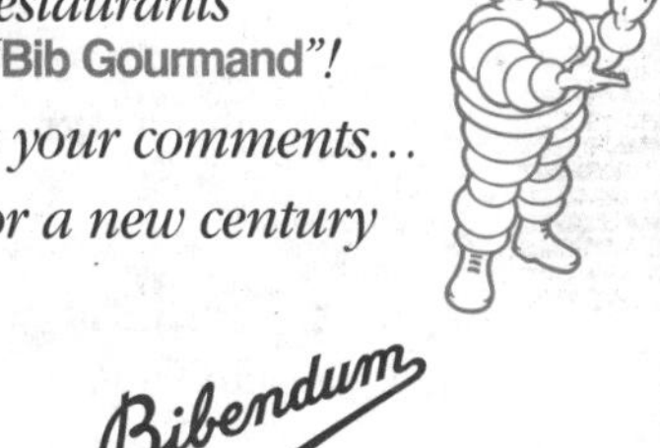

*Bibendum*

# *Contents*

*In addition to those situated in the main cities, restaurants renowned for their excellent cuisine will be found in the towns printed in light type in the list above.*

# *Dear Reader*

*With the aim of giving the maximum amount of information in a limited number of pages Michelin has adopted a system of symbols which is renowned the world over.*
*Failing this system the present publication would run to six volumes.*
*Judge for yourselves by comparing the descriptive text below with the equivalent extract from the Guide in symbol form.*

---

**La Résidence** (Paul) , 09 18 21 32 43,
*Fax 09 18 21 32 49,* lake, « Flowered garden »,
 -  . AE E JCB BX **a**
*March-November* – **Meals** *(closed Sunday)* 350/650 –
 75 – **25 rm** 500/800.
**Spec.** Goujonnettes de sole. Poulet aux écrevisses. Profiteroles.
**Wines.** Vouvray, Bourgueil.

*This demonstration clearly shows that each entry contains a great deal of information. The symbols are easily learnt and knowing them will enable you to understand the Guide and to choose those establishments that you require.*

---

*A very comfortable hotel where you will enjoy a pleasant stay and be tempted to prolong your visit.*
*The excellence of the cuisine, which is personally supervised by the proprietor Mr Paul, is worth a detour on your journey.*
*The hotel is in a quiet secluded setting, away from built-up areas.*
*To reserve phone 09 18 21 32 43 ; the Fax number is 09 18 21 32 49.*
*The hotel affords a fine view of the lake ; in good weather it is possible to eat out doors.*
*The hotel is enhanced by an attractive flowered garden and has an indoor swimming pool and a private tennis court. Smoking is not allowed in certain areas of the hotel. Direct dialling telephone in room.*
*Parking facilities, under cover, are available to hotel guests.*
*The hotel accepts payment by American Express, Eurocard and Japan Credit Bureau credit cards.*
*Letters giving the location of the hotel on the town plan :* BX **a**.
*The hotel is open from March to November but the restaurant closes every Sunday.*
*The set meal prices range from 350 F for the lowest to 650 F for the highest.*
*The cost of continental breakfast served in the bedroom is 75 F.*
*25 bedroomed hotel. The charges vary from 500 F for a single to 800 F for the best double or twin bedded room.*
*Included for the gourmet are some culinary specialities, recommended by the hotelier : Strips of deep-fried sole fillets, Chicken with crayfish, Choux pastry balls filled with ice cream and covered with chocolate sauce.*
*In addition to the best quality wines you will find many of the local wines worth sampling : Vouvray, Bourgueil.*

# Hotels, Restaurants

## Categories, standard of comfort

| | | |
|---|---|---|
| 🏨🏨🏨🏨🏨 | XXXXX | *Luxury in the traditional style* |
| 🏨🏨🏨🏨 | XXXX | *Top class comfort* |
| 🏨🏨🏨 | XXX | *Very comfortable* |
| 🏨🏨 | XX | *Comfortable* |
| 🏨 | X | *Quite comfortable* |
| | 🍺 | *Traditional pubs serving food* |
| M | | *In its class, hotel with modern amenities* |

## Atmosphere and setting

| | |
|---|---|
| 🏨🏨🏨🏨🏨 ... 🏨 | *Pleasant hotels* |
| XXXXX ... X | *Pleasant restaurants* |
| « Park » | *Particularly attractive feature* |
| | *Very quiet or quiet secluded hotel* |
| | *Quiet hotel* |
| < sea, ✱ | *Exceptional view, Panoramic view* |
| < | *Interesting or extensive view* |

## Cuisine

| | |
|---|---|
| ✿✿✿ | *Exceptional cuisine in the country, worth a special journey* |
| ✿✿ | *Excellent cooking : worth a detour* |
| ✿ | *A very good restaurant in its category* |
| Meals | *The* **"Bib Gourmand"** *:* *Good food at moderate prices* |

## Hotel facilities

30 rm — *Number of rooms*

*Lift (elevator) – Television in room*

*Non-smoking areas*

*Air conditioning*

*Telephone in room: direct dialling for outside calls*

*Minitel – modem point in the bedrooms*

*Tennis court(s) – Outdoor or indoor swimming pool*

*Sauna – Exercise room*

*Garden – Beach with bathing facilities*

*Meals served in garden or on terrace*

*Landing stage*

*Garage – Car park*

*Bedrooms accessible to disabled people*

150 — *Equipped conference room : maximum capacity*

*Dogs are not allowed*

without rest. — *The hotel has no restaurant*

## Prices

*These prices are given in the currency of the country in question. Valid for 1998 the rates shown should only vary if the cost of living changes to any great extent.*

### Meals

**Meals** 130/260 — *Set meal prices*

**Meals** a la carte 160/290 — *"a la carte" meal prices*

b.i. — *House wine included*

*Table wine available by the carafe*

### Hotels

**30 rm** 305/500 — *Lowest price for a comfortable single and highest price for the best double room.*

**30 rm** 345/580 — *Price includes breakfast*

### Breakfast

55 — *Price of breakfast*

### Credit cards

JCB VISA — *Credit cards accepted*

## Service and Taxes

*Except in Finland, Greece, Hungary and Spain, prices shown are inclusive, that is to say service and V.A.T. included. In the U.K. and Ireland, s = service only included, t = V.A.T. only included. In Italy, when not included, a percentage for service is shown after the meal prices, eg. (16 %).*

# *Town Plans*

## Main conventional signs

|  |  |
|---|---|
| | *Tourist Information Centre* |
| a | *Hotel, restaurant – Reference letter on the town plan* |
| | *Place of interest and its main entrance* } *Reference letter on the town plan* |
| B | *Interesting church or chapel* } *Reference letter on the town plan* |
| Thiers (R.) P | *Shopping street – Public car park* |
| | *Tram* |
| | *Underground station* |
| | *One-way street* |
| | *Church or chapel* |
| | *Poste restante, telegraph – Telephone* |
| | *Public buildings located by letters :* |
| POL T M | *Police (in large towns police headquaters) – Theatre – Museum* |
| | *Coach station – Airport – Hospital – Covered market* |
| | *Ruins – Monument, statue – Fountain* |
| | *Garden, park, wood – Cemetery, Jewish cemetery* |
| | *Outdoor or indoor swimming pool – Racecourse* |
| 18 | *Golf course* |
| | *Cable-car – Funicular* |
| | *Sports ground, stadium – View – Panorama* |

*Names shown on the street plans are in the language of the country to conform to local signposting.*

## Sights

| | |
|---|---|
| ★★★ | *Worth a journey* |
| ★★ | *Worth a detour* |
| ★ | *Interesting* |

# *Ami lecteur*

*C'est en 1898 que je suis né. Voici donc cent ans que, sous le nom de Bibendum, je vous accompagne sur toutes les routes du monde, soucieux du confort de votre conduite, de la sécurité de votre déplacement, de l'agrément de vos étapes.*

*L'expérience et le savoir-faire que j'ai acquis, c'est au Guide Rouge que je les confie chaque année.*

*Et dans cette 17e édition, pour trouver de bonnes adresses à petits prix, un conseil : suivez donc les nombreux restaurants que vous signale mon visage de* **"Bib Gourmand"** *!*

*N'hésitez pas à m'écrire...*

*Je reste à votre service pour un nouveau siècle de découvertes.*

*En toute confiance.*

*Bibendum*

# *Hôtels, Restaurants*

## Classe et confort

*Grand luxe et tradition*
*Grand confort*
*Très confortable*
*Bon confort*
*Assez confortable*
*Traditionnel "pub" anglais servant des repas*
M *Dans sa catégorie, hôtel d'équipement moderne*

## L'agrément

... *Hôtels agréables*
... *Restaurants agréables*
« Park » *Élément particulièrement agréable*
*Hôtel très tranquille, ou isolé et tranquille*
*Hôtel tranquille*
sea, *Vue exceptionnelle, panorama*
*Vue intéressante ou étendue*

## La table

*Une des meilleures tables du pays, vaut le voyage*
*Table excellente, mérite un détour*
*Une très bonne table dans sa catégorie*
Meals *Le* **"Bib Gourmand"** *:*
*Repas soignés à prix modérés*

## L'installation

| | |
|---|---|
| 30 rm | *Nombre de chambres* |
| | *Ascenseur – Télévision dans la chambre* |
| | *Non-fumeurs* |
| | *Air conditionné* |
| | *Téléphone dans la chambre direct avec l'extérieur* |
| | *Prise Modem – Minitel dans la chambre* |
| | *Tennis – Piscine : de plein air ou couverte* |
| | *Sauna – Salle de remise en forme* |
| | *Jardin – Plage aménagée* |
| | *Repas servis au jardin ou en terrasse* |
| | *Ponton d'amarrage* |
| P P P | *Garage – Parc à voitures* |
| | *Chambres accessibles aux handicapés physiques* |
| 150 | *Salles de conférences : capacité maximum* |
| | *Accès interdit aux chiens* |
| without rest. | *L'hôtel n'a pas de restaurant* |

## Les prix

*Les prix sont indiqués dans la monnaie du pays. Établis pour l'année 1998, ils ne doivent être modifiés que si le coût de la vie subit des variations importantes.*

### Au restaurant

| | |
|---|---|
| **Meals** 130/260 | *Prix des repas à prix fixes* |
| **Meals** à la carte 160/290 | *Prix des repas à la carte* |
| b.i. | *Boisson comprise* |
| | *Vin de table en carafe* |

### A l'hôtel

| | |
|---|---|
| **30 rm** 305/500 | *Prix minimum pour une chambre d'une personne et maximum pour la plus belle chambre occupée par deux personnes* |
| **30 rm** 345/580 | *Prix des chambres petit déjeuner compris* |

### Petit déjeuner

| | |
|---|---|
| 55 | *Prix du petit déjeuner* |

### Cartes de crédit

| | |
|---|---|
| AE GB JCB VISA | *Cartes de crédit acceptées* |

## Service et taxes

*A l'exception de la Finlande, de la Grèce, de la Hongrie et de l'Espagne, les prix indiqués sont nets.*
*Au Royaume Uni et en Irlande,* **s** *= service compris,* **t** *= T.V.A. comprise. En Italie, le service est parfois compté en supplément aux prix des repas. Ex. : (16 %).*

# Les Plans

## Principaux signes conventionnels

*Information touristique*
*Hôtel, restaurant – Lettre les repérant sur le plan*
*Monument intéressant et entrée principale* } *Lettre les repérant sur le plan*
*Église ou chapelle intéressante*
Thiers (R.) *Rue commerçante – Parc de stationnement public*
*Tramway*
*Station de métro*
*Sens unique*
*Église ou chapelle*
*Poste restante, télégraphe – Téléphone*
*Édifices publics repérés par des lettres :*
POL T M *Police (dans les grandes villes commissariat central) – Théâtre – Musée*
*Gare routière – Aéroport – Hôpital – Marché couvert*
*Ruines – Monument, statue – Fontaine*
*Jardin, parc, bois – Cimetière, Cimetière israélite*
*Piscine de plein air, couverte – Hippodrome – Golf*
*Téléphérique – Funiculaire*
*Stade – Vue – Panorama*

*Les indications portées sur les plans sont dans la langue du pays, en conformité avec la dénomination locale.*

## Les curiosités

★★★ *Vaut le voyage*
★★ *Mérite un détour*
★ *Intéressante*

# Lieber Leser

*Im Jahre 1898 habe ich das Licht der Welt erblickt. So bin ich schon seit hundert Jahren als Bibendum Ihr treuer Wegbegleiter auf all Ihren Reisen und sorge für Ihre Sicherheit während der Fahrt und für Ihre Bequemlichkeit bei Ihren Aufenthalten in Hotels und Restaurants.*

*Es sind meine Erfahrungen und mein Know how, die alljährlich in den Roten Hotelführer einfliessen.*

*Um in dieser 17. Ausgabe gute Restaurants mit kleinen Preisen zu finden, hier mein Typ: folgenSie meinem fröhlichen* **"Bib Gourmand"** *Gesicht, es wird Ihnen den Weg zu zahlreichen Restaurants mir besonders günstigem Preis-/Leistungsverhältnis weisen !*

*Ihre Kommentare sind uns jederzeit herzlich willkommen.*

*Stets zu Diensten im Hinblick auf ein neues Jahrhundert voller Entdeckungen.*

*Mit freundlichen Grüssen*

*Bibendum*

# *Hotels, Restaurants*

## Klasseneinteilung und Komfort

*Großer Luxus und Tradition*
*Großer Komfort*
*Sehr komfortabel*
*Mit gutem Komfort*
*Mit Standard-Komfort*
*Traditionelle Pubs die Spiesen anbieten*
M *Moderne Einrichtung*

## Annehmlichkeiten

*Angenehme Hotels*
*Angenehme Restaurants*
« Park » *Besondere Annehmlichkeit*
*Sehr ruhiges oder abgelegenes und ruhiges Hotel*
*Ruhiges Hotel*
sea, *Reizvolle Aussicht, Rundblick*
*Interessante oder weite Sicht*

## Küche

*Eine der besten Küchen des Landes : eine Reise wert*
*Eine hervorragende Küche : verdient einen Umweg*
*Eine sehr gute Küche : verdient Ihre besondere Beachtung*
Meals *Der* **"Bib Gourmand"** *:*
*Sorgfältig zubereitete preiswerte Mahlzeiten*

## Einrichtung

| | |
|---|---|
| **30 rm** | *Anzahl der Zimmer* |
| | *Fahrstuhl – Fernsehen im Zimmer* |
| | *Nichtraucher – Klimaanlage* |
| | *Zimmertelefon mit direkter Außenverbindung* |
| | *Minitel Anschluß im Zimmer* |
| | *Tennis – Freibad – Hallenbad* |
| | *Sauna – Fitneßraum* |
| | *Garten – Strandbad* |
| | *Garten-, Terrassenrestaurant* |
| | *Bootssteg* |
| | *Garage – Parkplatz* |
| | *Für Körperbehinderte leicht zugängliche Zimmer* |
| 150 | *Konferenzräume mit Höchstkapazität* |
| | *Hunde sind unerwünscht* |
| without rest. | *Hotel ohne Restaurant* |

## Die Preise

*Die Preise sind in der jeweiligen Landeswährung angegeben. Sie gelten für das Jahr 1998 und ändern sich nur bei starken Veränderungen der Lebenshaltungskosten.*

### Im Restaurant

| | |
|---|---|
| **Meals** 130/260 | *Feste Menupreise* |
| **Meals** à la carte 160/290 | *Mahlzeiten "a la carte"* |
| b.i. | *Getränke inbegriffen* |
| | *Preiswerter Wein in Karaffen* |

### Im Hotel

| | |
|---|---|
| **30 rm** 305/500 | *Mindestpreis für ein Einzelzimmer und Höchstpreis für das schönste Doppelzimmer für zwei Personen.* |
| **30 rm** 345/580 | *Zimmerpreis inkl. Frühstück* |

### Frühstück

| | |
|---|---|
| 55 | *Preis des Frühstücks* |

### Kreditkarten

| | |
|---|---|
| AE JCB VISA | *Akzeptierte Kreditkarten* |

## Bedienungsgeld und Gebühren

*Mit Ausnahme von Finnland, Griechenland, Ungarn und Spanien sind die angegebenen Preise Inklusivpreise. In den Kapiteln über Großbritannien und Irland bedeutet s = Bedienungsgeld inbegriffen, t = MWSt inbegriffen. In Italien wird für die Bedienung gelegentlich ein Zuschlag zum Preis der Mahlzeit erhoben, zB (16 %).*

# Stadtpläne

## Erklärung der wichtigsten Zeichen

- *Informationsstelle*
- a — *Hotel, Restaurant – Referenzbuchstabe auf dem Plan*
- *Sehenswertes Gebäude mit Haupteingang* } *Referenzbuchstabe auf dem Plan*
- B — *Sehenswerte Kirche oder Kapelle* } *Referenzbuchstabe auf dem Plan*
- Thiers (R.) P — *Einkaufsstraße – Parkplatz, Parkhaus*
- *Straßenbahn*
- *U-Bahnstation*
- *Einbahnstraße*
- *Kirche oder Kapelle*
- *Postlagernde Sendungen, Telegraph – Telefon*
- *Öffentliche Gebäude, durch Buchstaben gekennzeichnet :*
- POL T M — *Polizei (in größeren Städten Polizeipräsidium) – Theater – Museum*
- *Autobusbahnhof – Flughafen*
- *Krankenhaus – Markthalle*
- *Ruine – Denkmal, Statue – Brunnen*
- *Garten, Park, Wald – Friedhof, Jüd. Friedhof*
- *Freibad – Hallenbad – Pferderennbahn*
- 18 — *Golfplatz und Lochzahl*
- *Seilschwebebahn – Standseilbahn*
- *Sportplatz – Aussicht – Rundblick*

*Die Angaben auf den Stadtplänen erfolgen, übereinstimmend mit der örtlichen Beschilderung, in der Landessprache.*

## Sehenswürdigkeiten

- ★★★ *Eine Reise wert*
- ★★ *Verdient einen Umweg*
- ★ *Sehenswert*

# 読者のみなさまへ

わたしの名はビバンダム
（通称ビブ）、1898年の生まれです。
この100年、安全なドライブと
快適な宿泊、そしておいしい
料理など、世界各地の旅の情報を
お届けしてきました。

これまでのわたしの旅の経験と
知識とがふんだんに盛り込まれて
いるもの、それが毎年発行される
この『レッドガイド』です。

この第17版でも、手頃な値段で、
おいしい食事のレストランを
見つけていただけるよう、
お手伝いを致します。わたしの
赤い顔マーク、**“Bib Gourmand”!**
（ビブ・グルマン／食い道楽のビブ）が
目印です。

この本に挟みこまれているレターで
みなさまのご感想をお寄せください。

これからの新しい100年もまた、
お役に立てることを願っています。

ビバンダム

# ホテル　レストラン

## 等級と快適さ

| | | |
|---|---|---|
| | XXXXX | 豪華で伝統的様式 |
| | XXXX | トップクラス |
| | XXX | たいへん快適 |
| | XX | 快適 |
| | X | 割に快適 |
| | | 食事もできる伝統的なパブ |
| M | | 等級内での近代的設備のホテル |

## 居心地

| | |
|---|---|
| ... | 居心地よいホテル |
| XXXXX ... X | 居心地よいレストラン |
| « Park » | 特に魅力的な特徴 |
| | 大変静かなホテルまたは人里離れた静かなホテル |
| | 静かなホテル |
| sea, | 見晴らしがよい展望（例：海)、パノラマ |
| | 素晴らしい風景 |

## 料理

| | |
|---|---|
| ✿✿✿ | 最上の料理、出かける価値あり |
| ✿✿ | 素晴らしい料理、寄り道の価値あり |
| ✿ | 等級内では大変おいしい料理 |
| Meals | **"Bib Gourmand"!**：手頃な値段でおいしい料理 |

# 設備

| | |
|---|---|
| **30 rm** | ルームナンバー |
| | エレベーター、室内テレビ |
| | 非喫煙室 |
| | 空調設備 |
| | 室内に電話あり、外線直通 |
| | ミニテル／モデムの回線付き |
| | テニスコート。室外プール。室内プール。 |
| | サウナ。トレーニングルーム。 |
| | くつろげる庭。整備された海水浴場 |
| | 食事が庭またはテラスでできる。 |
| | 専用桟橋のあるホテル |
| | 駐車場、パーキング。 |
| | 体の不自由な方のための設備あり |
| 150 | 会議又は研修会の出来るホテル |
| | 犬の連れ込みおことわり |
| without rest. | レストランの無いホテル |

# 料金

料金は1998年のその国の貨幣単位で示してありますが、物価の変動などで変わる場合もあります。

## レストラン

| | |
|---|---|
| **Meals** 130/260<br>**Meals** à la carte 160/290 | 定食、ア・ラ・カルトそれぞれの最低料金と最高料金。 |
| b.i. | 飲食付 |
| | デカンター入りデーブルワイン有ります。 |

## ホテル

| | |
|---|---|
| **30 rm** 305/500 | 一人都室の最低料金と二人都室の最高料金。 |
| **30 rm** 345/580 | 朝食代は含まれています |

## 朝食

| | |
|---|---|
| 55 | 朝食代 |

## クレジット・カード

| | |
|---|---|
| JCB VISA | クレジット・カード使用可 |

# サービス料と税金

フィンランド、ギリシャ、スペイン以外の国に関しては正価料金。英国及びアイルランドでは、s.：サービス料込み、t.：付加価 値税込み、を意味する。イタリアでは、サービス料が料金に加算されることがある。例：（16%）

# 地図

## 主な記号

| | |
|---|---|
| i | ツーリストインフォメーション |
| □ ⓐ ● ● a | ホテル・レストラン ＿ 地図上での目印番号 |
| | 興味深い歴史的建造物と、その中央入口 } 地図上での |
| B | 興味深い教会または聖堂 } 目印番号 |
| Thiers (R.) P | 商店街　公共駐車場 |
| | 路面電車 |
| ● | 地下鉄駅 |
| → ► | 一方通行路 |
| | 教会または聖堂 ＿ 局留郵便、電報 ＿ 電話 |
| | 公共建造物、記号は下記の通り |
| POL T M | 警察（大都市では、中央警察書）＿ 劇場 ＿ 美術観、博物館 |
| | 長距離バス発着所 ＿ 空港 ＿ 病院 ＿ 屋内市場 |
| ∴ ■ ◎ | 遺跡 ＿ 歴史的建造物、像 ＿ 泉 |
| | 庭園、公園、森林 ＿ 墓地 ＿ ユダヤ教の墓地 |
| 18 | 屋外プール、屋内プール ＿ 競馬場 ＿ ゴルフ場 |
| | ロープウェイ ＿ ケーブルカー |
| | スタジアム ＿ 風景 ＿ パノラマ |

地図上の名称は、地方の標識に合わせてその国の言葉で表記されています。

# 名所

| | |
|---|---|
| ★★★ | 出かける価値あり |
| ★★ | 立ち寄る価値あり |
| ★ | 興味深い |

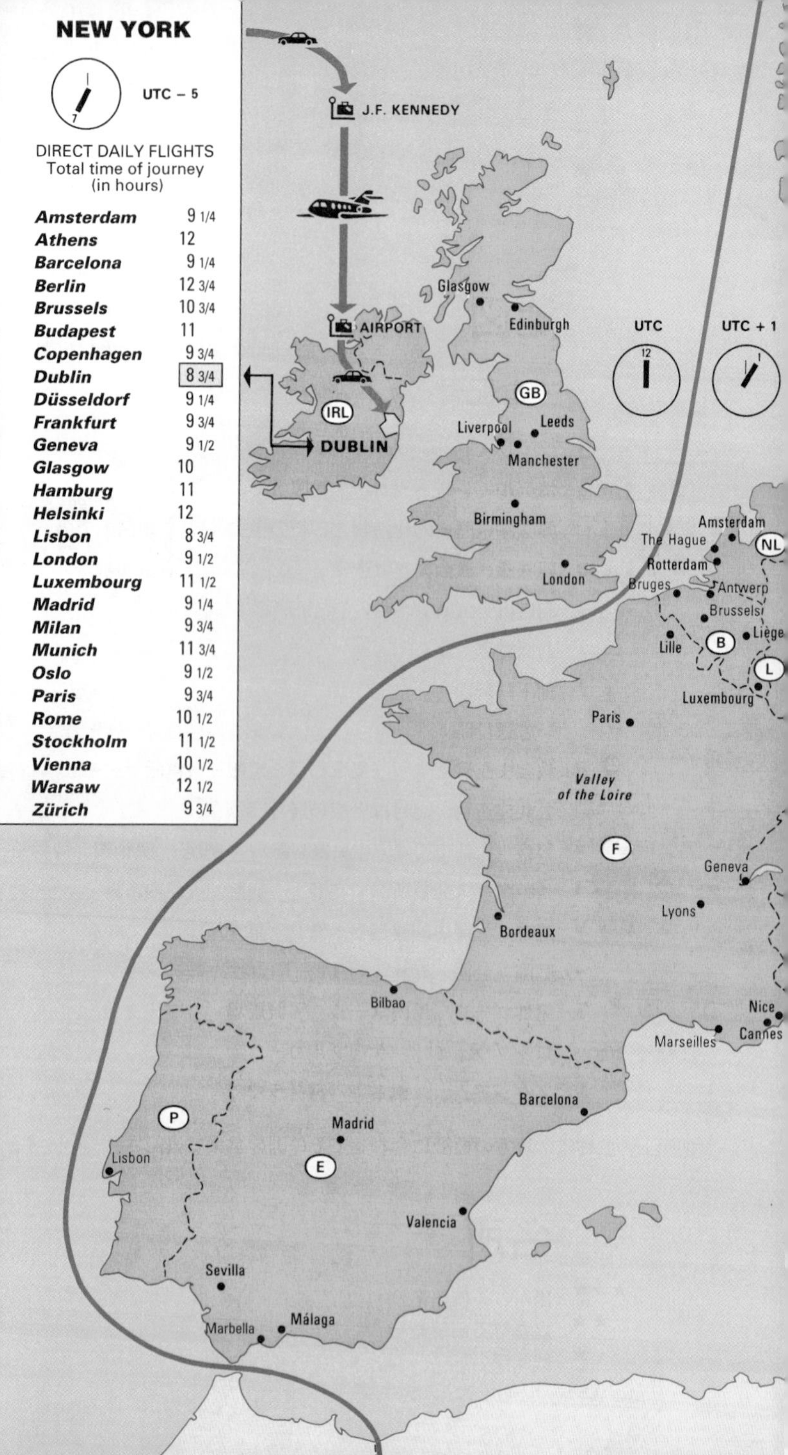

## NEW YORK

UTC – 5

DIRECT DAILY FLIGHTS
Total time of journey
(in hours)

| | |
|---|---|
| **Amsterdam** | 9 1/4 |
| **Athens** | 12 |
| **Barcelona** | 9 1/4 |
| **Berlin** | 12 3/4 |
| **Brussels** | 10 3/4 |
| **Budapest** | 11 |
| **Copenhagen** | 9 3/4 |
| **Dublin** | 8 3/4 |
| **Düsseldorf** | 9 1/4 |
| **Frankfurt** | 9 3/4 |
| **Geneva** | 9 1/2 |
| **Glasgow** | 10 |
| **Hamburg** | 11 |
| **Helsinki** | 12 |
| **Lisbon** | 8 3/4 |
| **London** | 9 1/2 |
| **Luxembourg** | 11 1/2 |
| **Madrid** | 9 1/4 |
| **Milan** | 9 3/4 |
| **Munich** | 11 3/4 |
| **Oslo** | 9 1/2 |
| **Paris** | 9 3/4 |
| **Rome** | 10 1/2 |
| **Stockholm** | 11 1/2 |
| **Vienna** | 10 1/2 |
| **Warsaw** | 12 1/2 |
| **Zürich** | 9 3/4 |

UTC + 2
FIN
Helsinki
N
Oslo
S
Stockholm
Gothenburg
DK
Copenhagen
Hamburg
Berlin
Hanover
Warsaw
PL
Leipzig
Düsseldorf
Dresden
Cologne
D
Prague
CZ
Frankfurt
Stuttgart
Vienna
Strasbourg
Munich
Salzburg
Budapest
A
Basle
Zürich
Innsbruck
H
CH
Berne
Venice
Milan
Turin
Florence
Monaco
I
Rome
Naples
GR
Athens
Palermo
Taormina
A Austria
B Belgium
CH Switzerland
CZ Czech Republic
D Germany
DK Denmark
E Spain
F France
FIN Finland
GB United Kingdom
GR Greece
H Hungary
I Italy
IRL Ireland
L Luxembourg
N Norway
NL Netherlands
PL Poland
P Portugal
S Sweden

# DISTANCES BY ROAD

*(in kilometres)*

| | Amsterdam | Athens | Barcelona | Berlin | Berne | Bordeaux | Brussels | Budapest | Cologne | Copenhagen | Dublin | Edinburgh | Frankfurt | Geneva | Hamburg | Helsinki | Lisbon | London | Luxembourg | Lyons | Madrid | Manchester | Marseilles | Milan | Munich | Oslo | Paris | Prague | Rome | Stockholm | Strasbourg | Stuttgart | Venice | Vienna | Warsaw |
|---|---|---|---|---|---|---|---|---|---|---|---|---|---|---|---|---|---|---|---|---|---|---|---|---|---|---|---|---|---|---|---|---|---|---|---|
| Athens | 2837 | | | | | | | | | | | | | | | | | | | | | | | | | | | | | | | | | | |
| Barcelona | 1562 | 3091 | | | | | | | | | | | | | | | | | | | | | | | | | | | | | | | | | |
| Berlin | 665 | 2584 | 1863 | | | | | | | | | | | | | | | | | | | | | | | | | | | | | | | | |
| Berne | 840 | 3316 | 925 | 913 | | | | | | | | | | | | | | | | | | | | | | | | | | | | | | | |
| Bordeaux | 1080 | 3240 | 567 | 1631 | 849 | | | | | | | | | | | | | | | | | | | | | | | | | | | | | | |
| Brussels | 205 | 2793 | 1366 | 774 | 648 | 892 | | | | | | | | | | | | | | | | | | | | | | | | | | | | | |
| Budapest | 1388 | 1510 | 1916 | 852 | 1107 | 2045 | 1347 | | | | | | | | | | | | | | | | | | | | | | | | | | | | |
| Cologne | 256 | 2579 | 1360 | 566 | 588 | 1068 | 211 | 1137 | | | | | | | | | | | | | | | | | | | | | | | | | | | |
| Copenhagen | 778 | 2938 | 2095 | 391 | 1222 | 1797 | 886 | 1252 | 732 | | | | | | | | | | | | | | | | | | | | | | | | | | |
| Dublin | 954 | 3587 | 1972 | 1538 | 1368 | 1164 | 796 | 2151 | 1015 | 1679 | | | | | | | | | | | | | | | | | | | | | | | | | |
| Edinburgh | 1101 | 3823 | 2119 | 1686 | 1515 | 1608 | 943 | 2298 | 1162 | 488 | 391 | | | | | | | | | | | | | | | | | | | | | | | | |
| Frankfurt | 441 | 2396 | 1331 | 537 | 429 | 1149 | 399 | 955 | 189 | 798 | 1203 | 1350 | | | | | | | | | | | | | | | | | | | | | | | |
| Geneva | 913 | 2446 | 762 | 1072 | 164 | 684 | 718 | 1268 | 748 | 1381 | 1335 | 1483 | 588 | | | | | | | | | | | | | | | | | | | | | | |
| Hamburg | 465 | 2780 | 1782 | 284 | 913 | 1483 | 573 | 1145 | 418 | 321 | 1365 | 1512 | 489 | 1072 | | | | | | | | | | | | | | | | | | | | | |
| Helsinki | 1205 | 2540 | 2389 | 505 | 1883 | 2182 | 1317 | 1630 | 1110 | 795 | 2154 | 2390 | 1101 | 1656 | 776 | | | | | | | | | | | | | | | | | | | | |
| Lisbon | 2278 | 4320 | 1238 | 2829 | 2146 | 1193 | 2091 | 3136 | 2266 | 2995 | 2361 | 2806 | 2347 | 1983 | 2681 | 3423 | | | | | | | | | | | | | | | | | | | |
| London | 479 | 3253 | 1496 | 1055 | 892 | 985 | 320 | 1672 | 536 | 1195 | 467 | 643 | 724 | 860 | 881 | 1820 | 2182 | | | | | | | | | | | | | | | | | | |
| Luxembourg | 379 | 2637 | 1155 | 765 | 436 | 928 | 215 | 1170 | 193 | 927 | 1004 | 1152 | 235 | 506 | 614 | 1303 | 2125 | 529 | | | | | | | | | | | | | | | | | |
| Lyons | 929 | 2560 | 635 | 1231 | 315 | 537 | 734 | 1419 | 728 | 1463 | 1341 | 1488 | 699 | 152 | 1149 | 1758 | 1855 | 865 | 522 | | | | | | | | | | | | | | | | |
| Madrid | 1775 | 3761 | 618 | 2326 | 1526 | 690 | 1588 | 2516 | 1763 | 2492 | 1858 | 2303 | 1844 | 1362 | 2178 | 2913 | 619 | 1680 | 1623 | 1235 | | | | | | | | | | | | | | | |
| Manchester | 820 | 3478 | 1837 | 1404 | 1233 | 1029 | 661 | 2016 | 880 | 1544 | 212 | 351 | 1068 | 1201 | 1231 | 2045 | 2226 | 333 | 870 | 1205 | 1723 | | | | | | | | | | | | | | |
| Marseilles | 1241 | 2622 | 504 | 1542 | 605 | 654 | 1046 | 1444 | 1039 | 1774 | 1652 | 1799 | 1010 | 441 | 1461 | 2070 | 1725 | 1177 | 833 | 314 | 1104 | 1518 | | | | | | | | | | | | | |
| Milan | 1085 | 2128 | 981 | 1033 | 357 | 1130 | 892 | 950 | 833 | 1426 | 1612 | 1760 | 674 | 317 | 1117 | 1575 | 2202 | 1137 | 680 | 445 | 1581 | 1478 | 509 | | | | | | | | | | | | |
| Munich | 831 | 2063 | 1378 | 585 | 434 | 1246 | 729 | 636 | 580 | 944 | 1541 | 1688 | 398 | 594 | 789 | 1120 | 2599 | 1065 | 514 | 745 | 1978 | 1406 | 1003 | 498 | | | | | | | | | | | |
| Oslo | 1047 | 3521 | 2363 | 970 | 1502 | 2065 | 1155 | 1833 | 1000 | 557 | 1000 | 728 | 1078 | 1662 | 591 | 690 | 3262 | 456 | 1196 | 1731 | 2759 | 768 | 2044 | 1707 | 1525 | | | | | | | | | | |
| Paris | 497 | 2913 | 1092 | 1048 | 551 | 581 | 309 | 1473 | 484 | 1213 | 877 | 1024 | 576 | 500 | 900 | 1605 | 1778 | 402 | 355 | 460 | 1275 | 743 | 773 | 846 | 822 | 1482 | | | | | | | | | |
| Prague | 847 | 2110 | 1706 | 338 | 756 | 1598 | 870 | 514 | 654 | 732 | 1674 | 1821 | 499 | 915 | 625 | 1095 | 2795 | 1199 | 722 | 1074 | 2306 | 1539 | 1386 | 868 | 379 | 1313 | 1025 | | | | | | | | |
| Rome | 1653 | 2389 | 1351 | 1494 | 925 | 1500 | 1460 | 1204 | 1401 | 1853 | 2180 | 2328 | 1242 | 871 | 1698 | 2041 | 2572 | 1705 | 1248 | 963 | 1951 | 2046 | 879 | 564 | 905 | 2434 | 1401 | 1288 | | | | | | | |
| Stockholm | 1386 | 3568 | 2702 | 998 | 1829 | 2404 | 1494 | 1861 | 1339 | 585 | 1056 | 965 | 1405 | 1989 | 928 | 165 | 3601 | 1799 | 1535 | 2070 | 3098 | 868 | 2383 | 2033 | 1553 | 538 | 1821 | 1341 | 2462 | | | | | | |
| Strasbourg | 588 | 2438 | 1129 | 753 | 243 | 1063 | 432 | 998 | 348 | 1007 | 1207 | 1355 | 214 | 402 | 698 | 1286 | 2260 | 732 | 220 | 497 | 1729 | 1073 | 810 | 488 | 361 | 1288 | 490 | 596 | 1056 | 1615 | | | | | |
| Stuttgart | 600 | 2302 | 1230 | 629 | 286 | 1182 | 515 | 858 | 348 | 968 | 1327 | 1474 | 189 | 445 | 659 | 1166 | 2450 | 851 | 300 | 596 | 1830 | 1192 | 888 | 477 | 220 | 1248 | 609 | 472 | 1045 | 1575 | 148 | | | | |
| Venice | 1243 | 1878 | 1235 | 1060 | 611 | 1384 | 1146 | 698 | 992 | 1420 | 1866 | 2013 | 874 | 579 | 1264 | 1615 | 2456 | 1391 | 933 | 707 | 1835 | 1731 | 763 | 269 | 472 | 2001 | 1109 | 810 | 523 | 2029 | 743 | 634 | | | |
| Vienna | 1146 | 1862 | 1788 | 623 | 865 | 1803 | 1105 | 243 | 895 | 1017 | 1909 | 2056 | 713 | 1024 | 910 | 924 | 3009 | 1433 | 928 | 1175 | 2389 | 1774 | 1316 | 823 | 394 | 1598 | 1231 | 285 | 1076 | 1626 | 758 | 617 | 571 | | |
| Warsaw | 1221 | 2249 | 2325 | 591 | 1375 | 2187 | 1330 | 670 | 1122 | 981 | 2094 | 2241 | 1093 | 1535 | 874 | 346 | 3384 | 1607 | 1321 | 1693 | 2881 | 1960 | 2006 | 1512 | 995 | 1401 | 1604 | 612 | 1766 | 852 | 1216 | 1087 | 1260 | 684 | |
| Zurich | 807 | 2417 | 1047 | 835 | 126 | 938 | 635 | 997 | 556 | 1174 | 1355 | 1502 | 396 | 286 | 865 | 1388 | 2268 | 879 | 422 | 437 | 1648 | 1220 | 728 | 280 | 313 | 1454 | 592 | 678 | 848 | 1781 | 232 | 208 | 533 | 757 | 1293 |

1286

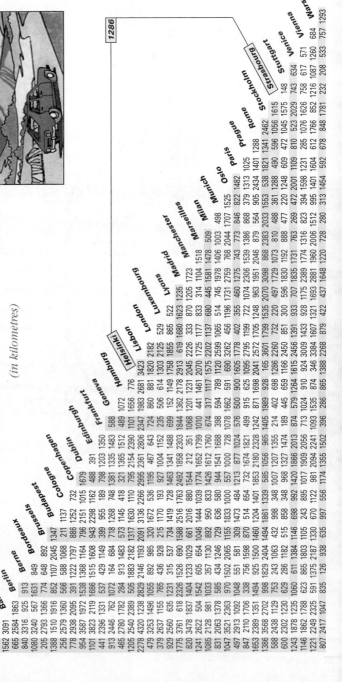

# AIR LINKS *(in hours)*

3½ not daily

| | Amsterdam | Athens | Barcelona | Berlin | Berne | Bordeaux | Brussels | Budapest | Cologne | Copenhagen | Dublin | Edinburgh | Frankfurt | Geneva | Hamburg | Helsinki | Lisbon | London | Luxembourg | Lyons | Madrid | Manchester | Marseilles | Milan | Munich | Oslo | Paris | Prague | Rome | Stockholm | Strasbourg | Stuttgart | Venice | Vienna | Warsaw |
|---|---|---|---|---|---|---|---|---|---|---|---|---|---|---|---|---|---|---|---|---|---|---|---|---|---|---|---|---|---|---|---|---|---|---|---|
| Athens | 5 | | | | | | | | | | | | | | | | | | | | | | | | | | | | | | | | | | |
| Barcelona | 3¾ | 4½ | | | | | | | | | | | | | | | | | | | | | | | | | | | | | | | | | |
| Berlin | 3 | 8 | 5¾ | | | | | | | | | | | | | | | | | | | | | | | | | | | | | | | | |
| Berne | 3¼ | | | | | | | | | | | | | | | | | | | | | | | | | | | | | | | | | | |
| Bordeaux | 2¾ | 9 | | 8½ | | | | | | | | | | | | | | | | | | | | | | | | | | | | | | | |
| Brussels | 2½ | 5 | 3¾ | 4¼ | 3½ | 5½ | | | | | | | | | | | | | | | | | | | | | | | | | | | | | |
| Budapest | 4 | 3¾ | | 3½ | | | 4 | | | | | | | | | | | | | | | | | | | | | | | | | | | | |
| Cologne | | 6 | 5¼ | 2¾ | | 7¼ | | 3¾ | | | | | | | | | | | | | | | | | | | | | | | | | | | |
| Copenhagen | 3 | 5 | 4½ | 4 | | 6 | 3¼ | 3¾ | 4¼ | | | | | | | | | | | | | | | | | | | | | | | | | | |
| Dublin | 3¼ | 8 | 6½ | 5½ | | 5¾ | 3¼ | | 5½ | 4 | | | | | | | | | | | | | | | | | | | | | | | | | |
| Edinburgh | 3¾ | 8½ | 6¼ | 6 | | 5½ | 4¾ | | 5¼ | 5½ | 2¾ | | | | | | | | | | | | | | | | | | | | | | | | |
| Frankfurt | 2¾ | 4½ | 3¾ | 2¾ | | 6¼ | 2¾ | 3½ | 2½ | 3¼ | 3¾ | 5¾ | | | | | | | | | | | | | | | | | | | | | | | |
| Geneva | 3 | 4½ | 3 | 4½ | 3½ | 3 | 3 | | 4½ | 3¾ | 4 | 5½ | 3 | | | | | | | | | | | | | | | | | | | | | | |
| Hamburg | 2¾ | 6½ | 5½ | 2½ | | 5¾ | 3 | 4 | 2¾ | 2½ | 5½ | 6¼ | 2¾ | 4¾ | | | | | | | | | | | | | | | | | | | | | |
| Helsinki | 5¼ | 9½ | 7½ | 5 | | 9¼ | 4½ | 4½ | 6 | 3¼ | 7¾ | 8¾ | 4¼ | 6 | 3¾ | | | | | | | | | | | | | | | | | | | | |
| Lisbon | 4½ | 9½ | 3¼ | 7½ | | | 4½ | | 7½ | 5½ | 6¾ | 7¼ | 4¾ | 3¼ | 6¼ | 8 | | | | | | | | | | | | | | | | | | | |
| London | 2¾ | 5¾ | 4¼ | 7 | 3¾ | 3¾ | 3¼ | 5 | 3½ | 4 | 3¼ | 3½ | 3½ | 3½ | 3¾ | 5¼ | 4¾ | | | | | | | | | | | | | | | | | | |
| Luxembourg | 2½ | 6½ | 6¾ | 4¾ | | 6¼ | 2¼ | | 4½ | 4¾ | 5½ | | 2½ | 4 | 4¾ | 5¾ | 6¾ | 3¼ | | | | | | | | | | | | | | | | | |
| Lyons | 3½ | 7¼ | 3 | 4 | | 3 | 3¼ | | 5 | 4 | 6 | 6 | 3¼ | | 5½ | 8 | 4¼ | 4 | | | | | | | | | | | | | | | | | |
| Madrid | 3 | 6¼ | 2¾ | 6¼ | | 3 | 4 | 5 | 5½ | 4¾ | 4 | 6 | 4¼ | 3½ | 6 | 7¾ | 2¾ | 4¼ | 6 | 4¾ | | | | | | | | | | | | | | | |
| Manchester | 3 | 7¼ | 6 | 5½ | | 5¾ | 3 | | 5½ | 3¾ | 2¾ | 3 | 3¾ | 4 | 5 | 7½ | 4¾ | 3¼ | 5¾ | 6 | 4¼ | | | | | | | | | | | | | | |
| Marseilles | 4½ | 5¾ | 2¾ | 7¼ | | 2¾ | 3½ | | 6½ | 5¼ | 6¼ | 6¼ | 4½ | 2½ | 6½ | 8¾ | 4 | 4 | 6 | 2¾ | 3¼ | 5¾ | | | | | | | | | | | | | |
| Milan | 3 | 3¾ | 3¼ | 5 | | 5¼ | 3¼ | 3¾ | 4¼ | 3¾ | 5¼ | 6¼ | 3 | 2½ | 4¾ | 6¼ | 5¼ | 4 | 4¾ | 3 | 3¾ | 4 | 3 | | | | | | | | | | | | |
| Munich | 3¼ | 4¼ | 3¾ | 3 | 2½ | 6 | 3 | 3¼ | 2¾ | 3¼ | 4¼ | 6¼ | 2¾ | 3½ | 3 | 4½ | 6½ | 4 | 4¼ | 5¼ | 5½ | 5½ | 8 | 2¾ | | | | | | | | | | | |
| Oslo | 3 | 8¾ | 6¼ | 4¼ | | 7¼ | 4¾ | | 6¾ | 3½ | 6 | 7½ | 3½ | 5¼ | 2¾ | 4 | 7¼ | 3 | 6 | 5¾ | 6½ | 5¼ | 7 | 5¼ | 5 | | | | | | | | | | |
| Paris | 2 | 5 | 3½ | 4¾ | 3 | 3 | 2¾ | 4¼ | 3 | 3¾ | 3¾ | 5 | 3¼ | 3 | 3½ | 5 | 4½ | 3½ | 2¾ | 3 | 3¾ | 3¼ | 3 | 3¼ | 3½ | 4 | | | | | | | | | |
| Prague | 3½ | 4½ | 4¼ | 3 | | | 3½ | 3¼ | 3½ | 3¾ | | | 3 | 3¾ | 3¾ | 4 | | 4½ | 3¾ | | 4¾ | 5½ | | 4¼ | 3 | | 3¾ | | | | | | | | |
| Rome | 3 | 3¾ | 3½ | 5¼ | | 8¼ | 4 | 4 | 5¾ | 4½ | 4¼ | 6¾ | 3¾ | 3½ | 5¾ | 7¼ | 4¾ | 4¾ | 3¾ | 5 | 4¼ | 5 | 3 | 3 | 3½ | 6½ | 4¼ | 4¼ | | | | | | | |
| Stockholm | 4 | 6¼ | 7¾ | 5 | | 6¾ | 5¼ | 6¼ | 6½ | 3¼ | 7 | 7¼ | 4 | 6 | 3½ | 2¾ | 9¼ | 5 | 6¾ | 6½ | 7 | 6 | 7¾ | 6 | 5¾ | 2¾ | 4¾ | 4¼ | 7 | | | | | | |
| Strasbourg | 2½ | 7¼ | 6¾ | | | 4½ | 2½ | | | 5¾ | 6½ | 5¾ | | 2¾ | | 8¼ | 6½ | 4½ | | 3¼ | 7 | 4¾ | 3¾ | 2¾ | | 6¾ | 3 | | 4¾ | 8½ | | | | | |
| Stuttgart | 3¾ | 8 | 3¾ | 3 | | 8 | 3¾ | 3½ | 2½ | 3¼ | 5½ | 6¾ | 2½ | 3¾ | 3 | 6¼ | 4¾ | 3¾ | 4¼ | 5 | 4¼ | 5 | 6¼ | 2¾ | 2½ | 5 | 3¼ | 3 | 5½ | 5½ | | | | | |
| Venice | 5½ | 6¼ | 5¾ | 5 | | | 4¾ | | 5¼ | 5¾ | 6¼ | | 3 | 4¾ | 5 | 7¼ | 7 | 4¼ | 5 | 5 | 4¾ | 6½ | 4¾ | 2½ | 3 | 6 | 3½ | | 3 | 6½ | | 5 | | | |
| Vienna | 3½ | 4 | 4 | 5 | 3¼ | 6 | 3½ | 2¾ | 4½ | 3¼ | 5¾ | 6¼ | 3 | 3¼ | 4¾ | 6 | 6½ | 4½ | 4¾ | 5½ | 5¼ | 5¾ | 6 | 3 | 2¾ | 5 | 3¾ | 3 | 3½ | 4¼ | | 3 | 3¼ | | |
| Warsaw | 4¾ | 5¼ | 7¾ | 4¼ | | | 4¾ | 4¼ | 6½ | 4 | | 7¾ | 4½ | 6½ | 5¼ | 4¼ | 8¾ | 5¾ | 7¼ | 7¼ | 6½ | 7½ | 8½ | 6¼ | 4¼ | 4¾ | 5¼ | 4¼ | 5½ | 4¾ | | 5¼ | 8 | 4 | |
| Zurich | 3 | 4½ | 3¼ | 3¼ | 3¼ | 6 | 3 | 3½ | 2¾ | 3½ | 5¾ | 5½ | 2¾ | 2½ | 3 | 5¾ | 4½ | 3¾ | 2½ | 3¼ | 3¾ | 3¾ | 5 | 2½ | 2½ | 5 | 3¾ | 3¾ | 3½ | 4½ | 2½ | 2½ | 3¾ | 3 | 4¾ |

2¾

HAMBURG

FUHLSBÜTTEL

FORNEBU

OSLO

# *Austria*

## *Österreich*

VIENNA

INNSBRUCK – SALZBURG

# PRACTICAL INFORMATION

## LOCAL CURRENCY

**Austrian Schilling;** *100 ATS = 7.95 USD ($) (Jan. 98)*

## TOURIST INFORMATION

**In Vienna:** *Österreich-Information, 1040 Wien, Margaretenstr. 1, ✆ (01) 587 20 00, Fax (01) 588 66 20*
*Niederösterreich Touristik-Information, 1010 Wien, Walfischgasse 6, ✆ (01) 513 80 220, Fax (01) 513 80 22 30*

**Austrian National Holiday:** *26 October*

## AIRLINES

**Austrian Swissair:** *1010 Wien, Kärntner Ring 18, ✆ (01) 17 66 76 00, Fax (01) 17 66 76 99*

**Air France:** *1010 Wien, Kärntner Str. 49, ✆ (01) 514 18 18, Fax (01) 513 94 26*

**British Airways:** *1010 Wien, Kärntner Ring 10, ✆ (01) 505 76 91, Fax (01) 504 20 84*

**Japan Airlines:** *1010 Wien, Kärntner Str. 11, ✆ (01) 512 75 22, Fax (01) 512 75 54*

**Lufthansa City Center:** *1010 Wien, Kärntner Str. 42, ✆ (01) 589 140, Fax (01) 589 14 10*

## FOREIGN EXCHANGE

*Hotels, restaurants and shops do not always accept foreign currencies and it is wise, therefore, to change money and cheques at the banks and exchange offices which are found in the larger stations, airports and at the border.*

## SHOPPING and BANK HOURS

*Shops are open from 9am to 6pm, but often close for a lunch break. They are closed Saturday afternoon, Sunday and Bank Holidays (except the shops in railway stations). Branch offices of banks are open from Monday to Friday between 8am and 12.30pm (in Salzburg 12am) and from 1.30pm to 3pm (in Salzburg 2pm to 4.30pm), Thursday to 5.30pm (only in Vienna).*
*In the index of street names, those printed in red are where the principal shops are found.*

## BREAKDOWN SERVICE

**ÖAMTC:** *See addresses in the text of each city.*

**ARBÖ:** *in Vienna: Mariahilfer Str. 180, ✆ (01) 89 12 17, Fax (01) 89 12 12 36*
*in Salzburg: Münchner Bundesstr. 9, ✆ (0662) 43 83 81, in Innsbruck: Stadlweg 7, ✆ (0512) 34 51 23*
*In Austria the ÖAMTC (emergency number ✆ 120) and the ARBÖ (emergency number ✆ 123) make a special point of assisting foreign motorists. They have motor patrols covering main roads.*

## TIPPING

*Service is generally included in hotel and restaurant bills. But in Austria, it is usual to give more than the expected tip in hotels, restaurants and cafés. Taxi-drivers, porters, barbers and theatre attendants also expect tips.*

## SPEED LIMITS

*The speed limit in built up areas (indicated by place name signs at the beginning and end of such areas) is 50 km/h - 31 mph; on motorways 130 km/h - 80 mph and on all other roads 100 km/h - 62 mph. Driving on Austrian motorways is subject to the purchase of a road tax obtainable from border posts and ÖAMTC.*

## SEAT BELTS

*The wearing of seat belts in Austria is compulsory for drivers and all passengers.*

# VIENNA

(WIEN) *Austria* 987 ⑩ 426 ⑫ - *pop. 1 640 000 - alt. 156 m.*

*Budapest 208 ④ - München 435 ⑦ - Praha 292 ① - Salzburg 292 ⑦ - Zagreb 362 ⑥.*

*Tourist-information, ✉ A-1010, Kärtner Str. 38, ☎ (01) 513 88 92 - ÖAMTC, ✉ A-1010, Schubertring 1, ☎ (01) 71 19 90, Fax (01) 7 13 18 07.*

18 *Freudenau 65a, ☎ (01) 728 95 64,*
18 *Weingartenallee 22, ☎ (01) 250 72*
9 *At Wienerberg ☎ (01) 661 23 70 00*
✈ *Wien-Schwechat by ③, ☎ (01) 70 07 22 31, Air Terminal, at Stadtpark (HY) ☎ (01) 58 00 23 00.*
*☎ (01) 58 00 29 89. - Exhibition Centre (Wiener Messe), Messeplatz 1, ☎ (01) 727 20.*

# Sights

## THE HOFBURG★★★ AND SOUVENIRS OF THE HABSBURGS

*Around the Hofburg* JR*: St Michael's Square (Michaelerplatz)★ – St Michael's Gate (Michaeltor)★ – Swiss Gate (Schweizertor)★ – Josefsplatz★ – Heroe's Square (Heldenplatz)★* HJR
*Souvenirs of the Habsburgs; Imperial Apartments (Kaiserappartments)★ – Imperial porcelain and silver collection. Milan centrpiece★★ – Imperial Treasury★★★; Rudolf Imperial Crown★★★; Insignia and regalia of the Holy Roman Germanic Empire★★★ – Spanish Riding School★★ – Austrian National Library★ – Albertina Collection of Graphic Art★★* JR
*Church of the Capucins (Kapuzinerkirche): Imperial Crypt of the Habqburg pantheon (Kaisergruft)★★* JR
*Other Museums in the Hofburg; Ephesos-Museum★★ (Frieze from the Parthian momument★★) Museum of Ancient Musical Instruments★★ – Collection of Arms Armour★ – Ethnographic Museum★*

## SCHÖNBRUNN★★★

*Schloss Schöbrunn* AZ*; Tour of the Palace★★ – Carriage Museum★ – Park★★ ⋞★ of the Gloriette★★ – Zoo★*

## BUILDINGS AND MONUMENTS

*St Stephen's Cathedral (Stephansdom)★★★* KR *– Stephansplatz★★ – Cathedral Museum (Dom-und DiözesanMuseum)★★* KR **M19**
*Unters Belvedere★★* CY *Museum of Austrian Medieval Art (Museum fûr mittelalterliche Österreichische Kunst)★ – Museumof Austrian Baroque Art (Barockmuseum)★★*
*Oberes Belvedere★* CY*: 19 and 20C Austrian and International Art (Galerie des 19. Und 20. Jahrhunderts)★★ – Staatsoper★★* JS *– Church of Charles Borromero (Karlskirche)★★* CY *– St Leopold's Church in Penzing (Kirche am Steinhof)★★ – Burgtheater★* HR *– St Peter's Church (Peterskirche)★* JR *– Church of the Jesuits (Jesuitenkirche)★* KLR *– Maria am Gestade★* JP *– Abbey of the Scots (Schottenstitt)★, Scotsaltar★★* JPR

## JUGENDSTIL AND SECESSION

*Post Office Savings Bank (Postsparkasse)★* KLR *– Wagner-Pavillons★* JS *– Secession Pavilion (Secessionsgebäude)★★* JS *– Buildings★ by Wagner on Linke Wienzeile – Wagner Villas★ (in Penzing)* BYZ

## STREETS, SQUARES AND PARKS

*The Tour of the Ring (Rundfahrt über den Ring)★★ – Graben★ (Plague Pillar★★)* JR *– Donner Brunner★★* JR *– Volksgarten★* HR *– Spittelberg Quarter★* HS *– Prater★ (Riesenrad★★)* CY

## MUSICAL VIENNA

*Pasquamatihaus★ (Beethoven)* HP **85** *– Figaro-Haus★ (Mozart)* KR *Schubert-Museum★* BY **M5** *– Haydn-Museum★* BYZ **M10** *– Strausshaus★* LP

## IMPORTANT MUSEUMS

*Museum of Art History (Kunsthistorisches Museum)★★★* HS *– Art Gallery of the Academy of Fine Arts (Gemäldegalerie der Akademie der Bildenden Künste)★★* JS *– Austrian Museum of Applied and Decorative Arts (Österreichische Museum für Angewandte Kunst)★★* LR *– Historical Museum of the City of Vienna (Historisches Museum der Stadt Wien)★* KS *Natural History Museum (Naturhistorisches Museum)★* HS *– City of Vienna Jewish Museum (Jüdisches Museum der Stadt Wien)★* JR *– Museum of Military History (Heeresgeschichtliches Museum)★* CZ **M23** *– Treasure Chamber of the Grand Masters (Schatzkammer des Deutschen Ordens)★* KR *– Josephinum★* BY *–* **M24** *– Sigmund Freud Museum★* BY **M25** *– Tram Museum (Wiener Strassenbahnmuseum)★* CY **M3** *– Clock and Watch Museum (Uhrenmuseum der Stadt Wien)★* JR **M17**

## EXCURSIONS

*UNO-City★* CY *– Donaupark★* CX *– Donauturm ⋞★★* CX *– Leopoldsberg★★ ⋞★★* BX *– Klosterneuburg Abbey (Stift Klosterneuburg)★ (Altarpiece by Nicolas of Verdun★★) N: 13km – Heiligenkreuz★ SW: 32 km by ⑥ – Grinzing★* BX *– Wienerwald★ SW by ⑥ – Heiligenstadt★ (Karl-Marx-Hof★)* BX.

## STREET INDEX TO WIEN TOWN PLANS

Write us...

If you have any comments on the contents of this Guide.

Your praise as well as your criticisms will receive careful consideration and, with your assistance, we will be able to add to our stock of information and, where necessary, amend our judgments.

Thank you in advance!

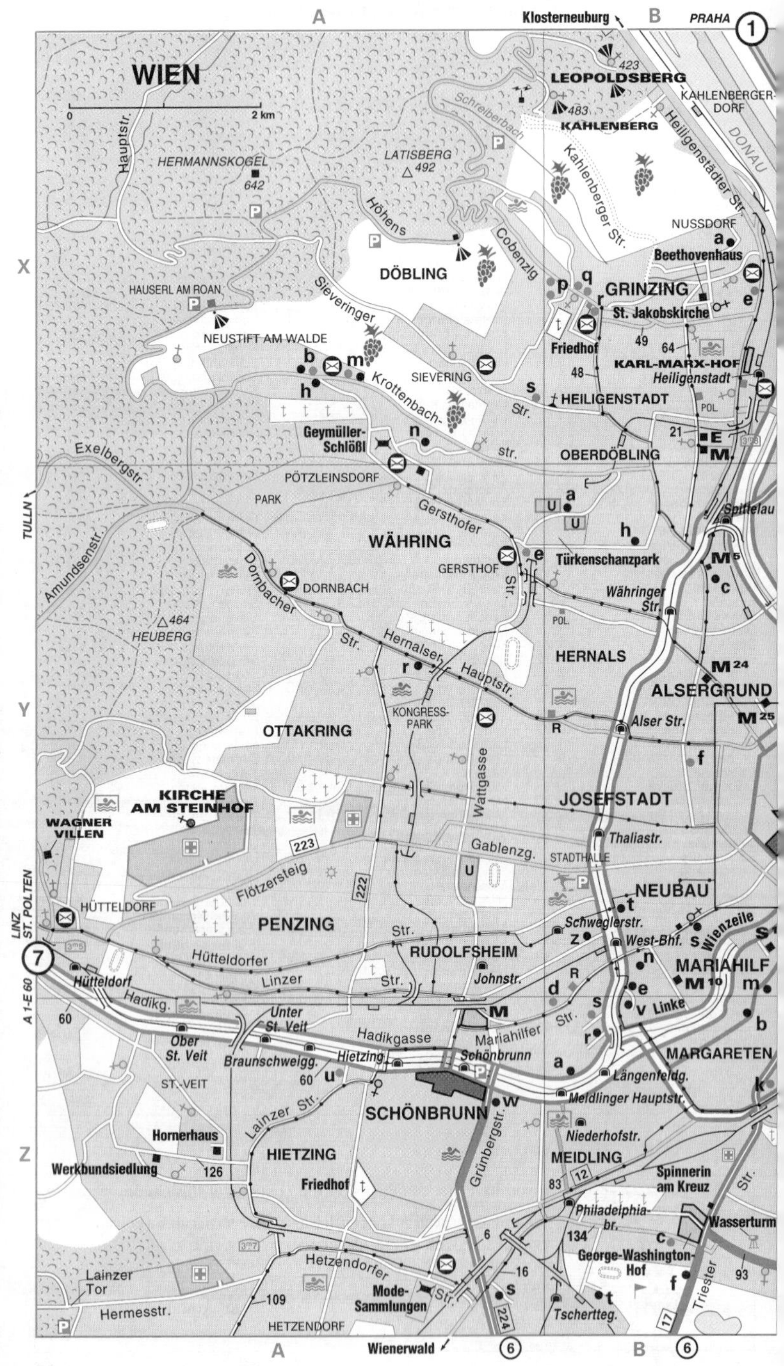
WIEN
Klosterneuburg
PRAHA
LEOPOLDSBERG
KAHLENBERG
KAHLENBERGERDORF
DONAU
Heiligenstädter Str.
Kahlenberger Str.
HERMANNSKOGEL
LATISBERG
DÖBLING
NUSSDORF
Beethovenhaus
GRINZING
St. Jakobskirche
Friedhof
KARL-MARX-HOF
Heiligenstadt
HEILIGENSTADT
HAUSERL AM ROAN
NEUSTIFT AM WALDE
SIEVERING
Krottenbach-str.
Geymüller-Schlößl
OBERDÖBLING
Spittelau
PÖTZLEINSDORF
PARK
WÄHRING
Türkenschanzpark
GERSTHOF
DORNBACH
Währinger Str.
HEUBERG
HERNALS
Hernalser Hauptstr.
ALSERGRUND
KONGRESS-PARK
Alser Str.
OTTAKRING
JOSEFSTADT
KIRCHE AM STEINHOF
WAGNER VILLEN
Thaliastr.
Gablenzg.
STADTHALLE
Flötzersteig
NEUBAU
HÜTTELDORF
PENZING
Schweglerstr.
West-Bhf.
Wienzeile
RUDOLFSHEIM
MARIAHILF
Hütteldorfer Str.
Linzer Str.
Johnstr.
Hütteldorf
Hadikg.
Ober St. Veit
Unter St. Veit
Hadikgasse
Braunschweigg.
Hietzing
Mariahilfer Str.
Schönbrunn
Linke
MARGARETEN
Längenfeldg.
Meidlinger Hauptstr.
ST.-VEIT
SCHÖNBRUNN
Lainzer Str.
Grünbergstr.
Niederhofstr.
Hornerhaus
Werkbundsiedlung
HIETZING
MEIDLING
Spinnerin am Kreuz
Friedhof
Philadelphiabr.
Wasserturm
George-Washington-Hof
Hetzendorfer Str.
Lainzer Tor
Hermesstr.
Mode-Sammlungen
HETZENDORF
Tschertteg.
Triester Str.
Wienerwald
TULLN
LINZ ST. POLTEN
A 1-E 60
Exelbergstr.
Amundsenstr.
Dombacher Str.
Gersthofer Str.
Wattgasse
Sieveringer Str.
Höhenstr.
Cobenzlg.
Hauptstr.
Schreiberbach
0
2 km
A
B
X
Y
Z

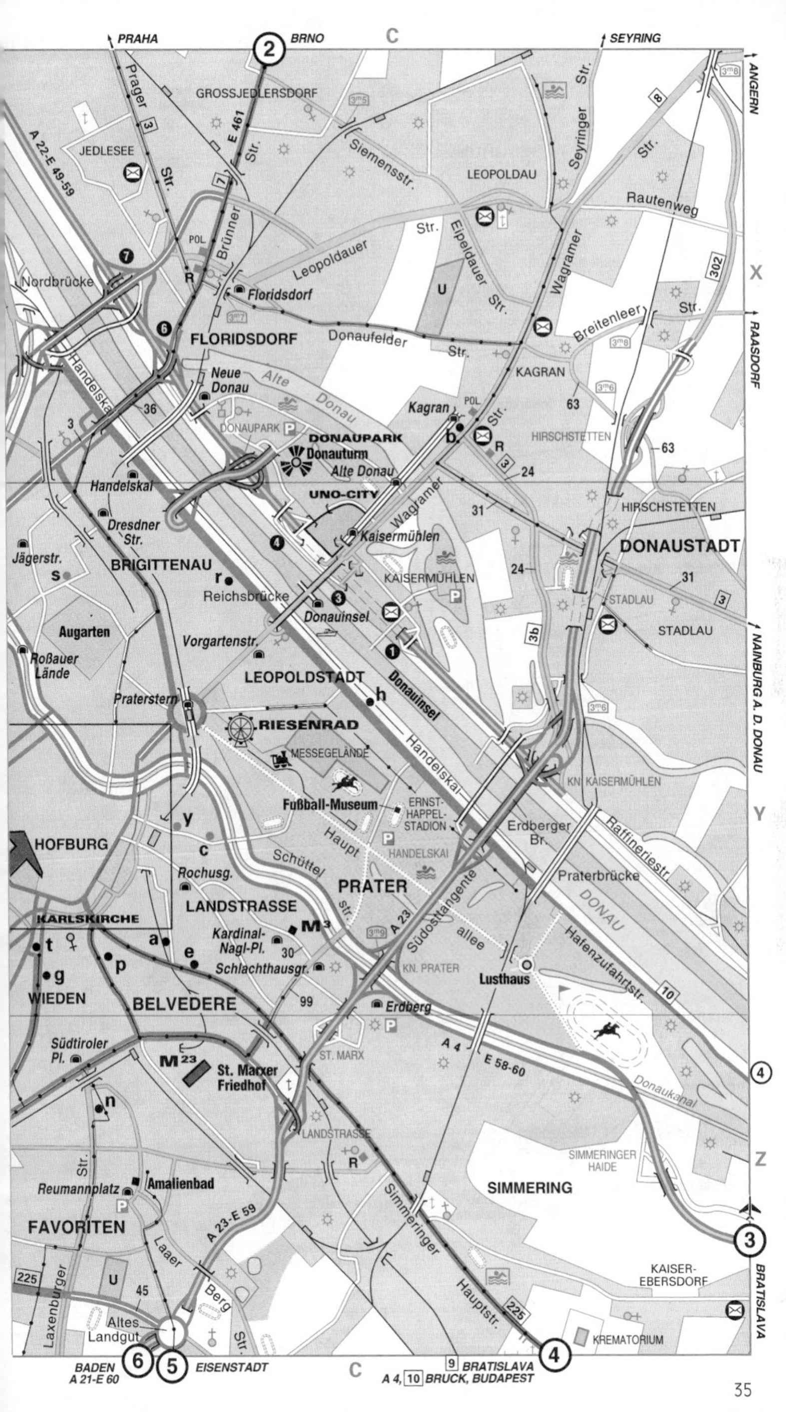

PRAHA
BRNO
SEYRING
ANGERN
RAASDORF
NAINBURG A. D. DONAU
BRATISLAVA
BADEN A 21-E 60
EISENSTADT
9 BRATISLAVA
A 4, 10 BRUCK, BUDAPEST
GROSSJEDLERSDORF
JEDLESEE
LEOPOLDAU
FLORIDSDORF
Floridsdorf
Nordbrücke
Neue Donau
Alte Donau
DONAUPARK
Donauturm
UNO-CITY
Kaisermühlen
KAISERMÜHLEN
Kagran
KAGRAN
HIRSCHSTETTEN
DONAUSTADT
STADLAU
Handelskai
Dresdner Str.
Jägerstr.
BRIGITTENAU
Reichsbrücke
Augarten
Roßauer Lände
Vorgartenstr.
Donauinsel
LEOPOLDSTADT
Praterstern
RIESENRAD
MESSEGELÄNDE
Fußball-Museum
ERNST-HAPPEL-STADION
HANDELSKAI
KN. KAISERMÜHLEN
Erdberger Br.
Raffineriestr.
Praterbrücke
DONAU
HOFBURG
KARLSKIRCHE
Rochusg.
LANDSTRASSE
Schüttel str.
Hauptallee
PRATER
Südosttangente
A 23
Kardinal-Nagl-Pl.
Schlachthausgr.
KN. PRATER
Lusthaus
Hafenzufahrtstr.
WIEDEN
BELVEDERE
Erdberg
Südtiroler Pl.
ST. MARX
St. Marxer Friedhof
A 4
E 58-60
Donaukanal
LANDSTRASSE
SIMMERINGER HAIDE
SIMMERING
Reumannplatz
Amalienbad
FAVORITEN
A 23-E 59
Simmeringer Hauptstr.
Laaer Berg Str.
Laxenburger Str.
Altes Landgut
KAISER-EBERSDORF
KREMATORIUM
Prager Str.
Brünner Str.
Siemensstr.
Leopoldauer Str.
Eipeldauer Str.
Wagramer Str.
Seyringer Str.
Rautenweg
Breitenleer Str.
Donaufelder Str.
A 22-E 49-59
E 461

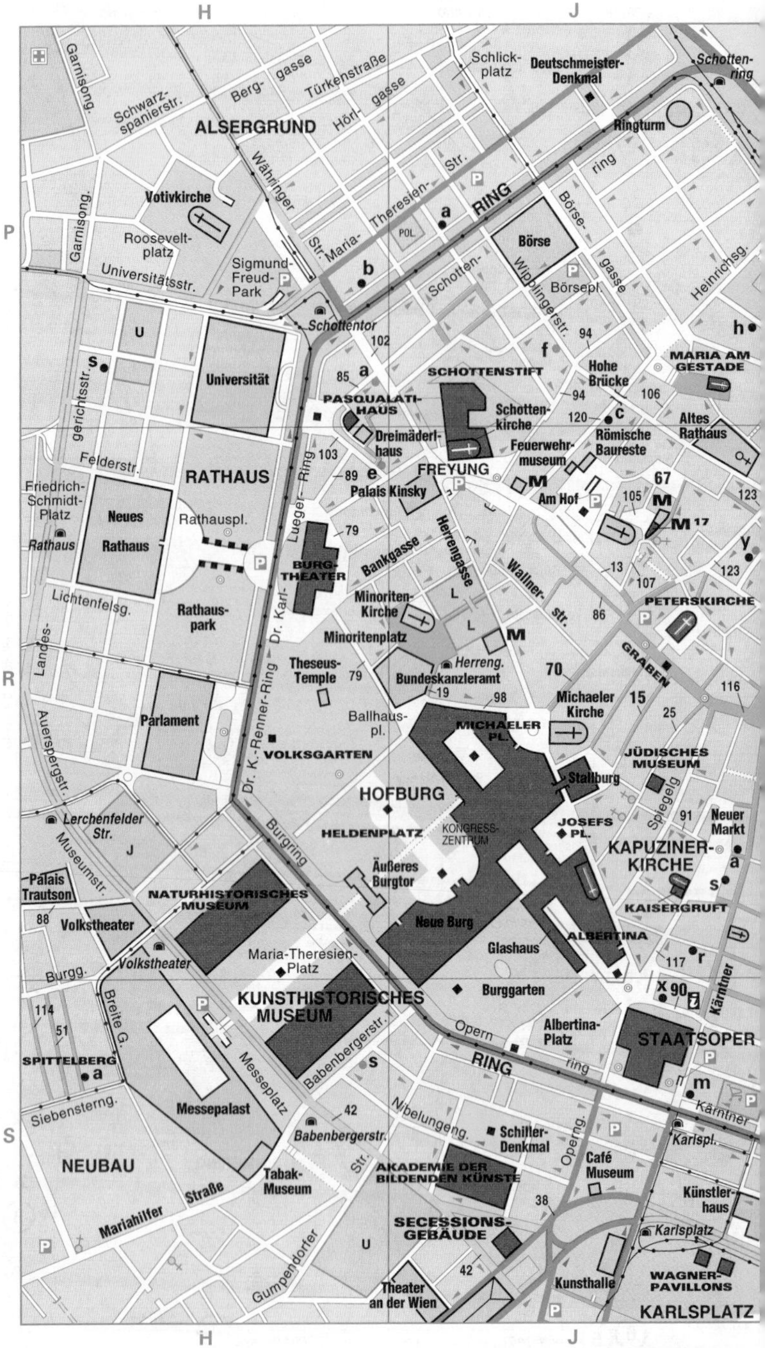

H J

Garnisong.
Schwarz-spanierstr.
Berg-gasse
Türkenstraße
Hörl-gasse
Schlick-platz
Deutschmeister-Denkmal
Schotten-ring
ALSERGRUND
Ringturm
Währinger Str.
Maria-Theresien-Str.
ring
Votivkirche
RING
Börse-gasse
Roosevelt-platz
POL
a
Börse
Garnisong.
Sigmund-Freud-Park
b
Wipplingerstr.
Heinrichsg.
Universitätsstr.
Schotten-
Börsepl.
P
Schottentor
102
94
h
U
f
MARIA AM GESTADE
s
85
a
SCHOTTENSTIFT
Hohe Brücke
Universität
106
PASQUALATI-HAUS
94
Schotten-kirche
120
c
Altes Rathaus
gerichtsstr.
Dreimäderlhaus
Römische Baureste
103
Feuerwehr-museum
Felderstr.
89
e
FREYUNG
RATHAUS
Palais Kinsky
M
67
Friedrich-Schmidt-Platz
Am Hof
105
123
Neues Rathaus
Rathauspl.
M
Rathaus
79
Herrengasse
M 17
y
Bankgasse
Wallner-str.
BURG-THEATER
13
123
Dr. Karl-Lueger-Ring
107
Lichtenfelsg.
Rathaus-park
L
Minoriten-Kirche
86
PETERSKIRCHE
L
Landes-gerichtsstr.
Minoritenplatz
M
GRABEN
Theseus-Temple
79
Herreng.
R
Bundeskanzleramt
70
19
116
Parlament
Ballhaus-pl.
98
Michaeler Kirche
15
25
Auerspergstr.
MICHAELER PL.
VOLKSGARTEN
JÜDISCHES MUSEUM
Stallburg
Dr. K.-Renner-Ring
HOFBURG
Spiegelg.
Lerchenfelder Str.
J
JOSEFS PL.
91
Neuer Markt
HELDENPLATZ
KONGRESS-ZENTRUM
KAPUZINER-KIRCHE
Museumstr.
Burgring
a
Palais Trautson
Äußeres Burgtor
s
NATURHISTORISCHES MUSEUM
KAISERGRUFT
88
Volkstheater
Neue Burg
ALBERTINA
Glashaus
Volkstheater
Maria-Theresien-Platz
117
r
Burgg.
Burggarten
x 90
Kärntner Str.
114
Breite G.
KUNSTHISTORISCHES MUSEUM
51
Albertina-Platz
Opern
STAATSOPER
SPITTELBERG
a
Babenbergerstr.
s
RING
ring
m
Messeplatz
Siebensterng.
Messepalast
42
Nibelungeng.
Kärntner
S
Babenbergerstr.
Schiller-Denkmal
Operng.
Karlspl.
NEUBAU
Str.
AKADEMIE DER BILDENDEN KÜNSTE
Café Museum
Tabak-Museum
Straße
Künstler-haus
Mariahilfer
38
SECESSIONS-GEBÄUDE
Karlsplatz
U
Gumpendorfer
42
Theater an der Wien
Kunsthalle
WAGNER-PAVILLONS
KARLSPLATZ
H J

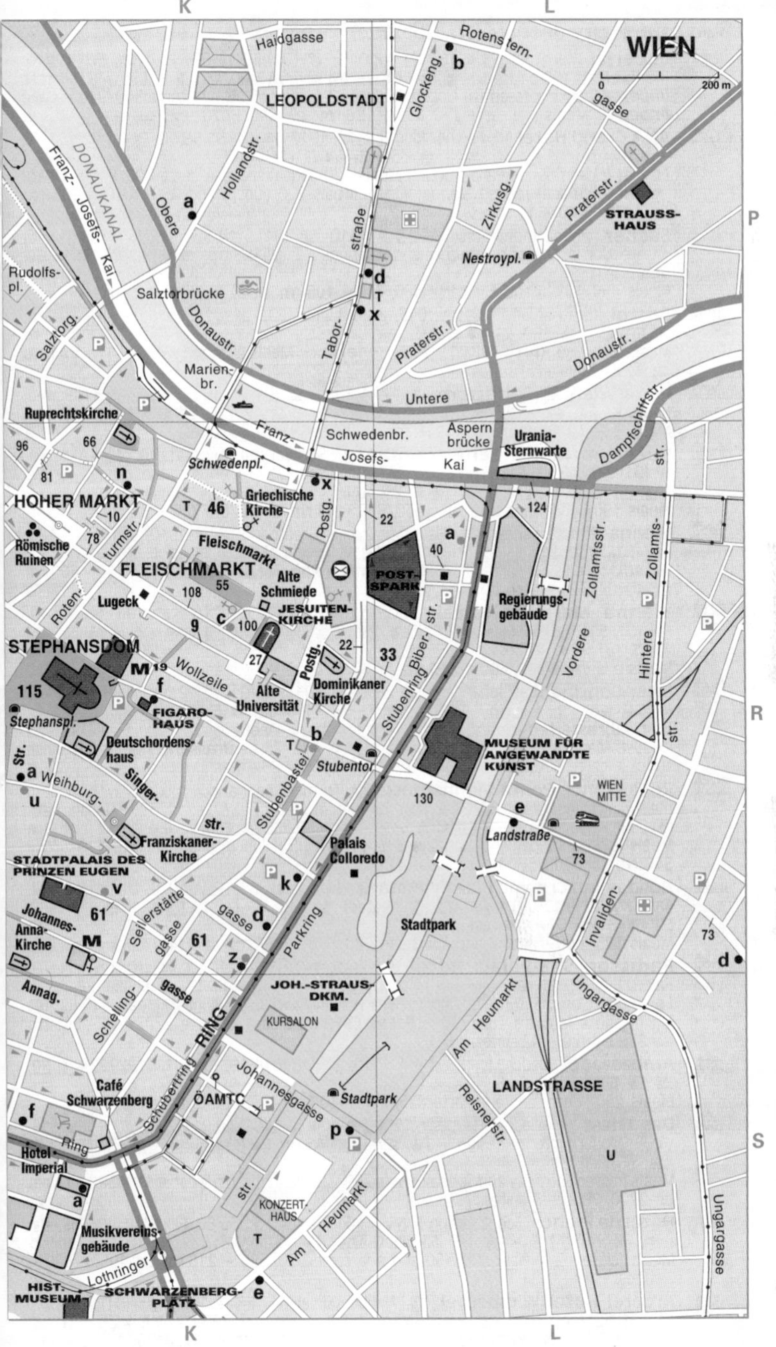

WIEN
0
200 m
K
L
P
R
S
LEOPOLDSTADT
Haidgasse
Rotenstern-gasse
Glockeng.
Hollandstr.
Obere
Donaukanal
Franz-Josefs-Kai
Rudolfs-pl.
Salztorbrücke
Donaustr.
Taborstraße
Zirkusg.
Praterstr.
STRAUSS-HAUS
Nestroypl.
Marien-br.
Salztorg.
Untere
Schwedenbr.
Aspernbrücke
Urania-Sternwarte
Dampfschiffstr.
Ruprechtskirche
Schwedenpl.
Franz-Josefs-Kai
HOHER MARKT
Römische Ruinen
Griechische Kirche
Fleischmarkt
FLEISCHMARKT
Alte Schmiede
JESUITENKIRCHE
POSTSPARK.
Regierungsgebäude
Zollamtsstr.
Vordere
Hintere
Lugeck
Rotenturmstr.
STEPHANSDOM
Wollzeile
Alte Universität
Postg.
Dominikaner Kirche
Stubenring
Biberstr.
Stephanspl.
FIGARO-HAUS
Deutschordenshaus
Stubentor
MUSEUM FÜR ANGEWANDTE KUNST
WIEN MITTE
Landstraße
Weihburg-
Singerstr.
Stubenbastei
Franziskaner-Kirche
Palais Colloredo
STADTPALAIS DES PRINZEN EUGEN
Johannes-Anna-Kirche
Seilerstätte
gasse
Parkring
Stadtpark
Invalidenstr.
Ungargasse
Annag.
Schellinggasse
JOH.-STRAUS-DKM.
KURSALON
Am Heumarkt
RING
Schubertring
Johannesgasse
ÖAMTC
Café Schwarzenberg
LANDSTRASSE
Reisnerstr.
Hotel Imperial
KONZERT-HAUS
Musikvereinsgebäude
Lothringer-
HIST. MUSEUM
SCHWARZENBERG-PLATZ

## Town Centre, city districts (Stadtbezirke) 1 - 9 :

**Imperial**, Kärntner Ring 16, ✉ A-1015, ☎ (01) 50 11 00, *Fax (01) 50110410*, « Converted 19C palace » – 🛗, ⇆ rm, ▤ TV ☎ – 🏛 200. AE ⓓ E VISA JCB. ✖ rest
***Imperial*** *(booking essential) closed 13 July - 2 August* **Meals** à la carte 540/910 – ***Café Imperial :*** **Meals** à la carte 350/600 – **128 rm** ☕ 4910/8420 – 22 suites. KS a

**ANA Grand Hotel** M, Kärtner Ring 9, ✉ A-1010, ☎ (01) 51 58 00, *Fax (01) 5151313* – 🛗, ⇆ rm, ▤ TV ☎ 🚗 – 🏛 350. AE ⓓ E VISA JCB KS f
***Le ciel*** *(closed Sunday and August)* **Meals** 370 (lunch) and à la carte 620/840 – ***Unkai*** (Japanese cuisine) *(closed Monday lunch)* **Meals** 220 (lunch) and 450/1020 – **205 rm** ☕ 3770/6040 – 11 suites.

**Sacher**, Philharmonikerstr. 4, ✉ A-1010, ☎ (01) 5 14 56, *Fax (01) 51457810*, « Collection of valuable furniture and paintings » – 🛗, ⇆ rm, ▤ TV ☎. AE ⓓ E VISA JCB. ✖ rest JS x
**Meals** 450 (lunch) and à la carte 560/760 – **108 rm** ☕ 2770/7540 – 3 suites.

**Bristol**, Kärntner Ring 1, ✉ A-1015, ☎ (01) 51 51 60, *Fax (01) 51516550* – 🛗, ⇆ rm, ▤ TV ☎ – 🏛 180. AE ⓓ E VISA JCB. ✖ rest JS m
**Meals** (see also ***Korso*** below) – ***Rôtisserie Sirk :*** **Meals** à la carte 470/770 – **141 rm** ☕ 4190/8080 – 11 suites.

**Plaza Wien** M, Schottenring 11, ✉ A-1010, ☎ (01) 31 39 00, *Fax (01) 31390160*, Massage, Fƒ, ≘s – 🛗, ⇆ rm, ▤ TV ☎ ♿ 🚗 – 🏛 180. AE ⓓ E VISA JCB. ✖ rest
**Meals** (see ***La Scala*** below) – **218 rm** ☕ 2970/4840 – 36 suites. JP a

**Hotel im Palais Schwarzenberg**, Schwarzenbergplatz 9, ✉ A-1030, ☎ (01) 7 98 45 15, *Fax (01) 7894714*, « Converted 1727 baroque palace, park », 🌳, 🎾 – 🛗 TV ☎ P – 🏛 250. AE ⓓ E VISA JCB CY p
**Meals** 390 (lunch) and à la carte 530/830 – **44 rm** ☕ 3270/7740 – 6 suites.

**Vienna Hilton**, Landstraßer Hauptstr. 2 (near Stadtpark), ✉ A-1030, ☎ (01) 7 17 00, *Fax (01) 7130691*, ≤ – 🛗, ⇆ rm, ▤ TV ☎ 🚗 – 🏛 660. AE ⓓ E VISA JCB
***Arcadia :*** **Meals** à la carte 425/580 – ***Terminal Pub :*** **Meals** à la carte 190/320 – **600 rm** ☕ 4060/4820 – 19 suites. LR e

**Vienna Marriott Hotel**, Parkring 12a, ✉ A-1010, ☎ (01) 51 51 80, *Fax (01) 515186736*, Massage, Fƒ, ≘s, 🏊 – 🛗, ⇆ rm, ▤ TV ☎ ♿ 🚗 – 🏛 600. AE ⓓ E VISA JCB. ✖ rest KR d
**Meals** à la carte 300/600 – **313 rm** ☕ 3860/4120 – 7 suites.

**Inter-Continental**, Johannesgasse 28, ✉ A-1037, ☎ (01) 71 12 20, *Fax (01) 714489*, ≤, Fƒ, ≘s – 🛗, ⇆ rm, ▤ TV ♿ 🚗 – 🏛 1100. AE ⓓ E VISA JCB. ✖ rest
***Vier Jahreszeiten*** *(closed Saturday and Sunday, 2 weeks January and 3 weeks July - August)* **Meals** 490 (buffet lunch) and à la carte 475/750 – ***Brasserie :*** **Meals** 220 lunch and à la carte 380/500 – **460 rm** ☕ 3820/5090 – 25 suites. KS p

**Renaissance Penta Vienna Hotel** M (former imperial riding school with modern hotel wing), Ungargasse 60, ✉ A-1030, ☎ (01) 71 17 50, *Fax (01) 7117590*, Massage, ≘s, 🏊, 🌳 – 🛗, ⇆ rm, ▤ TV ☎ ♿ 🚗 – 🏛 450. AE ⓓ E VISA JCB CY a
**Meals** *(closed Sunday and Monday dinner)* 350 (buffet lunch) and à la carte 310/530 – **342 rm** ☕ 2300/3600.

**Holiday Inn Crowne Plaza Vienna** M, Handelskai 269, ✉ A-1020, ☎ (01) 7 27 77, *Fax (01) 72777199*, 🍽, Fƒ, ≘s, 🏊 (heated), 🎾 – 🛗, ⇆ rm, ▤ TV ☎ ♿ P – 🏛 300. AE ⓓ E VISA JCB. ✖ rest CY h
**Meals** 325 (buffet lunch) and à la carte 380/570 – **367 rm** ☕ 2140/3250.

**Radisson SAS-Palais Hotel**, Parkring 16, ✉ A-1010, ☎ (01) 51 51 70, *Fax (01) 5122216*, ≘s – 🛗, ⇆ rm, ▤ TV ♿ 🚗 – 🏛 240. AE ⓓ E VISA JCB
***Le siècle*** *(closed Saturday, Sunday, Bank Holidays and July - August)* **Meals** 340 (buffet lunch) and à la carte 480/790 – ***Palais Café :*** **Meals** à la carte 270/470 – **245 rm** ☕ 2560/4420 – 42 suites. KR z

**Ambassador**, Neuer Markt 5, ✉ A-1010, ☎ (01) 5 14 66, *Fax (01) 5132999* – 🛗 TV. AE ⓓ E VISA JCB JR s
**Meals** 250 (lunch) and à la carte 425/550 – **105 rm** ☕ 2000/2900.

**Das Triest** M, Wiedner Hauptstr. 12, ✉ A-1040, ☎ (01) 58 91 80, *Fax (01) 5891818*, 🍽, « Modern interior design », Fƒ, ≘s – 🛗, ⇆ rm, ▤ TV ☎ 🚗 – 🏛 60. AE ⓓ E VISA JCB. ✖ rest CY t
**Meals** *(closed Saturday and Sunday lunch)* 290/390 (lunch) and à la carte 310/505 – **73 rm** ☕ 2200/2800 – 3 suites.

**Hotel de France**, Schottenring 3, ✉ A-1010, ☎ (01) 31 36 80, *Fax (01) 3195969*, ≘s – 🛗, ⇆ rm, TV ♿ – 🏛 120. AE ⓓ E VISA JCB HP b
**Meals** *(closed Saturday)* 300/350 and à la carte 370/560 – **216 rm** ☕ 1950/2800 – 7 suites.

**Arcotel Hotel Wimberger** M, Neubaugürtel 34, ✉ A-1070, ☎ (01) 52 16 50, *Fax (01) 52165810*, ≘s – 🛗, ⇆ rm, ▤ rm, TV ☎ ♿ 🚗 – 🏛 700. AE ⓓ E VISA BY t
**Meals** 290 (buffet lunch) and à la carte 335/590 – **225 rm** ☕ 1700/2300 – 13 suites.

**Biedermeier**, Landstraßer Hauptstr. 28 (at Sünnhof), ✉ A-1030, ☎ (01) 71 67 10, *Fax (01) 71671503*, « Bedrooms furnished in the Biedermeier style » – rm, – 100. AE VISA JCB LR d
Meals à la carte 323/535 – **203 rm** 1950/2450 – 11 suites.

**Kaiserin Elisabeth** without rest, Weihburggasse 3, ✉ A-1010, ☎ (01) 51 52 60, *Fax (01) 515267* – . AE VISA JCB KR a
**63 rm** 1450/2450.

**City-Central** without rest, Taborstr. 8a, ✉ A-1020, ☎ (01) 21 10 50, *Fax (01) 21105140* – . AE VISA KP x
**58 rm** 1700/2520.

**Stefanie**, Taborstr. 12, ✉ A-1020, ☎ (01) 21 15 00, *Fax (01) 21150160*, – , rm, – 70. AE VISA JCB KLP d
Meals 245/450 and à la carte 320/430 – **131 rm** 1480/2520.

**K. u. K. Hotel Maria Theresia** without rest, Kirchberggasse 6 - 8, ✉ A-1070, ☎ (01) 5 21 23, *Fax (01) 5212370* – , rm, – 40. AE VISA JCB HS a
**123 rm** 1770/2600.

**Sofitel Belvedere**, Am Heumarkt 35-37, ✉ A-1030, ☎ (01) 71 61 60, *Fax (01) 71616844* – , rm, – 30. AE VISA JCB. rest
Meals à la carte 200/490 – **211 rm** 2000/2740. KS e

**K u. K Palais Hotel** without rest, Rudolfsplatz 11, ✉ A-1010, ☎ (01) 5 33 13 53, *Fax (01) 533135370* – , rm, – 40. AE VISA JCB JP h
**66 rm** 1770/2350.

**Astron Suite Hotel** without rest, Mariahilfer Str. 78, ✉ A-1070, ☎ (01) 5 21 72, *Fax (01) 5217215*, , – – 20. AE VISA JCB BY x
**54 rm** 1620/2160.

**Kummer**, Mariahilfer Str. 71a, ✉ A-1070, ☎ (01) 5 88 95, *Fax (01) 5878133* – , rm, . AE VISA JCB BY s
Meals 135/185 and à la carte 280/400 – **100 rm** 1595/2400.

**Erzherzog Rainer**, Wiedner Hauptstr. 27, ✉ A-1040, ☎ (01) 50 11 10, *Fax (01) 50111350* – , rm, rest, – 50. AE VISA JCB
Meals à la carte 245/425 – **84 rm** 1720/2220. CY g

**Astoria** (19C period house with typical interior), Führichgasse 1, ✉ A-1015, ☎ (01) 51 57 70, *Fax (01) 5157782* – , rm, – 20. AE VISA JCB JR r
Meals *(closed Saturday and Sunday)* à la carte 300/600 – **108 rm** 1700/2700.

**Lassalle** without rest, Engerthstr. 173, ✉ A-1020, ☎ (01) 21 31 50, *Fax (01) 21315100*, – – 40. AE VISA JCB. rest
**140 rm** 1350/1850 – 4 suites. CY r

**Arkadenhof** without rest, Viriotgasse 5, ✉ A-1090, ☎ (01) 3 10 08 37, *Fax (01) 3107686* – – 20. AE VISA BY c
**44 rm** 1380/1880.

**Rathauspark** without rest, Rathausstr. 17, ✉ A-1010, ☎ (01) 40 41 20, *Fax (01) 40412761* – – 20. AE VISA JCB HP s
**117 rm** 1450/2700.

**Europa**, Neuer Markt 3, ✉ A-1015, ☎ (01) 51 59 40, *Fax (01) 5138138* – , rm, . AE VISA JCB. rest JR a
Meals 250/550 and à la carte 220/400 – **113 rm** 1750/2700.

**Falkensteiner Hotel Palace**, Margaretenstr. 92, ✉ A-1050, ☎ (01) 54 68 60, *Fax (01) 5468686*, – – 100. AE VISA BZ b
Meals (residents only) – **117 rm** 1430/1990.

**Mercure Nestroy** without rest, Rotensterngasse 12, ✉ A-1020, ☎ (01) 21 14 00, *Fax (01) 211407*, – – 50. AE VISA LP b
**62 rm** 1590/1990 – 7 suites.

**President**, Wallgasse 23, ✉ A-1060, ☎ (01) 5 99 90, *Fax (01) 5967646*, – – 50. AE VISA BZ v
Meals *(closed Sunday)* à la carte 240/460 – **77 rm** 1350/2350.

**Tigra** without rest, Tiefer Graben 14, ✉ A-1010, ☎ (01) 53 39 64 10, *Fax (01) 5339645* – , rm, . AE VISA JP c
**75 rm** 1180/1900.

**Amadeus** without rest, Wildpretmarkt 5, ✉ A-1010, ☎ (01) 5 33 87 38, *Fax (01) 533873838* – . AE VISA JR y
*closed 22 to 28 December* – **30 rm** 1100/1980.

**Mercure Europaplatz** M, Matrosengasse 6, ✉ A-1060, ☎ (01) 59 90 10, *Fax (01) 5976900* – |♦|, ⇔ rm, ▤ TV ☎ ♿ 🚗 – 🏛 70. AE ⓓ E VISA JCB BY n
**Meals** à la carte 240/430 – **210 rm** ☕ 1590/2400 – 5 suites.

**Am Parkring**, Parkring 12, ✉ A-1015, ☎ (01) 51 48 00, *Fax (01) 5148040*, ≤ Vienna – |♦|, ⇔ rm, ▤ TV ☎ 📞 🚗. AE ⓓ E VISA JCB. ⊘ rest KR k
**Meals** *(closed Sunday and Monday dinner)* à la carte 350/510 – **65 rm** ☕ 1770/2600 – 7 suites.

**Accadia**, Margaretenstr. 53, ✉ A-1050, ☎ (01) 58 85 00, *Fax (01) 58850899*, ♨, ≘ – |♦| TV ☎ 🚗 – 🏛 40. AE ⓓ E VISA JCB BY m
**Meals** (dinner only) à la carte 330/450 – **104 rm** ☕ 1390/2300.

**König von Ungarn**, Schulerstr. 10, ✉ A-1010, ☎ (01) 51 58 40, *Fax (01) 515848* – |♦|, ▤ rm, TV ☎ – 🏛 15. AE ⓓ E VISA JCB KR f
**Meals** *(closed Saturday)* 350/620 and à la carte – **33 rm** ☕ 1800/2290.

**Capricorno** without rest, Schwedenplatz 3, ✉ A-1010, ☎ (01) 53 33 10 40, *Fax (01) 53376714* – |♦| TV ☎ 🚗 P. AE ⓓ E VISA KR x
**46 rm** ☕ 1400/2320.

**Mercure Wien City** without rest, Hollandstr. 3, ✉ A-1020, ☎ (01) 21 31 30, *Fax (01) 21313230* – |♦|, ⇔ rm, ▤ TV ☎ 📞 ♿ 🚗. AE ⓓ E VISA JCB KP a
**63 rm** ☕ 1490/1960.

**Mercure**, Fleischmarkt 1a, ✉ A-1010, ☎ (01) 53 46 00, *Fax (01) 53460232* – |♦|, ⇔ rm, ▤ TV ☎ ♿. AE ⓓ E VISA KR n
**Meals** à la carte 240/360 – **154 rm** ☕ 1690/2150.

**Artis** without rest, Rennweg 51, ✉ A-1030, ☎ (01) 7 13 25 21, *Fax (01) 7145930* – |♦|, ⇔ rm, TV ☎ 🚗 – 🏛 50. AE ⓓ E VISA JCB CY e
**168 rm** ☕ 1500/2100.

**Ibis**, Mariahilfer Gürtel 22, ✉ A-1060, ☎ (01) 5 99 98, *Fax (01) 5979090* – |♦|, ⇔ rm, ▤ TV ☎ ♿ 🚗 – 🏛 60. AE ⓓ E VISA BY e
**Meals** à la carte 230/330 – **341 rm** ☕ 995/1325.

XXXX ✿✿ **Steirereck**, Rasumofskygasse 2 / Ecke Weißgerberlände, ✉ A-1030, ☎ (01) 7 13 31 68, *Fax (01) 71351682* – ▤. AE ⓓ E VISA CY c
*closed Saturday, Sunday, Bank Holidays and 1 to 20 January* – **Meals** *(outstanding wine list, tour of the wine-cellar possible)* (booking essential) 395 (lunch) and à la carte 620/880
**Spec.** Artischocke mit Käsetascherl. Wachtel mit Backplaumen und Kohlgemüse. Marzipanknödel mit Brombeeren.

XXXX ✿ **Korso** - Hotel Bristol, Kärntner Ring 1, ✉ A-1015, ☎ (01) 51 51 65 46, *Fax (01) 51516550* – ▤. AE ⓓ E VISA JCB. ⊘ JS m
*closed Saturday lunch* – **Meals** 380 (lunch) and à la carte 690/1000
**Spec.** Salat von Flusskrebsen auf Bohnen und Ruccola. Gefüllte Bauernente auf Apfel-Ingwerkraut. Maroni-Lebkuchendalken mit Eierliköreis.

XXXX **La Scala** - Hotel Plaza Wien, Schottenring 11, ✉ A-1010, ☎ (01) 31 39 01 50, *Fax (01) 31390160* – ▤. AE ⓓ E VISA JCB. ⊘ JP a
*closed Saturday lunch, Sunday and August* – **Meals** 320 (lunch) and à la carte 400/840.

XXX **Drei Husaren**, Weihburggasse 4, ✉ A-1010, ☎ (01) 51 21 09 20, *Fax (01) 512109218* – AE ⓓ E VISA JCB KR u
**Meals** 425 (lunch) and à la carte 610/915.

XXX ✿ **Academie**, Untere Viaduktgasse 45/Marxergasse, ✉ A-1030, ☎ (01) 7 13 82 56, *Fax (01) 7138257* – AE ⓓ E VISA JCB CY y
*closed Saturday, Sunday, Bank Holidays and 3 weeks August* – **Meals** *(booking essential)* (outstanding wine list) 330 (lunch) and à la carte 470/700
**Spec.** Waller über Limetten gedämft. Kalbstafelspitz geschmort mit Balsamico. Gestockte Schokolade mit weißem Trüffeleis (Okt.-Dez).

XXX ✿ **Selina**, Laudongasse 13, ✉ A-1080, ☎ (01) 4 05 64 04, *Fax (01) 4080459* – AE ⓓ E VISA JCB BY f
*closed Sunday and Bank Holidays* – **Meals** *(booking essential)* 620 and à la carte 460/670
**Spec.** Schaumsuppe von Teigtaschen mit Rindfleisch und Bohnen, Kürbiskern-Rahm. Kalbsrahmbeuscherl mit Griessknöderln. Schokolade-Schupfnudeln in Nußkrokant-Brösel.

XXX **Grotta Azzurra** (Italian rest.), Babenberger Str. 5, ✉ A-1010, ☎ (01) 58 61 04 40, *Fax (01) 586104415* – AE ⓓ E VISA JCB HS s
*closed 24 to 26 December* – **Meals** 270 (lunch) and à la carte 320/580.

XXX **Steirer Stub'n**, Wiedner Hauptstr. 111, ✉ A-1050, ☎ (01) 5 44 43 49, *Fax (01) 5440888* – ▤. AE ⓓ E VISA BZ k
*closed Saturday in summer, Sunday and Bank Holidays* – **Meals** *(booking essential)* à la carte 370/530.

XX **Walter Bauer**, Sonnenfelsgasse 17, ✉ A-1010, ☎ (01) 5 12 98 71, *Fax (01) 5129871* – AE KR c
*closed Saturday lunch, Sunday, Monday and 18 July - 17 August* – **Meals** (booking essential) 295/595 and à la carte 380/680.

XX **Kupferdachl**, Schottengasse 7 (entrance Mölker Bastei), ✉ A-1010, ☎ (01) 5 33 93 81, *Fax (01) 53393814* – AE ⓓ E VISA JCB HP a
*closed Christmas* – **Meals** 250/480 and à la carte 345/595.

XX **Schubertstüberln**, Schreyvogelgasse 4, ✉ A-1010, ☎ (01) 5 33 71 87, *Fax (01) 5353546*, – AE ⓓ E VISA JCB HR e
*closed Saturday and Sunday* – **Meals** à la carte 330/580.

XX **Salut**, Wildpretmarkt 3, ✉ A-1010, ☎ (01) 5 33 13 22 – AE ⓓ E VISA JR y
*closed Sunday and Bank Holidays* – **Meals** 220/600 and à la carte 445/580.

XX **Plachutta**, Wollzeile 38, ✉ A-1010, ☎ (01) 5 12 15 77, *Fax (01) 512157720*, – ▤. ⓓ E VISA – *closed 28 July - 11 August* – **Meals** à la carte 345/550. KR b

X **Fadinger**, Wipplingerstr. 29, ✉ A-1010, ☎ (01) 5 33 43 41 JP f
✿ *closed Saturday and Sunday* – **Meals** (booking essential) 150/420 (lunch) and à la carte 180/470.
**Spec.** Tafelspitzsulz mit Vogerlsalat und Gemüsevinaigrette mit Kernöl. Rehmedaillons in Morchelsauce mit Thymiannockerl. Gekochter Grießstrudel mit Nußbrösel und Zwetschkenröster.

X **Zum Kuckuck**, Himmelpfortgasse 15, ✉ A-1010, ☎ (01) 5 12 84 70, *Fax (01) 7741855* – AE ⓓ E VISA JCB – *closed Sunday* – **Meals** 255 (lunch) and à la carte 395/600. KR v

X **Hedrich**, Stubenring 2, ✉ A-1010, ☎ (01) 5 12 95 88 LR a
*open 11am - 9pm, closed Friday to Sunday, Bank Holidays and August* – **Meals** 200/400 à la carte 280/495.

**City districts (Stadtbezirke) 10 - 15 :**

**Holiday Inn** M, Triester Str. 72, ✉ A-1100, ☎ (01) 6 05 30, *Fax (01) 60530580*, ≤, – |‡|, ⇔ rm, ▤ TV ♿ – 🏛 420. AE ⓓ E VISA JCB BZ f
**Meals** *(closed Saturday and Sunday lunch)* 275 (buffet lunch) and à la carte – **176 rm** ☐ 2545/2940 – 4 suites.

**Renaissance Wien**, Ullmannstr. 71, ✉ A-1150, ☎ (01) 89 10 20, *Fax (01) 89102100*, – |‡|, ⇔ rm, ▤ TV ♿ – 🏛 200. AE ⓓ E VISA JCB BZ a
***Orangerie*** **: Meals** a la carte 355/765 – ***Allegro*** **: Meals** 375/480 (buffet only) – **309 rm** ☐ 2040/3410 – 3 suites.

**Gartenhotel Altmannsdorf**, Hoffingergasse 26, ✉ A-1120, ☎ (01) 8 04 75 27, *Fax (0B1) 804752751*, , Park, – |‡|, ⇔ rm, TV ☎ – 🏛 60. AE ⓓ E VISA
**Meals** 190/440 à la carte 290/460 – **95 rm** ☐ 1300/1850. AZ s

**Trend Hotel Bosei** M, Gutheil-Schoder-Gasse 9, ✉ A-1100, ☎ (01) 66 10 60, *Fax (01) 6610699* – |‡|, ⇔ rm, TV ☎ P – 🏛 200. AE ⓓ E VISA BZ t
**Meals** à la carte 270/420 – **192 rm** ☐ 1320/2400 – 8 suites.

**Trend Hotel Favorita** M without rest, Laxenburger Str. 8, ✉ A-1100, ☎ (01) 60 14 60, *Fax (01) 60146720*, – |‡| TV ☎ – 🏛 150. AE ⓓ E VISA
**161 rm** ☐ 1460/1900 – 3 suites. CZ n

**Kaiserpark-Schönbrunn**, Grünbergstr. 11, ✉ A-1120, ☎ (01) 8 13 86 10, *Fax (01) 8138183* – |‡|, ⇔ rm, ▤ rest, TV ☎ P – 🏛 20. AE ⓓ E VISA. ✂ rest
**Meals** (dinner only) à la carte 210/410 – **60 rm** ☐ 950/1800. AZ w

**Austrotel**, Felberstr. 4, ✉ A-1150, ☎ (01) 98 11 10, *Fax (01) 98111930*, – |‡|, ⇔ rm, TV ☎ ♿ – 🏛 280. AE ⓓ E VISA BY z
**Meals** 200/300 à la carte 280/450 – **252 rm** ☐ 1950/2600.

**Reither** without rest, Graumanngasse 16, ✉ A-1150, ☎ (01) 8 93 68 41, *Fax (01) 8936835*, – |‡| ⇔ TV ☎ . AE ⓓ E VISA BZ r
*closed 22 to 28 December* – **50 rm** ☐ 1100/1650.

XXX **Altwienerhof** with rm, Herklotzgasse 6, ✉ A-1150, ☎ (01) 8 92 60 00, *Fax (01) 89260008*, « Winter garden, courtyard-terrace » – |‡| TV ☎. AE ⓓ E VISA
*closed 1 to 24 January* – **Meals** *(closed Saturday lunch and Sunday)* (outstanding wine list) 298 (lunch) and à la carte 480/695 – **23 rm** ☐ 650/1400. BZ s

XX Windows of Vienna, Wienerbergstr. 7 (22th floor), ✉ A-1100, ☎ (01) 6 07 94 80, *Fax (01) 6072267*, ✳ Vienna – |‡| ▤ BZ c

XX **Vikerl's Lokal**, Würfelgasse 4, ✉ A-1150, ☎ (01) 8 94 34 30, *Fax (01) 8924183*
*closed Sunday dinner and Monday, 3 weeks July to August* – **Meals** 255/360 and à la carte 335/430. BYZ d

XX **Hietzinger Bräu**, Auhofstr. 1, ✉ A-1130, ☎ (01) 87 77 08 70, *Fax (01) 877708722*, – ▤. ⓓ E VISA – *closed 27 July - 16 August and 24 to 26 December* – **Meals** *(mainly boiled beef dishes)* (booking essential) à la carte 370/570. AZ u

**City districts (Stadtbezirke) 16 - 19 :**

**Modul**, Peter-Jordan-Str. 78, ✉ A-1190, ✆ (01) 47 66 00, *Fax (01) 47660117*, – – 500. BY a
Meals 180/280 à la carte 310/470 – **40 rm** 1450/1750 – 8 suites.

**Landhaus Fuhrgassl-Huber** without rest, Rathstr. 24, ✉ A-1190, ✆ (01) 4 40 30 33, *Fax (01) 4402714*, « Country house atmosphere », – . AX m
*closed 3 weeks January - February* – **22 rm** 960/1470.

**Gartenhotel Glanzing** without rest, Glanzinggasse 23, ✉ A-1190, ✆ (01) 47 04 27 20, *Fax (01) 470427214*, , , – .
**18 rm** 980/1880. AX n

**Clima Villenhotel**, Nussberggasse 2c, ✉ A-1190, ✆ (01) 37 15 16 (Hotel) 37 16 61 (Rest.), *Fax (01) 371392*, , « Rest. Bockkeller, vaulted cellar with Tyrolian farmhouse furniture », , , , – – 30. BX a
Meals *(closed Sunday)* 190/250 and à la carte 360/630 – **27 rm** 1300/2500.

**Jäger** without rest, Hernalser Hauptstr. 187, ✉ A-1170, ✆ (01) 48 66 62 00, *Fax (01) 48666208* – . AY r
**18 rm** 950/1600.

**Celtes** without rest, Celtesgasse 1a, ✉ A-1190, ✆ (01) 4 40 41 51, *Fax (01) 4404152116* – . AX b
**16 rm** 850/1400.

**Park-Villa** without rest, Hasenauerstr. 12, ✉ A-1190, ✆ (01) 3 19 10 05/3 67 57 00, *Fax (01) 319100541/367570041*, , – . BY h
**21 rm** 1280/1950.

**Schild** without rest, Neustift am Walde 97, ✉ A-1190, ✆ (01) 44 04 04 40, *Fax (01) 4404000*, – . AX v
**30 rm** 840/1580.

**Eckel**, Sieveringer Str. 46, ✉ A-1190, ✆ (01) 3 20 32 18, *Fax (01) 3206660*, – – *closed Sunday, Monday, Bank Holidays, 10 to 23 August and 24 December - January* – **Meals** à la carte 330/685. AX s

**Plachutta** with rm, Heiligenstädter Str. 179, ✉ A-1190, ✆ (01) 37 41 25, *Fax (01) 37412520*, – . BX e
*closed 22 July - 11 August* – **Meals** *(mainly boiled beef dishes)* à la carte 370/590 – **4 rm** 760/1180.

**Sailer**, Gersthofer Str. 14, ✉ A-1180, ✆ (01) 47 92 12 10, *Fax (01) 479212118*, – – **Meals** à la carte 330/585. AY e

**City district (Stadtbezirk) 22 :**

**Trend Hotel Donauzentrum** without rest, Wagramer Str. 83, ✉ A-1220, ✆ (01) 20 35 54 50, *Fax (01) 2035545183*, – , rm, – 40. CX b
**137 rm** 1460/1900.

**Mraz u. Sohn**, Wallensteinstr. 59, ✉ A-1200, ✆ (01) 3 30 45 94, *Fax (01) 3501536* – *closed Saturday - Sunday, 1 week January and 3 weeks August* – **Meals** 390/560 and à la carte 510/645. CY s

**Heurigen and Buschen-Schänken (wine gardens)** – *(mostly self-service, hot and cold dishes from buffet, prices according to weight of chosen meals, therefore not shown below. Buschen-Schänken sell their own wines only)* :

**Oppolzer**, Himmelstr. 22, ✉ A-1190, ✆ (01) 32 24 16, *Fax (01) 322416*, « Garden » – *closed Sunday, Bank Holidays and Christmas* – **Meals** (dinner only) à la carte 190/300. BX p

**Altes Preßhaus**, Cobenzlgasse 15, ✉ A-1190, ✆ (01) 3 20 02 03, *Fax (01) 320020323*, , « Old vaulted wine cellar with wine press » – BX p
*closed January and February* – **Meals** (dinner only) (buffet) and à la carte 190/370.

**Wolff**, Rathstr. 44, ✉ A-1190, ✆ (01) 4 40 23 35, *Fax (01) 4401403*, « Terraced garden » – **Meals** (buffet only). AX m

**Fuhrgassl Huber**, Neustift am Walde 68, ✉ A-1190, ✆ (01) 4 40 14 05, *Fax 4402730*, (wine-garden with Viennese Schrammelmusik), « Courtyard-terrace » – AX b
*open from 2pm* – **Meals** (buffet only).

Kirchenstöckl, Cobenzlgasse 3, ✉ A-1190, ✆ (01) 32 66 62, *Fax (01) 4403917*, – **Meals** (dinner only). BX r

Grinzinger Hauermandl, Cobenzlgasse 20, ✉ A-1190, ✆ (01) 32 30 27, *Fax (01) 320571322*, – **Meals** (dinner only). BX q

Grinzinger Weinbottich, Cobenzlgasse 28, ✉ A-1190, ✆ (01) 32 42 37, *Fax (01) 32071322*, – **Meals** (dinner only). BX q

**at Auhof motorway station** *W : 8 km by ⑦ :*

**Novotel Wien-West**, Am Auhof, ✉ A-1140, ✆ (01) 97 92 54 20, *Fax (01) 9794140*, (heated), – |‡|, ⇆ rm, ▤ TV ☎ ♿ P – 🕴 180. AE ⓓ E VISA
**Meals** à la carte 200/410 – **114 rm** ☕ 1155/1410.

**at Perchtoldsdorf** *SW : 13 km by B12 and Breitenfurter Str.* AZ :

XXX ✿ **Jahreszeiten**, Hochstr. 17, ✉ A-2380, ✆ (01) 8 65 31 29, *Fax (01) 865312973* – ▤. AE ⓓ E VISA
*closed Saturday lunch, Sunday dinner, Monday, Bank Holidays and 3 weeks July - August* – **Meals** 330 (lunch) and à la carte 560/695
**Spec.** Lasagne von Hummer. Hausgebeizter Lachs auf Trüffelnudeln mit Roter Butter. Nougatknöderl auf Schokolade-Karamelsauce.

**at Vienna-Schwechat Airport** ③ : *20 km :*

**Sofitel Vienna Airport** M, at the airport, ✉ A-1300, ✆ (01) 70 15 10, *Fax (01) 7062828* – |‡|, ⇆ rm, TV ♿ P – 🕴 30. AE ⓓ E VISA JCB
**Meals** 190 (lunch) and à la carte 360/400 – **142 rm** ☕ 3130/3760.

**Novotel Wien Airport**, at the airport, ✉ A-1300, ✆ (01) 70 10 70, *Fax (01) 7073239*, ≘s – |‡|, ⇆ rm, TV ☎ ♿ P – 🕴 30. AE ⓓ E VISA JCB
**Meals** à la carte 170/370 – **183 rm** ☕ 1640/2050.

XXX **Le Gourmet**, Terminal 2, first floor, ✉ A-1300, ✆ (01) 70 07 52 28, *Fax (01) 70073563* – AE ⓓ E VISA JCB – **Meals** à la carte 420/590.

---

**INNSBRUCK** *Austria* 426 *G 7,* 987 ⑳ *– pop. 120 000 – alt. 580 m – Wintersport : 580/2300 m* 3 7 – **See** : *Maria-Theresien-Strasse★* CZ – ≤★★ *on the Nordkette, Belfry (Stadtturm)* CZ **B** – ✻★ *over the city – Little Golden Roof (Goldenes Dachl)★* CZ – *Helblinghaus★* CZ – *Hofburg★* CZ – *Hofkirche* CZ *(Maximilian's Mausoleum★, Silver Chapel★★) – Tyrol Museum of Popular Art (Tiroler Volkskunstmuseum)★★* CDZ – *"Ferdinandeum" Tyrol Museum (Tiroler Landesmuseum "Ferdinandeum")★* DZ **M**[2] – *Wilten Basilica★* AY – **Envir.** : *Hafelekar ✻★★ – Upland Tour (Mittelgebirge)★★ (Hall in Tirol★, Volders★, Igls★, – Elbögen road★★) – The Stubaital★.*

9 *Innsbruck-Igls, Lans (0521) 37 71 65 ;* 18 *Innsbruck-Igls, Rinn (05223) 81 77.*

🅱 *Innsbruck Information, Burggraben 3, ✆ (0521) 53 56, Fax (0512) 535643.*

ÖAMTC, *Andechsstr. 81, ✆ (0512) 3 32 01 20, Fax (0512) 391612.*

*Wien 733 – München 140 – Salzburg 164.*

Plans on following pages

**Europa-Tyrol**, Südtiroler Platz 2, ✉ A-6020, ✆ (0512) 59 31, *Fax (0512) 587800*, ≘s – |‡|, ⇆ rm, ▤ rest, TV ✆ ⇔ – 🕴 200. AE ⓓ E VISA JCB. ✻ rest DZ a
**Meals** à la carte 340/650 – **122 rm** ☕ 1550/3400 – 6 suites.

**Holiday Inn**, Salurner Str. 15, ✉ A-6010, ✆ (0512) 5 93 50, *Fax (0512) 5935220*, ≘s – |‡|, ⇆ rm, ▤ TV ✆ – 🕴 300. AE ⓓ E VISA JCB. ✻ rest CDZ b
***Guggeryllis*** : **Meals** à la carte 300/510 – **176 rm** ☕ 1550/2800 – 4 suites.

**Goldener Adler** ⛰, Herzog-Friedrich-Str. 6, ✉ A-6020, ✆ (0512) 57 11 11, *Fax (0512) 584409*, , « 14C Tyrolian inn » – |‡| TV ☎. AE ⓓ E VISA CZ c
**Meals** à la carte 315/580 – **37 rm** ☕ 1080/1600.

**Central**, Gilmstr. 5, ✉ A-6020, ✆ (0512) 59 20, *Fax (0512) 580310*, ≘s – |‡|, ⇆ rm, TV ☎ – 🕴 30. AE ⓓ E VISA DZ d
**Meals** à la carte 195/442 – **87 rm** ☕ 1250/2100.

**Maria Theresia** without rest, Maria Theresienstr. 31, ✉ A-6020, ✆ (0512) 59 33, *Fax (0512) 575619* – |‡| ⇆ TV ☎ ⇔ – 🕴 20. AE ⓓ E VISA JCB CZ g
**103 rm** ☕ 1350/2200.

**Romantik Hotel Schwarzer Adler**, Kaiserjägerstr. 2, ✉ A-6020, ✆ (0512) 58 71 09, *Fax (0512) 561697* – |‡|, ⇆ rm, TV ☎ ⇔ – 🕴 40. AE ⓓ E VISA DZ e
**Meals** *(closed Sunday and Bank Holidays)* à la carte 310/550 – **26 rm** ☕ 1200/2100.

**Neue Post**, Maximilianstr. 15, ✉ A-6020, ✆ (0512) 5 94 76, *Fax (0512) 581818* – |‡|, ⇆ rm, TV ☎ ✆ P. AE ⓓ E VISA JCB CZ v
**Meals** *(closed Sunday)* à la carte 215/400 – **60 rm** ☕ 1100/2600.

**Alpotel Tirol**, Innrain 13, ✉ A-6020, ✆ (0512) 57 79 31, *Fax (0512) 57793115*, ≘s – |‡|, ▤ rest, TV ☎ ♿ ⇔ – 🕴 50. AE ⓓ E VISA – **Meals** *(closed Saturday lunch, Sunday and Bank Holidays)* à la carte 290/540 – **73 rm** ☕ 1040/1680. CZ f

**Grauer Bär**, Universitätsstr. 7, ✉ A-6021, ✆ (0512) 5 92 40, *Fax (0512) 574535*, ≘s – |‡| TV ☎ P – 🕴 150. AE ⓓ E VISA JCB. ✻ rest DZ k
**Meals** à la carte 265/465 – **98 rm** ☕ 1050/1900.

**Sporthotel Penz**, Fürstenweg 183, ✉ A-6020, ✆ (0512) 2 25 14, *Fax (0512) 22514124* – |‡| TV ☎ P – 🕴 50. AE E VISA. ✻ by Fürstenweg AY
**Meals** à la carte 195/410 – **70 rm** ☕ 780/1380.

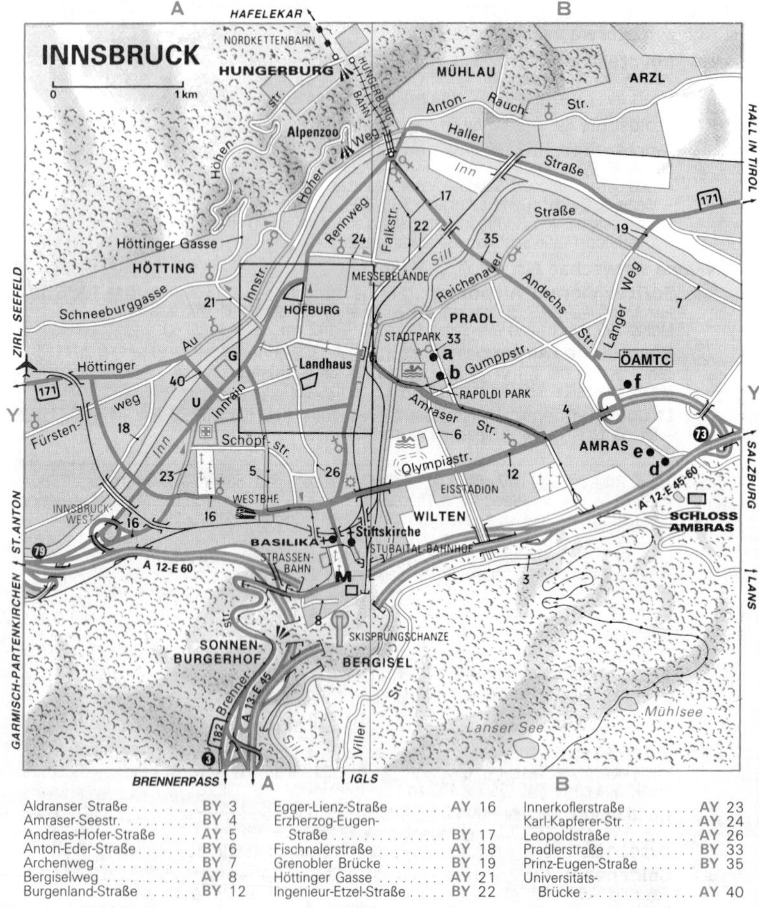


Aldranser Straße . . . . . . . . BY 3
Amraser-Seestr. . . . . . . . . . BY 4
Andreas-Hofer-Straße . . . . . AY 5
Anton-Eder-Straße . . . . . . . BY 6
Archenweg . . . . . . . . . . . . BY 7
Bergiselweg . . . . . . . . . . . AY 8
Burgenland-Straße . . . . . . . BY 12
Egger-Lienz-Straße . . . . . . AY 16
Erzherzog-Eugen-Straße . . . . . . . . . . . . BY 17
Fischnalerstraße . . . . . . . . AY 18
Grenobler Brücke . . . . . . . BY 19
Höttinger Gasse . . . . . . . . AY 21
Ingenieur-Etzel-Straße . . . . BY 22
Innerkoflerstraße . . . . . . . . AY 23
Karl-Kapferer-Str. . . . . . . . . AY 24
Leopoldstraße . . . . . . . . . . AY 26
Pradlerstraße . . . . . . . . . . BY 33
Prinz-Eugen-Straße . . . . . . . BY 35
Universitäts-Brücke . . . . . . . . . . . . . AY 40

**Maximilian** without rest, Marktgraben 7, ✉ A-6020, ✆ (0512) 5 99 67, *Fax (0512) 577450* – 🛗 TV ☎. AE ⓓ E VISA — CZ a
**40 rm** ☐ 850/1800.

**Innsbruck**, Innrain 3, ✉ A-6020, ✆ (0512) 5 98 68, *Fax (0512) 572280*, ≘s, 🏊 – 🛗 ▤ TV ☎ 🚗. AE ⓓ E VISA — CZ e
**Meals** (dinner only)(residents only) – **91 rm** ☐ 1100/1800.

**Zach** without rest, Wilhelm-Greil-Str. 11, ✉ A-6020, ✆ (0512) 58 96 67, *Fax (0512) 5896677* – 🛗 TV ☎. AE ⓓ E VISA — DZ h
**24 rm** ☐ 750/1300.

**Tourotel Breinössl**, Maria Theresien Str. 12, ✉ A-6020, ✆ (0512) 58 41 65, *Fax (0512) 58416526*, beer garden – 🛗, ⇷ rm, TV ☎ Ⓟ. AE ⓓ E VISA JCB — CZ p
**Meals** à la carte 170/300 – **40 rm** ☐ 950/1480.

**Weißes Rößl** 🐎, Kiebachgasse 8, ✉ A-6020, ✆ (0512) 58 30 57, *Fax (0512) 5830575*, 🍴 – 🛗 TV ☎. AE E VISA JCB — CZ n
*closed 2 weeks April and November* – **Meals** *(closed Sunday and Bank Holidays)* à la carte 210/410 – **14 rm** ☐ 850/1500.

**Weisses Kreuz** 🐎, Herzog-Friedrich-Str.31, ✉ A-6020, ✆ (0512) 5 94 79, *Fax (0512) 5947990*, 🍴, « 15C Tyrolian inn » – TV ☎. AE E VISA — CZ r
**Meals** à la carte 210/430 – **39 rm** ☐ 720/1380.

# INNSBRUCK

Anichstraße . . . . . . . . . . . . CZ
Burggraben . . . . . . . . . . . . CZ 14
Herzog-Friedrich-Straße . . . CZ 20
Maria-Theresien-Straße . . . . CZ
Marktgraben . . . . . . . . . . . . CZ
Museumstraße . . . . . . . . . CDZ

Adolf Pichler-Platz . . . . . . . . CZ 2
Bozner Platz . . . . . . . . . . . . DZ 10
Domplatz . . . . . . . . . . . . . . CZ 15
Ingenieur-Etzel-Straße . . . . . DZ 22
Landhausplatz . . . . . . . . . . . CZ 25
Leopoldstraße . . . . . . . . . . . CZ 26
Meinhardstr. . . . . . . . . . . . . DZ 28
Meraner Straße . . . . . . . . . CZ 30
Pfarrgasse . . . . . . . . . . . . . CZ 32
Stiftgasse . . . . . . . . . . . . . . CZ 37
Südbahnstraße . . . . . . . . . . DZ 38

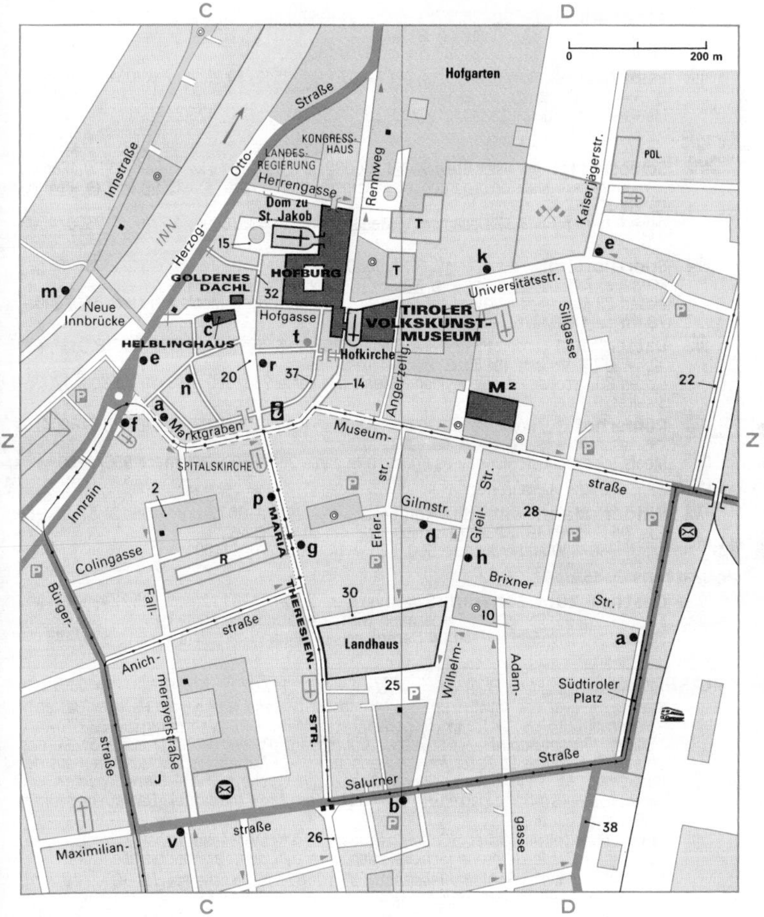


---

**Mondschein** without rest, Mariahilfstr. 6, A-6020, (0512) 2 27 84, *Fax (0512) 2278490* – AE E VISA JCB — CZ m
**34 rm** 700/1400.

**Altstadtstüberl**, Riesengasse 11, A-6020, (0512) 58 23 47, *Fax (0512) 583495* – AE E VISA JCB — CZ t
*closed Sunday and Bank Holidays* – **Meals** à la carte 310/450.

## at Innsbruck-Amras :

**Austrotel Innsbruck**, Bernhard-Höfel-Str. 16, A-6020, (0512) 34 43 33, *Fax (0512) 344428*, – rm, – 220. AE E VISA — BY f
**Meals** à la carte 180/430 – **135 rm** 1360/2090.

**Kapeller**, Philippine-Welser-Str. 96, A-6020, (0512) 34 31 06, *Fax (0512) 34310668*, – – 50. AE E VISA — BY e
Meals *(closed Monday lunch, Sunday and Bank Holidays)* 250/480 and à la carte 275/520 – **36 rm** 700/1650.

**Bierwirt**, Bichlweg 2, ✉ A-6020, ☎ (0512) 34 21 43, *Fax (0512) 3421435*, « Cosy lounge », – |♦|, rm, – 80. BY d
**Meals** *(closed Saturday lunch and Sunday)* à la carte 185/415 – **47 rm** 720/1100.

**at Innsbruck-Pradl :**

**Alpinpark**, Pradler Str. 28, ✉ A-6020, ☎ (0512) 34 86 00, *Fax (0512) 364172*, – – 30. AE E VISA BY a
**Meals** à la carte 210/500 – **87 rm** 970/1600.

**Leipzigerhof**, Defreggerstr. 13, ✉ A-6020, ☎ (0512) 34 35 25, *Fax (0512) 394357* – rm, . AE E VISA BY b
**Meals** *(closed Sunday)* à la carte 200/390 – **55 rm** 650/1250.

**at Igls** *S : 4 km by Viller Str.* AB *:*

**Schlosshotel**, Viller Steig 2, ✉ A-6080, ☎ (0512) 37 72 17, *Fax (0512) 378679*, ≤ mountains, « Mansion in garden, elegant installation », – – 15. AE E VISA. rest
*closed 15 October - 17 December* – **Meals** à la carte 400/600 – **20 rm** 2300/4500 – 6 suites.

**Sporthotel Igls**, Hilber Str. 17, ✉ A-6080, ☎ (0512) 37 72 41, *Fax (0512) 378679*, Massage, – – 50. AE E VISA. rest
*closed 22 March - 31 May and 4 October - 19 December* – **Meals** à la carte 350/600 – **78 rm** 1400/2760 – 6 suites.

**Batzenhäusl**, Lanserstr. 12, ✉ A-6080, ☎ (0512) 3 86 18, *Fax (0512) 386187*, – . AE E VISA. rest
*closed 20 October - 15 December* – **Meals** à la carte 235/560 – **30 rm** 800/1700 – 3 suites.

**Römerhof**, Römerstr. 62, ✉ A-6080, ☎ (0512) 37 89 02, *Fax (0512) 37890420*, – . AE E VISA
**Meals** *(closed lunch Monday to Friday)* à la carte 260/650 – **20 rm** 950/1700.

**at Lans** *SE : 6 km by Aldranser Str.* BY *:*

**Wilder Mann** with rm, Römerstr. 12, ✉ A-6072, ☎ (0512) 37 96 96, *Fax (0512) 379139*, – – 40. AE E VISA
**Meals** 350/420 and à la carte 300/525 – **14 rm** 700/1400.

**at Wattens** *E : 16 km : by A 12* BY *:*

**Gasthof Zum Schwan**, Swarovskistr. 2, ✉ A-6112, ☎ (05224) 5 21 21, *Fax (05224) 55175*, « Tyrolian inn with cosy atmosphere » –
*closed Saturday, Sunday and 24 December - 6 January* – **Meals** à la carte 320/445.

---

**SALZBURG** *Austria* 426 *L 5,* 420 *W 23,* 987 ㊶ *– pop. 147 000 – alt. 425 m –* ☎ *0662.*

**See :** *≤★★ over the town (from the Mönchsberg)* X *and ≤★★ (from Hettwer Bastei)* Y *– Hohensalzburg ★★* X, Z *: ≤★★ (from the Kuenburg Bastion), ★★ (from the Reck Tower), Museum (Burgmuseum)★ – St. Peter's Churchyard (Petersfriedhof)★★* Z *– St. Peter's Church (Stiftskirche St. Peter)★★* Z *– Residenz★★* Z *– Natural History Museum (Haus der Natur)★★* Y **M²** *– Franciscan's Church (Franziskanerkirche)★* Z **A** *– Getreidegasse★* Y *– Mirabell Gardens (Mirabellgarten)★* V *(Grand Staircase ★★ of the castle) – Baroquemuseum ★* V **M³** *– Dom★* Z.

**Envir. :** *Road to the Gaisberg (Gaisbergstraße)★★ (≤★) by ① – Untersberg★ by ② : 10 km (with ) – Castle Hellbrunn (Schloß Hellbrunn)★ by Nonntaler Hauptstraße* X.

*9 Salzburg-Wals, Schloß Klessheim, ☎ (0662) 85 08 51 ; 9 Hof (① : 20 km), ☎ (06229) 23 90 ; 18 St. Lorenz (① : 29 km), ☎ (06232) 38 35.*

*Innsbrucker Bundesstr. 95 (by ③), ☎ (0662) 85 12 23 - City Air Terminal, Südtiroler Platz (Autobus Station)* V.

*Lastenstraße – Exhibition Centre (Messegelände), Linke Glanzeile 65, ☎ 3 45 66.*

*Tourist Information, Mozartplatz 5, ☎ (0662) 88 98 73 30.*

ÖAMTC, *Alpenstr. 102 (by ②), ☎ (0662) 63 99 90, Fax (0662) 6399945.*

*Wien 292 ① – Innsbruck 177 ③ – München 140 ③*

Plans on following pages

**Österreichischer Hof**, Schwarzstr. 5, ✉ A-5020, ☎ (0662) 8 89 77, *Fax (0662) 8897714*, « Salzach-side setting, terrace with ≤ old town and castle » – rm, – 70. AE E VISA JCB Y b
***Zirbelzimmer* : Meals** à la carte 430/680 – ***Salzach-Grill* : Meals** à la carte 250/500 – **120 rm** 1800/7800 – 7 suites.

**Sheraton**, Auerspergstr. 4, ✉ A-5020, ☎ (0662) 88 99 90, *Fax (0662) 881776*, « Terrace in spa gardens », entrance to the spa facilities – rm, – 120. AE E VISA JCB V s
**Meals** à la carte 240/560 – **163 rm** 2100/5270 – 9 suites.

# SALZBURG

| | | | | | | | |
|---|---|---|---|---|---|---|---|
| Mirabellplatz | V 26 | Auerspergstraße | V 3 | Lindhofstr. | V 22 |
| Rainerstraße | V | Bürglsteinstraße | X 5 | Nonntaler Hauptstr. | X 29 |
| | | Erzabt-Klotz-Str. | X 9 | Schießstattstr. | V 33 |
| | | Gstättengasse | X 12 | Schwarzstr. | V 34 |
| | | Kaiserschützenstr. | V 20 | Späthgasse | X 37 |

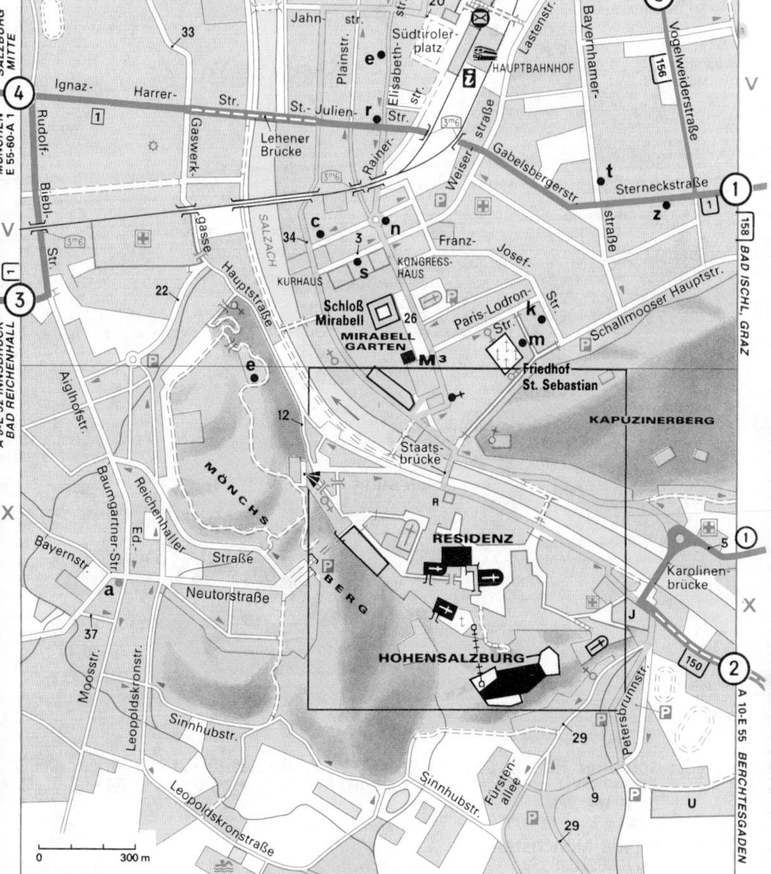


**Altstadt Radisson SAS**, Judengasse 15, ✉ A-5020, ☎ (0662) 8 48 57 10, *Fax (0662) 8485716*, « Modernised 14C nobleman's house, antique furnishings » – rm, rm, – 35. AE E VISA JCB. rest Y s
Meals à la carte 370/550 – **60 rm** 3325/6510 – 13 suites.

**Bristol**, Makartplatz 4, ✉ A-5020, ☎ (0662) 87 35 57, *Fax (0662) 8735576* – rm, – 60. AE E VISA JCB Y a
*closed early January - late March* – **Meals** (see ***Bei Bruno*** below) – **64 rm** 1960/5300 – 9 suites.

**Crowne Plaza-Pitter**, Rainerstr. 6, ✉ A-5020, ☎ (0662) 8 89 78, *Fax (0662) 878893*, rm, – 160. AE E VISA JCB V n
***Rainerstube*** *(dinner only)* **Meals** à la carte 360/510 – ***Auersberg* :** **Meals** à la carte 240/400 – **186 rm** 1900/4800 – 6 suites.

**Ramada**, Fanny-von-Lehnert-Str. 7, ✉ A-5020, ☎ (0662) 4 68 80, *Fax (0662) 4688298*, Massage, rm, – 800. AE E VISA JCB by Kaiserschützenstraße V
**Meals** à la carte 260/380 – **257 rm** 2370/4000.

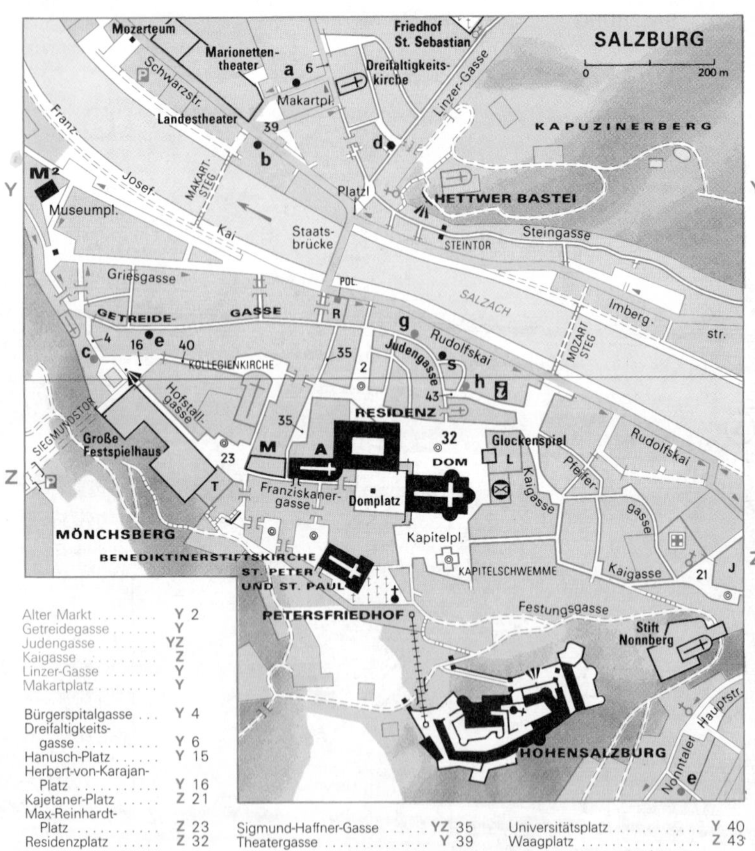


**Goldener Hirsch**, Getreidegasse 37, ✉ A-5020, ☎ (0662) 8 08 40, *Fax (0662) 843349*, « 15C nobleman's house, tastefully furnished » – |♦|, ⇔ rm, ▤ TV – 🏛 30. AE ⓓ E VISA JCB Y e
**Meals** à la carte 500/630 – **70 rm** ☐ 2370/7850 – 3 suites.

**Schloß Mönchstein** 🐌, Mönchsberg Park 26, ✉ A-5020, ☎ (0662) 8 48 55 50, *Fax (0662) 848559*, ≤ Salzburg and surroundings, 🌂, « Small castle with elegant, stylish furnishings, wedding chapel, park », 🌳, 🎾 – |♦| TV 🚗 Ⓟ. AE ⓓ E VISA JCB. 🚫 rest X e
*closed early February - mid March* – **Meals** à la carte 470/1150 – **17 rm** ☐ 2900/6500.

**Rosenberger**, Bessarabierstr. 94, ✉ A-5020, ☎ (0662) 4 35 54 60, *Fax (0662) 43951095*, ⇔ – |♦|, ⇔ rm, TV ♿ 🚗 Ⓟ – 🏛 360. AE ⓓ E VISA
**Meals** à la carte 250/410 🌡 – **120 rm** ☐ 1290/1850. by ④

**Dorint-Hotel**, Sterneckstr. 20, ✉ A-5020, ☎ (0662) 88 20 31, *Fax (0662) 8820319*, ⇔ – |♦|, ⇔ rm, TV ☎ ♿ 🚗 – 🏛 160. AE ⓓ E VISA. 🚫 rest V z
**Meals** à la carte 220/420 – **140 rm** ☐ 1530/2080 – 4 suites.

**Carlton** without rest, Markus-Sittikus-Str. 3, ✉ A-5020, ☎ (0662) 88 21 91, *Fax (0662) 87478447*, ⇔ – |♦| ⇔ TV ☎ 🚗 Ⓟ. AE ⓓ E VISA JCB V c
**39 rm** ☐ 1430/2520 – 13 suites.

**Mercure**, Bayerhamerstr. 14, ✉ A5020, ☎ (0662) 8 81 43 80, *Fax (0662) 871111411*, 🌂 – |♦|, ⇔ rm, TV ☎ ♿ 🚗 Ⓟ – 🏛 100. AE ⓓ E VISA JCB V t
**Meals** à la carte 220/370 – **121 rm** ☐ 1290/1990.

**Novotel Salzburg City**, Franz-Josef-Str. 26, ✉ A-5020, ☎ (0662) 88 20 41, *Fax (0662) 874240*, ⇔ – |♦|, ⇔ rm, TV ☎ ♿ 🚗 Ⓟ – 🏛 75. AE ⓓ E VISA JCB
**Meals** à la carte 200/380 – **140 rm** ☐ 1370/2280. V k

**Zum Hirschen**, St.-Julien-Str. 21, A-5020, (0662) 88 90 30, *Fax (0662) 8890358*, Massage, - . AE E VISA JCB V r
**Meals** à la carte 200/405 – **64 rm** 840/1750.

**Schaffenrath**, Alpenstr. 115, A-5020, (0662) 63 90 00, *Fax (0662) 639005*, , Massage, - , rm, - 90. AE E VISA JCB. rest by ②
**Meals** à la carte 185/370 – **51 rm** 990/1680.

**Kasererhof** without rest, Alpenstr. 6, A-5020, (0662) 6 39 65, *Fax (0662) 6396550*, - . AE E VISA JCB by ②
*closed February* – **53 rm** 995/3560.

**Wolf-Dietrich**, Wolf-Dietrich-Str. 7, A-5020, (0662) 87 12 75, *Fax (0662) 882320*, , - . AE E VISA JCB V m
*closed early February - mid March* – **Meals** *(closed Sunday)* (dinner only) à la carte 255/395 – **29 rm** 950/1720.

**Hohenstauffen** without rest, Elisabethstr. 19, A-5020, (0662) 8 77 66 90, *Fax (0662) 87219351* – . AE E VISA JCB V e
**27 rm** 790/1995.

**Fuggerhof** without rest, Eberhard-Fugger-Str. 9, A-5020, (0662) 6 41 29 00, *Fax (0662) 6412904*, ←, , , – . 
*closed 20 December - 26 January* – **20 rm** 980/2520. by Bürglsteinstr. X

Gablerbräu, Linzer Gasse 9, A-5020, (0662) 8 89 65, *Fax (0662) 8896555*, – – 25 – **52 rm.** Y d

**Alt Salzburg**, Bürgerspitalgasse 2, A-5020, (0662) 84 14 76, *Fax (0662) 841477* – AE E VISA JCB Y c
*closed Monday lunch and Sunday except festival period* – **Meals** à la carte 300/490.

**Bei Bruno** -Hotel Bristol, Makartplatz 4, A-5020, (0662) 87 84 17 – AE E VISA JCB – *closed Sunday except festival period, 1 week February and 2 weeks March* – **Meals** à la carte 270/560. Y a

**K+K Restaurant am Waagplatz**, Waagplatz 2 (1st floor), A-5020, (0662) 84 21 56, *Fax (0662) 84215633*, , « Medieval dinner with period performance in the Freysauff-Keller (by arrangement) » – AE E VISA Z h
*closed Sunday January to Easter* – **Meals** (booking essential) à la carte 315/480.

**Riedenburg**, Neutorstr. 31, A-5020, (0662) 83 08 15, *Fax (0662) 8443529*, – . AE E VISA – *closed Monday lunch and Sunday* – **Meals** à la carte 375/530. X a

**Zum Mohren**, Judengasse 9, A-5020, (0662) 84 23 87, *Fax (0662) 450179* – AE E VISA – *closed Sunday, Bank Holidays and mid June - mid July* – **Meals** (booking essential) à la carte 220/450. Y g

**at Salzburg-Aigen** *by Bürglsteinstr.* X :

**Rosenvilla** without rest, Höfelgasse 4, A-5026, (0662) 62 17 65, *Fax (0662) 6252308* – . AE – **15 rm** 1150/ 2270.

**Doktorwirt**, Glaser Str. 9, A-5026, (0662) 62 29 73, *Fax (0662) 62171724*, , , (heated), – – 25. AE E VISA JCB. rest
*closed 10 to 26 February and late October - late November* – **Meals** *(closed Monday)* à la carte 200/400 – **39 rm** 780/1900.

**Gasthof Schloß Aigen**, Schwarzenbergpromenade 37, A-5026, (0662) 62 12 84, *Fax (0662) 621284*, – . AE E VISA – *closed Thursday lunch, Wednesday and 3 weeks January - February* – **Meals** à la carte 315/495.

**at Salzburg-Gnigl** *by* ① :

**Pomodoro** (Italian rest.), Eichstr. 54, A-5023, (0662) 64 04 38, – AE E VISA
*closed Monday, Tuesday, Christmas to 6 January and mid July - late August* – **Meals** (booking essential) à la carte 305/440.

**at Salzburg-Liefering** *by* ④ :

**Brandstätter**, Münchner Bundesstr. 69, A-5020, (0662) 43 45 35, *Fax (0662) 43453590*, , , , – – 30. AE E VISA. rest
*closed 22 to 27 December* – **Meals** *(closed 2 to 16 January, 1 week May and Sunday except in season)* (booking essential) à la carte 295/600 – **34 rm** 980/2300
**Spec.** Vorspeisenvariation von geräucherten Mondseefischen. Lauwarmer Kalbsbrustsalat mit Gemüsevinaigrette. Bauernente im Rohr gebraten.

**at Salzburg-Maria Plain** *by Plainstr.* V :

**Maria Plain** (17C inn), Plainbergweg 41, A-5101, (0662) 4 50 70 10, *Fax (0662) 45070119*, « Garden with ← », – – 40. AE E VISA
*closed 1 week July* – **Meals** *(closed Tuesday and Wednesday except festival period)* à la carte 270/380 – **27 rm** 880/1400 – 5 suites.

**at Salzburg-Nonntal**

**Purzelbaum** (Bistro-rest.), Zugallistr. 7, A-5020, (0662) 84 88 43, *Fax (0662) 8443529,* – AE E VISA Z e
*closed Monday lunch and Sunday* – **Meals** (booking essential for dinner) à la carte 445/580.

**on the Heuberg** *NE : 3 km by ① – alt. 565 m*

**Schöne Aussicht**, Heuberg 3, A-5023 *Salzburg,* (0662) 64 06 08, *Fax (0662) 6406082,* « Garden with Salzburg and Alps », – 30. AE E VISA. rest
*closed November - March* – **Meals** (dinner only) a la carte 265/480 – **28 rm** 700/1800.

**on the Gaisberg** *by ① :*

**Vitalhotel Kobenzl**, Gaisberg 11, *alt. 730 m,* A-5020 *Salzburg,* (0662) 64 15 10, *Fax (0662) 642238,* « Beautiful panoramic location with Salzburg and Alps », Massage, – rm, – 40. AE E VISA. rest – **Meals** à la carte 325/520 – **40 rm** 1650/4500 – 5 suites.

**Romantik-Hotel Gersberg Alm**, Gersberg 37, *alt. 800 m,* A-5023 *Salzburg-Gnigl,* (0662) 64 12 57, *Fax (0662) 644278,* – – 55. AE E VISA. rest – **Meals** (booking essential) à la carte 280/485 – **40 rm** 990/2900.

**near Airport** *by ③ :*

**Radisson-SAS-Airport-Center-Hotel**, Bundesstr. 4, A-5073 *Salzburg-Wals,* (0662) 8 58 10, *Fax (0662) 85814000* – rm, – 90. AE E VISA – **Meals** à la carte 230/455 – **152 rm** 1300/1970 – 7 suites.

**Airporthotel**, Loigstr. 20a, A-5020 *Salzburg-Loig,* (0662) 85 00 20, *Fax (0662) 85002044,* – rm, – 20. AE E VISA JCB
**Meals** (residents only) – **37 rm** 990/1960.

**at Anif** *② : 7 km*

**Friesacher,** A-5081, (06246) 89 77, *Fax (06246) 897749,* Massage, – – 25 – *closed 2 to 22 January* – **Meals** *(closed Wednesday except festival period)* à la carte 180/400 – **52 rm** 720/1460.

**at Elixhausen** *N : 8 km by ⑤ :*

**Romantik-Hotel Gmachl**, Dorfstr. 14, A-5161, (0662) 48 02 12, *Fax (0662) 48021272,* (heated), (indoor), (indoor) – – 40. AE E VISA – *closed mid June - early July* – **Meals** *(closed Sunday dinner and Monday lunch)* à la carte 270/450 – **34 rm** 980/2200 – 3 suites.

**at Hallwang-Söllheim** *by ①, and Linzer Bundesstraße : 7 km :*

**Pfefferschiff**, Söllheim 3, A-5023, (0662) 66 12 42, *Fax (0662) 661841,* – . AE. – *closed Sunday, Monday, late June - mid July and 1 week September* – **Meals** à la carte 400/670
**Spec.** Blunzenguglhupf mit Stöcklkraut. Lammcrré auf Porree-Erdäpfelgratin. Marrillenschmarren mit Vanilleeis.

**at Hof** *by ① : 20 km :*

**Schloß Fuschl** (former 15C hunting seat with 3 guesthouses), A-5322, (06229) 2 25 30, *Fax (06229) 2253531,* Massage, – – 100. AE E VISA JCB. rest
**Meals** à la carte 480/745 – **84 rm** 2100/4000 – 12 suites.

**Jagdhof am Fuschlsee** (former 18C farmhouse with guesthouse), A-5322, (06229) 2 37 20, *Fax (06229) 2372413,* – – 90. AE E VISA JCB. rest – **Meals** à la carte 245/400 – **57 rm** 875/1925.

**at Fuschl am See** *① : 26 km :*

**Ebner's Waldhof**, Seepromenade, A-5330, (06226) 82 64, *Fax (06226) 8644,* Massage, – – 60. rest
*closed 3 weeks March - April and November - 15 December* – **Meals** (booking essential) à la carte 290/465 – **75 rm** 770/2560.

**at Mondsee** *① : 28 km (by motorway A 1)*

**Seehof** (SE : 7 km), A-5311 *Loibichl,* (06232) 50 31, *Fax (06232) 503151,* « Garden-terrace », Massage, – rest, – 15.
*closed mid September - mid May* – **Meals** à la carte 370/515 – **35 rm** 3600/5720 – 4 suites.

**at Werfen** *S : 42 km by ② and A 10 :*

**Karl-Rudolf Obauer** with rm, Markt 46, A-5450, (06468) 5 21 20, *Fax (06468) 521212* – rest, . AE
**Meals** (booking essential) 380/800 and à la carte 510/805 – **58 rm** 980/1700
**Spec.** Forellenstrudel "Obauer" mit Veltlinersauce. Schweinebackerl und Sauhaxl mit Rahmschwammerl. Mohnmarillen mit Honigschlag und Vanilleeis.

# *Benelux*

## Belgium

BRUSSELS – ANTWERP – BRUGES – LIÈGE

## Grand Duchy of Luxembourg

LUXEMBOURG

## Netherlands

AMSTERDAM – The HAGUE – ROTTERDAM

# PRACTICAL INFORMATION

## LOCAL CURRENCY

**Belgian Franc:** *100 BEF = 2,71 USD ($) (Jan. 98) can also be used in Luxembourg*

**Dutch Florin:** *100 NLG = 49,58 USD ($) (Jan. 98)*

## TOURIST INFORMATION

*Telephone numbers and addresses of Tourist Offices are given in the text of each city under* ℹ.

**National Holiday:** *Belgium: 21 July; Netherlands: 30 April; Luxembourg: 23 June.*

## AIRLINES

**SABENA :** *rue Marché-aux-Herbes 110, 1000 Bruxelles, ☎ (02) 723 89 40, Airport Findel – Terminal, L-1110 Luxembourg, ☎ 432 42 41, Strawinskylaan 813, 1077 XX Amsterdam, ☎ (020) 470 14 70.*

**LUXAIR :** *Luxembourg Airport, L-2987 Luxembourg, ☎ 4 79 81.*

**KLM :** *avenue Marnix 28, 1000 Bruxelles, ☎ (02) 507 70 70, avenue Marnix 28, 1000 Bruxelles, ☎ 42 48 42, Amsterdamseweg 55, 1182 GP Amstelveen, ☎ (020) 649 91 23.*

## FOREIGN EXCHANGE

**In Belgium,** *banks close at 4.30pm and weekends;*

**in the Netherlands,** *banks close at 5.00pm and weekends, Schiphol Airport exchange offices open daily from 6.30am to 11.30pm.*

## TRANSPORT

**Taxis:** *may be hailed in the street, at taxi ranks or called by telephone.*

**Bus, tramway:** *practical for long and short distances and good for sightseeing.*

*Brussels has a* **Métro** *(subway) network. In each station complete information and plans will be found.*

## POSTAL SERVICES – SHOPPING

*Post offices open Monday to Friday from 9am to 5pm in Benelux.*
*Shops and boutiques are generally open from 9am to 7pm in Belgium and Luxembourg, and from 9am to 6pm in the Netherlands. The main shopping areas are:*

**in Brussels:** *Rue Neuve, Porte de Namur, Avenue Louise, Avenue de la Toison d'Or, Boulevard de Waterloo, Rue de Namur - Also Brussels antique market on Saturday from 9am to 3pm, and Sunday from 9am to 1pm (around Place du Grand-Sablon) - Flower and Bird market (Grand-Place) on Sunday morning - Flea Market (Place du Jeu de Balles) – Shopping Centres: Basilix, Westland Shopping Center, Woluwé Shopping Center, City 2, Galerie Louise.*

**in Luxembourg:** *Grand'Rue and around Place d'Armes - Station Quarter.*

**in Amsterdam:** *Kalverstraat, Leidsestraat, Nieuwendijk, P.C. Hoofstraat, Beethovenstraat, Van Baerlestraat and Utrechtsestraat – Shopping Center, Magna Plaza – Second-hand goods and antiques (around Rijksmuseum and Spiegelgracht) – Flower Market – Amsterdam Flea Market (near Waterlooplein).*

## BREAKDOWN SERVICE *24 hour assistance:*

**Belgium:** *TCB, Brussels ☎ (02) 233 22 11 – VTB-VAB, Antwerp ☎ (03) 253 63 63 – RACB, Brussels ☎ (02) 287 09 00.*

**Luxembourg:** *ACL ☎ 45 00 451.*

**Netherlands:** *ANWB, The Hague ☎ (070) 314 71 47 – KNAC, The Hague ☎ (070) 383 16 12.*

## TIPPING *In Benelux, prices include service and taxes.*

## SPEED LIMITS – SEAT BELTS

*In Belgium and Luxembourg, the maximum speed limits are 120 km/h-74 mph on motorways and dual carriageways, 90 km/h-56 mph on all other roads and 50 km/h-31 mph in built-up areas. In the Netherlands, 100/120 km/h-62/74 mph on motorways and "autowegen", 80 km/h-50 mph on other roads and 50 km/h-31 mph in built-up areas. In each country, the wearing of seat belts is compulsory for drivers and passengers.*

# BRUSSELS

(BRUXELLES - BRUSSEL) *1000 Région de Bruxelles-Capitale - Brussels Hoofdstedelijk Gewest* 213 ⑱ *and* 409 G 3- ⑫ S *- Pop. 948 122.*

*Paris 308 - Amsterdam 204 - Düsseldorf 222 - Lille 116 - Luxembourg 219.*

*(T.I.B.) Town Hall (Hôtel de Ville), Grand'Place, ✉ 1000 ☎ (02) 513 89 40, Fax (02) 514 45 38 - Office de Promotion du Tourisme (O.P.T.) r. Marché-aux-Herbes 61, ✉ 1000, ☎ (02) 504 02 22, Fax (02) 513 69 50 - Vlaanderen Toerisme, Grasmarkt 61, ✉ 1000, ☎ (02) 504 03 00, Fax (02) 513 88 03.*

*18 9 at Tervuren SE : 14 km, Château de Ravenstein ☎ (02) 767 58 01, Fax (02) 767 28 41 - 18 at Melsbroek NE : 14 km, Steenwagenstraat 11 ☎ (02) 751 82 05, Fax (02) 751 84 25 - 18 at Anderlecht, Sports Area of la Pede, r. Scholle 1 ☎ (02) 521 16 87, Fax (02) 521 51 56 - 9 at Watermael-Boitsfort, chaussée de la Hulpe 53a ☎ (02) 672 22 22, Fax (02) 675 34 81 - 9 at Overijse SE : 16 km, Gemslaan 55 ☎ (02) 687 50 30, Fax (02) 687 37 68 - 9 at Itterbeek W : 8 km, Kerkstraat 22 ☎ (02) 567 00 38, Fax (02) 567 02 23 - 18 at Kampenhout NE : 20 km, Wildersedreef 56 ☎ (0 16) 65 12 16, Fax (0 16) 65 16 80 - 9 at Duisburg E : 18 km, Hertswegenstraat 39 ☎ (02) 769 45 82, Fax (02) 767 97 52.*

*Sabena office, r. Marché-aux-Herbes 110, ✉ 1000, ☎ (02) 723 89 40, direct railwayline ☎ (02) 753 21 11.*

*☎ (02) 203 36 40 and (02) 203 28 80.*

**See** : *Atomium★ (Heysel) - National basilica of Koekelberg★ - Place Royale★* KZ *- Market Square★★★ (Grand-Place)* JY *- Monnaie Theatre★* JY *- St-Hubert Arcades★★* JY *- Erasmus House★★ (Anderlecht) - Gauchie House★ (Etterbeek)* HS **W** *- Castle and park★★ (Gaasbeek, SW : 12 km) - Royal Plant Houses★★ (Laeken) - Horta Museum★★ (St-Gilles)* EFU **M10** *- Van Buuren House★ (Uccle)* EFV **M13** *- Old England★* KZ **B** *- Sts-Michaels and Gudule Cathedral★★* KY *- Church of N.-D. de la Chapelle★* JZ *- Church of N.-D. du Sablon★* JZ *- Cambre Abbey★★ (Ixelles)* FGV *- Church of Sts-Pierre and Guidon★ (Anderlecht) - Royal Museums of Belgian Fine Arts★★★* KZ *- Florist De Backer★* KY **F1** *- Grand et Petit Sablon★★* JZ *- Rue des Bouchers★* JY *- Manneken Pis★★* JZ.

**Museums** : *Ancien Art★★★* KZ *- Royal Museum of Art and History★★★* HS **M7** *- Modern Art★★* KZ **M1** *- Belgian Centre of Comic Strips★★* KY **M5** *- Autoworld★★* HS **M23** *- Natural Science (Royal Institute)★★* GS **M9** *- Musical Instruments★★* JZ **M2** *- Meunier★ (Ixelles)* FV **M12** *- Ixelles Municipal Museum★★* FGT **M11** *- Charlier★* FR **M21** *- Bibliotheca Wittockiana★ (Woluwé-St-Pierre) - Royal Museum of Central Africa★★ (Tervuren).*

# BRUXELLES
# BRUSSEL

Louise (Galerie) . . . . . . . . . **FS** 161
Midi (Bd du) . . . . . . . . . . . . **ES**
Baudouin (Bd) . . . . . . . . . **EQ** 16
Bienfaiteurs (Pl. des) . . . . **GQ** 21
Brabançonne (Av. de la) . **GR** 28
Edouard de Thibault (Av.). **HS** 72
Europe (Bd de l') . . . . . . . **ES** 89
Frans Courtens (Av.) . . . . **HQ** 102
Frère-Orban (Sq.) . . . . . . . **FR** 104
Froissart (R.) . . . . . . . . . . . **GS** 106
Gén. Eisenhower (Av.) . . . **GQ** 108
Hal (Porte de) . . . . . . . . . . **ES** 114
Henri Jaspar (Av.). . . . . . . **ES** 117
Herbert Hoover (Av.) . . . . **HR** 118
Industrie (Quai de l') . . . . **ER** 126
Jan Stobbaerts (Av.). . . . . **GQ** 133

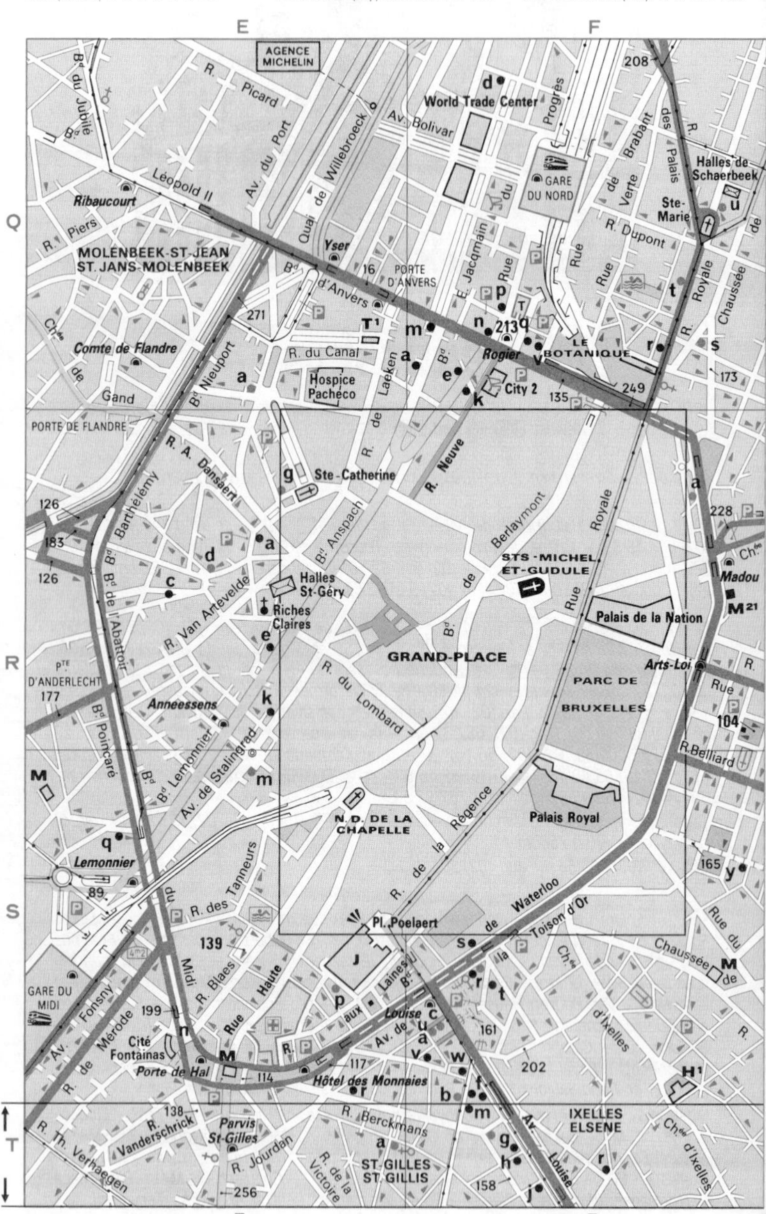

| Street | Grid | No. |
|---|---|---|
| Jardin Botanique (Bd du) | FQ | 135 |
| Jean Volders (Av.) | ET | 138 |
| Jeu de Balle (Pl. du) | ES | 139 |
| Livourne (R. de) | FT | 158 |
| Luxembourg (R. de) | FS | 165 |
| Marie-Louise (Sq.) | GR | 171 |
| Méridien (R. du) | FQ | 173 |
| Mons (Chée de) | ER | 177 |
| Nerviens (Av. des) | GS | 181 |
| Ninove (Chée de) | ER | 183 |
| Palmerston (Av.) | GR | 187 |
| Porte de Hal (Av. de la) | ES | 199 |
| Prince Royal (R. du) | FS | 202 |
| Reine (Av. de la) | FQ | 208 |
| Rogier (Pl.) | FQ | 213 |
| Roi Vainqueur (Pl. du) | HS | 216 |
| Saint-Antoine (Pl.) | GT | 220 |
| Scailquin (R.) | FR | 228 |
| Victoria Regina (Av) | FQ | 249 |
| Waterloo (Chée de) | ET | 256 |
| 9e de Ligne (Bd du) | EQ | 271 |

# BRUXELLES
# BRUSSEL



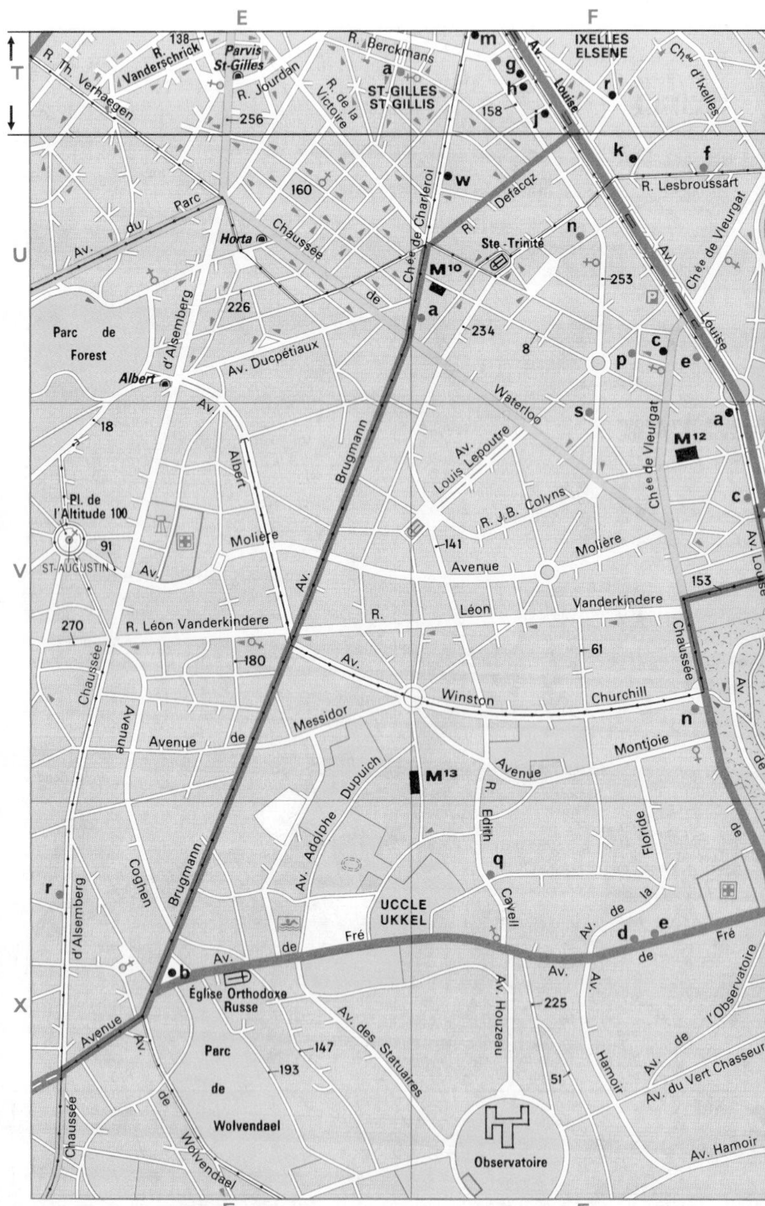

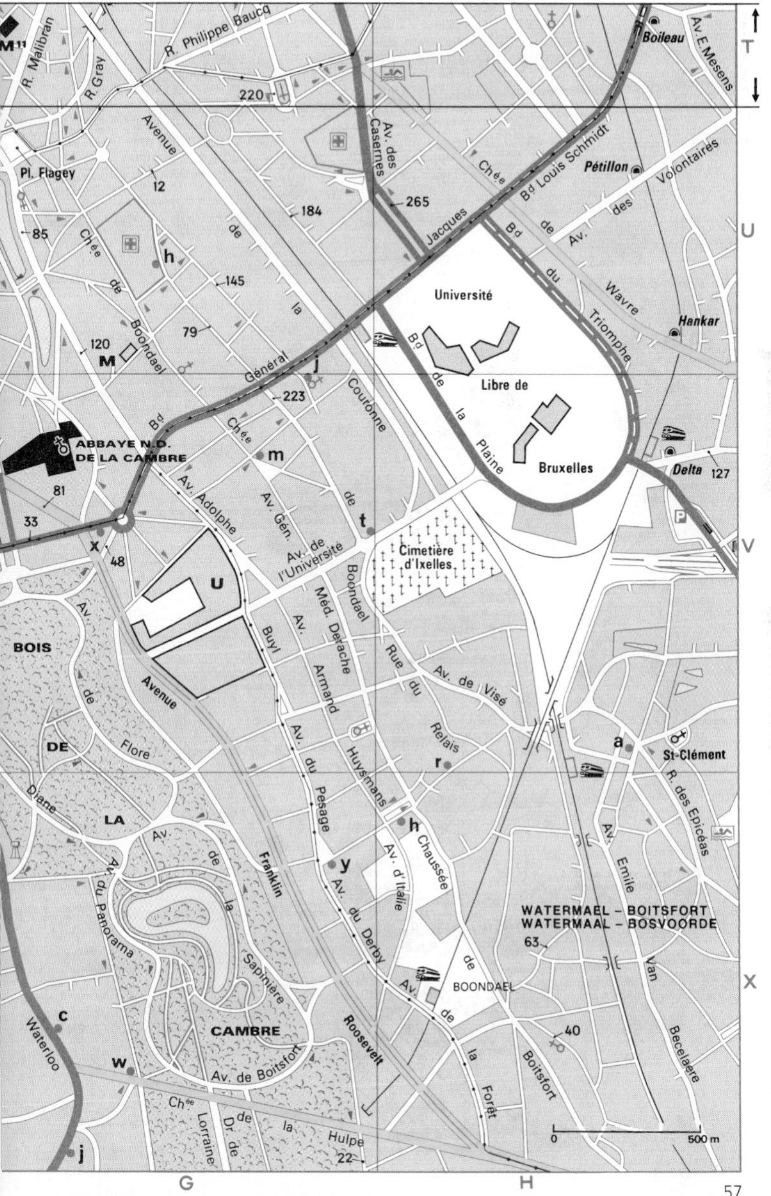

R. Philippe Baucq
R. Malibran
R. Gray
Pl. Flagey
Avenue de la Couronne
Av. des Casernes
Boileau
Av. E. Mesens
Bd Louis Schmidt
Pétillon
Av. des Volontaires
Chée de Wavre
Bd du Triomphe
Bd Général Jacques
Université Libre de Bruxelles
Bd de la Plaine
Hankar
Delta
Chée de Boondael
ABBAYE N.D. DE LA CAMBRE
Av. Adolphe Buyl
Av. Gén. Méd. Derache
Av. de l'Université
Cimetière d'Ixelles
Boondael
Rue du Relais
Av. de Visé
Av. Armand Huysmans
Av. du Pesage
Av. d'Italie
Chaussée de Boondael
Av. du Derby
Av. de la Forêt
St-Clément
R. des Epicéas
Av. Emile Van Becelaere
WATERMAEL - BOITSFORT
WATERMAAL - BOSVOORDE
BOIS DE LA CAMBRE
Av. de Flore
Diane
Av. du Panorama
Av. de la Sapinière
Avenue Franklin Roosevelt
Waterloo
Av. de Boitsfort
Chée de la Hulpe
Lorraine
Dr. de
Boitsfort
0
500 m
T
U
V
X
G
H

# BRUXELLES
# BRUSSEL

| Street | Grid | No. |
|---|---|---|
| Adolphe Max (Bd) | JY | 3 |
| Anspach (Bd) | JY | |
| Beurre (Rue au) | JY | 19 |
| Etuve (R. de l') | JZ | 88 |
| Fripiers (R. des) | JY | 105 |
| Grand Sablon (Pl. du) | KZ | 112 |
| Ixelles (Chée d') | KZ | 129 |
| Marché-aux-Herbes (R. du) | JY | 168 |
| Marché-aux-Poulets (R. du) | JY | 169 |
| Midi (R. du) | JYZ | |
| Neuve (Rue) | JY | |
| Reine (Galerie de la) | JY | 210 |
| Roi (Galerie du) | KY | 214 |
| Toison d'Or (Av. de la) | KZ | 238 |
| Albertine (Pl. de l') | KZ | 4 |
| Assaut (R. d') | KY | 10 |
| Baudet (R.) | KZ | 15 |
| Bortier (Galerie) | JZ | 23 |
| Bouchers (Petite rue des) | JY | 24 |
| Bouchers (R. des) | JY | 25 |
| Bourse (Pl. de la) | JY | 27 |
| Briques (Quai aux) | JY | 29 |
| Chêne (R. du) | JZ | 39 |
| Colonies (R. des) | KY | 43 |
| Comédiens (R. des) | KY | 45 |
| Commerce (R. du) | KZ | 46 |
| Croix-de-Fer (R. de la) | KY | 52 |
| Duquesnoy (Rue) | JYZ | 66 |
| Ernest Allard (R.) | JZ | 87 |
| Europe (Carr. de l') | KY | 90 |
| Fossé-aux-Loups (R. du) | JKY | 99 |
| Impératrice (Bd de l') | KY | 124 |
| Joseph Lebeau (R.) | JZ | 142 |
| Laeken (R. de) | JY | 151 |
| Louvain (R. de) | KY | 163 |
| Mercier (R. du Card.) | KY | 172 |
| Montagne (Rue de la) | KY | 178 |
| Musée (Pl. du) | KZ | 179 |
| Nord (Passage du) | JY | 182 |
| Petit Sablon (Sq. du) | KZ | 195 |
| Presse (R. de la) | KY | 201 |
| Princes (Galeries des) | JY | 205 |
| Ravenstein (R.) | KZ | 207 |
| Rollebeek (R. de) | JZ | 217 |
| Ruysbroeck (R. de) | KZ | 219 |
| Ste-Catherine (Pl.) | JY | 221 |
| Sainte-Gudule (Pl.) | KY | 222 |
| Trône (R. du) | KZ | 241 |
| Ursulines (R. des) | JZ | 243 |
| Waterloo (Bd de) | KZ | 255 |
| 6 Jeunes Hommes (R. des) | KZ | 268 |

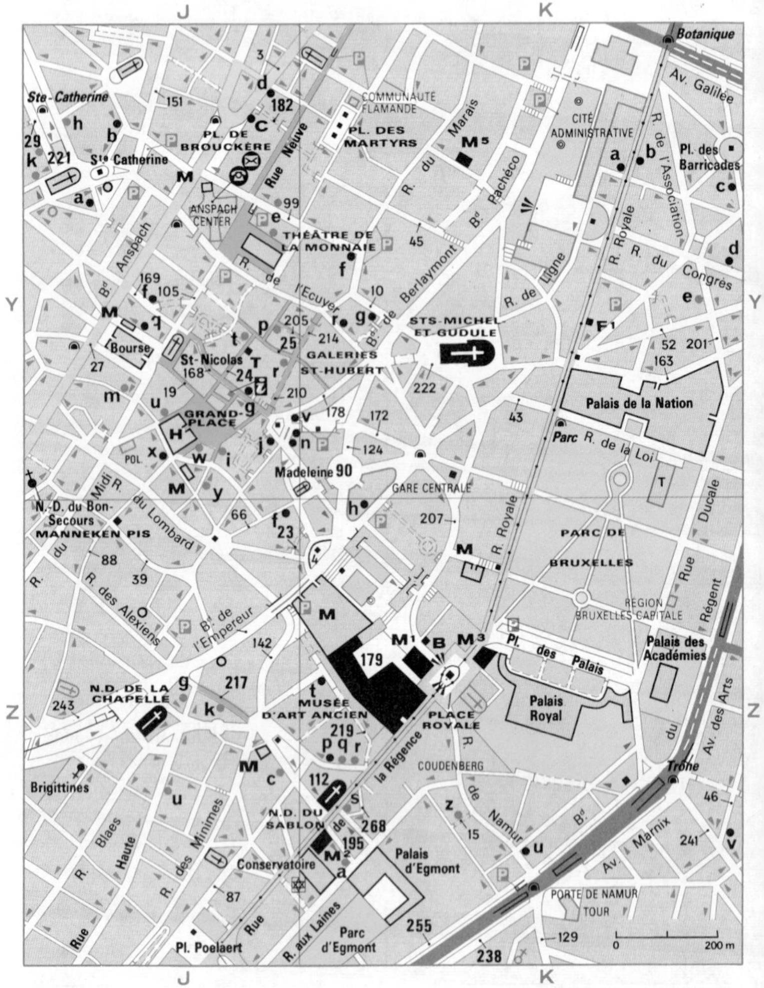

# *Alphabetical listing of hotels and restaurants*

## E



## F



## G



## H



## I – J – K



## L



## M



## N – O



## P – Q

## R



## S



## T



## U – V



## W – Y – Z

# *Starred establishments*

## ✿✿✿

| Page | Comfort | Establishment |
|---|---|---|
| 19 | XXXX | Bruneau |
| 13 | XXX | Comme Chez Soi |

## ✿✿

| Page | Comfort | Establishment |
|---|---|---|
| 24 | XXXXX | Bijgaarden (De) |
| 13 | XXXX | Sea Grill (at Radisson SAS H.) |
| 19 | XXX | Claude Dupont |
| 16 | XXX | Écailler du Palais Royal (L') |

## ✿

| Page | Comfort | Establishment |
|---|---|---|
| 17 | XXXXX | Villa Lorraine |
| 25 | XXXX | Barbizon |
| 16 | XXXX | Maison du Bœuf (at Hilton H.) |
| 15 | XXXX | Maison du Cygne (La) |
| 24 | XXXX | Michel |
| 23 | XXX | Des 3 Couleurs |
| 25 | XXX | André D'Haese |
| 15 | XXX | Les 4 Saisons (at Royal Windsor H.) |
| 17 | XXX | Truffe Noire (La) |
| 24 | XX | Aloyse Kloos |
| 18 | XX | Baguettes Impériales (Les) |
| 18 | XX | Grignotière (La) |
| 19 | XX | Stirwen |
| 23 | XX | Vignoble de Margot (Le) |

# Establishments according to style of cuisine

## Buffets

18 Adrienne Atomium *Q. Atomium*
14 Atelier (L') *Q. de l'Europe*
17 Café Wiltcher's (at Conrad H.) *Q. Louise*
17 Crescendo (at Sheraton Towers H.) *Q. Botanique, Gare du Nord*

## Grill

20 Aub. de Boendael (L') *Ixelles Q. Boondael*
25 Aub. Napoléon *Env. at Meise*
22 Hoef (De) *Uccle*

## Pub rest – Brasseries

20 Brasserie Marebœuf (La) *Ixelles Q. Boondael*
22 Brasseries Georges *Uccle*
25 Clarine *Env. at Strombeek-Bever*
22 Entre-Temps (L') *Watermael-Boitsfort*
18 Erasme *Anderlecht*
25 Istas *Env. at Overijse*
24 Kasteel Gravenhof *Env. at Dworp*
25 Lien Zana *Env. at Schepdaal*
26 Lindbergh Taverne (at Sheraton Airport H.) *Env. at Zaventem*
26 Met (De) *Env. at Vilvoorde*
15 Novotel off Grand'Place *Q. Grand'Place*
18 Paix (La) *Anderlecht*
15 Roue d'Or (La) *Q. Grand'Place*
26 Stockmansmolen *Env. at Zaventem*
15 Taverne du Passage *Q. Grand'Place*

## Regional

14 In 't Spinnekopke
15 Kelderke ('t) *Q. Grand'Place*

## Seafood – Oyster bar

16 Belle Maraîchère (La) *Q. Ste-Catherine*
20 Brasserie Mareboeuf (La) *Ixelles Q. Boondael*
22 Brasseries Georges *Uccle*
22 Cadre Noir (Le) *Schaerbeek Q. Meiser*
16 Écailler du Palais Royal (L') *Q. des Sablons*
16 François *Q. Ste-Catherine*
13 Sea Grill (at Radisson SAS H.)
15 Sirène d'Or (La) *Q. Ste-Catherine*
26 Stoveke ('t) *Env. at Strombeek-Bever*
15 Truite d'Argent and H. Welcome (La) *Q. Ste-Catherine*
23 Vignoble de Margot (Le) *Woluwé-St-Pierre*

## Chinese

22 Cité du Dragon (La) *Uccle*
18 Lychee *Q. Atomium*
19 Fontaine de Jade (La) *Etterbeek Q. Cinquantenaire*
18 Ming Dynasty *Q. Atomium*

## Indian

17 Porte des Indes (La) *Q. Louise*
22 Rives du Gange (Les) *Watermael-Boitsfort*

## Italian

22 Amici miei *Schaerbeek Q. Meiser*
25 Arlecchino (L') (at Aub. de Waterloo H.) *Env. at Sint-Genesius-Rode*
16 Castello Banfi *Q. des Sablons*
21 I Trulli *St-Gilles Q. Louise*
23 Mucha (Le) *Woluwé-St-Pierre*
14 Pappa e Citti *Q. de l'Europe*
14 Roma
19 San Daniele *Ganshoren*

## Japanese

19 Momotaro Etterbeek *Q. Cinquantenaire*
17 Tagawa *Q. Louise*
17 Taishin (at Mayfair H.) *Q. Louise*
14 Takesushi *Q. de l'Europe*

## Moroccan

18 Khaïma (La) *Auderghem*
21 Mamounia (La) *St-Gilles*

## Portuguese

21 Forcado (Le) *St-Gilles*

## Scandinavian

13 Atrium *(at Radisson SAS H.)*

## Spanish

14 Jardin d'Espagne (Le)
*Q. de l'Europe*

## Thaï

22 Blue Elephant *Uccle*
25 Bois Savanes
*Env. at Sint-Genesius-Rode*
16 Larmes du Tigre (Les)
*Q. Palais de Justice*
22 Maison de Thaïlande (La)
*Watermael-Boitsfort*
20 Perles de Pluie (Les) *Ixelles Q. Louise*

## Vietnamese

18 Baguettes Impériales (Les)
*Q. Atomium*
18 Citronnelle (La) *Auderghem*
20 Pagode d'Or (La) *Ixelles Q. Boondael*
19 Yen *Ixelles*

## BRUXELLES (BRUSSEL)

**Radisson SAS,** r. Fossé-aux-Loups 47, 1000, (0 2) 227 31 31 and 227 31 70 (rest), *Fax (0 2) 219 62 62*, « Patio with remains of 12C City enclosure wall », - - 25-380. AE VISA JCB KY f
Meals see rest ***Sea Grill*** below – ***Atrium*** *(partly Scandinavian cuisine)* 1250 b.i. – 1050 – **275 rm** 11000/14000, 6 suites.

**Astoria,** r. Royale 103, 1000, (0 2) 227 05 05, *Fax (0 2) 217 11 50*, « Early 20C residence, Belle Epoque style » – - 25-180. AE VISA JCB. 
Meals ***Le Palais Royal*** *(closed Saturday lunch, Sunday dinner and 15 July-15 August)* 1650/2100 b.i. – 850 – **106 rm** 9000, 14 suites. KY b

**Le Plaza,** bd. A. Max 118, 1000, (0 2) 227 67 00, *Fax (0 2) 227 67 20* – , rm, - 25-800. AE VISA JCB FQ e
Meals *(closed Saturday and Sunday)* a la carte 1250/1550 – **193 rm** 9900/11900, 5 suites.

**Métropole,** pl. de Brouckère 31, 1000, (0 2) 217 23 00, *Telex 21234, Fax (0 2) 218 02 20*, « Late 19C hall and lounges », - - 25-400. AE VISA JCB JY c
Meals see rest ***L'Alban Chambon*** below – **405 rm** 9500/14000, 5 suites.

**Bedford,** r. Midi 135, 1000, (0 2) 512 78 40, *Telex 24059, Fax (0 2) 514 17 59* – - 25-200. AE VISA JCB. ER k
Meals 1100 – **298 rm** 7700.

**Jolly Atlanta,** bd A. Max 7, 1000, (0 2) 217 01 20, *Telex 21475, Fax (0 2) 217 37 58* – , rest, - 25-50. AE VISA JCB. JY d
Meals (residents only) – **241 rm** 7050, 6 suites.

**Président Centre** without rest, r. Royale 160, 1000, (0 2) 219 00 65, *Telex 26784, Fax (0 2) 218 09 10* – . AE VISA JCB. 
**73 rm** 4900/5900. KY a

**Royal Embassy** without rest, bd Anspach 159, 1000, (0 2) 512 81 00, *Fax (0 2) 514 30 97*, - . AE VISA ER e
**54 rm** 3200/4200.

**Arctia** without rest, r. Arenberg 18, 1000, (0 2) 548 18 11, *Fax (0 2) 548 18 20*, - - 25-80. AE VISA JCB KY r
**95 rm** 3300/6900, 5 suites.

**Arenberg,** r. Assaut 15, 1000, (0 2) 501 16 16, *Fax (0 2) 501 18 18*, - , rest, - 25-75. AE VISA JCB. rest KY g
Meals (Pub rest) Lunch 700 – a la carte approx. 1000 – **155 rm** 4200/5000.

**Chambord** without rest, r. Namur 82, 1000, (0 2) 548 99 10, *Fax (0 2) 514 08 47* – . AE VISA. KZ u
**69 rm** 3400/5400.

**Queen Anne** without rest, bd E. Jacqmain 110, 1000, (0 2) 217 16 00, *Fax (0 2) 217 18 38* – . AE VISA EFQ a
**60 rm** 2750/3400.

**George V** without rest, r. 't Kint 23, 1000, (0 2) 513 50 93, *Fax (0 2) 513 44 93* – . VISA JCB ER c
**17 rm** 1980/2400.

**Sabina** without rest, r. Nord 78, 1000, (0 2) 218 26 37, *Fax (0 2) 219 32 39* – . AE VISA KY c
**24 rm** 1900/2400.

**Sea Grill** - (at Radisson SAS H.), r. Fossé-aux-Loups 47, 1000, (0 2) 227 31 20, *Telex 22202, Fax (0 2) 219 62 62*, Seafood – . AE VISA JCB. KY f
*closed Saturday lunch, Sunday, Bank Holidays, 12 to 19 April and 19 July-16 August* – **Meals** Lunch 1750 – a la carte 2200/2950
**Spec.** St-Jacques à la vapeur d'algues, crème légère au cresson (15 September-15 April). Manchons de crabe royal tièdis au beurre de persil plat. Homard à la presse.

**L'Alban Chambon** - (at Métropole H.), pl. de Brouckère 21, 1000, (0 2) 217 76 50, *Telex 21234, Fax (0 2) 218 02 20*, « Late 19C atmosphere » – . AE VISA JCB. JY c
*closed Saturday, Sunday and Bank Holidays* – **Meals** Lunch 1450 b.i. – a la carte 1500/1850.

**Comme Chez Soi** (Wynants), pl. Rouppe 23, 1000, (0 2) 512 29 21, *Fax (0 2) 511 80 52*, « Belle Epoque atmosphere with Horta decor » – . AE VISA
*closed Sunday, Monday, 5 July-3 August and Christmas-New Year* – **Meals** (booking essential) Lunch 1975 – 3500 (2 pers. min.), a la carte 2700/3300 ES m
**Spec.** Filets de sole et médaillon de homard cardinal. Couronne d'agneau de lait du pays aux fines herbes, mont d'or provençal (January-June). Fraîcheur d'été des Antilles aux fraises et crème citron à l'orange.

XX **Roma,** r. Princes 14, ✉ 1000, ☎ (0 2) 219 01 94, *Fax (0 2) 218 34 30,* Italian cuisine – ▤. AE ⓓ E VISA. ✂ JY e
*closed Saturday lunch, Sunday and mid July-mid August* – **Meals** a la carte 1100/2150.

XX **Astrid "Chez Pierrot",** r. Presse 21, ✉ 1000, ☎ (0 2) 217 38 31, *Fax (0 2) 217 38 31* – AE ⓓ E VISA JCB KY e
*closed Sunday, Easter week and 15 July-15 August* – **Meals** *Lunch 750* – 950/1500.

XX **J and B,** r. Baudet 5, ✉ 1000, ☎ (0 2) 512 04 84, *Fax (0 2) 511 79 30* – ▤. AE ⓓ E VISA JCB KZ z
*closed Saturday lunch, Sunday dinner, Bank Holidays and 21 July-6 August* – **Meals** – 995.

X **In 't Spinnekopke,** pl. du Jardin aux Fleurs 1, ✉ 1000, ☎ (0 2) 511 86 95, *Fax (0 2) 513 24 97,* 🏖, Partly regional cuisine, open until 11 p.m., « Typical ancient Brussels pub » – ▤. AE ⓓ E VISA ER d
*closed Saturday lunch* – **Meals** *Lunch 295* – a la carte 850/1350.

## Quartier de l'Europe

**Dorint** Ⓜ, bd Charlemange 11, ✉ 1000, ☎ (0 2) 231 09 09, *Fax (0 2) 230 33 71,* 🏋, ≘s – 🛗 ⇌ ▤ 📺 ☎ ♿ 🚗 – 🏛 25-150. AE ⓓ E VISA JCB GR c
Meals *Lunch 950* – a la carte approx. 1400 – ☕ 650 – **208 rm** 8200, 2 suites.

**Europa,** r. Loi 107, ✉ 1040, ☎ (0 2) 230 13 33, *Telex 25121, Fax (0 2) 230 36 82,* 🏋 – 🛗 ⇌ ▤ 📺 ☎ 🚗 Ⓟ – 🏛 25-350. AE ⓓ E VISA JCB. ✂ GR d
Meals 990/1650 – ☕ 650 – **236 rm** 8500/10500, 4 suites.

**Eurovillage** Ⓜ, bd Charlemagne 80, ✉ 1000, ☎ (0 2) 230 85 55, *Fax (0 2) 230 56 35,* 🏖, ≘s – 🛗 ⇌ ▤ 📺 ☎ 🚗 – 🏛 25-120. AE ⓓ E VISA JCB GR a
Meals *(closed Saturday, Sunday lunch and August) Lunch 750* – a la carte 1000/1350 – ☕ 600 – **80 rm** 5250/6500.

**Euroflat** without rest, bd Charlemagne 50, ✉ 1000, ☎ (0 2) 230 00 10, *Fax (0 2) 230 36 83,* ≘s – 🛗 📺 ☎ 🚗 – 🏛 25-80. AE ⓓ E VISA JCB GR b
**121 rm** ☕ 5700/6500, 12 suites.

**New Charlemagne** without rest, bd Charlemagne 25, ✉ 1000, ☎ (0 2) 230 21 35, *Fax (0 2) 230 25 10* – 🛗 ⇌ 📺 ☎ 🚗 – 🏛 30-60. AE ⓓ E VISA GR k
☕ 525 – **66 rm** 3200/5400.

**City Garden** without rest, r. Joseph II 59, ✉ 1000, ☎ (0 2) 282 82 82, *Fax (0 2) 230 64 37* – 🛗 ⇌ 📺 ☎ 🚗. AE ⓓ E VISA JCB GR f
**94 rm** ☕ 5000/5500, 2 suites.

XX **Le Jardin d'Espagne,** r. Archimède 65, ✉ 1000, ☎ (0 2) 736 34 49, *Fax (0 2) 735 17 45,* 🏖, Partly Spanish cuisine – AE ⓓ E VISA GR s
*closed Saturday lunch and Sunday* – **Meals** *Lunch 950* – 1150.

XX **Pappa e Citti,** r. Franklin 18, ✉ 1000, ☎ (0 2) 732 61 10, *Fax (0 2) 732 57 40,* 🏖, Italian cuisine – AE ⓓ E VISA JCB. ✂ GR e
*closed Saturday, Sunday, Bank Holidays, August and 24 December-3 January* – **Meals** *Lunch 1050* – a la carte 1200/1750.

X **L'Atelier,** r. Franklin 28, ✉ 1000, ☎ (0 2) 734 91 40, *Fax (0 2) 735 35 98,* 🏖, Buffets – AE ⓓ E VISA GR y
*closed weekends, August and Christmas-New Year* – **Meals** *Lunch 850* – 930 b.i./1200.

X **Takesushi,** bd Charlemagne 21, ✉ 1000, ☎ (0 2) 230 56 27, 🏖, Japanese cuisine – AE ⓓ E VISA GR z
*closed Saturday and Sunday lunch* – **Meals** *Lunch 450* – a la carte 1400/2450.

## Quartier Grand'Place (Ilot Sacré)

**Royal Windsor,** r. Duquesnoy 5, ✉ 1000, ☎ (0 2) 505 55 55, *Fax (0 2) 505 55 00,* 🏋, ≘s – 🛗 ⇌ ▤ 📺 ☎ 🚗 – 🏛 25-250. AE ⓓ E VISA JCB. ✂ JYZ f
Meals see rest ***Les 4 Saisons*** below – ☕ 650 – **264 rm** 11000/15000, 11 suites.

**Amigo,** r. Amigo 1, ✉ 1000, ☎ (0 2) 547 47 47, *Telex 21618, Fax (0 2) 513 52 77,* « Collection of works of art » – 🛗, ▤ rm, 📺 ☎ 🚗 – 🏛 25-200. AE ⓓ E VISA JCB. ✂ rest JY x
Meals *Lunch 1460 b.i.* – 1460/1740 – **171 rm** ☕ 6700/9000, 7 suites.

**Le Méridien** Ⓜ 🐚, Carrefour de l'Europe 3, ✉ 1000, ☎ (0 2) 548 42 11 and 548 47 16 (rest), *Fax (0 2) 548 40 80,* ≤, 🏋 – 🛗 ⇌ ▤ 📺 ☎ ♿ 🚗 – 🏛 25-200. AE ⓓ E VISA JCB. ✂ rm KZ h
Meals ***L'Epicerie*** *(closed Saturday lunch) Lunch 895* - a la carte 1300/1800 – ☕ 1050 – **212 rm** 5200/12000, 12 suites.

**Carrefour de l'Europe,** r. Marché-aux-Herbes 110, ✉ 1000, ☎ (0 2) 504 94 00, *Fax (0 2) 504 95 00* – 🛗 ⇌ ▤ 📺 ☎ – 🏛 25-150. AE ⓓ E VISA JCB. ✂ JKY n
**Meals** *(closed Saturday and Sunday)* a la carte approx. 1200 – ☕ 750 – **58 rm** 8100/9100, 5 suites.

**Novotel off Grand'Place,** r. Marché-aux-Herbes 120, ✉ 1000, ☎ (0 2) 514 33 33 – ⊞ ⇔ ≡ TV ☎ ♿ – 🏛 25. AE ⊙ E VISA JCB JKY n
Meals (Brasserie) a la carte approx. 1100 – ☕ 460 – **136 rm** 5600.

**Le Dixseptième** without rest, r. Madeleine 25, ✉ 1000, ☎ (0 2) 502 57 44, *Fax (0 2) 502 64 24*, « Elegant town house » – ⊞ TV ☎ – 🏛 25. AE ⊙ E VISA JCB. ✗ JY j
**16 rm** ☕ 5800/13600, 7 suites.

**Ibis off Grand'Place** without rest, r. Marché-aux-Herbes 100, ✉ 1000, ☎ (0 2) 514 40 40, *Fax (0 2) 514 50 67* – ⊞ ⇔ ≡ TV ☎ ♿ – 🏛 25-120. AE ⊙ E VISA JCB
☕ 250 – **180 rm** 3950. JKY v

**Matignon,** r. Bourse 10, ✉ 1000, ☎ (0 2) 511 08 88, *Fax (0 2) 513 69 27* – ⊞ TV ☎. AE ⊙ E VISA JY q
Meals *(closed Monday and 15 January-20 February)* a la carte approx. 1100 – **22 rm** ☕ 4100.

**La Maison du Cygne,** Grand'Place 9, ✉ 1000, ☎ (0 2) 511 82 44, *Fax (0 2) 514 31 48*, « Former 17C guildhouse » – ≡ P. AE ⊙ E VISA JCB. ✗ JY w
*closed Saturday lunch, Sunday, first 3 weeks August and late December* – **Meals** *Lunch 1400* – 2350/2650, a la carte 2450/2800
**Spec.** Huîtres au Champagne. Gibiers en saison. Cornets à la crème vanillée, sorbet à la pomme verte et son coulis.

**Les 4 Saisons** - (at Royal Windsor H.), 1st floor, r. Homme Chrétien 2, ✉ 1000, ☎ (0 2) 505 55 55, *Fax (0 2) 505 55 00* – ≡ P. AE ⊙ E VISA JCB. ✗ JYZ f
*closed Saturday lunch and 18 July-24 August* – **Meals** *Lunch 1490* – 1690/2290, a la carte 2000/2800
**Spec.** La salade de homard à la vinaigrette de fine champgagne. Sole pochée à la crème d'écrevisses et duxelles. Filet d'agneau gratiné au fromage de brebis et salpicon d'abats au jus.

**Aux Armes de Bruxelles,** r. Bouchers 13, ✉ 1000, ☎ (0 2) 511 55 98, *Fax (0 2) 514 33 81*, Brussels atmosphere, open until 11 p.m. – ≡. AE ⊙ E VISA JCB JY t
*closed Monday except Bank Holidays and 15 June-15 July* – **Meals** *Lunch 895* – 1100/1695.

**La Tête d'Or,** r. Tête d'Or 9, ✉ 1000, ☎ (0 2) 511 02 01, *Fax (0 2) 502 44 91*, « Ancient Brussels residence » – AE ⊙ E VISA JY u
*closed Saturday lunch and Sunday* – **Meals** 1000 b.i./1500.

**Falstaff Gourmand,** r. Pierres 38, ✉ 1000, ☎ (0 2) 512 17 61, *Fax (0 2) 512 17 61*, Open until 11 p.m. – ≡. AE ⊙ E VISA JY m
*closed Sunday dinner, Monday and last 3 weeks July* – **Meals** *Lunch 595* – 975 b.i./1300 b.i.

**L'Ogenblik,** Galerie des Princes 1, ✉ 1000, ☎ (0 2) 511 61 51, *Fax (0 2) 513 41 58*, Open until midnight, « Ancient pub interior » – AE ⊙ E VISA JCB JY p
*closed Sunday* – **Meals** a la carte 1700/2400.

**La Roue d'Or,** r. Chapeliers 26, ✉ 1000, ☎ (0 2) 514 25 54, *Fax (0 2) 512 30 81*, Open until midnight, « Typical ancient Brussels pub » – AE ⊙ E VISA JY y
*closed August* – **Meals** *Lunch 325* – a la carte approx. 1300.

**'t Kelderke,** Grand'Place 15, ✉ 1000, ☎ (0 2) 513 73 44, *Fax (0 2) 512 30 81*, Open until 2 a.m., « Pub in a vaulted cellar, Brussels atmosphere » – AE ⊙ E VISA JY i
**Meals** *Lunch 275* – a la carte approx. 1000.

**Taverne du Passage,** Galerie de la Reine 30, ✉ 1000, ☎ (0 2) 512 37 32, *Fax (0 2) 511 08 82*, 🏖, Open until midnight, « Brussels atmosphere » – AE ⊙ E VISA JY r
*closed Wednesday and Thursday in June and July* – **Meals** a la carte 1000/1850.

## Quartier Ste-Catherine (Marché-aux-Poissons)

**Atlas** 🐚 without rest, r. Vieux Marché-aux-Grains 30, ✉ 1000, ☎ (0 2) 502 60 06, *Fax (0 2) 502 69 35* – ⊞ TV ☎ ♿ 🚗 – 🏛 40. AE ⊙ E VISA ER a
**83 rm** ☕ 2900/4900, 5 suites.

**Astrid** M without rest, pl. du Samedi 11, ✉ 1000, ☎ (0 2) 219 31 19, *Fax (0 2) 219 31 70* – ⊞ TV ☎ ♿ 🚗 – 🏛 25-120. AE ⊙ E VISA JY b
**100 rm** ☕ 5500.

**Ibis Ste-Catherine** without rest, r. Joseph Plateau 2, ✉ 1000, ☎ (0 2) 513 76 20, *Fax (0 2) 514 22 14* – ⊞ ⇔ TV ☎ ♿ – 🏛 25-80. AE ⊙ E VISA JCB JY a
☕ 250 – **235 rm** 3450.

**La Sirène d'Or,** pl. Ste-Catherine 1a, ✉ 1000, ☎ (0 2) 513 51 98, *Fax (0 2) 502 13 05*, Seafood – ≡. AE ⊙ E VISA ER g
*closed Sunday, Monday, first 3 weeks September and 23 December-2 January* – **Meals** 890/1300.

**La Truite d'Argent and H. Welcome** with rm, quai au Bois-à-Brûler 23, ✉ 1000, ☎ (0 2) 219 95 46, *Fax (0 2) 217 18 87*, 🏖 – ≡ rest, TV ☎. AE ⊙ E VISA JY h
**Meals** (Seafood, open until 11.30 p.m.) *(closed Saturday lunch, Sunday, Bank Holidays, 1 week August and 20 December-12 January)* 1080/1540 – ☕ 280 – **6 rm** 2300/3400.

XX **François,** quai aux Briques 2, ✉ 1000, ✆ (0 2) 511 60 89, *Fax (0 2) 511 60 53*, Oyster bar, seafood – AE ◐ E VISA JCB JY k
*closed Monday* – **Meals** *Lunch 990* – a la carte 1850/2500.

XX **La Belle Maraîchère,** pl. Ste-Catherine 11, ✉ 1000, ✆ (0 2) 512 97 59, *Fax (0 2) 513 76 91*, Seafood – P. AE ◐ E VISA JY k
*closed Wednesday and Thursday* – **Meals** 995/1750.

X **Le Loup-Galant,** quai aux Barques 4, ✉ 1000, ✆ (0 2) 219 99 98, *Fax (0 2) 219 99 98*, – AE ◐ E VISA EQ a
*closed Saturday lunch, Sunday, Monday dinner, Bank Holidays, 1 week Easter, 1 to 15 August and 24 to 31 December* – **Meals** *Lunch 470* – 890/1390.

## Quartier des Sablons

**Jolly du Grand Sablon** M, r. Bodenbroek 2, ✉ 1000, ✆ (0 2) 512 88 00, *Telex 20397*, *Fax (0 2) 512 67 66* – 25-100. AE ◐ E VISA. KZ p
**Meals** (residents only) – **195 rm** 7800/8950, 6 suites.

**Alfa Sablon** M without rest, r. Paille 4, ✉ 1000, ✆ (0 2) 513 60 40, *Fax (0 2) 511 81 41*, – AE ◐ E VISA JCB KZ t
**28 rm** 4800/8600, 4 suites.

XXX **L'Écailler du Palais Royal** (Basso), r. Bodenbroek 18, ✉ 1000, ✆ (0 2) 512 87 51, *Fax (0 2) 511 99 50*, Seafood – AE ◐ E VISA JCB KZ r
*closed Sunday, Bank Holidays, 10 to 18 April and August* – **Meals** a la carte 2500/3150
**Spec.** Daube chaude de petites anguilles au Graves rouge. Fricassée de homard et petites lottes au Sauternes. Blanc de turbot grillé, sauce au Champagne.

XX **Au Duc d'Arenberg,** pl. du Petit Sablon 9, ✉ 1000, ✆ (0 2) 511 14 75, *Fax (0 2) 512 92 92*, « Collection of modern paintings » – E VISA KZ a
*closed Sunday, Bank Holidays and last week December* – **Meals** *Lunch 1600* – 2100.

XX **"Chez Marius" En Provence,** pl. du Petit Sablon 1, ✉ 1000, ✆ (0 2) 511 12 08, *Fax (0 2) 512 27 89* – AE ◐ E VISA KZ s
*closed Sunday, Bank Holidays and 15 July-15 August* – **Meals** *Lunch 850* – 1100/2000.

XX **Castello Banfi,** r. Bodenbroek 12, ✉ 1000, ✆ (0 2) 512 87 94, *Fax (0 2) 512 87 94*, Partly Italian cuisine – AE ◐ E VISA KZ q
*closed Sunday dinner, Monday, 12 to 20 April, 9 to 31 August and 20 to 28 December* – **Meals** *Lunch 995* – 1695.

X **Lola,** pl. du Grand Sablon 33, ✉ 1000, ✆ (0 2) 514 24 60, *Fax (0 2) 514 25 37*, Open until 11.30 p.m. – AE E VISA JZ c
**Meals** a la carte approx. 1300.

X **La Clef des Champs,** r. Rollebeek 23, ✉ 1000, ✆ (0 2) 512 11 93, *Fax (0 2) 513 89 49*, – AE ◐ E VISA. JZ k
*closed Sunday, Monday and Bank Holidays* – **Meals** 990/1290.

## Quartier Palais de Justice

**Hilton,** bd de Waterloo 38, ✉ 1000, ✆ (0 2) 504 11 11, *Telex 22744*, *Fax (0 2) 504 21 11*, ≤ town, – 45-600. AE ◐ E VISA JCB FS s
**Meals** see rest ***Maison du Bœuf*** below – ***Café d'Egmont*** 1090 – 690 – **421 rm** 6900/9500, 7 suites.

XXXX **Maison du Bœuf** - (at Hilton H.), 1st floor, bd de Waterloo 38, ✉ 1000, ✆ (0 2) 504 11 11, *Telex 22744*, *Fax (0 2) 504 21 11*, ≤ – P. AE ◐ E VISA JCB FS s
**Meals** *Lunch 1590* – a la carte 2700/3400
**Spec.** Fantaisie de crevettes de la mer du Nord. Train de côtes de bœuf américain rôti en croûte de sel. Tartare maison au caviar.

X **Les Larmes du Tigre,** r. Wynants 21, ✉ 1000, ✆ (0 2) 512 18 77, *Fax (0 2) 502 10 03*, Thaï cuisine – AE ◐ E VISA ES p
*closed Saturday lunch* – **Meals** *Lunch 395* – a la carte 900/1300.

## Quartier Léopold *(see also at Ixelles)*

**Stanhope,** r. Commerce 9, ✉ 1000, ✆ (0 2) 506 91 11, *Fax (0 2) 512 17 08*, « Town house with walled terrace », – AE ◐ E VISA JCB. KZ v
**Meals** *(closed Saturday, Sunday and 24 December-4 January)* *Lunch 1350* – a la carte 1850/2500 – **35 rm** 9900/12900, 15 suites.

**Swissôtel** M, r. Parnasse 19, ✉ 1050, ✆ (0 2) 505 29 29, *Fax (0 2) 505 22 76*, – 25-360. AE ◐ E VISA JCB. rest FS e
**Meals** (open until 11 p.m.) *Lunch 790* – 1240/1400 – 700 – **238 rm** 8300/9300, 19 suites.

## Quartier Louise *(see also at Ixelles and at St-Gilles)*

**Conrad**, av. Louise 71, 1050, (0 2) 542 42 42, *Fax (0 2) 542 42 00*, « Hotel complex around an early 20C mansion », – – 25-650. AE E VISA JCB. rest FS f
**Meals** see rest ***La Maison de Maître*** below – ***Café Wiltcher's*** (Buffet, open until 11 p.m.) *Lunch 1100* - a la carte 1450/1850 – 950 – **254 rm** 13000/17000, 15 suites.

**Bristol Stéphanie**, av. Louise 91, 1050, (0 2) 543 33 11, *Fax (0 2) 538 03 07*, – – 25-215. AE E VISA JCB. rest FT g
**Meals** *(closed Saturday, Sunday, 18 July-16 August and 19 December-3 January) Lunch 795* – a la carte 1250/1700 – 720 – **140 rm** 8200/10200, 2 suites.

**Mayfair,** av. Louise 381, 1050, (0 2) 649 98 00, *Fax (0 2) 649 22 49* – – 30-60. AE E VISA JCB. FV a
**Meals** see rest ***Taishin*** below – ***Louis XVI*** *(closed Saturday) Lunch 580* - a la carte approx. 1500 – 580 – **97 rm** 5900, 2 suites.

**Clubhouse** without rest, r. Blanche 4, 1000, (0 2) 537 92 10, *Fax (0 2) 537 00 18* – – 30. AE E VISA JCB. FT h
**80 rm** 4500/7400.

**L'Agenda** without rest, r. Florence 6, 1000, (0 2) 539 00 31, *Fax (0 2) 539 00 63* – . AE E VISA JCB FT j
300 – **38 rm** 3300/3600.

**La Maison de Maître** - (at Conrad H.), av. Louise 71, 1050, (0 2) 542 47 16, *Fax (0 2) 542 48 42* – . AE E VISA FS f
*closed Saturday lunch, Sunday, 3 to 31 August and 25 to 29 December* – **Meals** *Lunch 1400* – 1650/2550.

**La Porte des Indes,** av. Louise 455, 1050, (0 2) 647 86 51, *Fax (0 2) 640 30 59*, Indian cuisine, « Exotic decor » – . AE E VISA FV c
*closed Sunday lunch* – **Meals** *Lunch 650* – a la carte 1150/1550.

**Taishin** - (at Mayfair H.), av. Louise 381, 1050, (0 2) 647 84 04, *Fax (0 2) 649 22 49*, Japanese cuisine – . AE E VISA JCB. FV a
*closed Sunday* – **Meals** *Lunch 750* – 1500/3000.

**Tagawa,** av. Louise 279, 1050, (0 2) 640 50 95, *Fax (0 2) 648 41 36*, Japanese cuisine – . AE E VISA JCB. FU e
*closed Saturday lunch, Sunday and Bank Holidays* – **Meals** *Lunch 390* – a la carte 1400/1950.

## Quartier Bois de la Cambre

**Villa Lorraine** (Van de Casserie), av. du Vivier d'Oie 75, 1000, (0 2) 374 31 63, *Fax (0 2) 372 01 95*, , « Terrace » – . AE E VISA JCB GX w
*closed Sunday and 3 weeks July* – **Meals** *Lunch 1750* – 3000, a la carte 3100/3700
**Spec.** Émincé de homard et artichauts tièdes, vinaigrette aux truffes. Noisettes de chevreuil, jus de venaison au poivre noir (October-10 December). Escalopines de foie de canard au verjus et figues confites.

**La Truffe Noire,** bd de la Cambre 12, 1000, (0 2) 640 44 22, *Fax (0 2) 647 97 04*, « Elegant interior » – . AE E VISA GV x
*closed Saturday lunch, Sunday, 1 week Easter, last 2 weeks August and first week January* – **Meals** *Lunch 1975 b.i.* – 2100/3475, – a la carte 2500/3650
**Spec.** Carpaccio aux truffes. St-Pierre aux poireaux et truffes. Truffe au chocolat noir en cage de sucre.

## Quartier Botanique, Gare du Nord *(see also at St-Josse-ten-Noode)*

**Sheraton Towers,** pl. Rogier 3, 1210, (0 2) 224 31 11, *Fax (0 2) 224 34 56*, , , – – 25-600. AE E VISA JCB FQ n
**Meals** see rest ***Les Comtes de Flandre*** below – ***Crescendo*** (Partly buffets, open until 11 p.m.) *Lunch 1100* - a la carte 1050/1500 – 750 – **464 rm** 9500, 42 suites.

**Président World Trade Center,** bd E. Jacqmain 180, 1000, (0 2) 203 20 20, *Fax (0 2) 203 24 40*, , , – – 25-350. AE E VISA JCB
**Meals** (lunch only) 990 – **286 rm** 7500/8500, 16 suites. FQ d

**Le Dome** with annex Le Dome II, bd du Jardin Botanique 12, 1000, (0 2) 218 45 29, *Fax (0 2) 218 41 12*, – – 25-100. AE E VISA
**Meals** *Lunch 650* – a la carte approx. 1400 – **125 rm** 3000/8400. FQ m

**Président Nord** without rest, bd A. Max 107, 1000, (0 2) 219 00 60, *Telex 61417*, *Fax (0 2) 218 12 69* – . AE E VISA JCB. FQ k
**63 rm** 3850/5350.

**Les Comtes de Flandre** - (at Sheraton Towers H.), pl. Rogier 3, 1210, (0 2) 224 31 11, *Telex 26887*, *Fax (0 2) 224 34 56* – . AE E VISA JCB FQ n
*closed Saturday lunch, Sunday and August* – **Meals** *Lunch 1250* – 2250.

**Quartier Atomium (Centenaire - Trade Mart - Laeken)**

**Les Baguettes Impériales** (Mme Ma), av. J. Sobieski 70, ✉ 1020, ☎ (0 2) 479 67 32, *Fax (0 2) 479 67 32*, Partly Vietnamese cuisine, « Terrace » – AE VISA.
*closed Tuesday, Sunday dinner, 2 weeks Easter and August* – **Meals** a la carte 1800/2500
**Spec.** Mï au homard. Crêpe croustillante au homard. Pigeonneau farci aux nids d'hirondelle.

**Ming Dynasty,** av. de l'Esplanade BP 9, ✉ 1020, ☎ (0 2) 475 23 45, *Fax (0 2) 475 23 50*, Chinese cuisine, open until 11 p.m. – AE VISA
*closed Saturday lunch, Sunday and mid July-mid August* – **Meals** Lunch 750 – 980 (2 pers. min.)/1950.

**Lychee,** r. De Wand 118, ✉ 1020, ☎ (0 2) 268 19 14, *Fax (0 2) 268 19 14*, Chinese cuisine, open until 11.30 p.m. – AE VISA
*closed 15 July-15 August* – **Meals** Lunch 325 – a la carte approx. 1000.

**Adrienne Atomium,** Square Atomium, bd du Centenaire, ✉ 1020, ☎ (0 2) 478 30 00, *Fax (0 10) 68 80 41*, town, Buffets – AE VISA
*closed Sunday, 3 weeks July and 1 week Christmas* – **Meals** Lunch 690 – 840.

## ANDERLECHT

**Le Prince de Liège,** chaussée de Ninove 664, ✉ 1070, ☎ (0 2) 522 16 00, *Fax (0 2) 520 81 85* – 25. AE VISA
**Meals** *(closed Sunday dinner and 10 July-8 August)* Lunch 545 – 1050/1395 – **32 rm** 2100/3250.

**Ustel,** Square de l'Aviation 6, ✉ 1070, ☎ (0 2) 520 60 53, *Fax (0 2) 520 33 28* – 30. AE VISA. ES q
**Meals** ***La Grande Écluse*** « In the machinery room of a lock » *(closed lunch Saturday and Sunday)* Lunch 450 - a la carte 1150/1550 – **94 rm** 3600/4300.

**Erasme,** rte de Lennik 790, ✉ 1070, ☎ (0 2) 523 62 82, *Fax (0 2) 523 62 83*, rest, 25-80. AE VISA
**Meals** (Pub rest) *(closed 1 to 15 August)* 655 – **52 rm** 2150/2850.

**Saint-Guidon** 2nd floor, av. Théo Verbeeck 2 (in the Constant Vanden Stock stadium), ✉ 1070, ☎ (0 2) 520 55 36, *Fax (0 2) 523 38 27* – 25-500. VISA JCB
*closed Saturday, Sunday, Bank Holidays, first league match days, July and Christmas-New Year* – Meals (lunch only) 995/2100 b.i.

**Alain Cornelis,** av. Paul Janson 82, ✉ 1070, ☎ (0 2) 523 20 83, *Fax (0 2) 523 20 83*, – AE VISA
*closed Saturday lunch, Sunday, Bank Holidays, Easter week, August and Christmas-New Year* – **Meals** Lunch 870 – a la carte 1650/2000.

**La Brouette,** bd Prince de Liège 61, ✉ 1070, ☎ (0 2) 522 51 69, *Fax (0 2) 522 51 69* – AE VISA
*closed Monday, Saturday lunch and mid July-mid August* – **Meals** (lunch only except Saturday and Sunday) Lunch 750 – 1250/1500.

**La Paix** r. Ropsy-Chaudron 49 (opposite the slaughterhouse), ✉ 1070, ☎ (0 2) 523 09 58, *Fax (0 2) 520 10 39*, Pub rest – AE VISA
*closed Saturday, Sunday and last 3 weeks July* – **Meals** (lunch only except Friday) a la carte 1000/1400.

## AUDERGHEM (OUDERGEM)

**La Grignotière** (Chanson), chaussée de Wavre 2041, ✉ 1160, ☎ (0 2) 672 81 85, *Fax (0 2) 672 81 85* – AE VISA
*closed Sunday, Monday and August* – **Meals** Lunch 1350 – 1750/2000
**Spec.** Langoustines à la vapeur de verveine, ragoût de girolles. Ravioles de champignons aux herbes. Turbotin rôti à l'émulsion de cerfeuil.

**L'Abbaye de Rouge Cloître,** r. Rouge Cloître 8, ✉ 1160, ☎ (0 2) 672 45 25, *Fax (0 2) 660 12 01*, « On the edge of a forest » – 25-45. AE VISA
*closed Tuesday, 22 December-6 January and after 7 p.m. except in summer* – **Meals** Lunch 550 – 850.

**La Citronnelle,** chaussée de Wavre 1377, ✉ 1160, ☎ (0 2) 672 98 43, *Fax (0 2) 672 98 43*, Vietnamese cuisine – AE VISA
*closed Monday, Saturday lunch and last 2 weeks August* – Meals Lunch 420 – a la carte approx. 900.

**La Khaïma,** chaussée de Wavre 1390, ✉ 1160, ☎ (0 2) 675 00 04, *Fax (0 2) 675 00 04*, Moroccan cuisine, open until 11 p.m., « Berber tent interior theme » –
*closed August* – **Meals** 995.

## ETTERBEEK

XX **Stirwen,** chaussée St-Pierre 15, ✉ 1040, ℘ (0 2) 640 85 41, *Fax (0 2) 648 43 08* – AE ⓓ E VISA GS a
*closed Saturday lunch, Sunday and 2 weeks August* – **Meals** *Lunch 1050* – a la carte 1750/2450
**Spec.** Tête de veau ravigote. Cassoulet toulousain au confit de canard (September-June). Fricassée de chipirons à la basquaise.

**Quartier Cinquantenaire (Montgomery) :**

**Clubhouse Park** without rest, av. de l'Yser 21, ✉ 1040, ℘ (0 2) 735 74 00, *Fax (0 2) 735 19 67*, – TV – 25. AE ⓓ E VISA JCB. HS c
**51 rm** 4000/8500.

XX **Le Serpolet,** av. de Tervuren 59, ✉ 1040, ℘ (0 2) 736 17 01, *Fax (0 2) 736 67 85*, – AE ⓓ E VISA HS b
*closed Saturday lunch and Sunday dinner* – **Meals** *Lunch 695* – 995/1275.

X **La Fontaine de Jade,** av. de Tervuren 5, ✉ 1040, ℘ (0 2) 736 32 10, *Fax (0 2) 732 46 86*, Chinese cuisine, open until 11 p.m. – AE ⓓ E VISA HS a
*closed Saturday lunch* – **Meals** *Lunch 350* – 950.

X **Momotaro,** av. d'Auderghem 106, ✉ 1040, ℘ (0 2) 734 06 64, *Fax (0 2) 734 64 18*, Japanese cuisine with sushi-bar – AE ⓓ E VISA. GS f
*closed lunch Saturday and Sunday and 1 to 15 August* – **Meals** *Lunch 395* – 690/2700.

## EVERE

**Belson** without rest, chaussée de Louvain 805, ✉ 1140, ℘ (0 2) 705 20 30, *Fax (0 2) 705 20 43* – TV – 25. AE ⓓ E VISA JCB
650 – **131 rm** 2900/9000, 3 suites.

**Mercure,** av. J. Bordet 74, ✉ 1140, ℘ (0 2) 726 73 35, *Fax (0 2) 726 82 95*, – TV – 25-120. AE ⓓ E VISA JCB
**Meals** *(closed lunch Saturday and Sunday)* a la carte 1000/1600 – 600 – **113 rm** 4500/5950, 7 suites.

**Evergreen** without rest, av. V. Day 1, ✉ 1140, ℘ (0 2) 726 70 15, *Fax (0 2) 726 62 60* – TV. AE ⓓ E VISA JCB
**20 rm** 2300/2600.

## FOREST (VORST)

**De Fierlant** without rest, r. De Fierlant 67, ✉ 1190, ℘ (0 2) 538 60 70, *Fax (0 2) 538 91 99* – TV. AE ⓓ E VISA
**40 rm** 2000/2800.

## GANSHOREN

XXXX **Bruneau,** av. Broustin 75, ✉ 1083, ℘ (0 2) 427 69 78, *Fax (0 2) 425 97 26*, « Terrace » – AE ⓓ E VISA
*closed Bank Holidays Thursdays, Tuesday dinner, Wednesday, 30 July-26 August and 1 to 10 February* – **Meals** *Lunch 1750* – 3245/4675, a la carte 2300/3300
**Spec.** St-Jacques farcies d'embeurrée de chou et hachis de pieds de porc (October-15 April). Aile de raie gratinée de crevettes et mousseline aux poireaux. Noix de ris de veau en habit de dentelle.

XXX **Claude Dupont,** av. Vital Riethuisen 46, ✉ 1083, ℘ (0 2) 426 00 00, *Fax (0 2) 426 65 40* – AE ⓓ E VISA
*closed Monday, Tuesday and early July-early August* – **Meals** 1775/3250, a la carte approx. 2300
**Spec.** Barbue grillée en rosace de courgettes au Graves rouge. Timbale de homard en mousseline de jeunes poireaux. Gibiers (15 September-December).

XXX **San Daniele,** av. Charles-Quint 6, ✉ 1083, ℘ (0 2) 426 79 23, *Fax (0 2) 426 92 14*, Partly Italian cuisine – AE ⓓ E VISA
*closed Sunday, Monday dinner and 20 July-20 August* – **Meals** a la carte 1100/2050.

XX **Cambrils** 1st floor, av. Charles-Quint 365, ✉ 1083, ℘ (0 2) 465 35 82, *Fax (0 2) 465 76 63*, – AE E VISA
*closed dinner Monday and Thursday, Sunday, carnival and 15 July-15 August* – **Meals** *Lunch 890* – 1090/1230.

## IXELLES (ELSENE)

XX **Yen,** r. Lesbroussart 49, ✉ 1050, ℘ (0 2) 649 07 47, , Vietnamese cuisine – AE ⓓ E VISA. FU f
**Meals** *Lunch 320* – a la carte approx. 1000.

**Quartier Boondael (University)**

XXX **Le Couvert d'Argent,** pl. Marie-José 9, ✉ 1050, ☎ (0 2) 648 45 45, *Fax (0 2) 648 22 28,* ⛱, « Elegant pavilion in garden » – P. AE ⓓ E VISA JCB GX y
*closed Sunday, Monday, 15 to 30 August and 25 to 30 December* – **Meals** 995/2200.

XX **L'Aub. de Boendael,** square du Vieux Tilleul 12, ✉ 1050, ☎ (0 2) 672 70 55, *Fax (0 2) 660 75 82,* ⛱, Grill rest, « Rustic » – ▤ P. AE ⓓ E VISA HX h
*closed Saturday, Sunday, Bank Holidays, 25 July-16 August and 25 December-3 January* – **Meals** 1375 b.i.

X **La Pagode d'Or,** chaussée de Boondael 332, ✉ 1050, ☎ (0 2) 649 06 56, *Fax (0 2) 649 06 56,* ⛱, Vietnamese cuisine, open until 11 p.m. – AE ⓓ E VISA. ✻ GV m
*closed Monday* – **Meals** *Lunch 350* – a la carte approx. 1000.

X **La Brasserie Marebœuf,** av. de la Couronne 445, ✉ 1050, ☎ (0 2) 648 99 06, *Fax (0 2) 648 38 30,* Oyster bar, open until midnight – ▤. AE ⓓ E VISA GHV t
*closed Sunday* – **Meals** *Lunch 550* – 895.

X **le Toulon'Co,** av. du Bois de la Cambre 53, ✉ 1050, ☎ (0 2) 675 17 03, *Fax (0 2) 675 17 03,* ⛱ – E VISA HVX r
*closed lunch Saturday and Monday, Sunday and 15 July-15 August* – **Meals** *Lunch 950* – 1090/1350.

**Quartier Bascule**

**Capital** M without rest, chaussée de Vleurgat 191, ✉ 1050, ☎ (0 2) 646 64 20, *Fax (0 2) 646 33 14,* ⛱ – |♦| ⇆, ▤ rest, TV ☎ & ⇐ – 🏛 25-40. AE ⓓ E VISA JCB. ✻
**62 rm** ☕ 4300. FU c

XXX **La Mosaïque,** r. Forestière 23, ✉ 1050, ☎ (0 2) 649 02 35, *Fax (0 2) 647 11 49,* ⛱ – P. AE ⓓ E VISA FU p
*closed Saturday lunch, Sunday, 12 to 19 April, 15 August-6 September and 24 to 30 December* – **Meals** *Lunch 1200 b.i.* – 1400/1700.

XX **Maison Félix** 1st floor, r. Washington 149 (square Henri Michaux), ✉ 1050, ☎ (0 2) 345 66 93 – AE ⓓ E VISA FV s
*closed Sunday, Monday and last 2 weeks July* – **Meals** a la carte 2400/3300.

**Quartier Léopold** *(see also at Bruxelles)*

**Leopold,** r. Luxembourg 35, ✉ 1050, ☎ (0 2) 511 18 28, *Fax (0 2) 514 19 39,* ⛱, ≘ – |♦| ▤ TV ☎ ⇐ – 🏛 25-60. AE ⓓ E VISA. ✻ rm FS y
**Meals** *(closed Saturday lunch and Sunday) Lunch 1290* – a la carte approx. 1800 – ☕ 400 – **86 rm** ☕ 4450/4850.

**Quartier Louise** *(see also at Bruxelles and at St-Gilles)*

**Sofitel** without rest, av. de la Toison d'Or 40, ✉ 1050, ☎ (0 2) 514 22 00, *Fax (0 2) 514 57 44* – |♦| ⇆ ▤ TV ☎ – 🏛 25-120. AE ⓓ E VISA JCB FS r
☕ 750 – **171 rm** 12000.

**Mövenpick Cadettt** M, r. Paul Spaak 15, ✉ 1000, ☎ (0 2) 645 61 11, *Fax (0 2) 646 63 44,* ⛱, ≘, ⛱ – |♦| ⇆ ▤ TV ☎ & ⇐ – 🏛 25-40. AE ⓓ E VISA FU k
**Meals** (open until 11 p.m.) *Lunch 570* – a la carte approx. 1100 – ☕ 500 – **128 rm** 5350/5750.

**Beau-Site** without rest, r. Longue Haie 76, ✉ 1000, ☎ (0 2) 640 88 89, *Fax (0 2) 640 16 11* – |♦| TV ☎. AE ⓓ E VISA FT r
**38 rm** ☕ 3000/3950.

**Argus** without rest, r. Capitaine Crespel 6, ✉ 1050, ☎ (0 2) 514 07 70, *Fax (0 2) 514 12 22* – |♦| TV ☎. AE ⓓ E VISA FS t
**41 rm** ☕ 3200/3500.

X **Les Perles de Pluie,** r. Châtelain 25, ✉ 1050, ☎ (0 2) 649 67 23, *Fax (0 2) 644 07 60,* Thaï cuisine, open until 11 p.m. – AE ⓓ E VISA FU n
*closed Saturday lunch* – **Meals** *Lunch 460* – 850/1750.

## MOLENBEEK-ST-JEAN (SINT-JANS-MOLENBEEK)

XXX **Le Béarnais,** bd Louis Mettewie 318, ✉ 1080, ☎ (0 2) 411 51 51, *Fax (0 2) 410 70 81* – ▤. AE ⓓ E VISA
*closed Sunday, Monday dinner and 13 July-4 August* – **Meals** *Lunch 1090* – a la carte approx. 2100.

## ST-GILLES (SINT-GILLIS)

XX **Inada,** r. Source 73, ✉ 1060, ☎ (0 2) 538 01 13, *Fax (0 2) 538 01 13* – AE ⓓ E VISA ET a
*closed Saturday lunch, Sunday, Monday, Bank Holidays and mid July-August* – **Meals** *Lunch 750* – a la carte 1450/2400.

**Le Forcado,** chaussée de Charleroi 192, ✉ 1060, ☎ (0 2) 537 92 20, *Fax (0 2) 537 92 20,* Portuguese cuisine – ▤. AE ⓓ E VISA EFU a
*closed Sunday, Bank Holidays, carnival week and August* – **Meals** a la carte approx. 1300.

**La Mamounia,** av. Porte de Hal 9, ✉ 1060, ☎ (0 2) 537 73 22, *Fax (0 2) 539 39 59,* Moroccan cuisine, open until 11 p.m. – AE ⓓ E VISA JCB ES n
*closed Monday except Bank Holidays and mid July-mid August* – **Meals** *Lunch 495* – 745/1295.

**Quartier Louise** *(see also at Bruxelles and at Ixelles)*

**Holiday Inn City Centre,** chaussée de Charleroi 38, ✉ 1060, ☎ (0 2) 533 66 66, *Fax (0 2) 538 90 14* – AE ⓓ E VISA JCB – 25-250. AE ⓓ E VISA JCB FT m
**Meals** *(closed August) Lunch 750* – a la carte 1050/1500 – ☐ 600 – **201 rm** 7300.

**Manos Stephanie** without rest, chaussée de Charleroi 28, ✉ 1060, ☎ (0 2) 539 02 50, *Fax (0 2) 537 57 29,* « Mansion with particular atmosphere » – AE ⓓ E VISA JCB FS f
**48 rm** ☐ 6450/7850, 7 suites.

**Manos** without rest, chaussée de Charleroi 102, ✉ 1060, ☎ (0 2) 537 96 82, *Fax (0 2) 539 36 55,* – – 25. AE ⓓ E VISA JCB FU w
**35 rm** ☐ 4450/7450, 3 suites.

**Cascade** Ⓜ without rest, r. Berckmans 128, ✉ 1060, ☎ (0 2) 538 88 30, *Fax (0 2) 538 92 79* – – 25. AE ⓓ E VISA. ES r
**80 rm** ☐ 6000/6400.

**Tulip Inn Delta,** chaussée de Charleroi 17, ✉ 1060, ☎ (0 2) 539 01 60, *Fax (0 2) 537 90 11* – – 25-100. AE ⓓ E VISA JCB. rest FS w
**Meals** *Lunch 325* – 800 – **246 rm** ☐ 4900.

**Diplomat** without rest, r. Jean Stas 32, ✉ 1060, ☎ (0 2) 537 42 50, *Fax (0 2) 539 33 79* – . AE ⓓ E VISA JCB FS v
**68 rm** ☐ 6000/7000.

**I Trulli,** r. Jourdan 18, ✉ 1060, ☎ (0 2) 538 98 20, *Fax (0 2) 537 79 30,* , Partly Italian cuisine, open until midnight – AE ⓓ E VISA JCB FS c
*closed Sunday, 11 to 31 July and 22 December-1 January* – **Meals** *Lunch 460* – a la carte approx. 2000.

**Les Capucines,** r. Jourdan 22, ✉ 1060, ☎ (0 2) 538 69 24, *Fax (0 2) 538 69 24,* – AE ⓓ E VISA FS u
*closed Sunday, Monday dinner, 2 weeks Easter and 15 to 31 August* – **Meals** *Lunch 550* – 995.

## ST-JOSSE-TEN-NOODE (SINT-JOOST-TEN-NODE)

**Quartier Botanique** *(see also at Bruxelles)*

**Royal Crown Gd H. Mercure,** r. Royale 250, ✉ 1210, ☎ (0 2) 220 66 11, *Fax (0 2) 217 84 44,* – – 25-350. AE ⓓ E VISA JCB FQ r
Meals see rest ***Hugo's*** below – **304 rm** ☐ 7000/9000, 5 suites.

**Palace,** r. Gineste 3, ✉ 1210, ☎ (0 2) 203 62 00, *Fax (0 2) 203 55 55* – – 25-450. AE ⓓ E VISA JCB. rest FQ v
Meals ***Le Temps Présent*** *(closed lunch Saturday and Sunday and 15 July-20 August) Lunch 850* - a la carte approx. 1400 – ☐ 850 – **359 rm** 6800/7800, 1 suite.

**Art H. Siru** without rest, pl. Rogier 1, ✉ 1210, ☎ (0 2) 203 35 80, *Fax (0 2) 203 33 03,* « Each room decorated by a contemporary Belgian artist » – – 25-100. AE ⓓ E VISA JCB. FQ p
**101 rm** ☐ 4200/4700.

**Albert Premier** without rest, pl. Rogier 20, ✉ 1210, ☎ (0 2) 203 31 25, *Fax (0 2) 203 43 31* – – 25-60. AE ⓓ E VISA FQ q
**285 rm** ☐ 2500/3500.

**Hugo's** - (at Royal Crown Gd H. Mercure), r. Royale 250, ✉ 1210, ☎ (0 2) 220 66 11, *Fax (0 2) 217 84 44* – ▤ Ⓟ. AE ⓓ E VISA JCB FQ r
*closed Saturday and Sunday* – **Meals** *Lunch 1000* – a la carte 1450/1800.

**De Ultieme Hallucinatie,** r. Royale 316, ✉ 1210, ☎ (0 2) 217 06 14, *Fax (0 2) 217 72 40,* « Art Nouveau interior » – Ⓟ. AE ⓓ E VISA. FQ t
*closed Saturday lunch, Sunday, Bank Holidays and 20 July-16 August* – **Meals** *Lunch 1075* – 2750 b.i.

**Les Dames Tartine,** chaussée de Haecht 58, ✉ 1210, ☎ (0 2) 218 45 49, *Fax (0 2) 218 45 49* – AE ⓓ E VISA FQ s
*closed Saturday lunch, Sunday and Monday* – **Meals** *Lunch 750* – 990/1385.

## SCHAERBEEK (SCHAARBEEK)

### Quartier Meiser

**Lambermont** (with annex) without rest, bd Lambermont 322, ✉ 1030, ℘ (0 2) 242 55 95, *Fax (0 2) 215 36 13* – AE ⓓ E VISA
**42 rm** ☐ 3400/3900.

**Le Cadre Noir,** av. Milcamps 158, ✉ 1030, ℘ (0 2) 734 14 45, Seafood – AE ⓓ E VISA HR v
*closed Saturday lunch, Sunday dinner, Monday and 15 to 31 July* – Meals 885/1100.

**Amici miei,** bd. Gén. Wahis 248, ✉ 1030, ℘ (0 2) 705 49 80, *Fax (0 2) 705 29 65*, Italian cuisine – AE ⓓ E VISA HQ k
*closed Saturday lunch, Sunday and late July-early August* – **Meals** a la carte 900/1450.

## UCCLE (UKKEL)

**County House,** square des Héros 2, ✉ 1180, ℘ (0 2) 375 44 20, *Fax (0 2) 375 31 22* – rest, – 25-140. AE ⓓ E VISA. EX b
**Meals** a la carte 1100/1700 – **83 rm** ☐ 4000/4600, 16 suites.

**Les Frères Romano,** av. de Fré 182, ✉ 1180, ℘ (0 2) 374 70 98, *Fax (0 2) 374 04 18*, – ⓟ. AE ⓓ E VISA FX d
*closed Sunday, Bank Holidays and last 3 weeks August* – **Meals** Lunch 975 – a la carte approx. 1700.

**L'Amandier,** av. de Fré 184, ✉ 1180, ℘ (0 2) 374 03 95, *Fax (0 2) 374 86 92*, , Open until 11 p.m., « Terrace overlooking a garden » – AE ⓓ E VISA FX e
*closed Saturday lunch* – **Meals** Lunch 950 – a la carte approx. 1500.

**Villa d'Este,** r. Etoile 142, ✉ 1180, ℘ (0 2) 376 48 48, , « Terrace » – ⓟ. AE ⓓ E VISA
*closed Sunday dinner, Monday, July and late December* – Meals 990/1750.

**Blue Elephant,** chaussée de Waterloo 1120, ✉ 1180, ℘ (0 2) 374 49 62, *Fax (0 2) 375 44 68*, Thaï cuisine, « Exotic decor » – ⓟ. AE ⓓ E VISA GX j
*closed Saturday lunch* – **Meals** Lunch 850 – a la carte 1050/1650.

**Willy et Marianne,** chaussée d'Alsemberg 705, ✉ 1180, ℘ (0 2) 343 60 09 – AE ⓓ E VISA EX r
*closed Tuesday, Wednesday, 2 weeks carnival and 3 weeks July* – Meals Lunch 450 – 995.

**La Cité du Dragon,** chaussée de Waterloo 1024, ✉ 1180, ℘ (0 2) 375 80 80, *Fax (0 2) 375 69 77*, , Chinese cuisine, open until 11.30 p.m., « Exotic garden with fountains » – ⓟ. AE ⓓ E VISA GX c
Meals Lunch 485 – 810/2350.

**De Hoef,** r. Edith Cavell 218, ✉ 1180, ℘ (0 2) 374 34 17, *Fax (0 2) 375 30 84*, , Grill rest, « 17C inn » – AE ⓓ E VISA FX q
*closed 10 to 31 July* – **Meals** Lunch 395 – 795.

**Brasseries Georges,** av. Winston Churchill 259, ✉ 1180, ℘ (0 2) 347 21 00, *Fax (0 2) 344 02 45*, , Oyster bar, open until midnight – . AE ⓓ E VISA FV n
*closed dinner 24 December* – **Meals** Lunch 600 – a la carte 1100/1450.

## WATERMAEL-BOITSFORT (WATERMAAL-BOSVOORDE)

**Host. des 3 Tilleuls** with rm, Berensheide 8, ✉ 1170, ℘ (0 2) 672 30 14, *Fax (0 2) 673 65 52*, – AE ⓓ E VISA. rm
*closed 15 July-15 August* – **Meals** *(closed Sunday)* 1100 – **7 rm** ☐ 3000/4100.

**Les Rives du Gange** with rm, av. de la Fauconnerie 1, ✉ 1170, ℘ (0 2) 672 16 01, *Fax (0 2) 672 43 30*, – AE ⓓ E VISA
**Meals** (Indian cuisine, open until 1 a.m.) Lunch 595 – 990 – **19 rm** ☐ 2480/3480.

**Au Vieux Boitsfort,** pl. Bischoffsheim 9, ✉ 1170, ℘ (0 2) 672 23 32, *Fax (0 2) 660 22 94*, – AE ⓓ E VISA JCB
*closed Saturday lunch and Sunday* – **Meals** 1390.

**Le Bellini,** pl. Eug. Keym 4, ✉ 1170, ℘ (0 2) 673 83 83, *Fax (0 2) 662 07 07* – AE ⓓ E VISA HV a
*closed Saturday lunch, Sunday dinner, Monday and 2 weeks August* – **Meals** Lunch 750 – 1000/1595.

**L'Entre-Temps,** r. Philippe Dewolfs 7, ✉ 1170, ℘ (0 2) 672 87 20, *Fax (0 2) 672 87 20*, , Brasserie – AE ⓓ E VISA
*closed Tuesday dinner, Wednesday and 21 July-19 August* – **Meals** Lunch 525 – a la carte 850/1200.

**La Maison de Thaïlande,** r. Middelbourg 22, ✉ 1170, ℘ (0 2) 672 26 57, , Thaï cuisine – AE ⓓ E VISA
*closed lunch Saturday and Sunday and Tuesday* – **Meals** a la carte 900/1300.

## WOLUWÉ-ST-LAMBERT (SINT-LAMBRECHTS-WOLUWE)

**Sodehotel La Woluwe** M, av. E. Mounier 5, ✉ 1200, ℘ (0 2) 775 21 11, *Fax (0 2) 770 47 80*, – ... – 25-200. AE ⓓ E VISA
Meals : ***Le Lidrus*** *Lunch 745* - a la carte 1400/2000 – ☕ 645 – **112 rm** 7200, 8 suites.

**Lambeau** M without rest, av. Lambeau 150, ✉ 1200, ℘ (0 2) 732 51 70, *Fax (0 2) 732 54 90* – ... AE E VISA HR u
**24 rm** ☕ 2100/3100.

**Mon Manège à Toi,** r. Neerveld 1, ✉ 1200, ℘ (0 2) 770 02 38, *Fax (0 2) 762 95 80,* « Floral garden » – P. AE ⓓ E VISA
*closed Saturday, Sunday, Bank Holidays, 7 to 31 July and 24 December-1 January* – **Meals** *Lunch 1475* – a la carte 1950/2500.

Moulin de Lindekemale, av. J.-F. Debecker 6, ✉ 1200, ℘ (0 2) 770 90 57, *Fax (0 2) 762 94 57,* « Former watermill ».

## WOLUWÉ-ST-PIERRE (SINT-PIETERS-WOLUWE)

**Montgomery** M, av. de Tervuren 134, ✉ 1150, ℘ (0 2) 741 85 11, *Fax (0 2) 741 85 00,* ... – 25. AE ⓓ E VISA JCB. HS k
**Meals** *(closed weekends, Bank Holidays and 19 December-4 January) Lunch 1050* – 1790 – ☕ 600 – **61 rm** 9900/12700, 2 suites.

**Des 3 Couleurs** (Tourneur), av. de Tervuren 453, ✉ 1150, ℘ (0 2) 770 33 21, *Fax (0 2) 770 80 45*, , « Terrace » – AE E VISA
*closed Saturday lunch, Sunday dinner, Monday and mid August-mid September* – **Meals** *Lunch 1800 b.i.* – 2000, a la carte 2000/2350
**Spec.** Pigeonneau désossé façon Grand-Mère. Saumon Liliane. Chevreuil Arlequin (15 September-10 December).

**Le Vignoble de Margot,** av. de Tervuren 368, ✉ 1150, ℘ (0 2) 779 23 23, *Fax (0 2) 779 05 45*, ≤, Partly oyster bar, open until 11 p.m., « Overlooking park and ponds » – P. AE ⓓ E VISA
*closed Sunday* – **Meals** a la carte approx. 1700
**Spec.** Tronçon de turbotin rôti aux petis oignons caramélisés. Poularde à la broche et poêlée de champignons des bois (July-November). Croustillant aux amandes grillées, glace praliné, sauce au caramel mou.

**Le Mucha,** av. Jules Dujardin 23, ✉ 1150, ℘ (0 2) 770 24 14, *Fax (0 2) 770 24 14*, , Partly Italian cuisine, open until 11 p.m. – AE ⓓ E VISA
*closed Sunday and 1 to 22 September* – **Meals** *Lunch 460* – 850/1250.

## BRUSSELS ENVIRONS

**at Diegem** *Brussels-Zaventem motorway Diegem exit C Machelen pop. 11 518 – ✉ 1831 Diegem :*

**Holiday Inn Airport,** Holidaystraat 7 ℘ (0 2) 720 58 65, *Fax (0 2) 720 41 45*, ... – 25-400. AE ⓓ E VISA JCB. rest
**Meals** (open until 11 p.m.) *Lunch 1195 b.i.* – a la carte 1400/1700 – ☕ 650 – **310 rm** 8500.

**Sofitel Airport,** Bessenveldstraat 15 ℘ (0 2) 713 66 66, *Fax (0 2) 721 43 45*, ... – 25-300. AE ⓓ E VISA
**Meals** ***La Pléiade*** *(closed Saturday)* 1450 – ☕ 750 – **125 rm** 8000.

**Novotel Airport,** Olmenstraat ℘ (0 2) 725 30 50, *Fax (0 2) 721 39 58*, ... – 25-200. AE ⓓ E VISA JCB
**Meals** (open until midnight) a la carte 1150/1600 – ☕ 500 – **205 rm** 5450.

**Rainbow Airport** M, Berkenlaan 4 ℘ (0 2) 721 77 77, *Fax (0 2) 721 55 96*, ... – 25-60. AE ⓓ E VISA JCB.
**Meals** *(closed Saturday and Sunday)* a la carte 850/1250 – **99 rm** ☕ 4950.

**Ibis Airport,** Bessenveldstraat 17 ℘ (0 2) 725 43 21, *Fax (0 2) 725 40 40*, ..., rest, ... – 25-60. AE ⓓ E VISA JCB. rest
**Meals** *Lunch 595* – 695 – ☕ 250 – **95 rm** 2350/3150.

**at Dilbeek** *W : 7 km – pop. 37 352 – ✉ 1700 Dilbeek :*

**Relais Delbeccha**, Bodegemstraat 158 ℘ (0 2) 569 44 30, *Fax (0 2) 569 75 30*, ... – 25-120. AE ⓓ E VISA.
**Meals** *(closed Sunday dinner)* 1025/1450 – **12 rm** ☕ 3500/4500.

**Host. d'Arconati** with rm, d'Arconatistraat 77 ℘ (0 2) 569 35 00, *Fax (0 2) 569 35 04*, , « Floral terrace », ... – 60. AE E VISA. rm
**Meals** *(closed Sunday dinner, Monday, Tuesday and February) Lunch 1000* – 1775 b.i. – **6 rm** ☕ 3000.

**at Dworp** *(Tourneppe) S : 16 km* Ⓒ *Beersel pop. 22 711 – ✉ 1653 Dworp :*

**Kasteel Gravenhof**, Alsembergsesteenweg 676 ☎ (0 2) 380 44 99, *Fax (0 2) 380 40 60*, « Woodland setting, lake », – ⊡ – 25-120. AE ⓓ E VISA
**Meals** (Pub rest) *Lunch 625* – a la carte approx. 1200 – ☐ 395 – **24 rm** 4850.

**at Grimbergen** *N : 11 km – pop. 32 737 – ✉ 1850 Grimbergen :*

**Abbey,** Kerkeblokstraat 5 ☎ (0 2) 270 08 88, *Fax (0 2) 270 81 88*, – rest, ☎ ⓟ – 30-200. AE ⓓ E VISA. rm
*closed July* – **Meals** ***'t Wit Paard*** *(closed Saturday and Sunday) Lunch 1250* - a la carte 1750/2100 – ☐ 400 – **28 rm** 4200/4800.

**at Groot-Bijgaarden** *NW : 7 km* Ⓒ *Dilbeek pop. 37 352 – ✉ 1702 Groot-Bijgaarden :*

**Waerboom,** Jozef Mertensstraat 140 ☎ (0 2) 463 15 00, *Fax (0 2) 463 10 30*, – ☎ ⓟ – 25-270. AE ⓓ E VISA.
*closed mid July-mid August* – **Meals** (residents only) – **34 rm** ☐ 3800/4100.

**Gosset** Ⓜ, Alfons Gossetlaan 52 ☎ (0 2) 466 21 30, *Fax (0 2) 466 18 50*, – ☎ ⓟ – 25-200. AE ⓓ E VISA. rm
*closed 23 December-2 January* – **Meals** *Lunch 350* – a la carte 950/1300 – **48 rm** ☐ 2000/4100.

**De Bijgaarden,** I. Van Beverenstraat 20 (near castle) ☎ (0 2) 466 44 85, *Fax (0 2) 463 08 11*, – AE ⓓ E VISA
*closed Saturday lunch, Sunday, Bank Holidays, 12 to 20 April, 16 August-7 September and early January* – **Meals** 1850/3000, a la carte 3350/3800
**Spec.** Chou vert au caviar osciètre. Turbot rôti "château" et béarnaise de homard. Poularde fermière aux morilles crèmées (April-October).

**Michel** (Coppens), Schepen Gossetlaan 31 ☎ (0 2) 466 65 91, *Fax (0 2) 466 90 07*, – ⓟ. AE ⓓ E VISA
*closed Sunday, Monday and August* – **Meals** 1700/2250, a la carte 2000/2500
**Spec.** Bar rôti au risotto d'artichauts et fumet de fruits de mer. Blanc de turbot en papillote aux fines herbes. Escalopes de foie d'oie poêlées aux fruits de saison caramélisés.

**at Hoeilaart** *SE : 13 km – pop. 9 630 – ✉ 1560 Hoeilaart :*

**Groenendaal,** Groenendaalsesteenweg 145 (at Groenendaal) ☎ (0 2) 657 94 47, *Fax (0 2) 657 20 30*, – ☎ ⓟ – 25. AE ⓓ E VISA JCB
**Meals** *(closed Sunday) Lunch 790* – 980/1595 – **8 rm** ☐ 3200/3600.

**Aloyse Kloos,** Terhulpsesteenweg 2 (at Groenendaal) ☎ (0 2) 657 37 37, « On the edge of a forest » – ⓟ. E VISA JCB
*closed Sunday dinner, Monday, 2 weeks Easter and August* – **Meals** *Lunch 1450* – 2000, a la carte 1900/2300
**Spec.** Saumon mariné aux truffes. Ecrevisses à la luxembourgeoise (June-January). Poulet fermier aux morilles.

**at Huizingen** *S : 12 km* Ⓒ *Beersel pop. 22 711 – ✉ 1654 Huizingen :*

**Terborght,** Oud Dorp 16 (near E 19, exit ⑮) ☎ (0 2) 380 10 10, *Fax (0 2) 380 10 97*, « Rustic » – ⓟ. AE ⓓ E VISA.
*closed dinner Sunday and Tuesday, Monday, carnival and 13 July-3 August* – **Meals** *Lunch 1500 b.i.* – 950/1800.

**at Kobbegem** *NW : 11 km* Ⓒ *Asse pop. 27 501 – ✉ 1730 Kobbegem :*

**De Plezanten Hof,** Broekstraat 2 ☎ (0 2) 453 23 23, *Fax (0 2) 452 99 11*, – ⓟ. AE E VISA
*closed dinner Tuesday and Sunday, Wednesday, 1 week carnival and 3 weeks August* – **Meals** *Lunch 1150* – 2100/2950.

**at Kraainem** *E : 12 km – pop. 12 915 – ✉ 1950 Kraainem :*

**d'Oude Pastorie,** Pastoorkesweg 1 (Park Jourdain) ☎ (0 2) 720 63 46, *Fax (0 2) 720 63 46*, « Lakeside setting in park » – ⓟ. AE ⓓ E VISA.
*closed Monday dinner, Thursday, 13 to 20 April and 17 August-7 September* – **Meals** *Lunch 1200* – a la carte approx. 1700.

**at Linkebeek** *S : 12 km – pop. 4 647 – ✉ 1630 Linkebeek :*

**Le Saint-Sébastien,** r. Station 90 ☎ (0 2) 380 54 90, *Fax (0 2) 380 54 41*, – ⓟ. ⓓ E VISA
*closed Monday except Bank Holidays and 15 August-15 September* – **Meals** *Lunch 750* – 1150/1450.

**at Machelen** *NE : 12 km – pop. 11 518 – ✉ 1830 Machelen :*

XXX **André D'Haese,** Heirbaan 210 ☎ (0 2) 252 50 72, *Fax (0 2) 253 47 65,* ☂, « Modern interior, terrace with landscaped garden » – P. AE ① E VISA JCB. ✂
✿ *closed Saturday lunch, Sunday, Bank Holidays, 1 week after Easter, 12 July-2 August and 1 week after Christmas* – **Meals** *Lunch 1300* – 2250/2900, a la carte 2450/2950
**Spec.** Lotte et foie gras d'oie fumé aux haricots verts et tomates séchées. Filet de St-Pierre poêlé tout céleri. Ris de veau braisé à brun Zingara.

**at Meise** *N : 14 km – pop. 17 862 – ✉ 1860 Meise :*

XXX **Aub. Napoléon,** Bouchoutlaan 1 ☎ (0 2) 269 30 78, *Fax (0 2) 269 79 98,* Grill rest – P. AE ① E VISA
*closed August* – **Meals** *Lunch 1450* – a la carte 1850/2200.

XXX **Koen Van Loven,** Brusselsesteenweg 11 ☎ (0 2) 270 05 77, *Fax (0 2) 270 05 46,* ☂ – 🏛 25-150. AE ① E VISA
*closed Sunday dinner, Monday and Easter holidays* – **Meals** 1495/1845.

**at Melsbroek** *NE : 14 km* C *Steenokkerzeel pop. 10 130 – ✉ 1820 Melsbroek :*

XXX **Boetfort,** Sellaerstraat 42 ☎ (0 2) 751 64 00, *Fax (0 2) 751 62 00,* ☂, « 17C mansion, park » – P – 🏛 25-40. AE ① E VISA. ✂
*closed Wednesday dinner, Saturday lunch, Sunday and carnival week* – **Meals** *Lunch 1200* – 1500/2400.

**at Nossegem** *E : 13 km* C *Zaventem pop. 26 467 – ✉ 1930 Nossegem :*

XX **Roland Debuyst,** Leuvensesteenweg 614 ☎ (0 2) 757 05 59, ☂ – P. AE ① E VISA
*closed Saturday lunch, Sunday, Monday dinner, 3 weeks May and 1 week August* – **Meals** *Lunch 1300* – 1900/2450.

**at Overijse** *SE : 16 km – pop. 23 591 – ✉ 3090 Overijse :*

XXXX **Barbizon** (Deluc), Welriekendedreef 95 (at Jezus-Eik) ☎ (0 2) 657 04 62, *Fax (0 2) 657 40 66,* ☂, « Terrace and garden » – P. AE E VISA
✿ *closed Tuesday, Wednesday, February and late July-early August* – **Meals** *Lunch 1425* – 1750/3250, a la carte 2300/2800
**Spec.** Compression de homard et huîtres, vinaigrette aux herbes. Gibiers (September-January). Croustillant de ris de veau aux carottes, cumin et petits oignons.

X **Istas,** Brusselsesteenweg 652 (at Jezus-Eik) ☎ (0 2) 657 05 11, *Fax (0 2) 657 05 11,* ☂, Pub rest – P. E VISA
*closed Wednesday, Thursday and August* – **Meals** a la carte 850/1200.

**at Schepdaal** *W : 12 km* C *Dilbeek pop. 37 352 – ✉ 1703 Schepdaal :*

🏠 **Lien Zana,** Ninoofsesteenweg 1022 ☎ (0 2) 569 65 25, *Fax (0 2) 569 64 64,* ☂, ⛟ – 🛗, ▤ rest, TV ☎ P – 🏛 25. AE ① E VISA
*closed 21 July-early August and 24 December-3 January* – **Meals** (Pub rest) a la carte approx. 900 – **27 rm** ▭ 2600/4000.

**at Sint-Genesius-Rode** *(Rhode-St-Genèse) S : 13 km – pop. 18 099 – ✉ 1640 Sint-Genesius-Rode :*

🏠 **Aub. de Waterloo,** chaussée de Waterloo 212 ☎ (0 2) 358 35 80, *Fax (0 2) 358 38 06* – 🛗 ⇆ TV ☎ P – 🏛 25-80. AE ① E VISA
**Meals** see rest ***L'Arlecchino*** below – **83 rm** ▭ 2350/6250.

XX **L'Arlecchino** - (at Aub. de Waterloo H.), chaussée de Waterloo 212 ☎ (0 2) 358 34 16, *Fax (0 2) 358 28 96,* ☂, Italian cuisine, with trattoria – ▤ P. AE ① E VISA. ✂
**Meals** 850.

X **Bois Savanes,** chaussée de Waterloo 208 ☎ (0 2) 358 37 78, *Fax (0 2) 354 66 95,* ☂, Thaï cuisine – P. AE ① E VISA
*closed lunch Monday and Tuesday and first 3 weeks August* – **Meals** *Lunch 495* – a la carte approx. 1100.

**at Sint-Pieters-Leeuw** *SO : 13 km – pop. 29 643 – ✉ 1600 Sint-Pieters-Leeuw :*

🏠 **Green Park** M 🐎, V. Nonnemanstraat 15 ☎ (0 2) 331 19 70, *Fax (0 2) 331 03 11,* ☂, « Lakeside setting », 🏋, 🛶 – 🛗 TV ☎ ♿ P – 🏛 25-100. AE ① E VISA JCB
*closed July* – **Meals** *(closed Friday) Lunch 450* – a la carte 1300/1600 – **18 rm** ▭ 3850/4350.

**at Strombeek-Bever** *N : 9 km* C *Grimbergen pop. 32 737 – ✉ 1853 Strombeek-Bever :*

🏠 **Alfa Rijckendael** M 🐎, Luitberg 1 ☎ (0 2) 267 41 24 and 267 55 00 (rest), *Telex 20140, Fax (0 2) 267 94 01,* ☂, ⛟ – 🛗 TV ☎ P – 🏛 25-40. AE ① E VISA
**Meals** *(closed Wednesday) Lunch 880 b.i.* – a la carte 1700/2350 – **49 rm** ▭ 4300/4900.

🏠 **Clarine,** Romeinsesteenweg 572 ☎ (0 2) 461 00 21, *Fax (0 2) 461 04 84* – 🛗 TV ☎ P – 🏛 25 - 80. AE ① E VISA JCB. ✂ rest
**Meals** (Pub rest) *Lunch 580* – 850 – **75 rm** ▭ 3950/4150.

**Val Joli,** Leestbeekstraat 16 (0 2) 460 65 43, *Fax (0 2) 460 04 00,* , « Terrace and garden » - . AE E VISA
*closed Monday, Tuesday, 2 weeks June and 2 weeks November* – **Meals** 990/1390.

**'t Stoveke,** Jetsestraat 52 (0 2) 267 67 25, , Seafood – AE E VISA
*closed Sunday, Monday, 3 weeks June, Christmas and New Year* – **Meals** *Lunch 1190* – a la carte 1900/2500.

**at Vilvoorde** *(Vilvorde) N : 17 km – pop. 33 483 – ✉ 1800 Vilvoorde :*

**Barbay,** Romeinsesteenweg 220 (SW : 4 km at Koningslo) (0 2) 267 00 45, *Fax (0 2) 267 00 45,* – AE E VISA.
*closed Saturday lunch and Sunday* – **Meals** *Lunch 895* – 1450/1990.

**De Met** 1st floor, Grote Markt 7 (0 2) 253 30 00, *Fax (0 2) 253 31 00,* Partly pub rest, « Former covered market, Art Deco style » – 25-400. AE E VISA.
*closed Sunday* – **Meals** *Lunch 1375 b.i.* – a la carte 1600/2000.

**at Wemmel** *N : 12 km – pop. 13 738 – ✉ 1780 Wemmel :*

**Parkhof "Beverbos",** Parklaan 7 (0 2) 460 42 89, *Fax (0 2) 460 25 10,* , « Terrace » – . AE E VISA
*closed Wednesday, Thursday and late September-early October* – **Meals** *Lunch 850* – 1100/1400.

**at Wezembeek-Oppem** *E : 11 km – pop. 13 623 – ✉ 1970 Wezembeek-Oppem :*

**L'Aub. Saint-Pierre,** Sint-Pietersplein 8 (0 2) 731 21 79, *Fax (0 2) 731 28 28,* – AE E VISA
*closed Saturday lunch, Sunday, Bank Holidays, 18 July-16 August and 24 December-3 January* – **Meals** *Lunch 980* – a la carte 1650/2100.

**at Zaventem** *Brussels-Zaventem airport motorway – pop. 26 467 – ✉ 1930 Zaventem :*

**Sheraton Airport,** at airport (0 2) 725 10 00, *Telex 27085, Fax (0 2) 725 11 55,* – – 25-600. AE E VISA JCB. rest
Meals ***Concorde*** *Lunch 1375* - a la carte 1850/2450 – ***Lindbergh Taverne*** (open until 11.30 p.m.) *Lunch 690* - a la carte approx. 1000 – 890 – **297 rm** 11400/12400, 2 suites.

**Stockmansmolen** 1st floor, H. Henneaulaan 164 (0 2) 725 34 34, *Fax (0 2) 725 75 05,* Partly pub rest, « Former watermill » – . AE E VISA
*closed Saturday, Sunday, 21 July-10 August, Christmas and New Year* – **Meals** *Lunch 1675* – a la carte 2000/2650.

---

**ANTWERP** *(ANTWERPEN) 2000* 212 ⑮ *and* 409 G 2 - ⑧ S – *pop. 455 852.*

See : *Around the Market Square and the Cathedral★★★ : Market Square★ (Grote Markt)* FY, *Vlaaikensgang★* FY, *Cathedral★★★* FY *and its tower★★★* FY – *Butchers' House★ (Vleeshuis) : Musical instruments★* FY **D** – *Rubens' House★★ (Rubenshuis)* GZ – *Interior★ of St. James' Church (St-Jacobskerk)* GY - *Hendrik Conscience Place★* GY – *St. Charles Borromeo's Church★ (St-Carolus Borromeuskerk)* GY – *St. Paul's Church (St-Pauluskerk) : interior★* FY – *Zoo★★ (Dierentuin)* DEU – *Zurenborg Quater★* EV – *The port (Haven)* FY.

**Museums** : *Maritime "Steen"★ (Nationaal Scheepvaartmuseum Steen)* FY – *Etnographic Museum★* FY **M**[1] – *Plantin-Moretus★★★* FZ – *Mayer Van den Bergh★★ : Mad Meg★★ (Dulle Griet)* GZ – *Rockox House★ (Rockoxhuis)* GY **M**[4] – *Royal Art Gallery★★★ (Koninklijk Museum voor Schone Kunsten)* CV **M**[5] – *Museum of Photography★* CV **M**[6] – *Open-air Museum of Sculpture Middelheim★ (Openluchtmuseum voor Beeldhouwkunst).*

18 9 *at Kapellen N : 15,5 km, G. Capiaulei 2 (0 3) 666 84 56,* - 18 *at Aartselaar S : 10 km, Kasteel Cleydael (0 3) 887 00 79* - 18 9 *at Wommelgem E : 10 km, Uilenbaan 15 (0 3) 355 14 30* - 18 *at Broechem E : 13 km, Kasteel Bossenstein, Moor 16 (0 3) 485 64 46.*

*Grote Markt 15 (0 3) 232 01 03, Fax (0 3) 231 19 37 – Tourist association of the province, Karel Oomsstraat 11, ✉ 2018, (0 3) 216 28 10, Fax (0 3) 237 83 65.*

*Brussels 48 – Amsterdam 159 – Luxembourg 261 – Rotterdam 103.*

Plans on following pages

**Old Antwerp**

**Hilton** M, Groenplaats (0 3) 204 12 12, *Fax (0 3) 204 12 13,* « Facade of an early 20C department store », , – – 30-1000. AE E VISA JCB FZ m
Meals see rest ***Het Vijfde Seizoen*** below – 775 – **199 rm** 5700/12200, 12 suites.

**Alfa Theater** M, Arenbergstraat 30 (0 3) 231 17 20, *Fax (0 3) 233 88 58,* – – 25-50. AE E VISA. rest GZ t
Meals *(closed Saturday lunch, Sunday and Bank Holidays) Lunch 590* – 1350 b.i./1950 b.i. – **122 rm** 3400/6800, 5 suites.

**De Witte Lelie** without rest, Keizerstraat 16 (0 3) 226 19 66, *Fax (0 3) 234 00 19*, « Typical 17C terraced houses, patio » – AE E VISA JCB GY z
*closed 22 December-3 January* – **7 rm** 6500/15000, 3 suites.

**'t Sandt** without rest, Het Zand 17 (0 3) 232 93 90, *Fax (0 3) 232 56 13*, « 19C residence in rococo style » – – 25-150. AE E VISA JCB FZ w
**13 rm** 4500/8000, 1 suite.

**Rubens** M without rest, Oude Beurs 29 (0 3) 222 48 48, *Fax (0 3) 225 19 40*, « Floral inner courtyard » – P – 25-50. AE E VISA. FY y
**35 rm** 4500/6500, 1 suite.

**Prinse** without rest, Keizerstraat 63 (0 3) 226 40 50, *Fax (0 3) 225 11 48* – – 25-150. AE E VISA. GY a
**34 rm** 3700/5100, 1 suite.

**Villa Mozart,** Handschoenmarkt 3 (0 3) 231 30 31, *Fax (0 3) 231 56 85*, , – . AE E VISA JCB FY e
**Meals** (Pub rest) *Lunch 795* – a la carte approx. 1300 – 500 – **25 rm** 3500/5400.

**Antigone** without rest, Jordaenskaai 11 (0 3) 231 66 77, *Fax (0 3) 231 37 74* – P – 30. AE E VISA. FY a
**18 rm** 3000/3500.

**'t Fornuis** (Segers), Reyndersstraat 24 (0 3) 233 62 70, *Fax (0 3) 233 99 03*, « 17C residence, rustic interior » – AE E VISA. FZ c
*closed Saturday, Sunday, last 3 weeks August and 24 December - 2 January* – **Meals** (booking essential) *Lunch 2200* – a la carte 2200/2750
**Spec.** Salade de crabe frais. Sandre et anguille aux salsifis. Langues d'agneau aux haricots soissons, sauce Madère.

**Het Vijfde Seizoen** (at Hilton H.), Groenplaats (0 3) 204 12 29, *Fax (0 3) 204 12 13* – . AE E VISA JCB. FZ m
*closed Saturday lunch and mid-July-mid-August* – **Meals** a la carte approx. 2300.

**Huis De Colvenier,** St-Antoniusstraat 8 (0 3) 226 65 73, *Fax (0 3) 227 13 14*, , « Late 19C residence » – P. AE E VISA. FZ k
*closed Saturday lunch, Sunday dinner, Monday, 1 week carnival and 3 weeks August* – **Meals** *Lunch 1300* – 2750 b.i./3450 b.i.

**La Rade** 1st floor, E. Van Dijckkaai 8 (0 3) 233 37 37, *Fax (0 3) 233 49 63*, « Former 19C freemason's lodge » – AE E VISA FY g
*closed Saturday lunch, Sunday, Bank Holidays, carnival week and last 3 weeks July* – **Meals** *Lunch 1450* – a la carte 2400/3000.

**De Kerselaar** (Michiels), Grote Pieter Potstraat 22 (0 3) 233 59 69, *Fax (0 3) 233 11 49* – . AE E VISA JCB FY n
*closed lunch Saturday and Monday, Sunday, 3 to 13 April and 24 July - 9 August* – **Meals** *Lunch 1550* – 2950 b.i., a la carte 2200/2500
**Spec.** Carpaccio de foie gras en croûte d'épices et écrevisses au beurre pistaché. Langoustines rôties aux 10 épices. Gâteau chaud au chocolat, orangettes et sauce pistachée.

**'t Silveren Claverblat,** Grote Pieter Potstraat 16 (0 3) 231 33 88, *Fax (0 3) 231 31 46* – AE E VISA. FY k
*closed Tuesday and Saturday lunch* – **Meals** *Lunch 1000* – 2000 b.i./2650 b.i.

**P. Preud'homme,** Suikerrui 28 (0 3) 233 42 00, *Fax (0 3) 233 42 00*, , Open until 11 p.m. – . AE E VISA JCB. FY r
*closed January* – **Meals** *Lunch 1200* – a la carte 1550/2300.

**Het Nieuwe Palinghuis,** St-Jansvliet 14 (0 3) 231 74 45, *Fax (0 3) 231 50 53*, Seafood – . AE E VISA FZ e
*closed Monday, Tuesday and June* – **Meals** *Lunch 1150* – a la carte 1300/1900.

**De Gulden Beer,** Grote Markt 14 (0 3) 226 08 41, *Fax (0 3) 232 52 09*, , Partly Italian cuisine – . AE E VISA. FY v
**Meals** *Lunch 980* – 1500 (2 pers. min.)/2200.

**Neuze Neuze,** Wijngaardstraat 19 (0 3) 232 27 97, *Fax (0 3) 225 27 38* – AE E VISA JCB FY s
*closed Saturday lunch, Sunday and last 2 weeks July* – **Meals** *Lunch 1000* – 1650/2500 b.i.

**In de Schaduw van de Kathedraal,** Handschoenmarkt 17 (0 3) 232 40 14, *Fax (0 3) 226 88 14*, , Mussels in season – . AE E VISA. FY e
*closed Monday and Tuesday October - May and 10 January - 13 February* – **Meals** *Lunch 1095* – a la carte 1400/2000.

**De Matelote** (Garnich), Haarstraat 9 (0 3) 231 32 07, *Fax (0 3) 231 08 13*, Seafood – . AE E VISA FY u
*closed lunch Saturday and Monday, Sunday, Bank Holidays, July and 1 to 15 January* – **Meals** – a la carte 2200/2600
**Spec.** Saumon sauvage mariné aux aromates. Barbue au risotto de limon et champignons. Raie sauce au Champagne et échalotes.

# ANTWERPEN

| | | |
|---|---|---|
| Carnotstr. | EU | 3 |
| Dambruggestr. | ETU | 39 |
| Gemeentestr. | DU | 63 |
| de Keyserlei | DU | 103 |
| Leysstr. | DU | 123 |
| Offerandestr. | EU | 136 |
| Pelikaanstr. | DU | 151 |
| Quellinstr. | DU | 165 |
| Turnhoutsebaan (BORGERHOUT) | EU | |
| van Aerdtstr. | DT | 3 |
| Amsterdamstr. | DT | 4 |
| Ankerrui | DT | 6 |
| Ballaerstr. | DV | 12 |
| Bolivarplaats | CV | 15 |
| Borsbeekbrug | EX | 16 |
| van Breestr. | DV | 19 |
| Brialmontlei | DV | 21 |
| Britselei | DV | 22 |
| Broederminstr. | CV | 24 |
| Brouwersvliet | DT | 25 |
| Brusselstr. | CV | 27 |
| Cassiersstr. | DT | 31 |
| Charlottalei | DV | 33 |
| Cockerillkaai | CV | 36 |
| Cuperusstr. | EV | 37 |
| Diksmuidelaan | EX | 43 |
| Emiel Banningstr. | CV | 51 |
| Emiel Vloorsstr. | CX | 52 |
| Emile Verhaerenlaan | CT | 54 |
| Erwtenstr. | ET | 55 |
| van Eycklei | DV | 57 |
| Falconplein | DT | 58 |
| Franklin Rooseveltpl. | DU | 60 |
| Gén. Armstrongweg | CX | 64 |
| Gérard Le Grellelaan | DX | 66 |
| de Gerlachekaai | CV | 67 |
| Gitschotellei | EX | 70 |
| Graaf van Egmontstr. | CV | 72 |
| Haantjeslei | CDV | 79 |
| Halenstr. | ET | 81 |
| Hessenplein | DT | 84 |
| Jan de Voslei | CX | 90 |
| Jan van Gentstr. | CV | 91 |
| Jezusstr. | DU | 96 |
| Justitiestr. | DV | 97 |
| Kasteelpleinstr. | DV | 102 |
| Kloosterstr. | CU | 105 |
| Kol. Silvertopstr. | CX | 106 |
| Koningin Astridplein | DEU | 109 |
| Koningin Elisabethlei | DX | 110 |
| Korte Winkelstr. | DTU | 114 |
| Lange Lobroekstr. | ET | 117 |
| Lange Winkelstr. | DT | 118 |
| Léopold de Waelplein | CV | 120 |
| Léopold de Waelstr. | CV | 121 |
| Londenstr. | DT | 124 |
| Maria-Henriettalei | DV | 129 |
| Mercatorstr. | DEV | 130 |
| Namenstr. | CV | 133 |
| van den Nestlei | EV | 135 |
| Ommeganckstr. | EU | 138 |
| Orteliuskaai | DT | 141 |
| Osystr. | DU | 142 |
| Oude Leeuwenrui | DT | 148 |
| Plantinkaai | CU | 153 |
| Ploegstr. | EU | 154 |
| Pluvierstr. | CU | 156 |
| Posthofbrug | EX | 157 |
| Prins Albertlei | DX | 159 |
| Provinciestr. | EUV | 162 |
| Pyckestr. | CX | 163 |
| Quinlen Matsijslei | DUV | 166 |
| Rolwagenstr. | EV | 171 |
| Schijnpoortweg | ET | 174 |
| van Schoonhovestr. | DEU | 175 |
| Simonsstr. | DEV | 178 |
| Sint-Bernardse steenweg | CX | 180 |
| Sint-Gummarusstr. | DT | 181 |
| Sint-Jansplein | DT | 183 |
| Sint-Jozefsstr. | DV | 186 |
| Sint-Michielskaai | CU | 187 |
| Stuivenbergplein | ET | 196 |
| Viaduct Dam | ET | 202 |
| Visestr. | ET | 204 |
| Volkstr. | CV | 207 |
| Vondelstr. | DT | 208 |

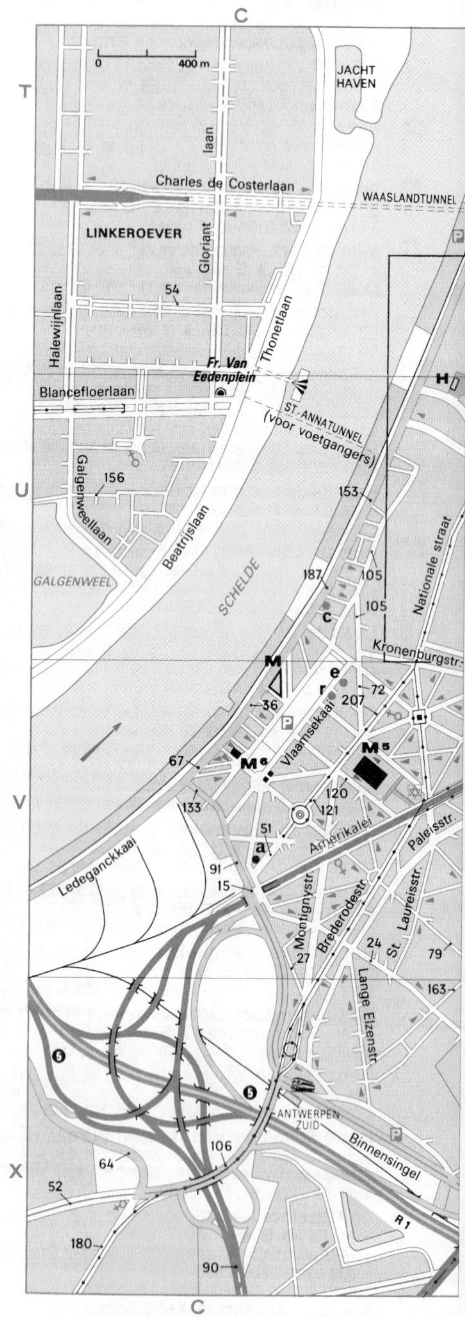

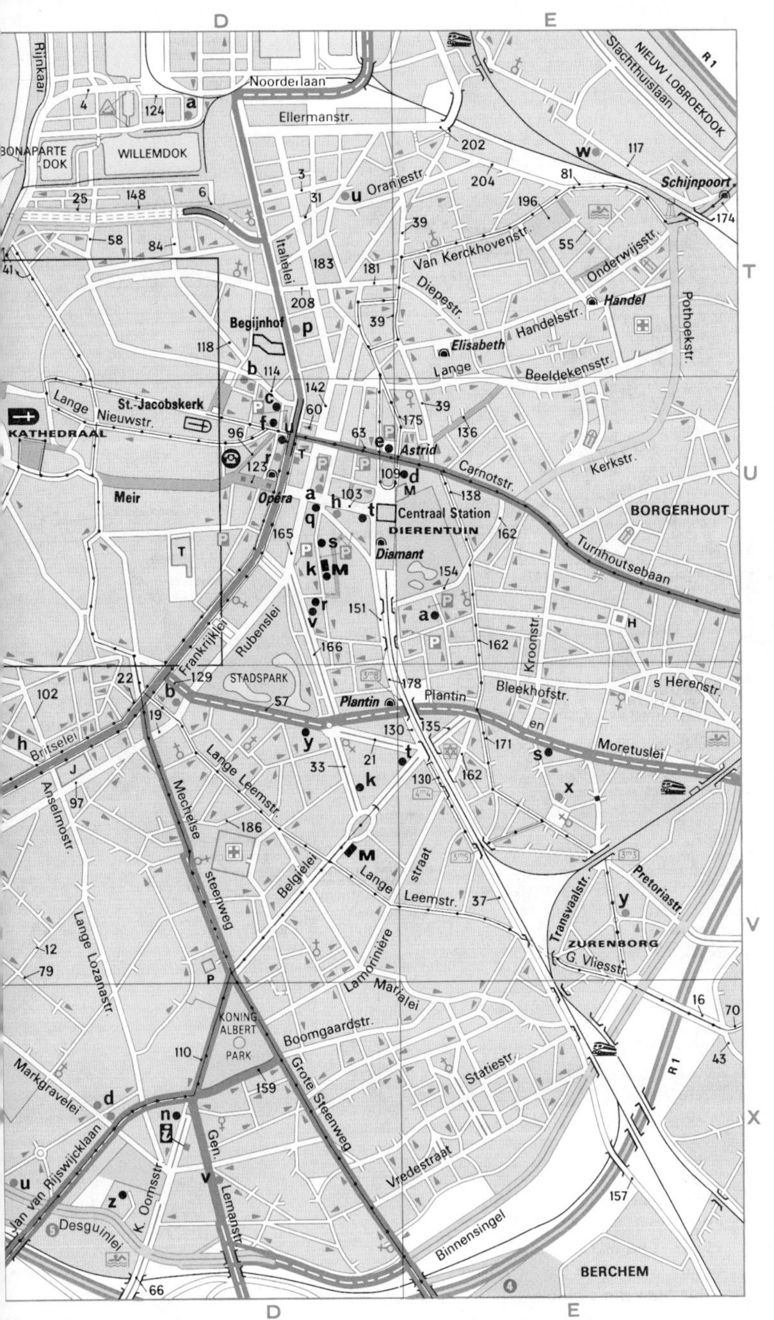

D
E
NIEUW LOBROEKDOK
Slachthuislaan
R1
Rijnkaai
Noorderlaan
Ellermanstr.
WILLEMDOK
BONAPARTE DOK
Oranjestr.
Schijnpoort
Italiëlei
Van Kerckhovenstr.
Onderwijsstr.
Diepestr.
Handel
Handelsstr.
Pothoekstr.
Begijnhof
Elisabeth
Lange Beeldekensstr.
St.-Jacobskerk
Lange Nieuwstr.
KATHEDRAAL
Astrid
Carnotstr.
Kerkstr.
Meir
Opéra
Centraal Station
DIERENTUIN
BORGERHOUT
Diamant
Turnhoutsebaan
Rubenslei
Frankrijklei
STADSPARK
Kroonstr.
Bleekhofstr.
s Herenstr.
Plantin
Plantin en Moretuslei
Britselei
Lange Leemstr.
Mechelse steenweg
Anselmostr.
Belgiëlei
Lange Leemstr.
straat
Pretoriastr.
Transvaalstr.
ZURENBORG
G. Vliesstr.
Lange Lozanastr.
Lamorinière
Marialei
KONING ALBERT PARK
Boomgaardstr.
Grote Steenweg
Statiestr.
Markgravelei
Gen. Lemanstr.
Vredestraat
Jan van Rijswijcklaan
K. Oomsstr.
Desguinlei
Binnensingel
BERCHEM
T
U
V
X

# ANTWERPEN

| Street | Square | No. |
|---|---|---|
| Groenplaats | FZ | |
| Klapdorp | GY | |
| Meir | GZ | |
| Nationalestr. | FZ | |
| Paardenmarkt | GY | |
| Schoenmarkt | FZ | |
| Gildekamerstr. | FY | 69 |
| Handschoenmarkt | FY | 82 |
| Korte Gasthuisstr. | GZ | 112 |
| Maria Pijpelinckxstr. | GZ | 127 |
| Oude Koornmarkt | FYZ | 147 |
| Repenstr. | FY | 168 |
| Rosier | FZ | 172 |
| Sint-Jansvliet | FZ | 184 |
| Sint-Rochusstr. | FZ | 189 |
| Steenhouwersvest | FZ | 193 |
| Twaalf Maandenstr. | GZ | 199 |
| Veemarkt | FY | 201 |
| Vleeshouwersstr. | FY | 205 |
| Vrijdagmarkt | FZ | 213 |
| Wisselstr. | FY | 214 |
| Zirkstr. | FY | 216 |
| Zwartzusterstr. | FY | 217 |

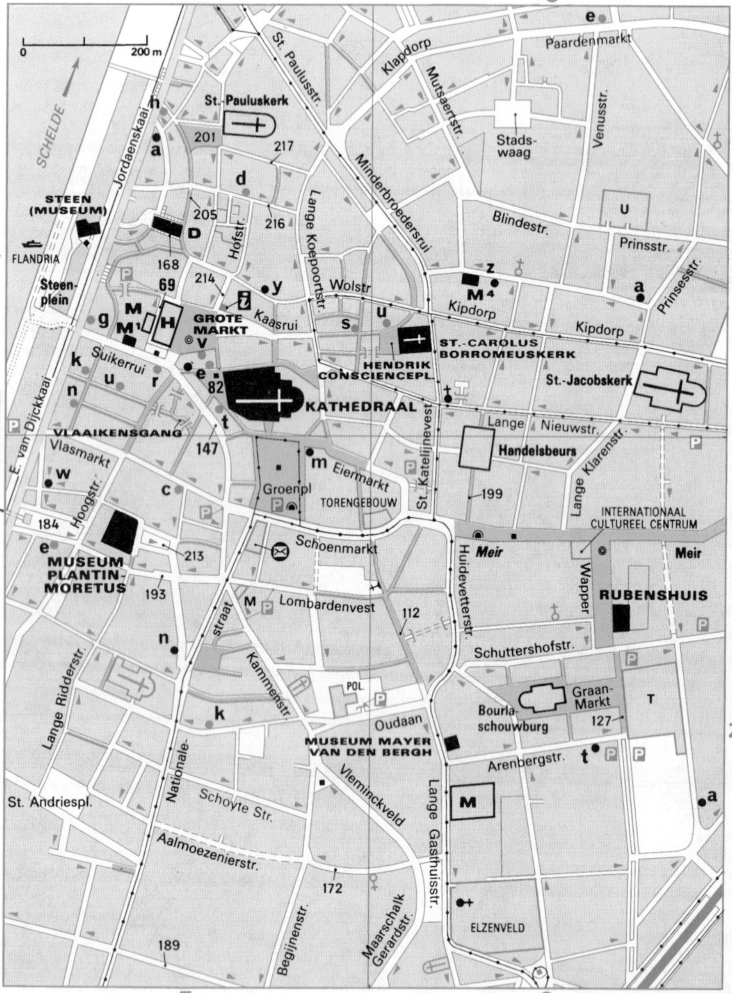

Pleasant hotels and restaurants
are shown in the Guide by a red sign.
Please send us the names
of any where you have enjoyed your stay.
Your **Michelin Guide** will be even better.

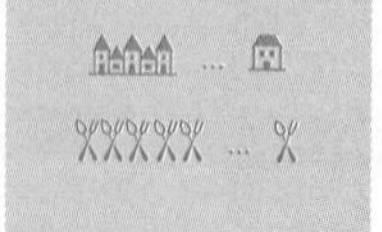

**Zirk,** Zirkstraat 29 ✆ (0 3) 225 25 86, *Fax (0 3) 226 51 77* – P. AE ⓓ E VISA. ✻
*closed Saturday lunch, Sunday, Monday, 1 week February and 3 weeks August* – **Meals** Lunch 950 – a la carte 2000/2550. FY d

**De Manie,** H. Conscienceplein 3 ✆ (0 3) 232 64 38, *Fax (0 3) 232 64 38,* – AE ⓓ E VISA GY u
*closed Wednesday, Sunday dinner and 16 August - 1 September* – **Meals** a la carte 1500/1850.

**Rooden Hoed,** Oude Koornmarkt 25 ✆ (0 3) 233 28 44, *Fax (0 3) 232 82 34,* Mussels in season, « Antwerp atmosphere » – AE E VISA FY t
**Meals** 950.

**Don Carlos,** St-Michielskaai 34 ✆ (0 3) 216 40 46, Partly Spanish cuisine – ✻ CU c
*closed Monday* – **Meals** (dinner only) a la carte approx. 1200.

**Town Centre**

**Park Lane** M, Van Eycklei 34, ✉ 2018, ✆ (0 3) 285 85 85 and 285 85 80 (rest), *Fax (0 3) 285 85 86,* <, Fö, ≘s, ◻, – 肖 ⇔ ▤ TV ☎ ⇔ – 🏛 25-450. AE ⓓ E VISA JCB. ✻
**Meals** ***Longchamps*** *(closed Saturday lunch, Sunday, Bank Holidays and 15 July-20 August)* Lunch 1100 - a la carte 1600/2300 – **166 rm** ☐ 8200/9900, 12 suites. DV y

**Astrid Park Plaza** M, Koningin Astridplein 1, ✉ 2018, ✆ (0 3) 203 12 34, *Fax (0 3) 203 12 51,* <, Fö, ≘s, ◻, – 肖 ⇔ ▤ TV ☎ ♿ ⇔ P – 🏛 25-340. AE ⓓ E VISA
**Meals** 950/1500 – ☐ 725 – **226 rm** 8050/9050, 3 suites. DEU e

**Carlton,** Quinten Matsijslei 25, ✉ 2018, ✆ (0 3) 231 15 15, *Fax (0 3) 225 30 90,* < – 肖 ⇔ ▤ TV ☎ ⇔ – 🏛 25-100. AE ⓓ E VISA JCB. ✻ rest DU v
**Meals** *(closed dinner Friday and Sunday, Saturday lunch, 15 July-15 August and 15 December-15 January)* Lunch 575 – a la carte approx. 1400 – **127 rm** ☐ 4500/13600, 1 suite.

**Alfa De Keyser** M, De Keyserlei 66, ✉ 2018, ✆ (0 3) 234 01 35, *Fax (0 3) 232 39 70,* Fö, ≘s, ◻, – 肖 ⇔ ▤ TV ☎ – 🏛 25-160. AE ⓓ E VISA JCB DU t
**Meals** Lunch 550 – a la carte 1100/1500 – **120 rm** ☐ 3200/5900, 3 suites.

**Hylitt** M without rest, De Keyserlei 28 (access by Appelmansstraat), ✉ 2018, ✆ (0 3) 202 68 00, *Fax (0 3) 202 68 90* – 肖 ▤ TV ☎ ⇔ – 🏛 30. AE ⓓ E VISA. ✻
☐ 550 – **24 rm** 4000/8500, 56 suites. DU q

**Plaza** without rest, Charlottalei 43, ✉ 2018, ✆ (0 3) 218 92 40, *Fax (0 3) 218 88 23* – 肖 ⇔ ▤ TV ☎ ⇔ – 🏛 25. AE ⓓ E VISA DV k
**80 rm** ☐ 6500/9000.

**Switel,** Copernicuslaan 2, ✉ 2018, ✆ (0 3) 231 67 80, *Fax (0 3) 233 02 90,* Fö, ≘s, ◻, ✻ – 肖 ⇔ ▤ TV ☎ ⇔ – 🏛 25-1000. AE ⓓ E VISA EU a
**Meals** *(closed Saturday, lunch Sunday and Monday)* 895/1275 – ☐ 260 – **296 rm** 5500, 2 suites.

**Residence** without rest, Molenbergstraat 9, ✉ 2018, ✆ (0 3) 232 76 75, *Fax (0 3) 233 73 28* – 肖 TV ☎ ⇔ – 🏛 40. AE ⓓ E VISA. ✻ DU c
**48 rm** ☐ 3400/8000.

**Alfa Empire** without rest, Appelmansstraat 31, ✉ 2018, ✆ (0 3) 231 47 55 – 肖 ⇔ ▤ TV ☎ P. AE ⓓ E VISA JCB DU s
**70 rm** ☐ 3200/5000.

**Astoria** M without rest, Korte Herentalsestraat 5, ✉ 2018, ✆ (0 3) 227 31 30, *Fax (0 3) 227 31 34* – 肖 ⇔ ▤ TV ☎ ⇔. AE ⓓ E VISA JCB DU r
**66 rm** ☐ 3900/4400.

**Colombus** without rest, Frankrijklei 4 ✆ (0 3) 233 03 90, *Fax (0 3) 226 09 46,* Fö, ◻ – 肖 TV ☎. AE ⓓ E VISA. ✻ DU u
**32 rm** ☐ 3300/3900.

**Alfa Congress,** Plantin en Moretuslei 136, ✉ 2018, ✆ (0 3) 235 30 00, *Fax (0 3) 235 52 31* – 肖 ⇔ ▤ TV ☎ ⇔ P – 🏛 25-120. AE ⓓ E VISA. ✻ EV s
**Meals** *(closed Saturday and Sunday)* Lunch 800 – a la carte approx. 1400 – **66 rm** ☐ 2600/3700.

**Ambassador** without rest, Belgiëlei 8, ✉ 2018, ✆ (0 3) 281 41 61, *Fax (0 3) 239 55 16* – 肖 TV ☎ ⇔ – 🏛 50. AE ⓓ E VISA. ✻ DEV t
**77 rm** ☐ 2350/6000.

**Antverpia** without rest, Sint-Jacobsmarkt 85 ✆ (0 3) 231 80 80, *Fax (0 3) 232 43 43* – 肖 TV ☎ ⇔ – 🏛 40. AE ⓓ E. ✻ DU f
*closed 20 December-5 January* – ☐ 400 – **19 rm** 3500/5000.

**Atlanta** without rest, Koningin Astridplein 14, ✉ 2018, ✆ (0 3) 203 09 19, *Fax (0 3) 226 37 37* – 肖 ⇔ TV ☎ – 🏛 30. AE ⓓ E VISA. ✻ DEU d
**60 rm** ☐ 2250/5000.

**Eden** without rest, Lange Herentalsestraat 25, ✉ 2018, ✆ (0 3) 233 06 08, *Fax (0 3) 233 12 28* – 肖 TV ☎ ⇔. AE ⓓ E VISA JCB DU k
**66 rm** ☐ 2600/3650.

**De Barbarie,** Van Breestraat 4, ✉ 2018, ☎ (0 3) 232 81 98, *Fax (0 3) 231 26 78*, – AE E VISA JCB DV b
*closed Saturday lunch, Sunday, Monday, 28 April-4 May and 1 to 14 September* – **Meals** Lunch 1450 – a la carte 2050/2500.

**De Lepeleer,** Lange St-Annastraat 10 ☎ (0 3) 225 19 31, *Fax (0 3) 231 31 24*, « Several small houses in a 16C cul-de-sac » – P. AE O E VISA DU b
*closed Saturday lunch, Sunday, Bank Holidays and 20 July-16 August* – **Meals** Lunch 1500 b.i. – 2700 b.i.

**De Zeste,** Lange Dijkstraat 36, ✉ 2060, ☎ (0 3) 233 45 49, *Fax (0 3) 232 34 18* – ▤. AE O E VISA DT u
*closed Saturday lunch and Sunday* – **Meals** Lunch 1200 – 2100.

**Fouquets,** De Keyserlei 17, ✉ 2018, ☎ (0 3) 232 62 09, *Fax (0 3) 226 16 88*, Open until midnight – ▤. AE O E VISA. DU a
**Meals** a la carte 900/1450.

**Blue Phoenix,** Frankrijklei 14 ☎ (0 3) 233 33 77, *Fax (0 3) 233 88 46*, Chinese cuisine – ▤. AE E VISA. DU r
*closed Monday, Saturday lunch and August* – **Meals** 850/1700.

**'t Peerd,** Paardenmarkt 53 ☎ (0 3) 231 98 25, *Fax (0 3) 231 59 40*, – ▤. AE O E VISA JCB
*closed Tuesday dinner, Wednesday, 2 weeks Easter and 2 weeks September* – **Meals** Lunch 995 – a la carte approx. 1600.

**La Luna,** Italiëlei 177 ☎ (0 3) 232 23 44, *Fax (0 3) 232 24 41*, Open until 11 p.m. – ▤. AE O E VISA. DT p
**Meals** 990.

**'t Lammeke,** Lange Lobroekstraat 51 (opposite the slaughterhouse), ✉ 2060, ☎ (0 3) 236 79 86, *Fax (0 3) 271 05 16*, – ▤. AE O E VISA ET w
*closed lunch Saturday and Sunday, Monday, 3 to 24 August and 24 to 31 December* – **Meals** Lunch 925 – 1550.

**Yamayu Santatsu,** Ossenmarkt 19 ☎ (0 3) 234 09 49, *Fax (0 3) 234 09 49*, Japanese cuisine – ▤. AE O E VISA DTU b
*closed Sunday lunch, Monday and first 2 weeks August* – **Meals** Lunch 450 – 1500 (2 pers. min.).

### South Quarter

**Holiday Inn Crowne Plaza,** G. Legrellelaan 10, ✉ 2020, ☎ (0 3) 237 29 00, *Fax (0 3) 216 02 96*, – ▤ TV ☎ P – 25-800. AE O E VISA JCB.
**Meals** Lunch 995 – a la carte 1350/1750 – 575 – **258 rm** 3600/5995, 4 suites.

**Sofitel,** Desguinlei 94, ✉ 2018, ☎ (0 3) 244 82 11, *Fax (0 3) 216 47 12*, – ▤ TV ☎ P – 25-600. AE O E VISA JCB. rest DX z
**Meals** ***Tiffany's*** *(closed Saturday lunch, Sunday and Bank Holidays)* Lunch 750 -975 – 650 – **210 rm** 3600/6500, 5 suites.

**Firean** without rest, Karel Oomsstraat 6, ✉ 2018, ☎ (0 3) 237 02 60, *Fax (0 3) 238 11 68*, « Period residence, Art Deco style » – ▤ TV ☎. AE O E VISA JCB.
*closed 25 July-17 August and 23 December-11 January* – **15 rm** 4300/5800. DX n

**Industrie** M without rest, Emiel Banningstraat 52 ☎ (0 3) 238 66 00, *Fax (0 3) 238 86 88* – TV ☎. AE O E VISA. CV a
**13 rm** 2500/3500.

**Loncin,** Markgravelei 127, ✉ 2018, ☎ (0 3) 248 29 89, *Fax (0 3) 248 38 66*, Open until midnight – ▤ P. AE O E VISA DX d
*closed Saturday lunch and Sunday* – **Meals** Lunch 1350 – a la carte 2000/2400.

**Liang's Garden,** Markgravelei 141, ✉ 2018, ☎ (0 3) 237 22 22, *Fax (0 3) 248 38 34*, Chinese cuisine – ▤. AE O E VISA DX d
*closed Sunday, 2 weeks July and 24 December-2 January* – **Meals** Lunch 950 – a la carte 1150/1750.

**Kommilfoo,** Vlaamse Kaai 17 ☎ (0 3) 237 30 00, *Fax (0 3) 237 30 00* – ▤. AE O E VISA
*closed 8 to 26 June* – **Meals** Lunch 1100 – a la carte 1200/1600. CV e

**De Poterne,** Desguinlei 186, ✉ 2018, ☎ (0 3) 238 28 24, *Fax (0 3) 248 59 67* – AE O E VISA DX u
*closed Saturday lunch, Sunday, 21 July-16 August and 24 December-2 January* – **Meals** Lunch 1350 – a la carte approx. 2100.

### Suburbs

**North** – ✉ *2030* :

**Novotel,** Luithagen-Haven 6 ☎ (0 3) 542 03 20, *Fax (0 3) 541 70 93*, – ▤ TV ☎ P – 25-180. AE O E VISA
**Meals** (open until midnight) Lunch 1050 – a la carte 850/1300 – 450 – **119 rm** 3500.

**at Borgerhout** *E : 3 km* ☐ *Antwerpen – ✉ 2140 Borgerhout :*

**Holiday Inn,** Luitenant Lippenslaan 66 ☎ (0 3) 235 91 91, *Fax (0 3) 235 08 96,* – AE ⓓ E VISA
**Meals** *(closed Sunday lunch)* *Lunch 990* – a la carte 1150/1600 – ☐ 550 – **201 rm** 3250/4950, 3 suites.

**at Deurne** *NE : 3 km* ☐ *Antwerpen – ✉ 2100 Deurne :*

XX De Violin, Bosuil 1 ☎ (0 3) 324 34 04, *Fax (0 3) 326 33 20,* « Small farmhouse » – Ⓟ.

XX **Périgord,** Turnhoutsebaan 273 ☎ (0 3) 325 52 00, *Fax (0 3) 325 52 00* – Ⓟ. AE ⓓ E VISA.
*closed Tuesday, Wednesday, Saturday lunch, 1 week carnival and July* – **Meals** *Lunch 875* – 1450/2800 b.i.

**at Ekeren** *N : 11 km* ☐ *Antwerpen – ✉ 2180 Ekeren :*

XX **Hof de Bist,** Veltwijcklaan 258 ☎ (0 3) 664 61 30, *Fax (0 3) 664 67 24,* – Ⓟ. AE ⓓ E
*closed Sunday, Monday, Tuesday, 2 weeks Easter and 2 weeks Christmas* – **Meals** 2000.

**at Merksem** *N : 2 km* ☐ *Antwerpen – ✉ 2170 Merksem :*

XXX **Maritime,** Bredabaan 978 ☎ (0 3) 646 22 23, *Fax (0 3) 646 22 71,* Seafood – Ⓟ. AE ⓓ E VISA
*closed Monday* – **Meals** *Lunch 995* – 1950/2600.

**at Wilrijk** *S : 6 km* ☐ *Antwerpen – ✉ 2610 Wilrijk :*

XX **Schans XV,** Moerelei 155 ☎ (0 3) 828 45 64, *Fax (0 3) 828 93 29,* « Early 20C redoubt » – AE ⓓ E VISA.
*closed Thursday dinner, Saturday lunch, Sunday, Bank Holidays, 2 weeks February and 2 weeks July* – **Meals** *Lunch 995 b.i.* – a la carte 1850/2250.

**Environs**

**at Aartselaar** *S : 10 km – pop. 14 390 – ✉ 2630 Aartselaar :*

**Kasteel Solhof** without rest, Baron Van Ertbornstraat 116 ☎ (0 3) 877 30 00, *Fax (0 3) 877 31 31,* « Terrace in public park », – Ⓟ – 25 à 50. AE ⓓ E VISA.
☐ 600 – **24 rm** 4800/6000.

XXXX **Host. Kasteelhoeve Groeninghe** with rm, Kontichsesteenweg 78 ☎ (0 3) 457 95 86, *Fax (0 3) 458 13 68,* ←, « Restored Flemish farm », – Ⓟ – 25-150. AE ⓓ E VISA.
**Meals** *(closed Saturday lunch, Sunday, 1 to 15 August and 20 December-3 January)* *Lunch 2000 b.i.* – 2350/3600 – ☐ 500 – **7 rm** 3900/5250.

XXX **Kasteel Cleydael** with rm, Cleydaellaan 36 (W : direction Hemiksem) ☎ (0 3) 887 05 04, *Fax (0 3) 877 20 18,* « Restored moated feudal castle » – Ⓟ – 25-60. AE ⓓ E VISA.
*closed Saturday lunch, Sunday, Monday, Bank Holidays, 19 July-19 August and 20 December-6 January* – **Meals** *Lunch 1750* – a la carte 2250/2600 – **6 rm** ☐ 4950/10000, 1 suite.

XX **Villa Verde,** Kleistraat 175 ☎ (0 3) 887 56 85, *Fax (0 3) 887 22 56,* ←, – Ⓟ. AE ⓓ E VISA.
*closed Saturday lunch, Sunday dinner, Monday, 12 July-4 August and 1 to 15 January* – **Meals** *Lunch 1100* – 1750/2450.

**at Boechout** *SE : 9 km – pop. 11 659 – ✉ 2530 Boechout :*

XX **De Schone van Boskoop** (Keersmaekers), Appelkantstraat 10 ☎ (0 3) 454 19 31, *Fax (0 3) 454 19 31,* « Terrace with ornamental pool » – Ⓟ. AE E VISA.
*closed Sunday, Monday, 1 week April, 3 weeks August and late December-early January* – **Meals** *Lunch 1500* – a la carte 2600/3000
**Spec.** St-Jacques avec ragoût de pâtes et tête de veau. Canard de Barbarie au foie d'oie et truffes. Ravioli caramélisé au pain d'épices.

**at Brasschaat** *N : 11 km – pop. 36 874 – ✉ 2930 Brasschaat :*

XXX **Halewijn,** Donksesteenweg 212 (Ekeren-Donk) ☎ (0 3) 647 20 10, *Fax (0 3) 647 08 95,* – E VISA
**Meals** *Lunch 980 b.i.* – a la carte approx. 1700.

**at Broechem** *E : 15 km* ☐ *Ranst pop.17 211 – ✉ 2520 Broechem :*

**Bossenstein,** Moor 16 (E 313, exit ⑲ - towards Ranst) ☎ (0 3) 485 64 46, *Fax (0 3) 485 78 41,* « Parkland golf course around a medieval castle », – Ⓟ – 25. AE ⓓ E VISA.
*closed first 2 weeks January* – **Meals** *(closed Monday)* 950/1680 – **16 rm** ☐ 4000/6000.

**at Kapellen** *N : 15,5 km – pop. 25 356 – ✉ 2950 Kapellen :*

XXX **De Bellefleur** (Buytaert), Antwerpsesteenweg 253 ☎ (0 3) 664 67 19, *Fax (0 3) 665 02 01*, « Veranda with pergola surrounded by floral garden » – P. AE ⊙ E VISA
*closed Saturday lunch, Sunday, Monday and July* – **Meals** *Lunch 1850 b.i.* – 3850 b.i., a la carte 2800/3450
**Spec.** Fettuccini de homard, sauce au basilic et tomates confites. Lotte rôtie, sauce hollandaise à la moutarde. Carré de chevreuil aux baies de cassis et champignons des bois.

**at Kontich** *S : 12 km – pop. 19 443 – ✉ 2550 Kontich :*

XXX **Carême,** Koningin Astridlaan 114 ☎ (0 3) 457 63 04, *Fax (0 3) 457 93 02*, – ▤ P. AE ⊙ E VISA
*closed Saturday lunch, Sunday, Monday and July* – **Meals** *Lunch 1095* – 1650/2350.

**at Schilde** *NE : 13 km* C *19 386 – ✉ 2970 Schilde :*

XX **Henri IV,** Louis Mariënlaan 5 ☎ (0 3) 383 11 49, *Fax (0 3) 383 11 49*, – ▤ P. AE ⊙ E VISA
*closed Tuesday, Saturday lunch, 31 August-24 September and 26 January-5 February* – **Meals** *Lunch 1625 b.i.* – a la carte 1400/1950.

**at Schoten** *NE : 10 km – pop. 31 912 – ✉ 2900 Schoten :*

XX **Kleine Barreel,** Bredabaan 1147 ☎ (0 3) 645 85 84, *Fax (0 3) 645 85 03* – ▤ P. AE ⊙ E VISA JCB.
**Meals** *Lunch 1175* – 1250/1585.

XX **Uilenspiegel,** Brechtsebaan 277 (3 km on N 115) ☎ (0 3) 651 61 45, *Fax (0 3) 652 08 08*, « Terrace and garden » – P. AE E VISA
*closed Monday and Tuesday* – **Meals** 975/1950.

**at Wijnegem** *E : 10 km – pop. 8 543 – ✉ 2110 Wijnegem :*

XXX **Ter Vennen,** Merksemsebaan 278 ☎ (0 3) 326 20 60, *Fax (0 3) 326 38 47*, « Terrace » – P. AE ⊙ E VISA
**Meals** *Lunch 1675 b.i.* – 2045/2295 b.i.

**Kruiningen** *Zeeland (Netherlands)* C *Reimerswaal pop. 20 417* 211 *E 14 and* 408 *D 7 – 56 km.*

**Le Manoir**, Zandweg 2 (W : 1 km), ✉ 4416 NA, ☎ (0 113) 38 17 53, *Fax (0 113) 38 17 63*, ←, – TV ☎ P. AE ⊙ E VISA JCB
*closed Monday, Tuesday, 1 week October and 3 weeks January* – **Meals** see rest ***Inter Scaldes*** below – ☕ 28 – **10 rm** 275/450, 2 suites.

XXXX **Inter Scaldes** (Mme Boudeling) - at Le Manoir H., Zandweg 2 (W : 1 km), ✉ 4416 NA, ☎ (0 113) 38 17 53, *Fax (0 113) 38 17 63*, « Terrace-veranda overlooking an English-style garden » – P. AE ⊙ E VISA JCB
*closed Monday, Tuesday, 1 week October and 3 weeks January* – **Meals** *Lunch 100* – 185, a la carte 185/205
**Spec.** Homard fumé, sauce au caviar. Huîtres meunières et St-Jacques grillées à la sauce d'huîtres (September-April). Turbot en robe de truffes et son beurre.

---

**BRUGES** *(BRUGGE) 8000 West-Vlaanderen* 213 ③ *and* 409 *C 2 – pop. 115 815.*

**See** : *Procession of the Holy Blood★★★ (Heilig Bloedprocessie) – Historic centre and canals★★★ (Historisch centrum en grachten) – Market square★★ (Markt)* AU, *Belfry and Halles★★★ (Belfort en Hallen) ←★★ from the top* AU – *Market-town★★ (Burg)* AU – *Basilica of the Holy Blood★ (Basiliek van het Heilig Bloed) : low Chapel★ or St. Basiles Chapel (beneden- of St-Basiliuskapel)* AU **B** – *Chimney of the "Brugse Vrije"★ in the Palace of the "Brugse Vrije"* AU **S** – *Rosery quay (Rozenhoedkaai) ←★★* AU **63** – *Dijver ←★★* AU – *St. Boniface bridge (Bonifatiusbrug) : site★★* AU – *Beguinage★★ (Begijnhof)* AV – *Trips on the canals★★★ (Boottocht)* AU – *Church of Our Lady★ (O.-L.-Vrouwekerk) : tower★★, statue of the Madonna★★, tombstone★★ of Mary of Burgundy★★* AV **N.**

**Museums** : *Groeninge★★★ (Stedelijk Museum voor Schone Kunsten)* AU – *Memling★★★ (St. John's Hospital)* AV – *Gruuthuse★ : bust of Charles the Fifth★ (borstbeeld van Karel-V)* AU **M¹** – *Brangwyn★* AU **M⁴** – *Folklore★ (Museum voor Volkskunde)* DY **M².**

**Envir** : *Zedelgem : baptismal font★ in the St. Lawrence's church SW : 10,5 km – Damme★ NE : 7 km.*

18 *at Sijsele NE : 7 km, Doornstraat 16 ☎ (0 50) 33 35 72, Fax (0 50) 35 89 25.*

*Burg 11 ☎ (0 50) 44 86 86, Fax (0 50) 44 86 00 and at railway station, Stationsplein – Tourist association of the province, Kasteel Tillegem ✉ 8200 Sint-Michiels, ☎ (0 50) 38 02 96, Fax (0 50) 38 02 92.*

*Brussels 96 – Ghent 45 – Lille 72 – Ostend 28.*

Plans on following pages

## Town Centre

**Crowne Plaza**, Burg 10 (0 50) 34 58 34, *Fax (0 50) 34 56 15*, « Interesting medieval remains and objects in basement », – 25-400. AE VISA JCB. AU a
Meals **'t Kapittel** *(closed Wednesday dinner, Saturday lunch and Sunday) Lunch 995 b.i.* - 1250 b.i./2155 b.i. – **De Linde** a la carte approx. 1100 – 620 – **93 rm** 6900/7600, 3 suites.

**de' Medici**, Potterierei 15 (0 50) 33 98 33 and 44 31 31 (rest), *Fax (0 50) 33 07 64 and 33 05 71 (rest)*, « Modern style », – – 25-60. AE E VISA JCB. rest CX g
Meals (Japanese cuisine with Teppan-Yaki) *(closed Monday and Tuesday lunch)* 850/1480 – **79 rm** 4000/5750.

**De Tuilerieën** without rest, Dijver 7 (0 50) 34 36 91, *Fax (0 50) 34 04 00*, – – 25-45. AE E VISA JCB AU c
*closed 2 weeks December* – **24 rm** 7100/12250.

**Relais Oud Huis Amsterdam** without rest, Spiegelrei 3 (0 50) 34 18 10, *Fax (0 50) 33 88 91*, « 17C residence, former Dutch trading post », – – 25. AE E VISA JCB AT d
**28 rm** 4100/6500.

**de orangerie** without rest, Kartuizerinnenstraat 10 (0 50) 34 16 49, *Fax (0 50) 33 30 16*, « Period canalside residence » – . AE E VISA JCB AU e
*closed 19 January-4 February* – **19 rm** 6950/7950.

**Die Swaene**, Steenhouwersdijk 1 (0 50) 34 27 98, *Fax (0 50) 33 66 74*, « Stylish furnishings », – – 30. AE E VISA JCB AU p
Meals *(closed Wednesday, Thursday lunch, 2 weeks July and 2 weeks January) Lunch 1250* – 1950 (2 pers. min.)/2650 – **21 rm** 6000/9150, 1 suite.

**Sofitel**, Boeveriestraat 2 (0 50) 34 09 71, *Fax (0 50) 34 40 53*, – – 25-150. AE E VISA JCB CZ b
Meals 1050/1700 – 550 – **155 rm** 5900/6900.

**Park** without rest, Vrijdagmarkt 5 (0 50) 33 33 64, *Fax (0 50) 33 47 63* – – 25-250. AE E VISA CY j
**86 rm** 4280/5560.

**Acacia** without rest, Korte Zilverstraat 3a (0 50) 34 44 11, *Fax (0 50) 33 88 17*, – – 25-40. AE E VISA JCB. AU n
*closed first 3 weeks January* – **34 rm** 3450/5450, 2 suites.

**Prinsenhof** without rest, Ontvangersstraat 9 (0 50) 34 26 90, *Fax (0 50) 34 23 21*, « Opulent interior » – . AE E VISA JCB CY s
**16 rm** 3500/6800.

**Pandhotel** without rest, Pandreitje 16 (0 50) 34 06 66, *Fax (0 50) 34 05 56*, « Opulent interior » – . AE E VISA JCB AU u
**24 rm** 4090/5090.

**Navarra** without rest, St-Jakobsstraat 41 (0 50) 34 05 61, *Fax (0 50) 33 67 90*, – – 25-110. AE E VISA AT n
**88 rm** 3500/5250.

**Novotel Centrum**, Katelijnestraat 65b (0 50) 33 75 33, *Telex 81799, Fax (0 50) 33 65 56*, – – 50-400. AE E VISA JCB AV h
Meals (dinner only) a la carte approx. 1100 – 450 – **126 rm** 3750/4100.

**Karos** without rest, Hoefijzerlaan 37 (0 50) 34 14 48, *Fax (0 50) 34 00 91*, – . AE E VISA BY f
*closed 2 January-15 February* – **60 rm** 2900/4800.

**Portinari** without rest, 't Zand 15 (0 50) 34 10 34, *Fax (0 50) 34 41 80* – – 25-80. AE E VISA JCB CY k
*closed 2 January-1 February* – **40 rm** 3500/5200.

**Jan Brito** without rest, Freren Fonteinstraat 1 (0 50) 33 06 01, *Fax (0 50) 33 06 52*, « Gabled façade, 16, 17 and 18C interior », – . AE E VISA JCB AU j
*closed 5 January-5 February* – **18 rm** 3200/6500.

**Alfa Dante**, Coupure 29a (0 50) 34 01 94, *Fax (0 50) 34 35 39*, – . AE E VISA JCB. DY m
Meals (vegetarian cuisine) *(closed Sunday dinner, Monday and Tuesday)* a la carte approx. 1100 – **22 rm** 3150/4650.

**De Castillion**, Heilige Geeststraat 1 (0 50) 34 30 01, *Fax (0 50) 33 94 75*, – – 25-50. AE E VISA JCB. rest AU r
Meals *(closed Sunday dinner and lunch Monday and Tuesday except Bank Holidays) Lunch 995* – 1850/1975 – **20 rm** 3500/7500.

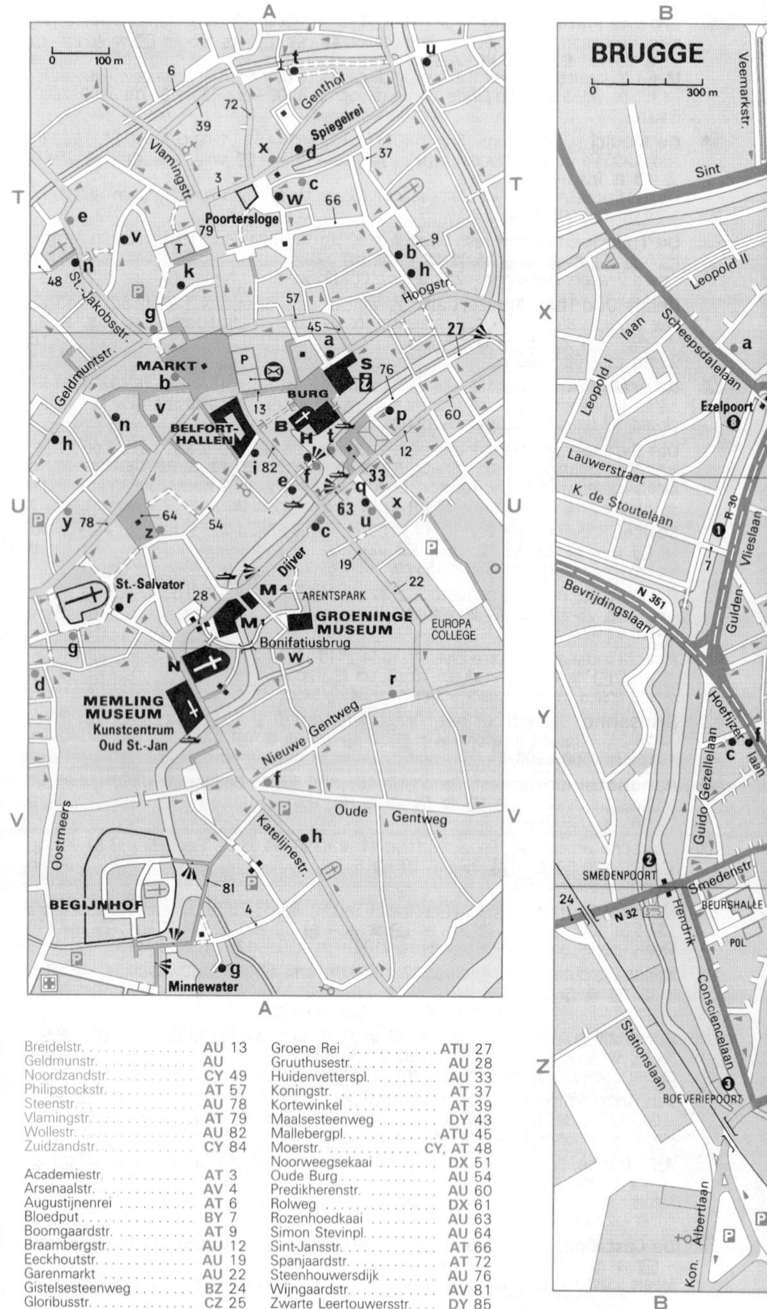


| | | |
|---|---|---|
| Breidelstr. | AU | 13 |
| Geldmunstr. | AU | |
| Noordzandstr. | CY | 49 |
| Philipstockstr. | AT | 57 |
| Steenstr. | AU | 78 |
| Vlamingstr. | AT | 79 |
| Wollestr. | AU | 82 |
| Zuidzandstr. | CY | 84 |
| Academiestr. | AT | 3 |
| Arsenaalstr. | AV | 4 |
| Augustijnenrei | AT | 6 |
| Bloedput | BY | 7 |
| Boomgaardstr. | AT | 9 |
| Braambergstr. | AU | 12 |
| Eeckhoutstr. | AU | 19 |
| Garenmarkt | AU | 22 |
| Gistelsesteenweg | BZ | 24 |
| Gloribusstr. | CZ | 25 |
| Groene Rei | ATU | 27 |
| Gruuthusestr. | AU | 28 |
| Huidenvetterspl. | AU | 33 |
| Koningstr. | AT | 37 |
| Kortewinkel | AT | 39 |
| Maalsesteenweg | DY | 43 |
| Mallebergpl. | ATU | 45 |
| Moerstr. | CY, AT | 48 |
| Noorweegsekaai | DX | 51 |
| Oude Burg | AU | 54 |
| Predikherenstr. | AU | 60 |
| Rolweg | DX | 61 |
| Rozenhoedkaai | AU | 63 |
| Simon Stevinpl. | AU | 64 |
| Sint-Jansstr. | AT | 66 |
| Spanjaardstr. | AT | 72 |
| Steenhouwersdijk | AU | 76 |
| Wijngaardstr. | AV | 81 |
| Zwarte Leertouwersstr. | DY | 85 |

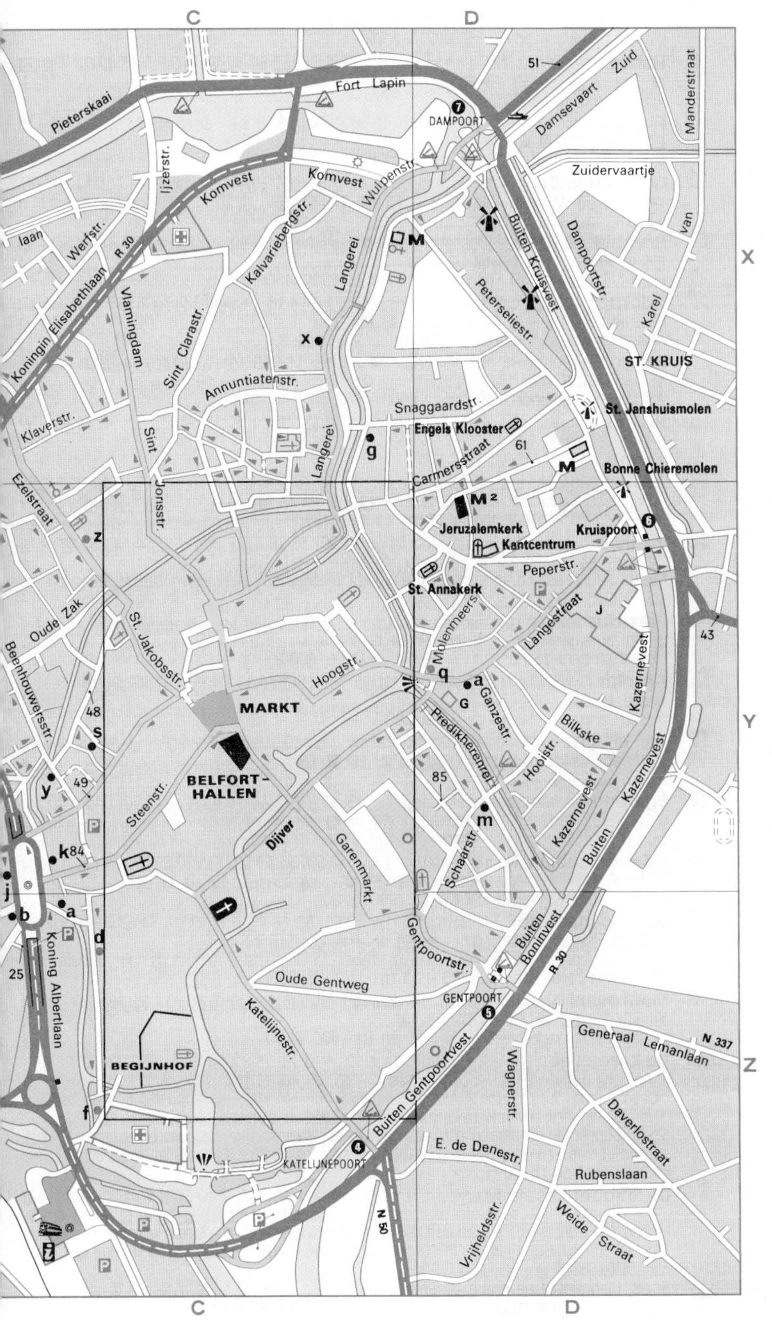

C
D
Pieterskaai
Fort Lapin
DAMPOORT
Damsevaart Zuid
Manderstraat
Zuidervaartje
Komvest
Wulpenstr.
Ijzerstr.
Werfstr.
R 30
Koningin Elisabethlaan
Kalvariebergstr.
Langerei
M
Buiten Kruisvest
Peterseliestr.
Dampoortstr.
Karel
Van
X
Vlamingdam
Sint Clarastr.
Annuntiatenstr.
Snaggaardstr.
ST. KRUIS
St. Janshuismolen
Klaverstr.
Sint Jorisstr.
Engels Klooster
Carmersstraat
61
Bonne Chieremolen
Ezelstraat
M²
Jeruzalemkerk
Kruispoort
Kantcentrum
Peperstr.
St. Annakerk
Langestraat
Oude Zak
St. Jakobsstr.
Molenmeers
Beenhouwersstr.
Hoogstr.
MARKT
Ganzestr.
Predikherenrei
Kazernevest
Bilkske
Y
BELFORT-HALLEN
Steenstr.
Dijver
Garenmarkt
Hooistr.
Buiten Kazernevest
Schaarstr.
Koning Albertlaan
Gentpoortstr.
Buiten Boninvest
Oude Gentweg
GENTPOORT
Katelijnestr.
Generaal Lemanlaan
N 337
Z
BEGIJNHOF
Wagnerstr.
Buiten Gentpoortvest
Daverlostraat
E. de Denestr.
KATELIJNEPOORT
Rubenslaan
N 50
Vrijheidsstr.
Weide Straat
C
D

**Ter Duinen** without rest, Langerei 52 (0 50) 33 04 37, *Fax (0 50) 34 42 16*, – . AE E VISA JCB. CX x
*closed January* – **20 rm** 2400/4200.

**Hansa** without rest, N. Desparsstraat 11 (0 50) 33 84 44, *Fax (0 50) 33 42 05* – – 30. AE E VISA JCB. AT k
**20 rm** 3500/5500.

**Flanders** without rest, Langestraat 38 (0 50) 33 88 89, *Fax (0 50) 33 93 45*, – . AE E VISA JCB DY a
*6 March-2 January* – **16 rm** 3500/4500.

**Gd H. Oude Burg** without rest, Oude Burg 5 (0 50) 44 51 11, *Fax (0 50) 44 51 00*, – – 25-210. AE E VISA JCB AU i
**138 rm** 4000/5000.

**Bryghia** without rest, Oosterlingenplein 4 (0 50) 33 80 59, *Fax (0 50) 34 14 30* – . AE E VISA JCB. AT t
*closed 5 January- 15 February* – **18 rm** 3500/4500.

**Adornes** without rest, St-Annarei 26 (0 50) 34 13 36, *Fax (0 50) 34 20 85*, , « Period vaulted cellars » – . AE E VISA JCB AT u
*closed January-13 February* – **20 rm** 2600/3600.

**Aragon** without rest, Naaldenstraat 24 (0 50) 33 35 33, *Fax (0 50) 34 28 05* – . AE E VISA AT v
*15 March-December* – **39 rm** 4000/4500.

**Biskajer** without rest, Biskajersplein 4 (0 50) 34 15 06, *Fax (0 50) 34 39 11* – . AE E VISA AT w
**17 rm** 3300/4150.

**Azalea** without rest, Wulfhagestraat 43 (0 50) 33 14 78, *Fax (0 50) 33 97 00*, « Canalside terrace » – . AE E VISA JCB CY y
*closed 22 to 26 December* – **25 rm** 3200/5200.

**'t Putje** (with annex ), 't Zand 31 (0 50) 33 28 47, *Fax (0 50) 34 14 23*, – – 30. AE E VISA JCB. rm CZ a
**Meals** (Pub rest, partly grill, open until midnight) Lunch 295 – 850/995 – **24 rm** 1700/3400.

**Patritius** without rest, Riddersstraat 11 (0 50) 33 84 54, *Fax (0 50) 33 96 34*, – – 25. AE E VISA JCB AT b
*closed January-15 February* – **16 rm** 2400/4000.

**Anselmus** without rest, Riddersstraat 15 (0 50) 34 13 74, *Fax (0 50) 34 19 16* – . AE E VISA AT h
*closed January* – **10 rm** 2700/2900.

**Ter Brughe** without rest, Oost-Gistelhof 2 (0 50) 34 03 24, *Fax (0 50) 33 88 73*, « Ancient vaulted cellars » – . AE E VISA AT a
**23 rm** 2900/4400.

**Egmond** without rest, Minnewater 15 (0 50) 34 14 45, *Fax (0 50) 34 29 40*, , « Early 20C residence in garden » – . AV g
*closed 5 to 31 January* – **8 rm** 3400/3950.

**Gd H. du Sablon,** Noordzandstraat 21 (0 50) 33 39 02, *Fax (0 50) 33 39 08*, « Early 20C hall with Art Deco cupola » – – 25-100. AE E VISA AU h
**Meals** (residents only) – **38 rm** 2950/3700.

**Bourgoensch Hof,** Wollestraat 39 (0 50) 33 16 45, *Fax (0 50) 34 63 78*, canals and old Flemish houses, – . E VISA AU f
*closed 10 January-15 February ; 18 November-15 March open weekends only* – **Meals** Lunch 1360 – a la carte approx. 1400 – **11 rm** 2450/5050.

**Montovani** without rest, Schouwvegerstraat 11 (0 50) 34 53 66, *Fax (0 50) 34 53 67* – . AE E VISA. BY c
*closed 12 January-2 February* – **13 rm** 1600/2600.

**De Karmeliet** (Van Hecke), Langestraat 19 (0 50) 33 82 59, *Fax (0 50) 33 10 11*, , « Ancient patrician residence, terrace » – . AE E VISA JCB. DY q
*closed Sunday lunch June-August, Sunday dinner, Monday, 16 August-3 September and 1 to 28 January* – **Meals** Lunch 2100 – 2600/3800, a la carte 2700/3700
**Spec.** Suprêmes de pigeon rôti, ses cuisses confites et pied de porc en saucisson. Tuile sucrée et salée aux grosses langoustines et chicons confits. Ravioli à la vanille et pommes caramélisées en chaud-froid.

**De Snippe** (Huysentruyt) with rm, Nieuwe Gentweg 53 (0 50) 33 70 70, *Fax (0 50) 33 76 62*, , « 18C residence with murals and shaded terrace » – . AE E VISA
*closed 15 February-12 March and 29 November-10 December* – **Meals** *(closed Sunday and Monday lunch)* Lunch 1950 b.i. – 2500, a la carte 2900/3700 – **9 rm** *(closed Sunday in winter)* 5000/5500 AV r
**Spec.** Blanquette de crabe au Champagne. Filets d'anguilles de rivière à la vinaigrette d'herbes. Ris de veau croustillant aux truffes et pointes vertes.

XXX ✿ **Den Gouden Harynck** (Serruys), Groeninge 25 ✆ (0 50) 33 76 37, *Fax (0 50) 34 42 70* – Ⓟ. AE ⓓ E VISA JCB AUV w
*closed Sunday, Monday, 1 week after Easter, last 2 weeks July-first week August and last week December* – **Meals** *Lunch 1300* – 2200, a la carte approx. 2600
**Spec.** Velouté de jeunes navets au foie gras poêlé. Homard vapeur à l'huile de noix et gingembre. St-Pierre à la purée d'aubergines fumées et jus aux aromates.

XXX **Duc de Bourgogne** with rm, Huidenvettersplein 12 ✆ (0 50) 33 20 38, *Fax (0 50) 34 40 37*, ≤ canals, « Rustic decor and murals of late medieval style » – ▤ rest, TV ☎. AE ⓓ E VISA AU t
*closed 3 weeks July and January* – **Meals** *(closed Monday and Tuesday lunch) Lunch 1250* – a la carte approx. 2500 – **10 rm** ☕ 3700/5300.

XXX **Den Braamberg,** Pandreitje 11 ✆ (0 50) 33 73 70, *Fax (0 50) 33 99 73* – AE E VISA
*closed Thursday and Sunday* – **Meals** a la carte 1650/2250. AU q

XXX **'t Pandreitje,** Pandreitje 6 ✆ (0 50) 33 11 90, *Fax (0 50) 34 00 70* – AE ⓓ E VISA JCB
*closed Wednesday, Sunday, 23 February-1 March, 5 to 22 July and 1 to 8 November* – **Meals** 1650/2350. AU x

XXX **De Witte Poorte,** Jan Van Eyckplein 6 ✆ (0 50) 33 08 83, *Fax (0 50) 34 55 60*, 🏕, « Vaulted dining room, walled inner garden » – AE ⓓ E VISA JCB AT x
*closed Sunday and Monday except Bank Holidays, 2 weeks June and 2 weeks January* – **Meals** *Lunch 1100* – 1700/1950.

XX **De Lotteburg,** Goezeputstraat 43 ✆ (0 50) 33 75 35, *Fax (0 50) 33 04 04*, 🏕, Seafood – ▤. AE E VISA JCB. ✂ AV d
*closed Monday, Tuesday, last week January-first week February and last week July-first week August* – **Meals** *Lunch 1195* – 1695/1895.

XX **'t Stil Ende,** Scheepsdalelaan 12 ✆ (0 50) 33 92 03, *Fax (0 50) 33 26 22*, 🏕, « Modern interior » – ▤. AE ⓓ E VISA JCB BX a
*closed Sunday dinner, Monday, 2 weeks late February and 2 weeks late July* – **Meals** 950/1950.

XX **'t Bourgoensche Cruyce** 🐚 with rm, Wollestraat 41 ✆ (0 50) 33 79 26, *Fax (0 50) 34 19 68*, ≤ canals and old Flemish houses – |♦|, ▤ rest, TV ☎. AE ⓓ E VISA AU f
**Meals** *(closed Tuesday, Wednesday, first week July and 17 November-11 December) Lunch 1750 b.i.* – 1800 – **8 rm** *(closed 17 November-11 December)* ☕ 3400/4400.

XX ✿ **Hermitage** (Dryepondt), Ezelstraat 18 ✆ (0 50) 34 41 73 – ⓓ E VISA JCB CY z
*closed Sunday, Monday and August* – **Meals** (dinner only) (booking essential) 2000 (2 pers. min.)/3000 b.i. – a la carte approx. 2400
**Spec.** Filet de rouget-barbet à la mousseline Soubise. Pot-au-feu de turbotin aux fines herbes. Éventail de magret au velouté de lentilles et salsifis confits.

XX **Kardinaalshof,** St-Salvatorskerkhof 14 ✆ (0 50) 34 16 91, *Fax (0 50) 34 20 62*, Seafood – AE ⓓ E VISA AUV g
*closed Wednesday, Thursday lunch and first 2 weeks July* – **Meals** 1100/1875.

XX **Patrick Devos,** Zilverstraat 41 ✆ (0 50) 33 55 66, *Fax (0 50) 33 58 67*, 🏕, « Belle Epoque interior, patio » – AE ⓓ E VISA JCB. ✂ AU y
*closed Sunday, 21 July-8 August and 24 to 30 December* – **Meals** *Lunch 1100* – 1700/2400.

XX **Bhavani,** Simon Stevinplein 5 ✆ (0 50) 33 90 25, *Fax (0 50) 34 89 52*, 🏕, Indian cuisine, open until 11 p.m. – AE ⓓ E VISA JCB AU z
**Meals** *Lunch 550* – a la carte approx. 1100.

XX **Den Dijver,** Dijver 5 ✆ (0 50) 33 60 69, *Fax (0 50) 44 62 51*, 🏕, Beer cuisine – AE E VISA AU c
*closed Wednesday, 1 week late February, 1 week late June and 1 week late August* – **Meals** 1300 b.i.

XX **Spinola,** Spinolarei 1 ✆ (0 50) 34 17 85, *Fax (0 50) 34 13 71*, « Rustic » – AE ⓓ E VISA JCB AT c
*closed Sunday, Monday lunch, 1 week late March, 2 last weeks June and 1 week late January* – **Meals** 1490/1850.

XX **Tanuki,** Oude Gentweg 1 ✆ (0 50) 34 75 12, *Fax (0 50) 33 82 42*, Japanese cuisine with Teppan-Yaki and sushi-bar – ▤. AE E VISA JCB AV f
*closed Monday, Tuesday, last 2 weeks July and last 2 weeks January* – **Meals** *Lunch 430* – 1390/2100.

X **Brasserie Raymond,** Eiermarkt 5 ✆ (0 50) 33 78 48, *Fax (0 50) 33 78 48*, 🏕, Open until 11.30 p.m. – AE ⓓ E VISA JCB AT g
*closed Tuesday, first week March, 2 weeks July and 1 week November* – **Meals** *Lunch 475* – 995 b.i.

X **Cafedraal,** Zilverstraat 38 ✆ (0 50) 34 08 45, *Fax (0 50) 33 52 41*, 🏕, Pub rest, open until 11.30 p.m., « Historical residence with inner terrace » – AE ⓓ E VISA JCB AU s
*closed Sunday and Monday* – **Meals** *Lunch 395* – a la carte 1250/1600.

**Huize Die Maene,** Markt 17 ☎ (0 50) 33 39 59, *Fax (0 50) 33 44 60*, Pub rest, open until 11 p.m. – AE ① E VISA AU b
**Meals** *Lunch 495* – 975.

**René,** St-Jakobsstraat 58 ☎ (0 50) 34 12 24 – AE E VISA. AT e
*closed Sunday dinner, Monday and July* – **Meals** 950/1295.

**Suburbs**

**North-West** – ✉ *8000* :

**De Gouden Korenhalm,** Oude Oostendsesteenweg 79a (Sint-Pieters) ☎ (0 50) 31 33 93, *Fax (0 50) 31 18 96*, « Typical Flemish farmhouse » – P. AE ① E VISA
*closed Monday, late February and late August* – **Meals** *Lunch 995* – 1450/1950.

**South** – ✉ *8200* :

**Novotel Zuid,** Chartreuseweg 20 (Sint-Michiels) ☎ (0 50) 40 21 40, *Fax (0 50) 40 21 41*, – rest, TV ☎ P – 25-200. AE ① E VISA JCB
**Meals** *Lunch 590* – 850 – 450 – **101 rm** 3000/3750.

**Casserole** (Hotel school), Groene-Poortdreef 17 (Sint-Michiels) ☎ (0 50) 40 30 30, *Fax (0 50) 40 30 35*, « Garden setting » – P – 25. AE ① E VISA.
*closed Saturday, Sunday and school Holidays* – **Meals** (lunch only) *Lunch 950* – a la carte approx. 1400.

**South-West** – ✉ *8200* :

**Host. Pannenhuis**, Zandstraat 2 ☎ (0 50) 31 19 07, *Fax (0 50) 31 77 66*, « Terrace and garden » – TV ☎ P – 25. AE ① E VISA JCB
**Meals** *(closed Tuesday dinner, Wednesday, 15 January-2 February and 2 to 17 July) Lunch 1300* – 1250/1750 – **18 rm** *(closed 15 January-2 February)* 3350/4080.

**Herborist** with rm, De Watermolen 15 (by N 32 : 6 km, then on the right after E 40, St-Andries) ☎ (0 50) 38 76 00, *Fax (0 50) 39 31 06*, « Inn with country atmosphere », – rest, TV ☎ P. AE E VISA. rm
*closed Sunday dinner, Monday, 22 March-4 April, 22 June-4 July, 22 September-4 October and 22 December-4 January* – **Meals** *Lunch 1750 b.i.* – 3150 b.i./3650 b.i. – **4 rm** 2850/3850.

**at Sint-Kruis** *E : 6 km* C *Bruges* – ✉ *8310 Sint-Kruis* :

**Wilgenhof** without rest, Polderstraat 151 ☎ (0 50) 36 27 44, *Fax (0 50) 36 28 21*, « An area of reclaimed land (polder) », – TV ☎ P. AE ① E VISA
*closed last week January* – **6 rm** 2500/4100.

**Ronnie Jonkman,** Maalsesteenweg 438 ☎ (0 50) 36 07 67, *Fax (0 50) 35 76 96*, « Terraces » – P. AE ① E VISA JCB
*closed Sunday, Monday, 1 to 15 April, 15 to 30 July and 1 to 15 October* – **Meals** *Lunch 1850 b.i.* – a la carte 2100/2700.

**Environs**

**at Hertsberge** *S by N 50 : 12,5 km* C *Oostkamp pop. 21 008* – ✉ *8020 Hertsberge* :

**Manderley,** Kruisstraat 13 ☎ (0 50) 27 80 51, *Fax (0 50) 27 80 51*, « Terrace and garden » – P. AE ① E VISA
*closed Thursday dinner in winter, Sunday dinner, Monday, first week October and last 3 weeks January* – **Meals** *Lunch 1250* – 1750/2100.

**at Ruddervoorde** *S by N 50 : 12 km* C *Oostkamp pop. 21 008* – ✉ *8020 Ruddervoorde* :

**Host. Leegendael** with rm, Kortrijkstraat 498 (N 50) ☎ (0 50) 27 76 99, *Fax (0 50) 27 58 80*, « Period residence, country atmosphere » – rest, TV ☎ P. AE ① E VISA
**Meals** *(closed Tuesday, Wednesday and Sunday dinner) Lunch 990* – a la carte 1600/2000 – **6 rm** 1750/2550.

**at Varsenare** *W : 6,5 km* C *Jabbeke pop. 13 282* – ✉ *8490 Varsenare* :

**Manoir Stuivenberg** (Scherrens frères) with rm, Gistelsteenweg 27 ☎ (0 50) 38 15 02, *Fax (0 50) 38 28 92*, – rest, TV ☎ P – 25-400. AE ① E VISA.
*closed 20 to 30 July* – **Meals** *(closed Sunday dinner and Monday) Lunch 1485* – 2450, a la carte 2150/3400 – **8 rm** 4700/6750, 1 suite
**Spec.** Filets de rouget à la brunoise de câpres et citron. Poitrine de pigeon grillée en crapaudine. Soufflé chaud à la vanille, sauce au chocolat.

**at Waardamme** *S by N 50 : 11 km* C *Oostkamp pop. 21 008* – ✉ *8020 Waardamme* :

**Ter Talinge,** Rooiveldstraat 46 ☎ (0 50) 27 90 61, *Fax (0 50) 28 00 52*, « Terrace » – P. AE E VISA
*closed Wednesday, Thursday, 20 February-6 March and 21 August-4 September* – **Meals** *Lunch 1100* – a la carte 1400/1800.

**at Zedelgem** *SW : 10,5 km – pop. 21 381 – ✉ 8210 Zedelgem :*

**Zuidwege,** Torhoutsesteenweg 128 ☎ (0 50) 20 13 39, *Fax (0 50) 20 17 39,* – rm
**Meals** (Pub rest) *(closed Saturday, Sunday lunch and 20 December-5 January)* *Lunch 310* – a la carte 850/1300 – **17 rm** 1850/2550.

**Ter Leepe,** Torhoutsesteenweg 168 ☎ (0 50) 20 01 97, *Fax (0 50) 20 88 54* – 220. AE VISA
*closed Wednesday dinner, Sunday, 22 to 28 February and last 2 weeks July* – **Meals** *Lunch 1300 b.i.* – a la carte approx. 1500.

**Kruishoutem** *9770 Oost-Vlaanderen 213 ⑯ and 409 D3 – pop. 7 718 – 44 km.*

**Hof van Cleve** (Goossens), Riemegemstraat 1 (near N 459, motorway E 17 - A 14, exit ⑥) ☎ (0 9) 383 58 48, *Fax (0 9) 383 77 25,* ≤, « Farmhouse in open fields » – P. AE VISA
*closed Sunday, Monday, 1 week Easter, 3 weeks August and late December-early January* – **Meals** *Lunch 1450* – 2200/3500, a la carte 2000/2900
**Spec.** Ravioli ouvert de girolles et joue de bœuf braisée, sabayon à l'estragon. Pigeonneau au lard croustillant, parmentière aux truffes et Banyuls. Moëlleux au chocolat, gelée au citron et glace au thé vert.

**Waregem** *8790 West-Vlaanderen 213 ⑮ and 409 D 3 – pop. 35 725 – 47 km.*

**'t Oud Konijntje** (Mmes Desmedt), Bosstraat 53 (S : 2 km near E 17) ☎ (0 56) 60 19 37, *Fax (0 56) 60 92 12,* « Floral terrace » – P. AE VISA
*closed dinner Thursday and Sunday, Friday, 21 July-13 August and 24 December-4 January* – **Meals** *Lunch 1500* – 2750 (2 pers. min.), a la carte 2250/3100
**Spec.** Fantaisie de bar de ligne et saumon de Norvège au caviar. Cristalline de homard à la pomme de terre. Nuage de fromage blanc et croustillant de chocolat Noir de Noir.

---

**LIÈGE** *4000 213 ㉒ and 409 J 4 ⑰ N – pop. 190 525.*

**See** : *Citadel ≤★★ DW – Cointe Park ≤★ CX – Old town★★ – Palace of the Prince-Bishops★ : court of honour★★ EY – The Perron★ (market cross) EY* **A** *– Baptismal font★★★ of St. Bartholomew's church FY – Treasury★★ of St. Paul's Cathedral : reliquary of Charles the Bold★★ EZ – St. James church★★ : vaults of the nave★★ EZ – Altarpiece★ in the St. Denis church EY – Church of St. John : Wooden Calvary statues★ EY – Aquarium★ FZ* **D.**

**Museums** : *Provincial Museum of Life in Wallonia★★ EY – Religious and Roman Art Museum★ FY* **M5** *– Curtius and Glass Museum★ : evangelistary of Notger★★★, collection of glassware★ FY* **M1** *– Arms★ FY* **M3** *– Ansembourg★ FY* **M2.**

**Envir** : *Blégny-Trembleur★★ NE : 20 km – Baptismal font★ in the church★ of St. Severin SW : 27 km – Visé N : 17 km, Reliquary of St. Hadelin★ in the collegiate church.*

*9 r. Bernalmont 2 ☎ 227 44 66, Fax 227 91 92 - 18 at Angleur S : 7,5 km, rte du Condroz 541 ☎ (0 4) 336 20 21, Fax (0 4) 337 20 26 - 18 at Gomzé-Andoumont SE : 18 km, r. Gomzé 30 ☎ (0 4) 360 92 07, Fax (0 4) 360 92 06.*

*☎ (0 4) 342 52 14.*

*En Féronstrée 92 ☎ (0 4) 221 92 21, Fax (0 4) 221 92 22 and Gare des Guillemins ☎ (0 4) 252 44 19 – Tourist association of the province, bd de la Sauvenière 77 ☎ (0 4) 232 65 10, Fax (0 4) 232 65 11.*

*Brussels 97 – Amsterdam 242 – Antwerp 119 – Cologne 122 – Luxembourg 159.*

Plans on following pages

**Bedford** M, quai St-Léonard 36 ☎ (0 4) 228 81 11, *Fax (0 4) 227 45 75,* « Inner garden » – P – 25-220. AE VISA DW g
**Meals** *Lunch 990* – a la carte approx. 1000 – **147 rm** 6950/8450, 2 suites.

**Old town**

**Mercure,** bd de la Sauveniere 100 ☎ (0 4) 221 77 11, *Fax (0 4) 221 77 01* – – 25-100. AE VISA. rest EY t
**Meals** *(closed Saturday lunch and Sunday dinner)* *Lunch 700* – a la carte approx. 1400 – **105 rm** 4500/4975.

**Au Vieux Liège,** quai Goffe 41 ☎ (0 4) 223 77 48, *Fax (0 4) 223 78 60,* « 16C residence » – AE VISA FY a
*closed Wednesday dinner, Sunday, Bank Holidays, 1 week Easter and mid July-mid August* – **Meals** 1250/1800.

**Chez Max,** pl. de la République Française 12 ☎ (0 4) 222 08 73, *Fax (0 4) 222 90 02,* Oyster bar, open until 11 p.m., « Elegant brasserie decorated by Luc Genot » – AE VISA EY a
*closed Saturday lunch and Sunday* – **Meals** *Lunch 1000* – a la carte approx. 1500.

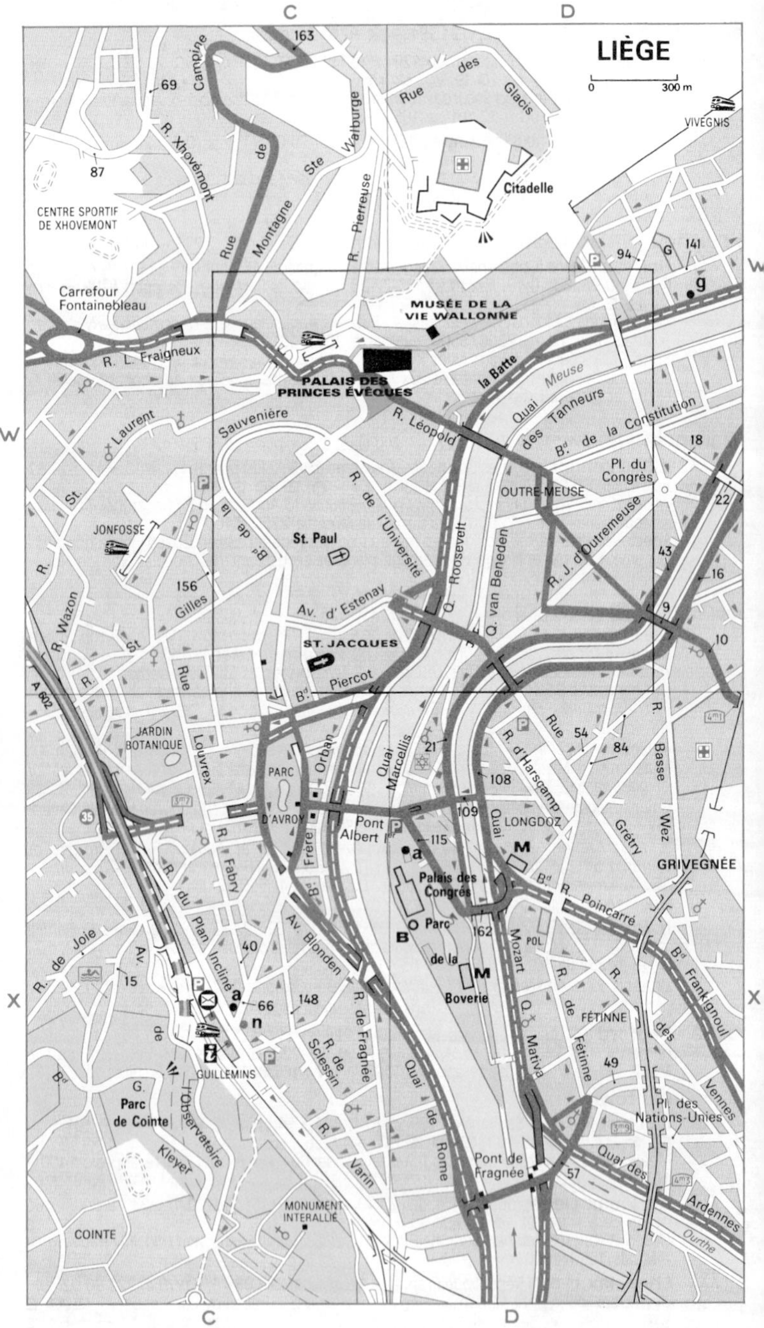
LIÈGE
0 300 m
C
D
W
X
VIVEGNIS
Citadelle
Rue des Glacis
MUSÉE DE LA VIE WALLONNE
PALAIS DES PRINCES ÉVÊQUES
CENTRE SPORTIF DE XHOVEMONT
Carrefour Fontainebleau
R. L. Fraigneux
R. Xhovémont
Rue de Campine
Montagne Ste Walburge
R. Pierreuse
la Batte
Meuse
Quai des Tanneurs
Bd de la Constitution
Pl. du Congrès
OUTRE-MEUSE
R. J. d'Outremeuse
R. Léopold
Sauvenière
St. Laurent
JONFOSSE
St. Paul
R. de l'Université
Bd de la Sauvenière
Av. d'Estenay
ST. JACQUES
Bd Piercot
Q. Roosevelt
Q. van Beneden
St Gilles
R. Wazon
A 602
JARDIN BOTANIQUE
Rue Louvrex
PARC D'AVROY
Bd Frère Orban
Quai Marcellis
Pont Albert Ier
Palais des Congrès
Parc de la Boverie
LONGDOZ
Quai
R. d'Harscamp
Rue Grétry
R. Basse Wez
GRIVEGNÉE
Bd R. Poincaré
Bd Frankignoul
R. des Vennes
Mozart
Q. Mativa
R. de Fétinne
FÉTINNE
Pl. des Nations-Unies
Quai des Ardennes
Ourthe
Pont de Fragnée
R. Fabry
R. du Plan Incliné
Av. Blonden
R. de Fragnée
R. de Sclessin
R. Varin
Quai de Rome
R. de Joie
Av. de l'Observatoire
Bd G. Kleyer
GUILLEMINS
Parc de Cointe
COINTE
MONUMENT INTERALLIÉ
POL
163
69
87
94
141
G
g
18
22
43
16
9
10
156
54
84
21
108
109
115
a
B
M
162
35
40
66
a
n
148
15
49
57

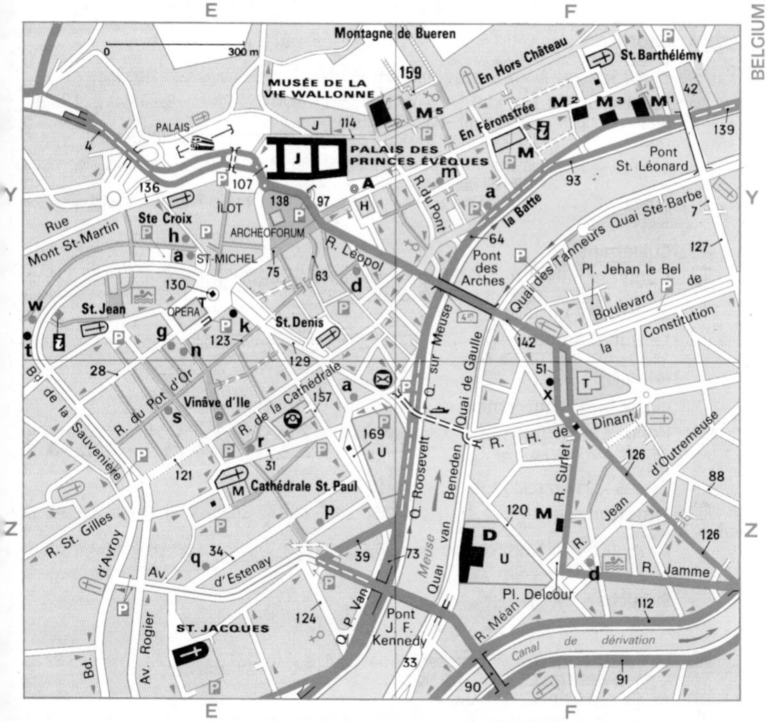

| Street | Grid | No. |
|---|---|---|
| Cathédrale (R. de la) | EZ | |
| En Féronstrée | FY | |
| Léopold (R.) | EFY | |
| Pont d'Ile | EY | 123 |
| Régence (R. de la ) | EYZ | 129 |
| Saint-Gilles (R.) | EZ | |
| Vinâve d'Ile (R.) | EZ | |
| Académie (R. de l') | EY | 4 |
| Adolphe Maréchal (R.) | FY | 7 |
| Amercoeur (Pont d') | DW | 9 |
| Amercoeur (R. d') | DW | 10 |
| Bois-l'Evêque (R.) | CX | 15 |
| Bonaparte (Quai) | DW | 16 |
| Bonnes-Villes (R. des) | DW | 18 |
| Boverie (Quai de la) | DX | 21 |
| Bressoux (Pont de) | DW | 22 |
| Bruxelles (R. de) | EY | 24 |
| Casquette (R. de la) | EYZ | 28 |
| Charles Magnette (R.) | EZ | 31 |
| Churchill (Quai) | FZ | 33 |
| Clarisses (R. des) | EZ | 34 |
| Croisiers (R. des) | EZ | 39 |
| Dartois (R.) | CX | 40 |
| Déportés (Pl. des) | FY | 42 |
| Dérivation (Quai de la) | DW | 43 |
| Emile de Laveleye (Bd) | DX | 49 |
| Est (Bd de l') | FYZ | 51 |
| Fer (R. du) | DX | 54 |
| Fétinne (Pont de) | DX | 57 |
| Georges Simenon (R.) | FZ | 61 |
| Gérardrie (R.) | EY | 63 |
| Goffe (Quai de la) | FY | 64 |
| Guillemins (R. des) | CX | 66 |
| Hauteurs (Bd des) | CW | 69 |
| Joffre (R.) | EY | 75 |
| Joie (R. de) | CX | 78 |
| Lairesse (R.) | DX | 84 |
| Léon Philippet (Bd) | CW | 87 |
| Liberté (R. de la) | FZ | 88 |
| Longdoz (Pont de) | FZ | 90 |
| Longdoz (Quai de) | FZ | 91 |
| Maastricht (Quai de) | FY | 93 |
| Marché (Pl. du) | EY | 97 |
| Maghin (R.) | DW | 94 |
| Notger (Square) | EY | 107 |
| Orban (Quai) | DX | 108 |
| Orban ou de Huy (Pont d') | DX | 109 |
| Ourthe (Quai de l') | FZ | 112 |
| Palais (R. du) | EY | 114 |
| Parc (R. du) | DX | 115 |
| Pitteurs (R. des) | FZ | 120 |
| Pont d'Avroy (R.) | EZ | 121 |
| Prémontrés (R. des) | EZ | 124 |
| Puits-en-Soc (R.) | FZ | 126 |
| Ransonnet (R.) | FY | 127 |
| Rép. Française (Pl. de la) | EY | 130 |
| Saint-Hubert (R.) | EY | 136 |
| Saint-Lambert (Pl.) | EY | 138 |
| Saint-Léonard (Quai) | FY | 139 |
| Saint-Léonard (R.) | DW | 141 |
| Saint-Pholien (R. et Pl.) | FY | 142 |
| Serbie (R. de) | CX | 148 |
| Trappé (R.) | CW | 156 |
| Université (R. de l') | EYZ | 157 |
| Ursulines (Imp. des) | FY | 159 |
| Vennes (Pont des) | DX | 162 |
| Victor-Hugo (Av.) | CW | 163 |
| 20-Août (Pl. du) | EZ | 169 |

XX **Le Déjeuner sur l'Herbe aux Bégards,** r. Bégards 2 ☎ (0 4) 222 92 34, *Fax (0 4) 223 54 02*, terrace, « Wine cellar backed on the city enclosure wall » – AE ⓓ E VISA
*closed lunch Saturday and Monday, Sunday, Bank Holidays, 1 week Easter, last 2 weeks August and 1 week late December* – **Meals** 1050/1900. EY w

XX **Robert Lesenne,** r. Boucherie 9 ☎ (0 4) 222 07 93, *Fax (0 4) 222 92 33*, « Ancient almshouse watchtower in an atrium » – ▤. AE ⓓ E VISA FY m
*closed Saturday lunch, Sunday and 2 to 16 August* – **Meals** 1390.

XX **Folies Gourmandes,** r. Clarisses 48 ☎ (0 4) 223 16 44, terrace, « Early 20C house with garden-terrace » – AE ⓓ E VISA EZ q
*closed Sunday dinner, Monday, Easter week and last 2 weeks September* – **Meals** 1150.

XX **Le Shanghai** 1st floor, Galeries Cathédrale 104 ☎ (0 4) 222 22 63, *Fax (0 4) 223 00 50*, Chinese cuisine – ▤. AE ⓓ E VISA EZ r
*closed Tuesday and 7 to 29 July* – **Meals** *Lunch 525* – a la carte approx. 1000.

X **Enoteca,** r. Casquette 5 ☎ (0 4) 222 24 64, *Fax (0 4) 223 20 65.*
E VISA EY g
*closed Saturday lunch, Sunday and Bank Holidays* – **Meals** *Lunch 590* – 1090.

X **Le Bistrot du Pot d'Or,** r. Pot d'Or 33 ☎ (0 4) 222 27 14, *Fax (0 4) 222 30 84*, Brasserie, open until 11 p.m. – AE ⓪ E VISA EZ s
*closed Sunday and dinner Monday and Tuesday* – **Meals** a la carte 1000/1300.

X **Lalo's Bar,** r. Madeleine 18 ☎ (0 4) 223 22 57, *Fax (0 4) 223 22 57*, Italian cuisine, open until 11 p.m. – ▤. ⓪ E VISA EY d
*closed Saturday lunch, Sunday, Bank Holidays and first 3 weeks August* – **Meals** *Lunch 650* – 850.

**Guillemins**

**L'Univers** without rest, r. Guillemins 116 ☎ (0 4) 254 55 55, *Fax (0 4) 254 55 00* – ⇕ ⇹ TV ☎ P – 25-80. AE ⓪ E VISA CX a
☕ 260 – **47 rm** 1840/2080.

X **Le Duc d'Anjou,** r. Guillemins 127 ☎ (0 4) 252 28 58, Mussels in season, open until 11.30 p.m. – ▤. AE ⓪ E VISA CX n
**Meals** 820.

**Right banc (Outremeuse - Palais des Congrès)**

**Holiday Inn** without rest, Esplanade de l'Europe 2, ✉ 4020, ☎ (0 4) 342 60 20, *Fax (0 4) 343 48 10*, ⩽, 🏋, ≘s, ▢ – ⇕ ⇹ ▤ TV ☎ ♿ 🚗 P – 25-70. AE ⓪ E VISA DX a
☕ 495 – **214 rm** 5400/6000, 5 suites.

**Simenon,** bd de l'Est 16, ✉ 4020, ☎ (0 4) 342 86 90 – ⇕ TV ☎. AE ⓪ E VISA FZ x
**Meals** (Pub rest, lunch only) *(closed 23 December-1 January)* a la carte approx. 900 – ☕ 250 – **11 rm** 2000.

**Suburbs**

**at Angleur** *S : 4 km* C *Liège* – ✉ *4031 Angleur :*

**Le Val de l'Ourthe** without rest, rte de Tilff 412 ☎ (0 4) 365 91 71, *Fax (0 4) 365 62 89* – TV ☎ 🚗 P. AE ⓪ E VISA. ⚡
☕ 300 – **12 rm** 3200/3800.

XX **L'Orchidée Blanche,** rte du Condroz 457 (N 680) ☎ (0 4) 365 11 48, *Fax (0 4) 367 09 16* – P. AE ⓪ E VISA
*closed Tuesday dinner, Wednesday and last 3 weeks July* – **Meals** 1000 b.i.

**at Chênée** *E : 7,5 km* C *Liège* – ✉ *4032 Chênée :*

XXX **Le Gourmet,** r. Large 91 ☎ (0 4) 365 87 97, *Fax (0 4) 365 38 12*, 🏠, « Winter garden » – P. AE ⓪ E VISA
*closed Monday dinner, Wednesday, Saturday lunch, last 2 weeks July and first 2 weeks January* – **Meals** 980/1500.

XX **Le Vieux Chênée,** r. Gravier 45 ☎ (0 4) 367 00 92, *Fax (0 4) 367 59 15*, Mussels in season – AE ⓪ E VISA
*closed Thursday except Bank Holidays* – **Meals** *Lunch 890* – a la carte 950/1350.

**Environs**

**at Ans** *NW : 4 km – pop. 27 600* – ✉ *4430 Ans :*

XX **Le Marguerite,** r. Walthère Jamar 171 ☎ (0 4) 226 43 46, *Fax (0 4) 226 38 35*, 🏠 – AE ⓪ E VISA
*closed Saturday lunch, Sunday, Monday, last 3 weeks July and Christmas-New Year* – **Meals** *Lunch 980* – 1450.

XX **La Fontaine de Jade,** r. Yser 321 ☎ (0 4) 246 49 72, *Fax (0 4) 263 69 53*, Chinese cuisine, open until 11 p.m. – ▤. AE ⓪ E VISA
*closed Tuesday* – **Meals** *Lunch 450* – a la carte 850/1200.

**at Flémalle** *SW : 14 km* C *Flémalle pop. 26 433* – ✉ *4400 Flémalle-Haute :*

XXX **La Ciboulette,** chaussée de Chokier 96 ☎ (0 4) 275 19 65, *Fax (0 4) 275 05 81*, 🏠 – ▤. AE ⓪ E VISA
*closed Monday, Saturday lunch, dinner Sunday and Wednesday, 27 July-13 August and 28 December-12 January* – **Meals** *Lunch 1900 b.i.* – a la carte 2000/2450.

XX **Le Gourmet Gourmand,** Grand-Route 411 ☎ (0 4) 233 07 56, *Fax (0 4) 233 19 21*, 🏠 – ▤. AE ⓪ E VISA
*closed Saturday lunch, Monday and dinner Tuesday, Wednesday and Thursday* – **Meals** *Lunch 1100* – 1300/1650.

**at Herstal** *NE : 8 km - pop. 36 565 - ✉ 4040 Herstal :*

**Post** ⛰, r. Hurbise 160 (by motorway E 40, exit ㉞) ☎ (0 4) 264 64 00, *Fax (0 4) 248 06 90*, 🌳, ⛰ - |‡|, ▤ rest, TV ☎ P - 🏃 25-80. AE ⦿ E VISA
**Meals** *Lunch 800* - a la carte 950/1450 - **98 rm** ☕ 4400/5900.

**at Neuville-en-Condroz** *S : 18 km* © *Neupré pop. 9 377 - ✉ 4121 Neuville-en-Condroz :*

XXXX **Le Chêne Madame** (Mme Tilkin), av. de la Chevauchée 70 (in Rognacs wood SE : 2 km)
✿ ☎ (0 4) 371 41 27, *Fax (0 4) 371 29 43*, 🌳, « Country Inn » - P. AE ⦿ E VISA
*closed Monday, dinner Sunday and Thursday and August* - **Meals** *Lunch 1100* - 2650 (2 pers. min.), a la carte 1700/2500
**Spec.** Salade de lapereau au vinaigre de Xérès. Truite au bleu. Gibiers en saison.

**Hasselt** *3500 Limburg* **213** ⑨ *and* **409** I 3 *- pop. 67 456 - 42 km.*

**at Stevoort** *by N 2 : 5 km to Kermt, then road on the left* © *Hasselt - ✉ 3512 Stevoort :*

XXXXX **Scholteshof** (Souvereyns) ⛰ with rm, Kermtstraat 130 ☎ (0 11) 25 02 02, *Fax (0 11) 25 43 28*, ≤, 🌳, « 18C farmhouse with vines, kitchen garden, orchard and gardens in countryside setting », ✂ - TV ☎ P - 🏃 25-60. AE ⦿ E VISA
✿✿ *closed 13 to 30 July and 2 to 21 January* - **Meals** *(closed Wednesday) Lunch 2650* - 4100, a la carte 3500/4600 - ☕ 600 - **11 rm** 3100/5800, 7 suites
**Spec.** Turbot farci de chicons et truffe. Mille-feuille de légumes en tête de veau. Croquant de fèves de cacao, bananes rôties au miel et glace à la chicorée.

**Namur** *5000 Namur* **213** ⑳ **214** ⑤ *and* **409** H 4 *- pop. 105 059 - 61 km.*

**at Lives-sur-Meuse** *E : 9 km* © *Namur - ✉ 5101 Lives-sur-Meuse :*

XXXX **La Bergerie** (Lefevere), r. Mosanville 100 ☎ (0 81) 58 06 13, *Fax (0 81) 58 19 39*, ≤,
✿✿ « Overlooking the valley, terrace and garden with ornamental fountain » - ▤ P. AE ⦿ E VISA
*closed Sunday dinner in winter, Monday, Tuesday, late February-early March and last 2 weeks August-early September* - **Meals** *Lunch 1750 b.i.* - 3000 b.i./4250 b.i., - a la carte 2500/3000
**Spec.** Foie d'oie poêlé, création du moment. Agneau rôti "Bergerie". Le gâteau de crêpes soufflées.

**Pepinster** *4860 Liège* **213** ㉓ *and* **409** K 4 *- pop. 9 080 - 26 km.*

XXX **Host. Lafarque** ⛰ with rm, Chemin des Douys 20 (W : 4 km by N 61, locality
✿✿ Goffontaine) ☎ (0 87) 46 06 51, *Fax (0 87) 46 97 28*, ≤, 🌳, « Park », 🌲 - TV ☎ P. AE ⦿ E VISA. ✂ rm
*closed Monday, Tuesday, 23 March-9 April and 1 week September* - **Meals** *Lunch 1550* - 2375/2675, a la carte 2400/2850 - ☕ 395 - **6 rm** 3000/3950
**Spec.** Langoustines aux artichauts et tomates confites à la badiane. Ravioles de raifort aux truffes (December-March). Gibiers en saison.

**St-Vith** *4780 Liège* **214** ⑨ *and* **409** L 5 *- pop. 8 880 - 78 km.*

XXX **Zur Post** (Pankert) with rm, Hauptstr. 39 ☎ (0 80) 22 80 27, *Fax (0 80) 22 93 10* - TV
✿✿ ☎. AE ⦿ E VISA. ✂ rest
*closed Sunday dinner, Monday, Tuesday lunch, first 2 weeks July and January* - **Meals** *Lunch 1450* - 3500 (2 pers. min.), a la carte approx. 2500 - ☕ 500 - **8 rm** 1800/3000
**Spec.** Fond d'artichaut farci d'une poêlée de foie d'oie aux épinards. Croustade de loup de mer et jeune fenouil au vinaigre balsamique et huile de noisettes. Cochon de lait en cocotte aux éclats de truffes et champignons sauvages (February-15 September).

**Tongeren** *3700 Limburg* **213** ㉒ *and* **409** J 3 *- pop. 29 798 - 19 km.*

**at Vliermaal** *N : 5 km* © *Kortessem pop. 7 916 - ✉ 3724 Vliermaal :*

XXXXX **Clos St. Denis** (Denis), Grimmertingenstraat 24 ☎ (0 12) 23 60 96, *Fax (0 12) 26 32 07*,
✿✿ « 17C farmhouse manor, shaded terrace and garden » - P. AE ⦿ E VISA. ✂
*closed Monday, Tuesday, 13 to 29 July, 4 and 5 November and 23 December-5 January* - **Meals** *Lunch 1750* - 3500/4500, a la carte 3000/3900
**Spec.** Jarret de veau confit et foie de canard mariné aux truffes façon mille-feuille. Marbré de foie d'oie et canard aux épices douces. Effilochée de crabe, mayonnaise et fondue de tomates fraîches.

**Maastricht** *Limburg (Netherlands)* **211** O 17 *and* **408** I 9 *- pop. 118 518 - 33 km.*

XXX **Toine Hermsen,** St-Bernardusstraat 2, ✉ 6211 HL, ☎ (0 43) 325 84 00, *Fax (0 43)*
✿✿ *325 83 73* - ▤. AE ⦿ E VISA JCB. ✂
*closed Saturday lunch, Sunday, Monday and 2 weeks carnival* - **Meals** *Lunch 60* - 135, a la carte 80/110
**Spec.** Salade d'asperges et petits œufs pochés, vinaigrette de truffes d'été (May-June). Queues de langoustines grillées à la provençale et risotto de homard à la fondue de tomates. Foie de veau aux pommes, raisins et oignons croustillants, sauce au Calvados.

**Weert** *Limburg (Netherlands)* 211 O 15 *and* 408 I 8 – *pop. 42 023 – 90 km.*

XXX ✿✿ **l'Auberge** (Mertens) with rm Wilhelminasingel 80, ✉ 6001 GV, ☎ (0 495) 53 10 57, *Fax (0 495) 54 45 96*, « Terrace » – TV – 25. AE E VISA.
**Meals** *(closed Sunday and Monday except Bank Holidays and Saturday lunch)* Lunch 75 – 100/165, a la carte approx. 135 – **14 rm** *(closed Sunday and Monday except Bank Holidays)* 158/233
**Spec.** Gâteau de crêpes persillées aux champignons des bois et foie d'oie. Viennoise de turbot à la mousseline de langoustines au homard. Lièvre de la région à la Royale (October-January).

# LUXEMBOURG

(LËTZEBUERG) 215 E 4 *and* 409 L 7 – *pop. 75 377.*

*Amsterdam 391 – Bonn 190 – Brussels 219 – Ettelbrück 30.*

*pl. d'Armes.* ✉ *2011,* ☎ *22 28 09, Fax 47 48 18 – Air Terminus gare centrale,* ✉ *1010,* ☎ *42 82 82 20, Fax 42 82 82 30 – Airport at Findel* ☎ *42 82 82 21.*

18 *Hoehenhof (Senningerberg) near Airport, rte de Trèves 1,* ✉ *2633,* ☎ *34 00 90, Fax 34 83 91.*

*Arrival and departure information* ☎ *47 98 50 50 and 47 98 50 51. Findel by E 44 : 6 km* ☎ *40 08 08 – Air Terminal : pl. de la Gare* ☎ *48 11 99.*

**See** : *Site*★★ – *Old Luxembourg*★★ G : *Place de la Constitution* ≤★★ F, *Plateau St. Esprit* ≤★★ G, *Chemin de la Corniche*★★, ≤★★ G, *The Bock cliff* ≤★★, *Bock Casemates*★★ G, *Boulevard Victor Thorn* ≤★ G **121**, *Grand-Ducal Palace*★ G, *Cathedral of Our Lady*★ *(Notre-Dame)* F – *Grand-Duchess Charlotte Bridge*★ DY – *The Trois Glands* ≤★ *(Three Acorns)* DY.

**Museum** : *National Museum of Art and History*★, *Gallo Romain section*★, *Luxembourg life section (decorative arts and folk traditions)*★★ G **M**[1].

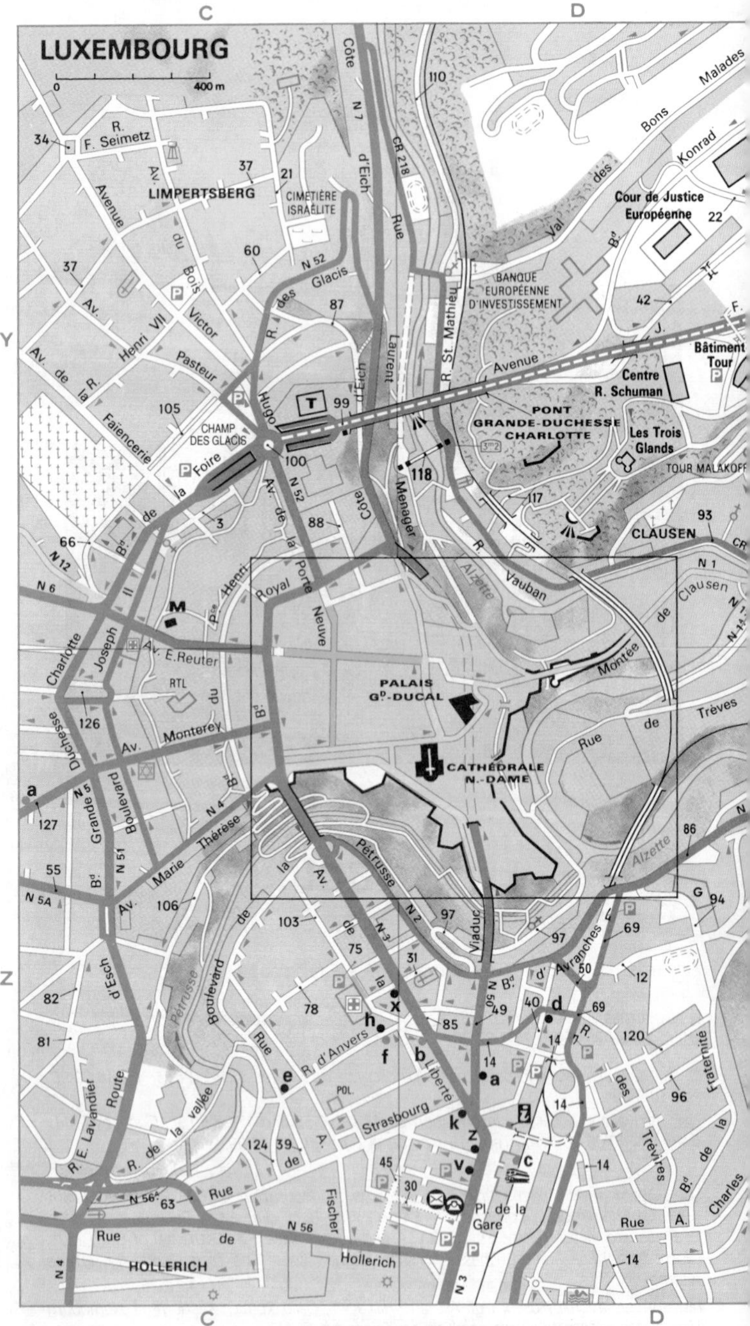
LUXEMBOURG
0
400 m
LIMPERTSBERG
CIMETIÈRE ISRAÉLITE
BANQUE EUROPÉENNE D'INVESTISSEMENT
Cour de Justice Européenne
Bâtiment Tour
Centre R. Schuman
PONT GRANDE-DUCHESSE CHARLOTTE
Les Trois Glands
TOUR MALAKOFF
CLAUSEN
CHAMP DES GLACIS
PALAIS Gᴰ-DUCAL
CATHÉDRALE N.-DAME
RTL
HOLLERICH
Pl. de la Gare
Av. de la Porte Neuve
Bd Royal
Av. E.Reuter
Av. Monterey
Av. Marie Thérèse
Bd Grande Duchesse Charlotte
Boulevard Joseph II
Av. de la Liberté
Av. de la Gare
Rue de Hollerich
Route d'Esch
R. E. Lavandier
R. de la Vallée
Boulevard de la Pétrusse
Rue de Strasbourg
R. d'Anvers
Rue Fischer
Bd d'Avranches
Rue de Trèves
Montée de Clausen
R. Vauban
Alzette
Pétrusse
Viaduc
Côte d'Eich
Rue Laurent Ménager
R. St. Mathieu
Val des Bons Malades
Bd Konrad Adenauer
Av. Victor Hugo
Av. du Bois
Av. Pasteur
Av. Henri VII
Av. de la Faïencerie
Av. de la Foire
R. des Glacis
R. F. Seimetz
Bd Prince Henri
R. des Trévires
Bd de la Fraternité
Rue A. Charles
N 1
N 2
N 3
N 4
N 5
N 5A
N 6
N 7
N 12
N 51
N 52
N 56
CR 218
C
D
Y
Z

Capucins (R. des) . . . . . F
Chimay (R.) . . . . . . . . . . F 24
Curé (R. du) . . . . . . . . . F
Fossé (R. du) . . . . . . . . . F 46
Gare (Av. de la) . . . . . . . DZ 49
Grand-Rue . . . . . . . . . . . F
Liberté (Av. de la) . . . . . CDZ
Philippe II (R.) . . . . . . . . F 91
Porte-Neuve (Av. de la) . CY
Strasbourg (R. de) . . . . . CDZ

Adames (R.) . . . . . . . . . . CY 3
Albert Wehrer (R.) . . . . . EY 4
Alcide de Gasperi (R.) . . EY 6
Aldringen (R.) . . . . . . . . F 7
Athénée (R. de l'Ancien) . F 9
Auguste Lumière (R.) . . DZ 12
Bains (R. des) . . . . . . . . F 13
Bonnevoie (R. de) . . . . . DZ 14
Boucherie (R. de la) . . . G 15
Bruxelles (Pl. de) . . . . . . F 16
Cerisiers (R. des) . . . . . . CY 21
Charles-Léon Hammes (R.) . . . . . . . . . . . . . . DY 22
Clairefontaine (Pl.) . . . . . FG 27
Clausen (R. de) . . . . . . . EY 28
Commerce (R. du) . . . . . CDZ 30
Dicks (R.) . . . . . . . . . . . . CDZ 31
Eau (R. de l') . . . . . . . . . G 33
Edouard André (Square) . . . . . . . . . . . CY 34
Ermesinde (R. ) . . . . . . . . CY 37
Etats-Unis (R. des) . . . . . CZ 39
Fort Neipperg (R. du) . . DZ 40
Fort Niedergrünewald (R. du) . . . . . . . . . . . DY 42
Fort Thüngen (R. du) . . . EY 43
Fort Wedell (R. du) . . . . CDZ 45
Franklin-Roosevelt (Bd) . F 48
Gaulle (Av. du Gén.-de) . DZ 50
Guillaume (Av.) . . . . . . . CZ 55
Guillaume Schneider (R.) . . . . . . . . . . . . . . CY 60
Jean Baptiste Merkels (R.) . . . . . . . . . . . . . . CZ 63
Jean Ulveling (Bd) . . . . . FG 64
J.P. Probst (R.) . . . . . . . CY 66
Jules Wilhem (R.) . . . . . EY 67
Laboratoire (R. du) . . . . DZ 69
Léon Hengen (R.) . . . . . EY 70
Marché (Pl. du) . . . . . . G 72
Marché aux Herbes (R. du) . . . . . . . . . . . . FG 73
Martyrs (Pl. des) . . . . . . CZ 75
Michel Rodange (R.) . . CZ 78
Nancy (Pl. de) . . . . . . . . CZ 81
Nassau (R. de) . . . . . . . CZ 82
Notre-Dame (R.) . . . . . . F 84
Paris (Pl. de) . . . . . . . . . DZ 85
Patton (Bd du Général) . DZ 86
Paul Eyschen (R.) . . . . . CY 87
Pescatore (Av.) . . . . . . . CY 88
Pfaffenthal (Montée de) . . . . . . . FG 90
Pierre de Mansfeld (Allée) . . . . . . . . . . . DY 93
Pierre et Marie Curie (R.) . . . . . . . . . . . . . DZ 94
Pierre Hentges (R.) . . . . DZ 96
Prague (R. de) . . . . . . . . DZ 97
Robert Schuman (Bd) . CY 99
Robert Schuman (Rond-Point) . . . . . . . CY 100
Sainte-Zithe (R.) . . . . . . CZ 103
Scheffer (Allée) . . . . . . . CY 105
Semois (R. de la) . . . . . CZ 106
Sigefroi (R.) . . . . . . . . . G 108
Sosthène Weis (R.) . . . G 109
Stavelot (R. de) . . . . . . . DY 110
Théâtre (Pl. du) . . . . . . F 114
Tour Jacob (Av. de la) . . . . . . . . . EY 115
Trois Glands (R. des) . . . . . . . . . . . . DY 117
Vauban (Pont) . . . . . . . . DY 118
Verger (R. du) . . . . . . . . DZ 120
Victor Thorn (Bd) . . . . . G 121
Willy Georgen (R.) . . . . F 123
Wilson (R.) . . . . . . . . . . . CZ 124
Winston Churchill (Pl.) . CZ 126
10-Septembre (Av. du) . . . . . . . . . . . CZ 127

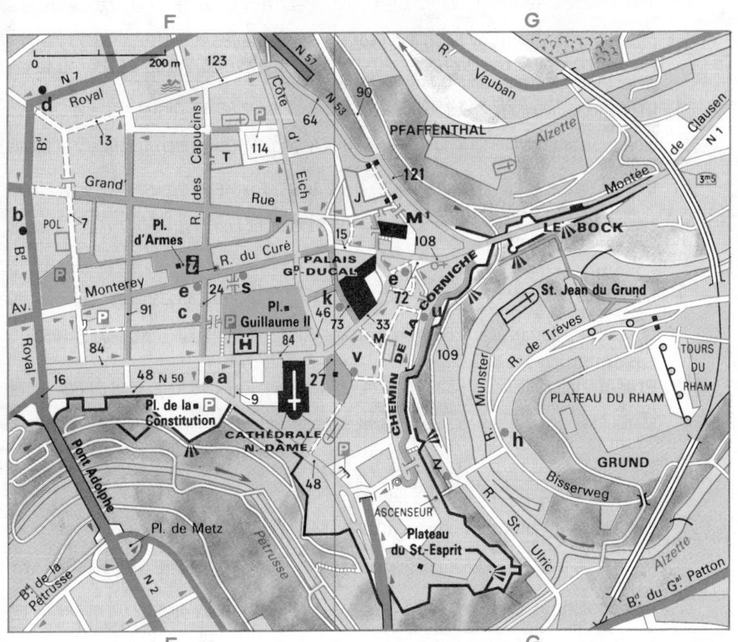

### Luxembourg-Centre

**Le Royal,** bd Royal 12, 2449, 241 61 61, *Fax 22 59 48*, - 25-350. F d
Meals see rest ***La Pomme Cannelle*** below - ***Le Jardin*** *Lunch 1080* - a la carte approx. 1300 - **190 rm** 8200/12500, 20 suites.

**Gd H. Cravat,** bd Roosevelt 29, 2450, 22 19 75, *Telex 2846, Fax 22 67 11* - rest, - 25. F a
Meals (Pub-rest) *(closed July-August)* *Lunch 490* - 950/1250 - **58 rm** 5900/7200.

**Rix** without rest, bd Royal 20, 2449, 47 16 66, *Fax 22 75 35* - . F b
*closed 18 December-4 January* - **20 rm** 4380/6480.

**Clairefontaine** (Tintinger), pl. de Clairefontaine 9, 1341, 46 22 11, *Fax 47 08 21*, - . G v
*closed Sunday dinner, Monday, 9 February-2 March and 15 to 31 August* - **Meals** *Lunch 1750* - 2560, a la carte approx. 2200
**Spec.** Foie gras d'oie et gelée au Porto. Poularde de Bresse en vessie, sauce Albufera. Tronçon de lotte à l'ardennaise. **Wines** Pinot gris, Riesling.

**St-Michel** (Glauben) 1st floor, r. Eau 32, 1449, 22 32 15, *Fax 46 25 93*, « In the old city, rustic interior » - G e
*closed Saturday lunch, Sunday, Bank Holidays, 1 to 17 August and 24 December-4 January* - **Meals** *Lunch 1750* - 3300 b.i., a la carte 2250/2700
**Spec.** Carpaccio de lotte et saumon parfumé au citron vert. Filet de St-Pierre au coulis de truffes (January-March). Pigeonneau à la fricassée de champignons des bois et ravioles de foie gras. **Wines** Riesling, Pinot gris.

**La Pomme Cannelle** (at Le Royal H.), bd Royal 12, 2449, 241 61 61, *Fax 22 59 48*, « Indian Empire style interior atmosphere » - . F d
*closed Saturday lunch, Sunday and Bank Holidays* - **Meals** *Lunch 1450* - 1920.

**Speltz,** r. Chimay 8, 1333, 47 49 50, *Fax 47 46 77*, - F c
*closed Saturday, Sunday, Bank Holidays, 11 to 19 April, 1 to 16 August and 24 December-3 January* - **Meals** 1450/2350.

**La Lorraine,** pl. d'Armes 7, 1136, 47 46 20, *Fax 47 09 64*, , Oyster bar and Seafood - . F e
*closed Sunday and 15 to 31 August* - **Meals** a la carte 1700/2400.

**Jan Schneidewind,** r. Curé 20, 1368, 22 26 18, *Fax 46 24 40*, , Seafood - . F s
*closed Monday, Saturday lunch and February* - **Meals** 1480/1980 b.i.

**Poêle d'Or,** r. Marché-aux-Herbes 20, 1728, 22 26 06, *Fax 22 26 05* -
*closed Monday dinner and Tuesday* - **Meals** *Lunch 990* - a la carte approx. 1300. G k

**L'Océan,** r. Louvigny 7, 1946, 22 88 66, *Fax 22 88 67*, Oyster bar and Seafood - F f
*closed Sunday dinner, Monday, 6 to 30 July and 24 December-4 January* - **Meals** a la carte 1550/2000.

**Breedewee,** r. Large 9, 1917, 22 26 96, *Fax 46 77 20*, , « Terrace with < Grund » - G u
*closed Sunday, last week August-first week September and first week January* - **Meals** *Lunch 550* - 1000/1200.

### Luxembourg-Grund

**Kamakura,** r. Münster 4, 2160, 47 06 04, *Fax 46 73 30*, Japanese cuisine - . G h
*closed lunch Saturday and Bank Holidays and Sunday* - **Meals** *Lunch 360* - 755/1650.

### Luxembourg-Station

**President,** pl. de la Gare 32, 1024, 48 61 61, *Telex 1510, Fax 48 61 80* - - 40. rest DZ v
**Meals** (dinner only) *(closed Sunday, Bank Holidays and August)* a la carte approx. 1400 - **35 rm** 4400/6500.

**City** without rest, r. Strasbourg 1, 2561, 29 11 22, *Fax 29 11 33* - - 25-100. DZ k
**35 rm** 3950/5350.

**Christophe Colomb,** r. Anvers 10, 1130, 408 41 41, *Fax 40 84 08*, - , rest, . CZ h
**Meals** (Pub-rest) *(closed Saturday and Sunday)* *Lunch 340* - a la carte 850/1300 - **24 rm** 3600/3950.

**International,** pl. de la Gare 20, 1616, 48 59 11, *Fax 49 32 27* - - 25-50. rm DZ z
**Meals** *(closed 22 December-10 January)* 1450 - **48 rm** 3950/7750, 1 suite.

**Arcotel** without rest, 1st floor, av. de la Gare 43, ✉ 1611, ✆ 49 40 01, *Fax 40 56 24* – 🛗 TV ☎. AE ⓓ E VISA. ✗ DZ a
22 rm ☐ 4800.

**Central Molitor,** av. de la Liberté 28, ✉ 1930, ✆ 48 99 11, *Fax 48 33 82* – 🛗, ▤ rest, TV ☎ 🚗. AE ⓓ E VISA CDZ x
Meals *(closed Saturday, Sunday dinner and 21 December-3 January)* *Lunch 360* – 750 – **36 rm** ☐ 3400/4400.

**Marco Polo** without rest, r. Fort Neipperg 27, ✉ 2230, ✆ 406 41 41, *Fax 40 48 84* – 🛗 TV ☎ 🚗. AE ⓓ E VISA DZ d
**18 rm** ☐ 3600/3950.

**Aub. Le Châtelet** (annex 🏠 - 9 rm), bd de la Pétrusse 2, ✉ 2320, ✆ 40 21 01, *Fax 40 36 66* – 🛗 TV ☎ P. AE ⓓ E VISA CZ e
Meals (dinner residents only) – **33 rm** ☐ 2300/4700.

**Cordial** 1st floor, pl. de Paris 1, ✉ 2314, ✆ 48 85 38, *Fax 40 77 76* – E VISA DZ b
*closed Friday, Saturday lunch, carnival week and 15 July-15 August* – **Meals** 1450/2650.

**Italia** with rm, r. Anvers 15, ✉ 1130, ✆ 48 66 26, *Fax 48 08 07*, 🏖, Partly Italian cuisine – TV ☎. AE ⓓ E VISA CZ f
Meals a la carte 1150/1800 – **20 rm** ☐ 2500/3100.

## Suburbs

**Airport** *NE : 8 km :*

**Sheraton Aérogolf** 🐌, rte de Trèves 1, ✉ 1019, ✆ 34 05 71, *Fax 34 02 17* – 🛗 ⇆ ▤ TV ☎ P – 🏛 25-120. AE ⓓ E VISA
Meals ***Le Montgolfier*** (open until midnight) *Lunch 900* - a la carte 1100/1700 – ☐ 590 – **137 rm** 6350/9050, 8 suites.

**Ibis,** rte de Trèves, ✉ 2632, ✆ 43 88 01, *Fax 43 88 02*, ⋖ – 🛗 ▤ TV ☎ P – 🏛 25-80. AE ⓓ E VISA
Meals *Lunch 380* – 850 – **120 rm** ☐ 2900/3700.

**Trust Inn** without rest, r. Neudorf 679, ✉ 2220, ✆ 42 30 51, *Fax 42 30 56* – ▤ TV ☎ P. AE ⓓ E VISA
☐ 200 – **7 rm** 1700/2400.

**Le Grimpereau,** r. Cents 140, ✉ 1319, ✆ 43 67 87, *Fax 42 60 26*, 🏖 – P. AE E VISA. ✗
*closed Tuesday July-15 September, Monday, 1 week carnival, 3 weeks August and 1 week All Saints* – **Meals** 1250/1550.

**at Belair** C *Luxembourg :*

**Parc Belair** M 🐌, av. du X Septembre 109, ✉ 2551, ✆ 44 23 23, *Fax 44 44 84*, ⋖ – 🛗 ⇆, ▤ rest, TV ☎ 🚗 – 🏛 25-60. AE ⓓ E VISA
Meals (dinner only except Sunday) a la carte 1100/1500 – **45 rm** ☐ 6150/6700, 7 suites.

**Astoria,** av. du X Septembre 44, ✉ 2550, ✆ 44 62 23, *Fax 45 82 96*, 🏖 – ▤– 🏛 25. AE ⓓ E VISA CZ a
*closed Saturday lunch and dinner Sunday and Monday* – **Meals** 1450.

**Thailand,** av. Gaston Diderich 72, ✉ 1420, ✆ 44 27 66, *Fax 37 91 73*, Thaï cuisine – AE ⓓ E VISA. ✗
*closed Monday, Saturday lunch and 15 August-4 September* – **Meals** *Lunch 690* – a la carte 1150/1500.

**at Dommeldange** *(Dummeldéng) N : 5,5 km* C *Luxembourg :*

**Inter.Continental** 🐌, r. Jean Engling 12, ✉ 1466, ✆ 4 37 81, *Fax 43 60 95*, ⋖, 🏖, 🏋, ≘s, 🏊 – 🛗 ⇆ ▤ TV ☎ P – 🏛 25-360. AE ⓓ E VISA JCB. ✗ rest
Meals ***Les Continents*** *(closed August and lunch Saturday and Sunday)* a la carte 1650/2500 – ***Café Stiffchen*** a la carte 1050/1500 – ☐ 690 – **324 rm** 7200/9450, 15 suites.

**Parc,** rte d'Echternach 120, ✉ 1453, ✆ 43 56 43, *Fax 43 69 03*, 🏋, ≘s, 🏊, 🌳, 🎾 – 🛗 TV ☎ ♿ P – 🏛 40-1500. AE ⓓ E VISA
Meals (open until 11.30 p.m.) *Lunch 750* – a la carte 850/1300 – **218 rm** ☐ 3800/5600, 3 suites.

**Host. du Grünewald,** rte d'Echternach 10, ✉ 1453, ✆ 43 18 82 and 42 03 14 (rest), *Fax 42 06 46 and 42 03 14 (rest)*, 🌳 – 🛗, ▤ rest, TV ☎ P – 🏛 25-40. AE ⓓ E VISA. ✗ rest
Meals *(closed Saturday lunch, Sunday, Bank Holidays and 1 to 22 January)* *Lunch 1590* – a la carte 1800/2450 – **23 rm** ☐ 3900/4900, 2 suites.

**at Gasperich** *(Gaasperech) S : 4 km* C *Luxembourg :*

**Inn Side** M, r. Henri Schnadt 1 (Cloche d'Or), ✉ 2530, ✆ 490 00 61, *Fax 49 06 80*, 🏖, « Design », 🏋, ≘s – 🛗 ⇆, ▤ rest, TV ☎ ♿ 🚗 – 🏛 25-200. AE ⓓ E VISA. ✗
Meals (buffets) a la carte approx. 1300 – **158 rm** ☐ 4900/9200.

**Upland of Kirchberg** *(Kiirchbierg)*

**Sofitel** M, r. Fort Niedergrünewald 6 (European Centre), ✉ 2015, ℘ 43 77 61, *Fax 42 50 91* – ☎ – 25-300. AE ⓓ E VISA. rest EY a
Meals ***Brasserie Europa*** Lunch 1200 – a la carte 1350/1650 – 750 – **100 rm** 8500/9000, 4 suites.

**Novotel,** r. Fort Niedergrünewald 6 (European Centre), ✉ 2015, ℘ 43 77 61, *Fax 43 86 58*, – ☎ – 25-300. AE ⓓ E VISA. rest
**Meals** (open until midnight) Lunch 750 – a la carte approx. 1200 – 500 – **258 rm** 4900, 1 suite. EY a

**at the skating-rink of Kockelscheuer** *(Kockelscheier) S by N 31 :*

**Patin d'Or** (Berring), rte de Bettembourg 40, ✉ 1899, ℘ 22 64 99, *Fax 40 40 11* – P. AE ⓓ E VISA.
*closed Saturday, Sunday, Bank Holidays, first week September and Christmas-New Year* – **Meals** 2000, a la carte 2200/2850
**Spec.** Salade de homard aux herbes du jardin et beurre de Sauternes. Médaillon de lotte au jambon de Parme et basilic. Pied de porc truffé et farci à l'ancienne, lentilles vertes.
**Wines** Pinot gris, Riesling Koëppchen.

**at Limpertsberg** *(Lampertsbierg)* C *Luxembourg :*

**Bouzonviller,** r. A. Unden 138, ✉ 2652, ℘ 47 22 59, *Fax 46 43 89*, – . AE E VISA
*closed Saturday, Sunday, Bank Holidays, 1 week Easter, last week July-first 2 weeks August and Christmas-New Year* – **Meals** Lunch 1600 – a la carte approx. 2100.

**at Rollingergrund** *(Rolléngergronn)* C *Luxembourg :*

**Sieweburen,** r. Septfontaines 36, ✉ 2534, ℘ 44 23 56, *Fax 44 23 53*, , « Woodland setting », – ☎ P. E VISA
*closed 23 December-6 January* – **Meals** (Pub rest) *(closed Wednesday)* Lunch 360 – a la carte 900/1500 – **14 rm** 2700/3700.

**Environs**

**at Bridel** *(Briddel) by N 12 : 7 km* C *Kopstal pop. 2 974 :*

**Le Rondeau,** r. Luxembourg 82, ✉ 8140, ℘ 33 94 73, *Fax 33 37 46* – P. AE ⓓ E VISA
*closed Monday dinner, Tuesday, last 3 weeks August and 2 weeks January* – **Meals** Lunch 900 – 980/1900.

**at Hesperange** *(Hesper) SE : 5,5 km – pop. 9 918 :*

**L'Agath** (Steichen) with rm, rte de Thionville 274 (Howald), ✉ 5884, ℘ 48 86 87, *Fax 48 55 05*, – ☎ P – 60. AE ⓓ E VISA
*closed Saturday lunch, Sunday dinner, Monday, July and 21 December-4 January* – **Meals** Lunch 1600 – 1850, a la carte approx. 2300 – **5 rm** 2200/3200
**Spec.** Carpaccio infusé à la truffe, salade et copeaux de foie gras. Filets de sole au Riesling et ciboulette. Poularde maison aux morilles. **Wines** Riesling, Pinot gris.

**Klein,** rte de Thionville 432, ✉ 5886, ℘ 36 08 42, *Fax 36 08 43* – AE E VISA
*closed Sunday dinner and Monday* – **Meals** Lunch 980 – 1400/2500.

**at Strassen** *(Strossen) W : 4 km – pop. 4 919 :*

**L'Olivier** with apartments, rte d'Arlon 140, ✉ 8008, ℘ 31 36 66, *Fax 31 36 27* – ☎ P – 25-350. AE ⓓ E VISA
Meals see rest ***La Cime*** below – **42 rm** 3290/4990, 4 suites.

**La Cime** - (at L'Olivier H.), rte d'Arlon 140a, ✉ 8008, ℘ 31 88 13, *Fax 31 36 27*, – P. AE ⓓ E VISA
*closed Sunday, Bank Holidays and 3 to 17 August* – **Meals** – 990/1590.

**Le Nouveau Riquewihr,** rte d'Arlon 373, ✉ 8011, ℘ 31 99 80, *Fax 31 97 05*, – P. AE ⓓ E VISA
*closed Sunday, 24, 25, 26 and 31 December and 1 January* – **Meals** Lunch 980 – a la carte approx. 1300.

**at Walferdange** *(Walfer) N : 5 km – pop. 5 818 :*

**Moris** M, pl. des Martyrs, ✉ 7201, ℘ 330 10 51, *Fax 33 30 70*, – , rest, ☎ P – 50. AE ⓓ E VISA
Meals 1050/1180 – **23 rm** 2700/3700.

**l'Etiquette,** rte de Diekirch 50, ✉ 7220, ℘ 33 51 67, *Fax 33 51 69*, – P. AE ⓓ E VISA
Meals 750/1600.

**Echternach** *(Iechternach)* 215 D 6 *and* 409 M 6 - *pop. 4 211 - 35 km.*

**at Geyershaff** *(Geieschhaff) SW : 6,5 km by E 27* C *Bech pop. 787 :*

XXX ✿✿ **La Bergerie** (Phal), ✉ 6251, ☎ 79 04 64, *Fax 79 07 71*, ≤, 🏠, « Floral country setting » - P. AE ⓓ E VISA
*closed Sunday dinner, Monday and January-February* - **Meals** *Lunch 1650* - 2650 (2 pers. min.), a la carte 2350/2650
**Spec.** Rosace de St-Jacques. Croustillant d'agneau aux amandes. Soufflé aux chocolat et son cœur glacé à la banane. **Wines** Pinot gris, Riesling.

**Paliseul** *6850 Luxembourg belge (Belgium)* 214 ⑯ *and* 409 I 6 - *pop. 4 853 - 94 km.*

XXX ✿✿ **Au Gastronome** (Libotte) with rm, r. Bouillon 2 (Paliseul-Gare) ☎ 53 30 64, *Fax 53 38 91*, « Ardennes country Inn, floral garden with ⛱ » - ▤ TV ☎ P. AE ⓓ E VISA
*closed Sunday dinner and Monday except Bank Holidays, last week June-first week July and 1 January dinner-7 February* - **Meals** *Lunch 1300* - 2980 (2 pers. min.), a la carte 2150/2800 - **9 rm** ☕ 3300/4800
**Spec.** Gâteau de pied de porc poêlé à la pancetta, girolles et queues d'écrevisses. Dos de turbot au four à l'ail et à la coriandre, sauce hollandaise au cresson. Cochon de lait rôti au miel, sauce aux épices.

# AMSTERDAM

*Noord-Holland* 210 J 8, 211 J 8 *and* 408 G 4 – ㉑ S – *Pop. 718 119*

*Brussels 204 – Düsseldorf 227 – The Hague 60 – Luxembourg 419 – Rotterdam 76.*

*Stationsplein,* ✉ *1012 AB* ☎ *0-900-400 40 40, Fax (020) 625 28 69.*

18 *Bauduinlaan 35* ✉ *1165 NE at Halfweg (W : 6 km)* ☎ *(020) 497 78 66, Fax (020) 497 59 66*
9 *Zwarte Laantje 4* ✉ *1099 CE at Duivendrecht (S : 5 km)* ☎ *(020) 694 36 50, Fax (020) 663 46 21* – 18 9 *Buikslotermeerdijk 41* ✉ *1027 AC* ☎ *(020) 632 56 50, Fax (020) 634 35 06* – 18 *Abcouderstraatweg 46* ✉ *1105 AA à Holendrecht* ☎ *(0294) 28 12 41, Fax (0294) 28 63 47.*

✈ *at Schiphol SW : 9,5 km* ☎ *(020) 601 91 11.*

**See:** *Old Amsterdam★★★ – The canals★★★ (Grachten) : Boat trips★ (Rondvaart) – Dam : Royal Palace★ (Koninklijk Paleis)* LY, *pulpit★ in the New Church★ (Nieuwe Kerk)* LY – *Beguine Convent★★ (Begijnhof)* LY – *Flower market★ (Bloemenmarkt)* LY – *Cromhout Houses★ (Cromhouthuizen) – Reguliersgracht ≤★ – Keizersgracht ≤★ – ≤★ from the sluice bridge Oudezijds Kolk-Oudezijds Voorburgwal* MX – *Groenburgwal ≤★* LMY – *Thin Bridge★ (Magere Brug)* MZ – *Artis★ (Zoological Garden) – Westerkerk★* KX.

**Museums:** *Amsterdam Historical Museum★★ (Amsterdams Historisch Museum)* LY – *Madame Tussaud's Scenerama★ : wax museum* LY **M¹** – *Rijksmuseum★★★* KZ – *Vincent van Gogh National Museum★★★ (Rijksmuseum) – Municipal★★ (Stedelijk Museum) : Modern Art – Amstelkringmuseum "Our Dear Lord in the Attic"★ (Museum Amstelkring Ons' Lieve Heer op Solder) : clandestine chapel* MX **M⁴** – *Rembrandt's House★ (Rembrandthuis) : works by the master* MY **M⁵** – *Jewish Museum★ (Joods Historisch Museum)* MY **M⁶** – *Allard Pierson★ : antiquities* LY **M⁷** – *Tropical Museum★ (Tropenmuseum) – Netherlands Maritime History Museum★ (Nederlands Scheepvaart Museum) – Anne Frank's House★★* KX **M⁸**.

*Casino, Max Euweplein 62,* ✉ *1017 MB (near Leidseplein)* ☎ *(020) 620 10 06, Fax (020) 620 36 66.*

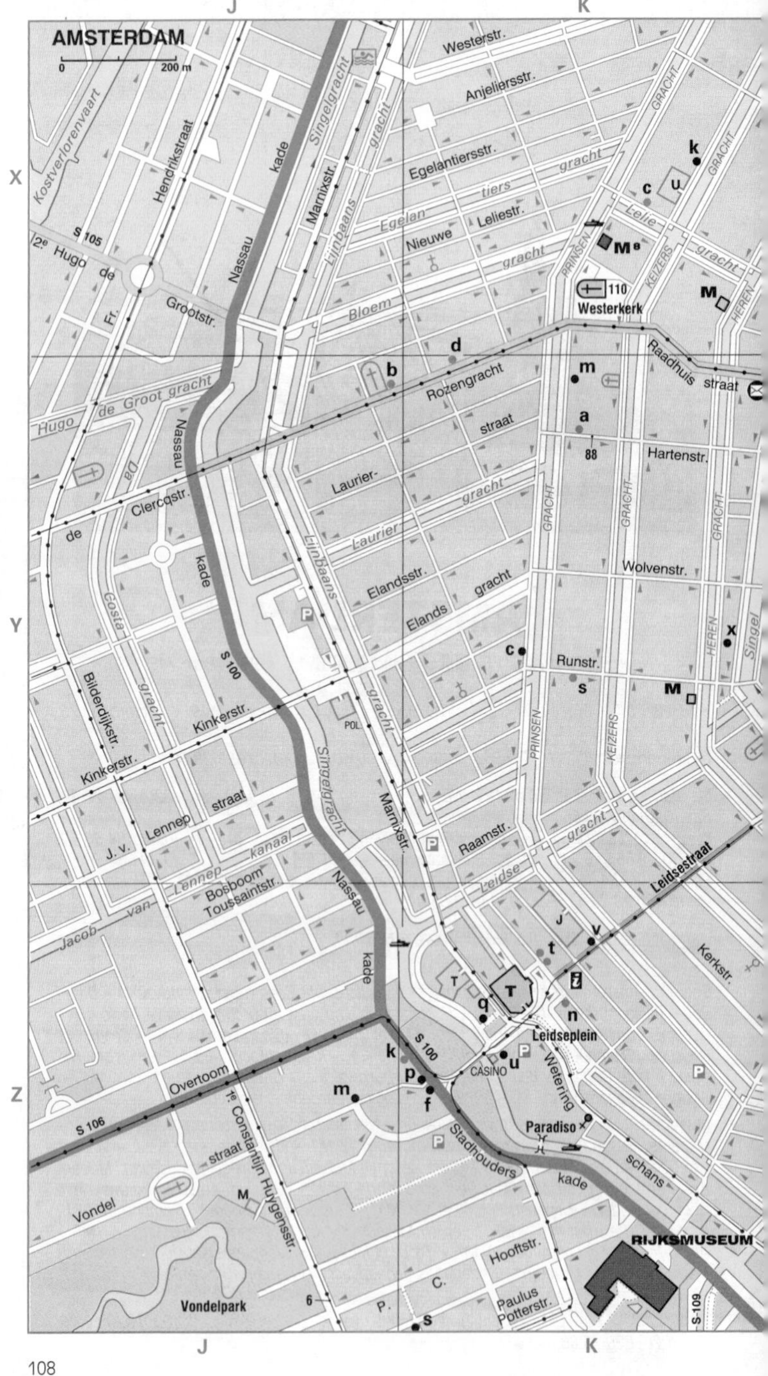

AMSTERDAM
0
200 m
J
K
X
Y
Z
Westerstr.
Anjeliersstr.
Egelantiersstr.
Egelantiersgracht
Leliestr.
Nieuwe
Bloemgracht
Westerkerk
110
Raadhuisstraat
Rozengracht
Laurier-straat
Lauriergracht
Elandsstr.
Elandsgracht
Runstr.
Hartenstr.
Wolvenstr.
Raamstr.
Leidsegracht
Leidsestraat
Kerkstr.
Leidseplein
CASINO
Paradiso
Weteringschans
Stadhouderskade
Hooftstr.
P. C.
Paulus Potterstr.
RIJKSMUSEUM
Vondelpark
Vondelstraat
1e Constantijn Huygensstr.
Overtoom
Nassaukade
Singelgracht
Marnixstr.
Lijnbaansgracht
Kostverlorenvaart
Hendrikstraat
2e Hugo de Grootstr.
Fr.
Hugo de Groot gracht
Da Costa gracht
de Clercqstr.
Bilderdijkstr.
Kinkerstr.
J. v. Lennepstraat
Lennepkanaal
Jacob van Lennep
Bosboom Toussaintstr.
PRINSENGRACHT
KEIZERSGRACHT
HERENGRACHT
Singel
S 105
S 100
S 106
S-109
POL
88
6

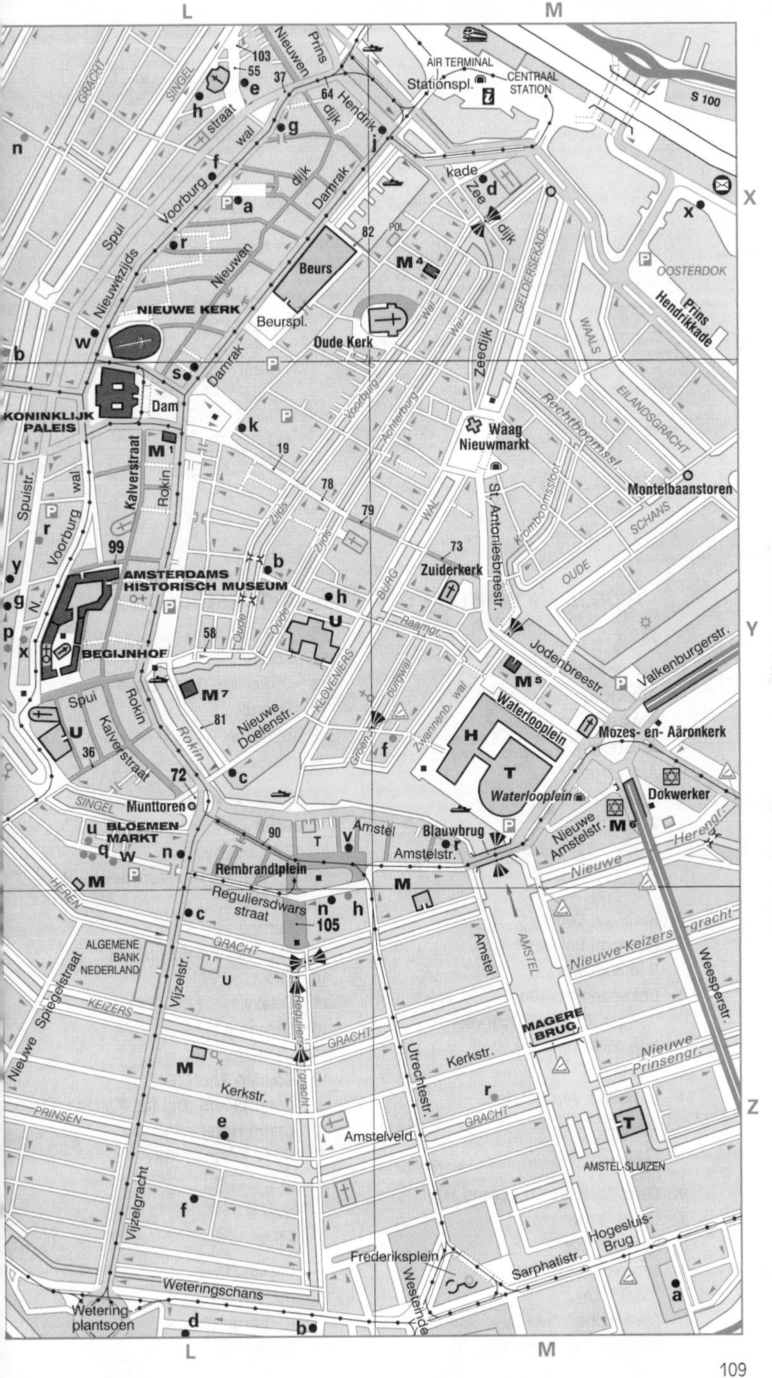
L
M
AIR TERMINAL
CENTRAAL STATION
Stationspl.
S 100
OOSTERDOK
Prins Hendrikkade
Beurs
Beurspl.
NIEUWE KERK
Oude Kerk
KONINKLIJK PALEIS
Dam
Damrak
Waag Nieuwmarkt
Montelbaanstoren
Zuiderkerk
AMSTERDAMS HISTORISCH MUSEUM
BEGIJNHOF
Kalverstraat
Rokin
Spui
Waterlooplein
Mozes- en- Aäronkerk
Dokwerker
Jodenbreestr.
Valkenburgerstr.
Munttoren
BLOEMEN MARKT
Rembrandtplein
Reguliersdwars straat
Amstelstr.
Blauwbrug
ALGEMENE BANK NEDERLAND
Vijzelstr.
MAGERE BRUG
Amstelveld
Utrechtestr.
Kerkstr.
Weesperstr.
AMSTEL-SLUIZEN
Hogesluis-Brug
Sarphatistr.
Frederiksplein
Weteringschans
Wetering-plantsoen
Vijzelgracht
Westeinde
X
Y
Z

## STREET INDEX TO AMSTERDAM TOWN PLAN



## *Alphabetical listing of hotels and restaurants*

# Establishments according to style of cuisine

## Buffets

12 Greenhouse (at Hilton Schiphol H.) *Env. at Schiphol*

## Pub rest – Brasseries

7 American *Centre*
7 Amstel Bar and Brasserie (The) (at Amstel H.) *Centre*
9 Bols Taverne *Centre*
11 Brasserie Camelia (at Okura H.) *South and West Q.*
7 Brasserie De Palmboom (at Radisson SAS H.) *Centre*
7 Brasserie Reflet (at Gd H. Krasnapolsky H.) *Centre*
11 Brasserie Van Baerle *Rijksmuseum*
7 Café Barbizon (at Barbizon Palace H.) *Centre*
7 Café Pulitzer (at Pulitzer H.) *Centre*
9 Café Roux (at The Grand H.) *Centre*
10 Garage (Le) *Rijksmuseum*
11 Keyzer *Rijksmuseum*
8 Die Port van Cleve *Centre*
12 Run-Way Café (at Sheraton Schiphol H.) *Env. at Schiphol*
8 Tulip Inn *Centre*

## Seafood – Oyster bar

9 Oesterbar (De) *Centre*
9 Pêcheur (Le) *Centre*
12 Pescadou (Le) *Env. at Amstelveen*

## Asian

10 Sea Palace *Centre*

## Chinese

9 Sichuan Food *Centre*

## Dutch regional

7 Dorrius (at Holiday Inn Crowne Plaza H.) *Centre*
8 Roode Leeuw (De) (at Amsterdam H.) *Centre*

## Indian

11 Pakistan *South and West Q.*

## Indonesian

9 Indrapura *Centre*
9 Long Pura *Centre*
10 Radèn Mas *Rijksmuseum*

## Italian

7 Caruso (at Jolly Carlton H.) *Centre*
11 Roberto's (at Hilton H.) *South and West Q.*
8 Tulip Inn *Centre*

## Japanese

10 Edo and Kyo (at Gd H. Krasnapolsky H.) *Centre*
9 Hosokawa *Centre*
11 Sazanka (at Okura H.) *South and West Q.*
11 Yamazato (at Okura H.) *South and West Q.*

## Oriental

9 Dynasty *Centre*
9 Manchurian *Centre*

## Swiss

7 Swissôtel *Centre*

## Thaï

10 Tom Yam *Centre*

## Centre

**Amstel**, Prof. Tulpplein 1, 1018 GX, (0 20) 622 60 60, *Fax (0 20) 622 58 08*, <, , , , , - - 25-180. AE E VISA JCB.
Meals see rest ***La Rive*** below - ***The Amstel Bar and Brasserie*** (open until 11.30 p.m.) a la carte approx. 65 - 40 - **64 rm** 775/925, 15 suites. MZ a

**The Grand**, O.Z. Voorburgwal 197, 1012 EX, (0 20) 555 31 11, *Fax (0 20) 555 32 22*, « Historic building, authentic Art Nouveau lounges, inner garden », , , - - 25-300. AE E VISA JCB. LY b
Meals see rest ***Café Roux*** below - 33 - **138 rm** 645/745, 13 suites.

**Europe,** Nieuwe Doelenstraat 2, 1012 CP, (0 20) 531 17 77, *Fax (0 20) 531 17 78*, <, , « Collection of Dutch landscape paintings in late 19C lounge », , , , - - 25-80. AE E VISA JCB LY c
Meals see rest ***Excelsior*** below - ***Le Relais*** *Lunch 43* - 45/53 - 40 - **94 rm** 420/820, 6 suites.

**Barbizon Palace,** Prins Hendrikkade 59, 1012 AD, (0 20) 556 45 64, *Fax (0 20) 624 33 53*, , - - 25-300. AE E VISA JCB. rest MX d
Meals see rest ***Vermeer*** below - ***Café Barbizon*** (open until 11 p.m.) *Lunch 48* - a la carte 59/86 - 35 - **265 rm** 395/545, 3 suites.

**Gd H. Krasnapolsky,** Dam 9, 1012 JS, (0 20) 554 91 11, *Fax (0 20) 622 86 07*, « 19C winter garden », , - , rm, - 25-700. AE E VISA JCB LY k
Meals see rest ***Edo and Kyo*** below - ***Brasserie Reflet*** (dinner only until 11 p.m.) 60 - 35 - **415 rm** 400/535, 14 suites.

**Radisson SAS** M, Rusland 17, 1012 CK, (0 20) 623 12 31, *Fax (0 20) 520 82 00*, « Patio with 18C presbytery », , , - - 25-300. AE E VISA JCB. LY h
Meals ***Laxen Oxen*** (dinner only) 58/68 - ***Brasserie De Palmboom*** 58 - 33 - **242 rm** 475/495, 1 suite.

**Holiday Inn Crowne Plaza,** N.Z. Voorburgwal 5, 1012 RC, (0 20) 620 05 00 and 420 22 24 (rest), *Fax (0 20) 620 11 73 and 420 04 65 (rest)*, , , - - 25-260. AE E VISA JCB LX g
Meals ***Dorrius*** (partly Dutch regional cooking, dinner only until 11 p.m.) a la carte 45/83 - 43 - **268 rm** 385/510, 2 suites.

**Pulitzer**, Prinsengracht 323, 1016 GZ, (0 20) 523 52 35, *Fax (0 20) 627 67 53*, , « 24 terraced canalside houses from 17 and 18C », , - - 25-150. AE E VISA JCB. rest KY m
Meals see rest ***De Goudsbloem*** below - ***Café Pulitzer*** (lunch only mid November-mid March) *Lunch 33* - 45 - **230 rm** 405/595, 2 suites.

**Victoria,** Damrak 1, 1012 LG, (0 20) 623 42 55, *Fax (0 20) 625 29 97*, , , - - 30-150. AE E VISA JCB LMX j
Meals 57 - 30 - **296 rm** 405, 9 suites.

**Renaissance,** Kattengat 1, 1012 SZ, (0 20) 621 22 23, *Fax (0 20) 627 52 45*, « Contemporary art collection », , , - - 25-400. AE E VISA JCB. rest LX e
Meals (open until 11 p.m.) *Lunch 45* - a la carte 68/88 - 33 - **370 rm** 395/455, 6 suites.

**Jolly Carlton,** Vijzelstraat 4, 1017 HK, (0 20) 622 22 66 and 623 83 20 (rest), *Telex 11670, Fax (0 20) 626 61 83* - - 25-180. AE E VISA JCB. rest LY n
Meals ***Caruso*** (Italian cuisine, dinner only until 11 p.m.) *(closed Monday)* a la carte 79/110 - 40 - **219 rm** 300/400.

**American,** Leidsekade 97, 1017 PN, (0 20) 624 53 22, *Fax (0 20) 625 32 36*, , , , - , rm, - 40-160. AE E VISA JCB. KZ q
Meals (Art Deco style pub rest) *Lunch 50* - a la carte 69/87 - 32 - **188 rm** 575.

**Swissôtel,** Damrak 95, 1012 LP, (0 20) 626 00 66, *Fax (0 20) 627 09 82* - - 25-60. AE E VISA JCB. LXY s
Meals (Swiss cuisine) *Lunch 37* - a la carte approx. 60 - 28 - **109 rm** 350/500.

**Sofitel** without rest, N.Z. Voorburgwal 67, 1012 RE, (0 20) 627 59 00, *Fax (0 20) 623 89 32*, , - - 25-80. AE E VISA LX r
30 - **148 rm** 360/399.

**Canal Crown** without rest, Herengracht 519, 1017 BV, (0 20) 420 00 55, *Fax (0 20) 420 09 93* - . AE E VISA LZ c
25 - **57 rm** 180/350.

**Ambassade** without rest, Herengracht 341, ✉ 1016 AZ, ☎ (0 20) 626 23 33, *Fax (0 20) 624 53 21*, ≤, « Typical 17C terraced houses » – |♦| TV ☎. AE ⓓ E VISA KY x
**46 rm** ☐ 245/325, 6 suites.

**Schiller,** Rembrandtsplein 26, ✉ 1017 CV, ☎ (0 20) 554 07 77, *Fax (0 20) 626 68 31*, 舍, Ⅎδ – |♦| ⋟ TV ☎. AE ⓓ E VISA JCB. ⋟ LZ n
**Meals** (open until 11 p.m.) a la carte approx. 55 – ☐ 30 – **90 rm** 320/455, 2 suites.

**Inntel** Ⓜ without rest, Nieuwezijdskolk 19, ✉ 1012 PV, ☎ (0 20) 530 18 18, *Fax (0 20) 422 19 19* – |♦| ⋟ ▤ TV ☎ ♿. AE ⓓ E VISA JCB LX a
☐ 28 – **236 rm** 325/350.

**Tulip Inn,** Spuistraat 288, ✉ 1012 VX, ☎ (0 20) 420 45 45, *Fax (0 20) 420 43 00*, ⚓ – |♦| ⋟ ▤ TV ☎ ♿ 🚗. AE ⓓ E VISA JCB. ⋟ LY g
**Meals** (Pub rest, partly Italian cuisine) a la carte approx. 45 – ☐ 20 – **208 rm** ☐ 225/275.

**Eden,** Amstel 144, ✉ 1017 AE, ☎ (0 20) 530 78 88, *Fax (0 20) 624 29 46*, ⚓ – |♦| ⋟ TV ☎ ♿. AE ⓓ E VISA JCB. ⋟ MY r
**Meals** a la carte 45/60 – **338 rm** ☐ 255/275.

**Mercure Arthur Frommer** without rest, Noorderstraat 46, ✉ 1017 TV, ☎ (0 20) 622 03 28, *Fax (0 20) 620 32 08* – |♦| ⋟ ▤ TV ☎ 🚗 P. AE ⓓ E VISA LZ f
☐ 24 – **90 rm** 170/275.

**Cok City** Ⓜ without rest, N.Z. Voorburgwal 50, ✉ 1012 SC, ☎ (0 20) 422 00 11, *Fax (0 20) 420 03 57* – |♦| ⋟ TV ☎. AE ⓓ E VISA JCB LX f
**106 rm** ☐ 225/265.

**Estheréa** without rest, Singel 305, ✉ 1012 WJ, ☎ (0 20) 624 51 46, *Fax (0 20) 623 90 01* – |♦| TV ☎. AE ⓓ E VISA JCB LY y
**70 rm** ☐ 335/385.

**Canal House** ⛵ without rest, Keizersgracht 148, ✉ 1015 CX, ☎ (0 20) 622 51 82, *Fax (0 20) 624 13 17*, « Antique furniture » – |♦| ☎. AE ⓓ E VISA JCB. ⋟ KX k
**26 rm** ☐ 270.

**Die Port van Cleve,** N.Z. Voorburgwal 178, ✉ 1012 SJ, ☎ (0 20) 624 48 60, *Fax (0 20) 622 02 40* – |♦| TV ☎ – 🎤 25-50. AE ⓓ E VISA JCB LX w
**Meals** (Brasserie) Lunch 43 – a la carte approx. 45 – **117 rm** ☐ 135/342.

**Amsterdam,** Damrak 93, ✉ 1012 LP, ☎ (0 20) 555 06 66, *Fax (0 20) 620 47 16* – |♦| ⋟ ▤ TV ☎. AE ⓓ E VISA JCB LXY s
**Meals** ***De Roode Leeuw*** (Dutch regional cooking) Lunch 38 - 50 – **80 rm** ☐ 204/240.

**Dikker en Thijs Fenice,** Prinsengracht 444, ✉ 1017 EK, ☎ (0 20) 626 77 21, *Fax (0 20) 625 89 86*, ⚓ – |♦| TV ☎ – 🎤 25. AE ⓓ E VISA JCB KZ v
***De Prinsenkelder*** (dinner only) a la carte 62/85 – **26 rm** ☐ 180/450.

**Caransa** without rest, Rembrandtsplein 19, ✉ 1017 CT, ☎ (0 20) 554 07 77, *Fax (0 20) 626 68 31* – |♦| ▤ TV ☎. AE ⓓ E VISA JCB. ⋟ LY v
☐ 30 – **66 rm** 300/435.

**Wiechmann** without rest, Prinsengracht 328, ✉ 1016 HX, ☎ (0 20) 626 33 21, *Fax (0 20) 626 89 62* – TV ☎. ⋟ – **38 rm** ☐ 250. KY c

**Asterisk** without rest, Den Texstraat 16, ✉ 1017 ZA, ☎ (0 20) 626 23 96, *Fax (0 20) 638 27 90* – |♦| TV ☎. E VISA – **29 rm** ☐ 149/185. LZ d

**Amstel Botel** without rest, Oosterdokskade 2, ✉ 1011 AE, ☎ (0 20) 626 42 47, *Fax (0 20) 639 19 52*, « Berthed boat » – |♦| TV ☎. AE ⓓ E VISA JCB. ⋟ MX x
☐ 11 – **176 rm** 113/153.

**La Rive** - (at Amstel H.), Prof. Tulpplein 1, ✉ 1018 GX, ☎ (0 20) 622 60 60, *Fax (0 20) 622 58 08*, ≤, 舍, « Amstel-side setting », ⚓ – ▤ P. AE ⓓ E VISA JCB. ⋟
✿✿ *closed Saturday lunch, Sunday and 1 to 11 January* – **Meals** Lunch 60 – 135/175, a la carte approx. 165 MZ a
**Spec.** Filet de rouget en persillade de jambon sec, crème de thon étuvée aux herbes. Loup fumé minute, vinaigrette aux truffes. Pigeonneau rôti parfumé au laurier, sauce salmis.

**Vermeer** - (at Barbizon Palace H.), Prins Hendrikkade 59, ✉ 1012 AD, ☎ (0 20) 556 48 85, *Fax (0 20) 624 33 53* – ▤ P. AE ⓓ E VISA JCB. ⋟ MX d
✿ *closed Saturday lunch, Sunday, 13 July-2 August and 26 December-10 January* – **Meals** Lunch 65 – 95/130, a la carte 100/148
**Spec.** Terrine de jambon Jabugo et foie d'oie en gelée de queue de bœuf. Turbot et truffe enrobés de spaghetti de pommes de terre. Quatre-quarts d'amandes et de chocolat.

**Excelsior** - (at Europe H.), Nieuwe Doelenstraat 2, ✉ 1012 CP, ☎ (0 20) 531 17 77, *Fax (0 20) 531 17 78*, ≤, 舍, Open until 11 p.m., ⚓ – ▤ P. AE ⓓ E VISA JCB
*closed Saturday lunch* – **Meals** Lunch 70 – 75/175 b.i. LY c

**De Goudsbloem** (at Pulitzer H.), Reestraat 8, ✉ 1016 GZ, ☎ (0 20) 523 52 35, *Fax (0 20) 627 67 53*, « Late 19C apothecary shop interior », ⚓ – ▤. AE ⓓ E VISA JCB. ⋟ – *closed 2 weeks July* – **Meals** (dinner only) a la carte 72/87. KY e

XXX **Christophe** (Royer), Leliegracht 46, ✉ 1015 DH, ✆ (0 20) 625 08 07, *Fax (0 20) 638 91 32* – ▤. AE ⓓ E VISA KX c
✿ *closed Sunday, Monday and early January* – **Meals** (dinner only) 85/105, a la carte 100/130
**Spec.** Vinaigrette de jeunes poireaux et langoustines (21 March-21 September). Turbot rôti aux épices, sauce au vin rouge. Pigeonneau à la marocaine.

XXX **D'Vijff Vlieghen,** Spuistraat 294, ✉ 1012 VX, ✆ (0 20) 624 83 69, *Fax (0 20) 623 64 04*, « Typical 17C houses », ⚓ – AE ⓓ E VISA JCB LY p
*closed 24 to 30 December and 1 January* – **Meals** (dinner only) a la carte 70/97.

XXX **'t Swarte Schaep** 1st floor, Korte Leidsedwarsstraat 24, ✉ 1017 RC, ✆ (0 20) 622 30 21, *Fax (0 20) 624 82 68*, Open until 11 p.m., « 17C Dutch interior » – ▤. AE ⓓ E VISA JCB KZ n
*closed 30 April, 25, 26 and 31 December and 1 January* – **Meals** Lunch 55 – a la carte 83/105.

XXX **Dynasty,** Reguliersdwarsstraat 30, ✉ 1017 BM, ✆ (0 20) 626 84 00, *Fax (0 20) 622 30 38*, 🏖, Oriental cuisine, « Terrace » – ▤. AE ⓓ E VISA. ✂ LY q
*closed Tuesday and January* – **Meals** (dinner only until 11 p.m.) 70/98.

XX **Het Tuynhuys,** Reguliersdwarsstraat 28, ✉ 1017 BM, ✆ (0 20) 627 66 03, *Fax (0 20) 627 66 03*, 🏖, « Terrace » – ▤. AE ⓓ E VISA LY q
**Meals** Lunch 55 – a la carte 83/102.

XX **Café Roux** (at The Grand H.), O.Z. Voorburgwal 197, ✉ 1012 EX, ✆ (0 20) 555 31 11, *Fax (0 20) 555 32 22*, 🏖, Open until 11 p.m. – ▤ Ⓟ. AE ⓓ E VISA JCB. ✂ LY b
☺ **Meals** Lunch 38 – 43.

XX **Les Quatre Canetons,** Prinsengracht 1111, ✉ 1017 JJ, ✆ (0 20) 624 63 07, *Fax (0 20) 638 45 99*, 🏖 – AE ⓓ E VISA JCB MZ r
*closed Sunday, Easter, Whitsun and New Year* – **Meals** Lunch 60 – 95/115.

XX **Bols Taverne,** Rozengracht 106, ✉ 1016 NH, ✆ (0 20) 624 57 52, *Fax (0 20) 620 41 94*, 🏖 – ▤. AE ⓓ E VISA JCB JKY b
*closed Sunday* – **Meals** Lunch 50 – 60/70.

XX **Tout Court,** Runstraat 13, ✉ 1016 GJ, ✆ (0 20) 625 86 37, *Fax (0 20) 625 44 11* – AE ⓓ E VISA KY s
☺ *closed late December-first week January* – **Meals** (dinner only until 11.30 p.m.) 53/105.

XX **Sancerre,** Reestraat 28, ✉ 1016 DN, ✆ (0 20) 627 87 94, *Fax (0 20) 623 87 49* – AE ⓓ E VISA JCB KY a
*closed 24 and 31 December and 1 January* – **Meals** (dinner only) a la carte 76/102.

XX **Sichuan Food,** Reguliersdwarsstraat 35, ✉ 1017 BK, ✆ (0 20) 626 93 27, *Fax (0 20) 627 72 81*, Chinese cuisine – ▤. AE ⓓ E VISA. ✂ LY u
✿ *closed 31 December* – **Meals** (dinner only until 11 p.m., booking essential) 58 (2 pers. min.), a la carte 60/85
**Spec.** Dim Sum. Canard laqué à la pékinoise. Huîtres sautées maison.

XX **Long Pura,** Rozengracht 46, ✉ 1016 ND, ✆ (0 20) 623 89 50, *Fax (0 20) 623 46 54*, Indonesian cuisine, « Exotic decor » – ▤. AE ⓓ E VISA. ✂ KXY d
**Meals** (dinner only until 11 p.m.) 55/95.

XX **Le Pêcheur,** Reguliersdwarsstraat 32, ✉ 1017 BM, ✆ (0 20) 624 31 21, *Fax (0 20) 624 31 21*, 🏖, Seafood, open until 11 p.m. – AE ⓓ E VISA JCB LY w
*closed Sunday* – **Meals** Lunch 52 b.i. – 66.

XX **d'theeboom,** Singel 210, ✉ 1016 AB, ✆ (0 20) 623 84 20, *Fax (0 20) 623 84 20*, 🏖 – AE ⓓ E VISA JCB LX b
*closed Saturday lunch, Sunday and 5 to 19 January* – **Meals** 48.

XX **Van Vlaanderen,** Weteringschans 175, ✉ 1017 XD, ✆ (0 20) 622 82 92, 🏖 – AE E VISA LZ k
☺ *closed Sunday, Monday, last 2 weeks July and 31 December-6 January* – **Meals** (dinner only) 58/68.

XX **Indrapura,** Rembrandtsplein 42, ✉ 1017 CV, ✆ (0 20) 623 73 29, *Fax (0 20) 624 90 78*, Indonesian cuisine – ▤. AE ⓓ E VISA JCB. ✂ LYZ h
**Meals** (dinner only until 11 p.m.) a la carte 47/76.

XX **Manchurian,** Leidseplein 10a, ✉ 1017 PT, ✆ (0 20) 623 13 30, *Fax (0 20) 626 21 05*, Oriental cuisine – ▤. AE ⓓ E VISA. ✂ KZ t
**Meals** 58/88.

XX **Hosokawa,** Max Euweplein 22, ✉ 1017 MB, ✆ (0 20) 638 80 86, *Fax (0 20) 638 22 19*, Japanese cuisine with Teppan-Yaki – AE ⓓ E VISA JCB. ✂ KZ u
*closed 3 weeks July* – **Meals** (dinner only) 85/120.

XX **De Oesterbar,** Leidseplein 10, ✉ 1017 PT, ✆ (0 20) 626 34 63, *Fax (0 20) 623 21 99*, Seafood, open until midnight – ▤. AE ⓓ E VISA. ✂ KZ t
*closed 25, 26 and 31 December* – **Meals** a la carte 81/106.

**Sea Palace,** Oosterdokskade 8, 1011 AE, (0 20) 626 47 77, *Fax (0 20) 620 42 66*, Asian cuisine, open until 11 p.m., « Floating restaurant with ≤ town » – AE E VISA JCB.
**Meals** 45.

**Bordewijk,** Noordermarkt 7, 1015 MV, (0 20) 624 38 99, *Fax (0 20) 420 66 03*, « Trendy Amsterdam atmosphere » – AE E VISA.
*closed Monday, late July-early August and late December-early January* – **Meals** (dinner only) a la carte approx. 85.

**De Gouden Reael,** Zandhoek 14, 1013 KT, (0 20) 623 38 83, « 17C house on old harbour site », – AE E VISA.
*closed Sunday and last week December-first week January* – **Meals** 55/95.

**Haesje Claes,** Spuistraat 275, 1012 VR, (0 20) 624 99 98, *Fax (0 20) 627 48 17*, « Amsterdam atmosphere » – AE E VISA JCB. LY x
**Meals** 45.

**Tom Yam,** Staalstraat 22, 1011 JM, (0 20) 622 95 33, *Fax (0 20) 624 90 62*, Thaï cuisine – AE E VISA JCB MY f
**Meals** (dinner only) 40 (2 pers. min.)/88.

**Edo and Kyo** - (at Gd H. Krasnapolsky), Dam 9, 1012 JS, (0 20) 554 60 96, *Fax (0 20) 639 31 46*, Japanese cuisine – AE E VISA JCB. LY k
**Meals** 45/100.

## Rijksmuseum (Vondelpark)

**Marriott,** Stadhouderskade 12, 1054 ES, (0 20) 607 55 55, *Fax (0 20) 607 55 67*, – – 25-500. AE E VISA. KZ f
**Meals** ***Port O'Amsterdam*** *(closed Sunday and Monday)* Lunch 30 - 45 – **387 rm** 335, 5 suites.

**Barbizon Centre** M, Stadhouderskade 7, 1054 ES, (0 20) 685 13 51, *Fax (0 20) 685 16 11*, – – 25-280. AE E VISA JCB KZ p
**Meals** Lunch 55 – a la carte 54/73 – 33 – **234 rm** 360/485, 2 suites.

**Memphis** without rest, De Lairessestraat 87, 1071 NX, (0 20) 673 31 41, *Telex 12450, Fax (0 20) 673 73 12* – – 25-60. AE E VISA JCB.
34 – **74 rm** 460.

**Toro** without rest, Koningslaan 64, 1075 AG, (0 20) 673 72 23, *Fax (0 20) 675 00 31*, « Waterside terrace, overlooking the park » – . AE E VISA JCB.
**22 rm** 195/240.

**Vondel** (with annex) without rest, Vondelstraat 28, 1054 GE, (0 20) 612 01 20, *Fax (0 20) 685 43 21*, « Opulent interior », – – 25. AE E VISA JCB. JZ m
31 – **38 rm** 245/320.

**Lairesse** without rest, De Lairessestraat 7, 1071 NR, (0 20) 671 95 96, *Fax (0 20) 671 17 56* – . AE E VISA JCB
**34 rm** 250/310.

**Cok Hotels** without rest, Koninginneweg 34, 1075 CZ, (0 20) 664 61 11, *Fax (0 20) 664 53 04* – – 25-80. AE E VISA JCB
**152 rm** 200/335.

**Villa Borgmann** without rest, Koningslaan 48, 1075 AE, (0 20) 673 52 52, *Fax (0 20) 676 25 80* – . AE E VISA JCB.
**15 rm** 125/235.

**Fita** without rest, Jan Luykenstraat 37, 1071 CL, (0 20) 679 09 76, *Fax (0 20) 664 39 69* – . AE E VISA. KZ s
**16 rm** 110/220.

**Radèn Mas,** Stadhouderskade 6, 1054 ES, (0 20) 685 40 41, *Fax (0 20) 685 39 81*, Indonesian cuisine, open until 11 p.m. – . AE E VISA JCB JKZ k
**Meals** Lunch 33 – 55/99.

**Le Garage,** Ruysdaelstraat 54, 1071 XE, (0 20) 679 71 76, *Fax (0 20) 662 22 49*, Open until 11 p.m., « Artistic atmosphere in a contemporary and cosmopolitan brasserie » – AE E VISA JCB.
*closed lunch Saturday and Sunday and Bank Holidays* – **Meals** Lunch 40 – 73.

**Aujourd'hui,** C. Krusemanstraat 15, 1075 NB, (0 20) 679 08 77, *Fax (0 20) 676 76 27*, – AE E VISA JCB
*closed Saturday, Sunday and last 3 weeks August* – **Meals** Lunch 55 – a la carte approx. 80.

**Beddington's,** Roelof Hartstraat 6, 1071 VH, (0 20) 676 52 01, *Fax (0 20) 671 74 29* – AE E VISA.
*closed lunch Saturday and Monday, Sunday, 19 July-9 August and 20 December-3 January* – **Meals** Lunch 55 – 70/85.

**Keyzer,** Van Baerlestraat 96, ✉ 1071 BB, ☎ (0 20) 671 14 41, *Fax (0 20) 673 73 53*, Pub rest, open until 11.30 p.m., « Amsterdam atmosphere » – AE ① E. ✻
*closed Sunday and Bank Holidays* – **Meals** 60.

**Brasserie van Baerle,** Van Baerlestraat 158, ✉ 1071 BG, ☎ (0 20) 679 15 32, *Fax (0 20) 671 71 96*, ☂, Pub rest – AE ① E VISA
*closed Saturday and 25 December-1 January* – **Meals** Lunch 45 – 57/68.

### South and West Quarters

**Okura** M ⛴, Ferdinand Bolstraat 333, ✉ 1072 LH, ☎ (0 20) 678 71 11, *Fax (0 20) 671 23 44*, ≤, Ⅎ, ≘s, ◻, ⚓ – 🛗 ✻ ≡ TV ☎ 🚗 P – 🏛 25-650. AE ① E VISA JCB. ✻
**Meals** see rest ***Ciel Bleu*** and ***Yamazato*** below – ***Sazanka*** *(closed lunch Saturday and Sunday)* (Japanese cuisine with Teppan-Yaki) Lunch 38 - 90/148 – ***Brasserie Le Camelia*** (open until 11 p.m.) a la carte approx. 65 – ☕ 42 – **358 rm** 385/555, 12 suites.

**Le Meridien Apollo,** Apollolaan 2, ✉ 1077 BA, ☎ (0 20) 673 59 22, *Fax (0 20) 570 57 44*, ☂, « Terrace with ≤ canal », ⚓ – 🛗 ✻, ≡ rm, TV ☎ P – 🏛 25-200. AE ① E VISA JCB. ✻ rest
**Meals** (open until 11 p.m.) Lunch 55 – a la carte 59/75 – ☕ 33 – **217 rm** 375/470, 2 suites.

**Garden,** Dijsselhofplantsoen 7, ✉ 1077 BJ, ☎ (0 20) 664 21 21, *Fax (0 20) 679 93 56* – 🛗 ✻ TV ☎ – 🏛 25-150. AE ① E VISA JCB
**Meals** see rest ***Mangerie De Kersentuin*** below – ☕ 38 – **96 rm** 225/495, 2 suites.

**Hilton,** Apollolaan 138, ✉ 1077 BG, ☎ (0 20) 678 07 80, *Telex 11025, Fax (0 20) 571 12 71*, ☂, « Canalside garden and terraces », Ⅎ, ≘s, ⚓ – 🛗 ✻ ≡ TV ☎ ♿ P – 🏛 25-350. AE ① E VISA JCB. ✻ rest
**Meals** ***Roberto's*** (Italian cuisine) a la carte 64/90 – ☕ 38 – **268 rm** 385/415, 3 suites.

**Mercure a/d Amstel,** Joan Muyskenweg 10, ✉ 1096 CJ, ☎ (0 20) 665 81 81, *Fax (0 20) 694 87 35*, Ⅎ, ≘s – 🛗 ✻, ≡ rm, TV ☎ P – 🏛 25-450. AE ① E VISA. ✻
**Meals** a la carte 62/82 – ☕ 35 – **178 rm** 325/350.

**La Casaló** ⛴ without rest, Amsteldijk 862, ✉ 1079 LN, ☎ (0 20) 642 36 80, *Fax (0 20) 644 74 09*, ≤, « Floating hotel on the Amstel », ⚓ – TV ☎. AE ① E VISA JCB
**4 rm** ☕ 225/275.

**Ciel Bleu** - (at Okura H.), 23th floor, Ferdinand Bolstraat 333, ✉ 1072 LH, ☎ (0 20) 678 71 11, *Fax (0 20) 671 23 44*, ≤ town, ⚓ – 🛗 ≡ P. AE ① E VISA JCB. ✻
**Meals** (dinner only) 80/120.

**Mangerie De Kerstentuin** - (at Garden H.), Dijsselhofplantsoen 7, ✉ 1077 BJ, ☎ (0 20) 664 21 21, *Fax (0 20) 679 93 56*, ☂, Open until 11 p.m. – ≡. AE ① E VISA JCB. ✻
*closed Sunday, 31 December and 1 January* – **Meals** Lunch 45 – 63/73.

**Yamazato** - (at Okura H.), Ferdinand Bolstraat 333, ✉ 1072 LH, ☎ (0 20) 678 71 11, *Fax (0 20) 671 23 44*, Japanese cuisine, ⚓ – ≡ P. AE ① E VISA JCB. ✻
**Meals** Lunch 45 – 80/130.

**Pakistan,** Scheldestraat 100, ✉ 1078 GP, ☎ (0 20) 675 39 76, *Fax (0 20) 675 39 76*, Indian cuisine – AE ① E VISA
**Meals** (dinner only until 11 p.m.) 43/65.

### Buitenveldert (RAI)

**Holiday Inn,** De Boelelaan 2, ✉ 1083 HJ, ☎ (0 20) 646 23 00, *Fax (0 20) 646 47 90* – 🛗 ✻ ≡ TV ☎ ♿ P – 🏛 25-350. AE ① E VISA JCB
**Meals** (open until 11 p.m.) 55/70 – ☕ 34 – **256 rm** 380/540, 2 suites.

**Novotel,** Europaboulevard 10, ✉ 1083 AD, ☎ (0 20) 541 11 23, *Fax (0 20) 646 28 23* – 🛗 ✻ ≡ TV ☎ ♿ P – 🏛 25-225. AE ① E VISA
**Meals** (open until midnight) Lunch 28 – 45 – ☕ 28 – **599 rm** 275.

**Halvemaan,** van Leyenberghlaan 320 (Gijsbrecht van Aemstelpark), ✉ 1082 DD, ☎ (0 20) 644 03 48, *Fax (0 20) 644 17 77*, ☂, « Terrace with ≤ private lake » – P. AE ① E VISA. ✻
*closed Saturday, Sunday and 24 December-mid January* – **Meals** Lunch 65 – 120.

### North

**Galaxy,** Distelkade 21, ✉ 1031 XP, ☎ (0 20) 634 43 66, *Telex 18607, Fax (0 20) 636 03 45* – 🛗, ≡ rest, TV ☎ P – 🏛 25-200. AE ① E VISA
**Meals** Lunch 25 – a la carte approx. 50 – **281 rm** ☕ 225/260.

### Suburbs

## by motorway The Hague (A 4) :

**Mercure Airport,** Oude Haagseweg 20 (exit ①), ✉ 1066 BW, ☎ (0 20) 617 90 05, *Fax (0 20) 615 90 27* – 🛗 ✻ ≡ TV ☎ P – 🏛 25-300. AE ① E VISA. ✻ rest
**Meals** Lunch 40 – 45/65 – ☕ 30 – **151 rm** 250/350.

**Environs**

**at Amstelveen** *S : 11 km – pop. 75 869 :*

*Thomas Cookstraat 1, 1181 ZS, (0 20) 441 55 45, Fax (0 20) 647 19 66*

**Grand Hotel**, Bovenkerkerweg 81 (S : 2,5 km direction Uithoorn), 1187 XC, (0 20) 645 55 58, *Fax (0 20) 641 21 21* – P. AE E VISA.
Meals see rest ***Résidence Fontaine Royale*** below, shuttle service – 35 – **81 rm** 200/320, 10 suites.

**De Jonge Dikkert,** Amsterdamseweg 104a, 1182 HG, (0 20) 641 13 78, *Fax (0 20) 645 91 62,* « 17C windmill » – P. AE E VISA
*closed Bank Holiday lunch and 31 December* – **Meals** 58/68.

**Résidence Fontaine Royale** - (at Grand Hotel), Dr Willem Dreesweg 1 (S : 2 km, direction Uithoorn), 1185 VA, (0 20) 640 15 01, *Fax (0 20) 640 16 61,* – P – 25-225. AE E VISA JCB
*closed Sunday* – **Meals** *Lunch 50* – a la carte 59/84.

**Le Pescadou,** Amsterdamseweg 448, 1181 BW, (0 20) 647 04 43, *Fax (0 20) 647 04 43,* Seafood – . AE E VISA JCB
*closed 23 December-4 January* – **Meals** *Lunch 50* – a la carte 75/90.

**at Badhoevedorp** *SW : 15 km Haarlemmermeer pop. 106 095 :*

**Dorint,** Sloterweg 299, 1171 VB, (0 20) 658 81 11, *Fax (0 20) 659 71 01,* , – , rm, P – 25-150. AE E VISA JCB. rest
Meals (open until 11 p.m.) *Lunch 40* – a la carte 45/76 – 30 – **196 rm** 330/385.

**De Herbergh** with rm, Sloterweg 259, 1171 CP, (0 20) 659 26 00, *Fax (0 20) 659 83 90,* – rest, P. AE E VISA. rm
**Meals** a la carte approx. 65 – 17 – **15 rm** 155/175.

**at Ouderkerk aan de Amstel** *S : 10 km Amstelveen pop. 75 869 :*

**Paardenburg,** Amstelzijde 55, 1184 TZ, (0 20) 496 12 10, *Fax (0 20) 496 40 17,* « 19C murals, riverside terrace » – P. AE E VISA JCB.
*closed Saturday lunch, Sunday and 26 December-19 January* – **Meals** 60/100.

**'t Jagershuis** with rm, Amstelzijde 2, 1184 VA, (0 20) 496 20 20, *Fax (0 20) 496 45 41,* <, , « Inn with Amstel-side terrace », – rest, P – 30. AE E VISA JCB.
*closed 31 December and 1 January* – **Meals** *Lunch 50* – 60/68 – 25 – **12 rm** 195/315.

**Klein Paardenburg,** Amstelzijde 59, 1184 TZ, (0 20) 496 13 35, « Waterside terrace » – AE E VISA
*closed Sunday and 25 December-4 January* – **Meals** *Lunch 68* – 95.

**Het Kampje,** Kerkstraat 56, 1191 JE, (0 20) 496 19 43, *Fax (0 20) 496 57 01,* – AE E VISA JCB
*closed Saturday, Sunday, 27 April-15 May and 21 December-4 January* – **Meals** *Lunch 40* – 50/60.

**at Schiphol** *(international airport) SW : 15 km Haarlemmermeer pop. 106 095 – Casino, Schiphol airport - Central Terminal (0 23) 571 80 44, Fax (0 23) 571 62 26 :*

**Sheraton Schiphol**, Schiphol bd 101, 1118 BG, (0 20) 316 43 00, *Fax (0 20) 316 43 99,* , , – P – 25-500. AE E VISA JCB
Meals ***Voyager*** (open until 11 p.m.) a la carte 74/98 – ***Run-Way Café*** (open until 1 a.m.) a la carte approx. 55 – 40 – **399 rm** 555/755, 9 suites.

**Hilton Schiphol,** Herbergierstraat 1, 1118 CA, (0 20) 603 45 67, *Fax (0 20) 648 09 17,* – P – 25-110. AE E VISA JCB.
Meals ***Greenhouse*** (buffets, open until 11.30 p.m.) *Lunch 62* - 65 – 38 – **265 rm** 425/605, 1 suite.

**Blokzijl** *Overijssel Brederwiede pop. 12 102* 210 *P 6 and* 408 *I 3 – 102 km.*

**Kaatje bij de Sluis**, Brouwerstraat 20, 8356 DV, (0 527) 29 18 33, *Fax (0 527) 29 18 36,* <, , « Terrace and garden along an intersection of canals », – P. AE E VISA
*closed Monday, Tuesday, Saturday lunch, February and late December-early January* – **Meals** 98, a la carte 110/165 – 38 – **8 rm** 210/270
**Spec.** Carpaccio de hareng au caviar. Gratin de homard aux tomates et basilic. Feuillantine aux chocolat et pamplemousse rose.

**Haarlem** *Noord-Holland* 210 H 8, 211 H 8 *and* 408 E 4 – *pop. 147 617 – 24 km.*

**at Overveen** *W : 4 km* C *Bloemendaal pop. 16 750 :*

XXX ✿✿ **De Bokkedoorns,** Zeeweg 53 (W : 2,5 km), ✉ 2051 EB, ℘ (0 23) 526 36 00, *Fax (0 23) 527 31 43,* ⛱, « Terrace, ≤ lake surrounded by wooded dunes » – ▤ P. AE ① E VISA. ✂
*closed Monday, Saturday lunch, 30 April lunch, 5 and 24 December and 28 December-4 January* – **Meals** *Lunch 70* – 98 (2 pers. min.), a la carte approx. 155
**Spec.** Homard braisé à l'ail, olives et safran. Perdrix sauvage, sauce à l'Armagnac et choucroute au Sauternes (in season). Salade de ris et rognon de veau aux pommes et Champagne.

**Hoorn** *Noord-Holland* 210 M 2 *and* 408 G 4 – *pop. 61 800 – 43 km.*

XX ✿✿ **De Oude Rosmolen** (Fonk), Duinsteeg 1, ✉ 1621 ER, ℘ (0 229) 21 47 52, *Fax (0 229) 21 49 38* – ▤. AE ① E VISA
*closed Thursday, 2 weeks February, 9 to 27 August and 28 December-7 January* – **Meals** (dinner only, booking essential) 125 b.i./150, a la carte 100/130
**Spec.** Profiteroles à la mousse de foie gras. Ris de veau à la financière. Pâtisseries maison.

---

**The HAGUE** *(Den HAAG or 's-GRAVENHAGE) Zuid-Holland* 211 F 10 - ① ② *and* 408 D 5 – *pop. 442 503.*

**See** : *Binnenhof★ : The Knight's Room★ (Ridderzaal)* JY – *Court pool (Hofvijver)* ≤★ HJY – *Lange Voorhout★* HJX – *Madurodam★★* – *Scheveningen★★.*

**Museums** : *Mauritshuis★★★* JY – *Prince William V art gallery★ (Schilderijengalerij Prins Willem V)* HY **M**² – *Panorama Mesdag★* HX – *Mesdag★* – *Municipal★★ (Gemeentehuis)* – *Bredius★* JY.

*18 at Rijswijk SE : 5 km, Delftweg 58, ✉ 2289 AL, ℘ (0 70) 319 24 24 - 18 at Wassenaar NE : 11 km, Groot Haesebroekseweg 22, ✉ 2243 EC, ℘ (0 70) 517 96 07 and 18 Hoge Klei 1, ✉ 2243 XZ, ℘ (0 70) 511 78 46.*

*✈ Amsterdam-Schiphol NE : 37 km ℘ (0 20) 601 91 11 – Rotterdam-Zestienhoven SE : 17 km ℘ (0 10) 446 34 44.*

*i Kon. Julianaplein 30, ✉ 2595 AA, ℘ 0 6-34 03 50 51, Fax (0 70) 347 21 02.*

*Amsterdam 55 – Brussels 182 – Rotterdam 24 – Delft 13.*

Plan on next page

**Centre**

**Des Indes,** Lange Voorhout 54, ✉ 2514 EG, ℘ (0 70) 363 29 32, *Fax (0 70) 345 17 21,* « Late 19C residence » – |♦| TV ☎ P – 🏛 25-75. AE ① E VISA JCB. ✂ rm JX s
Meals ***Le Restaurant*** *Lunch 55* - 65/100 – ☕ 38 – **70 rm** 320/530, 6 suites.

**Holiday Inn Crowne Plaza Promenade,** van Stolkweg 1, ✉ 2585 JL, ℘ (0 70) 352 51 61, *Fax (0 70) 354 10 46,* ≤, ⛱, « Collection of modern Dutch paintings » – |♦| ⚭ ▤ TV ☎ P – 🏛 25-400. AE ① E VISA JCB
Meals ***The Gallery*** a la carte 60/80 – ***Trattoria del'Arte*** (Italian cuisine) a la carte 50/65 – ☕ 38 – **91 rm** 225/250, 4 suites.

**Dorint** M, Johan de Wittlaan 42, ✉ 2517 JR, ℘ (0 70) 416 91 11, *Fax (0 70) 416 91 00,* Fø, ≘s – |♦| ⚭, ▤ rm, TV ☎ ♿ 🚗 – 🏛 25-2000. AE ① E VISA JCB. ✂ rest
Meals (open until 11 p.m.) a la carte approx. 65 – ☕ 28 – **214 rm** 315/370, 2 suites.

**Carlton Ambassador** M 🕭, Sophialaan 2, ✉ 2514 JP, ℘ (0 70) 363 03 63, *Fax (0 70) 360 05 35,* ⛱, « Dutch and English style interior » – |♦| ⚭ ▤ TV ☎ P – 🏛 25-150. AE ① E VISA JCB. ✂ HX c
Meals ***Brasserie Henricus*** *Lunch 40* - a la carte 49/85 – ☕ 35 – **71 rm** 345/405, 8 suites.

**Sofitel,** Koningin Julianaplein 35, ✉ 2595 AA, ℘ (0 70) 381 49 01, *Fax (0 70) 382 59 27* – |♦| ⚭ ▤ TV ☎ ♿ P – 🏛 25-150. AE ① E VISA
Meals 50 – ☕ 30 – **143 rm** 300/360.

**Bel Air,** Johan de Wittlaan 30, ✉ 2517 JR, ℘ (0 70) 352 53 54, *Fax (0 70) 353 53 53,* 🏊 – |♦| ⚭ TV ☎ P – 🏛 25-250. AE ① E VISA JCB
Meals *Lunch 46* – 53/58 – ☕ 25 – **350 rm** 260/295.

**Mercure Central** without rest, Spui 180, ✉ 2511 BW, ℘ (0 70) 363 67 00, *Fax (0 70) 363 93 98* – |♦| ⚭ ▤ TV ☎ ♿ P – 🏛 25-130. AE ① E VISA JCB JZ v
☕ 24 – **156 rm** 198/215, 3 suites.

**Corona,** Buitenhof 42, ✉ 2513 AH, ℘ (0 70) 363 79 30, *Fax (0 70) 361 57 85,* ⛱ – |♦|, ▤ rest, TV ☎ 🚗 – 🏛 30-100. AE ① E VISA JCB HY v
Meals ***Brasserie Buitenhof*** *Lunch 45* - 50/58 – ☕ 25 – **26 rm** 265/310.

**Parkhotel** without rest, Molenstraat 53, ✉ 2513 BJ, ℘ (0 70) 362 43 71, *Fax (0 70) 361 45 25* – |♦| TV ☎ – 🏛 25-100. AE ① E VISA HY a
**114 rm** ☕ 165/325.

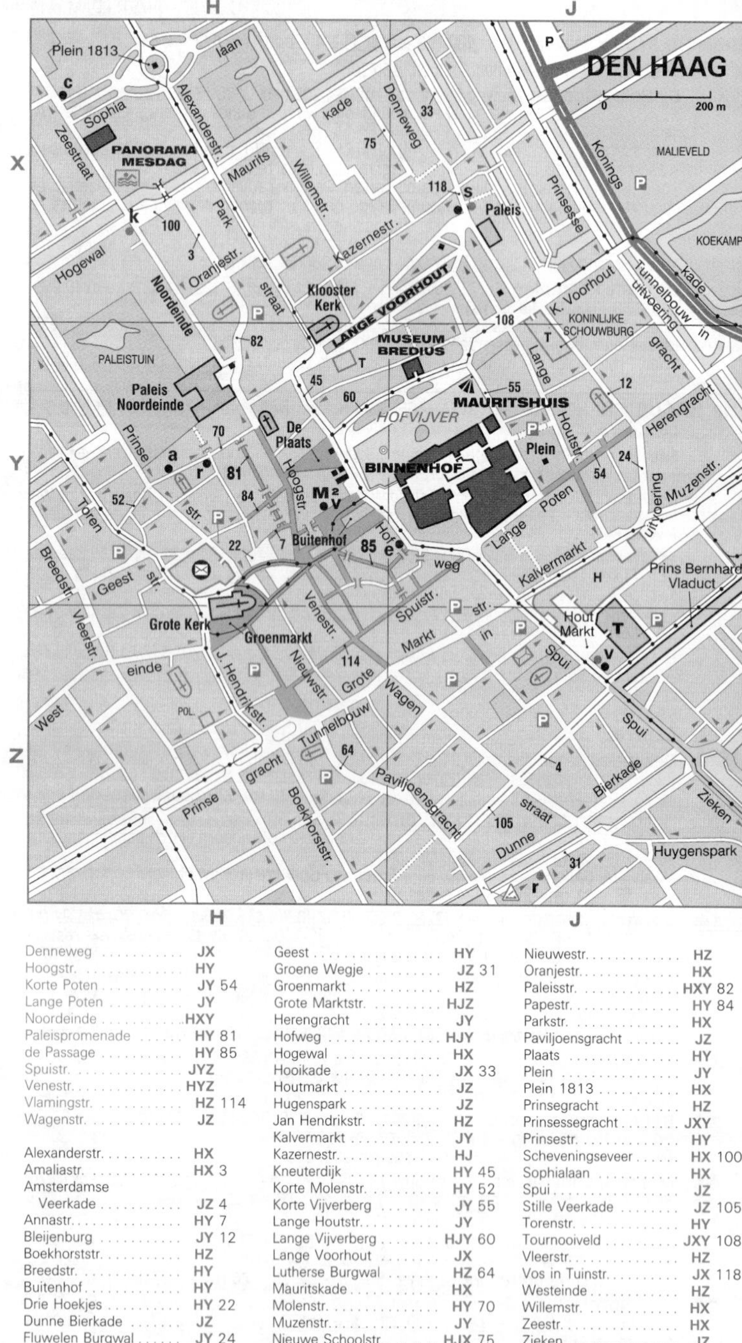
DEN HAAG
0
200 m
H
J
X
Y
Z
Plein 1813
Sophia
laan
Alexanderstr.
Zeestraat
PANORAMA MESDAG
Maurits
kade
Denneweg
Willemstr.
Park
Hogewal
Noordeinde
Oranjestr.
Kazernestr.
straat
Klooster Kerk
LANGE VOORHOUT
MUSEUM BREDIUS
Paleis
Prinsesse
Konings
MALIEVELD
KOEKAMP
Tunnelbouw in uitvoering
kade
K. Voorhout
KONINLIJKE SCHOUWBURG
Lange
Houtstr.
gracht
Herengracht
PALEISTUIN
Paleis Noordeinde
Prinse
De Plaats
HOFVIJVER
MAURITSHUIS
BINNENHOF
Plein
Hoogstr.
Buitenhof
Hof
weg
Lange Poten
Kalvermarkt
Muzenstr.
uitvoering
Prins Bernhard Vladuct
Toren
str.
Breedstr.
Geest
str.
Grote Kerk
Groenmarkt
Venestr.
Spuistr.
str.
Markt
in
Spui
Hout Markt
Vleerstr.
einde
J. Hendrikstr.
Nieuwstr.
Grote
Wagen
West
POL.
Tunnelbouw
Prinse
gracht
Boekhorststr.
Paviljoensgracht
Spui
Bierkade
straat
Dunne
Zieken
Huygenspark

**Novotel,** Hofweg 5, ✉ 2511 AA, ℘ (0 70) 364 88 46, *Fax (0 70) 356 28 89*, – |\$| , ▤ rest, TV ☎ – 25-100. AE ⓓ E VISA JCB HJY e
Meals (open until midnight) a la carte approx. 55 – ☕ 23 – **106 rm** 175/210.

**Paleis** without rest, Molenstraat 26, ✉ 2513 BL, ℘ (0 70) 362 46 21, *Fax (0 70) 361 45 33*, – |\$| TV ☎. AE ⓓ E VISA JCB HY r
☕ 16 – **20 rm** 155/219.

**De Hoogwerf,** Zijdelaan 20, ✉ 2594 BV, ℘ (0 70) 347 55 14, *Fax (0 70) 381 95 96*, , « 17C farmhouse, garden » – AE ⓓ E VISA JCB.
*closed Sunday and Bank Holidays except Christmas* – **Meals** *Lunch 45* – 55/125.

**Da Roberto,** Noordeinde 196, ✉ 2514 GS, ℘ (0 70) 346 49 77, *Fax (0 70) 362 52 86*, Italian cuisine – ▤ P. AE ⓓ E VISA HX k
*closed Sunday and first 2 weeks August* – **Meals** *Lunch 55* – a la carte approx. 90.

**'t Ganzenest** (Visbeen), Groenewegje 115, ✉ 2515 LP, ℘ (0 70) 389 67 09, *Fax (0 70) 380 07 41* – AE ⓓ E VISA. JZ r
*closed Monday, Easter, Whitsun, late July-early August and first week January* – **Meals** (dinner only) 55/110 b.i., a la carte 80/100
**Spec.** Carpaccio de thon mariné à la vinaigrette de soja. Crème de witlof aux St-Jacques (October-April). Ris de veau croustillant aux épinards et ravioles de petits-gris.

**It Rains Fishes,** Noordeinde 123, ✉ 2514 GG, ℘ (0 70) 365 25 98, *Fax (0 70) 365 25 22*, Partly Asian cuisine – ▤. AE ⓓ E VISA. HX k
*closed lunch Saturday and Sunday and Monday* – **Meals** *Lunch 38* – 55/65.

**Rousseau,** Van Boetzelaerlaan 134, ✉ 2581 AX, ℘ (0 70) 355 47 43, – AE ⓓ E VISA
*closed lunch Saturday and Sunday, Monday, 23 February-2 March, 3 to 17 August, 24 and 31 December and 1 January* – **Meals** *Lunch 45* – 55/98.

**Julien,** Vos in Tuinstraat 2a, ✉ 2514 BX, ℘ (0 70) 365 86 02, *Fax (0 70) 365 31 47*, « Art Deco interior » – AE ⓓ E VISA JX s
*closed Sunday* – **Meals** *Lunch 45* – 50/75.

**The Raffles,** Javastraat 63, ✉ 2585 AG, ℘ (0 70) 345 85 87, Indonesian cuisine – ▤. AE ⓓ E VISA JCB
*closed Sunday and late July-early August* – **Meals** (dinner only) 48/73.

**Shirasagi,** Spui 170, ✉ 2511 BW, ℘ (0 70) 346 47 00, *Fax (0 70) 346 26 01*, Japanese cuisine with Teppan-Yaki – ▤. AE ⓓ E VISA JCB. JZ v
*closed lunch Saturday, Sunday and Monday and 31 December-2 January* – **Meals** 55/135.

**at Scheveningen** C *'s-Gravenhage – Seaside resort★★ – Casino, Kurhausweg 1, ✉ 2587 RT, ℘ (0 70) 351 26 21, Fax (0 70) 354 31 83.*
ℹ *Gevers Deijnootweg 1134, ✉ 2586 BX, ℘ 0-6 34 03 50 51, Fax (0 70) 352 04 26 :*

**Kurhaus,** Gevers Deijnootplein 30, ✉ 2586 CK, ℘ (0 70) 416 26 36, *Fax (0 70) 416 26 46*, ⩽, , « Former late 19C concert hall », – |\$| TV ☎ ♿ P – 35-480. AE ⓓ E VISA JCB. rest
Meals see rest ***Kandinsky*** below – ***Kurzaal*** (buffets) *Lunch 45* - 55/75 – ☕ 41 – **247 rm** 390/500, 8 suites.

**Europa,** Zwolsestraat 2, ✉ 2587 VJ, ℘ (0 70) 416 95 95, *Fax (0 70) 461 95 55*, , , , – |\$| TV ☎ – 25-460. AE ⓓ E VISA JCB.
Meals (dinner only until 11 p.m.) a la carte approx. 65 – ☕ 28 – **173 rm** 275/385, 1 suite.

**Carlton Beach,** Gevers Deijnootweg 201, ✉ 2586 HZ, ℘ (0 70) 354 14 14, *Fax (0 70) 352 00 20*, ⩽, , , – |\$| TV ☎ P – 25-250. AE ⓓ E VISA.
Meals (open until midnight) *Lunch 28* – 45/90 – ☕ 30 – **183 rm** 245/370.

**Badhotel,** Gevers Deijnootweg 15, ✉ 2586 BB, ℘ (0 70) 351 22 21, *Fax (0 70) 355 58 70* – |\$| TV ☎ P – 25-150. AE ⓓ E VISA JCB. rest
Meals (dinner only) 45/90 – ☕ 19 – **90 rm** 168/195.

**Kandinsky** - (at Kurhaus H.), Gevers Deijnootplein 30, ✉ 2586 CK, ℘ (0 70) 416 26 34, *Fax (0 70) 416 26 46*, ⩽ – ▤ P. AE ⓓ E VISA JCB.
*closed Sunday except Bank Holidays and Saturday lunch* – **Meals** (dinner only July-August) *Lunch 58* – 70/93.

**Seinpost,** Zeekant 60, ✉ 2586 AD, ℘ (0 70) 355 52 50, *Fax (0 70) 355 50 93*, ⩽, Seafood – ▤. AE ⓓ E VISA
*closed Sunday and Bank Holidays* – **Meals** *Lunch 60* – 68 b.i.

**Radèn Mas,** Gevers Deijnootplein 125, ✉ 2586 CR, ℘ (0 70) 354 54 32, *Fax (0 70) 350 60 42*, Partly Indonesian cuisine, open until 11 p.m. – ▤. AE ⓓ E VISA JCB.
**Meals** *Lunch 30* – 50/95.

**Rederserf,** Schokkerweg 37, ✉ 2583 BH, ℘ (0 70) 350 50 23, *Fax (0 70) 350 84 54*, ⩽, – ▤. AE ⓓ E VISA JCB.
*closed 27 December-1 January* – **Meals** *Lunch 53* – a la carte 92/126.

**China Delight,** Dr Lelykade 116, ✉ 2583 CN, ℘ (0 70) 355 54 50, *Fax (0 70) 354 66 52*, Chinese cuisine – ⓓ E VISA JCB – **Meals** *Lunch 33* – a la carte 49/104.

XX **Ginza,** Dr Lelykade 28, ✉ 2583 CM, ☎ (0 70) 358 96 63, Japanese cuisine with Teppan-Yaki, open until midnight – ▤. AE ⓓ E VISA JCB. ✗
**Meals** *Lunch 28* – a la carte approx. 60.

XX **Bali** with rm, Badhuisweg 1, ✉ 2587 CA, ☎ (0 70) 350 24 34, *Fax (0 70) 354 03 63*, terrace, Indonesian cuisine – TV ☎ P. AE ⓓ E VISA. ✗
**Meals** (dinner only) 45/85 – **29 rm** ☕ 80/175.

**Environs**

**at Leidschendam** *E : 6 km – pop. 34 532 :*

**Green Park,** Weigelia 22, ✉ 2262 AB, ☎ (0 70) 320 92 80, *Fax (0 70) 327 49 07*, ≤, – lift ✗ TV ☎ P – 25-250. AE ⓓ E VISA JCB
**Meals** 45/73 – **92 rm** ☕ 275/315, 3 suites.

XXX **Villa Rozenrust,** Veursestraatweg 104, ✉ 2265 CG, ☎ (0 70) 327 74 60, *Fax (0 70) 327 50 62*, terrace, « Terrace » – P. AE ⓓ E VISA
✿ *closed Saturday lunch, Sunday and 27 July-15 August* – **Meals** *Lunch 70* – 98/120, a la carte 95/130
**Spec.** Sole au beurre de gambas. Taboulé de homard, thon et pamplemousse. Bœuf sauté à la chinoise aux chanterelles et truffes (July-February).

**at Voorburg** *E : 5 km – pop. 39 380 :*

**Mövenpick** M, Stationsplein 8, ✉ 2275 AZ, ☎ (0 70) 337 37 37, *Fax (0 70) 337 37 00*, terrace – lift ✗ ▤ TV ☎ ♿ – 25-160. AE ⓓ E VISA JCB
**Meals** (buffets) *Lunch 30* – 45 – ☕ 20 – **125 rm** 149/210.

XXX **Savelberg** ⛰ with rm, Oosteinde 14, ✉ 2271 EH, ☎ (0 70) 387 20 81, *Fax (0 70) 387 77 15*, ≤, terrace, « 17C residence with terrace in public park » – lift ✗ TV ☎ P – 35.
✿ AE ⓓ E VISA JCB
*closed 27 December-4 January* – **Meals** *(closed Sunday and Monday) Lunch 60* – 90, a la carte 105/130 – **14 rm** ☕ 250/350
**Spec.** Pot-au-feu de St-Jacques. Ris de veau en brioche à la truffe. L'assiette aux trois chocolats.

XX **Villa la Ruche,** Prinses Mariannelaan 71, ✉ 2275 BB, ☎ (0 70) 386 01 10, *Fax (0 70) 386 50 64* – ▤. AE ⓓ E VISA
*closed Sunday and 28 December-5 January* – **Meals** *Lunch 45* – 49.

XX **De Barbaars,** Kerkstraat 52, ✉ 2271 CT, ☎ (0 70) 386 29 00, *Fax (0 70) 386 29 00*, terrace, Open until 11 p.m., « 19C listed houses » – ▤. AE ⓓ E VISA
*closed lunch Saturday and Sunday* – **Meals** 50/88.

X **Papermoon,** Herenstraat 175, ✉ 2271 CE, ☎ (0 70) 387 31 61, *Fax (0 70) 386 80 36*, terrace – ▤. VISA. ✗
*closed Monday* – **Meals** (dinner only) 45.

**at Wassenaar** *NE : 11 km – pop. 25 840 :*

**Aub. de Kieviet** ⛰, Stoeplaan 27, ✉ 2243 CX, ☎ (0 70) 511 92 32, *Fax (0 70) 511 09 69*, terrace, « Floral terrace » – lift ▤ TV ☎ ♿ P – 25-90. AE ⓓ E VISA JCB. ✗ rest
**Meals** *Lunch 45* – 65/83 – ☕ 30 – **23 ch** 185/385, 1 suite.

---

**ROTTERDAM** *Zuid-Holland* 211 G 11 - ㊴ ㊵ *and* 408 E 6 - ㉕ N – *pop. 592 745 – Casino* JY, *Weena 624* ✉ *3012 CN*, ☎ *(0 10) 414 77 99, Fax (0 10) 414 92 33.*

**See :** *Lijnbaan*★ JKY – *St. Laurence Church (Grote- of St-Laurenskerk) : interior*★ KY – *Euromast*★ *(Tower)* ✱★★, ≤★ JZ – *The harbour*★★ ⛴ KZ – *Willemsbrug*★★ – *Erasmusbrug*★★ KZ – *Delftse Poort (building)*★ JY **R** – *World Trade Center*★ KY **A** – *The Netherlands architectural institute*★ JZ **B** – *Boompjes*★ KZ – *Willemswerf (building)*★ KY.

**Museums :** *History Museum Het Schielandshuis*★ KY **M**[4] – *Boijmans-van Beuningen*★★★ JZ – *History "De Dubbelde Palmboom"*★.

**Envir :** *SE : 7 km, Kinderdijk Windmils*★★.

⛳18 *at Capelle aan den IJssel E : 8 km, 's Gravenweg 311,* ✉ *2905 LB,* ☎ *(0 10) 442 21 09, Fax (0 10) 442 24 85* - ⛳9 *at Rhoon SW : 11 km, Veerweg 2a,* ✉ *3161 EX,* ☎ *(0 10) 501 80 58.*

✈ *Zestienhoven* ☎ *(0 10) 446 34 44.*

⛴ *Europoort to Hull : P and O North Sea Ferries Ltd* ☎ *(0 181) 25 55 00 (information) and (0 181) 25 55 55 (reservations), Fax (0 181) 25 52 15.*

ℹ *Coolsingel 67,* ✉ *3012 AC,* ☎ *0 900-403 40 65, Fax (0 10) 413 01 24 and – Central Station, Stationsplein 1,* ✉ *3013 AJ,* ☎ *0-900-403 40 65.*

*Amsterdam 76 – The Hague 24 – Antwerp 103 – Brussels 148 – Utrecht 57.*

# ROTTERDAM

| Street | Grid | No. |
|---|---|---|
| Beursplein | KY | 9 |
| Binnenweg | JY | |
| Botersloot | KY | 13 |
| Coolsingel | KY | |
| Hoogstr. | KY | |
| Karel Doormanstr. | JY | |
| Korte Hoogstr. | KY | 46 |
| Korte Lijnbaan | JY | 48 |
| Lijnbaan | JKY | |
| Stadhuispl. | KY | 93 |
| Aert van Nesstr. | JKY | 4 |
| Binnenwegpl. | KY | 10 |
| Delftsepl. | JY | 21 |
| Delftsestr. | JY | 22 |
| G.J. de Jonghweg | JZ | 25 |
| Grotekerkpl. | KY | 30 |
| Haagseveer | KY | 33 |
| Jonker Fransstr. | KY | 39 |
| Keizerstr. | KY | 40 |
| Kruiskade | JKY | 51 |
| Kruisplein | JY | 52 |
| Nieuwestr. | KY | 70 |
| van Oldenbarneveltplaats | JKY | 72 |
| Pompenburg | KY | 78 |
| Posthoornstr. | KY | 79 |
| Regentessebrug | KY | 82 |
| Scheepstimmermanslaan | KZ | 85 |
| Schouwburgplein | JY | 88 |
| Veerhaven | KZ | 102 |
| Veerkade | KZ | 103 |
| van Vollenhovenstr. | KZ | 107 |
| Westewagenstr. | KY | 110 |
| Wijnbrug | KY | 112 |
| Witte de Withstr. | KZ | 112 |

Don't get lost, use **Michelin Maps** which are kept up to date.

## Centre

**Parkhotel**, Westersingel 70, ✉ 3015 LB, ☎ (0 10) 436 36 11, *Fax (0 10) 436 42 12*, – 25-70. rest JZ a
**Meals** Lunch 43 – a la carte approx. 70 – ☕ 33 – **187 rm** 275/325, 2 suites.

**Hilton,** Weena 10, ✉ 3012 CM, ☎ (0 10) 414 40 44, *Fax (0 10) 411 88 84* – 25-365. KY a
**Meals** (open until 11 p.m.) a la carte approx. 50 – ☕ 37 – **246 rm** 385/550, 8 suites.

Holiday Inn City Centre, Schouwburgplein 1, ✉ 3012 CK, ☎ (0 10) 433 38 00, *Fax (0 10) 414 54 82* – 25-300. JY e
**98 rm**, 2 suites.

**Golden Tulip,** Aert van Nesstraat 4, ✉ 3012 CA, ☎ (0 10) 411 04 20, *Fax (0 10) 413 53 20* – 25-250. KY e
**Meals** 45/100 – ☕ 28 – **164 rm** 240/255.

**New York,** Koninginnehoofd 1, ✉ 3072 AD, ☎ (0 10) 439 05 00, *Fax (0 10) 484 27 01*, « Former head office of the Holland-America Line maritime company » – 25-120. rm KZ m
**Meals** (open until 11 p.m.) 35 – ☕ 15 – **72 rm** 135/250.

**Inntel,** Leuvehaven 80, ✉ 3011 EA, ☎ (0 10) 413 41 39, *Fax (0 10) 413 32 22*, rest, – 25-220. KZ d
**Meals** 45 – ☕ 25 – **150 rm** 185/410.

**Tulip Inn,** Willemsplein 1, ✉ 3016 DN, ☎ (0 10) 413 47 90, *Fax (0 10) 412 78 90*, – rest, – 25-70. rest KZ s
*closed 24 December-2 January* – **Meals** (dinner only) 45 – **103 rm** ☕ 160/240.

**Pax** without rest, Schiekade 658, ✉ 3032 AK, ☎ (0 10) 466 33 44, *Fax (0 10) 467 52 78* –
**45 rm** ☕ 135/250.

**Van Walsum,** Mathenesserlaan 199, ✉ 3014 HC, ☎ (0 10) 436 32 75, *Fax (0 10) 436 44 10* – rest JZ e
*closed 22 December-2 January* – **Meals** (dinner residents only) – **25 rm** ☕ 100/160.

**Parkheuvel** (Helder), Heuvellaan 21, ✉ 3016 GL, ☎ (0 10) 436 07 66, *Fax (0 10) 436 71 40*, « Terrace and maritime trade » – JZ n
*closed Saturday lunch, Sunday and 27 December-2 January* – **Meals** Lunch 73 – 93/148, a la carte approx. 115
**Spec.** Salade de langoustines au melon, gingembre et mayonnaise de curry. Turbot à la mousseline d'anchois, ragoût de champignons et jus de veau. Filet de bœuf poché au bouillon de truffes et ravioli de foie gras.

**Old Dutch,** Rochussenstraat 20, ✉ 3015 EK, ☎ (0 10) 436 03 44, *Fax (0 10) 436 78 26*, – JZ r
*closed Saturday mid June-mid September and Sunday* – **Meals** Lunch 53 – a la carte 73/100.

**Radèn Mas** 1st floor, Kruiskade 72, ✉ 3012 EH, ☎ (0 10) 411 72 44, *Fax (0 10) 411 97 11*, Indonesian cuisine, « Exotic decor » – JY a
**Meals** Lunch 33 – a la carte approx. 80.

**Brasserie La Vilette,** Westblaak 160, ✉ 3012 KM, ☎ (0 10) 414 86 92, *Fax (0 10) 414 33 91* – JKY t
*closed Sunday, 20 July-9 August and 24 December-3 January* – **Meals** 55/70.

**de Castellane,** Eendrachtsweg 22, ✉ 3012 LB, ☎ (0 10) 414 11 59, *Fax (0 10) 214 08 97*, « Terrace » – JZ h
*closed Saturday lunch, Sunday, 3 to 22 August and 25 December-5 January* – **Meals** Lunch 50 – a la carte 75/105.

**World Trade Center** 23rd floor, Beursplein 37, ✉ 3011 AA, ☎ (0 10) 405 44 65, *Fax (0 10) 405 51 20*, city – KY g
*closed Saturday lunch, Sunday and 27 July-9 August* – **Meals** Lunch 53 – 73.

**Brancatelli,** Boompjes 264, ✉ 3011 XD, ☎ (0 10) 411 41 51, *Fax (0 10) 404 57 34*, Italian cuisine, open until 11 p.m. – KZ n
**Meals** Lunch 60 – a la carte 53/78.

**Boompjes,** Boompjes 701, ✉ 3011 XZ, ☎ (0 10) 413 60 70, *Fax (0 10) 413 70 87*, Nieuwe Maas (Meuse), – KZ e
*closed Monday* – **Meals** Lunch 53 – 60/85.

**De Engel** (den Blijker), Eendrachtsweg 19, ✉ 3012 LB, ☎ (0 10) 413 82 56, *Fax (0 10) 412 51 96* – JZ h
*closed 25, 26 and 31 December* – **Meals** (dinner only) 58/70, a la carte approx. 85
**Spec.** Velouté de truffes au ris de veau croquant. Agneau au jus moutardé et basilic (April-October). Cabillaud au fumet de poisson et risotto aux tomates.

X **Engels,** Stationsplein 45, ✉ 3013 AK, ☎ (0 10) 411 95 50, *Fax (0 10) 413 94 21,* Multinational cuisines, open until 11 p.m. – ▤ P – 25-800. AE ⓓ E VISA JY v
**Meals** 45.

X **Anak Mas,** Meent 72a, ✉ 3011 JN, ☎ (0 10) 414 84 87, *Fax (0 10) 412 44 74,* Indonesian cuisine – ▤. AE ⓓ E VISA JCB. KY s
*closed Sunday* – **Meals** (dinner only) a la carte approx. 55.

**Suburbs**

**Airport** *N : 2,5 km :*

**Airport,** Vliegveldweg 59, ✉ 3043 NT, ☎ (0 10) 462 55 66, *Fax (0 10) 462 22 66,* – TV ☎ P – 25-425. AE ⓓ E VISA JCB
**Meals** 50 – 24 – **97 rm** 126/248, 1 suite.

**at Hillegersberg** *NE : 10 km C Rotterdam :*

X **Mangerie Lommerrijk,** Straatweg 99, ✉ 3054 AB, ☎ (0 10) 422 00 11, *Fax (0 10) 422 64 96,* ←, Pub rest – ▤ P – 250. AE ⓓ E VISA
*closed Monday and 24 and 31 December* – **Meals** *Lunch 35* – a la carte approx. 60.

**at Kralingen** *E : 2 km C Rotterdam :*

**Novotel Brainpark,** K.P. van der Mandelelaan 150 (near A 16), ✉ 3062 MB, ☎ (0 10) 453 07 77, *Fax (0 10) 453 15 03* – ▤ TV ☎ P – 25-400. AE ⓓ E VISA
**Meals** (open until 11 p.m.) *Lunch 43* – a la carte 53/76 – 23 – **196 rm** 180.

XXX **In den Rustwat,** Honingerdijk 96, ✉ 3062 NX, ☎ (0 10) 413 41 10, *Fax (0 10) 404 85 40,* , « 16C residence » – ▤ P. AE ⓓ E VISA JCB
*closed Saturday lunch and Sunday* – **Meals** *Lunch 63* – 89/110.

**at Ommoord** *NE : 10 km C Rotterdam :*

XX **Keizershof,** Martin Luther Kingweg 7, ✉ 3069 EW, ☎ (0 10) 455 13 33, *Fax (0 10) 456 80 23,* – P – 30. AE ⓓ E VISA
*closed 24 July-14 August* – **Meals** *Lunch 45* – 50/90.

**Europoort zone** *W : 25 km :*

**De Beer Europoort,** Europaweg 210 (N 15), ✉ 3198 LD, ☎ (0 181) 26 23 77, *Fax (0 181) 26 29 23,* ←, , , – TV ☎ P – 25-180. AE ⓓ E VISA
**Meals** *Lunch 45* – a la carte approx. 70 – **78 rm** 150/190.

**Environs**

**at Capelle aan den IJssel** *E : 8 km – pop. 61 421 :*

**Barbizon** M, Barbizonlaan 2 (near A 20), ✉ 2908 MA, ☎ (0 10) 456 44 55, *Telex 26514, Fax (0 10) 456 78 58,* ←, – TV ☎ P – 30-250. AE ⓓ E VISA JCB.
**Meals** 45 – 25 – **100 rm** 265/295, 1 suite.

**at Rhoon** *S : 10 km C Albrandswaard pop. 15 325 :*

XXX **Het Kasteel van Rhoon,** Dorpsdijk 63, ✉ 3161 KD, ☎ (0 10) 501 88 96, *Fax (0 10) 501 24 18,* ←, , « Situated in the outbuildings of the mansion » – P. AE ⓓ E VISA.
*closed 25 and 26 December* – **Meals** 68/98.

**at Schiedam** *W : 6 km – pop. 74 162*
*Buitenhavenweg 9, ✉ 3113 BC, ☎ (0 10) 473 30 00, Fax (0 10) 473 66 95 :*

**Novotel,** Hargalaan 2 (near A 20), ✉ 3118 JA, ☎ (0 10) 471 33 22, *Fax (0 10) 470 06 56,* , , – ▤ TV ☎ P – 25-200. AE ⓓ E VISA JCB
**Meals** (open until midnight) *Lunch 28* – a la carte approx. 60 – 23 – **133 rm** 169.

XXX **La Duchesse,** Maasboulevard 9, ✉ 3114 HB, ☎ (0 10) 426 46 26, *Fax (0 10) 473 25 01,* ← Nieuwe Maas (Meuse), – P. AE ⓓ E VISA JCB
*closed Saturday lunch, Sunday and 31 December* – **Meals** *Lunch 58* – 65.

XXX **Aub. Hosman Frères** 1st floor, Korte Dam 10, ✉ 3111 BC, ☎ (0 10) 426 40 96, « Collection of alcoholic spirits », Open until 11 p.m. – ▤. AE ⓓ E VISA JCB
*closed 31 December* – **Meals** *Lunch 48* – a la carte approx. 85.

X **Orangerie Duchesse,** Maasboulevard 9, ✉ 3114 HB, ☎ (0 10) 426 46 26, *Fax (0 10) 473 25 01,* ← Nieuwe Maas (Meuse), – P. AE ⓓ E VISA JCB
*closed Sunday and 25, 26 and 31 December* – **Meals** (dinner only) 55.

# Czech Republic

## Česká Republika

PRAGUE

# PRACTICAL INFORMATION

## LOCAL CURRENCY

**Crown** : *100 CRT = 2,89 US $ (Jan. 98)*

**National Holiday in the Czech Republic** : *28 October.*

## PRICES

*Prices may change if goods and service costs in the Czech Republic are revised and it is therefore always advisable to confirm rates with the hotelier when making a reservation.*

## FOREIGN EXCHANGE

*It is strongly advised against changing money other than in banks, exchange offices or authorised offices such as large hotels, tourist offices, etc... Banks are usually open on weekdays from 8am to 5pm. Some exchange offices in the old city are open 24 hours a day.*

## HOTEL RESERVATIONS

*In case of difficulties in finding a room through our hotel selection, it is always possible to apply to AVE Wilsonova 8, Prague 2, ☎ (02) 24 22 35 21. CEDOK Na příkopě 18, Prague 1 ☎ (02) 24 19 76 15.*

## POSTAL SERVICES

*Post offices are open from 8am to 6pm on weekdays and 12 noon on Saturdays. The* **General Post Office** *is open 24 hours a day : Jindřišska 14, Prague 1, ☎ (02) 24 22 85 88.*

## SHOPPING IN PRAGUE

*In the index of street names, those printed in red are where the principal shops are found. Typical goods to be bought include embroidery, puppets, glass, porcelain, ceramics... Shops are generally open from 9am to 7pm.*

## TIPPING

*Hotel, restaurant and café bills include service in the total charge but it is up to you to tip the staff.*

## CAR HIRE

*The international car hire companies have branches in Prague. Your hotel porter should be able to give details and help you with your arrangements.*

## BREAKDOWN SERVICE

*A 24 hour breakdown service is operated by YELLOW ANGELS, Limuzská 12, Prague 10, ☎ (02) 77 34 55, and Accident road service ☎ (02) 12 31 54.*

## SPEED LIMITS - SEAT BELTS - MOTORWAYS TAX

*The maximum permitted speed on motorways is 130 km/h - 80 mph, 90 km/h - 56 mph on other roads and 50 km/h - 31 mph in built up areas except where a lower speed limit is indicated.*

*The wearing of seat belts is compulsory for drivers and all passengers.*

*Driving on motorways is subject to the purchase of a single rate annual road tax obtainable from border posts and tourist offices.*

*In the Czech Republic, drivers must not drink alcoholic beverages at all.*

# PRAGUE

(PRAHA) *Česká Republika* 976 F 3 - *Pop. 1 203 230*

*Berlin 344 - Dresden 152 - Munich 384 - Nurnberg 287 - Wroclaw 272 - Vienna 291.*

*Prague Information Service : Na Příkope 20 (main office), Staroměstské nám 1, and Main Railway Station* ☎ *187*
*CEDOK : Na přikopě 18, Prague 1* ☎ *(02) 24 19 71 11, Fax (02) 232 16 56.*

*Golf Club Praha, Motol-Praha 5,* ☎ *(02) 651 24 64*
*Ruzyně (Prague Airport) NW 20 km, by road nº 7* ☎ *(02) 36 77 60.*
*Bus to airport : ČSA Bus at airlines Terminal V. Celnici 5* ☎ *(02) 20 11 42 96.*
*CZECH AIRLINES (ČESKÉ AEROLINIE) V. Celnici 5, PRAGUE 1* ☎ *(02) 20 10 41 11.*

**See:** *Castle District*★★★ *(Hradčany)* ABY : *Prague Castle*★★★ *(Pražský Hrad)* BY, *St Vitus' Cathedral*★★★ *(Katedrála sv. Víta)* BY, *Royal Palace*★★ *(Královský palác)* BY, *St George's Basilica and Convent*★★ *(National Gallery's Collection of Old Czech Art*★★★*) (Bazilika sv. Jiří/Jiřský Klašter)* BY, *Hradčany Square*★ *(Hradčanské náměstí)* AY **37**, *Schwarzenberg Palace*★ *(Schwarzenberský Palác)* ABY **P4**, *Loretto*★★ *(Loreta)* AY, *Strahov Monastery*★★ *(Strahovský Klášter)* AY – *Lesser Town*★★★ *(Malá Strana)* BY : *Charles Bridge*★★★ *(Karlův Most)* BCY, *Lesser Town Square*★★ *(Malostranské náměstí)* BY, *St Nicholas Church*★★★ *(Sv. Mikuláš)* BY, *Nerudova Street*★★ *(Nerudova)* BY, *Wallenstein Palace*★★ *(Valdštejnský Palác)* BY – *Old Town*★★★ *(Staré Město)* CY : *Old Town Square*★★★ *(Staroměstské náměstí)* CY, *Astronomical Clock*★★ *(Orloj)* CY **B**, *Old Town Hall – Extensive view*★★★ *(Staroměstská radnice)* CY **B**, *St Nicolas'*★ *(Sv. Mikuláš)* CY, *Týn Church*★ *(Týnský chrám)* CY, *Jewish Quarter*★★★ *(Josefov)* CY, *Old-New Synagogue*★★ *(Staronová Synagóga)* CY, *Old Jewish Cemetery*★★ *(Starý židovský hřbitov)* CY **V**, *St Agnes Convent*★★ *(National Gallery's Collection of 19 C Czech Painting and Sculpture) (Anežský klášter)* CY, *Celetná Street*★★ *(Celetná)* CDY, *Powder Tower*★ *(Prašná Brána)* DY, *House of the black Madonna*★ *(Dům u černe Matky boží)* CDY **E**, *Municipal House*★★ *(Obecní Dům)* DY **F** – *New Town*★★★ *(Nové Město)* CDZ : *Wenceslas Square*★★★ *(Václavské náměstí)* CDYZ.

**Museums**: *National Gallery*★★★ *(Národní Galérie)* AY, *National Museum*★ *(Národní muzeum)* DZ, *National Theatre*★★ *(Národní divadlo)* CZ, *Decorative Arts Museum*★ *(Umělecko průmyslové muzeum)* CY **M1**, *City Museum*★ *(Prague model*★★*) (Muzeum hlavního města Prahy)* DY **M2**, *Vila America*★ *(Dvořák Museum)* DZ.

**Outskirts:** *Karlštejn Castle SW : 30 km* ET – *Konopiště Castle SW : 40 km* FT.

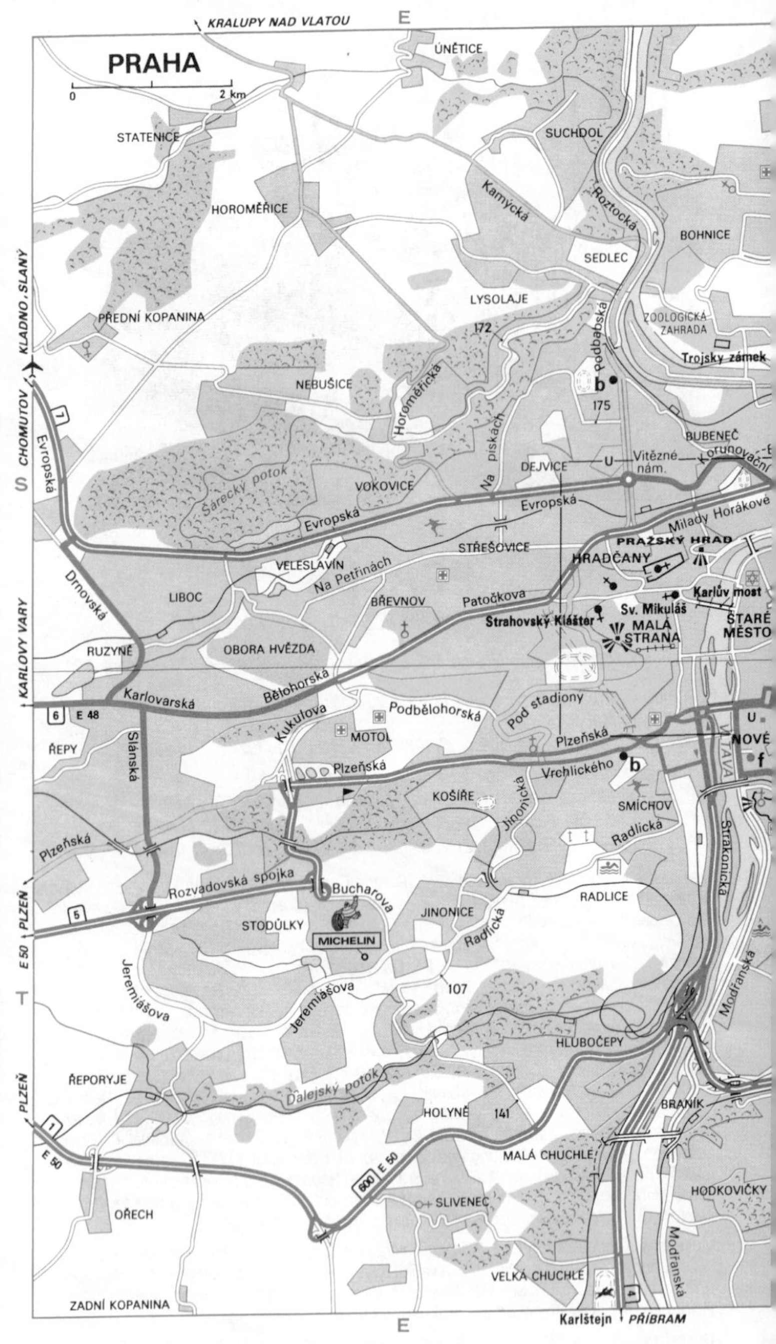
PRAHA
0
2 km
KRALUPY NAD VLATOU
E
ÚNĚTICE
STATENICE
SUCHDOL
HOROMĚŘICE
Kamýcká
Roztocká
BOHNICE
SEDLEC
LYSOLAJE
PŘEDNÍ KOPANINA
ZOOLOGICKÁ ZAHRADA
172
Trojský zámek
Podbabská
KLADNO, SLANÝ
NEBUŠICE
Horoměřická
b
175
CHOMUTOV
7
Evropská
Šárecký potok
Na piskách
BUBENEČ
DEJVICE
U
Vítězné nám.
Korunovační
S
VOKOVICE
Evropská
Evropská
Milady Horákové
PRAŽSKÝ HRAD
STŘEŠOVICE
HRADČANY
VELESLAVÍN
Na Petřinách
Drnovská
LIBOC
BŘEVNOV
Patočkova
Karlův most
Sv. Mikuláš
Strahovský Klášter
MALÁ STRANA
STARÉ MĚSTO
KARLOVY VARY
RUZYNĚ
OBORA HVĚZDA
Bělohorská
Karlovarská
Pod stadiony
6
E 48
Kukulova
Podbělohorská
U
Slánská
MOTOL
Plzeňská
NOVÉ
ŘEPY
Plzeňská
Vrchlického
b
VLTAVA
f
KOŠÍŘE
SMÍCHOV
Jinonická
Strakonická
Radlická
Plzeňská
Rozvadovská spojka
Bucharova
RADLICE
PLZEŇ
5
STODŮLKY
JINONICE
Radlická
MICHELIN
E 50
Jeremiášova
107
Modřanská
T
Jeremiášova
HLUBOČEPY
ŘEPORYJE
Dalejský potok
PLZEŇ
1
HOLYNĚ
141
BRANÍK
E 50
MALÁ CHUCHLE
600
E 50
SLIVENEC
HODKOVIČKY
OŘECH
Modřanská
VELKÁ CHUCHLE
4
ZADNÍ KOPANINA
Karlštejn
PŘÍBRAM
E

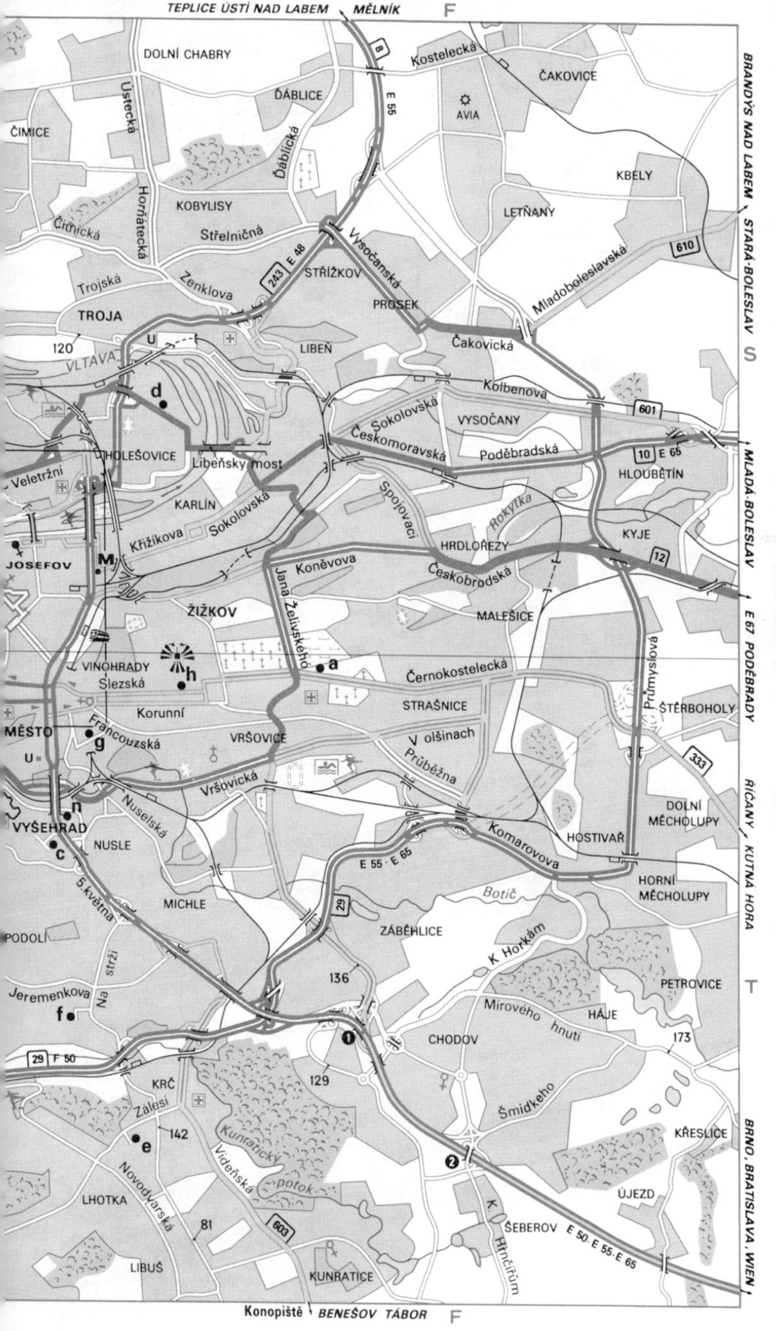
TEPLICE ÚSTÍ NAD LABEM
MĚLNÍK
F
BRANDÝS NAD LABEM, STARÁ-BOLESLAV
S
MLADÁ-BOLESLAV
E 67 PODĚBRADY
ŘÍČANY, KUTNÁ HORA
T
BRNO, BRATISLAVA, WIEN
Konopiště
BENEŠOV TÁBOR
DOLNÍ CHABRY
ČAKOVICE
ĎÁBLICE
ČIMICE
AVIA
KBELY
KOBYLISY
LETŇANY
STŘÍŽKOV
PROSEK
TROJA
LIBEŇ
VYSOČANY
HOLEŠOVICE
HLOUBĚTÍN
KARLÍN
KYJE
HRDLOŘEZY
JOSEFOV
ŽIŽKOV
MALEŠICE
VINOHRADY
STRAŠNICE
ŠTĚRBOHOLY
MĚSTO
VRŠOVICE
DOLNÍ MĚCHOLUPY
VYŠEHRAD
NUSLE
HOSTIVAŘ
HORNÍ MĚCHOLUPY
MICHLE
ZÁBĚHLICE
PODOLÍ
PETROVICE
HÁJE
CHODOV
KRČ
KŘESLICE
LHOTKA
ÚJEZD
ŠEBEROV
LIBUŠ
KUNRATICE
VLTAVA
Botič
Kunratický potok
Rokytka
Ústecká
Horňátecká
Čimická
Střelničná
Ďáblická
Kostelecká
Trojská
Zenklova
Vysočanská
Mladoboleslavská
Čakovická
Kolbenova
Sokolovská
Českomoravská
Poděbradská
Veletržní
Libeňský most
Spojovací
Křižíkova
Koněvova
Českobrodská
Jana Želivského
Černokostelecká
Průmyslová
Slezská
Korunní
Francouzská
V olšinach
Průběžná
Vršovická
Nuselská
Komarovova
5. května
K Horkám
Mírového hnutí
Na strži
Jeremenkova
Zálesí
Šmidkeho
Novodvarská
Vídeňská
K Hrnčířům
E 55
E 48
E 65
E 55 · E 65
E 50 · E 55 · E 65
F 50
8
243
610
601
10
12
333
29
603
120
136
129
173
142
81
a
c
d
e
f
g
h
n
M
U
1
2

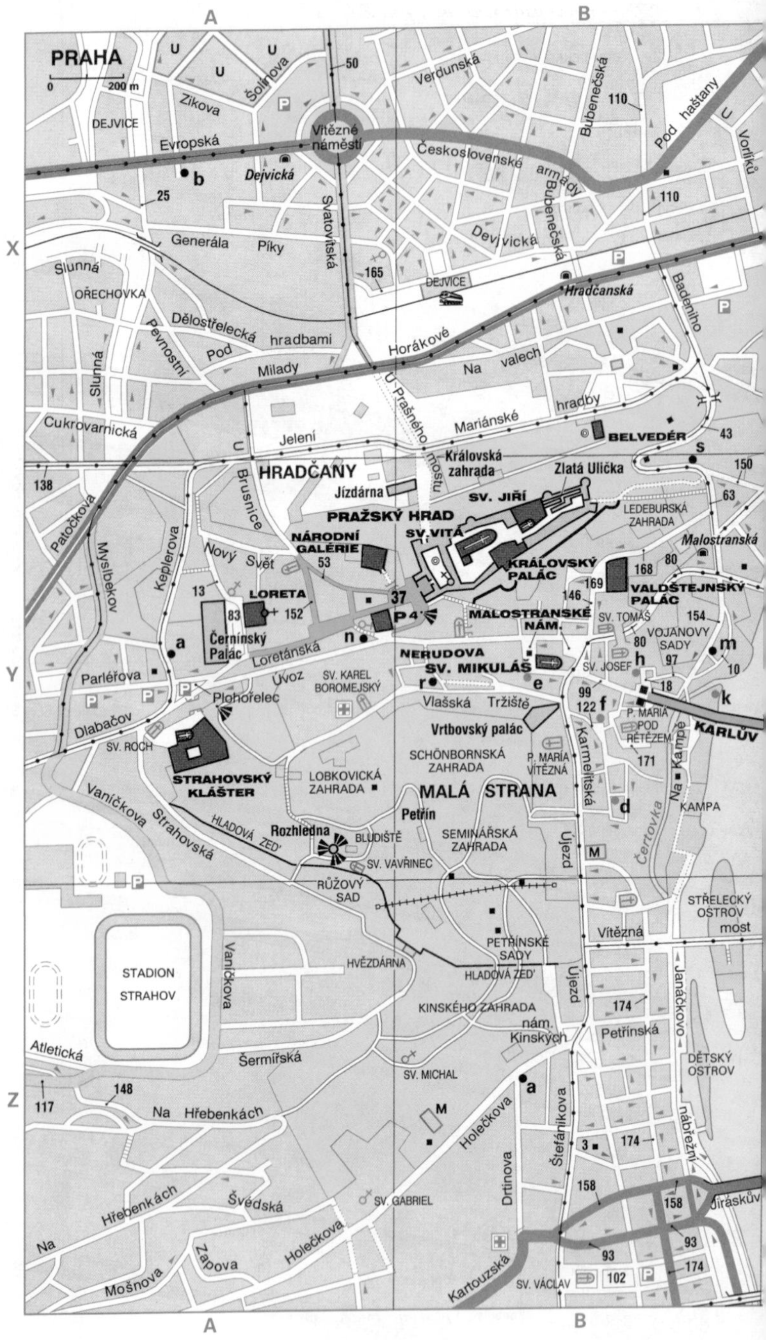
PRAHA
0
200 m
A
B
X
Y
Z
DEJVICE
Evropská
Zikova
Šolínova
Vítězné náměstí
Dejvická
Svatovítská
Verdunská
Bubenečská
Pod haštany
Vorlíků
Československé armády
Generála Píky
Dejvická
Hradčanská
Badeniho
Slunná
OŘECHOVKA
Dělostřelecká
Pevnostní
Pod hradbami
Milady Horákové
Na valech
U Prašného mostu
Mariánské hradby
Jelení
Cukrovarnická
BELVEDÉR
Královská zahrada
Zlatá Ulička
HRADČANY
Jízdárna
U Brusnice
SV. JIŘÍ
PRAŽSKÝ HRAD
LEDEBURSKÁ ZAHRADA
Malostranská
NÁRODNÍ GALÉRIE
SV. VITA
KRÁLOVSKÝ PALÁC
VALDŠTEJNSKÝ PALÁC
Patočkova
Myslbekov
Keplerova
Nový Svět
LORETA
MALOSTRANSKÉ NÁM.
SV. TOMÁŠ
VOJANOVY SADY
Černínský Palác
Loretánská
NERUDOVA
SV. MIKULÁŠ
SV. JOSEF
Parléřova
Úvoz
SV. KAREL BOROMEJSKÝ
Plohořelec
Vlašská
Tržiště
P. MARIA POD ŘETĚZEM
KARLŮV
Dlabačov
SV. ROCH
Vrtbovský palác
Karmelitská
STRAHOVSKÝ KLÁŠTER
SCHÖNBORNSKÁ ZAHRADA
P. MARIA VÍTĚZNÁ
LOBKOVICKÁ ZAHRADA
MALÁ STRANA
Na Kampě
KAMPA
Vaníčkova
Strahovská
HLADOVÁ ZEĎ
Rozhledna
BLUDIŠTĚ
Petřín
SEMINÁŘSKÁ ZAHRADA
Čertovka
SV. VAVŘINEC
Újezd
RŮŽOVÝ SAD
STŘELECKÝ OSTROV
most
Vítězná
PETŘÍNSKÉ SADY
HVĚZDÁRNA
STADION STRAHOV
Vaníčkova
HLADOVÁ ZEĎ
Újezd
Janáčkovo
KINSKÉHO ZAHRADA
nám. Kinských
Petřínská
Atletická
Šermířská
DĚTSKÝ OSTROV
SV. MICHAL
Na Hřebenkách
Štefánikova
nábřeží
Holečkova
Drtinova
SV. GABRIEL
Na Hřebenkách
Švédská
Jiráskův
Holečkova
Zapova
Mošnova
Kartouzská
SV. VÁCLAV

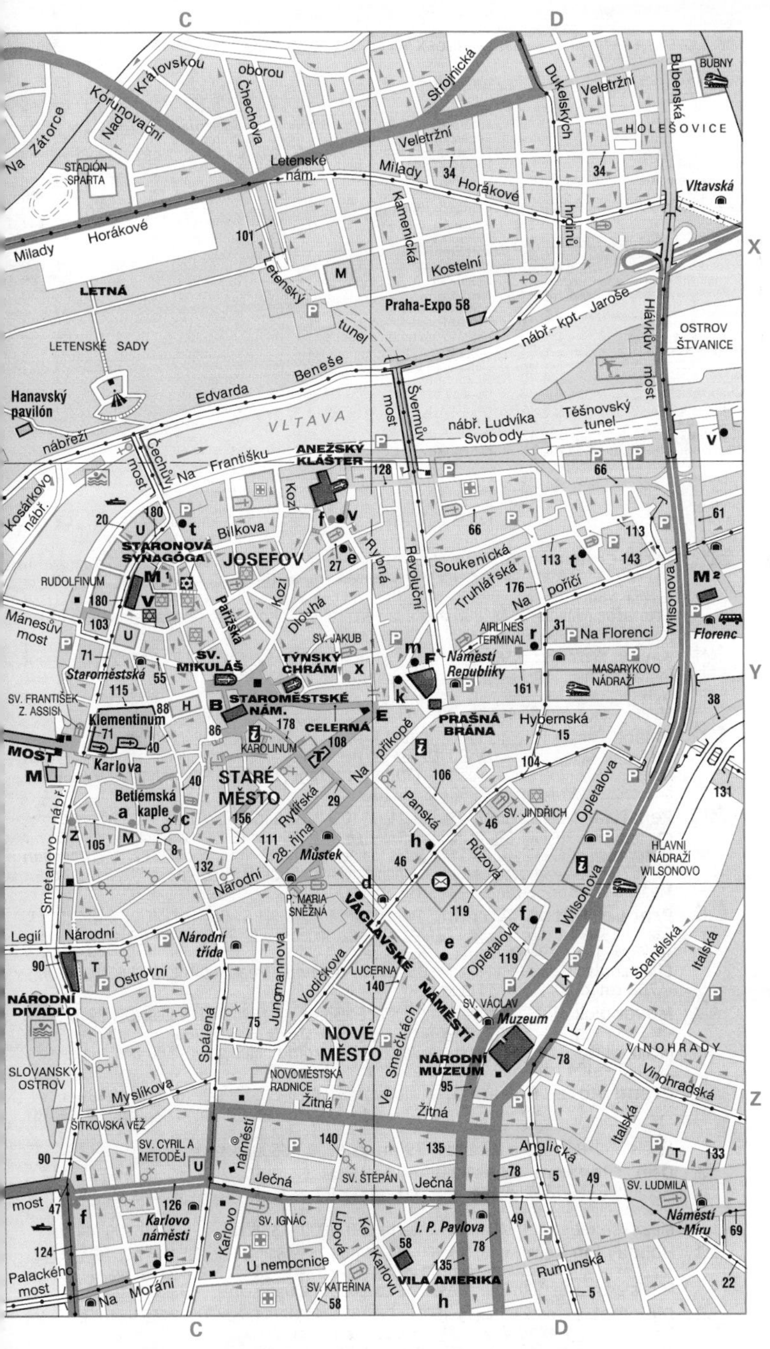
C
D
X
Y
Z
HOLEŠOVICE
LETNÁ
LETENSKÉ SADY
STADIÓN SPARTA
Hanavský pavilón
VLTAVA
JOSEFOV
STARÉ MĚSTO
NOVÉ MĚSTO
VINOHRADY
OSTROV ŠTVANICE
Praha-Expo 58
ANEŽSKÝ KLÁŠTER
STARONOVÁ SYNAGÓGA
RUDOLFINUM
SV. MIKULÁŠ
TÝNSKÝ CHRÁM
STAROMĚSTSKÉ NÁM.
Klementinum
KAROLINUM
CELERNÁ
PRAŠNÁ BRÁNA
MASARYKOVO NÁDRAŽÍ
AIRLINES TERMINAL
HLAVNÍ NÁDRAŽÍ WILSONOVO
NÁRODNÍ MUZEUM
VÁCLAVSKÉ NÁMĚSTÍ
NÁRODNÍ DIVADLO
SLOVANSKÝ OSTROV
NOVOMĚSTSKÁ RADNICE
VILA AMERIKA
Betlémská kaple
MOST
Florenc
Vltavská
Muzeum
Můstek
Národní třída
Staroměstská
Náměstí Republiky
Náměstí Míru
I. P. Pavlova
Karlovo náměstí
BUBNY
SV. JAKUB
SV. JINDŘICH
SV. VÁCLAV
SV. LUDMILA
SV. IGNÁC
SV. KATEŘINA
SV. ŠTĚPÁN
SV. CYRIL A METODĚJ
ŠITKOVSKÁ VĚŽ
SV. FRANTIŠEK Z. ASSISI
P. MARIA SNĚŽNÁ
LUCERNA

## STREET INDEX TO PRAHA TOWN PLAN

| Street | Grid | No. |
|---|---|---|
| Celetná | CDY | |
| Na příkopě | CDY | |
| Národní | CZ | |
| Václavské náměstí | CDZ | |
| Arbesovo náměstí | BZ | 3 |
| Bělehradská | DZ | 5 |
| Betlémské náměstí | CY | 8 |
| Çihelná | BY | 10 |
| Černínská | AY | 13 |
| Dlážděná | DY | 15 |
| Dražického náměstí | BY | 18 |
| Dvořákovo nábřeží | CY | 20 |
| Francouzská | DY | 22 |
| Gymnasijní | AX | 25 |
| Haštalské náměstí | CY | 27 |
| Havířská | CY | 29 |
| Havlíčkova | DY | 31 |
| Heřmanova | DX | 34 |
| Hradčanské náměstí | AY | 37 |
| Husitská | DY | 38 |
| Husova | CY | 40 |
| Chotkova | BX | 43 |
| Jindřišská | DY | 46 |
| Jiráskovo náměstí | CZ | 47 |
| Jugoslávská | DZ | 49 |
| Jugoslávských partyzánů | AX | 50 |
| Kanovnická | AY | 53 |
| Kaprova | CY | 55 |
| Kateřinská | CDZ | 58 |
| Ke Štvanici | DY | 61 |
| Klárov | BY | 63 |
| Klimentská | DY | 66 |
| Korunní | DZ | 69 |
| Křižovnická | CY | 71 |
| Lazarská | CZ | 75 |
| Legerova | DZ | 78 |
| Letenská | BY | 80 |
| Libušská | FT | 81 |
| Loretánské náměstí | AY | 83 |
| Malé náměstí | CY | 86 |
| Mariánské náměstí | CY | 88 |
| Masarykovo nábřeží | CZ | 90 |
| Matoušova | BZ | 93 |
| Mezibranská | DZ | 95 |
| Míšeňská | BY | 97 |
| Mostecká | BY | 99 |
| Nad štolou | CX | 101 |
| náměstí 14. října | BZ | 102 |
| náměstí Jana Palacha | CY | 103 |
| náměstí Maxima Gorkého | DY | 104 |
| Náprstkova | CY | 105 |
| Nekázanka | DY | 106 |
| Novoveská | ET | 107 |
| Ovocný trh | CY | 108 |
| Pelléova | BX | 110 |
| Perlová | CY | 111 |
| Petrská | DY | 113 |
| Platnéřská | CY | 115 |
| Pod Stadiony | AZ | 117 |
| Politických vězňů | DZ | 119 |
| Povltavská | FS | 120 |
| Prokopská | BY | 122 |
| Rašínovo nábřeží | CZ | 124 |
| Ŗesslova | CZ | 126 |
| Rásnovka | DY | 128 |
| Ryšaveho | FT | 129 |
| Seifertova | DY | 131 |
| Skořepka | CY | 132 |
| Slezská | DZ | 133 |
| Sokolská | DZ | 135 |
| Sporilovská | FT | 136 |
| Střešovická | AY | 138 |
| Štěpánská | DZ | 140 |
| Štěpařská | ÉT | 141 |
| Štúrova | FT | 142 |
| Těšnov | DY | 143 |
| Tomášská | BY | 146 |
| Turistiká | AZ | 148 |
| U Bruských Kasáren | BY | 150 |
| U kasáren | AY | 152 |
| U lužického semináře | BY | 154 |
| Uhelný trh | CY | 156 |
| V botanice | BZ | 158 |
| V celnici | DY | 161 |
| Václavkova | AX | 165 |
| Valdštejnská | BY | 168 |
| Valdštejnské náměstí | BY | 169 |
| Velkopřevorské náměstí | BY | 171 |
| V Šáreckém údolí | ES | 172 |
| Výstavní | FT | 173 |
| Zborovská | BZ | 174 |
| Zelená | ES | 175 |
| Zlatnická | DY | 176 |
| Železná | CY | 178 |
| 17. listopadu | CY | 180 |

**Inter-Continental**, Nám. Curieových 43-45, ✉ 110 00, ☎ (02) 2488 1111, *Fax (02) 2481 1216*, ←, Fø, ≘s, ⌂ – |‡|, ⇔ rm, ≡ TV ☎ ✆ ♿ – 🏛 400. AE ① E VISA JCB CY t
***Primator*** : Meals 700/1200 and a la carte – (see also ***Zlatá Praha*** below) – **340 rm** ⊡ 10030/11800, 24 suites.

**Savoy**, Keplerova Ul. 6, ✉ 118 00, ☎ (02) 2430 2430, *Fax (02) 2430 2128*, « Elegant installation », ≘s – |‡|, ⇔ rm, ≡ TV ☎ ✆ ♿ – 🏛 35. AE ① E VISA JCB AY a
Meals – (see ***Hradčany*** below) – **55 rm** ⊡ 7980/9435, 6 suites.

**Palace**, Panská 12, ✉ 111 21, ☎ (02) 2409 3111, *Fax (02) 2422 1240*, ≘s – |‡|, ⇔ rm, ≡ TV ☎ ✆ ♿ – 🏛 80. AE ① E VISA JCB DY h
Meals 1150/1250 and a la carte – ***Club Restaurant*** : Meals (dinner only) 2990/3550 and a la carte – **114 rm** ⊡ 7980/9510, 10 suites.

**Renaissance**, V Celnici 7, ✉ 111 21, ☎ (02) 2182 2100, *Fax (02) 2182 2200*, Fø, ≘s, ⌂ – |‡|, ⇔ rm, ≡ TV ☎ ✆ ♿ – 🏛 240. AE ① E VISA JCB. ⚹ rest DY r
***Potomac*** (*☎ (02) 2182 2431*) : Meals (dinner only) 930/1300 and a la carte – ***Pavillion*** (*☎ (02) 2182 2431*) : Meals (buffet lunch only) 470/550 – ***U Korbele*** (*☎ (02) 2182 2433*) : Meals a la carte 650/770 – **313 rm** ⊡ 6900/9100, 11 suites.

**Prague Hilton Atrium**, Pobřežní 1, ✉ 186 00, ☎ (02) 2484 1111, *Fax (02) 2484 2366*, ←, ⛱, Fø, ≘s, ⌂, ✂ indoor – |‡|, ⇔ rm, ≡ TV ☎ ✆ ♿ 🅟 – 🏛 1350. AE ① E VISA JCB. ⚹ rest DX v
***Chez Louis*** : Meals (dinner only) 850/950 – ***Atrium*** : Meals (buffet only) 650 – ⊡ 425 – **788 rm** 7600/8250, 34 suites.

**Mövenpick** Ⓜ, Mozartova 261/1, ✉ 151 33, ☎ (02) 5715 1111, *Fax (02) 5715 3131*, ⛱, *park* – |‡| ⇔ ≡ TV ☎ ♿ – 🏛 300. AE ① E VISA JCB ET b
Meals (buffet lunch) 490 and a la carte – ***Il Giardino*** : Meals 390/580 and a la carte – ⊡ 450 – **404 rm** 4590/4950, 31 suites.

**Grand Hotel Bohemia**, Králodvorská 4, ✉ 110 00, ☎ (02) 2480 4111, *Fax (02) 232 9545*, « Ballroom » – |‡|, ⇔ rm, ≡ TV ☎ ✆ ♿. AE ① E VISA JCB DY k
Meals 550/860 and a la carte – **75 rm** ⊡ 9800/13500, 3 suites.

**Don Giovanni** Ⓜ, Vinohradská 157a, ✉ 130 20, ☎ (02) 6703 1111, *Fax (02) 6703 6704*, ←, ≘s – |‡|, ⇔ rm, ≡ TV ☎ ✆ ♿ – 🏛 200. AE ① E VISA JCB FT a
Meals (buffet lunch) 540 and a la carte 650/1000 – **356 rm** ⊡ 5660/6700, 44 suites.

**Holiday Inn**, Koulova 15, ✉ 160 45, ☎ (02) 2439 3111, *Fax (02) 2431 0616*, ⛱, Fø, ≘s, ⛱ – |‡|, ⇔ rm, ≡ rest, TV ☎ ✆ ♿ 🅟 – 🏛 400. AE ① E VISA JCB ES b
Meals a la carte 330/590 – **237 rm** ⊡ 5650/6700, 6 suites.

**Diplomat**, Evropská 15, ✉ 160 41, ☎ (02) 2439 4111, *Fax (02) 2439 4215*, ≘s – |‡|, ⇔ rm, ≡ TV ☎ ✆ – 🏛 250. AE ① E VISA JCB AX b
Meals a la carte 410/630 – **364 rm** ⊡ 5800/6800, 18 suites.

**Hoffmeister,** Pod Bruskou 9, 118 00, (02) 5731 0942, *Fax (02) 5732 0906*, « Collection of Adolf Hoffmeister's artwork » – rm. BXY s
**Meals** a la carte 515/1520 – 325 – **34 rm** 6600/8800, 4 suites.

**Forum,** Kongresová 1, 140 69, (02) 6119 1111, *Fax (02) 420 684*, squash – rm, – 290. rest FT n
***Harmonie* : Meals** a la carte 790/1150 – ***Ceská* : Meals** (buffet only) 680 – **531 rm** 6235/7090.

**Maximilian** without rest., Haštalská 14, 110 00, (02) 2180 6111, *Fax (02) 2180 6110* – – 50. CY e
**71 rm** 5180/6150, 1 suite.

**Kinsky Garden,** Holečkova 7, 150 00, (02) 5731 1173, *Fax (02) 5731 1184* – rm, – 30. rest BZ a
**Meals** (dinner only) a la carte 600/820 – **60 rm** 4400/6180.

**Villa Voyta** (with guesthouse), K Novému Dvoru 124-54, 142 00, (02) 472 2711, *Fax (02) 472 2918*, – rm, rm, – 25.
**Meals** 750/2000 and a la carte – **20 rm** 4100/6300, 2 suites. FT e

**Esplanade,** Washingtonova 19, 110 00, (02) 2421 1715, *Fax (02) 2422 9306*, « Art Nouveau building » – rm, – 40. DZ f
**Meals** a la carte 500/900 – **68 rm** 6600/8400, 6 suites.

**Paříž,** U Obecního Domu 1, 110 00, (02) 2219 5111, *Fax (02) 2422 5475*, « Neo-Gothic and Art Nouveau architecture » – rm, – 55. DY m
**Meals** 510/1400 and a la carte – **93 rm** 7600/8600, 2 suites.

**U Krále Karla,** Úvoz 4, 118 00, (02) 538 805, *Fax (02) 538 811*, « 17C baroque house, antique furniture » – . AY n
**Meals** 240 (lunch) and a la carte 315/720 – **19 rm** 5000/6400.

**Vyšehrad,** Marie Cibulkové 29, 140 00, (02) 6122 5581, *Fax (02) 6122 5591* – . FT c
**Meals** a la carte 300/580 – **26 rm** 5300/5900, 1 suite.

**Adria,** Václavské Nám. 26, 110 00, (02) 2108 1111, *Fax (02) 2108 1300* – rm, rest, – 70. CZ d
**Meals** 380/1000 and a la carte – **61 rm** 4905/5850, 5 suites.

**City H. Moran,** Na Moráni 15, 120 00, (02) 2491 5208, *Fax (02) 297 533* – rm, . rest CZ e
**Meals** 350/750 and a la carte – **57 rm** 4940/5880.

**Jalta,** Václavské Nám. 45, 110 00, (02) 2422 9133, *Fax (02) 2421 3866* – – 130. DZ e
**Meals** 450/1900 and a la carte - also Japanese (Teppan-Yaki) - 950/1400 – **84 rm** 6850/8100, 5 suites.

**Alta,** Ortenovo Nám. 22, 170 00, (02) 800 252, *Fax (02) 6671 2011* – rm, rest, – 30. rest FS d
**Meals** 300/400 and a la carte – **82 rm** 2580/3220, 5 suites.

**Ametyst,** Jana Masaryka 11, 120 00, (02) 2425 4185, *Fax (02) 2425 1315*, – rm, rest, . FT g
**Meals** a la carte 500/730 – **84 rm** 4200/5250.

**Sax,** Jánský Vršek 328/3 Praha 1, 118 00, (02) 538 422, *Fax (02) 538 498* – rm, . BY r
**Meals** a la carte 205/375 – **19 rm** 3000/3700, 3 suites.

**Casa Marcello** , Rásnovka 783, 110 00, (02) 231 1230, *Fax (02) 231 3323*, – . CY v
**Meals** - Italian - *(closed lunch November-February)* a la carte 350/460 – **13 rm** 5100/6000, 4 suites.

**U Páva,** U Lužického Semináře 32, 118 00, (02) 5731 5867, *Fax (02) 533 379* – rm, . BY m
**Meals** a la carte 255/465 – **6 rm** 4600/4900, 5 suites.

**Vladař,** Na Dvorcích 144-149, 140 00, (02) 6126 1521, *Fax (02) 6126 4324* – . FT f
**Meals** a la carte 405/1030 – **16 rm** 2620/3240.

**Sieber,** Slezská 55, 130 00, (02) 2425 0025, *Fax (02) 2425 0027* – . FT h
**Meals** (dinner only) a la carte 265/530 – **12 rm** 3580/3800.

**Bílá Labuť,** Biskupská 9, 110 00, (02) 2481 1382, *Fax (02) 232 2905* – . DY t
**Meals** 250/540 and a la carte – **54 rm** 4500/5000.

XXXX **Zlatá** (at Inter-Continental H.), Nám. Curieových 43-45, ✉ 110 00, ✆ (02) 2488 1111, *Fax (02) 2481 1216*, ≤ Prague – ▤. AE ⓓ E VISA JCB. ⚡ CY t
**Meals** (dinner only) 1200/2500 and a la carte.

XXXX **Hradčany** (at Savoy H.), Keplerova Ul. 6, ✉ 118 00, ✆ (02) 2430 2430, *Fax (02) 2430 2128* – ▤. AE ⓓ E VISA JCB AY a
**Meals** 640/1000 and a la carte.

XXX **La Perle de Prague,** (7th floor), Rašínovo Nábřeží 80, ✉ 120 00, ✆ (02) 2198 4160, *Fax (02) 2198 4179*, ≤, 🏠 – |≑| ▤. AE ⓓ E VISA JCB CZ f
*closed Monday lunch and Sunday* – **Meals** a la carte 1050/2050.

XX **Flambée,** Betlém Palais, Husova 5, ✉ 110 00, ✆ (02) 2424 8512, *Fax (02) 2424 8513*, « 14C vaulted cellar » – Ⓟ. AE E VISA CY c
**Meals** (dinner booking essential) a la carte 1350/2050.

XX **Vinárna V Zatisi,** Liliová 1, Betlémské Nám., ✉ 110 00, ✆ (02) 2422 8977, *Fax (02) 2422 8932* – AE E VISA CY a
**Meals** (dinner booking essential) 675/975 and a la carte.

XX **Circle Line,** Malostranske Nám. 12, ✉ 110 00, ✆ (02) 530 308, *Fax (02) 2422 8932*, Vaulted cellar – AE E VISA BY e
*closed Sunday* – **Meals** (dinner only) 790/1390 and a la carte.

XX **Bellevue,** Smetanovo Nábřeží 18, ✉ 110 00, ✆ (02) 2422 1387, *Fax (02) 2422 8932* – AE E VISA CY z
**Meals** 890/1290 and a la carte.

XX **Francouzská,** Náměstí Republiky 5, ✉ 110 00, ✆ (02) 2200 2770, *Fax (02) 2200 2777*, « Restored 1912 Art Nouveau building » – AE E VISA JCB DY f
**Meals** a la carte 290/690 – ***Plzeňská :*** **Meals** a la carte 150/290.

X **Kampa Park,** Na Kampě 8b, ✉ 110 00, ✆ (02) 5731 3493, *Fax (02) 5731 3495*, 🏠, « Vltava riverside setting, ≤ Charles Bridge » – AE ⓓ E VISA BY k
**Meals** (dinner booking essential) 1000 and a la carte.

X **Bistrot de Marlène,** Plavecká 4, ✉ 120 00, ✆ (02) 291 077, *Fax (02) 291 077* – AE E VISA ET f
*closed Saturday lunch, Sunday and 24 December-5 January* – **Meals** (booking essential) a la carte 670/930.

X **U Patrona,** Dražického Nám. 4, ✉ 118 00, ✆ (02) 531 512, *Fax (02) 2422 8932* – AE E VISA BY h
*closed Sunday* – **Meals** (dinner only) 890/1090 and a la carte 1070/1270.

X **La Provence,** Štupartská 9, ✉ 110 00, ✆ (02) 232 4801, *Fax (02) 232 4801*, « Vaulted cellar » – AE E VISA CY x
**Meals** - Mediterranean Bistro - (booking essential) a la carte 370/795.

## LOCAL ATMOSPHERE AND CZECH CUISINE

XX **U Vladaře,** Maltézské Nám. 10, ✉ 118 00, ✆ (02) 538 128, *Fax (02) 530 842*, 🏠 – AE ⓓ E VISA JCB BY f
**Meals** a la carte 185/600.

XX **U Modre Kachnicky,** Nebovidská 6, ✉ 118 00, ✆ (02) 5732 0308, *Fax (02) 5732 0308*, « 14C house with modern murals » BY d
**Meals** (dinner booking essential) a la carte 475/700.

XX **U Červeného Kola,** Anežská 2, ✉ 110 00, ✆ (02) 2481 1118, *Fax (02) 2481 1118*, « Courtyard terrace » – AE ⓓ E VISA JCB. ⚡ CY f
**Meals** a la carte 340/755.

X **Hostinec U Kalicha,** Na Bojišti 12, ✉ 120 00, ✆ (02) 291 945, *Fax (02) 290 701*, Typical Prague beerhouse – AE ⓓ VISA JCB DZ h
**Meals** a la carte 240/420.

# Denmark

## Danmark

COPENHAGEN

# PRACTICAL INFORMATION

## LOCAL CURRENCY

**Danish Kroner:** *100 DKK = 14,67 USD ($) (Jan. 98)*

## TOURIST INFORMATION

*The telephone number and address of the Tourist Information office is given in the text under* 🅸.

**National Holiday in Denmark:** *5 June.*

## FOREIGN EXCHANGE

*Banks are open between 9.30am and 4.00pm (6.00pm on Thursdays) on weekdays except Saturdays. The main banks in the centre of Copenhagen, the Central Station and the Airport have exchange facilities outside these hours.*

## AIRLINES

**SAS:** *Hamerichsgade 1, ☎ 31 54 17 01*

**AIR FRANCE:** *Ved Versterpot 6, ☎ 33 12 76 76*

**BRITISH AIRWAYS:** *Rådhuspladsen 16, ☎ 33 14 60 00*

**LUFTHANSA:** *V. Farimagsgade 7, ☎ 33 37 73 33*

**UNITED AIRLINES:** *V. Farimagsgade 1, ☎ 33 13 47 47*

## MEALS

*At lunchtime, follow the custom of the country and try the typical buffets of Scandinavian specialities (smørrebrød).*

*At dinner, the a la carte and set menus will offer you more conventional cooking.*

## SHOPPING IN COPENHAGEN

*Strøget (Department stores, exclusive shops, boutiques).*

*Kompagnistræde (Antiques). Shops are generally open from 10am to 7pm (Saturday 9am to 4pm).*

*See also in the index of street names, those printed in red are where the principal shops are found.*

## THEATRE BOOKINGS

*Your hotel porter will be able to make your arrangements or direct you to Theatre Booking Agents.*

## CAR HIRE

*The international car hire companies have branches in Copenhagen. Your hotel porter should be able to give details and help you with your arrangements.*

## TIPPING

*In Denmark, all hotels and restaurants include a service charge. As for the taxis, there is no extra charge to the amount shown on the meter.*

## SPEED LIMITS

*The maximum permitted speed in cities is 50 km/h - 31 mph, outside cities 80 km/h - 50 mph and 110 km/h - 68 mph on motorways. Cars towing caravans 70 km/h – 44 mph and buses 80 km/h – 50 mph also on motorways.*

*Local signs may indicate lower or permit higher limits. On the whole, speed should always be adjusted to prevailing circumstances. In case of even minor speed limit offences, drivers will be liable to heavy fines to be paid on the spot. If payment cannot be made, the car may be impounded.*

## SEAT BELTS

*The wearing of seat belts is compulsory for drivers and all passengers except children under the age of 3 and taxi passengers.*

# COPENHAGEN

(KØBENHAVN) *Danmark* 985 *Q 9 - pop. 622 000, Greater Copenhagen 1 354 000.*

*Berlin 385 - Hamburg 305 - Oslo 583 - Stockholm 630.*

*Copenhagen Tourist Information, Bernstorffsgade 1, ✉ 1577 V ☎ 33 11 13 25, Fax 33 93 49 69.*

*Dansk Golf Union 56 ☎ 43 45 55 55.*

*Copenhagen/Kastrup SE : 10 km ☎ 31 54 17 01 – Air Terminal : main railway station.*

*Motorail for Southern Europe : ☎ 33 14 17 01.*

*Further information from the D S B, main railway station or tourist information centre (see above).*

**See** : *Rosenborg Castle★★★ (Rosenborg Slot)* CX – *Amalienborg Palace★★ (Amalienborg)* DY – *Nyhavn★★ (canal)* DY – *Tivoli★★ : May to mid September* BZ – *Christiansborg Palace★ (Christiansborg)* CZ – *Citadel★ (Kastellet)* DX – *Gråbrødretorv★* CY **28** – *Little Mermaid★★ (Den Lille Havfrue)* DX – *Marble Bridge★ (Marmorbroen)* CZ **50** – *Marble Church★ (Marmorkirke)* DY – *Kongens Nytorv★* DX – *Round Tower★ (Rundetårn)* CY **E** – *Stock Exchange★ (Børsen)* CDZ – *Strøget★* BCYZ – *Town Hall (Rådhuset)* BZ **H** : *Jens Olsen's astronomical clock★* BZ **H**.

**Museums** : *National Museum★★★ (Nationalmuseet)* CZ – *Ny Carlsberg Glyptotek★★★ : art collection* BZ – *National Fine Arts Museum★★ (Statens Museum for Kunst)* CX – *Thorvaldsen Museum★★ (Thorvaldsens Museum)* CZ **M1**.

**Outskirts** : *Ordrupgård★★ : art collection (Ordrupgårdsamlingen) N : 10 km* CX – *Louisiana Museum of Modern Art★★ (Museum for Moderne Kunst) N : 35 km* CX – *Dragør★ SW : 13 km* CZ – *Rungstedlund★ : Karen Blixen Museum N : 25 km* CX – *Open-Air Museum★ (Frilandsmuseet) NW : 12 km* AX.

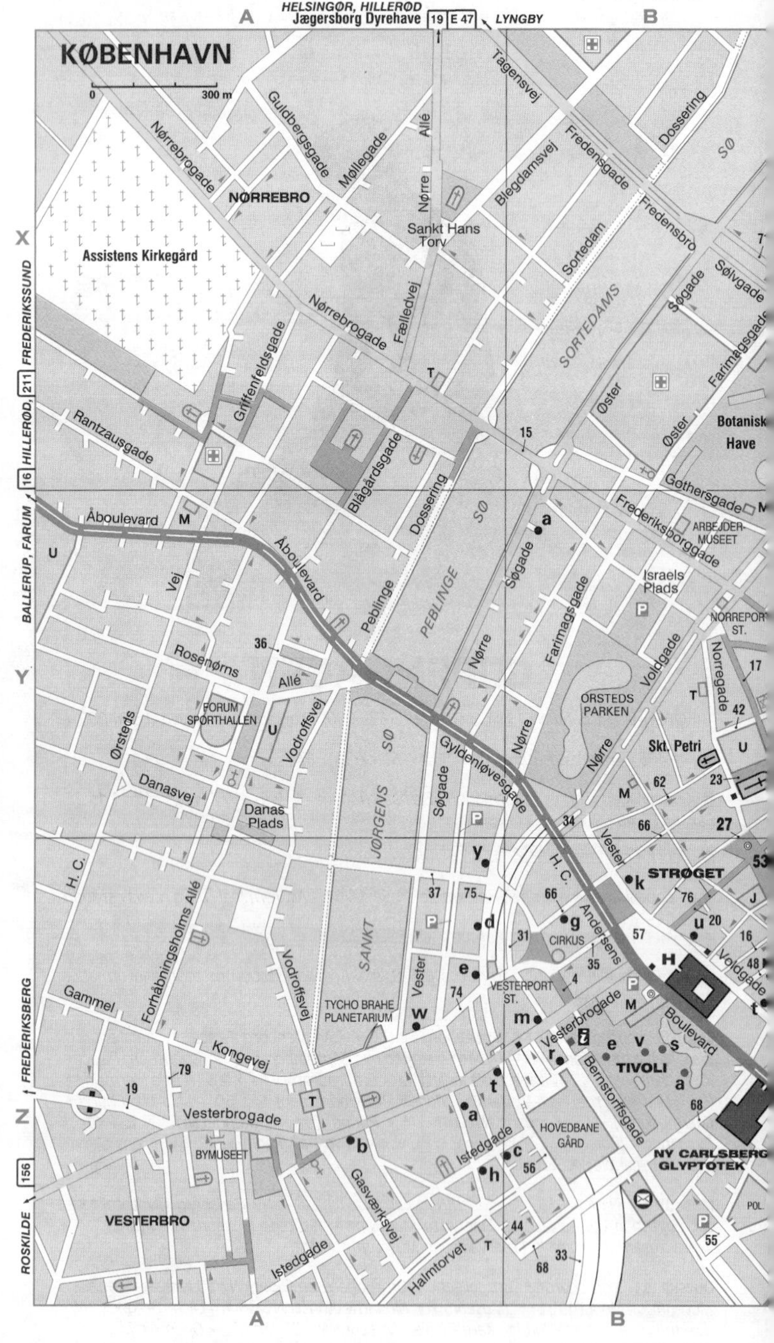
KØBENHAVN
0
300 m
HELSINGØR, HILLERØD
Jægersborg Dyrehave
19
E 47
LYNGBY
A
B
X
Y
Z
16 HILLERØD, 211 FREDERIKSSUND
BALLERUP, FARUM
FREDERIKSBERG
156
ROSKILDE
NØRREBRO
Assistens Kirkegård
Nørrebrogade
Guldbergsgade
Møllegade
Nørre Allé
Sankt Hans Torv
Tagensvej
Blegdamsvej
Fredensgade
Fredensbro
Dossering
SØ
Sortedam
SORTEDAMS
Sølvgade
Søgade
Farimagsgade
Øster
Botanisk Have
Fælledvej
Griffenfeldsgade
Rantzausgade
Blågårdsgade
Dossering
SØ
Gothersgade
Frederiksborggade
ARBEJDER-MUSEET
Israels Plads
NØRREPORT ST.
Åboulevard
Vej
Peblinge
PEBLINGE
Nørre
Farimagsgade
Voldgade
ØRSTEDS PARKEN
Norregade
Rosenørns Allé
FORUM SPORTHALLEN
Vodroffsvej
Ørsteds
Danasvej
Danas Plads
Gyldenløvesgade
Søgade
JØRGENS
SØ
Skt. Petri
Vester
STRØGET
H. C. Andersens
CIRKUS
VESTERPORT ST.
Vesterbrogade
Boulevard
TIVOLI
Bernstorffsgade
Voldgade
H. C.
Forhåbningsholms Allé
Gammel Kongevej
Vodroffsvej
TYCHO BRAHE PLANETARIUM
SANKT
Vester
Vesterbrogade
BYMUSEET
Gasværksvej
Istedgade
HOVEDBANE GÅRD
NY CARLSBERG GLYPTOTEK
POL.
VESTERBRO
Istedgade
Halmtorvet
M
U
T
P
H
J
a
k
g
d
e
y
w
m
r
t
b
c
h
u
v
s
15
17
20
23
27
31
33
34
35
36
37
4
42
44
48
53
55
56
57
62
66
68
74
75
76
79
16
19

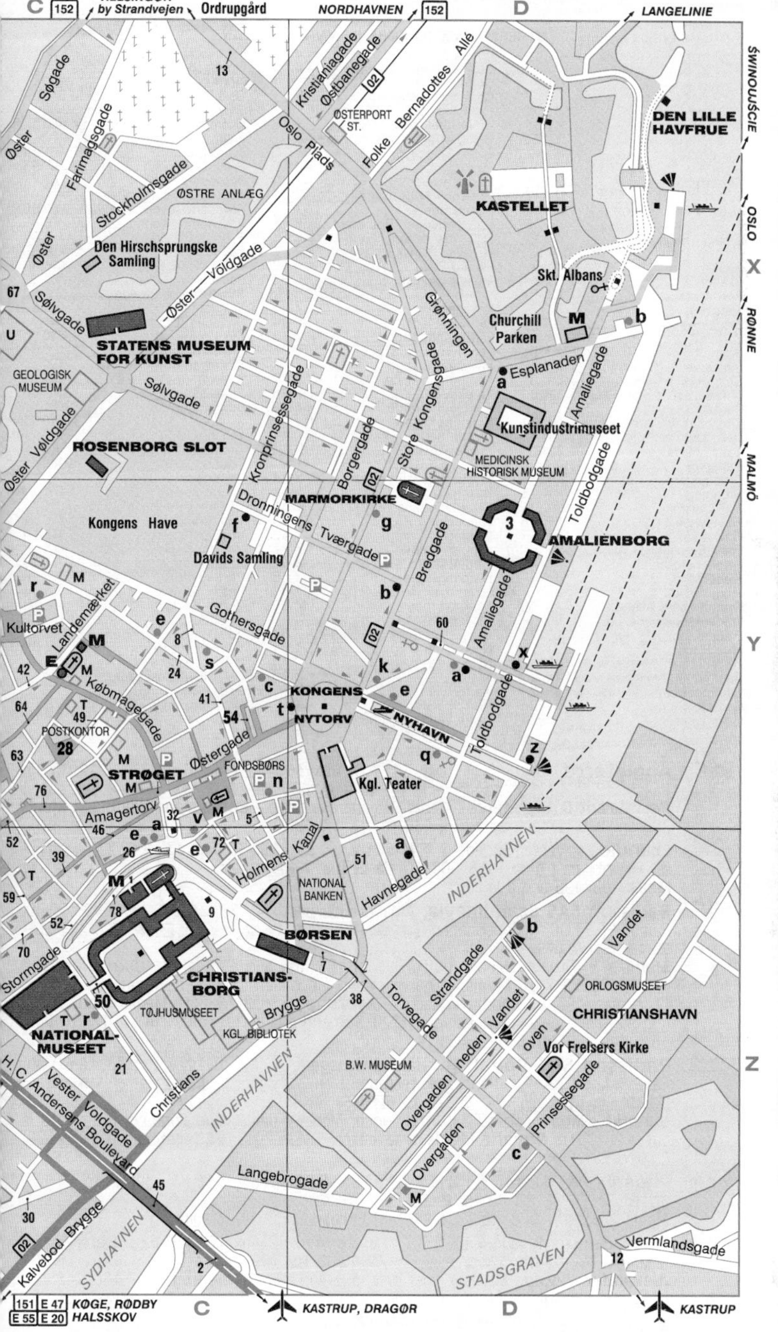
HELSINGØR by Strandvejen
Ordrupgård
NORDHAVNEN
LANGELINIE
DEN LILLE HAVFRUE
KASTELLET
Skt. Albans
Churchill Parken
Esplanaden
Kunstindustrimuseet
MEDICINSK HISTORISK MUSEUM
AMALIENBORG
MARMORKIRKE
STATENS MUSEUM FOR KUNST
GEOLOGISK MUSEUM
ROSENBORG SLOT
Kongens Have
Davids Samling
Den Hirschsprungske Samling
ØSTRE ANLÆG
ØSTERPORT ST.
Oslo Plads
Folke Bernadottes Allé
Kristianiagade
Østbanegade
Søgade
Farimagsgade
Stockholmsgade
Øster Voldgade
Sølvgade
Kronprinsessegade
Borgergade
Store Kongensgade
Grønningen
Bredgade
Amaliegade
Toldbodgade
Dronningens Tværgade
Gothersgade
Landemærket
Kultorvet
Købmagergade
POSTKONTOR
STRØGET
Østergade
FONDSBØRS
KONGENS NYTORV
NYHAVN
Kgl. Teater
Amagertorv
Holmens Kanal
NATIONAL BANKEN
Havnegade
BØRSEN
CHRISTIANSBORG
TØJHUSMUSEET
KGL. BIBLIOTEK
NATIONAL-MUSEET
Stormgade
Christians Brygge
H. C. Andersens Boulevard
Vester Voldgade
Kalvebod Brygge
SYDHAVNEN
INDERHAVNEN
Langebrogade
B.W. MUSEUM
Torvegade
Strandgade
Overgaden neden Vandet
Overgaden oven Vandet
ORLOGSMUSEET
CHRISTIANSHAVN
Vor Frelsers Kirke
Prinsessegade
Vermlandsgade
STADSGRAVEN
KØGE, RØDBY HALSSKOV
KASTRUP, DRAGØR
KASTRUP
ŚWINOUJŚCIE
OSLO
RØNNE
MALMÖ

## STREET INDEX TO KØBENHAVN TOWN PLAN

Amagertorv (Strøget) . . . . . CY
Bredgade . . . . . . . . . . . . . DY
Frederiksberggade (Strøget) . . . . . . . . . . . BZ 20
Købmagergade . . . . . . . . . . CY
Nygade (Strøget) . . . . . . . CYZ 52
Nørre Voldgade . . . . . . . . . BY
Store Kongensgade . . . . . DXY
Vesterbrogade . . . . . . . . . ABZ
Vimmelskaftet (Strøget) . . . CY 76
Østergade (Strøget) . . . . . . CY

Amager Boulevard . . . . . . . CZ 2
Amaliegade . . . . . . . . . . . DXY
Amalienborg Plads . . . . . . . DY 3
Axeltorv . . . . . . . . . . . . . BZ 4
Bernstorffsgade . . . . . . . . . BZ
Blegdamsvej . . . . . . . . . . . BX
Blågårdsgåde . . . . . . . . . . AX
Borgergade . . . . . . . . . . . DXY
Bremerholm . . . . . . . . . . . CY 5
Børsgade . . . . . . . . . . . . . DZ 7
Christan IX's Gade . . . . . . . CY 8
Christiansborg Slotsplads . . CZ 9
Christians Brygge . . . . . . . . CZ
Christmas Møllers Plads . . . DZ 12
Dag Hammarskjölds Allé . . CX 13
Danas Plads . . . . . . . . . . . AY
Danasvej . . . . . . . . . . . . . AY
Dronningens Tværgade . . CDY
Dronning Louises Bro . . . . . BX 15
Esplanaden . . . . . . . . . . . DX
Farvergade . . . . . . . . . . . . BZ 16
Fiolstræde . . . . . . . . . . . . BY 17
Folke Bernadottes Allé . . . . DX
Forhåbningsholms Allé . . . . AZ
Fredensbro . . . . . . . . . . . . BX
Fredensgade . . . . . . . . . . . BX
Frederiksberg Allé . . . . . . . AZ 19
Frederiksborggade . . . . . . . BY
Frederiksholms Kanal . . . . . CZ 21
Frue Plads . . . . . . . . . . . . BY 23
Fælledvej . . . . . . . . . . . . . AX
Gammel Kongevej . . . . . . . AZ
Gammel Mønt . . . . . . . . . . CY 24
Gammel Strand . . . . . . . . . CZ 26
Gammeltorv . . . . . . . . . . . BYZ 27
Gasværksvej . . . . . . . . . . . AZ
Gothersgade . . . . . . . . . . . BCY
Griffenfeldsgade . . . . . . . . AX
Grønningen . . . . . . . . . . . . DX
Gråbrødretorv . . . . . . . . . . CY 28
Guldbergsgade . . . . . . . . . . AX
Gyldenløvesgade . . . . . . . . AY
Halmtorvet . . . . . . . . . . . . AZ
Hambrosgade . . . . . . . . . . . CZ 30
Hammerichsgade . . . . . . . . BZ 31
Havnegade . . . . . . . . . . . . DZ
H.C. Andersens Boulevard . BCZ
H.C. Ørsteds Vej . . . . . . . . AY
Holmens Kanal . . . . . . . . . CDZ
Højbro Plads . . . . . . . . . . . CY 32
Ingerslevsgade . . . . . . . . . BZ 33
Israels Plads . . . . . . . . . . . BY
Istedgade . . . . . . . . . . . . . AZ
Jarmers Plads . . . . . . . . . . BY 34
Jernbanegade . . . . . . . . . . BZ 35
Julius Thomsens Gade . . . . AY 36
Kalvebod Brygge . . . . . . . . CZ
Kampmannsgade . . . . . . . . AZ 37
Knippelsbro . . . . . . . . . . . DZ 38
Kompagnistræde . . . . . . . . CZ 39
Kongens Nytorv . . . . . . . . . DY
Kristen Bernikows Gade . . . CY 41
Kristianiagade . . . . . . . . . . DX
Kronprinsessegade . . . . . . CXY
Krystalgade . . . . . . . . . . . BCY 42
Kultorvet . . . . . . . . . . . . . CY
Kvægtorvsgade . . . . . . . . . ABZ 44
Landemaerket . . . . . . . . . . CY
Langebro . . . . . . . . . . . . . CZ 45
Langebrogade . . . . . . . . . . CDZ
Læderstræde . . . . . . . . . . . CYZ 46
Løngangstræde . . . . . . . . . BZ 48
Løvstræde . . . . . . . . . . . . . CY 49
Marmorbroen . . . . . . . . . . . CZ 50
Møllegade . . . . . . . . . . . . . AX
Niels Juels Gade . . . . . . . . DZ 51
Nybrogade . . . . . . . . . . . . CZ 52
Nyhavn . . . . . . . . . . . . . . . DY
Nytorv . . . . . . . . . . . . . . . BZ 53
Nørre Allé . . . . . . . . . . . . . AX
Nørrebrogade . . . . . . . . . . AX
Nørre Farimagsgade . . . . . BY
Nørregade . . . . . . . . . . . . . BY
Nørre Søgade . . . . . . . . . . ABY
Oslo Plads . . . . . . . . . . . . DX
Overgaden neden Vandet . DZ
Overgaden oven Vandet . . DZ
Peblinge Dossering . . . . . . AY
Pistolstræde . . . . . . . . . . . CY 54
Polititorvet . . . . . . . . . . . . BZ 55
Prinsessegade . . . . . . . . . . DZ
Rantzausgade . . . . . . . . . . AX
Reventlowsgade . . . . . . . . . BZ 56
Rosenørns Allé . . . . . . . . . AY
Rådhuspladsen . . . . . . . . . BZ 57
Rådhusstræde . . . . . . . . . . CZ 59
Sankt Annæ Plads . . . . . . . DY 60
Sankt Hans Torv . . . . . . . . AX
Sankt Peders Stræde . . . . . BY 62
Skindergade . . . . . . . . . . . CY 63
Sortedam Dossering . . . . . . BX
Stockholmsgade . . . . . . . . . CX
Store Kannikestræde . . . . . CY 64
Stormgade . . . . . . . . . . . . CZ
Strandgade . . . . . . . . . . . . DZ
Studiestræde . . . . . . . . . . . BYZ 66
Sølvgade . . . . . . . . . . . . . BCX
Sølvtorvet . . . . . . . . . . . . . CX 67
Tagensvej . . . . . . . . . . . . . BX
Tietgensgade . . . . . . . . . . . BZ 68
Toldbodgade . . . . . . . . . . . DXY
Torvegade . . . . . . . . . . . . . DZ
Vandkunsten . . . . . . . . . . . CZ 70
Webersgade . . . . . . . . . . . . BX 71
Ved Stranden . . . . . . . . . . . CZ 72
Ved Vesterport . . . . . . . . . AZ 74
Vermlandsgade . . . . . . . . . DZ
Vester Farimagsgade . . . . . AZ 75
Vestergade . . . . . . . . . . . . BZ 76
Vester Søgade . . . . . . . . . . AYZ
Vester Voldgade . . . . . . . . BCZ
Vindebrogade . . . . . . . . . . CZ 78
Vodroffsvej . . . . . . . . . . . . AYZ
Værnedamsvej . . . . . . . . . . AZ 79
Østbanegade . . . . . . . . . . . DX
Øster Farimagsgade . . . . . BCX
Øster Søgade . . . . . . . . . . BCX
Øster Voldgade . . . . . . . . . CX
Aboulevard . . . . . . . . . . . . AY

**Angleterre,** Kongens Nytorv 34, P.O. Box 3044, ✉ 1021 K, ☎ 33 12 00 95, *Fax 33 12 11 18*, – ☎ – 400. CDY t
***Restaurant D'Angleterre*** : **Meals** 395 and a la carte – ***Restaurant Wiinblad*** : **Meals** 295 and a la carte – 120 – **130 rm** 1875/2350.

**Scandic**, Vester Søgade 6, ✉ 1601 V, ☎ 33 14 35 35, *Fax 33 32 12 23*, rm, ☎ – 800. rest AZ w
**Meals** 165/195 and a la carte – **465 rm** 1050/1745.

**Radisson SAS Scandinavia,** Amager Boulevard 70, ✉ 2300 S, ☎ 33 96 50 00, *Fax 33 96 55 00*, Copenhagen, squash – rm, ☎ – 1200. rest CZ
***Mama's & Papa's*** : **Meals** (buffet lunch) 185/400 and a la carte – ***Blue Elephant*** *(☎ 33 96 59 70)* : **Meals** - Thai - *(closed lunch Saturday and Sunday, Easter and Christmas)* 195/495 and a la carte – ***Kyoto*** *(☎ 33 32 16 74)* : **Meals** - Japanese - *(closed Bank Holidays)* (dinner only) 220/380 and a la carte – **507 rm** 1745/1845, 35 suites.

**Radisson SAS Royal**, Hammerichsgade 1, ✉ 1611 V, ☎ 33 42 60 00, *Fax 33 42 61 00*, « Panoramic restaurant on 20th floor », – rm, ☎ – 250. rest BZ m
***Summit*** : **Meals** *(closed Saturday lunch, Monday dinner and Sunday)* 450 and a la carte – ***Café Royal*** : **Meals** a la carte 185/370 – **263 rm** 1890/2190, 2 suites.

**Phoenix,** Bredgade 37, ✉ 1260 K, ☎ 33 95 95 00, *Fax 33 33 98 33* – rm, rest, ☎ – 80. rest DY b
**Meals** 275 and a la carte – 110 – **209 rm** 1120/2390, 3 suites.

**Plaza,** Bernstorffsgade 4, ✉ 1577 V, ☎ 33 14 92 62, *Fax 33 93 93 62*, « Library bar » – rm, rm, ☎ – 35. rest BZ r
***Alexander Nevski*** : **Meals** (dinner only) 325 and a la carte – **93 rm** 1650/1850.

**Kong Frederik,** Vester Voldgade 25, ✉ 1552 V, ☎ 33 12 59 02, *Fax 33 93 59 01* – ☎ – 80. BZ k
**Meals** 155/295 and a la carte – 100 – **110 rm** 1150/1650.

**Kong Arthur**, Nørre Søgade 11, 1370 K, 33 11 12 12, *Fax 33 32 61 30*, – rm, – 50. BY a
***Brochner*** *(33 93 58 05)* : **Meals** *(closed Sunday and Bank Holidays)* (dinner only) 195/285 and a la carte – ***Sticks 'n' Sushi*** *(33 11 14 07)* : **Meals** - Japanese - *(closed Bank Holidays)* (dinner only) 155/180 and a la carte – **107 rm** 995/1300.

**Radisson SAS Falconer** M, Falkoner Allé 9, 2000 Frederiksberg C, 38 19 80 01, *Fax 31 87 11 91*, Copenhagen, – rm, rm, – 2000. rest by Gammel Kongevej AZ
**Meals** (buffet lunch) 175/375 and a la carte – **163 rm** 1195/1540, 3 suites.

**Imperial** M, Vester Farimagsgade 9, 1606 V, 33 12 80 00, *Fax 33 93 80 31* – , rm, – 100. rest AZ e
***Imperial Garden*** : **Meals** *(closed 22 December-4 January)* (dinner only) 345/495 and a la carte – ***Imperial Brasserie*** : **Meals** (buffet lunch) 250 and a la carte – **163 rm** 1160/2310.

**Palace,** Rådhuspladsen 57, 1550 V, 33 14 40 50, *Fax 33 14 52 79*, – , rm, – 50. BZ u
**Meals** a la carte 165/300 – **162 rm** 1390/1590.

**Neptun,** Sankt Annae Plads 14-20, 1250 K, 33 13 89 00, *Fax 33 14 12 50* – , rm, rm, – 40. DY a
*closed 20 December-4 January* – **Meals** *(closed Sunday, July and Bank Holidays)* 190/270 and a la carte – **118 rm** 1270/1705, 15 suites.

**Sophie Amalie** M, Sankt Annae Plads 21, P.O. Box 3015, 1021 K, 33 13 34 00, *Fax 33 11 77 07*, – , rest, – 50. DY x
**Meals** 145/500 and a la carte – 90 – **134 rm** 835/1080.

**Richmond** without rest., Vester Farimagsgade 33, 1606 V, 33 12 33 66, *Fax 33 12 97 17* – , rm, – 120. AZ y
**122 rm** 995/1260, 5 suites.

**Crown** M without rest., Vesterbrogade 41, 1620 V, 31 21 21 66, *Fax 31 21 00 66* – , rm, – 25. AZ b
**80 rm** 945/1190.

**Star** M without rest., Colbjørnsensgade 13, 1652 V, 31 22 11 00, *Fax 31 21 21 86* – , rm, – 25. rest ABZ c
**132 rm** 945/1190, 2 suites.

**Ascot** without rest., Studiestraede 61, 1554 V, 33 12 60 00, *Fax 33 14 60 40*, – – 50. BZ g
**140 rm** 870/1290, 10 suites.

**City** M without rest., Peder Skrams Gade 24, 1054 K, 33 13 06 66, *Fax 33 13 06 67* – . DZ a
**81 rm** 825/1185.

**71 Nyhavn,** Nyhavn 71, 1051 K, 33 11 85 85, *Fax 33 93 15 85*, « Former warehouse » – , rm, . rest DY z
**Meals** *(closed Sunday and Bank Holidays)* (dinner only) 275/310 and a la carte – **76 rm** 1050/1695, 6 suites.

**Mercur** without rest., Vester Farimagsgade 17, 1606 V, 33 12 57 11, *Fax 33 12 57 17*, – . AZ d
**108 rm** 945/1290, 1 suite.

**Christian IV** without rest., Dronningens Tvaergade 45, 1302 K, 33 32 10 44, *Fax 33 32 07 06* – . . CY f
*closed 23 to 29 December* – **42 rm** 890/1090.

**Esplanaden** M without rest., Bredgade 78, 1260 K, 33 91 32 00, *Fax 33 91 32 39* – . . DX a
*closed 20 December-4 January* – **112 rm** 720/1040, 4 suites.

**Komfort,** Løngangstraede 27, 1468 K, 33 12 65 70, *Fax 33 15 28 99* – , rm, . . BZ n
*closed 20 to 30 December* – **Meals** a la carte 180/240 – **201 rm** 900/1200.

**Absalon** without rest., Helgolandsgade 15, 1653 V, 33 24 22 11, *Fax 33 24 34 11* – . . AZ h
*closed 20 December-4 January* – **177 rm** 775/1100.

**Danmark** without rest., Vester Voldgade 89, 1552 V, 33 11 48 06, *Fax 33 14 36 30* – . BZ t
*closed 20 December-4 January* – **49 rm** 625/995, 2 suites.

XXX **Kong Hans Kaelder,** Vingårdsstraede 6, ✉ 1070 K, ☎ 33 11 68 68, *Fax 33 32 67 68,* « Vaulted Gothic cellar » – AE ⓓ E VISA CY n
*closed 20 July-2 August and 22 to 30 December* – **Meals** (booking essential) (dinner only) 425 and a la carte 600/685
**Spec.** Foie gras prepared three ways with Banyuls sauce. Home smoked salmon with fennel and aquavit. Variations on Valrhona chocolate with citrus fruit marmalade.

XX **Kommandanten,** Ny Adelgade 7, ✉ 1104 K, ☎ 33 12 09 90, *Fax 33 93 12 23,* « 17C town house, contemporary furnishings » – AE ⓓ E VISA JCB CY c
*closed Saturday lunch, Sunday, 24 December-5 January and Bank Holidays* – **Meals** (booking essential) 330/580 and a la carte 485/605
**Spec.** Oysters with salmon trout, blinis and sevruga caviar. Miroton of oxtail, fried lobster and potato purée, sauce Lyonnaise. Selection of chocolate desserts.

XX **Nouvelle** (Kyllesbech), Gammel Strand 34 (1st floor), ✉ 1202 K, ☎ 33 13 50 18, *Fax 33 32 07 97* – AE ⓓ E VISA JCB CZ a
*closed Saturday lunch, Sunday, July, Christmas-New Year and Bank Holidays* – **Meals** (booking essential) 275/425 and a la carte 405/495
**Spec.** Egg "Nouvelle" filled with lobster, mousseline sauce and sevruga caviar. Bornholm herrings served as appetisers. Grilled zander with shallots and thyme, Burgundy sauce.

XX **Restaurationen,** Møntergade 19, ✉ 1116 K, ☎ 33 14 94 95 – AE ⓓ E VISA
*closed Sunday, Monday, July, 23 December-5 January and Bank Holidays* – **Meals** (booking essential) (dinner only except December) 455. CY e

XX **Pierre André** (Houdet), Ny Østergade 21, ✉ 1101 K, ☎ 33 16 17 19 – AE ⓓ E VISA CY s
*closed Saturday lunch, Sunday, last 3 weeks July and Bank Holidays* – **Meals** (booking essential) 210/435 and a la carte 335/475
**Spec.** Foie gras 'Emilia Romagna'. Noisettes de chevreuil aux épices. Gâteau chaud au Gianduja.

XX **Era Ora** (Milleri), Torvegade 62, ✉ 1400 K, ☎ 31 54 06 93, *Fax 32 96 02 09* – ▤. AE ⓓ E VISA JCB DZ c
*closed Sunday, 23 to 26 December and 1 January* – **Meals** - Italian - (booking essential) (dinner only) 395/550
**Spec.** Rugoli with cinnamon, sage, lemon and Parmesan. Lamb with liquorice stick, dried figs, balsamico and rosemary. Sea bass with artichokes, dried tomatoes and spumante.

XX **Krogs,** Gammel Strand 38, ✉ 1202 K, ☎ 33 15 89 15, *Fax 33 15 83 19,* 🍽, 18C house – AE ⓓ E VISA JCB CZ a
*closed Sunday, Easter and Christmas* – **Meals** - Seafood - (booking essential) 180/355 and a la carte.

XX **Lumskebugten,** Esplanaden 21, ✉ 1263 K, ☎ 33 15 60 29, *Fax 33 32 87 18,* 🍽, « Mid 19C café-pavilion » – AE ⓓ E VISA JCB DX b
*closed Saturday lunch, Sunday and 23 December-2 January* – **Meals** 265/375 and a la carte 340/460.

XX **St. Gertruds Kloster,** Hauser Plads 32, ✉ 1127 K, ☎ 33 14 66 30, *Fax 33 93 93 65,* « Part 14C monastic cellars » – ▤. AE ⓓ E VISA JCB CY r
*closed 24 December-2 January* – **Meals** (dinner only) 350/770 and a la carte.

XX **Leonore Christine,** Nyhavn 9 (1st floor), ✉ 1051 K, ☎ 33 13 50 40, *Fax 33 13 50 40,* 18C house – AE ⓓ E VISA JCB DY e
*closed 23 December-1 January* – **Meals** 225/395 and a la carte.

X **Kanalen,** Christianshavn-Wilders Plads 2, ✉ 1403 K, ☎ 32 95 13 30, *Fax 32 95 13 38,* ≤, 🍽, « Canalside house » – Ⓟ. AE ⓓ E VISA JCB DZ b
*closed Sunday and 22 to 28 December* – **Meals** (booking essential) 160/285 and a la carte 285/375.

X **Den Gyldne Fortun,** Ved Stranden 18, ✉ 1061 K, ☎ 33 12 20 11, *Fax 33 93 35 11* – AE ⓓ E VISA JCB CZ e
*closed Saturday, Sunday and Bank Holidays* – **Meals** - Seafood - 175/325 and a la carte.

X **Den Sorte Ravn,** Nyhavn 14, ✉ 1051 K, ☎ 33 13 12 33, *Fax 33 13 24 72* – ▤. AE ⓓ E VISA DY q
*closed Sunday June-August, 9 to 13 April, 30 May-1 June, 24 to 26 December and 1 January* – **Meals** 130/445 and a la carte.

X **Els,** Store Strandstraede 3, ✉ 1255 K, ☎ 33 14 13 41, *Fax 33 91 07 00,* « 19C murals » – ▤. AE ⓓ E VISA JCB DY k
*closed Sunday lunch* – **Meals** 295/380 and a la carte.

X **Thorvaldsen,** Gammel Strand 34 (ground floor), ✉ 1202 K, ☎ 33 32 04 00, *Fax 33 32 07 97,* 🍽 – AE ⓓ E VISA JCB CZ a
*closed dinner in winter, Sunday, Christmas-New Year and Bank Holidays* – **Meals** (booking essential) 175/225 and a la carte.

**in Tivoli** : *Vesterbrogade 3 ✉ 1620 V (Entrance fee payable)*

XXX **Divan 2,** ☎ 33 12 51 51, *Fax 33 91 08 82*, ≤, 余, « Floral decoration and terrace » – AE ⓓ E VISA JCB BZ a
*24 April-13 September* – **Meals** 345/650 and a la carte.

XXX **Belle Terrasse,** ☎ 33 12 11 36, *Fax 33 15 00 31*, ≤, 余, « Floral decoration and terrace » – AE ⓓ E VISA JCB BZ s
*25 April-13 September* – **Meals** 295/555 and a la carte.

XX **Divan No 1,** ☎ 33 11 42 42, *Fax 33 11 74 07*, ≤, 余, « 19C pavilion » – AE ⓓ E VISA JCB BZ v
*25 April-14 September* – **Meals** 195/395 and a la carte.

XX **La Crevette,** Bernstorffsgade 5, ✉ 1577 V, ☎ 33 14 68 47, *Fax 33 14 60 06*, ≤, 余, « Terrace overlooking flowered garden » – AE ⓓ E VISA JCB BZ e
*24 April-13 September* – **Meals** - Seafood - 315/380 and a la carte.

**SMØRREBRØD**

*The following list of simpler restaurants and cafés/bars specialize in Danish open sandwiches and are generally open from 10.00am to 4.00pm.*

X **Ida Davidsen,** St. Kongensgade 70, ✉ 1264 K, ☎ 33 91 36 55, *Fax 33 11 36 55* – AE ⓓ E VISA JCB DY g
*closed Saturday, Sunday, July, Christmas-New Year and Bank Holidays* – **Meals** (buffet lunch) a la carte 170/385.

X **Slotskaelderen-Hos Gitte Kik,** Fortunstraede 4, ✉ 1065 K, ☎ 33 11 15 37, *Fax 33 11 15 37* – AE ⓓ E VISA JCB CYZ v
*closed Sunday, Monday, 22 June-12 July and Bank Holidays* – **Meals** (buffet lunch only) a la carte 30/70.

X **Sankt Annae,** Sankt Annae Plads 12, ✉ 1250 K, ☎ 33 12 54 97 – ⓓ E VISA JCB DY a
*closed Saturday, Sunday and 3 weeks July* – **Meals** (lunch only) a la carte 115/145.

X **Kanal Caféen,** Frederiksholms Kanal 18, ✉ 1220 K, ☎ 33 11 57 70, *Fax 33 13 79 62*, 余 – AE ⓓ E VISA CZ r
*closed Sunday and Bank Holidays* – **Meals** (lunch only) 30/70 and a la carte.

**at Hellerup** *N : 7 ½ km by Østbanegade* – DX – *and Road 2* – ✉ *2900 Hellerup :*

**Hellerup Parkhotel,** Strandvejen 203, ☎ 39 62 40 44, *Fax 39 62 56 57*, Fø, ≘s – |‡|, ⇔ rm, TV ☎ P – 🏃 150. AE ⓓ E VISA. ✂ rest
**Meals** – (see ***Saison*** below) – **71 rm** ☐ 995/1450.

XX **Saison** (at Hellerup Parkhotel), Strandvejen 203, ☎ 39 62 48 42, *Fax 39 62 56 57* – P. AE ⓓ E VISA JCB. ✂
*closed Sunday* – **Meals** 250/525 and a la carte.

**at Klampenborg** *N : 12 km by Østbanegade* – DX –, *Road 2 and Road 152 (coast rd)* – ✉ *2930 :*

X **Den Gule Cottage,** Staunings Plaene, Strandvejen 506, ☎ 39 64 06 91, *Fax 39 64 27 77*, ≤, 余, « Thatched cottage beside the sea » – P. AE ⓓ E VISA JCB
**Meals** (booking essential) 245/385 and a la carte.

X **Den Røde Cottage,** Strandvejen 550, ✉ 2930 K, ☎ 39 90 46 14, *Fax 39 90 86 14*, 余, « Small cottage in a clearing » – AE ⓓ E VISA JCB
**Meals** (booking essential) 210/375 and a la carte.

**at Søllerød** *N : 20 km by Tagensvej* – BX – *and Road 19* – ✉ *2840 Holte :*

XXX ✿ **Søllerød Kro,** Søllerødvej 35, ✉ 2840 K, ☎ 45 80 25 05, *Fax 45 80 22 70*, 余, « 17C thatched inn, terrace » – P. AE ⓓ E VISA JCB. ✂
*closed 24 December and 1 January* – **Meals** 525 and a la carte 490/595
**Spec.** Terrine of foie gras with poached veal shank, potatoes and parsley. Roasted Danish wood pigeon with langoustines, confit of onions and fondant potatoes. Warm chocolate fondant with an orange sorbet and crisp pineapple.

**at Kastrup Airport** *SE : 10 km by Amager Boulevard* – CZ – ✉ *2300 S :*

**Radisson SAS Globetrotter** M, Engvej 171, ✉ 2300, *NW : 3 km by coastal rd* ☎ 32 87 02 02, *Fax 32 87 02 20*, Fø, ≘s, 🏊 – |‡|, ⇔ rm, TV ☎ P – 🏃 360. AE ⓓ E VISA JCB. ✂ rest
**Meals** (buffet lunch) 305 and a la carte – **197 rm** ☐ 1260/1460.

**Dan** M, Kastruplundgade 15, Kastrup, ✉ 2770, *N : 2 ½ km by coastal rd* ☎ 32 51 14 00, *Fax 32 51 37 01*, 余, ≘s – |‡|, ⇔ rm, ▤ rest, TV P – 🏃 120. AE ⓓ E VISA JCB. ✂ rest
**Meals** (buffet lunch) 170/265 and a la carte – **218 rm** ☐ 795/1095, 10 suites.

# Finland

## Suomi

HELSINKI

# PRACTICAL INFORMATION

## LOCAL CURRENCY

**Finnish Mark:** *100 FIM = 18,45 USD ($) (Jan. 98)*

## TOURIST INFORMATION

*The Tourist Office is situated near the Market Square, Pohjoisesplanadi 19 ✆ (09) 169 3757. Open from 2 May to 30 September, Monday to Friday 9am - 7pm, Saturday and Sunday 9am - 3pm, and from 1 October to 30 April, Monday to Friday 9am - 5pm and Saturday from 9am to 3pm. Hotel bookings are possible from a reservation board situated in the airport arrival lounge and in the main railway station; information is also available free.*

**National Holiday in Finland:** *6 December.*

## FOREIGN EXCHANGE

*Banks are open between 9.15am and 4.15pm on weekdays only. Exchange office at Helsinki-Vantaa airport and Helsinki harbour open daily between 6.30am and 11pm.*

## MEALS

*At lunchtime, follow the custom of the country and try the typical buffets of Scandinavian specialities.*

*At dinner, the a la carte and set menus will offer you more conventional cooking. Booking is essential.*

*Many city centre restaurants are closed for a few days over the Midsummer Day period.*

## SHOPPING IN HELSINKI

*Furs, jewelry, china, glass and ceramics, Finnish handicraft and wood.*

*In the index of street names, those printed in red are where the principal shops are found. Your hotel porter will be able to help you with information.*

## THEATRE BOOKINGS

*A ticket service - Lippupalvelu, Mannerheimintie 5, sells tickets for cinema, concert and theatre performances - Telephone (09) 613 8611, open Mon-Fri 9am to 6pm, Sat. 9am to 2pm. Tickets can also be purchased from the Tourist Office.*

## CAR HIRE

*The international car hire companies have branches in Helsinki and at Vantaa airport. Your hotel porter should be able to help you with your arrangements.*

## TIPPING

*Service is normally included in hotel and restaurant bills. Doormen, baggage porters etc. are generally given a gratuity; taxi drivers are not usually tipped.*

## SPEED LIMITS

*The maximum permitted speed on motorways is 120 km/h - 74 mph (in winter 100 km/h - 62 mph), 80 km/h - 50 mph on other roads and 50 km/h - 31 mph in built-up areas.*

## SEAT BELTS

*The wearing of seat belts in Finland is compulsory for drivers and all passengers.*

# HELSINKI

*Finland* 985 L 21 – *Pop. 491 777.*

*Lahti 103 – Tampere 176 – Turku 165.*

*City Tourist Office Pohjoisesplanadi 19 ☎ (09) 169 37 57, Fax (09) 169 38 39 – Automobile and Touring Club of Finland: Autoliitto ☎ (09) 694 00 22, Fax (09) 693 25 78.*

18 *Tali Manor ☎ (09) 550 235.*

*Helsinki-Vantaa N : 19 km ☎ (09) 821 122 – Finnair Head Office, Tietotie 11 A – 01053 ☎ (09) 818 8114, Fax (09) 818 40 92 – Air Terminal : Hotel Intercontinental, Mannerheimintie 46 – Finnair City Terminal : Asema – Aukio 3, ☎ (09) 818 77 50, Fax (09) 818 77 65.*

*To Sweden, Estonia, Poland and boat excursions : contact the City Tourist Office (see above) – Car Ferry: Silja Line – Finnjet Line ☎ (09) 180 41.*

See: *Senate Square★★★ (Senaatintori)* DY **53** – *Market Square★★ (Kauppatori* DY **26** – *Esplanadi★★* CDY **8/43** – *Railway Station★★ (Rautatiesema)* CX – *Finlandia Hall★★ (Finlandia-talo)* BX – *National Opera House★★ (Kansallisoopera)* BX – *Church in the Rock★★ (Temppeliaukion kirkko)* BX – *Ateneum Art Museum★★ (Ateneum, Suomen Taiteen Museo)* CY **M¹** – *National Museum★★ (Kansallismuseo)* BX **M²** – *Lutheran Cathedral★ (Tuomiokirkko)* DY – *Parliament House★ (Eduskuntatalo)* BX – *Amos Anderson Collection★ (Amos Andersinin taidemuseo)* BY **M⁴** – *Uspensky Cathedral★ (Uspenskin katedraali)* DY – *Cygnaeus home and collection★ (Cynaeuksen galleria)* DZ **B** – *Mannerheim home and collection★ (Mannerheim-museo)* DZ **M⁵** – *Olympic Stadium★ (Olympiastadion)* ✲★★ BX **21** – *Museum of Applied Arts★ (Taideteollisuusmuseo)* CZ **M⁶** – *Sibelius Monument★ (Sibelius-monumentti)* AX **S** – *Ice-breaker fleet★* DX.

Outskirts: *Fortress of Suomenlinna★★ by boat* DZ – *Seurasaari Open-Air Museum★★* BX – *Urho Kekkonen Museum★ (Urho Kekkosen museo)* BX.

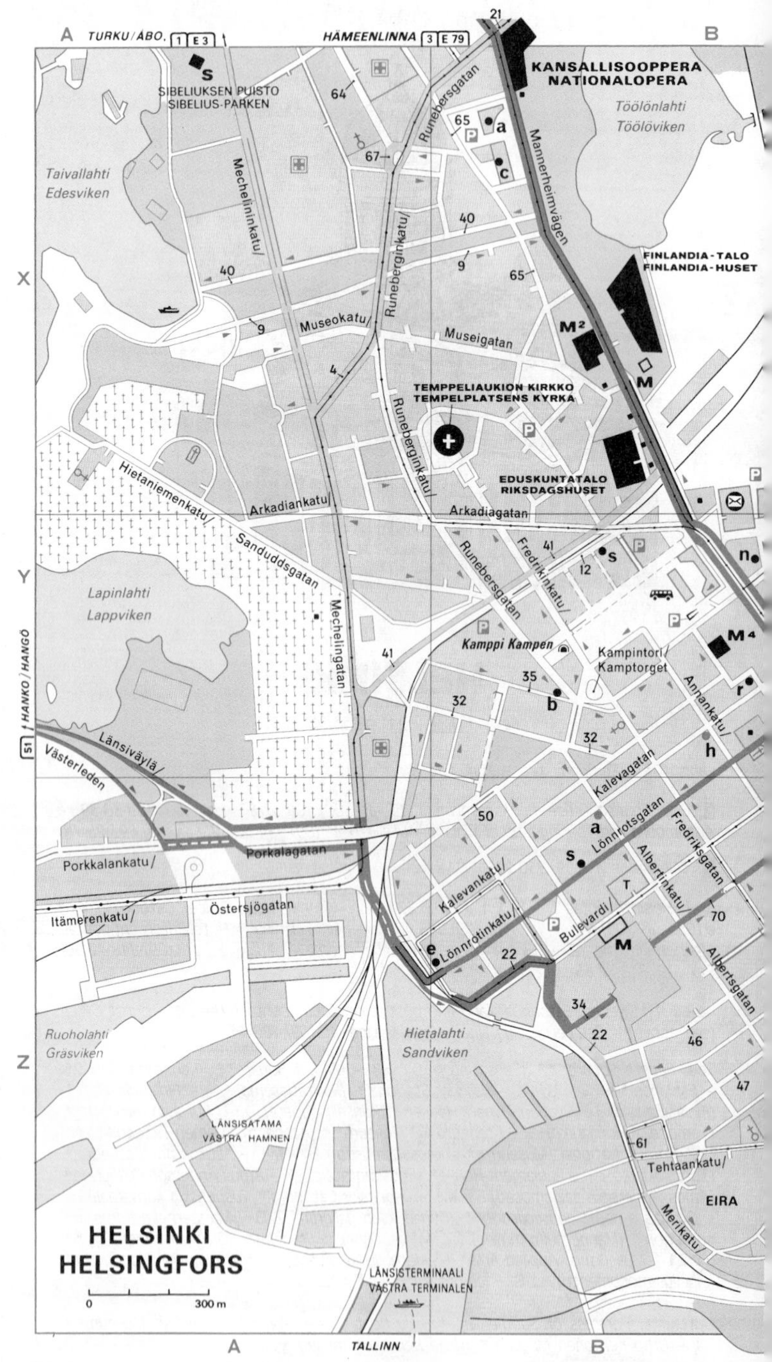
TURKU/ÅBO
HÄMEENLINNA
KANSALLISOOPPERA
NATIONALOPERA
SIBELIUKSEN PUISTO
SIBELIUS-PARKEN
Töölönlahti
Töölöviken
Taivallahti
Edesviken
Mechelininkatu/
Runebergsgatan
Runeberginkatu/
Mannerheimvägen
FINLANDIA-TALO
FINLANDIA-HUSET
Museokatu/
Museigatan
TEMPPELIAUKION KIRKKO
TEMPELPLATSENS KYRKA
EDUSKUNTATALO
RIKSDAGSHUSET
Hietaniemenkatu/
Sanduddsgatan
Arkadiankatu/
Arkadiagatan
Fredrikinkatu/
Lapinlahti
Lappviken
Mechelingatan
Kamppi Kampen
Kampintori/
Kamptorget
Annankatu/
HANKO/HANGÖ
Länsiväylä/
Västerleden
Kalevagatan
Lönnrotsgatan
Fredriksgatan
Albertinkatu/
Porkkalankatu/
Porkalagatan
Itämerenkatu/
Östersjögatan
Kalevankatu/
Lönnrotinkatu/
Bulevardi/
Albertsgatan
Ruoholahti
Gräsviken
Hietalahti
Sandviken
LÄNSISATAMA
VÄSTRA HAMNEN
Tehtaankatu/
EIRA
Merikatu/
HELSINKI
HELSINGFORS
LÄNSISTERMINAALI
VÄSTRA TERMINALEN
0
300 m
TALLINN

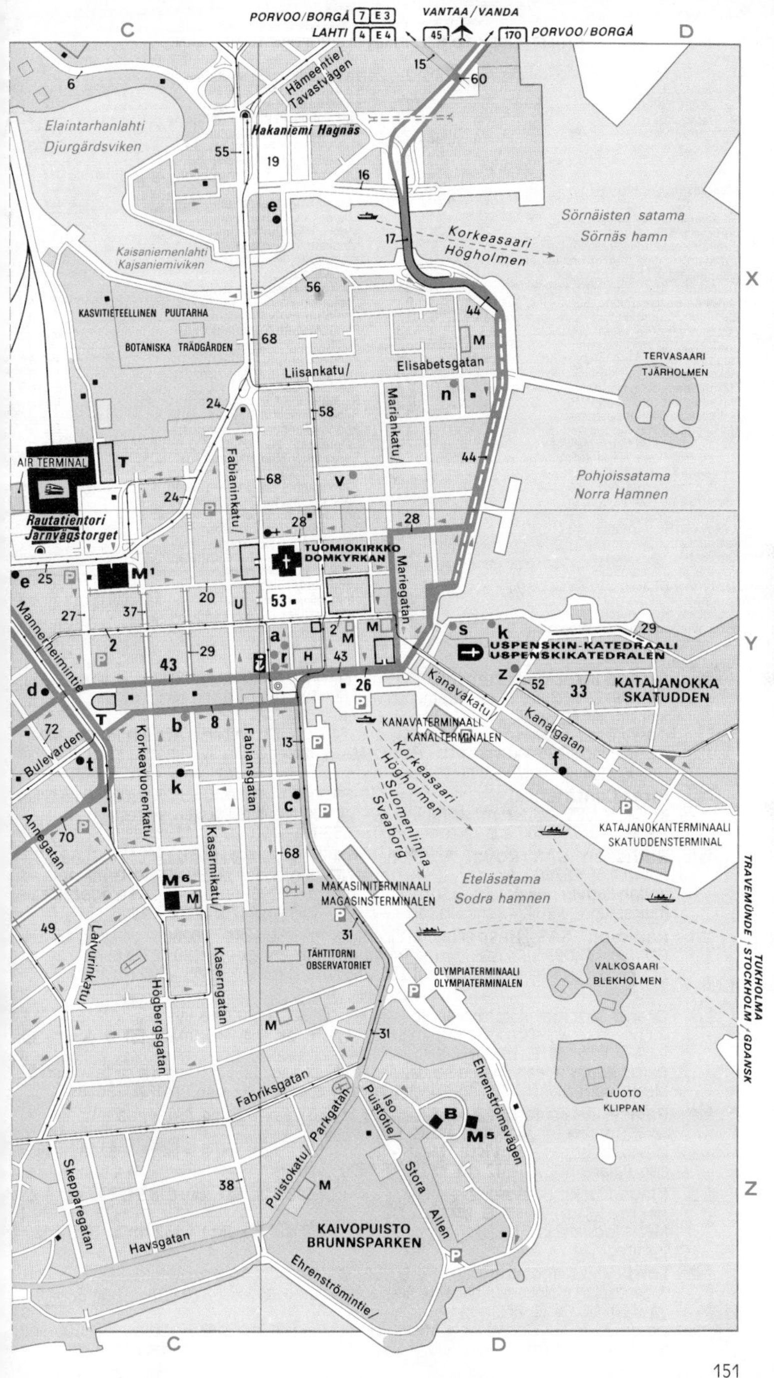
PORVOO/BORGÅ 7 E 3
LAHTI 4 E 4
VANTAA/VANDA
45
170 PORVOO/BORGÅ
Elaintarhanlahti
Djurgårdsviken
Hämeentie/
Tavastvägen
Hakaniemi Hagnäs
Sörnäisten satama
Sörnäs hamn
Korkeasaari
Högholmen
Kaisaniemenlahti
Kajsaniemiviken
KASVITIETEELLINEN PUUTARHA
BOTANISKA TRÄDGÅRDEN
Liisankatu/
Elisabetsgatan
Mariankatu/
TERVASAARI
TJÄRHOLMEN
AIR TERMINAL
Rautatientori
Järnvägstorget
Fabianinkatu/
Pohjoissatama
Norra Hamnen
TUOMIOKIRKKO
DOMKYRKAN
Mariegatan
Mannerheimintie
USPENSKIN-KATEDRAALI
USPENSKIKATEDRALEN
KATAJANOKKA
SKATUDDEN
Kanavakatu/
Kanalgatan
KANAVATERMINAALI
KANALTERMINALEN
Bulevarden
Korkeavuorenkatu/
Fabiansgatan
Korkeasaari
Högholmen
Suomenlinna
Sveaborg
KATAJANOKANTERMINAALI
SKATUDDENSTERMINAL
Annegatan
Kasarmikatu/
MAKASIINITERMINAALI
MAGASINSTERMINALEN
Eteläsatama
Sodra hamnen
TRAVEMÜNDE / TUKHOLMA / STOCKHOLM / GDANSK
Laivurinkatu/
Högbergsgatan
Kaserngatan
TÄHTITORNI
OBSERVATORIET
OLYMPIATERMINAALI
OLYMPIATERMINALEN
VALKOSAARI
BLEKHOLMEN
Fabriksgatan
Puistokatu/
Parkgatan
Iso
Puistotie/
Ehrenströmsvägen
LUOTO
KLIPPAN
Stora
Allen
Skepparegatan
Havsgatan
KAIVOPUISTO
BRUNNSPARKEN
Ehrenströmintie/

## STREET INDEX TO HELSINKI/HELSINGFORS TOWN PLAN

Aleksanterinkatu/Alexandersgatan . . . . . . . . . CDY 2
Fabianinkatu/Fabiansgatan . . . . . . . . . . . . . CXYZ
Keskuskatu/Centralgatan . . . . . . . . . . . . . . CY 27
Kluuvikatu/Glogatan . . . . . . . . . . . . . . . . CY 29
Mannerheimintie/Mannerheimvägen . . . . . . BCXY
Mikonkatu/Mikaelsgatan . . . . . . . . . . . . . . CY 37
Pohjoisesplanadi/Norra esplanaden . . . . . . . . CDY 43

Albertinkatu/Albertsgatan . . . . . . . . . . . . . BZ
Annankatu/Annegatan . . . . . . . . . . . . . . . BCYZ
Arkadiankatu/Arkadiagatan . . . . . . . . . . . . ABX
Bulevardi/Bulevarden . . . . . . . . . . . . . . . BCXY
Caloniuksenkatu/Caloniusgatan . . . . . . . . . . AX 4
Ehrenströmintie/Ehrenströmsvägen . . . . . . . . DZ
Eläintarhantie/Djurgårdsvägen . . . . . . . . . . CX 6
Eteläesplanadi/Södra esplanaden . . . . . . . . . CY 8
Eteläinen Hesperiankatu/Södra Hesperiagatan . . ABX 9
Eteläinen Rautatiekatu/Södra Järnvägsgatan . . BY 12
Eteläranta/Södra kajen . . . . . . . . . . . . . . DY 13
Fredrikinkatu/Fredriksgatan . . . . . . . . . . . . BYZ
Haapaniemenkatu/Aspnäsgatan . . . . . . . . . . DX 15
Hakaniemenranta/Hagnäskajen . . . . . . . . . . DX 16
Hakaniemen silta/Hagnäs bro . . . . . . . . . . . DX 17
Hakaniemen tori/Hagnäs torg . . . . . . . . . . . DX 19
Hallituskatu/Regeringsgatan . . . . . . . . . . . CY 20
Helsinginkatu/Helsingegatan . . . . . . . . . . . BX 21
Hietalahdenranta/Sandvikskajen . . . . . . . . . BZ 22
Hietaniemenkatu/Sanduddsgatan . . . . . . . . . AXY
Hämeentie/Tavastvägen . . . . . . . . . . . . . . DX
Iso Puistotie/Stora Allen . . . . . . . . . . . . . DZ
Itämerenkatu/Östersjögatan . . . . . . . . . . . AZ
Kaisaniemenkatu/Kajsaniemigatan . . . . . . . . CX 24
Kaivokatu/Brunnsgatan . . . . . . . . . . . . . . CY 25
Kalevankatu/Kalevagatan . . . . . . . . . . . . . BYZ
Kampintori/Kamptorget . . . . . . . . . . . . . . BY
Kanavakatu/Kanalgatan . . . . . . . . . . . . . . DXY
Kasarmikatu/Kaserngatan . . . . . . . . . . . . . CZ
Kauppatori/Salutorget . . . . . . . . . . . . . . DY 26
Kirkkokatu/Kyrkogatan . . . . . . . . . . . . . . DY 28
Korkeavuorenkatu/Högbergsgatan . . . . . . . . . CYZ
Laivasillankatu/Skeppsbrogatan . . . . . . . . . DZ 29
Laivastokatu/Maringatan . . . . . . . . . . . . . DY 31
Laivurinkatu/Skepparegatan . . . . . . . . . . . CZ
Lapinlahdenkatu/Lappviksgatan . . . . . . . . . BY 32
Liisankatu/Elisabetsgatan . . . . . . . . . . . . DX
Luotsikatu/Lotsgatan . . . . . . . . . . . . . . . DY 33
Länsiväylä/Västerleden . . . . . . . . . . . . . . AYZ
Lönnrotinkatu/Lönnrotsgatan . . . . . . . . . . . BZ
Mallaskatu/Maltgatan . . . . . . . . . . . . . . . BZ 34
Malminkatu/Malmgatan . . . . . . . . . . . . . . BY 35
Mariankatu/Mariegatan . . . . . . . . . . . . . . DXY
Mechelininkatu/Mechelingatan . . . . . . . . . . AXY
Merikatu/Havsgatan . . . . . . . . . . . . . . . . BCZ
Museokatu/Museigatan . . . . . . . . . . . . . . ABX
Neitsytpolku/Jungfrustigen . . . . . . . . . . . . CZ 38
Pohjoinen Hesperiankatu/Norra Hesperiagatan . ABX 40
Pohjoinen Rautatiekatu/Norra Järnvägsgatan . ABY 41
Pohjoisranta/Norra kajen . . . . . . . . . . . . . DX 44
Porkkalankatu/Porkalagatan . . . . . . . . . . . AZ
Puistokatu/Parkgatan . . . . . . . . . . . . . . . DZ
Punavuorenkatu/Rödbergsgatan . . . . . . . . . BZ 46
Pursimiehenkatu/Båtsmansgatan . . . . . . . . . BZ 47
Ratakatu/Bangatan . . . . . . . . . . . . . . . . CZ 49
Rautatientori/Järnvägstorget . . . . . . . . . . . CY
Runeberginkatu/Runebersgatan . . . . . . . . . ABXY
Ruoholahdenkatu/Gräsviksgatan . . . . . . . . . BZ 50
Satamakatu/Hamngatan . . . . . . . . . . . . . . DY 52
Senaatintori/Senatstorget . . . . . . . . . . . . DY 53
Siltasaarenkatu/Broholmsgatan . . . . . . . . . . CX 55
Siltavuorenranta/Brobergskajen . . . . . . . . . DX 56
Snellmaninkatu/Snellmansgatan . . . . . . . . . DX 58
Sörnäisten rantatie/Sörnäs strandväg . . . . . . DX 60
Tehtaankatu/Fabriksgatan . . . . . . . . . . . . BCDZ
Telakkakatu/Docksgatan . . . . . . . . . . . . . BZ 61
Topeliuksenkatu/Topeliusgatan . . . . . . . . . AX 64
Töölönkatu/Tölögatan . . . . . . . . . . . . . . BX 65
Töölöntori/Tölötorg . . . . . . . . . . . . . . . . AX 67
Unioninkatu/Unionsgatan . . . . . . . . . . . . . DXYZ 68
Uudenmaankatu/Nylandsgatan . . . . . . . . . . BCZ 70
Yrjönkatu/Georgsgatan . . . . . . . . . . . . . . BCY 72

**Strand Inter-Continental** M, John Stenbergin Ranta 4, ✉ 00530, ✆ (09) 39 351, *Fax (09) 393 5255*, ←, « Contemporary Finnish architecture and decor », rm, – 300. AE VISA JCB. rest — DX e
*closed Good Friday to Easter Monday and 24 to 26 December* – ***Atrium Plaza*** **: Meals** (buffet lunch) 225 and a la carte – ***Pamir*** **: Meals** *(closed Saturday, Sunday and 19 June-mid August)* (dinner only) a la carte 190/425 – 50 – **192 rm** 1340/1490, 8 suites.

**Inter-Continental,** Mannerheimintie 46, ✉ 00260, ✆ (09) 40 551, *Fax (09) 405 53255*, ←, rm, – 700. AE VISA JCB. rest
**Meals** 100/250 and a la carte – 70 – **552 rm** 1150/2000, 12 suites. — BX c

**Radisson SAS Royal** M, Runeberginkatu 2, ✉ 00100, ✆ (09) 69 580, *Fax (09) 695 87100*, rm, – 250. AE VISA JCB.
***Johan Ludvig*** **: Meals** *(closed Sunday)* (grill rest.) 155/295 and a la carte – ***Ströget*** **: Meals** (buffet lunch) 120/240 and a la carte – 75 – **253 rm** 1170/1290, 7 suites. — BY b

**Radisson SAS Hesperia,** Mannerheimintie 50, ✉ 00260, ✆ (09) 43 101, *Fax (09) 431 0995*, rm, – 120. AE VISA. rest
***Fransmanni*** **: Meals** (buffet lunch) 230/250 and a la carte – 85 – **372 rm** 1100/1350, 4 suites. — BX a

**Grand Marina,** Katajanokanlaituri 7, ✉ 00160, ✆ (09) 16 661, *Fax (09) 664 764*, « Converted warehouse in contemporary style », rm, – 70. AE VISA JCB. — DYZ f
***Baltic Room*** **: Meals** *(closed Sunday and Bank Holidays)* 125/210 and a la carte – ***Bistro*** **: Meals** (buffet lunch) 49 and dinner a la carte approx. 140 – **462 rm** 790/990.

**Palace,** Eteläranta 10, ✉ 00130, ✆ (09) 134 561, *Fax (09) 654 786*, ←, rm, – 60. AE VISA. — DZ c
*closed Christmas* – ***La Vista*** **: Meals** - Italian - 180 (lunch) and a la carte 155/260 – (see also ***Palace*** below) – **42 rm** 1060/1490, 2 suites.

**Klaus Kurki,** Bulevardi 2, ✉ 00120, ✆ (09) 618 911, *Fax (09) 618 91234*, rm, AE VISA JCB. — CY t
**Meals** *(closed Bank Holidays)* (dinner only) 130/260 and a la carte – **132 rm** 875/1120, 2 suites.

**Lord**, Lönnrotinkatu 29, ✉ 00180, ✆ (09) 615 815, *Fax (09) 680 1315*, « Part Jugendstil (Art Nouveau) building, fireplaces », rm, rm, – 200. AE VISA. — BZ s
*closed 23 to 27 December* – **Meals** *(closed Sunday and Bank Holidays)* 150/300 and a la carte – **47 rm** 650/800, 1 suite.

**Marski,** Mannerheimintie 10, ✉ 00100, ℘ (09) 68 061, *Fax (09) 642 377,* ≘s – |≑|, ⇜ rm, ▤ TV ☎ ♿ ⇔ – 🛋 200. AE ⓓ E VISA. ⇹ rest CY d
*closed 23 to 26 December* – ***Marskin Kellari :*** **Meals** 200 and a la carte – **230 rm** ⊐ 690/940, 6 suites.

**Vaakuna,** Asema-aukio 2, ✉ 00100, ℘ (09) 131 181, *Fax (09) 131 18234,* 🏠, ≘s – |≑|, ⇜ rm, TV ☎ ♿. AE ⓓ E VISA JCB. ⇹ rest BY n
***10th Floor Dining :*** **Meals** *(closed Sunday)* (dinner only) 175/255 and a la carte – ***Brasserie :*** **Meals** *(closed Sunday)* 120/180 and a la carte – **259 rm** ⊐ 960/1140, 10 suites.

**Seaside,** Ruoholahdenranta 3, ✉ 00180, ℘ (09) 69 360, *Fax (09) 69 32123,* ≘s – |≑|, ⇜ rm, ▤ TV ☎ ♿ ⇔ – 🛋 60. AE ⓓ E VISA. ⇹ rest ABZ e
**Meals** 150/175 and a la carte – **280 rm** ⊐ 700/860.

**Ramada Presidentti,** Eteläinen Rautatiekatu 4, ✉ 00100, ℘ (09) 6911, *Fax (09) 694 7886,* ≘s, 🏊 – |≑|, ⇜ rm, ▤ TV ☎ ♿ ⇔ – 🛋 400. AE ⓓ E VISA JCB. ⇹ rest BY s
**Meals** 160/250 and a la carte – ⊐ 30 – **485 rm** 1050/1245, 5 suites.

**Torni,** Yrjönkatu 26, ✉ 00100, ℘ (09) 131 131, *Fax (09) 131 1361,* ≘s – |≑|, ⇜ rm, TV ☎ – 🛋 35. AE ⓓ E VISA JCB. ⇹ BY r
*closed 23 to 28 December* – **Meals** *(closed Saturday lunch and Sunday)* 95/430 and a la carte – **152 rm** ⊐ 1075/1320.

**Rivoli Jardin** 🐌 without rest., Kasarmikatu 40, ✉ 00130, ℘ (09) 177 880, *Fax (09) 656 988,* ≘s – |≑| ⇜ TV ☎ ♿. AE ⓓ E VISA CYZ k
*closed 1 week Christmas* – **53 rm** ⊐ 810/930.

**Pasila,** Maistraatinportti 3, ✉ 00240, *N : 3 km by Mannerheimintie* ℘ (09) 148 841, *Fax (09) 143 771,* ≘s, squash – |≑| ⇜ ▤ TV ☎ ♿ ⇔ Ⓟ – 🛋 120. AE ⓓ E VISA JCB. ⇹ rest
**Meals** 170/290 and a la carte – **246 rm** ⊐ 695/840, 2 suites.

**Seurahuone,** Kaivokatu 12, ✉ 00100, ℘ (09) 69 141, *Fax (09) 691 4010,* ≘s – |≑|, ⇜ rm, TV ☎ – 🛋 60. AE ⓓ E VISA. ⇹ rest CY e
**Meals** 120/260 and a la carte – **118 rm** ⊐ 830/1120.

Aurora, Helsinginkatu 50, ✉ 00530, *NE : 2 km on Lahti road* ℘ (09) 770 100, *Fax (09) 770 10200,* Ꮭδ, ≘s, 🏊, squash – |≑|, ⇜ rm, ▤ TV ☎ Ⓟ – 🛋 220.
**70 rm**

**Savoy,** Eteläesplanadi 14 (8th floor), ✉ 00130, ℘ (09) 176 571, *Fax (09) 628 715,* ≤, 🏠, « Typical Finnish design dating from 1937 » – AE ⓓ E VISA CY b
*closed Saturday, Sunday and Bank Holidays* – **Meals** 170/450 and a la carte.

**Palace** (at Palace H.), Eteläranta 10 (10th floor), ✉ 00130, ℘ (09) 134 561, *Fax (09) 654 786,* ≤ harbour and city – |≑| ▤. AE ⓓ E VISA DZ c
*closed Saturday, Sunday and Bank Holidays* – **Meals** 200/470 and a la carte.

**Alexander Nevski,** Pohjoisesplanadi 17, ✉ 00700, ℘ (09) 639 610, *Fax (09) 631 435* – ▤. AE ⓓ E VISA. ⇹ DY r
*closed lunch Sunday and July and 24 to 26 December* – **Meals** - Russian - 140/350 and a la carte.

**Havis Amanda,** Unioninkatu 23, ✉ 00170, ℘ (09) 666 882, *Fax (09) 631 435* – ▤. AE ⓓ E VISA. ⇹ DY r
*closed Sunday, Easter and Christmas* – **Meals** - Seafood - (booking essential) 120/330 and a la carte.

**Sipuli,** Kanavaranta 3 (2nd floor), ✉ 00160, ℘ (09) 179 900, *Fax (09) 630 662,* « Picture window ≤ Uspensky Cathedral (orthodox) » – AE ⓓ E VISA JCB DY s
*closed Saturday, Sunday, 21 to 24 April, 19 June-2 August, 24 December-10 January and Bank Holidays* – **Meals** (booking essential) a la carte 225/325.

**Bellevue,** Rahapajankatu 3, ✉ 00160, ℘ (09) 179 560, *Fax (09) 636 985* – ▤. AE ⓓ E VISA DY z
*closed lunch Saturday and Sunday* – **Meals** - Russian - 110 (lunch) and a la carte 160/265.

**Svenska Klubben,** Maurinkatu 6, ✉ 00170, ℘ (09) 135 4706, *Fax (09) 135 4896,* « Scottish style house » – AE ⓓ E VISA DX n
*closed 1 July-3 August* – **Meals** 140/250 and a la carte.

**Rivoli,** Albertinkatu 38, ✉ 00180, ℘ (09) 643 455, *Fax (09) 647 780* – ▤. AE ⓓ E VISA BZ a
*closed Saturday lunch, Saturday in summer, Sunday, Easter, midsummer, Christmas and Bank Holidays* – **Meals** 130/200 and a la carte.

**Amadeus,** Sofiankatu 4, ✉ 00170, ℘ (09) 626 676, *Fax (09) 636 064* – AE ⓓ E VISA DY a
*closed Saturday lunch, Sunday and Bank Holidays* – **Meals** - Brasserie - 150/280 and dinner a la carte.

**Kanavaranta,** Kanavaranta 3E-F, ✉ 00160, ☎ (09) 6222 633, *Fax (09) 6222 616,* « Mid 19C harbour warehouse with nautical tavern » – ▤. AE ⓓ E VISA DY k
*closed lunch Monday and Saturday and Sunday* – **Meals** (booking essential) 295 (dinner) and a la carte 150/250.

**Safka,** Vironkatu 8, ✉ 00170, ☎ (09) 135 7287, *Fax (09) 278 3178* – AE ⓓ E VISA
*closed Saturday lunch, Monday dinner, Sunday, Easter, July and Christmas* – **Meals** (booking essential) 130/220 and dinner a la carte 150/170. DX v

**Lappi,** Annankatu 22, ✉ 00100, ☎ (09) 645 550, *Fax (09) 645 551,* « Typical Finnish atmosphere » – AE ⓓ E VISA JCB BY h
*closed Easter* – **Meals** - Finnish - (booking essential) 240/250 and a la carte.

**at Vantaa** *N : 19 km by A 137* – DX :

**Vantaa** M, Hertaksentie 2 (near Tikkurila Railway Station), ✉ 01300, ☎ (09) 857 851, *Fax (09) 857 85555,* ≘s, 18 – |≑|, ⇹ rm, ▤ TV ☎ ♿ 🚗 P – 🏛 95. AE ⓓ E VISA. ✻ rest
*closed Christmas* – **Meals** a la carte 95/200 – **150 rm** ☕ 750/800, 8 suites.

**Holiday Inn Garden Court Helsinki Airport** ⚘, Rälssitie 2, ✉ 01510, *(near the airport)* ☎ (09) 870 900, *Fax (09) 870 90101,* ≘s – |≑|, ⇹ rm, TV ☎ ♿ P – 🏛 30. AE ⓓ E VISA JCB. ✻ rest
**Meals** - Bistro - *(closed Saturday and Sunday lunch, Easter and Christmas)* a la carte 130/240 – **287 rm** ☕ 880/1100.

**Airport H. Rantasipi,** Robert Huberin Tie 4, ✉ 01510, *(near the airport)* ☎ (09) 415 77100, *Fax (09) 415 77101,* ≘s, ▢ – |≑|, ⇹ rm, TV ☎ ♿ P – 🏛 250. AE ⓓ E VISA JCB. ✻ rest
**Meals** *(closed Saturday and Sunday lunch)* (buffet lunch) 200/250 and dinner a la carte – **276 rm** ☕ 720/860, 4 suites.

# France

PARIS AND ENVIRONS – BORDEAUX
CANNES – LILLE – LYONS
MARSEILLES – PRINCIPALITY OF MONACO
NICE – STRASBOURG
VALLEY OF THE LOIRE

# PRACTICAL INFORMATION

## LOCAL CURRENCY

**French Franc:** *100 FRF = 16,70 USD ($) (Jan. 98)*

## TOURIST INFORMATION IN PARIS

**Paris "Welcome" Office** *(Office du Tourisme et des Congrès de Paris - Accueil de France): 127 Champs-Élysées, 8th, ☎ 01 49 52 53 54, Fax 01 49 52 53 00*

**American Express** *11 Rue Scribe, 9th, ☎ 01 47 14 50 00, Fax 01 42 68 17 17*

**National Holiday in France:** *14 July*

## AIRLINES

**AMERICAN AIRLINES:** *109, rue Fg-St-Honoré, 8th, ☎ 01 69 32 73 07, Fax 01 42 99 99 95*

**UNITED AIRLINES:** *55 rue Raspail, Levallois Perret (92) ☎ 01 41 40 30 30*

**T.W.A.:** *6, rue Christophe-Colomb, 8th, ☎ 01 49 19 20 00, Fax 01 49 19 20 09*

**DELTA AIRLINES:** *4, rue Scribe, 9th, ☎ 01 47 68 92 92, Fax 01 47 68 52 82*

**BRITISH AIRWAYS:** *13 boulevard de la Madeleine, 1st, ☎ 01 47 78 14 14, Fax 01 78 53 34 43*

**AIR FRANCE:** *119 Champs-Élysées, 8th, ☎ 08 02 80 28 02, Fax 01 42 99 21 99*

**AIR INTER EUROPE:** *119 Champs-Élysées, 8th, ☎ 01 42 99 21 01, Fax 01 47 23 74 58*

## FOREIGN EXCHANGE OFFICES

**Banks:** *close at 5pm and at weekends*

**Orly Airport:** *daily 6.30am to 11.30pm*

**Roissy-Charles de Gaulle Airport:** *daily 7am to 11.30pm*

## TRANSPORT IN PARIS

**Taxis:** *may be hailed in the street when showing the illuminated sign-available day and night at taxi ranks or called by telephone*

**Bus-Métro (subway):** *for full details see the Michelin Plan de Paris n° 11. The metro is quicker but the bus is good for sightseeing and practical for short distances.*

## POSTAL SERVICES

**Local post offices:** *open Mondays to Fridays 8am to 7pm; Saturdays 8am to noon*

**General Post Office:** *52 rue du Louvre, 1st: open 24 hours*

## SHOPPING IN PARIS

**Department stores:** *Boulevard Haussmann, Rue de Rivoli and Rue de Sèvres*

**Exclusive shops and boutiques:** *Faubourg St-Honoré, Rue de la Paix and Rue Royale, Avenue Montaigne.*

**Antiques and second-hand goods:** *Swiss Village (Avenue de la Motte Picquet), Louvre des Antiquaires (Place du Palais Royal), Flea Market (Porte Clignancourt).*

## TIPPING

*Service is generally included in hotel and restaurants bills but you may choose to leave more than the expected tip to the staff. Taxi-drivers, porters, barbers and theatre or cinema attendants also expect a small gratuity.*

## BREAKDOWN SERVICE

*Certain garages in central and outer Paris operate a 24 hour breakdown service. If you breakdown the police are usually able to help by indicating the nearest one.*

## SPEED LIMITS

*The maximum permitted speed in built up areas is 50 km/h - 31 mph; on motorways the speed limit is 130 km/h - 80 mph and 110 km/h - 68 mph on dual carriageways. On all other roads 90 km/h - 56 mph.*

## SEAT BELTS

*The wearing of seat belts is compulsory for drivers and all passengers.*

# PARIS AND ENVIRONS

*Maps:* 10, 11, 12 G. Paris.



**Population:** *Paris 2 152 333 ; Ile-de-France region : 10 651 000.*

**Altitude:** *Observatory : 60 m ; Place Concorde : 34 m*

**Air Terminals – To Orly:** *Esplanade des Invalides, 7th, ☎ 01 43 17 21 65*
**To Charles de Gaulle** *(Roissy): Palais des Congrès, Porte Maillot, 17th, ☎ 01 44 09 51 52 and Montparnasse r. du Cdt-Mouchotte (near SNCF railways station) 14th, ☎ 01 48 64 14 24*

**Paris'Airports:** *see Orly and Charles de Gaulle (Roissy)*

**Railways, motorail:** *information ☎ 01 36 35 35 35.*

# ARRONDISSEMENTS

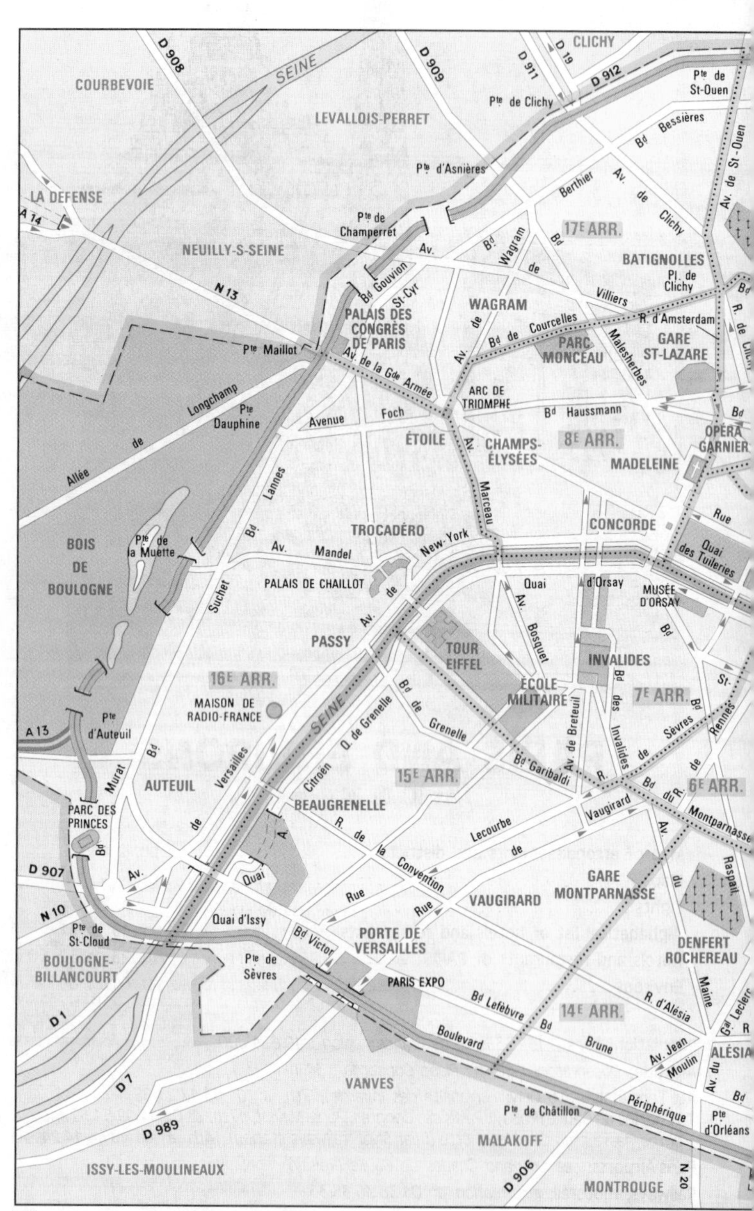

# AND DISTRICTS

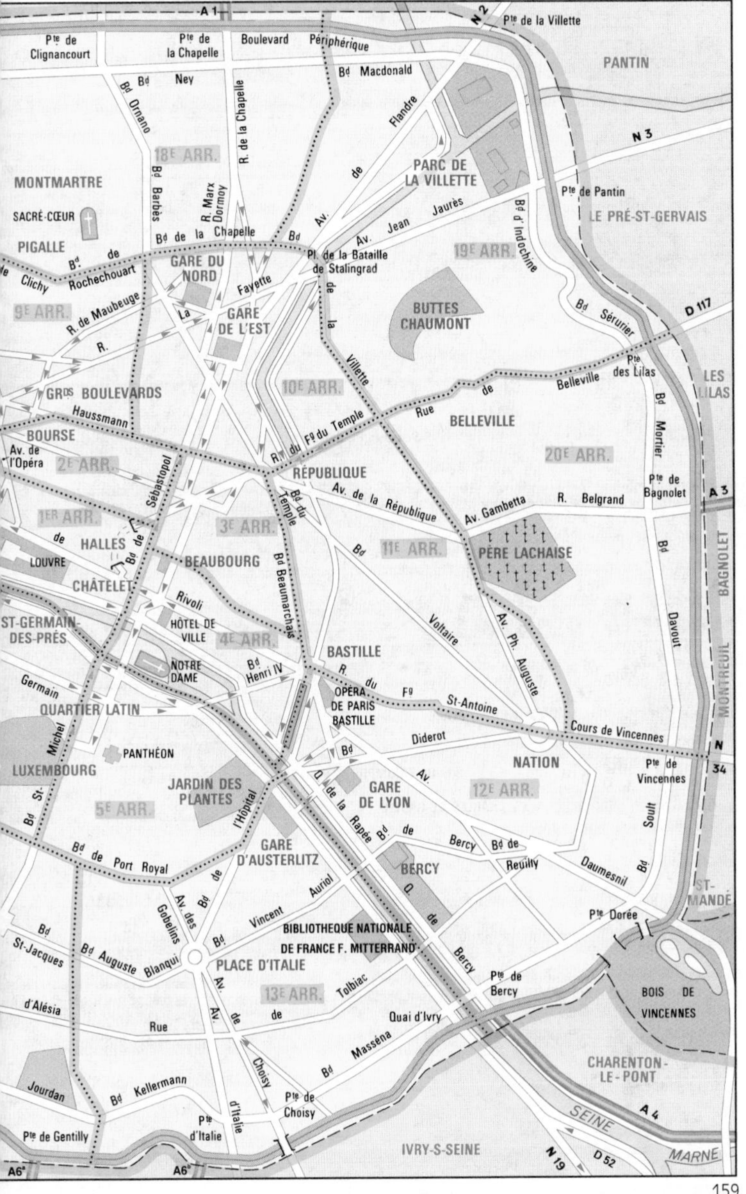

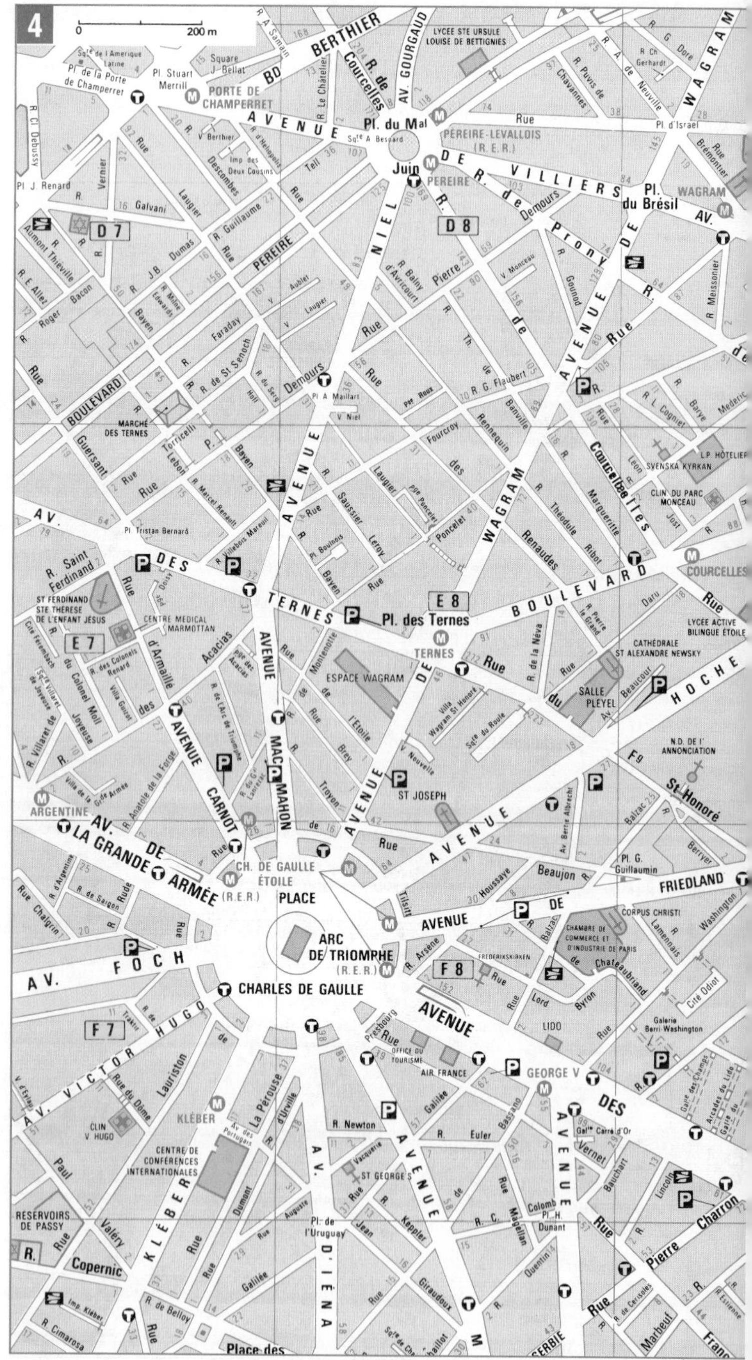
4
0
200 m
BD BERTHIER
PORTE DE CHAMPERRET
Pl. de la Porte de Champerret
Pl. Stuart Merrill
Square J.-Bellat
R. de Courcelles
AV. GOURGAUD
LYCEE STE URSULE
LOUISE DE BETTIGNIES
R. Puvis de Chavannes
R. A. de Neuville
R. G. Doré
R. Ch. Gerhardt
WAGRAM
AVENUE
Pl. du Mal Juin
PEREIRE-LEVALLOIS (R.E.R.)
PEREIRE
Pl. d'Israel
R. Brémontier
R. DE VILLIERS
Pl. du Brésil
WAGRAM
R. de Demours
R. de Prony
D 7
D 8
R. Cl. Debussy
Pl. J. Renard
R. Vernier
Galvani
R. Laugier
R. Guillaume
R. Descombes
Imp. des Deux Cousins
R. Tell
V. Berthier
R. d'Héliopolis
Sq. A. Besnard
R. Aumont Thiéville
R. E. Allez
R. Roger Bacon
R. J.B. Dumas
R. Mlle Edwards
Bayen
R. Faraday
PEREIRE
NIEL
R. Balny d'Avricourt
R. Pierre Demours
R. Th. de Banville
R. G. Flaubert
R. Gounod
R. Meissonier
AVENUE DE
BOULEVARD
R. de St Senoch
R. du Sergent Hoff
MARCHÉ DES TERNES
R. Torricelli
R. Lebon
P. Guersant
Rue Bayen
Pl. A. Maillart
V. Niel
Pge Roux
Rue Fourcroy
Rennequin
R. Laugier
Pge Poncelet
R. Poncelet
R. Saussier Leroy
Pl. Boulnois
R. Théodule Ribot
R. Renaudes
R. Marguerite
R. de Courcelles
R. L. Cogniet
R. Barye
R. Médéric
R. Léon Jost
SVENSKA KYRKAN
L.P. HÔTELIER
CLIN. DU PARC MONCEAU
COURCELLES
AV. DES TERNES
R. Marcel Renault
Pl. Tristan Bernard
R. Villebois Mareuil
R. Saint Ferdinand
ST FERDINAND
STE THÉRESE DE L'ENFANT JÉSUS
CENTRE MEDICAL MARMOTTAN
Pl. des Ternes
TERNES
E 8
BOULEVARD
R. Pierre le Grand
R. Daru
Rue de la Néva
LYCÉE ACTIVE BILINGUE ÉTOILE
CATHÉDRALE ST ALEXANDRE NEWSKY
SALLE PLEYEL
Av. Beaucour
HOCHE
E 7
Cité Férembach
Sq. Villaret de Joyeuse
R. du Colonel Moll
R. des Colonels Renard
Villa Guizot
Rue d'Armaillé
Acacias
Pge des Acacias
R. de l'Arc de Triomphe
AVENUE MAC MAHON
Rue Montenotte
ESPACE WAGRAM
R. de l'Étoile
R. Brey
Villa Wagram St Honoré
Sq. du Roule
R. du Fg St Honoré
N.D. DE L'ANNONCIATION
R. Villaret de Joyeuse
Joyeuse
AVENUE CARNOT
R. Anatole de la Forge
Villa de la Gde Armée
R. du Gal Lanrezac
ARGENTINE
AV. DE LA GRANDE ARMÉE
R. Troyon
V. Nouvelle
ST JOSEPH
AVENUE DE
Av. Bertie Albrecht
R. Balzac
R. Berryer
Pl. G. Guillaumin
CH. DE GAULLE ÉTOILE (R.E.R.)
PLACE
ARC DE TRIOMPHE (R.E.R.)
Rue de Tilsitt
AVENUE HOUSSAYE
Beaujon
FRIEDLAND
R. Washington
CORPUS CHRISTI
CHAMBRE DE COMMERCE ET D'INDUSTRIE DE PARIS
R. de Chateaubriand
R. Lamennais
R. d'Argentine
R. de Saigon
Rue Rude
Rue Chalgrin
R. Arsène Houssaye
FREDERIKSKIRKEN
F 8
Rue Lord Byron
AV. FOCH
CHARLES DE GAULLE
AVENUE
LIDO
Cité Odiot
Galerie Berri-Washington
F 7
R. de Traktir
HUGO
AV. VICTOR
R. de Presbourg
OFFICE DU TOURISME
AIR FRANCE
GEORGE V
DES
Galerie des Champs
Arcades du Lido
Rue du Dôme
Lauriston
CLIN. V. HUGO
KLÉBER
Av. des Portugais
Rue La Pérouse
R. d'Urville
R. Newton
R. Galilée
R. Euler
R. Bassano
Galie Carré d'Or
R. Vernet
R. Bauchart
R. Lincoln
R. Charron
CENTRE DE CONFÉRENCES INTERNATIONALES
V. d'Eylau
Paul Valéry
RESERVOIRS DE PASSY
KLÉBER
R. Dumont d'Urville
Auguste Vacquerie
ST GEORGE'S
R. C. Colomb
Pl. H. Dunant
Magellan
Rue Pierre
R. Quentin Bauchart
Rue Copernic
Pl. de l'Uruguay
AV. D'IÉNA
R. Jean Giraudoux
Keppler
Galilée
R. de Cerisoles
Rue Marbeuf
R. Boccador
R. Esienne
Franç
Imp. Kléber
R. Cimarosa
R. de Belloy
Rue
Sq. de Chaillot
Place des
SERBIE
M

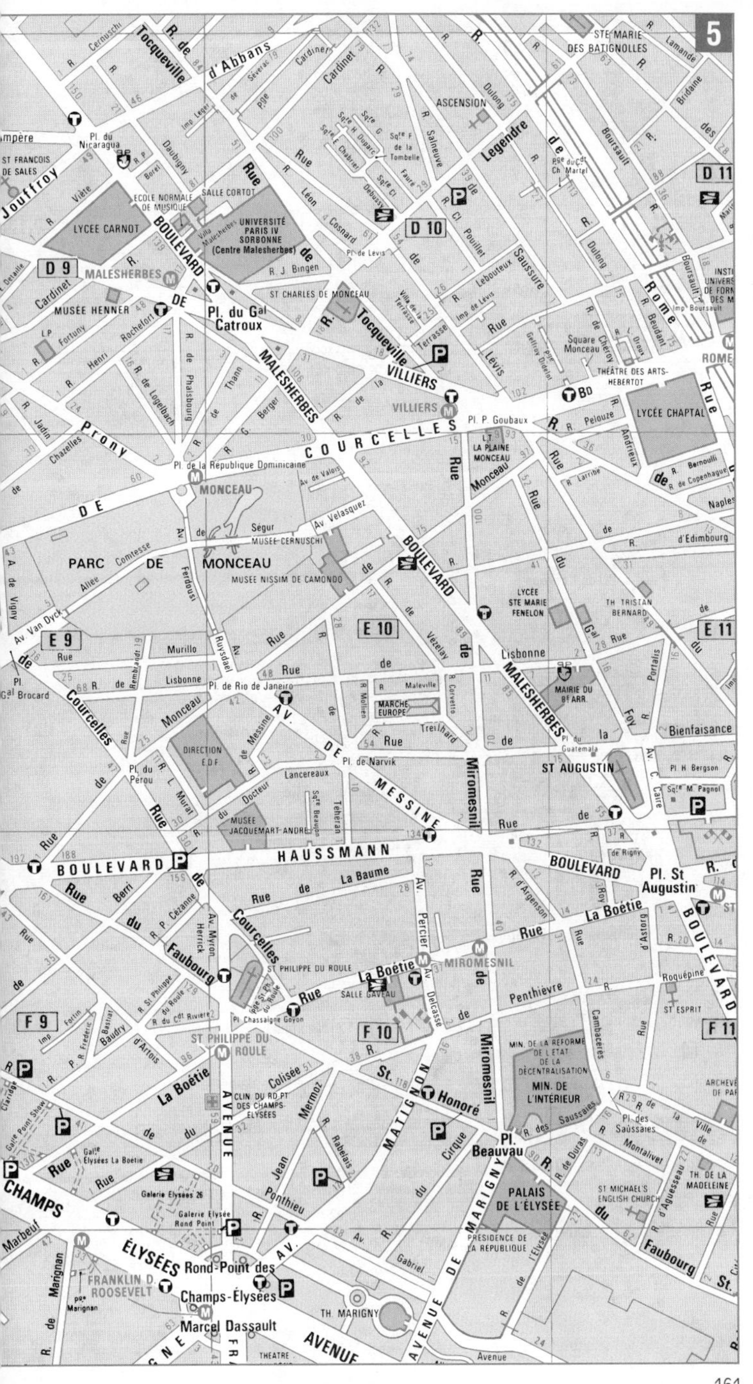

6
GARE ST LAZARE
PL. DE CLICHY
Pl. Blanche
STE TRINITÉ
Pl. de l'Europe
OPÉRA GARNIER
STE MARIE MADELEINE
BD DE LA MADELEINE
BD DES CAPUCINES
HAUSSMANN
BATIGNOLLES
LYCEE CONDORCET
MAGASINS DU PRINTEMPS
GALERIES LAFAYETTE
MUSÉE DE LA VIE ROMANTIQUE
MUSÉE GUSTAVE MOREAU
CASINO DE PARIS
D 11
D 12
D 13
E 11
E 12
E 13
F 11
F 12
F 13

7
BASILIQUE DU SACRÉ CŒUR
BOULEVARD DE ROCHECHOUART
AVENUE TRUDAINE
BOULEVARD BARBÈS
BD DE MAGENTA
D 14
D 15
E 14
E 15
F 14
F 15
BD MONTMARTRE
BD POISSONNIÈRE
BD DE BONNE NOUVELLE
LA BOURSE

8
Place des États Unis
G 7
G 8
H 7
H 8
J 7
J 8
K 7
K 8
MUSÉE GUIMET
Pl. d'Iéna
PRÉSIDENT
WILSON
Pl. de l'Alma
PALAIS DE TOKYO
MUSÉE D'ART MODERNE
PALAIS DE CHAILLOT
JARDINS
TROCADÉRO
Pl. de Varsovie
Pont d'Iéna
Pont de l'Alma
TOUR EIFFEL
CHAMP DE MARS TOUR EIFFEL (R.E.R.)
ESPACE EIFFEL-BRANLY
Pl. de la Résistance
Pl. du Général Gouraud
Pl. Jacques Rueff
BIR HAKEIM
DUPLEIX
Place Dupleix
ÉCOLE SUPRE DE GUERRE
ÉCOLE SUPRE D'INTENDANCE
BOULEVARD DE GRENELLE
AVENUE DE SUFFREN
CHAMP DE MARS
AVENUE BOSQUET
AVENUE RAPP

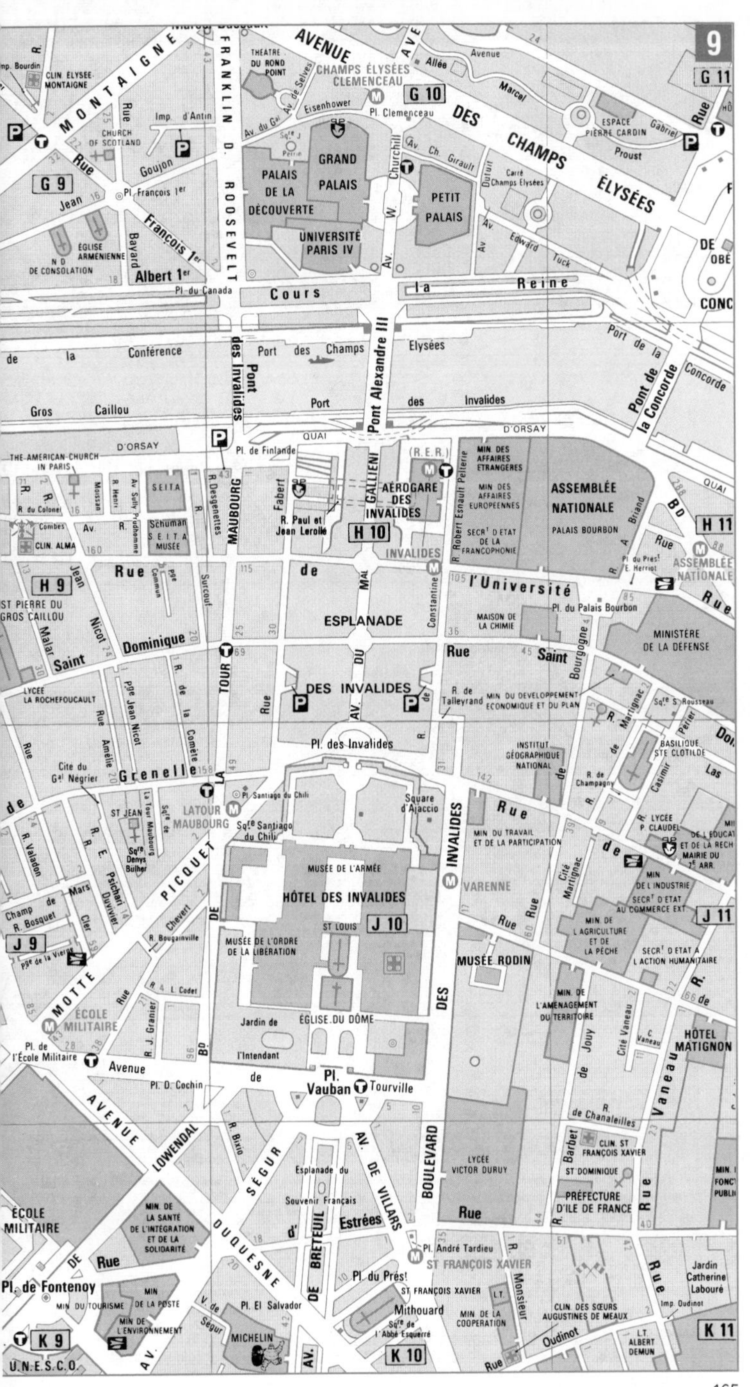

9
G 9
G 10
G 11
H 9
H 10
H 11
J 9
J 10
J 11
K 9
K 10
K 11
AVENUE DES CHAMPS ÉLYSÉES
MONTAIGNE
FRANKLIN D. ROOSEVELT
GRAND PALAIS
PALAIS DE LA DÉCOUVERTE
UNIVERSITÉ PARIS IV
PETIT PALAIS
CHAMPS ÉLYSÉES CLEMENCEAU
Cours la Reine
Port des Champs Elysées
Port des Invalides
Pont des Invalides
Pont Alexandre III
Pont de la Concorde
QUAI D'ORSAY
ASSEMBLÉE NATIONALE
PALAIS BOURBON
AÉROGARE DES INVALIDES
INVALIDES
ESPLANADE DES INVALIDES
Rue de l'Université
Rue Saint Dominique
Rue de Grenelle
MINISTÈRE DE LA DÉFENSE
HÔTEL DES INVALIDES
MUSÉE DE L'ARMÉE
MUSÉE DE L'ORDRE DE LA LIBÉRATION
ÉGLISE DU DÔME
MUSÉE RODIN
HÔTEL MATIGNON
BD DE LA TOUR MAUBOURG
BOULEVARD DES INVALIDES
AVENUE DE LA MOTTE PICQUET
ÉCOLE MILITAIRE
AVENUE DE SÉGUR
AV. DE VILLARS
AV. DE BRETEUIL
AVENUE DUQUESNE
Pl. Vauban
Pl. de Fontenoy
U.N.E.S.C.O.
LATOUR MAUBOURG
VARENNE
ST FRANÇOIS XAVIER
LYCÉE VICTOR DURUY
PRÉFECTURE D'ILE DE FRANCE
MICHELIN

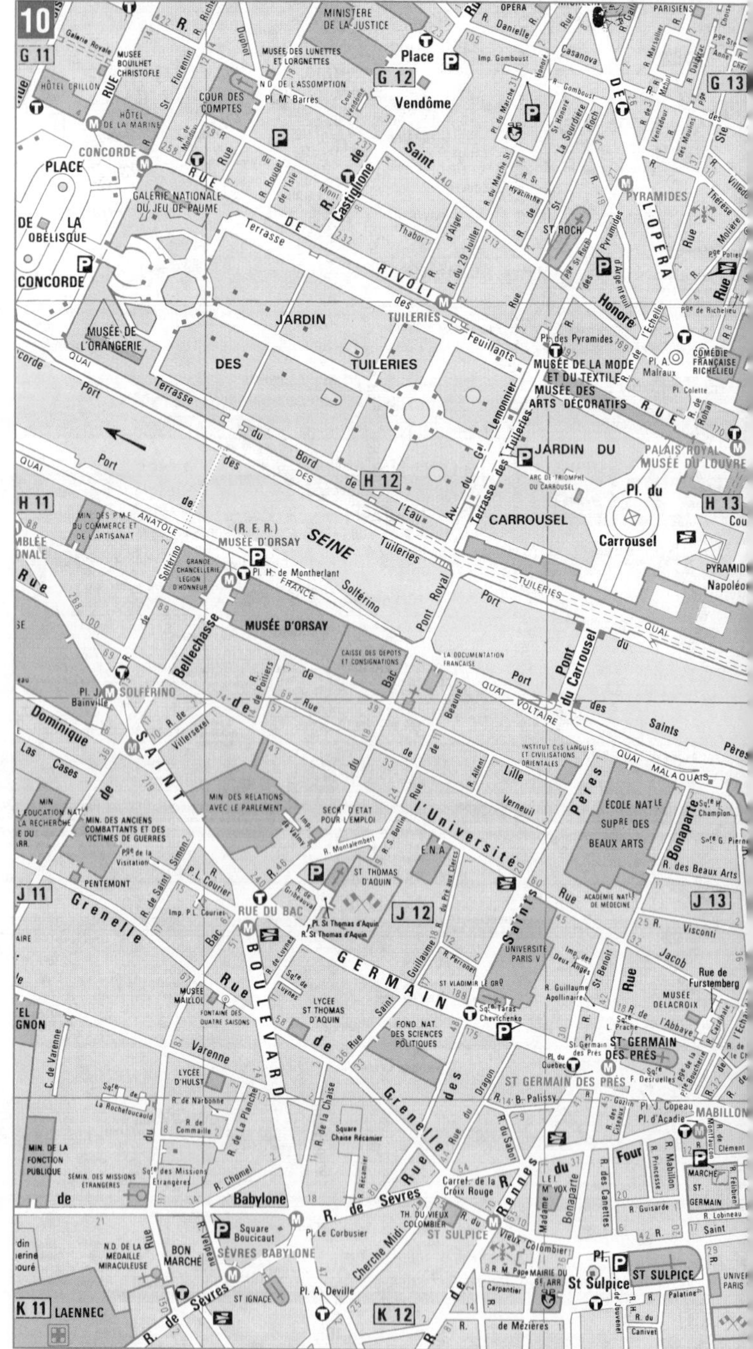
10
G 11
G 12
G 13
H 11
H 12
H 13
J 11
J 12
J 13
K 11
K 12
Place Vendôme
MINISTERE DE LA JUSTICE
PLACE DE LA CONCORDE
OBÉLISQUE
HÔTEL CRILLON
HÔTEL DE LA MARINE
GALERIE NATIONALE DU JEU DE PAUME
MUSÉE DE L'ORANGERIE
JARDIN DES TUILERIES
RUE DE RIVOLI
ST ROCH
PYRAMIDES
COMÉDIE FRANÇAISE RICHELIEU
MUSÉE DE LA MODE ET DU TEXTILE
MUSÉE DES ARTS DÉCORATIFS
PALAIS ROYAL MUSÉE DU LOUVRE
JARDIN DU CARROUSEL
Pl. du Carrousel
SEINE
MUSÉE D'ORSAY
Pont Royal
Pont du Carrousel
QUAI VOLTAIRE
QUAI MALAQUAIS
ÉCOLE NAT^LE SUP^RE DES BEAUX ARTS
SOLFÉRINO
RUE DU BAC
BOULEVARD SAINT GERMAIN
Rue de Grenelle
Rue de Varenne
Babylone
UNIVERSITE PARIS V
MUSÉE DELACROIX
ST GERMAIN DES PRÉS
MABILLON
MARCHÉ ST-GERMAIN
BON MARCHÉ
SÈVRES BABYLONE
ST SULPICE
Pl. St Sulpice
MAIRIE DU 6^E ARR.
LAENNEC
R. de Sèvres
Rue de Rennes

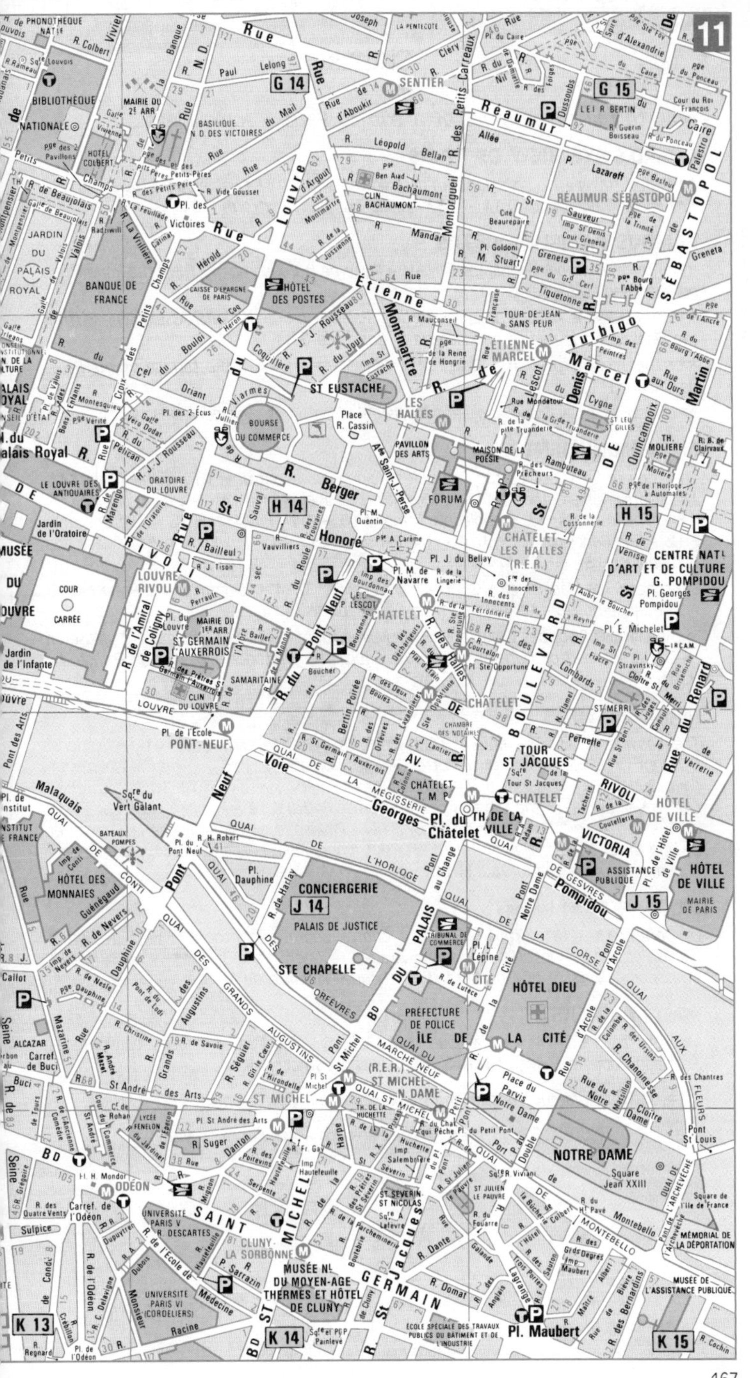
11
G 14
G 15
H 14
H 15
J 14
J 15
K 13
K 14
K 15
BIBLIOTHÈQUE NATIONALE
BANQUE DE FRANCE
JARDIN DU PALAIS ROYAL
HÔTEL DES POSTES
BOURSE DU COMMERCE
ST EUSTACHE
LES HALLES
FORUM
CENTRE NATL D'ART ET DE CULTURE G. POMPIDOU
MUSÉE DU LOUVRE
COUR CARRÉE
ST GERMAIN L'AUXERROIS
SAMARITAINE
PONT-NEUF
TOUR ST JACQUES
CHÂTELET
HÔTEL DE VILLE
CONCIERGERIE
PALAIS DE JUSTICE
STE CHAPELLE
HÔTEL DIEU
PRÉFECTURE DE POLICE
ÎLE DE LA CITÉ
NOTRE DAME
HÔTEL DES MONNAIES
ST MICHEL
ODÉON
CLUNY-LA SORBONNE
MUSÉE NL DU MOYEN-AGE THERMES ET HÔTEL DE CLUNY
Pl. Maubert
RÉAUMUR SÉBASTOPOL
ÉTIENNE MARCEL
SENTIER

# Sights

*How to make the most of a trip to Paris – some ideas :*

## A BIRD'S-EYE VIEW OF PARIS

★★★ *Eiffel Tower* J 7 – ★★★ *Montparnasse Tower* LM 11 – ★★★ *Notre-Dame Towers* K 15 – ★★★ *Sacré Cœur Dome* D 14 – ★★★ *Arc de Triomphe platform* F 8.

## FAMOUS PARISIAN VISTAS

★★★ *Arc de Triomphe – Champs-Élysées – Place de la Concorde : ⩽ from the Rond Point on the Champs-Élysées* G 10.

★★ *The Madeleine – Place de la Concorde – Palais Bourbon (National Assembly) : ⩽ from the Obelisk in the middle of Place de la Concorde* G 11.

★★★ *The Trocadéro – Eiffel Tower – Ecole Militaire : ⩽ from the terrace of the Palais de Chaillot* H 7.

★★ *The Invalides – Grand and Petit Palais : ⩽ from Pont Alexandre III* H 10.

## MAIN MONUMENTS

*The Louvre*★★★ *(Cour Carrée, Perrault's Colonnade, Pyramid)* H 13 – *Eiffel Tower*★★★ J 7 – *Notre-Dame Cathedral*★★★ K 15 – *Sainte-Chapelle*★★★ J 14 – *Arc de Triomphe*★★★ F 8 – *The Invalides*★★★ *(Napoleon's Tomb)* J 10 – *Palais-Royal*★★ H 13 – *The Opéra*★★ F 12 – *The Conciergerie*★★ J 14 – *The Panthéon*★★ L 14 – *Luxembourg*★★ *(Palace and Gardens)* KL 13.

**Churches :** *The Madeleine*★★ G 11 – *Sacré Cœur*★★ D 14 – *St-Germain-des-Prés*★★ J 13 – *St-Etienne-du-Mont*★★ – *St-Germain-l'Auxerrois*★★ H 14.

**In the Marais :** *Place des Vosges*★★ – *Hôtel Lamoignon*★★ – *Hôtel Guénégaud*★★ *(Museum of the Chase and of Nature)* – *Hôtel de Soubise*★★ *(Historical Museum of France)* by HJ 15.

## MAIN MUSEUMS

*The Louvre*★★★ H 13 – *Musée d'Orsay*★★★ *(mid-19C to early 20C)* H 12 – *National Museum of Modern Art*★★★ *(Centre Georges-Pompidou)* H 15 – *Army Museum*★★★ *(Invalides)* J 10 – *Museum of Decorative Arts*★★ *(107 rue de Rivoli)* H 13 – *Hôtel de Cluny*★★ *(Museum of the Middle Ages and Roman Baths)* K 14 – *Rodin*★★ *(Hôtel de Biron)* J 10 – *Carnavalet*★★ *(History of Paris)* J 17 – *Picasso*★★ H 17 – *Cité de la Science et de l'Industrie*★★★ *(La Villette)* – *Marmottan*★★ *(Impressionist artists)* – *Orangerie*★★ *(from the Impressionists until 1930)* H 11.

## MODERN MONUMENTS

*La Défense*★★ *(CNIT, Grande Arche)* – *Centre Georges-Pompidou*★★ H 15 – *Forum des Halles* H 14 – *Institut du Monde Arabe*★ – *Opéra Paris-Bastille*★ – *Bercy (Palais Omnisports, Ministry of Finance)* – *Bibliothèque Nationale de France.*

## PRETTY AREAS

*Montmartre*★★★ D 14 – *Ile St-Louis*★★ J 14 J 15 – *the Quays*★★ *(between Pont des Arts and Pont de Sully)* J 14 J 15 – *St Séverin district*★★ K 14.

K 14, G 10 : *Reference letters and numbers on the town plans.*

*Use MICHELIN Green Guide Paris for a well-informed visit.*

# Alphabetical list (Hotels and restaurants)

## C

## D



## E

## F



## G



## H - I

## J - K



## L



## M

## U - V



## W



## Y - Z

# HOTELS, RESTAURANTS

## Listed by districts and arrondissements

(List of Hotels and Restaurants in alphabetical order, see pp 13 to 21)

G 12: These reference letters and numbers correspond to the squares on the Michelin Map of Paris no 10. Paris Atlas no 11. Map with street index no 12 and Map of Paris no 14.

Consult any of the above publications when looking for a car park nearest to a listed establishment.

## Opéra, Palais-Royal, Halles, Bourse.

*1st and 2nd arrondissements - 1st: ✉ 75001 - 2nd: ✉ 75002*

**Ritz,** 15 pl. Vendôme (1st) ✆ 01 43 16 30 30, *Fax 01 43 16 31 78,* « Attractive pool and luxurious fitness centre » - AE ⓞ GB JCB G 12
see ***Espadon*** below - ***Bar Vendôme*** (lunch only) **Meals** a la carte 360/540 - ☕ 190 - **142 rm** 3300/4300, 45 suites.

**Meurice,** 228 r. Rivoli (1st) ✆ 01 44 58 10 10, *Fax 01 44 58 10 15* - |‡|, ⊭ rm, ▤ rm, TV ☎ - 🅰 100. AE ⓞ GB JCB. ⚔ rest G 12
**Meals** see ***Le Meurice*** below - ☕ 150 - **134 rm** 2800/3900, 46 suites.

**Inter - Continental,** 3 r. Castiglione (1st) ✆ 01 44 77 11 11, *Fax 01 44 77 14 60,* 余 - |‡|, ⊭ rm, ▤ TV ☎ ♿ - 🅰 500. AE ⓞ GB JCB. ⚔ rest G 12
***Brasserie 234 Rivoli*** ✆ 01 44 77 10 40 **Meals** a la carte 200/400 - ***Terrasse Fleurie*** ✆ *01 44 77 10 44 (open May-September and closed Saturday and Sunday)* **Meals** 280 - ☕ 195 - **415 rm** 2600/3000, 30 suites.

**Castille** M, 37 r. Cambon (1st) ✆ 01 44 58 44 58, *Fax 01 44 58 44 00,* 余 - |‡|, ⊭ rm, ▤ TV ☎ ♿ - 🅰 30. AE ⓞ GB JCB. ⚔ rest G 12
see ***Il Cortile*** below - ☕ 140 - **107 rm** 2100/2750, 7 suites, 14 duplex.

**Westminster,** 13 r. Paix (2nd) ✆ 01 42 61 57 46, *Fax 01 42 60 30 66* - |‡|, ⊭ rm, ▤ rm, TV ☎ - 🅰 60. AE ⓞ GB JCB G 12
**Meals** see ***Céladon*** below - ☕ 110 - **84 rm** 1850/2600, 18 suites.

**Costes,** 239 r. St-Honoré (1st) ✆ 01 42 44 50 00, *Fax 01 42 44 50 01,* 余, « Elegant mansion tastefully decorated », Fō, ▣ - |‡| ▤ TV ☎ ♿ - 🅰 30. AE ⓞ GB JCB
**Meals** a la carte 250/440 - ☕ 130 - **85 rm** 1750/3250. G 12

**du Louvre,** pl. A. Malraux (1st) ✆ 01 44 58 38 38, *Fax 01 44 58 38 01,* 余 - |‡| ▤ TV ☎ ♿ - 🅰 100. AE ⓞ GB JCB H 13
***Brasserie Le Louvre :*** **Meals** 180 (dinner) and a la carte 190/370 - ☕ 120 - **194 rm** 1650/2800, 5 suites.

**Lotti,** 7 r. Castiglione (1st) ✆ 01 42 60 37 34, *Fax 01 40 15 93 56* - |‡|, ⊭ rm, ▤ TV ☎. AE ⓞ GB JCB G 12
**Meals** 160/220 and a la carte 260/430 - ☕ 120 - **129 rm** 1710/3330.

**Édouard VII** without rest, 39 av. Opéra (2nd) ✆ 01 42 61 56 90, *Fax 01 42 61 47 73* - |‡| ▤ TV ☎. AE ⓞ GB G 13
☕ 100 - **65 rm** 1400/1600, 4 suites.

**Opéra Richepanse** M without rest, 14 r. Richepanse (1st) ✆ 01 42 60 36 00, *Fax 01 42 60 13 03* - |‡| ▤ TV ☎. AE ⓞ GB JCB G 12
☕ 70 - **35 rm** 1250/1450, 3 suites.

**Normandy,** 7 r. Échelle (1st) ✆ 01 42 60 30 21, *Fax 01 42 60 45 81* - |‡|, ⊭ rm, TV ☎ - 🅰 30. AE ⓞ GB JCB H 13
***L'Échelle*** *(closed Saturday and Sunday)* **Meals** 150 - ☕ 68 - **111 rm** 1155/1510, 4 suites.

**Royal St-Honoré** M without rest, 221 r. St-Honoré (1st) ✆ 01 42 60 32 79, *Fax 01 42 60 47 44* - |‡| ▤ TV ☎ ♿. AE ⓞ GB JCB. ⚔ G 12
☕ 95 - **67 rm** 1500/2000, 5 suites.

**Régina**, 2 pl. Pyramides (1st) ✆ 01 42 60 31 10, *Fax 01 40 15 95 16*, « "Art Nouveau" lobby » – rm, – 30. AE GB JCB. rest H 13
**Meals** *(closed August, Saturday, Sunday and Bank Holidays)* 170/270 b.i. – 95 – **116 rm** 1650/2250, 14 suites.

**Stendhal** without rest, 22 r. D. Casanova (2nd) ✆ 01 44 58 52 52, *Fax 01 44 58 52 00* – AE GB JCB G 12
95 – **20 rm** 1380/1560.

**L'Horset Opéra** M without rest, 18 r. d'Antin (2nd) ✆ 01 44 71 87 00, *Fax 01 42 66 55 54* – rm, AE GB JCB G 13
80 – **54 rm** 990/1350.

**Cambon** M without rest, 3 r. Cambon (1st) ✆ 01 44 58 93 93, *Fax 01 42 60 30 59* – AE GB JCB G 12
80 – **40 rm** 1680.

**Mansart** without rest, 5 r. Capucines (1st) ✆ 01 42 61 50 28, *Fax 01 49 27 97 44* – AE GB JCB. G 12
55 – **57 rm** 700/980.

**Novotel Les Halles** M, 8 pl. M.-de-Navarre (1st) ✆ 01 42 21 31 31, *Fax 01 40 26 05 79*, – rm, – 120. AE GB JCB H 14
**Meals** a la carte approx. 170 – 68 – **280 rm** 1075/1145, 5 suites.

**de Noailles** M without rest, 9 r. Michodière (2nd) ✆ 01 47 42 92 90, *Fax 01 49 24 92 71*, contemporary decor – AE GB JCB G 13
50 – **58 rm** 880.

**Favart** without rest, 5 r. Marivaux (2nd) ✆ 01 42 97 59 83, *Fax 01 40 15 95 58* – AE GB JCB F 13
20 – **37 rm** 495/600.

**Violet** M without rest, 7 r. J. Lantier (1st) ✆ 01 42 33 45 38, *Fax 01 40 28 03 56* – AE GB JCB. J 14
50 – **30 rm** 550/730.

**Place du Louvre** M without rest, 21 r. Prêtres-St-Germain-L'Auxerrois (1st) ✆ 01 42 33 78 68, *Fax 01 42 33 09 95* – AE GB JCB H 14
50 – **20 rm** 510/830.

**Gd H. de Besançon** M without rest, 56 r. Montorgueil (2nd) ✆ 01 42 36 41 08, *Fax 01 45 08 08 79* – rm, AE GB JCB. G 14
60 – **20 rm** 620/680.

**Baudelaire Opéra** without rest, 61 r. Ste Anne (2nd) ✆ 01 42 97 50 62, *Fax 01 42 86 85 85* – AE GB JCB G 13
39 – **24 rm** 480/670, 5 duplex.

**Vivienne** without rest, 40 r. Vivienne (2nd) ✆ 01 42 33 13 26, *Fax 01 40 41 98 19* – GB F 14
40 – **44 rm** 365/505.

**L'Espadon** - Hôtel Ritz, 15 pl. Vendôme (1st) ✆ 01 43 16 30 80, *Fax 01 43 16 33 75*, – AE GB JCB. G 12
**Meals** 390 (lunch)/750 and a la carte 490/850
**Spec.** Pastilla de foie gras chaud en gelée de poulette. Noix de Saint-Jacques (October-April). Suprême de volaille de Bresse.

**Grand Vefour,** 17 r. Beaujolais (1st) ✆ 01 42 96 56 27, *Fax 01 42 86 80 71*, « Pre-Revolutionary (late 18C) café style » – AE GB JCB. G 13
*closed August, Saturday and Sunday* – **Meals** 335 (lunch)/750 and a la carte 590/850
**Spec.** Ravioles de foie gras à l'émulsion de crème truffée. Noisettes d'agneau panées au moka, jus de café, pulpe d'aubergine confite. Tourte d'artichaut et légumes confits, sorbet aux amandes amères (dessert).

**Le Meurice** - Hôtel Meurice, 228 r. Rivoli (1st) ✆ 01 44 58 10 50, *Fax 01 44 58 10 15* – AE GB JCB. G 12
**Meals** 290 (lunch), 430 b.i./550 and a la carte 370/520
**Spec.** Homard breton en vinaigrette d'herbes de mer. Tronçon de turbot rôti, sabayon acidulé de carottes à la badiane. Pigeon de Bretagne en cocotte, farce d'herbes et de pignons.

**Goumard-Prunier,** 9 r. Duphot (1st) ✆ 01 42 60 36 07, *Fax 01 42 60 04 54* – AE GB JCB G 12
*closed 10 to 23 August, Sunday and Monday* – **Meals** - Seafood - 390 b.i. and a la carte 420/800
**Spec.** Soupe tiède de homard breton aux cocos. Coquilles Saint-Jacques cuites au "repère". Daurade royale grillée aux tomates confites.

XXXX ⚘⚘ **Carré des Feuillants** (Dutournier), 14 r. Castiglione (1st) ✆ 01 42 86 82 82, *Fax 01 42 86 07 71* – ▤. AE ⓓ GB JCB G 12
*closed August, Saturday lunch and Sunday* – **Meals** 285 (lunch) and a la carte 480/680
**Spec.** Velouté de châtaignes à la truffe blanche (October-November). Langoustines à la nougatine d'ail doux. Noisettes de brebis en croûte parfumée.

XXXX ⚘ **Drouant,** pl. Gaillon (2nd) ✆ 01 42 65 15 16, *Fax 01 49 24 02 15,* « Home of the Academie Goncourt since 1914 » – ▤. AE ⓓ GB JCB G 13
**Meals** 290 (lunch)/650 and a la carte 560/720 - ***Café Drouant :*** **Meals** 200 and a la carte 280/360
**Spec.** Salade de homard à l'huile pimentée. Bar rôti à la tapenade et pissala, légumes confits au basilic. Canette fermière de Challans en cabessal (autumn-winter).

XXXX ⚘⚘ **Gérard Besson,** 5 r. Coq Héron (1st) ✆ 01 42 33 14 74, *Fax 01 42 33 85 71* – ▤. AE ⓓ GB JCB H 14
*closed Saturday except dinner from 15 September to 15 June and Sunday* – **Meals** 280 (lunch), 420/550 and a la carte 430/660
**Spec.** Cocotte de queue et pinces de homard. Gibier (season). Fenouil confit aux épices, glace vanille et nougatine aux amandes.

XXX ⚘ **Céladon** - Hôtel Westminster, 15 r. Daunou (2nd) ✆ 01 42 61 77 42, *Fax 01 42 61 33 78* – ▤. AE ⓓ GB JCB G 12
*closed August, Saturday, Sunday and Bank Holidays* – **Meals** 260/390 and a la carte 340/500
**Spec.** Risotto de cèpes au lard paysan. Tronçon de turbot en cocotte au céleri rave et parfum de truffes. Mirliton d'Aix aux fruits rouges, glace au basilic.

XXX **Macéo,** 15 r. Petits-Champs (1st) ✆ 01 42 96 98 89, *Fax 01 42 96 08 89* – GB G 13
*closed Sunday* – **Meals** 185 (lunch), 200/240.

XXX ⚘ **Il Cortile** - Hôtel de Castille, 37 r. Cambon (1st) ✆ 01 44 58 45 67, *Fax 01 44 58 44 00*
*closed Saturday and Sunday* – **Meals** - Italian rest. - a la carte 240/340 G 12
**Spec.** Farfalle à l'encre, crustacés et coquillages au basilic. Picatta de veau à la sauge. Tartelette chocolat et noisette du Piémont.

XXX **Pierre " A la Fontaine Gaillon ",** pl. Gaillon (2nd) ✆ 01 47 42 63 22, *Fax 01 47 42 82 84,* ☂ – ▤. AE ⓓ GB JCB G 13
*closed August, Saturday lunch and Sunday* – **Meals** 165 and a la carte 220/380.

XX ⚘ **Pierre Au Palais Royal,** 10 r. Richelieu (1st) ✆ 01 42 96 09 17, *Fax 01 42 96 09 62* – ▤. AE ⓓ GB JCB H 13
*closed 24 December-1 January and Sunday* – **Meals** a la carte 200/300
**Spec.** Escalope de foie gras de canard. Quenelles de brochet à la Nantua. Bœuf ficelle à la ménagère.

XX **Palais Royal,** 110 Galerie de Valois - Jardin du Palais Royal (1st) ✆ 01 40 20 00 27, *Fax 01 40 20 00 82,* ☂, « Terrace in Palais Royal garden » – AE ⓓ GB JCB G 13
*closed 22 December-2 January, Saturday lunch and Sunday from September-May* – **Meals** a la carte 200/310.

XX **Chez Pauline,** 5 r. Villédo (1st) ✆ 01 42 96 20 70, *Fax 01 49 27 99 89* – AE ⓓ GB JCB
*closed Saturday except lunch from October-March and Sunday* – **Meals** 220 and a la carte 290/480. G 13

XX **Pays de Cocagne,** -Espace Tarn- 111 r. Réaumur (2nd) ✆ 01 40 13 81 81, *Fax 01 40 13 87 70* – AE GB JCB G 14
*closed 3 to 22 August, Saturday lunch, Sunday and Bank Holidays* – **Meals** 138/190.

XX **Rôtisserie Monsigny,** 1 r. Monsigny (2nd) ✆ 01 42 96 16 61, *Fax 01 42 97 40 97* – ▤. AE GB JCB G 13
*closed 10 to 20 August and Saturday lunch* – **Meals** 160 and a la carte 190/350.

XX **Kinugawa,** 9 r. Mont-Thabor (1st) ✆ 01 42 60 65 07, *Fax 01 42 60 45 21* – ▤. AE ⓓ GB JCB. ✱ G 12
*closed Christmas Holidays and Sunday* – **Meals** - Japanese rest. - 510/700 and a la carte 180/400.

XX **Pharamond,** 24 r. Grande-Truanderie (1st) ✆ 01 42 33 06 72, *Fax 01 40 28 01 81,* bistrot, « Fine 1900 decor » – AE ⓓ GB G 14
*closed Monday lunch and Sunday* – **Meals** 200 b.i. (lunch)/310 b.i. and a la carte 250/450.

XX **Au Pied de Cochon** (24 hr service), 6 r. Coquillière (1st) ✆ 01 40 13 77 00, *Fax 01 40 13 77 09,* ☂, brasserie – |♦| ▤. AE ⓓ GB H 14
**Meals** 178 and a la carte 200/380.

XX **Gallopin,** 40 r. N.-D.-des Victoires (2nd) ✆ 01 42 36 45 38, *Fax 01 42 36 10 32,* « Late 19C brasserie » – AE ⓓ GB G 14
*closed Saturday lunch and Sunday* – **Meals** 149 and a la carte 160/300 ♁.

XX **Vaudeville,** 29 r. Vivienne (2nd) ✆ 01 40 20 04 62, *Fax 01 49 27 08 78,* brasserie – AE ⓓ GB G 14
**Meals** 169 b.i. and a la carte 160/300.

XX **Grand Colbert,** 2 r. Vivienne (2nd) ☎ 01 42 86 87 88, *Fax 01 42 86 82 65*, brasserie – AE ⓓ GB JCB G 13
*closed 10 to 25 August* – **Meals** 155 and a la carte 190/280 🍷.

XX **Poquelin,** 17 r. Molière (1st) ☎ 01 42 96 22 19, *Fax 01 42 96 05 72* – AE ⓓ GB JCB G 13
*closed 1 to 20 August, Saturday lunch and Sunday* – **Meals** 189 and a la carte 250/380.

XX **Bonne Fourchette,** 320 r. St-Honoré, in the backyard (1st) ☎ 01 42 60 45 27 – ▤. ⓓ GB. ✂ G 12
*closed August, February Holidays, Sunday lunch and Saturday* – **Meals** 130/170 and a la carte 200/300.

XX **Saudade,** 34 r. Bourdonnais (1st) ☎ 01 42 36 30 71, *Fax 01 42 36 27 77* – ▤. AE GB JCB. ✂ H 14
*closed Sunday* – **Meals** - Portuguese rest. - 129 (lunch) and a la carte 170/310.

X **A la Grille St-Honoré,** 15 pl. Marché St-Honoré (1st) ☎ 01 42 61 00 93, *Fax 01 47 03 31 64*, 🏠 – ▤. AE ⓓ GB G 12
*closed 1 to 25 August, 24 December-2 January, Sunday and Monday* – **Meals** 180/250.

X **Bistrot St-Honoré,** 10 r. Gomboust (1st) ☎ 01 42 61 77 78, *Fax 01 42 61 77 78* – AE GB G 13
*closed 10 to 16 August and Sunday* – **Meals** 130 and a la carte 180/360.

X **Chez Georges,** 1 r. Mail (2nd) ☎ 01 42 60 07 11, bistro – AE GB G 14
*closed 1 to 24 August, Sunday and Bank Holidays* – **Meals** a la carte 190/340.

X **Café Marly,** 93 r. Rivoli - Cour Napoléon (1st) ☎ 01 49 26 06 60, *Fax 01 49 26 07 06*, 🏠, « Original decor at the Louvre museum, terrace » – ▤. AE ⓓ GB H 13
**Meals** a la carte 180/220.

X **L'Ardoise,** 28 r. Mont-Thabor (2nd) ☎ 01 42 96 28 18 – GB G 12
*closed 10 to 31 August and Monday* – **Meals** 165.

X **Willi's Wine Bar,** 13 r. Petits-Champs (1st) ☎ 01 42 61 05 09, *Fax 01 47 03 36 93* – GB. ✂ G 13
*closed Sunday* – **Meals** 145 (lunch), 180/195.

X **Poule au Pot,** 9 r. Vauvilliers (1st) ☎ 01 42 36 32 96, bistro – GB. ✂ H 14
**Meals** (dinner only) 160 and a la carte 210/280.

X **Souletin,** 6 r. Vrillière (1st) ☎ 01 42 61 43 78, *Fax 01 42 61 43 78*, bistro – GB G 14
*closed Sunday and Bank Holidays* – **Meals** a la carte approx. 190.

X **Lescure,** 7 r. Mondovi (1st) ☎ 01 42 60 18 91, bistro – GB G 11
*closed 1 to 25 August, 22 December-5 January, Saturday dinner and Sunday* – **Meals** 100 b.i. and a la carte 100/200.

X **Entre Ciel et Terre,** 5 r. Hérold (1st) ☎ 01 45 08 49 84, no smoking rest. – GB G 14
*closed 25 July-30 August, Saturday and Sunday* – **Meals** - Vegetarian rest. - 87 and a la carte approx. 120.

X **Victoire Suprême du Cœur,** 41 r. Bourdonnais (1st) ☎ 01 40 41 93 95, *Fax 01 40 41 94 57* – GB H 14
*closed 15 to 31 August and Sunday* – **Meals** - Vegetarian rest. - 71 (lunch), 87/131 and a la carte 100/140.

## Bastille, République, Hôtel de Ville.

*3rd, 4th and 11th arrondissements.*
*3rd: ✉ 75003*
*4th: ✉ 75004*
*11th: ✉ 75011*

🏨 **Pavillon de la Reine** 🐕 without rest, 28 pl. Vosges (3rd) ☎ 01 40 29 19 19, *Fax 01 40 29 19 20*, « Fine decor » – 🛗 ▤ TV ☎ 🚗. AE ⓓ GB JCB J 17
☕ 110 – **31 rm** 1650/2000, 14 suites, 10 duplex.

🏨 **Holiday Inn** M, 10 pl. République (11th) ☎ 01 43 55 44 34, *Fax 01 47 00 32 34* – 🛗, ✂ rm, ▤ TV ☎ ♿ – 🏛 200. AE ⓓ GB JCB G 17
***Belle Époque*** : **Meals** a la carte 170/260 – ☕ 125 – **318 rm** 2300/2995.

**Jeu de Paume** without rest, 54 r. St-Louis-en-l'Ile (4th) 01 43 26 14 18, *Fax 01 40 46 02 76*, « 17C tennis court » – 30. AE GB JCB K 16
80 – **32 rm** 895/1385.

**Bretonnerie** without rest, 22 r. Ste-Croix-de-la-Bretonnerie (4th) 01 48 87 77 63, *Fax 01 42 77 26 78* – GB. J 16
*closed 31 July-27 August* – 50 – **27 rm** 650/790, 3 suites.

**Caron de Beaumarchais** M without rest, 12 r. Vieille-du-Temple (4th) 01 42 72 34 12, *Fax 01 42 72 34 63* – AE GB JCB. J 16
54 – **19 rm** 690/770.

**Beaubourg** without rest, 11 r. S. Le Franc (4th) 01 42 74 34 24, *Fax 01 42 78 68 11* – AE GB JCB. H 15
40 – **28 rm** 620/720.

**Verlain** without rest, 97 r. St-Maur (11th) 01 43 57 44 88, *Fax 01 43 57 32 06* – AE GB G 19
40 – **38 rm** 520/580.

**Lutèce** without rest, 65 r. St-Louis-en-l'Ile (4th) 01 43 26 23 52, *Fax 01 43 29 60 25* – AE GB. K 16
47 – **23 rm** 840/860.

**Bel Air** M without rest, 5/7 r. Rampon (11th) 01 47 00 41 57, *Fax 01 47 00 21 56* – AE GB JCB G 17
45 – **48 rm** 540/610.

**Rivoli Notre Dame** without rest, 19 r. Bourg Tibourg (4th) 01 42 78 47 39, *Fax 01 40 29 07 00* – AE GB JCB. J 16
42 – **31 rm** 525/715.

**Grand Prieuré** without rest, 20 r. Grand Prieuré (11th) 01 47 00 74 14, *Fax 01 49 23 06 64* – AE GB. G 17
30 – **32 rm** 330/370.

**Croix de Malte** M without rest, 5 r. Malte (11th) 01 48 05 09 36, *Fax 01 43 57 02 54* – rm, AE GB JCB H 17
45 – **29 rm** 510/570.

**de Nice** without rest, 42 bis r. Rivoli (4th) 01 42 78 55 29, *Fax 01 42 78 36 07* – GB. J 16
35 – **23 rm** 400/500.

**Allegro République** M without rest, 39 r. J.-P. Timbaud (11th) 01 48 06 64 97, *Fax 01 48 05 03 38* – AE GB G 18
40 – **42 rm** 410/470.

**Beauséjour** M without rest, 71 av. Parmentier (11th) 01 47 00 38 16, *Fax 01 43 55 47 89* – AE GB H 18
30 – **31 rm** 290/350.

**L'Ambroisie** (Pacaud), 9 pl. des Vosges (4th) 01 42 78 51 45 – AE GB. J 17
*closed 3 to 23 August, February Holidays, Sunday and Monday* – **Meals** a la carte 690/1 160
**Spec.** Feuillantine de queues de langoustines aux graines de sésame, sauce au curry. Pigeon confit à l'ail doux, ragoût de févettes à la sarriette. Tarte fine sablée au chocolat.

**Miravile,** 72 quai Hôtel de Ville (4th) 01 42 74 72 22, *Fax 01 42 74 67 55* – AE GB J 15
*closed 3 to 25 August, 15 to 22 February, Saturday lunch and Sunday* – **Meals** 240 and a la carte 330/400.

**Ambassade d'Auvergne,** 22 r. Grenier St-Lazare (3rd) 01 42 72 31 22, *Fax 01 42 78 85 47* – AE GB JCB H 15
**Meals** 170 and a la carte 170/300.

**Benoît,** 20 r. St-Martin (4th) 01 42 72 25 76, *Fax 01 42 72 45 68*, bistro –
*closed August* – **Meals** 200 (lunch) and a la carte 350/460 J 15
**Spec.** Saumon fumé mariné, salade tiède de pommes de terre. Daube de joues de bœuf au vin de Beaujolais. Filet de rouget barbet rôti, canapé d'aubergine et tapenade.

**Bofinger,** 5 r. Bastille (4th) 01 42 72 87 82, *Fax 01 42 72 97 68*, brasserie, « Belle Epoque decor » – AE GB J 17
**Meals** 169 b.i. and a la carte 160/300.

**L'Aiguière,** 37bis r. Montreuil (11th) 01 43 72 42 32, *Fax 01 43 72 96 36* – AE GB JCB K 20
*closed Saturday lunch and Sunday* – **Meals** 135 b.i./248 b.i. (except dinner Fri. and Sat.) and a la carte 270/380.

XX **A Sousceyrac,** 35 r. Faidherbe (11th) ✆ 01 43 71 65 30, *Fax 01 40 09 79 75* – ▤. AE ⓓ GB J 19
*closed Saturday lunch and Sunday* – **Meals** 180 and a la carte 210/330.

XX **L'Excuse,** 14 r. Charles V (4th) ✆ 01 42 77 98 97, *Fax 01 42 77 88 55* – AE GB J 16
*closed 2 to 20 August and Sunday* – **Meals** 150/185 and a la carte 270/360.

XX **Vin et Marée,** 276 bd Voltaire (11th) ✆ 01 43 72 31 23, *Fax 01 40 09 05 24* – ▤. AE GB JCB K 21
**Meals** - Seafood - a la carte approx. 170.

XX **Blue Elephant,** 43 r. Roquette (11th) ✆ 01 47 00 42 00, *Fax 01 47 00 45 44*, « Typical decor » – ▤. AE ⓓ GB J 18
*closed Saturday lunch* – **Meals** - Thai rest. - 150 (lunch), 275/300 and a la carte approx. 270 ♁.

XX **L'Alisier,** 26 r. Montmorency (3rd) ✆ 01 42 72 31 04, *Fax 01 42 72 74 83* – GB H 16
*closed August, Saturday and Sunday* – **Meals** 185 b.i./195.

XX **Péché Mignon,** 5 r. Guillaume Bertrand (11th) ✆ 01 43 57 68 68 – GB H 19
*closed August, Sunday dinner and Monday* – **Meals** 139.

XX **Les Amognes,** 243 r. Fg St-Antoine (11th) ✆ 01 43 72 73 05 – GB K 20
*closed 3 to 23 August, Monday lunch and Sunday* – **Meals** 190.

XX **Repaire de Cartouche,** 99 r. Amelot (11th) ✆ 01 47 00 25 86 – GB. ✂ H 17
*closed 15 July-15 August, Sunday and Monday* – **Meals** a la carte 150/220.

X **Bistrot du Dôme,** 2 r. Bastille (4th) ✆ 01 48 04 88 44, *Fax 01 48 04 00 59* – ▤. AE GB J 17
**Meals** - Seafood - a la carte 180/230.

X **Petit Bofinger,** 6 r. Bastille (4th) ✆ 01 42 72 05 23, *Fax 01 42 72 97 68* – ▤. AE ⓓ GB J 17
**Meals** 128.

X **Chardenoux,** 1 r. J. Vallès (11th) ✆ 01 43 71 49 52, bistrot, « Early 20C decor » – AE ⓓ GB K 20
*closed August, Saturday lunch and Sunday* – **Meals** a la carte 160/260.

X **Relais St-Paul,** 33 r. F. Miron (4th) ✆ 01 48 87 34 20 – GB J 16
*closed 1 to 23 August, Saturday lunch, Sunday and Bank Holidays* – **Meals** 90/135 and a la carte 190/240.

X **Mansouria,** 11 r. Faidherbe (11th) ✆ 01 43 71 00 16, *Fax 01 40 24 21 97* – ▤. GB K 19
*closed Monday lunch* – **Meals** Moroccan rest. 172/195 and a la carte 200/300.

X **Au Bascou,** 38 r. Réaumur (3rd) ✆ 01 42 72 69 25, bistro – AE GB G 16
*closed August, Christmas-New Year, Saturday lunch and Sunday* – **Meals** a la carte 180/250.

X **Grizzli,** 7 r. St-Martin (4th) ✆ 01 48 87 77 56, ☂, bistro – AE GB JCB J 15
*closed Sunday* – **Meals** 120 (lunch)/160 and a la carte approx. 180.

X **Astier,** 44 r. J.-P. Timbaud (11th) ✆ 01 43 57 16 35, bistro – GB G 18
*closed spring Holidays, Saturday and Sunday* – **Meals** 110 (lunch)/135.

X **Monde des Chimères,** 69 r. St-Louis-en-l'Ile (4th) ✆ 01 43 54 45 27, *Fax 01 43 29 84 88* – GB K 16
*closed Sunday and Monday* – **Meals** 89/160 and a la carte 250/350.

X **Clos du Vert Bois,** 13 r. Vert Bois (3rd) ✆ 01 42 77 14 85 – GB G 16
*closed 1 to 25 August, Monday dinner and Sunday lunch* – **Meals** 78 (lunch), 98/175 b.i. and a la carte 180/260.

X **Anjou-Normandie,** 13 r. Folie-Méricourt (11th) ✆ 01 47 00 30 59, *Fax 01 47 00 30 59* – GB H 18
*closed Saturday and Sunday* – **Meals** (lunch only) 137/150 and a la carte 150/200 ♁.

X **Les Fernandises,** 19 r. Fontaine au Roi (11th) ✆ 01 48 06 16 96, bistro – GB G 18
*closed 1 to 24 August, Sunday and Monday* – **Meals** 100/130 and a la carte 150/260.

Pleasant hotels and restaurants
are shown in the Guide by a red sign.
Please send us the names
of any where you have enjoyed your stay.
Your **Michelin Guide** will be even better.

XXXXX ... X

# Quartier Latin, Luxembourg, Jardin des Plantes.

*5th and 6th arrondissements.*
*5th: ✉ 75005*
*6th: ✉ 75006*

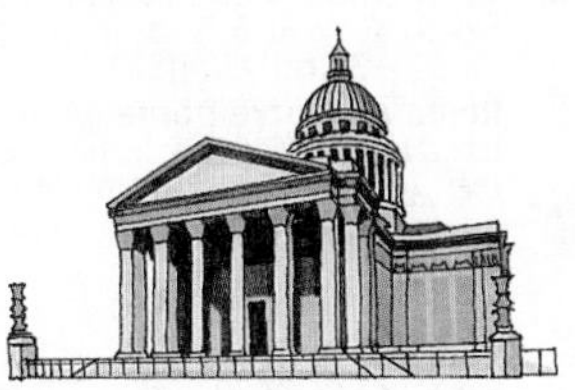

**Lutétia,** 45 bd Raspail (6th) ✆ 01 49 54 46 46, *Fax 01 49 54 46 00* – |$|, ⇔ rm, ▤ TV ☎ – 🅰 300. AE ⓓ GB JCB K 12
see *Paris* below - ***Brasserie Lutétia*** ✆ 01 49 54 46 76 **Meals** 189/245 – ☕ 135 – **220 rm** 1190/2050, 30 suites.

**Relais Christine** M without rest, 3 r. Christine (6th) ✆ 01 40 51 60 80, *Fax 01 40 51 60 81*, « Elegant decor » – |$|, ⇔ rm, ▤ TV ☎. AE ⓓ GB JCB J 14
☕ 110 – **36 rm** 1650/2000, 15 duplex.

**Relais St-Germain** M without rest, 9 carrefour de l'Odéon (6th) ✆ 01 43 29 12 05, *Fax 01 46 33 45 30*, « Attractive interior » – |$| kitchenette ▤ TV ☎. AE ⓓ GB JCB
**22 rm** ☕ 1290/2000. K 13

**Relais Médicis** M without rest, 23 r. Racine (6th) ✆ 01 43 26 00 60, *Fax 01 40 46 83 39* – |$| ▤ TV ☎. AE ⓓ GB JCB K 13
**16 rm** ☕ 1230/1595.

**d'Aubusson** without rest, 33 r. Dauphine (6e) ✆ 01 43 29 43 43, *Fax 01 43 29 12 62* – |$|, ⇔ rm, ▤ TV ☎ ♿. AE GB. ✻ J 13
☕ 80 – **49 rm** 1900/2100.

**de l'Abbaye** without rest, 10 r. Cassette (6th) ✆ 01 45 44 38 11, *Fax 01 45 48 07 86* – |$| ▤ TV ☎. AE GB. ✻ K 12
**42 rm** ☕ 1050/1600, 4 duplex.

**Left Bank St-Germain** without rest, 9 r. Ancienne Comédie (6th) ✆ 01 43 54 01 70, *Fax 01 43 26 17 14* – |$| ▤ TV ☎ ♿. AE ⓓ GB JCB K 13
**30 rm** ☕ 980/1100.

**Victoria Palace** without rest, 6 r. Blaise-Desgoffe (6th) ✆ 01 45 49 70 00, *Fax 01 45 49 23 75* – |$|, ⇔ rm, ▤ TV ☎ ♿ – 🅰 30. AE ⓓ GB JCB L 11
☕ 95 – **76 rm** 992/2000, 3 suites.

**Madison** M without rest, 143 bd St-Germain (6th) ✆ 01 40 51 60 00, *Fax 01 40 51 60 01* – |$| ▤ TV ☎. AE ⓓ GB JCB J 13
**55 rm** ☕ 800/2000.

**Holiday Inn Saint Germain des Prés** M without rest, 92 r. Vaugirard (6th) ✆ 01 42 22 00 56, *Fax 01 42 22 05 39* – |$|, ⇔ rm, ▤ TV ☎ ♿ – 🅰 50. AE ⓓ GB JCB L 12
☕ 80 – **134 rm** 1050/1230.

**Angleterre** without rest, 44 r. Jacob (6th) ✆ 01 42 60 34 72, *Fax 01 42 60 16 93* – |$| TV ☎. AE ⓓ GB JCB. ✻ J 13
☕ 52 – **24 rm** 680/1200, 3 suites.

**Sainte Beuve** M without rest, 9 r. Ste-Beuve (6th) ✆ 01 45 48 20 07, *Fax 01 45 48 67 52* – |$| TV ☎. AE GB JCB. ✻ L 12
☕ 90 – **22 rm** 760/1600.

**Littré** without rest, 9 r. Littré (6th) ✆ 01 45 44 38 68, *Fax 01 45 44 88 13* – |$| TV ☎ – 🅰 25. AE ⓓ GB JCB L 11
☕ 70 – **93 rm** 720/1000, 4 suites.

**St-Grégoire** M without rest, 43 r. Abbé Grégoire (6th) ✆ 01 45 48 23 23, *Fax 01 45 48 33 95* – |$| ▤ TV ☎. AE ⓓ GB JCB. ✻ L 12
☕ 60 – **20 rm** 790/1390.

**Villa** M without rest, 29 r. Jacob (6th) ✆ 01 43 26 60 00, *Fax 01 46 34 63 63*, « Contemporary decor » – |$|, ⇔ rm, ▤ TV ☎. AE ⓓ GB. ✻ J 13
☕ 80 – **29 rm** 1100/2000, 3 suites.

**Alliance St-Germain-des-Prés** M without rest, 7-11 r. St-Benoit (6th) ✆ 01 42 61 53 53, *Fax 01 49 27 09 33* – |$| ▤ TV ☎ ♿. AE ⓓ GB JCB J 13
☕ 75 – **117 rm** 1190/1290.

**St-Germain-des-Prés** without rest, 36 r. Bonaparte (6th) ℘ 01 43 26 00 19, *Fax 01 40 46 83 63* – lift, rm, TV ☎. AE GB. J 13
50 – **30 rm** 750/1350.

**Rives de Notre-Dame** M without rest, 15 quai St-Michel (5th) ℘ 01 43 54 81 16, *Fax 01 43 26 27 09*, ≤, « 16C house, Provencal decor » – lift, rm, TV ☎. AE GB JCB – 85 – **10 rm** 995/2500. J 14

**Ferrandi** without rest, 92 r. Cherche-Midi (6th) ℘ 01 42 22 97 40, *Fax 01 45 44 89 97* – lift TV ☎. AE GB JCB L 11
65 – **41 rm** 580/1280.

**Villa des Artistes** M without rest, 9 r. Grande Chaumière (6th) ℘ 01 43 26 60 86, *Fax 01 43 54 73 70* – lift TV ☎. AE GB JCB. L 12
40 – **59 rm** 1200.

**Régent** M without rest, 61 r. Dauphine (6th) ℘ 01 46 34 59 80, *Fax 01 40 51 05 07* – lift TV ☎. AE GB JCB. J 13
55 – **25 rm** 750/1000.

**de Buci** M without rest, 6 r. Buci (6th) ℘ 01 43 26 89 22, *Fax 01 46 33 80 31* – lift TV ☎ ♿. AE GB JCB. J 13
70 – **24 rm** 950/1400.

**Relais St-Jacques** without rest, 3 r. Abbé de l'Épée (5th) ℘ 01 53 73 26 00, *Fax 01 43 26 17 81* – lift TV ☎. AE GB JCB. L 14
66 – **23 rm** 1080/1300.

**Résidence Henri IV** M without rest, 50 r. Bernardins (5th) ℘ 01 44 41 31 81, *Fax 01 46 33 93 22* – lift kitchenette TV ☎. AE GB JCB. K 15
40 – **8 rm** 630/800, 5 suites.

**Odéon H.** M without rest, 3 r. Odéon (6th) ℘ 01 43 25 90 67, *Fax 01 43 25 55 98* – lift TV ☎. AE GB JCB. K 13
60 – **33 rm** 756/1412.

**de Fleurie** without rest, 32 r. Grégoire de Tours (6th) ℘ 01 53 73 70 00, *Fax 01 53 73 70 20* – lift TV ☎. AE GB. K 13
50 – **29 rm** 680/1200.

**Saints-Pères** without rest, 65 r. Sts-Pères (6th) ℘ 01 45 44 50 00, *Fax 01 45 44 90 83* – lift TV ☎. AE GB. J 12
55 – **36 rm** 750/1250, 3 suites.

**Select** M without rest, 1 pl. Sorbonne (5th) ℘ 01 46 34 14 80, *Fax 01 46 34 51 79* – lift TV ☎. AE GB JCB K 14
30 – **67 rm** 650/890.

**Panthéon** without rest, 19 pl. Panthéon (5th) ℘ 01 43 54 32 95, *Fax 01 43 26 64 65* – lift TV ☎. AE GB JCB. L 14
*closed 3 to 24 August* – 45 – **34 rm** 680/800.

**Grands Hommes** without rest, 17 pl. Panthéon (5th) ℘ 01 46 34 19 60, *Fax 01 43 26 67 32*, ≤ – lift TV ☎. AE GB JCB. L 14
45 – **32 rm** 680/800.

**Sully St-Germain** M without rest, 31 r. Écoles (5th) ℘ 01 43 26 56 02, *Fax 01 43 29 74 42*, – lift, rm, TV ☎. AE GB JCB. K 15
50 – **56 rm** 700/1200.

**Relais St-Sulpice** M without rest, 3 r. Garancière (6th) ℘ 01 46 33 99 00, *Fax 01 46 33 00 10* – lift, rm, TV ☎ ♿. AE GB JCB. K 13
55 – **26 rm** 1120/1490.

**Royal St-Michel** M without rest, 3 bd St-Michel (5th) ℘ 01 44 07 06 06, *Fax 01 44 07 36 25* – lift TV ☎. AE GB JCB K 14
45 – **39 rm** 990/1160.

**Belloy St-Germain** M without rest, 2 r. Racine (6th) ℘ 01 46 34 26 50, *Fax 01 46 34 66 18* – lift TV ☎. GB JCB K 14
50 – **50 rm** 690/910.

**Jardins du Luxembourg** M without rest, 5 imp. Royer-Collard (5th) ℘ 01 40 46 08 88, *Fax 01 40 46 02 28* – lift, rm, TV ☎ ♿. AE GB JCB.
55 – **26 rm** 1025. L 14

**Au Manoir St-Germain des Prés** without rest, 153 bd St-Germain (6th) ℘ 01 42 22 21 65, *Fax 01 45 48 22 25* – lift TV ☎. AE GB JCB J 12
**32 rm** 1100/1300.

**de l'Odéon** without rest, 13 r. St-Sulpice (6th) ℘ 01 43 25 70 11, *Fax 01 43 29 97 34*, « 16C house » – lift TV ☎. AE GB JCB K 13
55 – **29 rm** 680/970.

**Jardin de l'Odéon** M without rest, 7 r. Casimir Delavigne (6th) ℘ 01 46 34 23 90, *Fax 01 43 25 28 12* – lift TV ☎ ♿. AE GB JCB K 13
55 – **41 rm** 650/1050.

**Clos Médicis** without rest, 56 r. Monsieur Le Prince (6th) 01 43 29 10 80, *Fax 01 43 54 26 90* – AE GB JCB K 14
60 – **38 rm** 790/1200.

**Parc St-Séverin** without rest, 22 r. Parcheminerie (5th) 01 43 54 32 17, *Fax 01 43 54 70 71* – AE GB. K 14
50 – **27 rm** 500/1500.

**St-Christophe** without rest, 17 r. Lacépède (5th) 01 43 31 81 54, *Fax 01 43 31 12 54* – AE GB L 15
50 – **31 rm** 550.

**Notre Dame** without rest, 1 quai St-Michel (5th) 01 43 54 20 43, *Fax 01 43 26 61 75*, – AE GB JCB K 14
40 – **23 rm** 620/820, 3 duplex.

**Jardin de Cluny** without rest, 9 r. Sommerard (5th) 01 43 54 22 66, *Fax 01 40 51 03 36* – AE GB JCB. K 14
50 – **40 rm** 690/1200.

**Millésime H.** without rest, 15 r. Jacob (6th) 01 44 07 97 97, *Fax 01 46 34 55 97* – AE GB. J 13
55 – **21 rm** 800/950.

**Marronniers** without rest, 21 r. Jacob (6th) 01 43 25 30 60, *Fax 01 40 46 83 56* – GB. J 13
50 – **37 rm** 755/985.

**California** without rest, 32 r. Écoles (5th) 01 46 34 12 90, *Fax 01 46 34 75 52* – AE GB. K 14-15
45 – **44 rm** 650/1200.

**Sèvres Azur** without rest, 22 r. Abbé-Grégoire (6th) 01 45 48 84 07, *Fax 01 42 84 01 55* – AE GB JCB K 11-12
38 – **31 rm** 445/500.

**Familia** without rest, 11 r. Écoles (5th) 01 43 54 55 27, *Fax 01 43 29 61 77* – AE GB. K-L 15
35 – **30 rm** 380/520.

**Maxim** without rest, 28 r. Censier (5th) 01 43 31 16 15, *Fax 01 43 31 93 87* – , rm, AE GB JCB M 15
45 – **36 rm** 510/570.

**Albe** without rest, 1 r. Harpe (5th) 01 46 34 09 70, *Fax 01 40 46 85 70* – , rm, rm, AE GB JCB. K 14
47 – **45 rm** 540/800.

**Pierre Nicole** without rest, 39 r. Pierre Nicole (5th) 01 43 54 76 86, *Fax 01 43 54 22 45* – AE GB. M 13
35 – **33 rm** 330/430.

**Sorbonne** without rest, 6 r. Victor Cousin (5th) 01 43 54 58 08, *Fax 01 40 51 05 18* – AE GB K 14
35 – **37 rm** 425/500.

**Tour d'Argent** (Terrail), 15 quai Tournelle (5th) 01 43 54 23 31, *Fax 01 44 07 12 04*, Notre-Dame, « Small museum showing the development of eating utensils. In the cellar : an illustrated history of wine » – . AE GB JCB K 16
*closed Monday* – **Meals** 350 (lunch) and a la carte 750/980
**Spec.** Quenelles de brochet "André Terrail". Caneton "Tour d'Argent". Flambée de pêches à l'eau de vie de framboise.

**Jacques Cagna,** 14 r. Grands Augustins (6th) 01 43 26 49 39, *Fax 01 43 54 54 48*, « Old Parisian house » – . AE GB JCB J 14
*closed 1 to 26 August, 24 December-2 January, Saturday lunch and Sunday* – **Meals** 240 (lunch)/470 and a la carte 430/700
**Spec.** Escargots "petits gris" en surprise. Poularde de Houdan en deux services. Gibier (season).

**Paris** - Hôtel Lutétia, 45 bd Raspail (6th) 01 49 54 46 90, *Fax 01 49 54 46 00*, « "Art Deco" decor » – . AE GB K 12
*closed 27 July-24 August, Saturday, Sunday and Bank Holidays* – **Meals** 275 (lunch), 375/565 and a la carte 390/540
**Spec.** Turbot cuit dans le sel de Guérande et algues bretonnes. Jarret de veau cuit en cocotte. Le "tout chocolat".

**Relais Louis XIII** (Martinez), 8 r. Grands Augustins (6th) 01 43 26 75 96, *Fax 01 44 07 07 80*, « Historical house, 16C cellar » – . AE GB JCB J 14
*closed 12 to 20 April, 3 to 25 August, Monday lunch and Sunday* – **Meals** 195/250 and a la carte 270/390
**Spec.** Soufflé de poularde et ris de veau aux écrevisses (September-December). Tronçon de turbot de ligne cuisiné comme une matelotte. Millefeuille tiède à la vanille.

XXX **Closerie des Lilas,** 171 bd Montparnasse (6th) ☎ 01 40 51 34 50, *Fax 01 43 29 99 94*, ⛱, « Former literary café » – AE ⓓ GB JCB M 13
**Meals** 250 b.i. (lunch), 350/450 and a la carte 300/420 - ***Brasserie :*** **Meals** 180 b.i./300 b.i.

XXX **Procope,** 13 r. Ancienne Comédie (6th) ☎ 01 40 46 79 00, *Fax 01 40 46 79 09*, « Former 18C literary café » – ▤. AE ⓓ GB K 13
**Meals** 109 (lunch)/178 and a la carte 170/320.

XX **Yugaraj,** 14 r. Dauphine (6th) ☎ 01 43 26 44 91, *Fax 01 46 33 50 77* – ▤. AE ⓓ GB JCB. ✻ J 14
*closed Monday lunch* – **Meals** - Indian rest. - 130 (lunch), 170/220 and a la carte 220/350.

XX **Mavrommatis,** 42 r. Daubenton (5th) ☎ 01 43 31 17 17, *Fax 01 43 36 13 08* – ▤. GB. ✻ M 15
*closed Monday* – **Meals** - Greek rest. - 150 and a la carte 170/270.

XX **Timonerie** (de Givenchy), 35 quai Tournelle (5th) ☎ 01 43 25 44 42 – ▤. GB
✿ *closed 2 to 31 August, Monday lunch and Sunday* – **Meals** 250 (lunch)/350 K 15
**Spec.** Tarte de pain et pomme de terre à la tomme de montagne. Poitrine de porc rôtie et sa croûte de pain farcie. Tarte au chocolat.

XX **Chez Maître Paul,** 12 r. Monsieur-le-Prince (6th) ☎ 01 43 54 74 59, *Fax 01 46 34 58 33* – ▤. AE ⓓ GB K 13
**Meals** 160/195 b.i. and a la carte 210/320.

XX **Truffière,** 4 r. Blainville (5th) ☎ 01 46 33 29 82, *Fax 01 46 33 64 74*, « 17C house » – ▤. AE ⓓ GB JCB. ✻ L 15
*closed Monday* – **Meals** 110 (lunch)(except Sunday) 240.

XX **Chat Grippé,** 87 r. Assas (6th) ☎ 01 43 54 70 00, *Fax 01 43 26 42 05* – ▤. AE GB. ✻
*closed 27 July-28 August, Saturday lunch and Monday* – **Meals** 140 (lunch)/200 and a la carte 220/300. LM 13

XX **Marty,** 20 av. Gobelins (5th) ☎ 01 43 31 39 51, *Fax 01 43 37 63 70*, brasserie, « 1930 decor » – AE ⓓ GB JCB M 15
**Meals** 168 b.i./195 and a la carte 180/310.

XX **Inagiku,** 14 r. Pontoise (5th) ☎ 01 43 54 70 07, *Fax 01 40 51 74 44* – ▤. GB K 15
*closed 1 to 15 August and Sunday* – **Meals** - Japanese rest. - 88 (lunch), 148/248 and a la carte 230/300.

XX **L'Arrosée,** 12 r. Guisarde (6th) ☎ 01 43 54 66 59, *Fax 01 43 54 66 59*, « 18C house » – ▤. AE ⓓ GB JCB. ✻ K 13
*closed lunch Saturday and Sunday* – **Meals** 150/210 and a la carte 270/450.

XX **Bastide Odéon,** 7 r. Corneille (6th) ☎ 01 43 26 03 65, *Fax 01 44 07 28 93* – GB
*closed 3 to 23 August, Sunday and Monday* – **Meals** 190. K 13

XX **Aub. des Deux Signes,** 46 r. Galande (5th) ☎ 01 43 25 46 56, *Fax 01 46 33 20 49*, « Medieval decor » – AE ⓓ GB JCB K 14
*closed August, Saturday lunch and Sunday* – **Meals** 150/230 and a la carte 290/450.

XX **Rond de Serviette,** 97 r. Cherche-Midi (6th) ☎ 01 45 44 01 02, *Fax 01 42 22 50 10* – ▤. AE ⓓ GB JCB L 11
*closed 1 to 23 August, Saturday lunch and Sunday* – **Meals** 138 b.i. (lunch), 178/270 b.i.

XX **Chez Toutoune,** 5 r. Pontoise (5th) ☎ 01 43 26 56 81, *Fax 01 40 46 80 34* – AE GB
*closed Monday lunch* – **Meals** 178/198. K 15

XX **Atelier Maître Albert,** 1 r. Maître Albert (5th) ☎ 01 46 33 13 78, *Fax 01 44 07 01 86* – ▤. AE GB K 15
*closed Monday lunch and Sunday* – **Meals** 180/240 b.i.

X **Campagne et Provence,** 25 quai Tournelle (5th) ☎ 01 43 54 05 17, *Fax 01 43 29 74 93* – ▤. GB K 15
*closed 1 to 15 August, Monday lunch, Saturday lunch and Sunday* – **Meals** 125/220.

X **Bouillon Racine,** 3 r. Racine (6th) ☎ 01 44 32 15 60, *Fax 01 44 32 15 61*, brasserie, « "Art Nouveau" decor » – ▤. AE GB K 14
**Meals** 98 (lunch)/159 and a la carte 170/260.

X **Les Bouchons de François Clerc,** 12 r. Hôtel Colbert (5th) ☎ 01 43 54 15 34, *Fax 01 46 34 68 07*, « Old Parisian house » – ▤. AE GB K 15
*closed Saturday lunch and Sunday* – **Meals** 117/219.

X **Les Bookinistes,** 53 quai Grands Augustins (6th) ☎ 01 43 25 45 94, *Fax 01 43 25 23 07* – ▤. AE GB JCB J 14
*closed lunch Saturday and Sunday* – **Meals** 190 b.i. (lunch) and a la carte 200/260.

X **Dominique,** 19 r. Bréa (6th) ☎ 01 43 27 08 80, *Fax 01 43 26 88 35* – ▤. AE ⓓ GB JCB
*closed 18 July-18 August, Monday lunch and Sunday* – **Meals** - Russian rest. - (dinner only) 160 b.i. and a la carte 230/270. L 12

X **L'O à la Bouche,** 157 bd Montparnasse (6th) ✆ 01 43 26 26 53, *Fax 01 43 26 43 40* - GB M 13
*closed 6 to 12 April, 3 to 23 August, 4 to 10 January, Sunday and Monday* – **Meals** 190.

X **Rotonde,** 105 bd Montparnasse (6th) ✆ 01 43 26 48 26, *Fax 01 46 34 52 40*, brasserie - ▤. AE GB JCB L 12
**Meals** 180.

X **Rôtisserie d'en Face,** 2 r. Christine (6th) ✆ 01 43 26 40 98, *Fax 01 43 54 54 48* – ▤. AE ⊕ GB JCB J 14
*closed Saturday lunch and Sunday* – **Meals** 159 (lunch)/210.

X **Rôtisserie du Beaujolais,** 19 quai Tournelle (5th) ✆ 01 43 54 17 47, *Fax 01 44 07 12 04* – ▤. GB K 15
*closed Monday* – **Meals** a la carte 160/250.

X **Bistrot d'Alex,** 2 r. Clément (6th) ✆ 01 43 54 09 53, *Fax 01 43 25 77 66* – ▤. AE GB JCB
*closed 9 to 16 August, 24 December-2 January, Saturday lunch and Sunday* – **Meals** 140/170 and a la carte 170/280. K 13

X **Joséphine "Chez Dumonet",** 117 r. Cherche Midi (6th) ✆ 01 45 48 52 40, *Fax 01 42 84 06 83*, bistro – AE GB L 11
*closed August, Saturday and Sunday* – a la carte 200/370 - ***Rôtisserie :*** grills and spit roast over wood fire - ✆ 01 42 22 81 19 *(closed July, Monday and Tuesday)* **Meals** 128/210.

X **L'Épi Dupin,** 11 r. Dupin (6th) ✆ 01 42 22 64 56, *Fax 01 42 22 30 42* – AE GB K 12
*closed 1 to 23 August, Saturday and Sunday* – **Meals** 165.

X **Bauta,** 129 bd Montparnasse (6th) ✆ 01 43 22 52 35, *Fax 01 43 22 10 99* – ▤. GB M 12
*closed 9 to 23 August, Saturday lunch, Sunday and Bank Holidays* – **Meals** - Italian rest. - 150/200 and a la carte 210/300.

X **Cafetière,** 21 r. Mazarine (6th) ✆ 01 46 33 76 90, *Fax 01 43 25 76 90* – GB J 13
*closed 9 to 30 August, 21 December-4 January and Sunday* – **Meals** - Italian rest. - a la carte 200/310.

X **Allard,** 41 r. St-André-des-Arts (6th) ✆ 01 43 26 48 23, *Fax 01 46 33 04 02*, bistro – ▤. AE ⊕ GB JCB K 14
*closed August and Sunday* – **Meals** 200 and a la carte 250/420.

X **Moulin à Vent "Chez Henri",** 20 r. Fossés-St-Bernard (5th) ✆ 01 43 54 99 37, bistrot - GB. ✗ K 15
*closed late July-late August, Sunday and Monday* – **Meals** a la carte 230/320.

X **Balzar,** 49 r. Écoles (5th) ✆ 01 43 54 13 67, *Fax 01 44 07 14 91*, brasserie – ▤. AE GB
*closed August* – **Meals** a la carte 140/280. K 14

X **Moissonnier,** 28 r. Fossés-St-Bernard (5th) ✆ 01 43 29 87 65, bistro – GB K 15
*closed August, Sunday dinner and Monday* – **Meals** 150 and a la carte 170/290.

X **Reminet,** 3 r. Grands Degrés (5th) ✆ 01 44 07 04 24, *Fax 01 44 07 17 37* – AE GB
*closed 10 to 25 August, 1 to 14 January, Tuesday lunch and Monday* – **Meals** 85 (lunch)/110 and a la carte 170/210. K 15

X **Palanquin,** 12 r. Princesse (6th) ✆ 01 43 29 77 66 – GB K 13
*closed Sunday* – **Meals** - Vietnamese rest. - 70 (lunch), 110/148 and a la carte 150/240.

## Faubourg-St-Germain, Invalides, École Militaire.

*7th arrondissement.*
*7th: ✉ 75007*

**Montalembert** M, 3 r. Montalembert ✆ 01 45 49 68 68, *Fax 01 45 49 69 49*, 🍽, « Original decor » – 🛗 ▤ TV ☎ – 🏛 25. AE ⊕ GB JCB J 12
**Meals** a la carte 250/350 – ☕ 100 – **51 rm** 1695/2200, 5 suites.

**Duc de Saint-Simon** 🐎 without rest, 14 r. St-Simon ✆ 01 44 39 20 20, *Fax 01 45 48 68 25*, « Tastefully furnished interior » – 🛗 TV ☎. AE GB. ✗ J 11
☕ 70 – **29 rm** 1075/1475, 5 suites.

**Cayré** without rest, 4 bd Raspail ✆ 01 45 44 38 88, *Fax 01 45 44 98 13* – 🛗, ⊁ rm, TV ☎. AE ⊕ GB JCB J 12
☕ 80 – **119 rm** 1200.

**Tourville** M without rest, 16 av. Tourville ☎ 01 47 05 62 62, *Fax 01 47 05 43 90* – TV ☎. AE ⓓ GB JCB J 9
☕ 60 – **30 rm** 790/1690.

**Bellechasse** M without rest, 8 r. Bellechasse ☎ 01 45 50 22 31, *Fax 01 45 51 52 36* – rm, TV ☎ ♿. AE ⓓ GB JCB H 11
☕ 75 – **41 rm** 910/975.

**La Bourdonnais,** 111 av. La Bourdonnais ☎ 01 47 05 45 42, *Fax 01 45 55 75 54* – TV ☎. AE ⓓ GB JCB J 9
Meals see ***Cantine des Gourmets*** below – ☕ 45 – **57 rm** 580/780, 3 suites.

**Lenox Saint-Germain** without rest, 9 r. Université ☎ 01 42 96 10 95, *Fax 01 42 61 52 83* – TV ☎. AE ⓓ GB JCB J 12
☕ 45 – **29 rm** 650/1200.

**Splendid** M without rest, 29 av. Tourville ☎ 01 45 51 29 29, *Fax 01 44 18 94 60* – TV ☎ ♿. AE ⓓ GB J 9
☕ 46 – **45 rm** 590/990.

**Bourgogne et Montana** without rest, 3 r. Bourgogne ☎ 01 45 51 20 22, *Fax 01 45 56 11 98* – TV ☎. AE ⓓ GB JCB H 11
☕ 70 – **28 rm** 690/1060, 6 suites.

**Les Jardins d'Eiffel** M without rest, 8 r. Amélie ☎ 01 47 05 46 21, *Fax 01 45 55 28 08* – rm, TV ☎ ♿. AE ⓓ GB JCB H 9
☕ 60 – **80 rm** 710/970.

**Eiffel Park H.** M without rest, 17 bis r. Amélie ☎ 01 45 55 10 01, *Fax 01 47 05 28 68* – TV ☎ ♿ – 25. AE ⓓ GB JCB. J 9
☕ 55 – **36 rm** 650/700.

**Verneuil St-Germain** without rest, 8 r. Verneuil ☎ 01 42 60 82 14, *Fax 01 42 61 40 38* – TV ☎. AE ⓓ GB. J 12
**26 rm** ☕ 650/950.

**Muguet** M without rest, 11 r. Chevert ☎ 01 47 05 05 93, *Fax 01 45 50 25 37* – TV ☎. AE GB J 9
☕ 47 – **45 rm** 460/530.

**du Cadran** M without rest, 10 r. Champ-de-Mars ☎ 01 40 62 67 00, *Fax 01 40 62 67 13* – rm, TV ☎. AE ⓓ GB. J 9
☕ 50 – **42 rm** 850/920.

**Relais Bosquet** without rest, 19 r. Champ-de-Mars ☎ 01 47 05 25 45, *Fax 01 45 55 08 24* – TV ☎. AE ⓓ GB J 9
☕ 53 – **40 rm** 700/850.

**Sèvres Vaneau** without rest, 86 r. Vaneau ☎ 01 45 48 73 11, *Fax 01 45 49 27 74* – rm, TV ☎. AE ⓓ GB JCB K 11
☕ 75 – **39 rm** 825/890.

**St-Germain** without rest, 88 r. Bac ☎ 01 49 54 70 00, *Fax 01 45 48 26 89* – TV. AE GB. J 11
☕ 50 – **29 rm** 450/800.

**de Varenne** without rest, 44 r. Bourgogne ☎ 01 45 51 45 55, *Fax 01 45 51 86 63* – TV ☎. AE GB J 10
☕ 48 – **24 rm** 590/720.

**Beaugency** without rest, 21 r. Duvivier ☎ 01 47 05 01 63, *Fax 01 45 51 04 96* – TV ☎. AE ⓓ GB J 9
☕ 40 – **30 rm** 600/700.

**Bersoly's** without rest, 28 r. Lille ☎ 01 42 60 73 79, *Fax 01 49 27 05 55* – TV ☎. AE GB – *closed August* – ☕ 50 – **16 rm** 600/750. J 13

**Londres** without rest, 1 r. Augereau ☎ 01 45 51 63 02, *Fax 01 47 05 28 96* – TV ☎. AE ⓓ GB JCB J 8
☕ 45 – **30 rm** 495/595.

**France** without rest, 102 bd La Tour Maubourg ☎ 01 47 05 40 49, *Fax 01 45 56 96 78* – TV ☎ ♿. AE ⓓ GB JCB J 9
☕ 35 – **60 rm** 385/500.

**Champ-de-Mars** without rest, 7 r. Champ-de-Mars ☎ 01 45 51 52 30, *Fax 01 45 51 64 36* – TV ☎. AE GB JCB. J 9
☕ 35 – **25 rm** 355/420.

**L'Empereur** without rest, 2 r. Chevert ☎ 01 45 55 88 02, *Fax 01 45 51 88 54* – TV ☎. AE GB – ☕ 37 – **38 rm** 420/500. J 9

**Turenne** without rest, 20 av. Tourville ☎ 01 47 05 99 92, *Fax 01 45 56 06 04* – TV ☎. AE ⓓ GB. J 9
☕ 38 – **34 rm** 340/550.

XXXX ✿ **Jules Verne,** Eiffel Tower : 2nd platform, lift in south leg ✆ 01 45 55 61 44, *Fax 01 47 05 29 41*, ≤ Paris – ▤. AE ⓓ GB JCB. ⚡ J 7
**Meals** 290/680 and a la carte 520/680
**Spec.** Langoustines et gros homard poêlés, jus aux agrumes. Entrecôte de veau de Corrèze aux champignons du moment. Cristalline aux framboises, sorbet au vin de Brouilly.

XXXX ✿✿✿ **Arpège** (Passard), 84 r. Varenne ✆ 01 45 51 47 33, *Fax 01 44 18 98 39* – ▤. AE ⓓ GB JCB J 10
*closed Sunday and Saturday* – **Meals** 390 (lunch)/690 and a la carte 540/780
**Spec.** Consommé de crustacés et ravioles d'oignons au citron et basilic. Dragée de pigeonneau vendéen à l'hydromel. Tomate confite farcie aux douze saveurs (dessert).

XXXX ✿✿ **Le Divellec,** 107 r. Université ✆ 01 45 51 91 96, *Fax 01 45 51 31 75* – ▤. AE ⓓ GB JCB. ⚡ H 10
*closed 23 December-3 January, Sunday and Monday* – **Meals** - Seafood - 290/390 and a la carte 460/760
**Spec.** Homard à la presse avec son corail. Sole braisée au coulis d'écrevisses. Blanc de turbot braisé aux truffes.

XXX ✿ **Paul Minchelli,** 54 bd La Tour Maubourg ✆ 01 47 05 89 86, *Fax 01 45 56 03 84* – ▤. GB. ⚡ J 9
*closed August, 21 December-6 January, Sunday and Monday* – **Meals** - Seafood - a la carte 440/630
**Spec.** Rougets grillés à l'ail et au genièvre. Escalopes de thon blanc. Ventrèche de thon à la tomate confite.

XXX ✿ **Violon d'Ingres** (Constant), 135 r. St-Dominique ✆ 01 45 55 15 05, *Fax 01 45 55 48 42* – ▤. AE GB J 8
*closed August, Sunday and Monday* – **Meals** 240 (lunch), 290/400 b.i. and a la carte 260/380
**Spec.** Mousseline d'œufs brouillés. Tatin de pied de porc caramélisé, moelleux de pomme ratte. Tarte sablée au chocolat noir, glace vanille.

XXX ✿ **Cantine des Gourmets,** 113 av. La Bourdonnais ✆ 01 47 05 47 96, *Fax 01 45 51 09 29* – ▤. AE GB J 9
**Meals** 240 b.i. (lunch), 320/420 and a la carte 340/470 ♁
**Spec.** Rémoulade de langoustines et tourteaux, vinaigrette de corail. Saint-Pierre à l'étouffée, poireaux-pommes à la marjolaine. Pintade rôtie vanillée, endives meunière au vieux vinaigre.

XXX **Boule d'Or,** 13 bd La Tour Maubourg ✆ 01 47 05 50 18, *Fax 01 47 05 91 21* – ▤. AE ⓓ GB H 10
*closed Saturday lunch* – **Meals** 175/210.

XXX **Petit Laurent,** 38 r. Varenne ✆ 01 45 48 79 64, *Fax 01 45 44 15 95* – AE ⓓ GB J 11
*closed August, Saturday lunch and Sunday* – **Meals** 185/250 and a la carte 260/420.

XX ✿ **Bellecour** (Goutagny), 22 r. Surcouf ✆ 01 45 51 46 93, *Fax 01 45 50 30 11* – ▤. AE ⓓ GB H 9
*closed August, Saturday lunch and Sunday* – **Meals** 160 (lunch)/220
**Spec.** Tartare d'huîtres et Saint-Jacques, crème de beaufort. Saint-Jacques rôties, févettes et courgettes à la vinaigrette d'andouille au cidre. Quenelles de brochet, bisque de langoustines.

XX ✿ **Récamier** (Cantegrit), 4 r. Récamier ✆ 01 45 48 86 58, *Fax 01 42 22 84 76*, ☂ – ▤. AE ⓓ GB JCB K 12
*closed Sunday* – **Meals** 300 b.i. and a la carte 280/450
**Spec.** Oeufs en meurette. Mousse de brochet sauce Nantua. Sauté de bœuf bourguignon.

XX **Maison de l'Amérique Latine,** 217 bd St-Germain ✆ 01 45 49 33 23, *Fax 01 40 49 03 94*, ☂, « 18C mansion, terrace opening onto the garden » – AE ⓓ GB. ⚡ J 11
*closed 1 to 23 August, 25 December-3 January, dinner from November-April, Saturday, Sunday and Bank Holidays* – **Meals** 225 (lunch) and a la carte approx. 340.

XX **Beato,** 8 r. Malar ✆ 01 47 05 94 27, *Fax 01 45 55 64 41* – ▤. AE GB H 9
*closed August, Christmas-New Year and Sunday* – **Meals** - Italian rest. - 145 (lunch) and a la carte 250/350.

XX **Ferme St-Simon,** 6 r. St-Simon ✆ 01 45 48 35 74, *Fax 01 40 49 07 31* – ▤. AE ⓓ GB J 11
*closed 1 to 17 August, Saturday lunch and Sunday* – **Meals** 170 (lunch)/190 and a la carte 250/370.

XX **6 Bosquet,** 6 av. Bosquet ✆ 01 45 56 97 26, *Fax 01 45 56 98 44* – ▤. AE GB H 9
*closed 1 to 24 August, Christmas Holidays, Saturday and Sunday* – **Meals** 165.

XX **Vin sur Vin,** 18 r. Monttessuy ✆ 01 47 05 14 20, *Fax 01 47 05 05 55* – ▤. GB H 8
*closed 1 to 9 May, 1 to 16 August, 24 December-3 January, Saturday lunch, Monday lunch and Sunday* – **Meals** a la carte 270/360.

XX **Les Glénan,** 54 r. Bourgogne ✆ 01 47 05 96 65, *Fax 01 45 51 05 79* – ▤. AE GB J 10
*closed August, February Holidays, Saturday and Sunday* – **Meals** - Seafood - 200 b.i. and a la carte 290/360.

XX **Bamboche,** 15 r. Babylone ✆ 01 45 49 14 40, *Fax 01 45 49 14 44* – ▤. AE GB K 11
*closed 3 to 16 August, Saturday and Sunday* – **Meals** 190/320 and a la carte 300/430.

XX **Gildo,** 153 r. Grenelle ✆ 01 45 51 54 12, *Fax 01 45 51 54 12* – ▤. AE GB JCB J 9
*closed 25 July-25 August, Monday lunch and Sunday* – **Meals** - Italian rest. - 149 b.i. and a la carte 250/390.

XX **D'Chez Eux,** 2 av. Lowendal ✆ 01 47 05 52 55, *Fax 01 45 55 60 74* – AE ⓓ GB J 9
*closed 1 to 20 August and Sunday* – **Meals** 270/570 b.i. and a la carte 300/410.

XX **Bar au Sel,** 43 quai d'Orsay ✆ 01 45 51 58 58, *Fax 01 45 56 98 42* – AE ⓓ GB H 9
**Meals** - Seafood - 190 and a la carte 200/340.

XX **Foc Ly,** 71 av. Suffren ✆ 01 47 83 27 12, *Fax 01 46 24 48 46* – ▤. AE GB K 8
*closed Monday in July-August* – **Meals** - Chinese and Thai rest. - 160 and a la carte 150/240.

XX **Tan Dinh,** 60 r. Verneuil ✆ 01 45 44 04 84, *Fax 01 45 44 36 93* J 12
*closed August and Sunday* – **Meals** - Vietnamese rest. - a la carte 270/310.

XX **Champ de Mars,** 17 av. La Motte-Picquet ✆ 01 47 05 57 99, *Fax 01 44 18 94 69* – AE ⓓ GB J 9
*closed 19 July-19 August and Monday* – **Meals** 155 b.i./198 b.i. and a la carte 180/310.

X **Gaya Rive Gauche,** 44 r. Bac ✆ 01 45 44 73 73, *Fax 01 45 44 73 73* – AE GB J 12
*closed 26 July-24 August and Sunday* – **Meals** - Seafood - a la carte 250/350.

X **P'tit Troquet,** 28 r. Exposition ✆ 01 47 05 80 39, *Fax 01 47 05 80 39*, bistro – GB J 9
*closed August, Sunday and Monday* – **Meals** 153/183.

X **Les Olivades,** 41 av. Ségur ✆ 01 47 83 70 09, *Fax 01 42 73 04 75* – AE GB K 9
*closed August, Monday lunch, Saturday lunch and Sunday* – **Meals** 169 and a la carte 210/290.

X **Bistrot de Paris,** 33 r. Lille ✆ 01 42 61 16 83, *Fax 01 49 27 06 09*, 1900 bistro – AE GB – **Meals** 185. J 12

X **Thoumieux** with rm, 79 r. St-Dominique ✆ 01 47 05 49 75, *Fax 01 47 05 36 96*, brasserie – ▤ rest, TV ☎. AE GB H 9
**Meals** 82/160 b.i. and a la carte 170/250 – ☕ 35 – **10 rm** 550/600.

X **Maupertu,** 94 bd La Tour Maubourg ✆ 01 45 51 37 96 – GB J 10
*closed 8 to 31 August, Saturday lunch and Sunday* – **Meals** 135 and a la carte 190/280.

X **Clémentine,** 62 av. Bosquet ✆ 01 45 51 41 16, *Fax 01 45 55 76 79* – AE GB JCB J 9
*closed August, Saturday lunch and Sunday* – **Meals** a la carte approx. 170.

X **L'Oeillade,** 10 r. St-Simon ✆ 01 42 22 01 60 – ▤. GB J 11
*closed 15 to 31 August, Saturday lunch and Sunday* – **Meals** 158 and a la carte 190/330.

X **Chez Collinot,** 1 r. P. Leroux ✆ 01 45 67 66 42 – GB K 11
*closed August, Saturday except dinner from October-June and Sunday* – **Meals** 135.

X **Fontaine de Mars,** 129 r. St-Dominique ✆ 01 47 05 46 44, *Fax 01 47 05 11 13*, 🏠, bistro – AE GB J 9
*closed Sunday* – **Meals** a la carte 170/300 🍷.

X **Table d'Eiffel,** 39 av. La Motte-Picquet ✆ 01 45 55 90 20, *Fax 01 44 18 36 73* – AE ⓓ GB JCB – **Meals** 175 b.i. H 9

X **Sédillot,** 2 r. Sédillot ✆ 01 45 51 95 82, « Art Nouveau decor » – AE GB H 8
*closed Saturday and Sunday* – **Meals** 95/130 and a la carte 160/280.

X **Calèche,** 8 r. Lille ✆ 01 42 60 24 76, *Fax 01 47 03 31 10* – ▤. AE ⓓ GB JCB J 12
*closed 10 to 31 August, 25 December-1 January, Saturday and Sunday* – **Meals** 100/175 and a la carte 170/280.

X **Aub. Bressane,** 16 av. La Motte-Picquet ✆ 01 47 05 98 37, *Fax 01 47 05 92 21* – ▤. AE GB JCB H 9
*closed 10 to 20 August and Saturday lunch* – **Meals** 139 b.i. (lunch) and a la carte 190/290.

X **Du Côté 7ème,** 29 r. Surcouf ✆ 01 47 05 81 65, bistro – AE ⓓ GB JCB H 9-10
*closed 9 to 17 August and Monday* – **Meals** 185 b.i.

X **Florimond,** 19 av. La Motte-Picquet ✆ 01 45 55 40 38 – GB H 9
*closed 1 to 24 August, Saturday lunch and Sunday* – **Meals** 98/157 and a la carte 190/260.

X **Au Bon Accueil,** 14 r. Monttessuy ✆ 01 47 05 46 11 - GB. ✻ H 8
*closed August, Saturday lunch and Sunday* - **Meals** 120 (lunch)/145 and a la carte 250/320.

X **Apollon,** 24 r. J. Nicot ✆ 01 45 55 68 47, *Fax 01 47 05 13 60* H 9
*closed 20 December-10 January* - **Meals** - Greek rest. - 128 b.i. (lunch), 150 b.i./200 b.i. and a la carte 150/220.

## Champs-Élysées, St-Lazare, Madeleine.

*8th arrondissement.*
*8th: ✉ 75008*

**Plaza Athénée,** 25 av. Montaigne ✆ 01 53 67 66 65, *Fax 01 53 67 66 66*, ☂, Fö - |‡| ▤ TV ☎ - 🏛 30 - 100. AE ⓪ GB JCB. ✻ G 9
see rest. ***Régence*** below - ***Relais-Plaza*** ✆ 01 53 67 64 00 **Meals** 165/290 and a la carte 310/470 - ***La Cour Jardin*** (terrace) *(May-September)* **Meals** 400/500 - ☐ 160 - **163 rm** 3700/4650, 42 suites.

**Crillon,** 10 pl. Concorde ✆ 01 44 71 15 00, *Fax 01 44 71 15 02*, Fö - |‡|, ⇔ rm, ▤ TV ☎ - 🏛 30 - 60. AE ⓪ GB JCB G 11
see ***Les Ambassadeurs*** below - ***L'Obélisque*** ✆ 01 44 71 15 15 *(closed August and Bank Holidays)* **Meals** 270 - ☐ 230 - **118 rm** 2950/4200, 45 suites.

**Bristol,** 112 r. Fg St-Honoré ✆ 01 53 43 43 00, *Fax 01 53 43 43 01*, Fö, ▣, ☂ - |‡|, ▤ rm, TV ☎ ⇔ - 🏛 30 - 60. AE ⓪ GB JCB. ✻ F 10
Meals see ***Bristol*** below - ☐ 170 - **153 rm** 2500/3950, 42 suites.

**Royal Monceau,** 37 av. Hoche ✆ 01 42 99 88 00, *Fax 01 42 99 89 90*, ☂, « Pool and fitness centre » - |‡|, ⇔ rm, ▤ TV ☎ ⇔ - 🏛 25 - 100. AE ⓪ GB JCB. ✻ E 8
see ***Le Jardin*** below - ***Carpaccio*** ✆ 01 42 99 98 90, Fax 01 42 99 89 94, Italian rest. *(closed August)* **Meals** 280 (dinner) and a la carte 320/390 - ☐ 150 - **180 rm** 2800/3600.

**Prince de Galles,** 33 av. George-V ✆ 01 53 23 77 77, *Fax 01 53 23 78 78*, ☂ - |‡|, ⇔ rm, ▤ TV ☎ - 🏛 25 - 100. AE ⓪ GB JCB. ✻ rest G 8
***Jardin des Cygnes*** ✆ 01 53 23 78 50 **Meals** 260 - ☐ 155 - **138 rm** 2495/3660, 30 suites.

**Vernet,** 25 r. Vernet ✆ 01 44 31 98 00, *Fax 01 44 31 85 69* - |‡| ▤ TV ☎. AE ⓪ GB JCB. ✻ rest F 8
see ***Les Élysées*** below - ☐ 130 - **54 rm** 1950/2550, 3 suites.

**de Vigny** M without rest, 9 r. Balzac ✆ 01 42 99 80 80, *Fax 01 42 99 80 40*, « Tasteful decor » - |‡|, ⇔ rm, ▤ TV ☎ ⇔. AE ⓪ GB JCB F 8
☐ 90 - **25 rm** 1900/2200, 12 suites.

**Lancaster,** 7 r. Berri ✆ 01 40 76 40 76, *Fax 01 40 76 40 00*, ☂, Fö - |‡|, ⇔ rm, ▤ rm, TV ☎. AE ⓪ GB JCB F 9
Meals (residents only) a la carte approx. 290 - ☐ 120 - **52 rm** 1650/2650, 8 suites.

**San Régis,** 12 r. J. Goujon ✆ 01 44 95 16 16, *Fax 01 45 61 05 48*, « Tasteful decor » - |‡| ▤ TV ☎. AE ⓪ GB JCB. ✻ G 9
Meals 200/250 (except weekends) and a la carte 280/420 - ☐ 110 - **34 rm** 1700/2950, 10 suites.

**Astor** M ⛭, 11 r. d'Astorg ✆ 01 53 05 05 05, *Fax 01 53 05 05 30*, Fö - |‡|, ⇔ rm, ▤ rm, TV ☎ ♿. AE ⓪ GB JCB F 11
Meals see ***L'Astor*** below - ☐ 140 - **130 rm** 1650/1850, 4 suites.

**Trémoille,** 14 r. La Trémoille ✆ 01 47 23 34 20, *Fax 01 40 70 01 08* - |‡| ▤ TV ☎ - 🏛 25. AE ⓪ GB JCB G 9
***Louis d'Or*** *(closed August, Saturday, Sunday and Bank Holidays)* **Meals** 220 and a la carte 240/330 - ☐ 110 - **104 rm** 1960/2950, 3 suites.

**Élysées Star** M without rest, 19 r. Vernet ✆ 01 47 20 41 73, *Fax 01 47 23 32 15* - |‡|, ⇔ rm, ▤ TV ☎ - 🏛 30. AE ⓪ GB F 8
☐ 90 - **38 rm** 1700/2100.

**Balzac** M, 6 r. Balzac ✆ 01 44 35 18 00, *Fax 01 44 35 18 05* - |‡|, ▤ rm, TV ☎. AE ⓪ GB JCB F 8
see ***Pierre Gagnaire*** below - ☐ 90 - **56 rm** 1950/2200, 14 suites.

**Marriott** Ⓜ, 70 av. Champs-Élysées ✆ 01 53 93 55 00, *Fax 01 53 93 55 01*, – rm, – 150. AE GB JCB. F 9
***Pavillon*** ✆ 01 53 93 55 44 **Meals** 250/270 – 175 – **174 rm** 2800/3200, 18 suites.

**Sofitel Arc de Triomphe,** 14 r. Beaujon ✆ 01 53 89 50 50, *Fax 01 53 89 50 51* – rm, – 40. AE GB JCB F 8
see ***Clovis*** below – 120 – **135 rm** 2400/3150.

**Hyatt Regency** Ⓜ, 24 bd Malheshertes ✆ 01 55 27 12 34, *Fax 01 55 27 12 35*, – rm, AE GB JCB F 11
***Café M*** ✆ 01 55 27 12 57 **Meals** 230/280 (lunch) and a la carte 260/310 – 150 – **86 rm** 2400/2800.

**Golden Tulip St-Honoré** Ⓜ, 218 r. Fg St-Honoré ✆ 01 49 53 03 03, *Fax 01 40 75 02 00* – kitchenette, rm, – 140. AE GB JCB
***Relais Vermeer*** *(closed Saturday, Sunday and Bank Holidays)* **Meals** 210 – 110 – **54 rm** 1600/1900, 18 suites. E 8

**Château Frontenac** without rest, 54 r. P. Charron ✆ 01 53 23 13 13, *Fax 01 53 23 13 01* – – 25. AE GB. G 9
85 – **100 rm** 980/1500, 4 suites.

**Bedford,** 17 r. de l'Arcade ✆ 01 44 94 77 77, *Fax 01 44 94 77 97* – – 50. AE GB. rest F 11
**Meals** *(closed 1 to 30 August, Saturday and Sunday)* (lunch only) 170 and a la carte 200/330 – 70 – **135 rm** 830/1050, 11 suites.

**Warwick** Ⓜ, 5 r. Berri ✆ 01 45 63 14 11, *Fax 01 45 63 75 81* – rm, – 30 - 110. AE GB JCB. rest F 9
***La Couronne*** ✆ 01 45 61 82 08 *(closed August, Saturday lunch, Sunday and Bank Holidays)* **Meals** 250 and a la carte 290/410 – 110 – **142 rm** 2100/2600, 5 suites.

**California,** 16 r. Berri ✆ 01 43 59 93 00, *Fax 01 45 61 03 62*, « Important collection of paintings » – rm, – 25 - 80. AE GB JCB. F 9
**Meals** *(closed August, Saturday and Sunday)* (lunch only) 175 – 120 – **157 rm** 2100/2450.

**Résidence du Roy** Ⓜ without rest, 8 r. François 1[er] ✆ 01 42 89 59 59, *Fax 01 40 74 07 92* – kitchenette – 25. AE GB JCB G 9
95, 28 suites1300/1800, 4 studios, 3 duplex.

**Concorde St-Lazare,** 108 r. St-Lazare ✆ 01 40 08 44 44, *Fax 01 42 93 01 20*, « Late 19C lobby, superb billiards room » – rm, – 25 - 150. AE GB JCB. E 12
***Café Terminus*** : **Meals** 148/198 – 105 – **274 rm** 1350/1950, 5 suites.

**Napoléon** without rest, 40 av. Friedland ✆ 01 47 66 02 02, *Fax 01 47 66 82 33* – rm, – 30 - 60. AE GB JCB F 8
110 – **70 rm** 1300/2100, 32 suites.

**Queen Elizabeth,** 41 av. Pierre-1[er]-de-Serbie ✆ 01 53 57 25 25, *Fax 01 53 57 25 26* – rm, – 30. AE GB JCB G 8
**Meals** *(closed August, Saturday and Sunday)* (lunch only) 170/230 b.i. – 95 – **50 rm** 1300/2000, 12 suites.

**Beau Manoir** without rest, 6 r. de l'Arcade ✆ 01 42 66 03 07, *Fax 01 42 68 03 00*, « Attractive interior » – AE GB JCB F 11
**29 rm** 1100/1300, 3 suites.

**Sofitel Champs-Élysées** Ⓜ, 8 r. J. Goujon ✆ 01 40 74 64 64, *Fax 01 40 74 64 99*, – rm, – 200. AE GB JCB G 9
***Les Saveurs*** ✆ 01 40 74 64 94 *(closed 1 to 25 August, Saturday and Sunday)* **Meals** 230 – 125 – **40 rm** 1850/2500.

**Claridge-Bellman,** 37 r. François 1[er] ✆ 01 47 23 54 42, *Fax 01 47 23 08 84* – AE GB. G 9
**Meals** *(closed August, Saturday and Sunday)* a la carte 170/280 – 70 – **42 rm** 1150/1350.

**Rochester Champs-Élysées** Ⓜ without rest, 92 r. La Boétie ✆ 01 43 59 96 15, *Fax 01 42 56 01 38* – – 25. AE GB. F 9
85 – **90 rm** 900/1200.

**Montaigne** Ⓜ without rest, 6 av. Montaigne ✆ 01 47 20 30 50, *Fax 01 47 20 94 12* – AE GB JCB G 9
95 – **29 rm** 1340/1900.

**Royal H.** Ⓜ without rest, 33 av. Friedland ✆ 01 43 59 08 14, *Fax 01 45 63 69 92* – rm, AE GB JCB F 8
105 – **58 rm** 1200/1950.

**Chateaubriand** Ⓜ without rest, 6 r. Chateaubriand ✆ 01 40 76 00 50, *Fax 01 40 76 09 22* – rm, AE GB JCB F 9
80 – **28 rm** 1500.

**Royal Alma** without rest, 35 r. J. Goujon ☎ 01 53 93 63 00, *Fax 01 45 63 68 64* – |‡|, ⇔ rm, TV ☎. AE ① GB JCB. ✻ G 9
☕ 95 – **61 rm** 1380/1620, 3 suites.

**Élysées-Ponthieu and Résidence** without rest, 24 r. Ponthieu ☎ 01 53 89 58 58, *Fax 01 53 89 59 59* – |‡| kitchenette, ⇔ rm, ▤ TV ☎ ♿. AE ① GB JCB F 9
☕ 75 – **92 rm** 985/1050, 6 suites.

**Powers** without rest, 52 r. François 1er ☎ 01 47 23 91 05, *Fax 01 49 52 04 63* – |‡| ▤ TV ☎. AE ① GB JCB G 9
☕ 65 – **53 rm** 826/1392.

**Résidence Monceau** without rest, 85 r. Rocher ☎ 01 45 22 75 11, *Fax 01 45 22 30 88* – |‡|, ⇔ rm, TV ☎ ♿. AE ① GB JCB. ✻ E 11
☕ 55 – **51 rm** 940.

**Concortel** without rest, 19 r. Pasquier ☎ 01 42 65 45 44, *Fax 01 42 65 18 33* – |‡| ▤ TV ☎. AE ① GB F 11
☕ 50 – **46 rm** 570/770.

**Mathurins** M without rest, 43 r. Mathurins ☎ 01 44 94 20 94, *Fax 01 44 94 00 44* – |‡| ▤ TV ☎ ♿ 🚗. AE ① GB F 11
☕ 65 – **33 rm** 1000/1200, 3 suites.

**New Roblin and rest. Le Mazagran,** 6 r. Chauveau-Lagarde ☎ 01 44 71 20 80, *Fax 01 42 65 19 49* – |‡|, ⇔ rm, ▤ TV ☎. AE ① GB JCB F 11
Meals *(closed Saturday, Sunday and Bank Holidays)* 92/155 – ☕ 60 – **77 rm** 920/1050.

**L'Arcade** M without rest, 9 r. de l'Arcade ☎ 01 53 30 60 00, *Fax 01 40 07 03 07* – |‡| ▤ TV ☎ ♿ – 🏛 25. AE GB JCB F 11
☕ 55 – **37 rm** 780/960, 4 duplex.

**de l'Élysée** without rest, 12 r. Saussaies ☎ 01 42 65 29 25, *Fax 01 42 65 64 28* – |‡| ▤ TV ☎. AE ① GB JCB. ✻ F 11
☕ 65 – **32 rm** 780/1180.

**West-End** without rest, 7 r. Clément-Marot ☎ 01 47 20 30 78, *Fax 01 47 20 34 42* – |‡| TV ☎. AE ① GB JCB G 9
☕ 65 – **53 rm** 820/1330.

**Lido** M without rest, 4 passage Madeleine ☎ 01 42 66 27 37, *Fax 01 42 66 61 23* – |‡| ▤ TV ☎. AE ① GB JCB F 11
**32 rm** ☕ 980/1100.

**Étoile Friedland** without rest, 177 r. Fg St-Honoré ☎ 01 45 63 64 65, *Fax 01 45 63 88 96* – |‡|, ⇔ rm, ▤ TV ☎ ♿. AE ① GB JCB F 9
☕ 75 – **40 rm** 1300.

**Queen Mary** M without rest, 9 r. Greffulhe ☎ 01 42 66 40 50, *Fax 01 42 66 94 92* – |‡| ▤ TV ☎. AE GB JCB. ✻ F 12
☕ 85 – **35 rm** 765/935.

**Galiléo** without rest, 54 r. Galilée ☎ 01 47 20 66 06, *Fax 01 47 20 67 17* – |‡| ▤ TV ☎ ♿. AE GB JCB. ✻ F 8
☕ 50 – **27 rm** 800/950.

**Franklin Roosevelt** without rest, 18 r. Clément-Marot ☎ 01 47 23 61 66, *Fax 01 47 20 44 30* – |‡| TV ☎. AE GB JCB. ✻ G 9
☕ 80 – **45 rm** 945/1400.

**Élysées Mermoz** M without rest, 30 r. J. Mermoz ☎ 01 42 25 75 30, *Fax 01 45 62 87 10* – |‡| ▤ TV ☎ ♿. AE ① GB F 10
☕ 47 – **21 rm** 720/890, 5 suites.

**Relais Mercure Opéra Garnier** M without rest, 4 r. de l'Isly ☎ 01 43 87 35 50, *Fax 01 43 87 03 29* – |‡|, ⇔ rm, ▤ TV ☎ ♿. AE ① GB JCB F 12
☕ 65 – **141 rm** 985/1315.

**Flèche d'Or** M without rest, 29 r. Amsterdam ☎ 01 48 74 06 86, *Fax 01 48 74 06 04* – |‡| ▤ TV ☎ ♿. AE ① GB E 12
☕ 40 – **61 rm** 580/780.

**Cordélia** without rest, 11 r. Greffulhe ☎ 01 42 65 42 40, *Fax 01 42 65 11 81* – |‡| ▤ TV ☎. AE ① GB F 11
☕ 50 – **30 rm** 740/850.

**Atlantic H.** without rest, 44 r. Londres ☎ 01 43 87 45 40, *Fax 01 42 93 06 26* – |‡| TV ☎. AE GB JCB. ✻ E 12
☕ 52 – **87 rm** 530/805.

**Mayflower** without rest, 3 r. Chateaubriand ☎ 01 45 62 57 46, *Fax 01 42 56 32 38* – |‡| TV ☎. AE GB F 9
☕ 50 – **24 rm** 660/970.

**Newton Opéra** without rest, 11 bis r. de l'Arcade ☎ 01 42 65 32 13, *Fax 01 42 65 30 90* – . AE GB JCB. F 11
60 – **31 rm** 700/830.

**Fortuny** without rest, 35 r. de l'Arcade ☎ 01 42 66 42 08, *Fax 01 42 66 00 32* – rm, . AE GB JCB F 11
50 – **30 rm** 700/730.

**Les Ambassadeurs** - Hôtel Crillon, 10 pl. Concorde ☎ 01 44 71 16 16, *Fax 01 44 71 15 02*, « 18C decor » – . AE GB JCB. G 11
**Meals** 340 (lunch)/630 and a la carte 510/750
**Spec.** Saumon fumé, chantilly au caviar et croustillant de pommes de terre. Turbot rôti et poché au lait fumé, confiture d'oignons rouges et céleri rave. Truffe glacée à la fleur de thym frais, ganache fondue et violettes cristalisées.

**Taillevent** (Vrinat), 15 r. Lamennais ☎ 01 44 95 15 01, *Fax 01 42 25 95 18* – . AE GB JCB. F 9
*closed 25 July-25 August, Saturday, Sunday and Bank Holidays* – **Meals** (booking essential) a la carte 570/700
**Spec.** Cannelloni de tourteau. Pigeon rôti en bécasse. Fondant au thé fumé.

**Lasserre,** 17 av. F.-D.-Roosevelt ☎ 01 43 59 53 43, *Fax 01 45 63 72 23*, « Retractable roof » – . AE GB JCB. G 10
*closed 2 to 3 August, Monday lunch and Sunday* – **Meals** a la carte 550/710
**Spec.** Poêlée de petits gris aux herbes fraîches. Côte de veau de lait fermier, lardons à la moëlle. Truffes en beignet, sabayon au muscat.

**Lucas Carton** (Senderens), 9 pl. Madeleine ☎ 01 42 65 22 90, *Fax 01 42 65 06 23*, « Authentic 1900 decor » – . AE GB JCB. G 11
*closed 1 to 24 August, Saturday lunch and Sunday* – **Meals** 395 (lunch), 650/1200 and a la carte 650/970
**Spec.** Homard de Bretagne et sa polenta au corail. Selle d'agneau cuite dans sa panoufle, aubergine au masala. Ananas rôti aux clous de girofle et son petit baba aux épices.

**Ledoyen,** carré Champs-Élysées (1st floor) ☎ 01 53 05 10 01, *Fax 01 47 42 55 01*, see also rest. ***Le Cercle*** – P. AE GB JCB. G 10
*closed August, Saturday and Sunday* – **Meals** 300/530 and a la carte 500/780
**Spec.** Truffe en feuilleté de pomme de terre (December-February). Turbot rôti à la bière de garde, oignons frits. Mousse chaude au cacao aux deux cuissons, glace à la kriek.

**Laurent,** 41 av. Gabriel ☎ 01 42 25 00 39, *Fax 01 45 62 45 21*, « Pleasant summer terrace » – AE GB. G 10
*closed Saturday lunch, Sunday and Bank Holidays* – **Meals** 390/650 and a la carte 540/970
**Spec.** Homard entier en salade. Pigeonneau rôti à la broche. Crêpes Suzette.

**Bristol** - Hôtel Bristol, 112 r. Fg St-Honoré ☎ 01 53 43 43 40, *Fax 01 53 43 43 01*, – . AE GB JCB. F 10
**Meals** 360/600 and a la carte 650/780
**Spec.** Lobe de foie gras de canard rôti et servi froid (autumn-winter). Pavé de turbot rôti, têtes de cèpes poêlées au magret fumé et noix fraîches (autumn). Pigeon cuit à la broche, escalope de foie gras poêlée, jus aux truffes.

**Régence** - Hôtel Plaza Athénée, 25 av. Montaigne ☎ 01 53 67 65 00, *Fax 01 53 67 66 76* – . AE GB JCB. G 9
**Meals** 310 (lunch), 480/620 and a la carte 430/680
**Spec.** Gelée d'oursins en coque au fondant de fenouil (October-April). Pavé de lieu aux aubergines, jus léger à la poutargue. Ris de veau meunière au beurre salé et au citron confit (October-April).

**Les Élysées** - Hôtel Vernet, 25 r. Vernet ☎ 01 44 31 98 98, *Fax 01 44 31 85 69*, « Fine glass roof » – . AE GB JCB. F 8
*closed 27 July-30 August, 24 to 30 December, Saturday, Sunday and Bank Holidays* – **Meals** 330 (lunch), 430/790 and a la carte 470/720
**Spec.** Epeautre du pays de Sault cuisiné comme un risotto à l'encre de seiche. Turbot côtier du Guilvinec doré aux câpres, citron et truffe écrasée. Chausson feuilleté au chocolat amer, crème glacée aux fèves de cacao torréfiées.

**Pierre Gagnaire** - Hôtel Balzac, 6 r. Balzac ☎ 01 44 35 18 25, *Fax 01 44 35 18 37* – . AE GB F 8
*closed 14 July-15 August, February Holidays, Sunday lunch and Saturday* – **Meals** 450 (lunch), 520/860 and a la carte 550/940
**Spec.** Grosses langoustines en scampi, feuilles croustillantes de légumes. Pièce de turbot de ligne poêlée au vadouvan. Soufflé au chocolat pur Caraïbe, parfait de Sicile et fromage blanc glacé.

XXXX ✿ **L'Astor** - Hôtel Astor, 11 rue d'Astorg ☎ 01 53 05 05 20, *Fax 01 53 05 05 30* – ▤. AE ⓓ GB JCB F 11
*closed Saturday and Sunday* – **Meals** 290 b.i./600 and a la carte 280/510
**Spec.** Araignée de mer en gelée anisée à la crème de fenouil. Blanc de bar cuit en peau, sauce verjutée. Cristalline à la pomme verte, crème croustillante au thé.

XXXX ✿ **Chiberta,** 3 r. Arsène-Houssaye ☎ 01 45 63 77 90, *Fax 01 45 62 85 08* – ▤. AE ⓓ GB JCB F 8
*closed August, Saturday and Sunday* – **Meals** 290 b.i. and a la carte 340/590
**Spec.** Ravioli de poireaux aux truffes. Salade de pigeonneau aux petits épeautres. Fondant au chocolat chaud, sorbet cacao.

XXXX ✿ **La Marée,** 1 r. Daru ☎ 01 43 80 20 00, *Fax 01 48 88 04 04* – ▤. AE ⓓ GB E 8
*closed 1 August-2 September, Saturday lunch and Sunday* – **Meals** - Seafood - a la carte 350/560
**Spec.** Belons au champagne (mid-September-May). Langoustines poêlées aux carottes confites. Cabillaud à la diable, purée de pommes de terre "minute".

XXX ✿ **Clovis** - Hôtel Sofitel Arc de Triomphe, 14 r. Beaujon ☎ 01 53 89 50 53, *Fax 01 53 89 50 51* – AE ⓓ GB JCB F 8
*closed 25 July-25 August, 23 December-2 January, Saturday, Sunday and Bank Holidays* – **Meals** 250/520 and a la carte 300/430
**Spec.** Marbré de lapin au ris de veau, langue écarlate. Tronçon de lotte à la livèche, mousseline de céleri. Cristallines d'ananas, sorbet coco.

XXX **Maison Blanche,** 15 av. Montaigne (6th floor) ☎ 01 47 23 55 99, *Fax 01 47 20 09 56*, ≤, 帝, « Contemporary decor » – ▤. AE GB G 9
*closed August, Saturday lunch and Sunday* – **Meals** a la carte 400/540.

XXX ✿ **Jardin** - Hôtel Royal Monceau, 37 av. Hoche ☎ 01 42 99 98 70, *Fax 01 42 99 89 94*, 帝 – ▤. AE ⓓ GB JCB. ✻ E 8
*closed Saturday and Sunday except August* – **Meals** 290/440 and a la carte 420/590
**Spec.** Cocotte de langoustines rôties au poivre frais. Carré d'agneau grillé aux pignons de pin et sarriette. Figues noires rôties dans leurs feuilles aux épices.

XXX ✿ **Copenhague,** 142 av. Champs-Élysées (1st floor) ☎ 01 44 13 86 26, *Fax 01 42 25 83 10*, 帝 – ▤. AE ⓓ GB JCB. ✻ F 8
*closed 3 to 30 August, 4 to 10 January, Saturday lunch, Sunday and Bank Holidays* – **Meals** - Danish rest. - 250 b.i. and a la carte 280/420 - ***Flora Danica :*** **Meals** 170 and a la carte 270/380
**Spec.** Carrelet poêlé à la danoise. Mignons de renne aux saveurs nordiques. Crêpes aux mûres jaunes.

XXX **Marcande,** 52 r. Miromesnil ☎ 01 42 65 19 14, *Fax 01 40 76 03 27*, 帝 – AE GB F 10
*closed 8 to 24 August, Saturday, Sunday and Bank Holidays* – **Meals** 240 and a la carte 270/400.

XXX **Yvan,** 1bis r. J. Mermoz ☎ 01 43 59 18 40, *Fax 01 42 89 30 95* – ▤. AE ⓓ GB JCB F-G 10
*closed Saturday lunch and Sunday* – **Meals** 178/288 and a la carte 240/370.

XXX **Indra,** 10 r. Cdt-Rivière ☎ 01 43 59 46 40, *Fax 01 44 07 31 19* – ▤. AE ⓓ GB F 9
*closed Sunday* – **Meals** - Indian rest. - 195 (lunch), 220/300 and a la carte 180/220.

XXX **Le 30 - Fauchon,** 30 pl. Madeleine ☎ 01 47 42 56 58, *Fax 01 47 42 96 02*, 帝 – ▤. AE ⓓ GB JCB F 12
*closed Sunday* – **Meals** 245/259 b.i. and a la carte 300/400.

XX **Luna,** 69 r. Rocher ☎ 01 42 93 77 61, *Fax 01 40 08 02 44* – ▤. AE GB E 11
*closed Sunday* – **Meals** - Seafood - a la carte 270/500.

XX **Chez Tante Louise,** 41 r. Boissy-d'Anglas ☎ 01 42 65 06 85, *Fax 01 42 65 28 19* – ▤. AE ⓓ GB JCB F 11
*closed August, Saturday and Sunday* – **Meals** 190 and a la carte 250/360.

XX **Cercle Ledoyen,** carré Champs-Élysées (ground floor) ☎ 01 53 05 10 02, *Fax 01 47 42 55 01*, 帝 – ▤. AE ⓓ GB JCB. ✻ G 10
*closed Sunday* – **Meals** a la carte 220/280.

XX **El Mansour,** 7 r. Trémoille ☎ 01 47 23 88 18 – AE GB. ✻ G 9
*closed Monday lunch and Sunday* – **Meals** - Moroccan rest. - a la carte 250/350.

XX **Sarladais,** 2 r. Vienne ☎ 01 45 22 23 62, *Fax 01 45 22 23 62* – ▤. AE GB E 11
*closed Saturday except dinner from September-June and Sunday* – **Meals** 155 (dinner), 200/300 and a la carte 220/330.

XX **Grenadin,** 46 r. Naples ☎ 01 45 63 28 92, *Fax 01 45 61 24 76* – ▤. AE GB E 11
*closed Saturday lunch and Sunday* – **Meals** 250/330.

XX **Pavillon Élysée,** 10 av. Champs Élysées ☎ 01 42 65 85 10, *Fax 01 42 65 76 23,* – ▤. AE ⓓ GB JCB G 10
*closed Saturday lunch and Sunday* – **Meals** 200 and a la carte 240/350.

XX **Hédiard,** 21 pl. Madeleine ☎ 01 43 12 88 99, *Fax 01 43 12 88 98* – ▤. AE ⓓ GB F 11
*closed Sunday* – **Meals** a la carte 230/310.

XX **Fermette Marbeuf 1900,** 5 r. Marbeuf ☎ 01 53 23 08 00, *Fax 01 53 23 08 09,* « 1900 decor with original ceramics and stained glass windows » – ▤. AE ⓓ GB G 9
**Meals** 178 and a la carte 190/370.

XX ✿ **Marius et Janette,** 4 av. George-V ☎ 01 47 23 41 88, *Fax 01 47 23 07 19,* – ▤. AE ⓓ GB JCB G 8
**Meals** - Seafood - 300 b.i. and a la carte 360/570
**Spec.** Ravioles de langoustines au persil plat. Merlan frit, sauce tartare. Blanc de Saint-Pierre, huile d'olive et anchois.

XX **Suntory,** 13 r. Lincoln ☎ 01 42 25 40 27, *Fax 01 45 63 25 86* – ▤. AE ⓓ GB JCB. ✻
**Meals** - Japanese rest. - 145 (lunch), 430/630 and a la carte 270/400. F 9

XX **Shozan,** 11 r. de la Trémoille ☎ 01 47 23 37 32, *Fax 01 47 23 67 30* – ▤. AE ⓓ GB JCB G 9
*closed 2 to 19 August, 25 to 30 December, Saturday lunch and Sunday* – **Meals** - French and Japanese rest. - 90 (lunch), 200/400 and a la carte 280/410.

XX **Stella Maris,** 4 r. Arsène Houssaye ☎ 01 42 89 16 22, *Fax 01 42 89 16 01* – AE ⓓ GB JCB. ✻ F 8
*closed 1 to 15 August, Bank Holidays lunch, Saturday lunch and Sunday* – **Meals** - Seafood - 175/480 and a la carte 300/430.

XX **Stresa,** 7 r. Chambiges ☎ 01 47 23 51 62 – ▤. AE ⓓ GB. ✻ G 9
*closed 11 to 31 August, 20 December-4 January, Saturday dinner and Sunday* – **Meals** - Italian rest. - (booking essential) a la carte 380/450.

XX **Kinugawa,** 4 r. St-Philippe du Roule ☎ 01 45 63 08 07, *Fax 01 42 60 45 21* – ▤. AE ⓓ GB JCB. ✻ F 9
*closed Christmas Holidays and Sunday* – **Meals** - Japanese rest. - 510/700 and a la carte 180/400.

XX **Bistrot du Sommelier,** 97 bd Haussmann ☎ 01 42 65 24 85, *Fax 01 53 75 23 23* – ▤. AE GB F 11
*closed August, Christmas-New Year, Saturday and Sunday* – **Meals** 390 (dinner only) and a la carte 280/360 ♁.

XX **Les Bouchons de François Clerc,** 7 r. Boccador ☎ 01 47 23 57 80, *Fax 01 47 23 74 54* – AE GB G 9
*closed Saturday lunch and Sunday* – **Meals** 195.

XX **Village d'Ung et Li Lam,** 10 r. J. Mermoz ☎ 01 42 25 99 79, *Fax 01 42 25 12 06* – ▤. AE ⓓ GB F 10
**Meals** - Chinese and Thai rest. - 118/178 and a la carte 160/220.

XX **Le Pichet,** 68 r. P. Charron ☎ 01 43 59 50 34, *Fax 01 42 89 68 91* – ▤. AE ⓓ GB GF 9
*closed Saturday except dinner from September-June and Sunday* – **Meals** a la carte 280/510.

XX **Bistro de l'Olivier,** 13 r. Quentin Bauchart ☎ 01 47 20 17 00, *Fax 01 47 20 17 04* – ▤. AE ⓓ GB G 8
*closed 1 to 30 August, Saturday lunch and Sunday* – **Meals** (booking essential) 190.

XX **L'Alsace** (24 hr service), 39 av. Champs-Élysées ☎ 01 53 93 97 00, *Fax 01 53 93 97 09,* , brasserie – ▤. AE ⓓ GB F 9
**Meals** 123 b.i. (dinner)/178 and a la carte 180/270.

XX **Kok Ping,** 4 r. Balzac ☎ 01 42 25 28 85, *Fax 01 53 75 11 49* – ▤. AE ⓓ GB. ✻ F 8
*closed lunch Saturday and Sunday* – **Meals** - Chinese and Thai rest - 89/135 and a la carte 130/270.

X **Cap Vernet,** 82 av. Marceau ☎ 01 47 20 20 40, *Fax 01 47 20 95 36,* – ▤. AE GB JCB F 8
**Meals** - Seafood - a la carte 200/280.

X **L'Appart',** 9 r. Colisée ☎ 01 53 75 16 34, *Fax 01 53 76 15 39* – ▤. AE GB JCB F 9
**Meals** 175 and a la carte 210/270.

X **Ferme des Mathurins,** 17 r. Vignon ☎ 01 42 66 46 39 – ⓓ GB JCB F 12
*closed August, Sunday and Bank Holidays* – **Meals** 160/210 and a la carte 190/330.

X **Boucoléon,** 10 r. Constantinople ☎ 01 42 93 73 33, *Fax 01 42 93 17 44* – GB E 11
*closed August, Saturday and Sunday* – **Meals** (booking essential) a la carte approx. 140.

# Opéra, Gare du Nord, Gare de l'Est, Grands Boulevards.

*9th and 10th arrondissements.*
*9th: ✉ 75009*
*10th: ✉ 75010*

**Grand Hôtel Inter-Continental,** 2 r. Scribe (9th) ✆ 01 40 07 32 32, *Fax 01 42 66 12 51,* – ⛛, ⇔ rm, ▤ TV ☎ ♿ – 🏠 300. AE ⓓ GB JCB. ✗ rest F12
see **Rest. Opéra** and **Brasserie Café de la Paix** below - **La Verrière** ✆ 01 40 07 31 00 *(closed August and Saturday) (lunch only)* **Meals** 285 – ☕ 160 – **488 rm** 1750/3600, 22 suites.

**Scribe** M, 1 r. Scribe (9th) ✆ 01 44 71 24 24, *Fax 01 44 71 24 42* – ⛛, ⇔ rm, ▤ TV ☎ ♿ – 🏠 50. AE ⓓ GB JCB F 12
see **Les Muses** below - **Jardin des Muses :** **Meals** 160 – ☕ 110 – **206 rm** 1600/2450, 11 suites.

**Ambassador,** 16 bd Haussmann (9th) ✆ 01 44 83 40 40, *Fax 01 40 22 08 74* – ⛛ ▤ TV ☎ – 🏠 110. AE ⓓ GB JCB F 13
**Venantius** ✆ 01 48 00 06 38, fax 01 42 46 19 84 *(closed Saturday and Sunday)* **Meals** 160 – ☕ 110 – **288 rm** 1500/2200.

**Millennium Commodore,** 12 bd Haussmann (9th) ✆ 01 42 46 72 82, *Fax 01 47 70 23 81* – ⛛, ⇔ rm, TV ☎ – 🏠 25. AE ⓓ GB JCB F 13
**Brasserie Haussmann :** **Meals** 120/250 – ☕ 110 – **159 rm** 2000/2600, 5 suites.

**Terminus Nord** M without rest, 12 bd Denain (10th) ✆ 01 42 80 20 00, *Fax 01 42 80 63 89* – ⛛, ⇔ rm, TV ☎ ♿ – 🏠 80. AE ⓓ GB JCB E 16
☕ 75 – **236 rm** 985/1500.

**Lafayette** M without rest, 49 r. Lafayette (9th) ✆ 01 42 85 05 44, *Fax 01 49 95 06 60* – ⛛, ⇔ rm, TV ☎ ♿. AE ⓓ GB JCB F 14
☕ 75 – **96 rm** 1075, 7 suites.

**St-Pétersbourg,** 33 r. Caumartin (9th) ✆ 01 42 66 60 38, *Fax 01 42 66 53 54* – ⛛ ▤ TV ☎ – 🏠 25. AE ⓓ GB JCB. ✗ rest F 12
**Le Relais** *(closed August, Saturday and Sunday)* **Meals** 140 – ☕ 70 – **100 rm** 875/975.

**Brébant,** 32 bd Poissonnière (9th) ✆ 01 47 70 25 55, *Fax 01 42 46 65 70* – ⛛, ⇔ rm, ▤ TV ☎ – 🏠 25 - 100. AE ⓓ GB JCB F 14
**Vieux Pressoir :** **Meals** 98/198 – ☕ 48 – **122 rm** 760/1050.

**L'Horset Pavillon,** 38 r. Échiquier (10th) ✆ 01 42 46 92 75, *Fax 01 42 47 03 97* – ⛛, ⇔ rm, ▤ TV ☎. AE ⓓ GB JCB F 15
**Meals** *(closed Saturday lunch and Sunday)* 90/180 b.i. – ☕ 80 – **92 rm** 890/990.

**Richmond Opéra** without rest, 11 r. Helder (9th) ✆ 01 47 70 53 20, *Fax 01 48 00 02 10* – ⛛ ▤ TV ☎. AE ⓓ GB JCB. ✗ F 13
☕ 40 – **58 rm** 710/840.

**Bergère Opéra** without rest, 34 r. Bergère (9th) ✆ 01 47 70 34 34, *Fax 01 47 70 36 36* – ⛛ ▤ TV ☎ – 🏠 40. AE ⓓ GB JCB. ✗ F 14
☕ 70 – **134 rm** 790/990.

**Franklin** without rest, 19 r. Buffault (9th) ✆ 01 42 80 27 27, *Fax 01 48 78 13 04* – ⛛, ⇔ rm, TV ☎ ♿. AE ⓓ GB JCB E 14
☕ 75 – **68 rm** 825/890.

**Blanche Fontaine** 🐎 without rest, 34 r. Fontaine (9th) ✆ 01 44 63 54 95, *Fax 01 42 81 05 52* – ⛛, ⇔ rm, TV ☎. AE ⓓ GB JCB. ✗ D 13
☕ 45 – **45 rm** 507/570, 4 suites.

**Carlton's H.** without rest, 55 bd Rochechouart (9th) ✆ 01 42 81 91 00, *Fax 01 42 81 97 04,* « Rooftop panoramic terrace, ≤ Paris » – ⛛ TV ☎. AE ⓓ GB JCB D 14
☕ 47 – **103 rm** 619/688.

**Anjou-Lafayette** without rest, 4 r. Riboutté (9th) ✆ 01 42 46 83 44, *Fax 01 48 00 08 97* – ⛛ TV ☎. AE ⓓ GB JCB E 14
☕ 50 – **39 rm** 490/680.

**Frantour Paris-Est** M without rest, 4 r. 8 Mai 1945 (cour d'Honneur gare de l'Est) (10th) ✆ 01 44 89 27 00, *Fax 01 44 89 27 49* – ⛛ ▤ TV ☎ – 🏠 250. AE GB E 16
☕ 55 – **45 rm** 535/1055.

**Albert 1er** without rest, 162 r. Lafayette (10th) 01 40 36 82 40, *Fax 01 40 35 72 52* – . AE GB JCB. E 16
45 – **57 rm** 500/698.

**Opéra Cadet** without rest, 24 r. Cadet (9th) 01 53 34 50 50, *Fax 01 53 34 50 60* – . AE GB JCB F 14
65 – **82 rm** 755/980, 3 suites.

**Touraine Opéra** without rest, 73 r. Taitbout (9th) 01 48 74 50 49, *Fax 01 42 81 26 09* – , rm, . AE GB JCB E 13
75 – **39 rm** 825/990.

**Paix République** without rest, 2 bis bd St-Martin (10th) 01 42 08 96 95, *Fax 01 42 06 36 30* – , rm, . AE GB JCB. G 16
40 – **45 rm** 550/980.

**Mercure Monty** without rest, 5 r. Montyon (9th) 01 47 70 26 10, *Fax 01 42 46 55 10* – , rm, – 50. AE GB JCB F 14
60 – **71 rm** 990.

**Corona** without rest, 8 cité Bergère (9th) 01 47 70 52 96, *Fax 01 42 46 83 49* – . AE GB JCB F 14
45 – **56 rm** 580/700, 4 suites.

**Capucines** without rest, 6 r. Godot de Mauroy (9th) 01 47 42 25 05, *Fax 01 42 68 05 05* – . AE GB JCB F 12
38 – **45 rm** 520/550.

**Amiral Duperré** without rest, 32 r. Duperré (9th) 01 42 81 55 33, *Fax 01 44 63 04 73* – , rm, . AE GB JCB D 13
45 – **52 rm** 540/570.

**Suède** without rest, 106 bd Magenta (10th) 01 40 36 10 12, *Fax 01 40 36 11 98* – , rm, . AE GB JCB E 15-16
45 – **52 rm** 510/570.

**Ibis Gare de l'Est** without rest, 197 r. Lafayette (10th) 01 44 65 70 00, *Fax 01 44 65 70 07* – , rm, . AE GB E 17
41 – **165 rm** 420/470.

**Modern' Est** without rest, 91 bd Strasbourg (10th) 01 40 37 77 20, *Fax 01 40 37 17 55* – . GB. E 16
35 – **30 rm** 380/460.

**Alba** without rest, 34 ter r. La Tour d'Auvergne (9th) 01 48 78 80 22, *Fax 01 42 85 23 13* – kitchenette, rm, . AE GB JCB. E 14
40 – **24 rm** 500/1400.

**Trois Poussins** without rest, 15 r. Clauzel (9th) 01 53 32 81 81, *Fax 01 53 32 81 82* – , rm, . AE GB. E 13
38 – **40 rm** 350/490.

XXXX ✿✿ **Rest. Opéra** - Grand Hôtel Inter-Continental, pl. Opéra (9th) 01 40 07 30 10, *Fax 01 40 07 33 86,* « Second Empire decor » – . AE GB JCB. F 12
*closed August, Saturday, Sunday and Bank Holidays* – **Meals** 240 (lunch)/345 b.i. and a la carte 380/600
**Spec.** Grosses langoustines croustillantes, émulsion d'agrumes à l'huile d'olive. Blanc de turbot braisé, rattes écrasées au beurre de truffe. Noix de ris de veau poêlée au beurre d'herbes.

XXXX ✿ **Les Muses** - Hôtel Scribe, 1 r. Scribe (9th) 01 44 71 24 26, *Fax 01 44 71 24 64* – . AE GB JCB. F 12
*closed August, Saturday, Sunday and Bank Holidays* – **Meals** 250/320
**Spec.** Parmentier de foie gras de canard chaud. Noisettes de biche poêlées au macis, poire au vin rouge et palets de charlotte (October-February). Tarte chocolat "Manjari", soupe d'oranges aux fleurs séchées.

XXX ✿ **Table d'Anvers** (Conticini), 2 pl. Anvers (9th) 01 48 78 35 21, *Fax 01 45 26 66 67* – . AE GB JCB D 14
*closed Saturday lunch and Sunday* – **Meals** 180 (lunch)/270 and a la carte 440/630
**Spec.** "Céviche" de langoustines. Saint-Pierre au "nuoc-mâm". Croquettes au chocolat coulant.

XXX **Charlot "Roi des Coquillages",** 12 pl. Clichy (9th) 01 53 20 48 00, *Fax 01 53 20 48 09* – . AE GB D 12
**Meals** - Seafood - 178 and a la carte 240/360.

XX **Au Chateaubriant,** 23 r. Chabrol (10th) 01 48 24 58 94, *Fax 01 42 47 09 75,* Collection of paintings – . AE GB JCB E 15
*closed August, Sunday and Monday* – **Meals** - Italian rest. - 159 and a la carte 230/330.

XX **Brasserie Café de la Paix** - Grand Hôtel Inter-Continental, 12 bd Capucines (9th) ✆ 01 40 07 30 20, *Fax 01 40 07 33 86* – ▤. AE ⓓ GB JCB F 12
**Meals** 179 and a la carte 220/360.

XX **Julien,** 16 r. Fg St-Denis (10th) ✆ 01 47 70 12 06, *Fax 01 42 47 00 65*, « Belle Epoque brasserie » – ▤. AE ⓓ GB F 15
**Meals** 169 b.i. (lunch)/183 b.i. and a la carte 160/300.

XX **Grand Café Capucines** (24 hr service), 4 bd Capucines (9th) ✆ 01 43 12 19 00, *Fax 01 43 12 19 09*, brasserie, « Belle Epoque decor » – ▤. AE ⓓ GB F 13
**Meals** 178 and a la carte 190/340 ♫.

XX **Grange Batelière,** 16 r. Grange Batelière (9th) ✆ 01 47 70 85 15, *Fax 01 47 70 85 15* – ▤. AE GB G 10
*closed August, Saturday lunch, Sunday and Bank Holidays* – **Meals** 190/300 and a la carte 270/360.

XX **Quercy,** 36 r. Condorcet (9th) ✆ 01 48 78 30 61, *Fax 01 48 78 16 29* – AE ⓓ GB JCB E 14
*closed August, Sunday and Bank Holidays* – **Meals** 152 and a la carte 190/310.

XX **Bistrot Papillon,** 6 r. Papillon (9th) ✆ 01 47 70 90 03, *Fax 01 48 24 05 59* – ▤. AE ⓓ GB E 15
*closed 1 to 20 April, 8 to 30 August, Saturday and Sunday* – **Meals** 150 and a la carte 200/250.

XX **Au Petit Riche,** 25 r. Le Peletier (9th) ✆ 01 47 70 68 68, *Fax 01 48 24 10 79*, bistro, « Late 19C decor » – ▤. AE ⓓ GB JCB F 13
*closed Sunday* – **Meals** 135 (dinner)/175 and a la carte 170/300 ♫.

XX **Brasserie Flo,** 7 cour Petites-Écuries (10th) ✆ 01 47 70 13 59, *Fax 01 42 47 00 80*, « 1900 decor » – ▤. AE ⓓ GB F 15
**Meals** 169 and a la carte 160/300 ♫.

XX **Terminus Nord,** 23 r. Dunkerque (10th) ✆ 01 42 85 05 15, *Fax 01 40 16 13 98*, brasserie – ▤. AE ⓓ GB E 16
**Meals** 169 b.i. and a la carte 160/300.

XX **Paprika,** 28 av. Trudaine (9th) ✆ 01 44 63 02 91, *Fax 01 44 63 09 62* – ▤. GB E 14
*closed Monday dinner and Sunday* – **Meals** - Hungarian rest. - 75 (lunch), 120/180 and a la carte 210/330.

XX **Saintongeais,** 62 r. Fg Montmartre (9th) ✆ 01 42 80 39 92 – AE ⓓ GB E 14
*closed 15 to 25 August, Saturday and Sunday* – **Meals** 135/168 and a la carte 180/260.

XX **Comme Chez Soi,** 20 r. Lamartine (9th) ✆ 01 48 78 00 02, *Fax 01 42 85 09 78* – ▤. AE GB JCB E 14
*closed August, Saturday and Sunday* – **Meals** 90/140 and a la carte 220/310.

XX **Wally Le Saharien,** 36 r. Rodier (9th) ✆ 01 42 85 51 90, *Fax 01 45 86 08 35* – ▤. ✂
*closed Monday lunch and Sunday* – **Meals** - North African rest. - 140 (lunch)/240 and a la carte 160/230. E 14

XX **P'tite Tonkinoise,** 56 r. Fg Poissonnière (10th) ✆ 01 42 46 85 98 – AE ⓓ GB JCB F 15
*closed 25 July-3 September, 24 December-15 January, Saturday lunch and Sunday* – **Meals** - Vietnamese rest. - 135 and a la carte approx. 170.

X **Pré Cadet,** 10 r. Saulnier (9th) ✆ 01 48 24 99 64 – ▤. AE ⓓ GB JCB F 14
*closed 1 to 8 May, 5 to 25 August, 24 to 31 December, Saturday lunch and Sunday* – **Meals** (booking essential) 150 and a la carte 190/290.

X **Paludier,** 5 r. Clichy (9th) ✆ 01 48 74 32 13, *Fax 01 48 74 32 13* – ▤. AE GB E 12
*closed Saturday and Sunday* – **Meals** 158/171 and a la carte approx. 250.

X **L'Oenothèque,** 20 r. St-Lazare (9th) ✆ 01 48 78 08 76, *Fax 01 40 16 10 27* – ▤. AE GB JCB E 13
*closed 4 to 10 May, 10 to 30 August, Saturday and Sunday* – **Meals** a la carte 240/380.

X **Chez Jean,** 8 r. St-Lazare (9th) ✆ 01 48 78 62 73, *Fax 01 48 78 35 30* E 14
*closed 18 to 24 May, 17 to 23 August, Saturday lunch and Sunday* – **Meals** 165.

X **Bistro de Gala,** 45 r. Fg Montmarte (9th) ✆ 01 40 22 90 50, *Fax 01 40 22 90 50* – ▤. AE ⓓ GB JCB F 14
*closed Saturday lunch and Sunday* – **Meals** 160 and a la carte 160/230.

X **I Golosi,** 6 r. Grange Batelière (9th) ✆ 01 48 24 18 63, *Fax 01 45 23 18 96*, « Venetian decor » – ▤. GB F 14
*closed August, Saturday dinner and Sunday* – **Meals** - Italian rest - a la carte 160/240.

X **Aux Deux Canards,** 8 r. Fg Poissonnière (10th) ✆ 01 47 70 03 23 – AE ⓓ GB F 15
*closed 31 July-23 August, Saturday lunch and Sunday* – **Meals** a la carte 150/250.

X **Bistro des Deux Théâtres,** 18 r. Blanche (9th) ✆ 01 45 26 41 43, *Fax 01 48 74 08 92* – ▤. AE GB E 12
**Meals** 169 b.i.

**Chez Michel,** 10 r. Belzunce (10th) ✆ 01 44 53 06 20, *Fax 01 44 53 61 31* – GB F 15
*closed 26 July-26 August, 20 December-2 January, Sunday and Monday* – **Meals** 170.

**Casa Olympe,** 48 r. St-Georges (9th) ✆ 01 42 85 26 01, *Fax 01 45 26 49 33* – ▤. E 13
*closed August, 23 December-2 January, Saturday and Sunday* – **Meals** 190/280 b.i.

**Petite Sirène de Copenhague,** 47 r. N.-D. de Lorette (9th) ✆ 01 45 26 66 66 – GB E 13
*closed August, Sunday and Monday* – **Meals** - Danish rest. - (booking essential) 120 and a la carte 170/240.

**Relais Beaujolais,** 3 r. Milton (9th) ✆ 01 48 78 77 91, bistro – GB E 14
*closed August, Saturday and Sunday* – **Meals** a la carte 130/220.

**Petit Batailley,** 26 r. Bergère (9th) ✆ 01 47 70 85 81 – AE ⓓ GB JCB F 14
*closed 25 July-24 August, 19 to 28 December, Saturday lunch, Sunday and Bank Holidays* – **Meals** 145.

**L'Alsaco Winstub,** 10 r. Condorcet (9th) ✆ 01 45 26 44 31 – AE GB E 15
*closed August, Saturday lunch and Sunday* – **Meals** 79 (lunch), 87/170 b.i. and a la carte 120/230.

**Chez Catherine - Le Poitou,** 65 r. Provence (9th) ✆ 01 45 26 72 88, *Fax 01 42 80 96 88*, bistro – GB F 13
*closed August, 1 to 11 January, Monday dinner, Saturday and Sunday* – **Meals** a la carte 170/200.

**L'Excuse Mogador,** 21 r. Joubert (9th) ✆ 01 42 81 98 19 – GB F 12
*closed August, Monday dinner, Saturday and Sunday* – **Meals** 75 (lunch)/95 and a la carte 110/170.

## Bastille, Gare de Lyon, Place d'Italie, Bois de Vincennes.

*12th and 13th arrondissements.*
*12th: ✉ 75012*
*13th: ✉ 75013*

**Holiday Inn Bastille** M without rest, 11 r. Lyon (12th) ✆ 01 53 02 20 00, *Fax 01 53 02 20 01* – ⧖, ⋟ rm, ▤ TV ☎ – 🏛 80. AE ⓓ GB JCB L 18
☕ 80 – **125 rm** 1130/1330.

**Novotel Bercy** M, 86 r. Bercy (12th) ✆ 01 43 42 30 00, *Fax 01 43 45 30 60*, 🏫 – ⧖, ⋟ rm, ▤ TV ☎ ♿ 🚗 – 🏛 80. AE ⓓ GB M 19
Meals a la carte approx. 170 – ☕ 68 – **128 rm** 720/760.

**Holiday Inn Tolbiac** M without rest, 21 r. Tolbiac (13th) ✆ 01 45 84 61 61, *Fax 01 45 84 43 38* – ⧖, ⋟ rm, ▤ TV ☎ ♿ – 🏛 25. AE ⓓ GB JCB P 18
☕ 65 – **71 rm** 890.

**Mercure Pont de Bercy** M without rest, 6 bd Vincent Auriol (13th) ✆ 01 45 82 48 00, *Fax 01 45 82 19 16* – ⧖ ▤ TV ☎ ♿ – 🏛 60. AE ⓓ GB JCB M 18
☕ 60 – **90 rm** 810.

**Mercure Vincent Auriol** M without rest, 178 bd Vincent Auriol (13th) ✆ 01 44 24 01 01, *Fax 01 44 24 07 07* – ⧖, ⋟ rm, TV ☎ ♿ – 🏛 50. AE ⓓ GB N 16
☕ 62 – **70 rm** 680/785.

**Mercure Blanqui** M without rest, 25 bd Blanqui (13th) ✆ 01 45 80 82 23, *Fax 01 45 81 45 84* – ⧖, ⋟ rm, ▤ TV ☎ ♿. AE ⓓ GB JCB P 15
☕ 60 – **50 rm** 790.

**Pavillon Bastille** M without rest, 65 r. Lyon (12th) ✆ 01 43 43 65 65, *Fax 01 43 43 96 52*, « Elegant contemporary decor » – ⧖, ⋟ rm, ▤ TV ☎ ♿. AE ⓓ GB JCB K 18
☕ 65 – **24 rm** 955.

**Paris Bastille** M without rest, 67 r. Lyon (12th) ✆ 01 40 01 07 17, *Fax 01 40 01 07 27* – ⧖ ▤ TV ☎ ♿ – 🏛 25. AE ⓓ GB JCB. ✂ K 18
☕ 55 – **30 rm** 766/950.

**Allegro Nation** M without rest, 33 av. Dr A. Netter (12th) 01 40 04 90 90, *Fax 01 40 04 99 20* – AE GB. M 12
40 – **49 rm** 500/610.

**Ibis Gare de Lyon** M without rest, 43 av. Ledru-Rollin (12th) 01 53 02 30 30, *Fax 01 53 02 30 31* – rm, – 25. AE GB K 18
40 – **119 rm** 450.

**Ibis Place d'Italie** M without rest, 25 av. Stephen Pichon (13th) 01 44 24 94 85, *Fax 01 44 24 20 70* – rm, AE GB N 16
39 – **58 rm** 415/455.

**Ibis Italie Tolbiac** M without rest, 177 r. Tolbiac (13th) 01 45 80 16 60, *Fax 01 45 80 95 80* – rm, AE GB P 15
39 – **60 rm** 380/420.

**Touring H. Magendie** M without rest, 2 r. Magendie (13th) 01 43 36 13 61, *Fax 01 43 36 47 48* – – 30. GB N 14
**112 rm** 325/395.

**Nouvel H.** without rest, 24 av. Bel Air (12th) 01 43 43 01 81, *Fax 01 43 44 64 13* – AE GB L 21
40 – **28 rm** 360/555.

**Viator** without rest, 1 r. Parrot (12th) 01 43 43 11 00, *Fax 01 43 43 10 89* – AE GB. L 18
35 – **45 rm** 320/370.

**Au Pressoir** (Seguin), 257 av. Daumesnil (12th) 01 43 44 38 21, *Fax 01 43 43 81 77* – AE GB M 22
*closed August, Saturday and Sunday* – **Meals** 400 and a la carte 360/610
**Spec.** Millefeuille de champignons aux truffes. Pot-au-feu de homard. Lièvre à la royale (October-November).

**Train Bleu,** Gare de Lyon (12th) 01 43 43 09 06, *Fax 01 43 43 97 96*, brasserie, « Murals depicting the journey from Paris to the Mediterranean » – AE GB JCB
**Meals** (1st floor) 250 b.i. and a la carte 220/370. L 18

**L'Oulette,** 15 pl. Lachambeaudie (12th) 01 40 02 02 12, *Fax 01 40 02 04 77*, – AE GB N 20
*closed Saturday lunch and Sunday* – **Meals** 165/245 b.i. and a la carte approx. 340.

**Au Trou Gascon,** 40 r. Taine (12th) 01 43 44 34 26, *Fax 01 43 07 80 55* – AE GB JCB M 21
*closed August, Christmas-New Year, Saturday lunch and Sunday* – **Meals** (booking essential) 190 (lunch)/285 and a la carte 290/410
**Spec.** Chipirons sautés façon pibale (June-September). Petit pâté chaud de cèpes au jus de persil (season). Volaille de Chalosse rôtie, jus clair.

**Frégate,** 30 av. Ledru-Rollin (12th) 01 43 43 90 32 – AE GB L 18
*closed Saturday and Sunday* – **Meals** - Seafood - 160/220 and a la carte 280/410.

**Gourmandise,** 271 av. Daumesnil (12th) 01 43 43 94 41, *Fax 01 43 43 94 41* – AE GB
*closed 1 to 10 May, 3 to 23 August, Monday dinner and Sunday* – **Meals** 165/199 b.i. and a la carte 250/370. M 22

**Petit Marguery,** 9 bd Port-Royal (13th) 01 43 31 58 59, bistro – AE GB M 15
*closed August, 23 December-2 January, Sunday and Monday* – **Meals** 165 (lunch), 210/270.

**Traversière,** 40 r. Traversière (12th) 01 43 44 02 10, *Fax 01 43 44 64 20* – AE GB JCB K 18
*closed August, dinner Sunday and Monday* – **Meals** 130/170 and a la carte 260/360.

**Les Marronniers,** 53 bis bd Arago (13th) 01 47 07 58 57, *Fax 01 43 36 85 20* – AE GB JCB N 14
*closed August, 1 to 8 March and Sunday* – **Meals** 230/300 and a la carte 180/290.

**Bistrot de la Porte Dorée,** 5 bd Soult (12th) 01 43 43 80 07, *Fax 01 43 42 32 66* – GB N 22
**Meals** 185 b.i.

**Jean-Pierre Frelet,** 25 r. Montgallet (12th) 01 43 43 76 65 – GB L 20
*closed late July-late August, Saturday lunch and Sunday* – **Meals** 140 and a la carte 200/250.

**Quincy,** 28 av. Ledru-Rollin (12th) 01 46 28 46 76, bistro – L 17
*closed 8 August-10 September, Saturday, Sunday and Monday* – **Meals** a la carte 220/370.

**Aub. Etchégorry,** 41 r. Croulebarbe (13th) 01 44 08 83 51, *Fax 01 44 08 83 69*, bistro – AE GB JCB N 15
*closed Sunday* – **Meals** 145/220 b.i. and a la carte 210/380.

**Chez Jacky,** 109 r. du Dessous-des-Berges (13th) 01 45 83 71 55, *Fax 01 45 86 57 73* – GB P 18
*closed August, Saturday and Sunday* – **Meals** 188 and a la carte 230/390.

**L'Escapade en Touraine,** 24 r. Traversière (12th) ✆ 01 43 43 14 96 – GB L 18
*closed August, Saturday, Sunday and Bank Holidays* – **Meals** 110/140 and a la carte 140/250.

**Anacréon,** 53 bd St-Marcel (13th) ✆ 01 43 31 71 18, *Fax 01 43 31 94 94* – ▤. AE ⓓ GB. ✻ M 16
*closed August, 20 February-2 March, Sunday and Monday* – **Meals** 120/180.

**L'Avant Goût,** 26 r. Bobillot (13th) ✆ 01 53 80 24 00, bistro – GB P 15
*closed 2 to 24 August, 3 to 8 January, Sunday and Monday* – **Meals** (booking essential) 135.

**Temps des Cerises,** 216 r. Fg St-Antoine (12th) ✆ 01 43 67 52 08, *Fax 01 43 67 60 91* – ▤. AE GB JCB K 20
*closed 10 to 24 August and Monday* – **Meals** 97/230 ♁.

**A la Biche au Bois,** 45 av. Ledru-Rollin (12th) ✆ 01 43 43 34 38 – AE ⓓ GB K 18
*closed Saturday and Sunday* – **Meals** 105/125 and a la carte 110/220.

**St-Amarante,** 4 r. Biscornet (12th) ✆ 01 43 43 00 08, bistro – GB K 18
*closed 14 July-15 August, Saturday and Sunday* – **Meals** (booking essential) a la carte approx. 180.

**Chez Françoise,** 12 r. Butte aux Cailles (13th) ✆ 01 45 80 12 02, *Fax 01 45 65 13 67*, bistro – AE ⓓ GB JCB. ✻ P 15
*closed 31 July-27 August, 25 December-1 January and Sunday* – **Meals** 69/146 and a la carte 160/250.

**Sipario,** 69 r. Charenton (12th) ✆ 01 43 45 70 26 – AE ⓓ GB JCB K 18
*closed 10 to 17 August, Saturday lunch and Sunday* – **Meals** - Italian rest. - 70 (lunch), 95/250 and a la carte 160/250.

**Rhône,** 40 bd Arago (13th) ✆ 01 47 07 33 57, ☂ – GB N 14
*closed August, Saturday, Sunday and Bank Holidays* – **Meals** 75/165 and a la carte 180/210.

**Chez Paul,** 22 r. Butte aux Cailles (13th) ✆ 01 45 89 22 11, bistro – GB. ✻ P 15
**Meals** a la carte 170/260.

**Michel,** 20 r. Providence (13th) ✆ 01 45 89 99 27, *Fax 01 45 89 99 27* – GB P 15
*closed 2 to 16 August and Sunday* – **Meals** 120/190 and a la carte 190/320 ♁.

**Les Zygomates,** 7 r. Capri (12th) ✆ 01 40 19 93 04, *Fax 01 44 73 46 63*, bistro – GB. ✻
*closed 24 December-3 January, Saturday lunch and Sunday* – **Meals** 75 (lunch)/130 and a la carte 160/210. N 21

## Vaugirard, Gare Montparnasse, Grenelle, Denfert-Rochereau.

*14th and 15th arrondissements.*
*14th: ✉ 75014*
*15th: ✉ 75015*

**Hilton,** 18 av. Suffren (15th) ✆ 01 44 38 56 00, *Fax 01 44 38 56 10*, ☂ – |≑|, ⇔ rm, ▤ TV ☎ ♿ ⇔ – 🏃 400. AE ⓓ GB JCB J 7
***La Terrasse*** : **Meals** 144 (lunch), 167/179 – ☐ 120 – **453 rm** 1650/2250, 9 suites.

**Nikko** Ⓜ, 61 quai Grenelle (15th) ✆ 01 40 58 20 00, *Fax 01 40 58 24 44*, ≤, Ꮃ, ▣ – |≑|, ⇔ rm, ▤ TV ☎ ♿ ⇔ – 🏃 600. AE ⓓ GB JCB K 6
see ***Les Célébrités*** below - ***Brasserie Pont Mirabeau*** : **Meals** 170 – ***Benkay*** Japanese rest. **Meals** 135 (lunch), 340/750 – ☐ 110 – **755 rm** 1900/2500, 9 suites.

**Sofitel Forum Rive Gauche** Ⓜ, 17 bd St-Jacques (14th) ✆ 01 40 78 79 80, *Fax 01 45 88 43 93*, Convention centre, Ꮃ – |≑|, ⇔ rm, ▤ TV ☎ ♿ ⇔ – 🏃 25 - 1 200. AE ⓓ GB JCB N 13-14
***Le Café Français*** (lunch only) *(closed 25 July-24 August, Saturday and Sunday)* **Meals** 169 – ***La Table et la Forme*** (low-calorie menu) *(closed 18 July-17 August)* **Meals** 175 ♁ – ***Patio*** (lunch only) **Meals** 135 – ☐ 110 – **772 rm** 1250/1500, 13 suites.

**Sofitel Porte de Sèvres** Ⓜ, 8 r. L. Armand (15th) ✆ 01 40 60 30 30, *Fax 01 45 57 04 22*, ≤, Ꮃ, ▣ – |≑|, ⇔ rm, ▤ TV ☎ ♿ ⇔ – 🏃 450. AE ⓓ GB JCB. ✻ rest N 5
***Relais de Sèvres*** ✆ 01 40 60 33 66 *(closed August, 24 December- 1 January, Saturday, Sunday and Bank Holidays)* **Meals** 385 b.i. and a la carte 290/410 – ***La Tonnelle*** : **Meals** 140 and a la carte approx. 210 – ☐ 115 – **524 rm** 1500/2200, 14 suites.

**Méridien Montparnasse,** 19 r. Cdt Mouchotte (14th) ✆ 01 44 36 44 36, *Fax 01 44 36 49 00*, <, – |♦|, ⇹ rm, ≡ TV ☎ ♿ – 🏛 25 - 1 000. AE ◑ GB JCB M 11
see ***Montparnasse 25*** below - ***Justine*** ✆ 01 44 36 44 00 **Meals** 198 and a la carte 200/320 – ☕ 115 – **918 rm** 1875/2075, 35 suites.

**Novotel Porte d'Orléans** M, 15-19 bd R. Rolland (14th) ✆ 01 41 17 26 00, *Fax 01 41 17 26 26* – |♦|, ⇹ rm, ≡ TV ☎ ♿ – 🏛 100. AE ◑ GB S 12
Meals 132 – ☕ 67 – **150 rm** 720/780.

**Novotel Vaugirard** M, 253 r. Vaugirard (15th) ✆ 01 40 45 10 00, *Fax 01 40 45 10 10*, – |♦|, ⇹ rm, ≡ TV ☎ ♿ – 🏛 300. AE ◑ GB JCB M 9
***Transatlantique*** : Meals 170 – ☕ 75 – **184 rm** 820/880, 3 suites.

**Mercure Montparnasse** M, 20 r. Gaîté (14th) ✆ 01 43 35 28 28, *Fax 01 43 27 98 64* – |♦|, ⇹ rm, ≡ rest, TV ☎ ♿ – 🏛 50. AE ◑ GB JCB M 11
***Bistrot de la Gaîté*** ✆ 01 43 22 86 46 **Meals** 135b.i/175b.i – ☕ 75 – **181 rm** 1080, 4 suites.

**L'Aiglon** without rest, 232 bd Raspail (14th) ✆ 01 43 20 82 42, *Fax 01 43 20 98 72* – |♦| ≡ TV ☎. AE ◑ GB JCB M 12
☕ 40 – **38 rm** 610/740, 9 suites.

**Mercure Porte de Versailles** M, 69 bd Victor (15th) ✆ 01 44 19 03 03, *Fax 01 48 28 22 11* – |♦|, ⇹ rm, ≡ TV ☎ ♿ – 🏛 250. AE ◑ GB N 7
Meals 105/160 – ☕ 72 – **91 rm** 1162/1240.

**Mercure Tour Eiffel** M without rest, 64 bd Grenelle (15th) ✆ 01 45 78 90 90, *Fax 01 45 78 95 55* – |♦|, ⇹ rm, ≡ TV ☎ ♿ – 🏛 25. AE ◑ GB JCB K 7
☕ 70 – **64 rm** 1200.

**Raspail Montparnasse** without rest, 203 bd Raspail (14th) ✆ 01 43 20 62 86, *Fax 01 43 20 50 79* – |♦| ≡ TV ☎. AE ◑ GB JCB. ✻ M 12
☕ 50 – **38 rm** 520/1160.

**Lenox Montparnasse** without rest, 15 r. Delambre (14th) ✆ 01 43 35 34 50, *Fax 01 43 20 46 64* – |♦| TV ☎. AE ◑ GB JCB M 12
☕ 45 – **46 rm** 540/650, 6 suites.

**Delambre** M without rest, 35 r. Delambre (14th) ✆ 01 43 20 66 31, *Fax 01 45 38 91 76* – |♦| TV ☎ ♿. AE GB M 12
☕ 38 – **30 rm** 440/490.

**Apollinaire** without rest, 39 r. Delambre (14th) ✆ 01 43 35 18 40, *Fax 01 43 35 30 71* – |♦| TV ☎. AE ◑ GB JCB M 12
☕ 45 – **36 rm** 500/700.

**Tour Eiffel Dupleix** M without rest, 11 r. Juge (15th) ✆ 01 45 78 29 29, *Fax 01 45 78 60 00* – |♦|, ⇹ rm, TV ☎. AE ◑ GB JCB K 7
☕ 43 – **40 rm** 480/670.

**Mercure Paris XV** M without rest, 6 r. St-Lambert (15th) ✆ 01 45 58 61 00, *Fax 01 45 54 10 43* – |♦|, ⇹ rm, ≡ rm, TV ☎ ♿ – 🏛 30. AE ◑ GB JCB M 7
☕ 55 – **56 rm** 870.

**Daguerre** M without rest, 94 r. Daguerre (14th) ✆ 01 43 22 43 54, *Fax 01 43 20 66 84* – |♦| TV ☎ ♿. AE ◑ GB JCB. ✻ N 11
☕ 40 – **30 rm** 400/600.

**Lilas Blanc** M without rest, 5 r. Avre (15th) ✆ 01 45 75 30 07, *Fax 01 45 78 66 65* – |♦|, ⇹ rm, TV ☎. AE ◑ GB K 8
☕ 35 – **32 rm** 380/455.

**Ibis Brancion** M without rest, 105 r. Brancion (15th) ✆ 01 42 50 86 00, *Fax 01 42 50 99 63* – |♦|, ⇹ rm, TV ☎ ♿. AE ◑ GB P 8-9
☕ 39 – **71 rm** 410/430.

**Istria** without rest, 29 r. Campagne Première (14th) ✆ 01 43 20 91 82, *Fax 01 43 22 48 45* – |♦| TV ☎. AE ◑ GB JCB M 12
☕ 40 – **26 rm** 470/590.

**Apollon Montparnasse** without rest, 91 r. Ouest (14th) ✆ 01 43 95 62 00, *Fax 01 43 95 62 10* – |♦| TV ☎. AE ◑ GB JCB N 10-11
☕ 35 – **33 rm** 395/470.

**Ariane Montparnasse** without rest, 35 r. Sablière (14th) ✆ 01 45 45 67 13, *Fax 01 45 45 39 49* – |♦|, ⇹ rm, TV ☎. AE ◑ GB N 11
☕ 35 – **30 rm** 375/460.

**Carladez Cambronne** without rest, 3 pl. Gén. Beuret (15th) ✆ 01 47 34 07 12, *Fax 01 40 65 95 68* – |♦| TV ☎. AE ◑ GB M 9
☕ 36 – **27 rm** 385/435.

XXXX ✿ **Les Célébrités** - Hôtel Nikko, 61 quai Grenelle (15th) ✆ 01 40 58 20 00, *Fax 01 40 58 24 44*, ≤ - ▤. AE ① GB JCB K 6
*closed August* – **Meals** 290/390 and a la carte 400/670
**Spec.** Royale de crustacés et soupe de poissons crémeuse. Tronçon poêlé de gros turbot de Saint-Guénolé, girolles sautées. Ris de veau de lait braisé aux langoustines, mousserons des prés.

XXXX ✿ **Montparnasse 25** - Hôtel Méridien Montparnasse, 19 r. Cdt Mouchotte (14th) ✆ 01 44 36 44 25, *Fax 01 44 36 49 03* – ▤ P. AE ① GB JCB. ✂ M 11
*closed August, 21 to 27 December, Saturday and Sunday* – **Meals** 240 (lunch), 300/390 and a la carte 390/500
**Spec.** Tourte de pommes de terre, truffes fraîches au pied de porc et foie gras (January-March). Darne de bar au confit de coco, jus acidulé (September-December). Colvert légèrement laqué aux épices (September-December).

XXX **Morot Gaudry,** 6 r. Cavalerie (15th) (8th floor) ✆ 01 45 67 06 85, *Fax 01 45 67 55 72*, 余 - ⇅ ▤. AE ① GB K 8
*closed 8 to 23 August, Saturday and Sunday* – **Meals** 180 (lunch)/340 and a la carte 340/450.

XXX **Mille Colonnes,** 20 bis r. Gaîté (14th) ✆ 01 40 47 08 34, *Fax 01 40 64 37 49*, 余 – ▤. AE ① GB JCB M 11
*closed 26 July-23 August, 21 to 30 December, Saturday lunch and Sunday* – **Meals** 165.

XXX ✿ **Le Duc,** 243 bd Raspail (14th) ✆ 01 43 20 96 30, *Fax 01 43 20 46 73* – ▤. AE ① GB JCB M 12
*closed Saturday lunch, Sunday, Monday and Bank Holidays* – **Meals** - Seafood - 260 (lunch) and a la carte 350/450
**Spec.** Poissons crus. Aiguillettes de bar au citron vert. Queue de lotte aux branches de fenouil.

XXX **Pavillon Montsouris,** 20 r. Gazan (14th) ✆ 01 45 88 38 52, *Fax 01 45 88 63 40*, ≤, 余, « 1900 pavilion beside the park » – P. GB. ✂ R 14
**Meals** 198.

XXX **Moniage Guillaume,** 88 r. Tombe-Issoire (14th) ✆ 01 43 22 96 15, *Fax 01 43 27 11 79* – AE ① GB JCB P 12
*closed Sunday* – **Meals** 185/245 and a la carte 300/430.

XXX **Dôme,** 108 bd Montparnasse (14th) ✆ 01 43 35 25 81, *Fax 01 42 79 01 19*, brasserie – ▤. AE ① GB LM 12
**Meals** - Seafood - a la carte 280/460.

XXX **Chen,** 15 r. Théâtre (15th) ✆ 01 45 79 34 34, *Fax 01 45 79 07 53* – ▤. AE GB JCB K 6
*closed Sunday* – **Meals** - Chinese rest. - 190 b.i. (lunch), 250/450 and a la carte 260/380.

XX **Lous Landès,** 157 av. Maine (14th) ✆ 01 45 43 08 04, *Fax 01 45 45 91 35* – ▤. AE ① GB N 11
*closed August, Saturday lunch and Sunday* – **Meals** 195/320 and a la carte 270/410.

XX **Lal Qila,** 88 av. É. Zola (15th) ✆ 01 45 75 68 40, *Fax 01 45 79 68 61*, « Original decor » – ▤. AE GB L 7
**Meals** - Indian rest. - 55 (lunch), 125/250 and a la carte 150/250.

XX **Philippe Detourbe,** 8 r. Nicolas Charlet (15th) ✆ 01 42 19 08 59, *Fax 01 45 67 09 13* – ▤. GB L 10
*closed August, Saturday lunch and Sunday* – **Meals** 180 (lunch)/220.

XX **Yves Quintard,** 99 r. Blomet (15th) ✆ 01 42 50 22 27, *Fax 01 42 50 22 27* – ▤. GB M 8
*closed 15 August-1 September, Saturday lunch and Sunday* – **Meals** 135 (lunch), 185/235.

XX **La Dînée,** 85 r. Leblanc (15th) ✆ 01 45 54 20 49, *Fax 01 40 60 73 76* – AE GB M 5
*closed 2 to 23 August, Saturday lunch and Sunday* – **Meals** 210/450 and a la carte 250/410.

XX **Coupole,** 102 bd Montparnasse (14th) ✆ 01 43 20 14 20, *Fax 01 43 35 46 14*, « 1920 Parisian brasserie » – ▤. AE ① GB L 12
**Meals** 169 b.i. and a la carte 160/300.

XX **Caroubier,** 122 av. Maine (14th) ✆ 01 43 20 41 49 – ▤. GB N 11
*closed 26 July-17 August* – **Meals** - North African rest. - 140 and a la carte 150/180.

XX **Erawan,** 76 r. Fédération (15th) ✆ 01 47 83 55 67, *Fax 01 47 34 85 98* – ▤. AE GB. ✂ K 8
*closed August and Sunday* – **Meals** Thaï rest. a la carte 170/250.

XX **Aux Senteurs de Provence,** 295 r. Lecourbe (15th) ✆ 01 45 57 11 98, *Fax 01 45 58 66 84* – AE ① GB JCB M 6
*closed 10 to 23 August, Saturday lunch and Sunday* – **Meals** - Seafood - 148 and a la carte 190/280.

XX **L'Etape,** 89 r. Convention (15th) ☏ 01 45 54 73 49, *Fax 01 45 58 20 91* – ▤. GB M 6
*closed 15 to 25 August, Saturday lunch and Sunday* – **Meals** 160/230 and a la carte 180/250.

XX **Petite Bretonnière,** 2 r. Cadix (15th) ☏ 01 48 28 34 39, *Fax 01 48 28 20 90* – AE ⓓ GB JCB N 7
*closed 2 to 24 August, Saturday lunch and Sunday* – **Meals** 150/220.

XX **Gauloise,** 59 av. La Motte-Picquet (15 th) ☏ 01 47 34 11 64, *Fax 01 40 61 09 70,* 🏠 – AE GB K 8
**Meals** 155 and a la carte 180/330.

X **Chaumière,** 54 av. F. Faure (15th) ☏ 01 45 54 13 91, *Fax 01 45 54 41 96* – AE ⓓ GB
**Meals** a la carte 200/250. M 7

X **de la Tour,** 6 r. Desaix (15th) ☏ 01 43 06 04 24 – GB J 8
*closed Saturday lunch and Sunday* – **Meals** 138 (lunch), 185/230 and a la carte 220/330.

X **Fontana Rosa,** 28 bd Garibaldi (15th) ☏ 01 45 66 97 84 – AE GB L 9
**Meals** - Italian rest. - 120 and a la carte 200/290.

X **L'Épopée,** 89 av. É. Zola (15th) ☏ 01 45 77 71 37 – AE GB JCB L 7
*closed August, Saturday lunch and Sunday* – **Meals** 185.

X **Bistrot du Dôme,** 1 r. Delambre (14th) ☏ 01 43 35 32 00, *Fax 01 48 04 00 59* – ▤. AE GB M 12
**Meals** - Seafood - a la carte 170/280.

X **Petit Plat,** 49 av. É. Zola (15th) ☏ 01 45 78 24 20, *Fax 01 45 78 23 13* – ▤. GB L 6
*closed 1 to 17 August, Christmas-New Year, Sunday and Monday* – **Meals** 140 and a la carte 180/290.

X **Gastroquet,** 10 r. Desnouettes (15th) ☏ 01 48 28 60 91, *Fax 01 45 33 23 70* – AE GB N 7
*closed August, Saturday and Sunday* – **Meals** 155 and a la carte 200/250.

X **Les Cévennes,** 55 r. Cévennes (15th) ☏ 01 45 54 33 76, *Fax 01 44 26 46 95* – AE GB L 6
*closed 1 to 20 August, Saturday lunch and Sunday* – **Meals** 165/350 and a la carte approx. 240.

X **Contre-Allée,** 83 av. Denfert-Rochereau (14th) ☏ 01 43 54 99 86, *Fax 01 43 25 05 28* – AE GB N 13
*closed Sunday* – **Meals** 200 b.i.

X **L'Armoise,** 67 r. Entrepreneurs (15th) ☏ 01 45 79 03 31, *Fax 01 45 79 44 69* – ▤. GB L 7
*closed 1 to 19 August, Saturday lunch and Sunday* – **Meals** 138.

X **Chez Pierre,** 117 r. Vaugirard (15th) ☏ 01 47 34 96 12, *Fax 01 47 34 96 12,* bistro – ▤. AE GB L 11
*closed 1 to 25 August, Saturday except dinner from October-March, Sunday and Bank Holidays* – **Meals** 140/165 and a la carte 180/250.

X **Père Claude,** 51 av. La Motte-Picquet (15th) ☏ 01 47 34 03 05, *Fax 01 40 56 97 84* – AE GB K 8
**Meals** 110/165 and a la carte 210/440.

X **Château Poivre,** 145 r. Château (14th) ☏ 01 43 22 03 68 – AE GB N 11
*closed 9 to 23 August, 23 December-3 January and Sunday* – **Meals** 89 and a la carte 140/270.

X **Les P'tits Bouchons de François Clerc,** 32 bd Montparnasse (15th) ☏ 01 45 48 52 03, *Fax 01 45 48 52 17,* bistrot – AE GB L 11
*closed Saturday lunch and Sunday* – **Meals** 169.

X **Quercy,** 5 r. Mouton-Duvernet (14th) ☏ 01 45 39 39 61, *Fax 01 45 39 39 61* – GB N 12
*closed August, Sunday dinner and Monday* – **Meals** 149.

X **Régalade,** 49 av. J. Moulin (14th) ☏ 01 45 45 68 58, *Fax 01 45 40 96 74,* bistro – ▤. GB R 11
*closed August, Sunday and Monday* – **Meals** (booking essential) 170.

X **L'Os à Moelle,** 3 r. Vasco de Gama (15th) ☏ 01 45 57 27 27, *Fax 01 45 57 27 27,* bistro – AE GB. ✗ M 6
*closed 25 July-25 August, Sunday and Monday* – **Meals** 145/190.

X **L'Agape,** 281 r. Lecourbe (15th) ☏ 01 45 58 19 29 – GB. ✗ M 7
*closed August, Saturday lunch and Sunday* – **Meals** 120.

X **Les Gourmands,** 101 r. Ouest (14th) ☏ 01 45 41 40 70 – AE GB N 10
*closed August, Sunday and Monday* – **Meals** 143.

X **St-Vincent,** 26 r. Croix-Nivert (15th) ☏ 01 47 34 14 94, *Fax 01 45 66 02 80,* bistro – ▤. AE GB. ✗ L 8
*closed 10 to 16 August, Saturday lunch and Sunday* – **Meals** 165 b.i. and a la carte 150/240.

X **Petit Mâchon,** 123 r. Convention (15th) ✆ 01 45 54 08 62, bistro – GB. ✻ N 7
*closed 1 to 25 August and Sunday* – **Meals** 85 (lunch), 135/200 and a la carte 170/270.

X **Les Coteaux,** 26 bd Garibaldi (15th) ✆ 01 47 34 83 48, bistro – GB L 9
*closed August, Monday dinner, Saturday and Sunday* – **Meals** 130.

X **L'Amuse Bouche,** 186 r. Château (14th) ✆ 01 43 35 31 61 – GB N 11
*closed 3 to 23 August, Saturday lunch and Sunday* – **Meals** (booking essential) 168.

# Passy, Auteuil, Bois de Boulogne, Chaillot, Porte Maillot.

*16th arrondissement.*
*16th: ✉ 75016*

**Parc** M, 55 av. R. Poincaré ✉ 75116 ✆ 01 44 05 66 66, *Fax 01 44 05 66 00*, « Fine English furniture » – rm, – 30 - 250. AE GB JCB. G 6
see ***Alain Ducasse*** below - ***Relais du Parc*** ✆ 01 44 05 66 10 **Meals** 220/600 – 140 – **116 rm** 1990/2650, 3 duplex.

**Raphaël,** 17 av. Kléber ✉ 75116 ✆ 01 44 28 00 28, *Fax 01 45 01 21 50*, « Elegant period decor, fine furniture » – rm, – 50. AE GB JCB F 7
***La Salle à Manger*** *(closed August, Saturday and Sunday)* **Meals** 298/450 and a la carte 300/440 – 165 – **75 rm** 1950/2350, 25 suites.

**St-James Paris**, 43 av. Bugeaud ✉ 75116 ✆ 01 44 05 81 81, *Fax 01 44 05 81 82*, « Attractive 19C mansion », – 25. AE GB JCB F 5
**Meals** *(closed weekends and Bank Holidays)* (residents only) 250 and a la carte 310/410 – 110 – **20 rm** 1900/2150, 20 suites2650/3800, 8 duplex 2400.

**Baltimore** M, 88bis av. Kléber ✉ 75116 ✆ 01 44 34 54 54, *Fax 01 44 34 54 44*, « Attractive decor » – rm, – 30 - 100. AE GB JCB G 7
***Bertie's*** ✆ 01 44 34 54 34 - English rest. *(closed 1 to 15 August)* **Meals** 220 and a la carte 220/400 – 140 – **105 rm** 1990/3500.

**K. Palace** M without rest, 81 av. Kléber ✉ 75116 ✆ 01 44 05 75 75, *Fax 01 44 05 74 74*, « Contemporary decor », – rm, – 40. AE GB JCB G 7
115 – **83 rm** 1790/2690.

**Villa Maillot** M without rest, 143 av. Malakoff ✉ 75116 ✆ 01 53 64 52 52, *Fax 01 45 00 60 61* – – 25. AE GB JCB F 6
110 – **39 rm** 1580/1800, 3 suites.

**Square** M, 3 r. Boulainvilliers ✉ 75016 ✆ 01 44 14 91 90, *Fax 01 44 14 91 99*, « Contemporary decor » – rm, . AE GB JCB. ✻ rm K 5
**Meals** see ***Zébra Square*** below – 90 – **22 rm** 1350/2500.

**Pergolèse** M without rest, 3 r. Pergolèse ✉ 75116 ✆ 01 40 67 96 77, *Fax 01 45 00 12 11*, « Contemporary decor » – rm, . AE GB JCB E 6
80 – **40 rm** 950/1700.

**Majestic** without rest, 29 r. Dumont d'Urville ✉ 75116 ✆ 01 45 00 83 70, *Fax 01 45 00 29 48* – rm, . AE GB JCB F 7
70 – **27 rm** 1200/1500, 3 suites.

**Élysées Régencia** M without rest, 41 av. Marceau ✉ 75016 ✆ 01 47 20 42 65, *Fax 01 49 52 03 42*, « Attractive decor » – rm, . AE GB JCB. ✻
115 – **41 rm** 1260/1860. G 8

**Garden Élysée** M without rest, 12 r. St-Didier ✉ 75116 ✆ 01 47 55 01 11, *Fax 01 47 27 79 24* – . AE GB JCB. ✻ G 7
85 – **48 rm** 1100/1600.

**Alexander** without rest, 102 av. V. Hugo ✉ 75116 ✆ 01 45 53 64 65, *Fax 01 45 53 12 51* – . AE GB JCB. ✻ G 6
85 – **62 rm** 840/1600.

**Rond-Point de Longchamp** without rest, 86 r. Longchamp ✉ 75116 ☎ 01 45 05 13 63, *Fax 01 47 55 12 80* – |‡|, ⇆ rm, ▤ TV ☎ – 50. AE ⓓ GB G 6
☕ 70 – **57 rm** 1006/2012.

**Élysées Sablons** M without rest, 32 r. Greuze ✉ 75116 ☎ 01 47 27 10 00, *Fax 01 47 27 47 10* – |‡|, ⇆ rm, TV ☎ ♿. AE ⓓ GB JCB G 6
☕ 75 – **41 rm** 910/1125.

**Frémiet** without rest, 6 av. Frémiet ✉ 75016 ☎ 01 45 24 52 06, *Fax 01 42 88 77 46* – |‡|, ⇆ rm, ▤ TV ☎. AE ⓓ GB JCB J 6
☕ 50 – **34 rm** 697/990.

**Élysées Bassano** without rest, 24 r. Bassano ✉ 75116 ☎ 01 47 20 49 03, *Fax 01 47 23 06 72* – |‡|, ⇆ rm, TV ☎. AE ⓓ GB JCB G 8
☕ 75 – **40 rm** 920/1270.

**Union H. Étoile** without rest, 44 r. Hamelin ✉ 75116 ☎ 01 45 53 14 95, *Fax 01 47 55 94 79* – |‡| kitchenette TV ☎. AE ⓓ GB JCB G 7
☕ 42 – **29 rm** 715/830, 13 suites.

**Résidence Impériale** M without rest, 155 av. Malakoff ✉ 75116 ☎ 01 45 00 23 45, *Fax 01 45 01 88 82* – |‡|, ⇆ rm, ▤ TV ☎. AE ⓓ GB E 6
☕ 55 – **37 rm** 740/850.

**Les Jardins du Trocadéro** M without rest, 35 r. Franklin ✉ 75116 ☎ 01 53 70 17 70, *Fax 01 53 70 17 80* – |‡|, ⇆ rm, ▤ TV ☎. AE ⓓ GB JCB. ✗ H 6
☕ 75 – **18 rm** 1350/1550.

**Floride Étoile** without rest, 14 r. St-Didier ✉ 75116 ☎ 01 47 27 23 36, *Fax 01 47 27 82 87* – |‡| TV ☎ – 40. AE ⓓ GB JCB. ✗ G 7
☕ 45 – **60 rm** 850/950.

**Kléber** without rest, 7 r. Belloy ✉ 75116 ☎ 01 47 23 80 22, *Fax 01 49 52 07 20* – |‡|, ⇆ rm, TV ☎. AE ⓓ GB JCB G 7
☕ 60 – **23 rm** 790/890.

**Victor Hugo** without rest, 19 r. Copernic ✉ 75116 ☎ 01 45 53 76 01, *Fax 01 45 53 69 93* – |‡| ▤ TV ☎. AE ⓓ GB JCB. ✗ G 7
☕ 65 – **75 rm** 740/890.

**Sévigné** without rest, 6 r. Belloy ✉ 75116 ☎ 01 47 20 88 90, *Fax 01 40 70 98 73* – |‡| TV ☎. AE ⓓ GB JCB G 7
☕ 50 – **30 rm** 650/750.

**Résidence Chambellan Morgane** without rest, 6 r. Keppler ✉ 75116 ☎ 01 47 20 35 72, *Fax 01 47 20 95 69* – |‡| TV ☎. AE ⓓ GB JCB GF 8
☕ 50 – **20 rm** 650/900.

**Holiday Inn Garden Court** M without rest, 21 r. Gudin ✉ 75016 ☎ 01 46 51 99 22, *Fax 01 46 51 07 24* – |‡|, ⇆ rm, ▤ TV ☎. AE ⓓ GB JCB M 3
☕ 65 – **47 rm** 980.

**Étoile Maillot** without rest, 10 r. Bois de Boulogne (angle r. Duret) ✉ 75116 ☎ 01 45 00 42 60, *Fax 01 45 00 55 89* – |‡| TV ☎. AE ⓓ GB F 6
☕ 45 – **28 rm** 570/750.

**Royal Élysées** without rest, 6 av. V. Hugo ✉ 75116 ☎ 01 45 00 05 57, *Fax 01 45 00 13 88* – |‡| ▤ TV ☎. AE ⓓ GB JCB F 7
☕ 50 – **35 rm** 1107/1214.

**Passy Eiffel** without rest, 10 r. Passy ✉ 75016 ☎ 01 45 25 55 66, *Fax 01 42 88 89 88* – |‡| ▤ TV ☎. AE ⓓ GB JCB J 6
☕ 40 – **48 rm** 580/850.

**Murat** without rest, 119 bis bd Murat ✉ 75016 ☎ 01 46 51 12 32, *Fax 01 46 51 70 01* – |‡| TV ☎. AE ⓓ GB. ✗ M 3
☕ 45 – **28 rm** 600/700.

**Hameau de Passy** M ⛰ without rest, 48 r. Passy ✉ 75016 ☎ 01 42 88 47 55, *Fax 01 42 30 83 72* – TV ☎. AE ⓓ GB JCB J 5-6
☕ 30 – **32 rm** 510/550.

**Palais de Chaillot** M without rest, 35 av. R. Poincaré ✉ 75016 ☎ 01 53 70 09 09, *Fax 01 53 70 09 08* – |‡| TV ☎. AE ⓓ GB JCB. ✗ G 6
☕ 39 – **28 rm** 460/590.

**Eiffel Kennedy** without rest, 12 r. Boulainvilliers ✉ 75016 ☎ 01 45 24 45 75, *Fax 01 42 30 83 32* – |‡|, ⇆ rm, ▤ TV ☎. AE ⓓ GB JCB K 5
☕ 45 – **30 rm** 480/700.

**Nicolo** without rest, 3 r. Nicolo ✉ 75116 ☎ 01 42 88 83 40, *Fax 01 42 24 45 41* – |‡| TV ☎. AE GB JCB J 6
☕ 35 – **28 rm** 380/450.

XXXX ✿✿✿ **Alain Ducasse,** 59 av. R. Poincaré ✉ 75116 ✆ 01 47 27 12 27, *Fax 01 47 27 31 22*, « Elegant mansion with Art Nouveau decor » – ▤. AE ⓓ GB JCB. ✻ G 6
*closed 17 July-17 August, 24 December-4 January, Saturday, Sunday and Bank Holidays* – **Meals** 480 (lunch)/920 and a la carte 760/1 100
**Spec.** Pâtes mi-séchées crémées et truffées au ris de veau, crêtes et rognons de coq. Lard paysan croustillant aux pommes de terre caramélisées, tête de porc en salade d'herbes amères truffée. Coupe glacée de saison.

XXXX ✿✿ **Faugeron,** 52 r. Longchamp ✉ 75116 ✆ 01 47 04 24 53, *Fax 01 47 55 62 90*, « Attractive decor » – ▤. AE GB JCB. ✻ G 7
*closed August, 23 December-3 January, Saturday except dinner from September-April and Sunday* – **Meals** 320 (lunch), 470/550 b.i. and a la carte 490/600
**Spec.** Oeufs coque à la purée de truffes. Truffes (January-March). Gibier (15 October-10 January).

XXXX ✿ **Prunier-Traktir,** 16 av. V. Hugo ✉ 75116 ✆ 01 44 17 35 85, *Fax 01 44 17 90 10*, « Art Deco decor » – ▤. AE ⓓ GB JCB FG 8
*closed 19 July-17 August, Monday lunch and Sunday* – **Meals** - Seafood - a la carte 420/670
**Spec.** Soupe crémeuse de homard aux haricots blancs et chorizo. Gros filets de sole cuits au beurre demi-sel et aux herbes fraîches. Petits pots de crème Emile Prunier.

XXXX ✿✿ **Vivarois** (Peyrot), 192 av. V. Hugo ✉ 75116 ✆ 01 45 04 04 31, *Fax 01 45 03 09 84* – ▤. AE ⓓ GB JCB G 5
*closed August, Saturday and Sunday* – **Meals** 345 (lunch) and a la carte 430/700
**Spec.** Terrine de ris de veau, pied de veau, queue de boeuf et lentilles. Turbot viennoise. Gâteau de pommes au miel et à l'orange (season).

XXX ✿ **Relais d'Auteuil** (Pignol), 31 bd Murat ✉ 75016 ✆ 01 46 51 09 54, *Fax 01 40 71 05 03* – ▤. AE GB L 3
*closed 3 to 28 August, Saturday lunch and Sunday* – **Meals** 250 (lunch), 440/540 and a la carte 390/560
**Spec.** Amandine de foie gras. Dos de bar au poivre. Madeleines au miel de bruyére, glace miel et noix.

XXX ✿✿ **Jamin** (Guichard), 32 r. Longchamp ✉ 75116 ✆ 01 45 53 00 07, *Fax 01 45 53 00 15* – ▤. AE ⓓ GB G 7
*closed 25 July-17 August, Saturday and Sunday* – **Meals** 280/375 and a la carte 300/420
**Spec.** Fantaisie d'araignée de mer (April-September). Fricassée de langoustines. Fine volaille fermière cuite à l'étouffée.

XXX **Tsé-Yang,** 25 av. Pierre 1er de Serbie ✉ 75016 ✆ 01 47 20 70 22, *Fax 01 49 52 03 68*, « Tasteful decor » – ▤. AE ⓓ GB JCB. ✻ G 8
**Meals** - Chinese rest. - 115 (lunch), 245/340 and a la carte 190/320.

XXX ✿ **Port Alma** (Canal), 10 av. New-York ✉ 75116 ✆ 01 47 23 75 11, *Fax 01 47 20 42 92* – ▤. AE ⓓ GB H 8
*closed August and Sunday* – **Meals** - Seafood - 200 and a la carte 290/440
**Spec.** Croustillant de langoustines. Bar en croûte de sel de Guérande. Rouget poêlé au vinaigre, trilogie de poivrons.

XXX **Pavillon Noura,** 21 av. Marceau ✉ 75116 ✆ 01 47 20 33 33, *Fax 01 47 20 60 31* – ▤. AE ⓓ GB. ✻ G 8
**Meals** - Lebanese rest. - 168 (lunch), 245/350 and a la carte 200/250.

XXX ✿ **Pergolèse** (Corre), 40 r. Pergolèse ✉ 75116 ✆ 01 45 00 21 40, *Fax 01 45 00 81 31* – AE GB F 6
*closed August, Saturday and Sunday* – **Meals** 230 and a la carte 310/440
**Spec.** Carpaccio de jambon d'agneau fumé. Saint-Jacques en robe des champs (winter). Moelleux au chocolat, glace vanille.

XXX **Chez Ngo,** 70 r. Longchamp ✉ 75116 ✆ 01 47 04 53 20, *Fax 01 47 04 53 20* – ▤. AE ⓓ GB JCB G 6
**Meals** - Chinese and Thai rest. - 98 b.i. (lunch)/168 b.i. and a la carte 110/230.

XX **Zébra Square,** 3 pl. Clément Ader ✉ 75016 ✆ 01 44 14 91 91, *Fax 01 45 20 46 41*, « Original contemporary decor » – AE ⓓ GB JCB K 5
**Meals** a la carte 210/280.

XX **Al Mounia,** 16 r. Magdebourg ✉ 75116 ✆ 01 47 27 57 28 – ▤. AE GB. ✻ G 7
*closed 10 July-31 August and Sunday* – **Meals** - Moroccan rest. - (dinner booking essential) a la carte 200/300.

XX ✿ **Conti,** 72 r. Lauriston ✉ 75116 ✆ 01 47 27 74 67, *Fax 01 47 27 37 66* – ▤. AE ⓓ GB G 7
*closed 3 to 24 August, 25 December-3 January, Saturday, Sunday and Bank Holidays* – **Meals** - Italian rest. - 198 (lunch) and a la carte 310/420
**Spec.** Tortellini au crabe (20 April-31 October). Cacciuco à la livournaise. Agneau de lait sauté aux poivrades et romarin (1 March-30 June).

XX **Giulio Rebellato,** 136 r. Pompe ✉ 75116 ✆ 01 47 27 50 26 – ▤. AE GB. ✻ G 6
*closed 26 July-16 August* – **Meals** - Italian rest. - a la carte 270/410.

XX **Tang,** 125 r. de la Tour ✉ 75116 ☎ 01 45 04 35 35, *Fax 01 45 04 58 19* – AE GB. ✻ H 5
*closed 11 to 15 July, August, Saturday lunch and Monday* – **Meals** - Chinese and Thai rest. - 200 and a la carte 250/360.

XX **Marius,** 82 bd Murat ✉ 75016 ☎ 01 46 51 67 80, *Fax 01 47 43 10 24,* ☂ – AE GB M 2
*closed 3 to 23 August, Saturday lunch and Sunday* – **Meals** a la carte 200/290.

XX **Villa Vinci,** 23 r. P. Valéry ✉ 75116 ☎ 01 45 01 68 18 – ▤. AE GB F 7
*closed August, Saturday and Sunday* – **Meals** - Italian rest. - 182 and a la carte 250/370.

XX **Paul Chêne,** 123 r. Lauriston ✉ 75116 ☎ 01 47 27 63 17, *Fax 01 47 27 53 18* – ▤. AE ⓓ GB G 6
*closed 3 to 23 August, 24 December-1 January, Saturday lunch and Sunday* – **Meals** 200/250 and a la carte 220/380.

XX **Fontaine d'Auteuil,** 35bis r. La Fontaine ✉ 75016 ☎ 01 42 88 04 47, *Fax 01 42 88 95 12* – ▤. AE ⓓ GB K 5
*closed 2 to 23 August, Saturday lunch and Sunday* – **Meals** 175 (lunch), 230/350 and a la carte 240/370.

XX **Chez Géraud,** 31 r. Vital ✉ 75016 ☎ 01 45 20 33 00, *Fax 01 45 20 46 60,* « Attractive Longwy porcelain mural » – AE GB H 5
*closed August, Sunday dinner and Saturday* – **Meals** 180 and a la carte 230/340.

XX **Detourbe Duret,** 23 r. Duret ✉ 75016 ☎ 01 45 00 10 26, *Fax 01 45 00 10 16* – ▤. GB F 6
**Meals** one menu only 180 (lunch)/220.

XX **Petite Tour,** 11 r. de la Tour ✉ 75116 ☎ 01 45 20 09 31 – AE ⓓ GB JCB H 6
*closed 1 to 25 August and Sunday except in June* – **Meals** a la carte 310/440.

XX **Bellini,** 28 r. Lesueur ✉ 75116 ☎ 01 45 00 54 20, *Fax 01 45 00 11 74* – ▤. AE GB F 7
*closed Saturday lunch and Sunday* – **Meals** - Italian rest. - 180 and a la carte 240/320.

X **Beaujolais d'Auteuil,** 99 bd Montmorency ✉ 75016 ☎ 01 47 43 03 56, *Fax 01 46 51 27 81,* bistro – ▤. GB K 3
*closed 10 to 16 August* – **Meals** 127 b.i./147 b.i. and a la carte 180/220.

X **Butte Chaillot,** 110 bis av. Kléber ✉ 75116 ☎ 01 47 27 88 88, *Fax 01 47 04 85 70* – ▤. AE GB JCB G 7
**Meals** 150/195 and a la carte 210/280.

X **Cuisinier François,** 19 r. Le Marois ✉ 75016 ☎ 01 45 27 83 74, *Fax 01 45 27 83 74* – AE GB M 3
*closed August, February Holidays, Wednesday dinner, Sunday dinner and Monday* – **Meals** 160 and a la carte 310/400 ♁.

X **Rosimar,** 26 r. Poussin ✉ 75016 ☎ 01 45 27 74 91, *Fax 01 45 20 75 05* – ▤. AE GB JCB K 3
*closed August, 21 to 27 December, Saturday lunch, Sunday and Bank Holidays* – **Meals** - Fish and Spanish specialities - 175 and a la carte 190/270.

X **Driver's,** 6 r. G. Bizet ✉ 75016 ☎ 01 47 23 61 15, *Fax 01 47 23 80 17,* « Racing car accessories » – ▤. AE GB G 8
*closed Saturday lunch and Sunday* – **Meals** a la carte 140/210 ♁.

X **Vin et Marée,** 2 r. Daumier ✉ 75016 ☎ 01 46 47 91 39, *Fax 01 46 47 69 07* – ▤. AE ⓓ GB JCB M 3
**Meals** - Seafood - a la carte 160/270.

X **Bistrot de l'Étoile,** 19 r. Lauriston ✉ 75016 ☎ 01 40 67 11 16, *Fax 01 45 00 99 87* – ▤. AE GB JCB F 7
*closed Saturday lunch and Sunday* – **Meals** 165 (lunch) and a la carte 200/250.

X **Scheffer,** 22 r. Scheffer ✉ 75016 ☎ 01 47 27 81 11, bistro – AE GB H 6
*closed Saturday, Sunday and Bank Holidays* – **Meals** a la carte 140/190.

**in the Bois de Boulogne :**

XXXX ✿ **Pré Catelan,** rte Suresnes ✉ 75016 ☎ 01 44 14 41 14, *Fax 01 45 24 43 25,* ☂, ⛱ – P. AE ⓓ GB JCB H 2
*closed February Holidays, Sunday dinner and Monday* – **Meals** 295 (lunch), 550/750 and a la carte 530/830
**Spec.** Choux-fleurs et artichauts à la grecque (April-September). Fricassée de grosses langoustines aux pommes de terre. Poire rôtie, petite gaufre caramélisée, crème glacée à la bergamote.

XXXX ✿ **Grande Cascade,** allée de Longchamp (opposite the hippodrome) ✉ 75016 ☎ 01 45 27 33 51, *Fax 01 42 88 99 06,* « Second Empire pavilion » – P. AE ⓓ GB H 12
*closed 20 December-20 January* – **Meals** 295/600 and a la carte 450/700
**Spec.** Macaroni aux germes de blé fourrés au foie gras et céleri, lamelles de truffes glacées au porto. Dos de Saint-Pierre clouté de citrons confits. Caneton de Challans aux épices, rôti à la broche, en aigre-doux.

# Clichy, Ternes, Wagram.

*17th arrondissement.*
*17th: ✉ 75017*

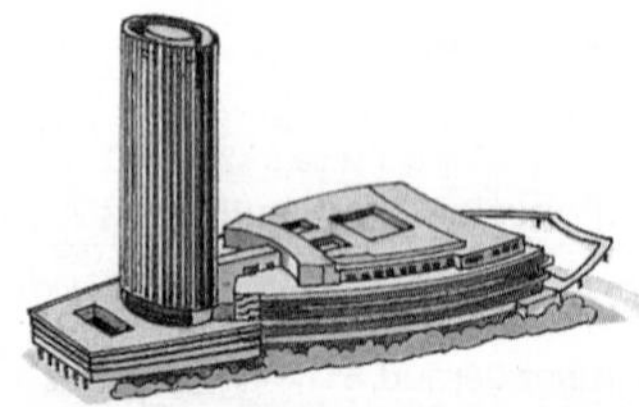

**Concorde La Fayette** M, 3 pl. Gén. Koenig ☎ 01 40 68 50 68, *Fax 01 40 68 50 43,* « Panoramic bar on 33rd floor with ≤ Paris » – |‡|, ⇆ rm, ▤ TV ☎ – 🏛 40 - 2 000. AE ⓓ GB JCB. ✂ rm E 6
see ***L'Étoile d'Or*** below - ***L'Arc-en-Ciel*** ☎ 01 40 68 51 25 *(closed August and 21 February-1 March)* **Meals** 194/225 – ***Les Saisons*** (coffee shop) ☎ 01 40 68 51 19 **Meals** 159 b.i. – ☕ 133 – **943 rm** 1750/2150, 27 suites.

**Meridien** M, 81 bd Gouvion St-Cyr ☎ 01 40 68 34 34, *Fax 01 40 68 31 31* – |‡|, ⇆ rm, ▤ rest, TV ☎ ♿ – 🏛 50 - 1 500. AE ⓓ GB JCB E 6
***Café Arlequin*** ☎ 01 40 68 30 85, **Meals** 165 – ***Le Yamato*** ☎ 01 40 68 30 41, Japanese rest. *(closed Aug., 4 to 10 January, Saturday lunch, Sunday, Monday and Bank Holidays)* **Meals** 160 (dinner) and a la carte 160/250 – ☕ 115 – **1 008 rm** 2000/2600, 17 suites.

**Splendid Étoile** without rest, 1bis av. Carnot ☎ 01 45 72 72 00, *Fax 01 45 72 72 01* – |‡| ▤ TV ☎. AE ⓓ GB. ✂ F 7
☕ 85 – **57 rm** 980/1300.

**Balmoral** without rest, 6 r. Gén. Lanrezac ☎ 01 43 80 30 50, *Fax 01 43 80 51 56* – |‡|, ⇆ rm, ▤ TV ☎. AE ⓓ GB E 7
☕ 40 – **57 rm** 550/800.

**Quality Inn Pierre** M without rest, 25 r. Th.-de-Banville ☎ 01 47 63 76 69, *Fax 01 43 80 63 96* – |‡|, ⇆ rm, TV ☎ ♿ – 🏛 30. AE ⓓ GB JCB D 8
☕ 70 – **50 rm** 720/1500.

**Regent's Garden** without rest, 6 r. P. Demours ☎ 01 45 74 07 30, *Fax 01 40 55 01 42,* « Garden » – |‡| ▤ TV ☎. AE ⓓ GB JCB. ✂ E 7
☕ 50 – **39 rm** 830/980.

**Ternes Arc de Triomphe** M without rest, 97 av. Ternes ☎ 01 53 81 94 94, *Fax 01 53 81 94 95* – |‡|, ⇆ rm, ▤ TV ☎ ♿. AE ⓓ GB JCB E 6
☕ 68 – **39 rm** 690/1120.

**Étoile St-Ferdinand** without rest, 36 r. St-Ferdinand ☎ 01 45 72 66 66, *Fax 01 45 74 12 92* – |‡| ▤ TV ☎. AE ⓓ GB JCB E 6-7
☕ 50 – **42 rm** 900/1100.

**Magellan** 🐚 without rest, 17 r. J.B.-Dumas ☎ 01 45 72 44 51, *Fax 01 40 68 90 36,* 🌳 – |‡| TV ☎. AE ⓓ GB. ✂ D 7
☕ 45 – **75 rm** 595/635.

**Champerret Elysées** M without rest, 129 av. Villiers ☎ 01 47 64 44 00, *Fax 01 47 63 10 58* – |‡|, ⇆ rm, ▤ TV ☎. AE ⓓ GB JCB D 7
☕ 60 – **45 rm** 515/665.

**Banville** without rest, 166 bd Berthier ☎ 01 42 67 70 16, *Fax 01 44 40 42 77* – |‡| ▤ TV ☎. AE ⓓ GB D 8
☕ 60 – **38 rm** 735/860.

**Mercure Étoile** M without rest, 27 av. Ternes ☎ 01 47 66 49 18, *Fax 01 47 63 77 91* – |‡|, ⇆ rm, ▤ TV ☎. AE ⓓ GB E 8
☕ 70 – **56 rm** 880.

**de Neuville** without rest, 3 r. Verniquet ☎ 01 43 80 26 30, *Fax 01 43 80 38 55* – |‡| TV ☎. AE ⓓ GB JCB C 8
☕ 55 – **28 rm** 750.

**Cheverny** without rest, 7 villa Berthier ✆ 01 43 80 46 42, *Fax 01 47 63 26 62* – 50. AE GB JCB. D 7
55 – **48 rm** 530/670.

**Neva** without rest, 14 r. Brey ✆ 01 43 80 28 26, *Fax 01 47 63 00 22* – rm, AE GB E 8
45 – **31 rm** 520/790.

**Mercédès** without rest, 128 av. Wagram ✆ 01 42 27 77 82, *Fax 01 40 53 09 89* – AE GB D 9
55 – **37 rm** 590/740.

**Étoile Park H.** without rest, 10 av. Mac Mahon ✆ 01 42 67 69 63, *Fax 01 43 80 18 99* – AE GB JCB E 8
*closed 24 December-1 January* – 52 – **28 rm** 450/650.

**Astrid** without rest, 27 av. Carnot ✆ 01 44 09 26 00, *Fax 01 44 09 26 01* – AE GB JCB E 7
50 – **40 rm** 470/750.

**Campanile,** 4 bd Berthier ✆ 01 46 27 10 00, *Fax 01 46 27 00 57,* – rm, – 40. AE GB B 10
**Meals** 92 b.i./119 b.i. – 36 – **247 rm** 416.

**Champerret-Héliopolis** without rest, 13 r. Héliopolis ✆ 01 47 64 92 56, *Fax 01 47 64 50 44* – AE GB D 7
38 – **22 rm** 350/495.

**Guy Savoy,** 18 r. Troyon ✆ 01 43 80 40 61, *Fax 01 46 22 43 09* – AE GB JCB
*closed 13 to 19 July, Saturday lunch and Sunday* – **Meals** 500/1000 and a la carte 570/770
**Spec.** Huîtres en nage glacée. Soupe d'artichauts à la truffe. Bar en écailles grillées aux épices douces. E 8

**Michel Rostang,** 20 r. Rennequin ✆ 01 47 63 40 77, *Fax 01 47 63 82 75,* « Elegant decor » – AE GB JCB D 8
*closed 1 to 16 August, Saturday lunch and Sunday* – **Meals** 325 (lunch), 595/795 and a la carte 640/880
**Spec.** Brochettes de langoustines au romarin, grappes de tomates farcies. Canette au sang en deux services. Carte des truffes (15 December-15 March).

**L'Étoile d'Or** - Hôtel Concorde La Fayette, 3 pl. Gén. Koenig ✆ 01 40 68 51 28, *Fax 01 40 68 50 43* – AE GB JCB E 6
*closed August, Saturday and Sunday* – **Meals** 270 and a la carte 330/580
**Spec.** Marinière de moules aux épices (April-September). Joue de bœuf aux choux en ravigote. Soufflé chaud au chocolat.

**Apicius** (Vigato), 122 av. Villiers ✆ 01 43 80 19 66, *Fax 01 44 40 09 57* – AE GB JCB D 8
*closed August, Saturday and Sunday* – **Meals** 450 (lunch), 550/750 and a la carte 380/560
**Spec.** Foie gras et canard rôti aux poivres noirs, orange et chocolat (winter-spring). Crème de cèpes et sabayon de truffes blanches (October-December). Blanc-manger au lait d'amandes.

**Amphyclès** (Groult), 78 av. Ternes ✆ 01 40 68 01 01, *Fax 01 40 68 91 88* – AE GB JCB E 7
*closed Saturday lunch and Sunday* – **Meals** 260 (lunch), 540/680 and a la carte 440/600
**Spec.** Délicat fondant frais d'artichauts à la crème d'oursins. Petits gris de garrigue, pignons de pin et basilic. Cocotte lutée de langoustes "puces" aux truffes et foie gras.

**Sormani** (Fayet), 4 r. Gén. Lanrezac ✆ 01 43 80 13 91, *Fax 01 40 55 07 37* – GB
*closed 13 to 17 April, 1 to 21 August, 23 December-2 January, Saturday, Sunday and Bank Holidays* – **Meals** - Italian rest. - 250 (lunch) and a la carte 330/400 E 7
**Spec.** Gratin de pommes de terre au parmesan, œufs et truffes blanches (1 October-15 December). Ravioli de canard aux navets (October-March). Chaud-Froid de macaroni farcis d'asperges et de foie gras à la crème de basilic (April-May).

**Faucher,** 123 av. Wagram ✆ 01 42 27 61 50, *Fax 01 46 22 25 72* – AE GB D 8
*closed Saturday lunch and Sunday* – **Meals** 390 and a la carte 240/440
**Spec.** Millefeuille de bœuf. Montgolfière de Saint-Jacques aux cèpes (1 October-31 March). Canette rôtie et ses filets laqués.

**Pétrus,** 12 pl. Mar. Juin ✆ 01 43 80 15 95, *Fax 01 43 80 06 96* – AE GB D 8
**Meals** - Seafood - 250 and a la carte 310/450.

**Timgad,** 21 r. Brunel ✆ 01 45 74 23 70, *Fax 01 40 68 76 46,* « Moorish decor » – AE GB. E 7
**Meals** - North African rest. - a la carte 250/380
**Spec.** Couscous princier. Pastilla. Tagine.

**Manoir Detourbe,** 6 r. P. Demours ✆ 01 45 72 25 25, *Fax 01 45 74 80 98* – GB E 7
*closed August, Saturday lunch and Sunday* – **Meals** 230 and a la carte 230/270.

XXX **Augusta,** 98 r. Tocqueville ✆ 01 47 63 39 97, *Fax 01 42 27 21 71* – ▤. GB C 9
*closed 3 to 24 August, Saturday except dinner from October-April and Sunday* – **Meals** - Seafood - a la carte 320/540.

XXX **Il Ristorante,** 22 r. Fourcroy ✆ 01 47 54 91 48, *Fax 01 47 63 34 00* – ▤. AE GB
*closed 10 to 23 August, Saturday lunch and Sunday* – **Meals** - Italian rest. - 165 (lunch) and a la carte 220/370. D 8

XX ✿ **Petit Colombier** (Fournier), 42 r. Acacias ✆ 01 43 80 28 54, *Fax 01 44 40 04 29* – AE GB E 7
*closed 1 to 20 August, Saturday and Sunday from 1 May-15 September* – **Meals** 190 (lunch)/360 and a la carte 280/460
**Spec.** Œufs à la broche aux truffes fraîches (15 December-15 March). Pigeonneau fermier, farce fine à la croque au sel et jus truffé. Lièvre à la royale (October-December).

XX **Table de Pierre,** 116 bd Péreire ✆ 01 43 80 88 68, *Fax 01 47 66 53 02* – ▤. AE GB
*closed Saturday lunch and Sunday* – **Meals** a la carte 220/370. D 8

XX **Graindorge,** 15 r. Arc de Triomphe ✆ 01 47 54 00 28, *Fax 01 47 54 00 28* – AE GB JCB
*closed 1 to 15 August, Saturday lunch and Sunday* – **Meals** 168 (lunch), 188/230 and a la carte 210/330. E 7

XX **Les Béatilles,** 11 bis r. Villebois-Mareuil ✆ 01 45 74 43 80, *Fax 01 45 74 43 81* – ▤. AE GB E 7
*closed 1 to 21 August, Christmas Holidays, Saturday and Sunday* – **Meals** 170/290 and a la carte 240/330.

XX **Truite Vagabonde,** 17 r. Batignolles ✆ 01 43 87 77 80, *Fax 01 43 87 31 50*, 🏠 – AE GB JCB D 11
*closed Sunday dinner* – **Meals** 190 and a la carte 270/380.

XX **Billy Gourmand,** 20 r. Tocqueville ✆ 01 42 27 03 71 – AE GB D 10
*closed 1 to 25 August, Saturday except dinner from 15 September-15 June, Sunday and Bank Holidays* – **Meals** 165 and a la carte 250/300.

XX **Beudant,** 97 r. des Dames ✆ 01 43 87 11 20, *Fax 01 43 87 27 35* – ▤. AE ⓓ GB JCB
*closed 8 to 27 August, Saturday lunch, Monday dinner and Sunday* – **Meals** 160/300 and a la carte 200/360. D 11

XX **Aub. des Dolomites,** 38 r. Poncelet ✆ 01 42 27 94 56, *Fax 01 47 66 38 54* – AE GB E 8
*closed 24 July-23 August, Saturday lunch and Sunday* – **Meals** 139/188 and a la carte 210/330.

XX **Les Marines de Pétrus,** 27 av. Niel ✆ 01 47 63 04 24, *Fax 01 44 15 92 20* – ▤. AE ⓓ GB D 8
*closed Sunday* – **Meals** - Seafood - 200/250 and a la carte 220/310.

XX **Dessirier,** 9 pl. Mar. Juin ✆ 01 42 27 82 14, *Fax 01 47 66 82 07* – AE ⓓ GB D 8
**Meals** - Seafood - 198 and a la carte 270/460.

XX ✿ **Braisière** (Vaxelaire), 54 r. Cardinet ✆ 01 47 63 40 37, *Fax 01 47 63 04 76* – AE GB. ✂ D 9
*closed April, Saturday and Sunday* – **Meals** 185 and a la carte 260/340
**Spec.** Saint-Jacques aux patates et fleur de sel (October-April). Saint-Pierre à la peau et olives noires. Rognon de veau à la lie de vin.

XX **Taïra,** 10 r. Acacias ✆ 01 47 66 74 14, *Fax 01 47 66 74 14*.– ▤. AE ⓓ GB E 7
*closed 15 to 31 August, Saturday lunch and Sunday* – **Meals** - Seafood - 170/330 and a la carte 280/370.

XX **Petite Auberge,** 38 r. Laugier ✆ 01 47 63 85 51, *Fax 01 47 63 85 81* – GB D 7-8
*closed August, Monday lunch and Sunday* – **Meals** (booking essential) 160 and a la carte 200/310.

XX **Chez Guyvonne,** 14 r. Thann ✆ 01 42 27 25 43, *Fax 01 42 27 25 43* – ▤. AE GB JCB. ✂
*closed 3 to 31 August, 24 December-4 January, Saturday and Sunday* – **Meals** 150/180 and a la carte 280/400. D 10

XX **Soupière,** 154 av. Wagram ✆ 01 42 27 00 73 – ▤. AE GB D 9
*closed 10 to 23 August, Saturday lunch and Sunday* – **Meals** 138/165 and a la carte 200/340.

XX **Chez Georges,** 273 bd Péreire ✆ 01 45 74 31 00, *Fax 01 45 74 02 56*, bistro – GB JCB. ✂ E 6
**Meals** a la carte 210/310.

XX **Epicure 108,** 108 r. Cardinet ✆ 01 47 63 50 91 – GB D 10
*closed 10 to 22 August, Saturday lunch and Sunday* – **Meals** 175/250.

XX **Ballon des Ternes,** 103 av. Ternes ✆ 01 45 74 17 98, *Fax 01 45 72 18 84*, brasserie – AE GB JCB E 6
*closed 1 to 21 August* – **Meals** a la carte 180/290.

XX **Chez Léon,** 32 r. Legendre ✆ 01 42 27 06 82, bistro – ⓓ GB D 10
*closed August, Saturday and Sunday* – **Meals** 185.

**Rôtisserie d'Armaillé,** 6 r. Armaillé ☎ 01 42 27 19 20, *Fax 01 40 55 00 93* – ▤. AE ⓓ GB JCB E 7
*closed 8 to 16 August, Saturday lunch and Sunday* – **Meals** 218.

**L'Impatient,** 14 passage Geffroy Didelot ☎ 01 43 87 28 10 – GB D 10-11
*closed 10 to 22 April, 8 to 31 August, Monday dinner, Saturday and Sunday* – **Meals** 102 (lunch), 120/158 and a la carte 210/320.

**Caves Petrissans,** 30 bis av. Niel ☎ 01 42 27 52 03, *Fax 01 40 54 87 56,* , bistro – AE GB D 8
*closed 31 July-23 August, Saturday, Sunday and Bank Holidays* – **Meals** 170 and a la carte 220/400.

**Troyon,** 4 r. Troyon ☎ 01 40 68 99 40, *Fax 01 40 68 99 57* – AE GB. E 8
*closed 2 to 23 August, Saturday lunch and Sunday* – **Meals** (booking essential) a la carte 160/260.

**Bistro du 17ᵉ,** 108 av. Villiers ☎ 01 47 63 32 77, *Fax 01 42 27 67 66* – ▤. AE GB D 8
**Meals** 169 b.i.

**Bistrot d'à Côté Flaubert,** 10 r. G. Flaubert ☎ 01 42 67 05 81, *Fax 01 47 63 82 75* – AE GB D 8
**Meals** a la carte 210/310.

**Café d'Angel,** 16 r. Brey ☎ 01 47 54 03 33, *Fax 01 47 54 03 33*, bistro – GB E 8
*closed 1 to 15 August, 23 December-2 January, Saturday and Sunday* – **Meals** 92 (lunch)/165.

**Bistrot de l'Étoile,** 13 r. Troyon ☎ 01 42 67 25 95, *Fax 01 46 22 43 09* – ▤. AE GB JCB E 8
*closed in August, Saturday and Sunday* – **Meals** 180 and a la carte approx. 250.

**L'Huitrier,** 16 r. Saussier-Leroy ☎ 01 40 54 83 44, *Fax 01 40 54 83 86* – AE GB E 8
*closed August, Sunday lunch and Monday* – **Meals** - Seafood - a la carte 220/340.

**Petite Provence,** 69 rue des Dames ☎ 01 45 22 03 03 – GB D 11
*closed August, Saturday lunch and Monday* – **Meals** 135 and a la carte 190/260.

## Montmartre, La Villette, Belleville.

*18th, 19th and 20th arrondissements.*
*18th: ✉ 75018*
*19th: ✉ 75019*
*20th: ✉ 75020*

**Terrass'H.** M, 12 r. J. de Maistre (18th) ☎ 01 46 06 72 85, *Fax 01 42 52 29 11,* , « Rooftop terrace, ≤ Paris » – ▮, ⋈ rm, ▤ TV ☎ – 🏛 160. AE ⓓ GB JCB C 13
*La Terrasse* ☎ 01 44 92 34 00 **Meals** 130b.i./168 – ☕ 70 – **88 rm** 840/1430, 13 suites.

**Holiday Inn** M, 216 av. J. Jaurès (19th) ☎ 01 44 84 18 18, *Fax 01 44 84 18 20,* Lδ – ▮, ⋈ rm, ▤ TV ☎ ♿ 🚗 – 🏛 180. AE ⓓ GB JCB C 21
**Meals** 89/110 – ☕ 75 – **174 rm** 890, 8 suites.

**Mercure Montmartre** without rest, 1 r. Caulaincourt (18th) ☎ 01 44 69 70 70, *Fax 01 44 69 70 71* – ▮, ⋈ rm, ▤ TV ☎ ♿ – 🏛 120. AE ⓓ GB D 12
☕ 68 – **308 rm** 895/1220.

**Roma Sacré Cœur** without rest, 101 r. Caulaincourt (18th) ☎ 01 42 62 02 02, *Fax 01 42 54 34 92* – ▮ TV ☎. AE ⓓ GB JCB C 14
☕ 37 – **57 rm** 410/480.

**Laumière** without rest, 4 r. Petit (19th) ☎ 01 42 06 10 77, *Fax 01 42 06 72 50* – ▮ TV ☎. GB D 19
☕ 32 – **54 rm** 285/370.

**Regyn's Montmartre** without rest, 18 pl. Abbesses (18th) ☎ 01 42 54 45 21, *Fax 01 42 23 76 69* – ▮ TV ☎. AE GB D 13
☕ 40 – **22 rm** 380/460.

**Palma** without rest, 77 av. Gambetta (20th) ✆ 01 46 36 13 65, *Fax 01 46 36 03 27* – G 21
☕ 33 – **32 rm** 345/395.

**Super H.** without rest, 208 r. Pyrénées (20th) ✆ 01 46 36 97 48, *Fax 01 46 36 26 10* – G 21
*closed August* – ☕ 35 – **32 rm** 250/520.

**Eden H.** without rest, 90 r. Ordener (18th) ✆ 01 42 64 61 63, *Fax 01 42 64 11 43* – B 14
☕ 35 – **35 rm** 380/420.

**Damrémont** without rest, 110 r. Damrémont (18th) ✆ 01 42 64 25 75, *Fax 01 46 06 74 64* – rm, B 13
☕ 40 – **35 rm** 440/490.

**Crimée** without rest, 188 r. Crimée (19th) ✆ 01 40 36 75 29, *Fax 01 40 36 29 57* – C 18
☕ 35 – **31 rm** 310/350.

**des Arts** without rest, 5 r. Tholozé (18th) ✆ 01 46 06 30 52, *Fax 01 46 06 10 83* – D 13
☕ 35 – **50 rm** 460/500.

**Abricotel** without rest, 15 r. Lally Tollendal (19th) ✆ 01 42 08 34 49, *Fax 01 42 40 83 95* – D 18
☕ 33 – **39 rm** 295/400.

**Beauvilliers** (Carlier), 52 r. Lamarck (18th) ✆ 01 42 54 54 42, *Fax 01 42 62 70 30*, « 1900 decor, terrace » – C 14
*closed Monday lunch and Sunday* – **Meals** 185/400 b.i. and a la carte 430/580
**Spec.** "Cul" d'artichaut frais au tourteau, jus de moutarde à la pistache. Escalopines de foie de canard poêlées aux pêches de vigne (June-October). Timbale de macaroni aux ris de veau et morilles.

**Pavillon Puebla,** Parc Buttes-Chaumont, entrance : av. Bolivar, r. Botzaris (19th) ✆ 01 42 08 92 62, *Fax 01 42 39 83 16*, « Pleasant setting in the park » – E 19
*closed 9 to 24 August, Sunday and Monday* – **Meals** 180/250 and a la carte 380/460.

**Cottage Marcadet,** 151 bis r. Marcadet (18th) ✆ 01 42 57 71 22 – C 13
*closed 12 to 19 April, 25 July - 24 August and Sunday* – **Meals** 160 (lunch)/215 b.i. and a la carte 230/320.

**Les Allobroges,** 71 r. Grands-Champs (20th) ✆ 01 43 73 40 00 – K 22
*closed 12 to 21 April, 31 July-25 August, Sunday, Monday and Bank Holidays* – **Meals** 95/169 and a la carte 200/340.

**Relais des Buttes,** 86 r. Compans (19th) ✆ 01 42 08 24 70, *Fax 01 42 03 20 44*, – E 20
*closed 8 to 31 August, Saturday lunch and Sunday* – **Meals** 178 and a la carte 230/320.

**Chaumière,** 46 av. Secrétan (19th) ✆ 01 42 06 54 69, *Fax 01 42 06 28 12* – E 18
*closed 15 to 31 August and Sunday dinner* – **Meals** 143/198 b.i. and a la carte 180/340.

**Au Clair de la Lune,** 9 r. Poulbot (18th) ✆ 01 42 58 97 03 – D 14
*closed 17 August-6 September, Monday lunch and Sunday* – **Meals** 165 and a la carte 210/320.

**Eric Frechon,** 10 r. Gén. Brunet (19th) ✆ 01 40 40 03 30, *Fax 01 40 40 03 30* – E 20
*closed August, Sunday and Monday* – **Meals** 200.

**Poulbot Gourmet,** 39 r. Lamarck (18th) ✆ 01 46 06 86 00 – C 14
*closed Sunday except lunch from October-May* – **Meals** 170 and a la carte 210/300.

**L'Étrier,** 154 r. Lamarck (18th) ✆ 01 42 29 14 01, bistro – C 12
*closed 9 to 31 August, Sunday and Monday* – **Meals** (booking essential) 76 (lunch)/160.

**Bistrot du 19e,** 45 r. Alouettes (19th) ✆ 01 42 00 84 85 – E 20
*closed August, Sunday dinner and Monday* – **Meals** 165.

**Aucune Idée ?,** 2 pl. St-Blaise (20th) ✆ 01 40 09 70 67, *Fax 01 43 56 12 34* – H 22
*closed 3 to 17 August, Sunday dinner and Monday* – **Meals** 175 and a la carte 180/260.

**Marie-Louise,** 52 r. Championnet (18th) ✆ 01 46 06 86 55, bistro – B 15
*closed 31 July-1 September, Easter Holidays, Sunday, Monday and Bank Holidays* – **Meals** 130 and a la carte 150/260.

# ENVIRONS

## The outskirts of Paris up to 25Km

K 11: These reference letters and numbers correspond to the squares on the **Michelin plans of Parisian suburbs** nos 18, 20, 22, 24, 25.

**La Défense** *92 Hauts-de-Seine* 101 ⑭, 18 – ✉ *92400 Courbevoie.*
See : *Quarter★★ : perspective★ from the parvis.*
*Paris 8,5.*

**Sofitel CNIT** M, 2 pl. Défense ✆ 01 46 92 10 10, *Fax 01 46 92 10 50* – rm, rm, – 70. AE GB JCB AV-AW40
see ***Les Communautés*** below – 100 – **141 rm** 1500, 6 suites.

**Sofitel La Défense** M, 34 cours Michelet by ring road, exit La Défense 4 ✉ 92060 Puteaux ✆ 01 47 76 44 43, *Fax 01 47 76 72 20*, – rm, – 80. AE GB AW 41
***Les 2 Arcs*** *(closed Friday dinner, Sunday lunch and Saturday)* **Meals** 295 (lunch) and a la carte 190/300 – ***Le Botanic*** *(closed dinner except Friday and Saturday)* **Meals** 160 – 105 – **149 rm** 1450.

**Renaissance** M, 60 Jardin de Valmy, by ring road, exit La Défense 7 ✉ 92918 Puteaux ✆ 01 41 97 50 50, *Fax 01 41 97 51 51*, – rm, – 200. AE GB AW 40
**Meals** 170 – 95 – **314 rm** 1400/1600, 20 suites.

**Novotel La Défense** M, 2 bd Neuilly ✆ 01 41 45 23 23, *Fax 01 41 45 23 24*, – rm, – 25 - 150. AE GB JCB AW 42
**Meals** a la carte approx. 170 – 70 – **280 rm** 810/850.

**Ibis La Défense** M, 4 bd Neuilly ✆ 01 41 97 40 40, *Fax 01 41 97 40 50*, – rm, – 50. AE GB AW 42
**Meals** a la carte 100/130 – 39 – **284 rm** 530.

**Les Communautés** - Hôtel Sofitel CNIT, 2 pl. Défense, 5th floor ✆ 01 46 92 10 30, *Fax 01 46 92 10 50* – . AE GB JCB AV-AW40
*closed Saturday and Sunday* – **Meals** 190 (dinner) and a la carte 290/340.

**Marne-la-Vallée** *77206 S.-et-M.* 101 ⑲.
*18 of Bussy-St-Georges (private) ✆ 01 64 66 00 00 ; 9 18 of Disneyland Paris ✆ 01 60 45 69 14.*
*Maison du Tourisme d'Ile de France, Disney Village, ✆ 01 60 43 33 33, Fax 01 60 43 36 91.*
*Paris 28.*

**at Collégien** – *pop. 2 331 alt. 105 – ✉ 77080 :*

**Novotel,** at Motorway junction Lagny A 4 ✆ 01 64 80 53 53, *Fax 01 64 80 48 37*, – rm, – 250. AE GB
**Meals** 118 – 70 – **197 rm** 610/690.

**at Disneyland Paris** *access by Highway A 4 and Disneyland exit.*
See : *Disneyland Paris ★★★*

**Disneyland Hôtel** M, ✆ 01 60 45 65 00, *Fax 01 60 45 65 33*, « Victorian style architecture, at the entrance to the Disneyland Resort », – rm, – 25 - 50. AE GB JCB.
***California*** : **Meals** 195/275 – ***Inventions*** : **Meals** 180 (lunch)/250 – **478 rm** 2250/3500, 18 suites.

**New-York** M, ✆ 01 60 45 73 00, *Fax 01 60 45 73 33*, « Evokes the architecture of Manhattan », – rm, – 1 500. AE GB JCB.
***Manhattan Restaurant*** (dinner only) **Meals** 195/260 – ***Parkside Diner*** : **Meals** a la carte approx. 150 – **532 rm** 1400/1600, 31 suites.

**Newport Bay Club** M, ✆ 01 60 45 55 00, *Fax 01 60 45 55 33*, Convention centre, « In the style of a New England seaside resort », – rm, – 5 000. AE GB JCB.
***Cape Cod*** : **Meals** 145 – ***Yacht Club*** : **Meals** 150/195 – **1 077 rm** 1180/1580, 15 suites.

**Séquoia Lodge** M, ✆ 01 60 45 51 00, *Fax 01 60 45 51 33*, « The atmosphere of an American mountain lodge », – rm, – 35. AE GB JCB.
***Hunter's Grill*** (dinner only) **Meals** 150 – ***Beaver Creek Tavern*** : **Meals** (115)-150 – **997 rm** 1060/1260, 14 suites.

**Cheyenne,** ☏ 01 60 45 62 00, *Fax 01 60 45 62 33*, « Resembles a frontier town of the American Wild West » – rm, rest, AE GB JCB.
***Chuck Wagon Café :*** **Meals** a la carte approx. 150 – **1 000 rm** 925.

**Santa Fé,** ☏ 01 60 45 78 00, *Fax 01 60 45 78 33*, « Evokes a New Mexican pueblo » – rm, rest, AE GB JCB.
***La Cantina :*** **Meals** a la carte approx. 130 – **1 000 rm** 780.

## Orly (Paris Airports) *94396 Val-de-Marne 101 ㉖, 24 – pop. 21 646.*

☏ *01 49 75 15 15.*
*Paris 15.*

**Hilton Orly** M, near airport station ✉ 94544 ☏ 01 45 12 45 12, *Fax 01 45 12 45 00*, – rm, – 300. AE GB JCB BR 51
**Meals** 195/245 – 95 – **357 rm** 1080/1500.

**Mercure** M, N 7, Z.I. Nord, Orlytech ✉ 94547 ☏ 01 46 87 23 37, *Fax 01 46 87 71 92* – rm, – 40. AE GB
**Meals** a la carte 160/230 – 67 – **190 rm** 695/865.

### Orly Airport West :

**Maxim's,** 2nd floor ✉ 94547 ☏ 01 49 75 16 78, *Fax 01 46 87 05 39* – . AE GB
*closed 31 July-30 August, 25 December-3 January, Saturday, Sunday and Bank Holidays* – **Meals** 230/480 and a la carte 290/420
**Spec.** Terrine de canard "Alex Humbert". Sole braisée au vermouth. Filet de bœuf aux pommes Maxim's.

**See also** *Rungis*

## Roissy-en-France (Paris Airports) *95700 Val-d'Oise 101 ⑧ – pop. 2 054 alt. 85.*

☏ *01 48 62 22 80.*
*Paris 26.*

### at Roissy-Town :

**Copthorne** M, allée Verger ☏ 01 34 29 33 33, *Fax 01 34 29 03 05*, – rm, – 150. AE GB JCB
**Meals** *(closed Sunday lunch and Saturday)* 160 b.i. (lunch), 200/250 – 85 – **237 rm** 1050/1450.

**Mercure,** allée Verger ☏ 01 34 29 40 00, *Fax 01 34 29 00 18*, – rm, – 90. AE GB
**Meals** 146 b.i. – 70 – **202 rm** 800, 4 suites.

**Bleu Marine** M, Z.A. parc de Roissy ☏ 01 34 29 00 00, *Fax 01 34 29 00 11*, – rm, – 80. AE GB JCB
**Meals** 145 – 60 – **153 rm** 610.

**Ibis** M, av. Raperie ☏ 01 34 29 34 34, *Fax 01 34 29 34 19* – rm, – 70. AE GB
**Meals** 95 b.i. and a la carte approx. 140 – 42 – **291 rm** 650.

### in Airport terminal nr 2 :

**Sheraton** M, Aérogare nº 2 ☏ 01 49 19 70 70, *Fax 01 49 19 70 71*, ←, « Original contemporary architecture », – rm, – 80. AE GB JCB
***Les Étoiles*** *(closed August, Saturday and Sunday)* **Meals** 310 – ***Les Saisons :*** **Meals** 260 – 130 – **242 rm** 1500/3700, 14 suites.

### at Roissypole :

**Hilton** M, ☏ 01 49 19 77 77, *Fax 01 49 19 77 78*, – rm, – 500. AE GB JCB. rest
***Gourmet*** *(closed 14 July-15 August, Saturday and Sunday)* **Meals** 220/400 – ***Aviateurs*** - brasserie **Meals** 79/185 – ***Oyster bar*** - Seafood *(closed 14 July-15 August, Sunday and Monday)* **Meals** a la carte approx. 250 – 95 – **378 rm** 1450/1800, 4 suites.

**Sofitel** M, Zone centrale Ouest ☏ 01 49 19 29 29, *Fax 01 49 19 29 00*, – rm, – 150. AE GB JCB
**Meals** brasserie 145 b.i. – 100 – **344 rm** 980/1520, 8 suites.

**Novotel** M, ☏ 01 49 19 27 27, *Fax 01 49 19 27 99* – rm, – 60. AE GB JCB
**Meals** a la carte approx. 170 – 65 – **201 rm** 860/900.

**Z.I. Paris Nord II** - ✉ *95912* :

**Hyatt Regency** Ⓜ, 351 av. Bois de la Pie ✆ 01 48 17 12 34, *Fax 01 48 17 17 17*, « Original contemporary decor », - rm, - 300. AE GB
**Meals** 185/220 - 105 - **383 rm** 1500, 5 suites.

**Rungis** *94150 Val-de-Marne* 101 ㉖, 24 - *pop. 2 939 alt. 80.*
*Paris 14.*

**at Pondorly** : *Access : from Paris, Highway A 6 and take Orly Airport exit ; from outside of Paris, A 6 and Rungis exit :*

**Gd H. Mercure Orly** Ⓜ, 20 av. Ch. Lindbergh ✉ 94656 ✆ 01 46 87 36 36, *Fax 01 46 87 08 48*, - rm, - 180. AE GB BM 50
***La Rungisserie*** : **Meals** 190 - 66 - **190 rm** 830/930.

**Holiday Inn** Ⓜ, 4 av. Ch. Lindbergh ✉ 94656 ✆ 01 46 87 26 66, *Fax 01 45 60 91 25* - rm, - 150. AE GB BM 50
**Meals** 140 - 70 - **172 rm** 860/1060.

**Novotel** Ⓜ, Zone du Delta, 1 r. Pont des Halles ✆ 01 45 12 44 12, *Fax 01 45 12 44 13*, - rm, - 150. AE GB BM 50
**Meals** a la carte approx. 170 - 65 - **181 rm** 680/850.

**Ibis,** 1 r. Mondétour ✉ 94656 ✆ 01 46 87 22 45, *Fax 01 46 87 84 72*, - rm, - 60. AE GB BM 50
**Meals** 95 - 39 - **119 rm** 350.

**Versailles** *78000 Yvelines* 101 ㉒, 22 - *pop. 87 789 alt. 130.*
**See** : *Palace*★★★ Y - *Gardens*★★★ *(fountain display*★★★ *- grandes eaux - and illuminated night performances*★★★ *- fêtes de nuit - in summer) - Ecuries Royales*★ Y - *The Trianons*★★ - *Lambinet Museum*★ Y **M**.
*of la Boulie (private)* ✆ *01 39 50 59 41 by* ③ *: 2,5 km.*
*Tourist Office 7 r. Réservoirs* ✆ *01 39 50 36 22, Fax 01 39 50 68 07.*
*Paris 20* ①.

Plan on next page

**Trianon Palace** Ⓜ, 1 bd Reine ✆ 01 30 84 38 00, *Fax 01 39 49 00 77*, ←, park, « Tasteful early 20C decor », - , rm, - 30. AE GB JCB X r
see ***Les Trois Marches*** below - ***Brasserie La Fontaine*** ✆ 01 30 84 38 47 **Meals** a la carte 180/290 - 140 - **163 rm** 1400/2100, 27 suites.

**Sofitel Château de Versailles** Ⓜ, 2 av. Paris ✆ 01 39 07 46 46, *Fax 01 39 07 46 47*, - rm, - 150. AE GB JCB Y a
**Meals** 195/320 and a la carte 260/450 - 105 - **146 rm** 1200, 6 suites.

**Versailles** Ⓜ without rest, 7 r. Ste-Anne (Petite place) ✆ 01 39 50 64 65, *Fax 01 39 02 37 85* - rm, . AE GB JCB Y p
57 - **46 rm** 480/580.

**Résidence du Berry** Ⓜ without rest, 14 r. Anjou ✆ 01 39 49 07 07, *Fax 01 39 50 59 40* - rm, . AE GB JCB Z s
50 - **38 rm** 420/750.

**Relais Mercure** Ⓜ without rest, 19 r. Ph. de Dangeau ✆ 01 39 50 44 10, *Fax 01 39 50 65 11* - - 35. AE GB JCB Y n
42 - **60 rm** 410/430.

**Ibis** without rest, 4 av. Gén. de Gaulle ✆ 01 39 53 03 30, *Fax 01 39 50 06 31* - rm, . AE GB Y u
39 - **85 rm** 390/490.

**Les Trois Marches** (Vié), 1 bd Reine ✆ 01 39 50 13 21, *Fax 01 30 21 01 25*, ←, - . AE GB JCB X r
*closed 1 August-2 September* - **Meals** 270 (lunch)/610 and a la carte 470/740
**Spec.** Gâteau de poireaux, mousse de morilles, escalope de foie gras. Homard rôti aux aromates. Côte de veau rôtie en cocotte "grand-mère".

**Rescatore,** 27 av. St-Cloud ✆ 01 39 25 06 34, *Fax 01 39 51 68 11* - AE GB Y s
*closed August, Saturday lunch and Sunday* - **Meals** - Seafood - 180 and a la carte 280/340.

**Potager du Roy,** 1 r. Mar.-Joffre ✆ 01 39 50 35 34, *Fax 01 30 21 69 30* - . AE GB
*closed Sunday dinner and Monday* - **Meals** 169. Z r

**Marée de Versailles,** 22 r. au Pain ✆ 01 30 21 73 73, *Fax 01 39 50 55 87* - . AE GB Y t
*closed 3 to 15 August, 22 to 25 December, February Holidays, Monday dinner and Sunday* - **Meals** - Seafood - 260 and a la carte 200/280.

# VERSAILLES

Carnot (R.) . . . . . . . . . . . . Y
Clemenceau
(R. Georges) . . . . . . . . . Y 7
États-Généraux (R. des) . . Z
Foch (R. du Mar.) . . . . . XY
Hoche (R.) . . . . . . . . . . . . Y
Leclerc (R. du Gén.) . . . . Z 24
Marché N.D. (Pl. du) . . . Y 25
Orangerie (R. de l') . . . . YZ
Paroisse (R. de la) . . . . . Y
Royale (R.) . . . . . . . . . . . Z
Satory (R. de) . . . . . . . . YZ 42
Vieux-Versailles (R. du) . YZ 47

Chancellerie (R. de la) . . Y 3
Cotte (R. Robert-de) . . . Y 10
Europe (Av. de l') . . . . . Y 14
Gambetta (Pl.) . . . . . . . . Y 17
Gaulle (Av. Gén.-de) . . . YZ 19
Indép. Américaine (R.) . Y 20
Mermoz (R. Jean) . . . . . Z 27
Nolhac (R. Pierre-de) . . . Y 30
Porte de Buc (R. de la) . Z 34
Rockefeller (Av.) . . . . . . Y 37

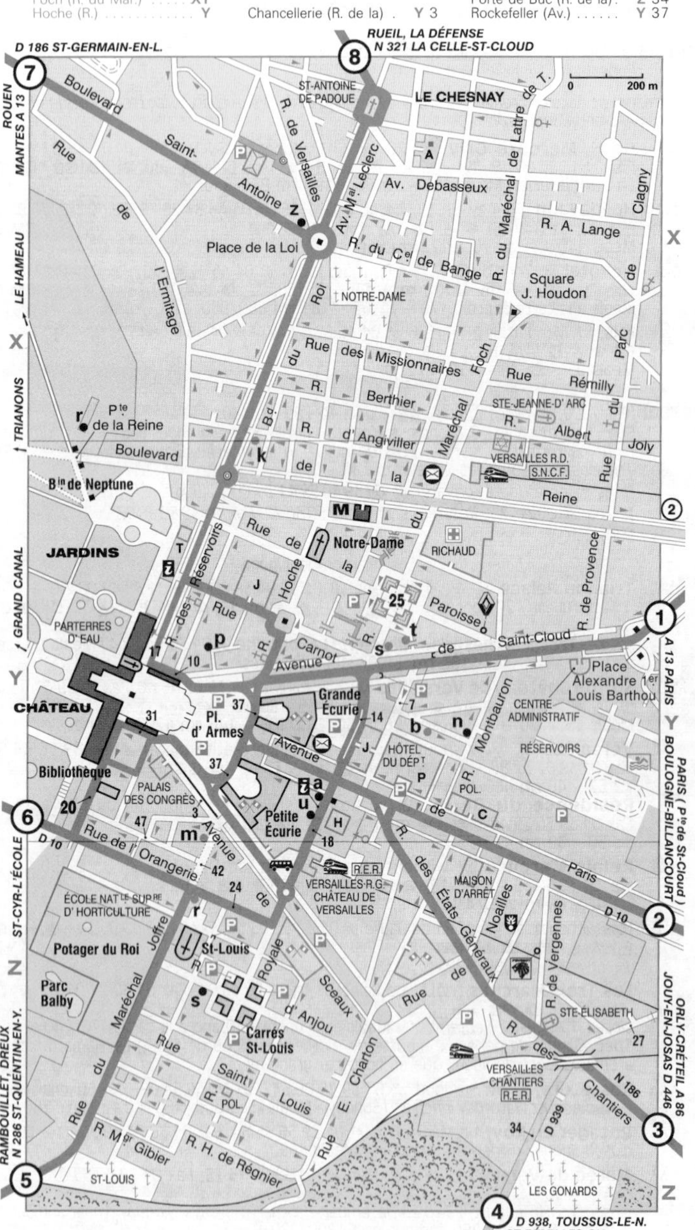

**Cuisine Bourgeoise,** 10 bd Roi ✆ 01 39 53 11 38, *Fax 01 39 53 25 26* – AE GB XY k
*closed 9 to 24 August, Saturday lunch and Sunday* – **Meals** 168/290 b.i. and a la carte 250/340.

**Chevalet,** 6 r. Ph. de Dangeau ✆ 01 39 02 03 13, *Fax 01 39 50 81 41* – GB JCB Y b
*closed 10 to 25 August, February Holidays, Monday dinner and Sunday* – **Meals** 118 (lunch), 145/180.

**Le Falher,** 22 r. Satory ✆ 01 39 50 57 43, *Fax 01 39 49 04 66* – AE GB. Y m
*closed 14 to 26 August, Saturday lunch and Sunday* – **Meals** 128/180 and a la carte 220/300.

**at Le Chesnay** – *pop. 29 542 alt. 120* – ✉ *78150* :

**Novotel** M, 4 bd St-Antoine ✆ 01 39 54 96 96, *Fax 01 39 54 94 40* – rm, – 25 - 150. AE GB X z
Meals 120 – 60 – **105 rm** 560.

**Mercure** M without rest, r. Marly-le-Roi, in front of Commercial Centre Parly II ✆ 01 39 55 11 41, *Fax 01 39 55 06 22* – rm, P. AE GB JCB
55 – **80 rm** 580.

**Ibis** without rest, av. Dutartre, Commercial Centre Parly II ✆ 01 39 63 37 93, *Fax 01 39 55 18 66* – rm, AE GB JCB
39 – **72 rm** 390.

**Au Comptoir Nordique,** 6 av. Rocquencourt ✆ 01 39 55 13 31, *Fax 01 39 55 40 57*, – P. AE GB
*closed spring Holidays, 2 to 23 August, Christmas Holidays and Sunday* – **Meals** 145 and a la carte 170/240 - ***Brasserie*** : **Meals** 90.

**Connemara,** 41 rte Rueil ✆ 01 39 55 63 07, *Fax 01 39 55 63 07* – AE GB
*closed 20 July-15 August, February Holidays, Sunday dinner and Monday* – **Meals** 170/300 and a la carte 200/290.

# AND BEYOND...

**Joigny** *89300 Yonne* 65 ④ – *pop. 9 697 alt. 79.*
See : *Vierge au Sourire★ in St-Thibault's Church – Côte St-Jacques ≤★ 1,5 km by D 20.*
*of Roncemay ✆ 03 86 73 68 87.*
*Tourist Office 4 quai H.-Ragobert ✆ 03 86 62 11 05, Fax 03 86 91 76 38.*
*Paris 147 – Auxerre 27 – Gien 75 – Montargis 59 – Sens 30 – Troyes 76.*

✿✿✿ **Côte St-Jacques** (Lorain) Ⓜ, 14 fg Paris ✆ 03 86 62 09 70, *Fax 03 86 91 49 70,* ≤, « Tasteful decor », – – 30. AE GB
*closed 4 to 21 January* – **Meals** (Sunday booking essential) 340 b.i. (lunch)/740 and a la carte 610/950 – ☕ 120 – **25 rm** 740/1780, 4 suites
**Spec.** Huîtres bretonnes en petite terrine océane. Noix de Saint-Jacques, endives et chanterelles, jus de champignons monté en capuccino (October-April). Canard croisé rôti entier, sauce aux petits fruits, tarte fine de légumes nouveaux. **Wines** Bourgogne Irancy.

**Pontoise** *95300 Val d'Oise* 106 ⑤ – *pop. 27 150 alt. 48.*
*Paris 36 – Beauvais 50 – Dieppe 135 – Mantes-la-Jolie 39 – Rouen 91.*

**at Cormeilles-en-Vexin** *NW – alt. 111 – ✉ 95830 :*

✿✿ **Relais Ste-Jeanne** (Cagna), on D 915 ✆ 01 34 66 61 56, *Fax 01 34 66 40 31,* « Garden » – . AE GB
*closed 25 July-18 August, 23 to 28 December, Sunday and Monday* – **Meals** 220/600 b.i.
**Spec.** Paupiettes de sole au persil plat et champignons sylvestres. Douceur de homard aux aromates à l'huile d'olive. Pigeon de Bretagne aux griottes et jus acidulé.

**Rheims** *51100 Marne* 56 ⑥ ⑯ – *pop. 180 620 alt. 85.*
See : *Cathedral★★★ – St-Remi Basilica★★ : interior★★★ – Palais du Tau★★ – Champagne cellars★ – Place Royale★ – Porte Mars★ – Hôtel de la Salle★ – Foujita Chapel★ – Library★ of Ancien Collège des Jésuites – St-Remi Museum★★ – Hôtel le Vergeur Museum★ – Fine Arts Museum★ – French Automobile Heritage Centre★.*
Envir. : *Fort de la Pompelle : German helmets★ 9 km to the SE by N 44.*
*Rheims-Champagne ✆ 03 26 03 60 14 at Gueux ; to the NW by N 31-E 46 : 9,5 km.*
*Rheims-Champagne ✆ 03 26 05 46 10 : 6 km. – ✆ 08 36 35 35 35.*
*Tourist Office 2 r. Guillaume-de-Machault ✆ 03 26 77 45 25, Fax 03 26 77 45 27 – A.C. de Champagne 7 bd Lundy ✆ 03 26 47 34 76, Fax 03 26 88 52 24.*
*Paris 144 – Brussels 214 – Châlons-sur-Marne 48 – Lille 199 – Luxembourg 232.*

✿✿✿ **Boyer "Les Crayères"** Ⓜ, 64 bd Vasnier ✆ 03 26 82 80 80, *Fax 03 26 82 65 52,* ≤, , « Elegant mansion in park », – . AE GB
*closed 21 December-11 January* – **Meals** *(closed Tuesday lunch and Monday)* (booking essential) 950 b.i. and a la carte 650/720 – ☕ 110 – **16 rm** 1250/1950, 3 suites
**Spec.** Pied de porc farci au foie gras, braisé en cocotte. Filet de Saint-Pierre poêlé, crème de chou-fleur. Canon d'agneau truffé en croûte feuilletée, pommes rattes. **Wines** Champagne.

**Saulieu** *21210 Côte-d'Or* 65 ⑰ – *pop. 2 917 alt. 535* – **See** : *St-Andoche Basilica★.*
*Tourist Office r. d'Argentine ✆ 03 80 64 00 21, Fax 03 80 64 21 96.*
*Paris 249 – Autun 41 – Avallon 38 – Beaune 64 – Clamecy 76 – Dijon 73.*

✿✿✿ **Côte d'Or** (Loiseau) Ⓜ, 2 r. Argentine ✆ 03 80 90 53 53, *Fax 03 80 64 08 92,* « Tasteful inn with flowered garden » – – 30. AE GB JCB
**Meals** 420 (lunch), 580/890 and a la carte 570/940 – ☕ 150 – **24 rm** 340/2100, 3 duplex
**Spec.** Jambonnettes de grenouilles à la purée d'ail et au jus de persil. Sandre à la fondue d'échalotes sauce au vin rouge. Blanc de volaille au foie gras chaud et purée truffée. **Wines** Bourgogne.

**Vézelay** *89450 Yonne* 65 ⑮ – *pop. 571 alt. 285.*
See : *Ste-Madeleine Basilica★★★ : tower ★.* – **Envir.** : *Site★ of Pierre-Perthuis SE : 6 km.*
*Tourist Office r. St-Pierre ✆ 03 86 33 23 69, Fax 03 86 33 34 00.*
*Paris 223 – Auxerre 51 – Avallon 15 – Château-Chinon 60 – Clamecy 22.*

**at St-Père** : *SE : 3 km by D 957 – alt. 148 – ✉ 89450.*
See : *Church of N.-Dame★*

✿✿✿ **L'Espérance** (Meneau), ✆ 03 86 33 39 10, *Fax 03 86 33 26 15,* ≤, « Conservatory restaurant opening onto the garden », – rest, – 50. AE GB
*closed February* – **Meals** *(closed Tuesday except dinner from 15 June-15 October and Wednesday lunch except Bank Holidays)* (booking essential) 360 (lunch), 650/860 and a la carte 490/910 – ☕ 130 – **34 rm** 500/1300, 6 suites
**Spec.** Galets de pomme de terre au caviar. Turbot en croûte de sel, beurre de homard. Sabayon à la mousse de lait, tarte à la confiture. **Wines** Vézelay, Chablis.

**BORDEAUX** *33000 Gironde 71 ⑨ – pop. 210 336 alt. 4 Greater Bordeaux 696 364 h.*

See : *18C Bordeaux : façades along the quayside★★* EX, *Esplanade des Quinconces* DX, *Grand Théâtre★★* DX, *Notre-Dame Church★* DX, *Allées de Tourny* DX, *Cours Clemenceau* DX, *Place Gambetta* DX, *Cours de l'Intendance* DX – *Old Bordeaux★★ : Place de la Bourse★★* EX, *Place du Parlement★* EX **109**, *St-Michel Basilica★* EY, *Great Bell★ (Grosse Cloche)* EY **D** – *Pey-Berland district : St-André Cathedral★* DY *(Pey-Berland Tower★ : ←★★* **E**) – *Mériadeck district* CY – *Battle-Cruiser Colbert★★* – *Museums : Fine Arts★ (Beaux-Arts)* CDY **M**[3], *Decorative Arts★* DY **M**[2], *Aquitaine★★* DY **M**[4] – *Entrepôt Lainé★★ : Museum of Contemporary Art★.*

*18 Golf Bordelais ✆ 05 56 28 56 04 by av. d'Eysines : 4 km ; 18 18 de Bordeaux Lac ✆ 05 56 50 92 72, to the N by D 209 : 10 km ; 18 18 of Medoc at Louens ✆ 05 56 70 21 10 to the NW by D 6 : 6 km ; 9 9 9 9 Internat. of Bordeaux-Pessac ✆ 05 56 36 03 33 by N 250 ; 18 Bordeaux-Cameyrac ✆ 05 56 72 96 79 by N 89 : 18 km.*

*of Bordeaux-Mérignac : ✆ 05 56 34 50 50 to the W : 11 km.*

*✆ 08 36 35 35 35.*

*Tourist Office 12 cours 30-Juillet ✆ 05 56 00 66 00, Fax 05 56 00 66 01, at the Gare St-Jean ✆ 05 56 91 64 70 and the airport ✆ 05 52 34 39 39 – Automobile-Club du Sud-Ouest 8 Espl. des Quinconces ✆ 05 56 44 22 92, Fax 05 56 48 57 47 – Bordeaux wine Exhibition (Maison du vin de Bordeaux) 3 cours 30-juil. (closed weekend from mid Oct.-mid May) ✆ 05 56 00 22 66* DX.

*Paris 579 – Lyons 531 – Nantes 324 – Strasbourg 919 – Toulouse 245.*

Plans on following pages

**Burdigala** M, 115 r. G. Bonnac ✆ 05 56 90 16 16, *Fax 05 56 93 15 06,* « Tasteful decor » – 🛗 ▤ TV ☎ ♿ – 🏋 100. AE ⓓ GB JCB — CX r
**Meals** 200/300 – ☕ 90 – **68 rm** 900/1500, 8 suites, 7 duplex.

**Mercure Château Chartrons** M, 81 cours St-Louis ✉ 33300 ✆ 05 56 43 15 00, *Fax 05 56 69 15 21,* – 🛗, rm, ▤ rest, TV ☎ ♿ – 🏋 150. AE ⓓ GB
**Meals** 110/200 – ☕ 56 – **144 rm** 520/720.

**Claret** M, Cité Mondiale du Vin, 18 parvis des Chartrons ✆ 05 56 01 79 79, *Fax 05 56 01 79 00,* – 🛗 ▤ TV ☎ ♿ – 🏋 800. AE ⓓ GB
***Le 20*** *(closed 20 December- 5 January, Saturday and Sunday)* **Meals** a la carte approx 160 – ☕ 65 – **94 rm** 540/620, 4 suites.

**Mercure Mériadeck** M, 5 r.-Lateulade ✆ 05 56 56 43 43, *Fax 05 56 96 50 59* – 🛗, rm, ▤ TV ☎ – 🏋 150. AE ⓓ GB — CY v
***Festival*** *(closed Saturday, Sunday and Bank Holidays)* **Meals** 98 – ☕ 55 – **194 rm** 495/520.

**Holiday Inn Garden Court,** 30 r. de Tauzia ✉ 33800 ✆ 05 56 92 21 21, *Fax 05 56 91 08 06,* – 🛗, rm, ▤ TV ☎ ♿ – 🏋 70. AE ⓓ GB JCB — FZ v
**Meals** *(closed Saturday and Sunday)* 95 b.i. – ☕ 60 – **89 rm** 450/600.

**Novotel Bordeaux-Centre** M, 45 cours Mar. Juin ✆ 05 56 51 46 46, *Fax 05 56 98 25 56,* – 🛗, rm, ▤ TV ☎ ♿ P – 🏋 80. AE ⓓ GB — CY m
**Meals** 97 – ☕ 55 – **138 rm** 480/530.

**Ste-Catherine** M without rest, 27 r. Parlement Ste-Catherine ✆ 05 56 81 95 12, *Fax 05 56 44 50 51* – 🛗, rm, ▤ TV ☎ – 🏋 40. AE ⓓ GB JCB — DX m
☕ 70 – **84 rm** 530/1200.

**Normandie** without rest, 7 cours 30-Juillet ✆ 05 56 52 16 80, *Fax 05 56 51 68 91* – 🛗 TV ☎ – 🏋 30. AE ⓓ GB JCB — DX z
☕ 55 – **100 rm** 320/700.

**Majestic** without rest, 2 r. Condé ✆ 05 56 52 60 44, *Fax 05 56 79 26 70* – 🛗 ▤ TV ☎. AE ⓓ GB JCB — DX a
☕ 50 – **50 rm** 390/580.

**Gd H. Français** without rest, 12 r. Temple ✆ 05 56 48 10 35, *Fax 05 56 81 76 18* – 🛗 ▤ TV ☎ ♿. AE ⓓ GB JCB — DX v
☕ 60 – **35 rm** 380/650.

**Bayonne Etche-Ona** M without rest, 4 r. Martignac ✆ 05 56 48 00 88, *Fax 05 56 48 41 60* – 🛗 ▤ TV ☎. AE ⓓ GB JCB. — DX f
☕ 60 – **36 rm** 390/595.
**Annexe** M without rest, 11 r. Mautrec – 🛗 ▤ TV ☎ – 🏋 25
☕ 60 – **27 rm** 390/595.

**Presse** M without rest, 6 r. Porte Dijeaux ✆ 05 56 48 53 88, *Fax 05 56 01 05 82* – 🛗 ▤ TV ☎. AE ⓓ GB — DX k
☕ 38 – **29 rm** 340/450.

**Continental** without rest, 10 r. Montesquieu ✆ 05 56 52 66 00, *Fax 05 56 52 77 97* – 🛗 TV ☎. AE ⓓ GB — DX b
☕ 35 – **50 rm** 300/430.

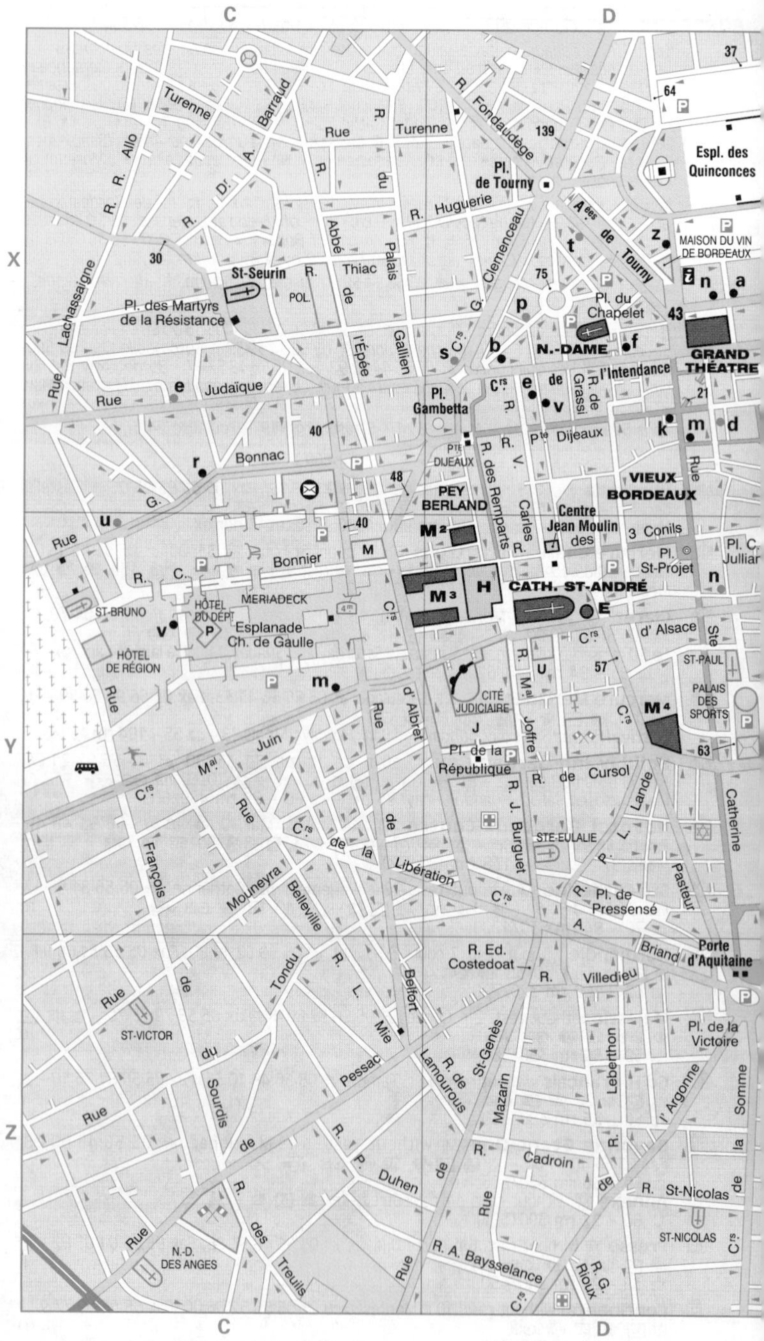
C
D
X
Y
Z
Turenne
Barraud
Rue
R.
Turenne
R. Fondaudège
139
37
64
Espl. des Quinconces
Pl. de Tourny
R. Huguerie
Allées de Tourny
MAISON DU VIN DE BORDEAUX
R. Allo
Dr A.
Abbé
Palais
du
30
St-Seurin
R. Thiac
POL.
Pl. des Martyrs de la Résistance
Lachassaigne
G. Clemenceau
75
Pl. du Chapelet
43
GRAND THÉATRE
N.-DAME
Cours de l'Intendance
R. de Grassi
l'Épée
Gallien
Rue Judaïque
Pl. Gambetta
Pte Dijeaux
PTE DIJEAUX
40
Bonnac
48
PEY BERLAND
R. des Remparts
V. Carles
VIEUX BORDEAUX
Centre Jean Moulin
des 3 Conils
Pl. St-Projet
Pl. C. Julliar
Rue G.
Bonnier
R. C.
MERIADECK
HÔTEL DU DÉPT
Esplanade Ch. de Gaulle
ST-BRUNO
HÔTEL DE RÉGION
CATH. ST-ANDRÉ
Cours d'Alsace
57
ST-PAUL
PALAIS DES SPORTS
CITÉ JUDICIAIRE
R. Mal Joffre
Pl. de la République
R. de Cursol
63
Cours Mal Juin
Rue d'Albret
Rue de
Cours de la Libération
R. J. Burguet
STE-EULALIE
R. P. L. Lande
Pasteur
Ste Catherine
Pl. de Pressensé
A. Briand
Porte d'Aquitaine
François
Mouneyra
Belleville
Tondu
R. L. Mie
Belfort
R. Ed. Costedoat
R. Villedieu
Rue de
ST-VICTOR
du
Sourdis
Pessac
R. de Lamourous
St-Genès
Mazarin
Leberthon
l'Argonne
Pl. de la Victoire
Somme
la
de
Cours
Rue
R. P. Duhen
R. Cadroin
Rue de
R. St-Nicolas
ST-NICOLAS
R. des Treuils
N.-D. DES ANGES
R. A. Bayssalance
R. G. Rioux
Cours
Rue

E F

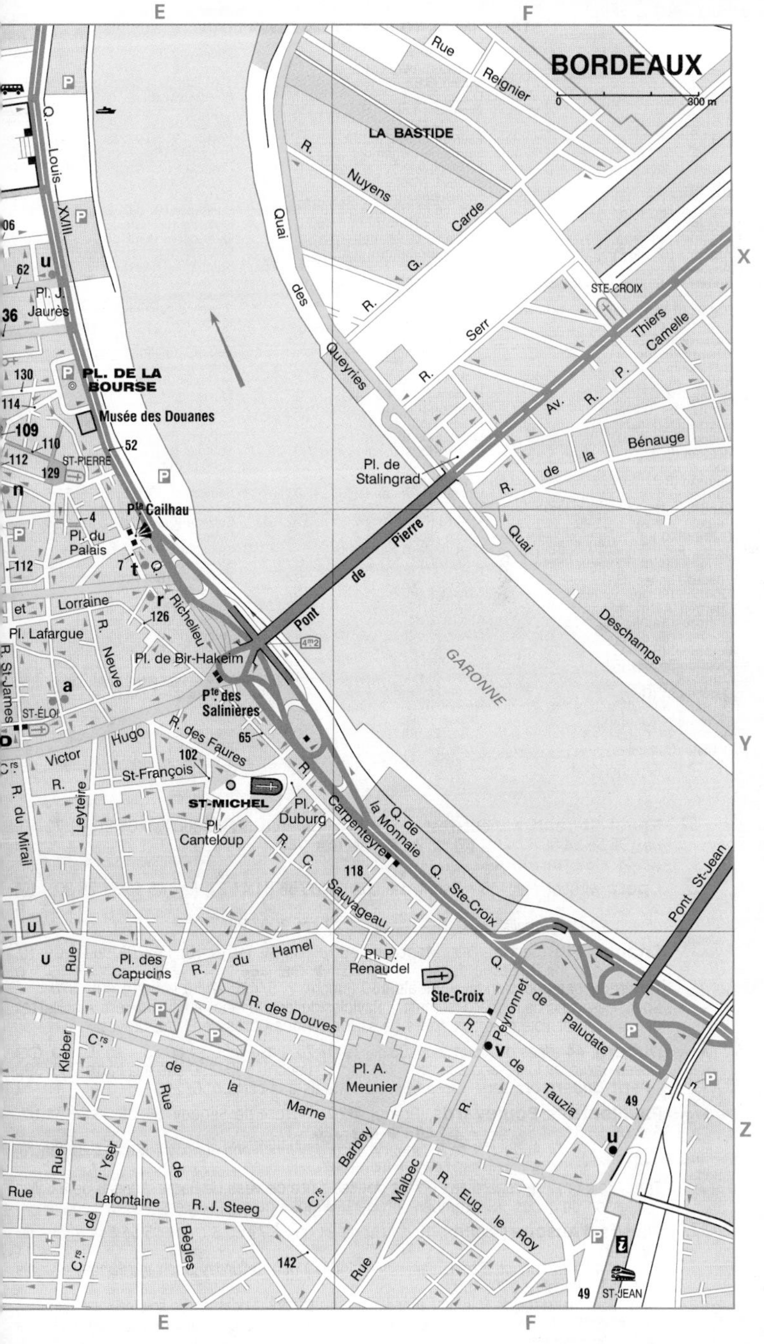
BORDEAUX
0
300 m
LA BASTIDE
Rue Reignier
R. Nuyens
R. G. Carde
R. Serr
Quai des Queyries
STE-CROIX
Thiers
Camelle
Av. R. P.
R. de la Bénauge
Pl. de Stalingrad
Pont de Pierre
Quai Deschamps
GARONNE
Q. Louis XVIII
Pl. J. Jaurès
PL. DE LA BOURSE
Musée des Douanes
ST-PIERRE
Pte Cailhau
Pl. du Palais
Q. Richelieu
Lorraine
Pl. Lafargue
R. Neuve
Pl. de Bir-Hakeim
R. St-James
ST-ÉLOI
Pte des Salinières
R. des Faures
Victor Hugo
R. St-François
ST-MICHEL
Pl. Duburg
Pl. Canteloup
R. Leyteire
R. du Mirail
R. Carpenteyre
Q. de la Monnaie
Q. Ste-Croix
R. C. Sauvageau
Pont St-Jean
Pl. des Capucins
R. du Hamel
Pl. P. Renaudel
Ste-Croix
R. des Douves
Q. de Paludate
R. Peyronnet
R. de Tauzia
Crs de la Marne
Pl. A. Meunier
Rue Kléber
Rue de l' Yser
Rue de Bègles
Rue Lafontaine
R. J. Steeg
Crs de la Somme
Crs Barbey
Rue Malbec
R. Eug. le Roy
ST-JEAN
X
Y
Z

E F

## STREET INDEX TO BORDEAUX TOWN PLAN



**Royal St-Jean** without rest, 15 r. Ch. Domercq ✉ 33800 ✆ 05 56 91 72 16, *Fax 05 56 94 08 32* – ▮ TV ☎ ♿. AE ⓓ GB JCB FZ u
☕ 45 – **37 rm** 330/440.

**Opéra** without rest, 35 r. Esprit des Lois ✆ 05 56 81 41 27, *Fax 05 56 51 78 80* – TV ☎. GB DX n
*closed 24 December-2 January* – ☕ 35 – **27 rm** 200/310.

**Chapon Fin** (Garcia), 5 r. Montesquieu ✆ 05 56 79 10 10, *Fax 05 56 79 09 10*, « Authentic 1900 rocaille decor » – ▤. AE ⓓ GB JCB DX p
*closed Sunday and Monday* – **Meals** 160 (lunch), 275/420 and a la carte 400/620
**Spec.** Gaspacho de homard (summer). Ravioles de langoustines au citron vert. Aiguillettes de caneton et foie gras aux fruits de saison. **Wines** Côtes de Blaye, Graves.

**Dubern,** 44 allées de Tourny ✆ 05 56 79 07 70, *Fax 05 56 51 60 38* – ▤. AE ⓓ GB
*closed Saturday lunch and Sunday* – **Meals** 150 (lunch), 190/290 and a la carte 280/390 - ***Petit Dubern*** brasserie *(closed Sunday)* **Meals** a la carte 150/210. DX t

**Pavillon des Boulevards** (Franc), 120 r. Croix de Seguey ✆ 05 56 81 51 02, *Fax 05 56 51 14 58*, ☂ – ▤. AE ⓓ GB JCB
*closed 10 to 24 August, 1 to 8 January, Saturday lunch and Sunday* – **Meals** 220 (lunch), 270/320 and a la carte 340/450
**Spec.** Foie gras de canard aux épices douces. Côte de veau de Bazas. Agneau de Pauillac "paillasson de cèpes" (September-October). **Wines** Entre-Deux-Mers, Pessac-Léognan.

**Plaisirs d'Ausone** (Gauffre), 10 r. Ausone ✆ 05 56 79 30 30, *Fax 05 56 51 38 16* – AE ⓓ GB EY t
*closed 14 to 25 August, 3 to 12 January, Monday lunch, Saturday lunch and Sunday* – **Meals** 170 and a la carte 270/400
**Spec.** Gourmandises de foie de canard aux trois façons. Fricassée de sole et Saint-Jacques aux cèpes (September-October). Oreille de cochon farcie, étuvée aux morilles. **Wines** Côtes de Castillon, Graves.

XXX **Jean Ramet,** 7 pl. J. Jaurès ✆ 05 56 44 12 51, *Fax 05 56 52 19 80* – ▤. AE GB EX u
*closed 10 to 30 August, Saturday lunch and Sunday* – **Meals** 160 (lunch), 250/300 and a la carte 270/460
**Spec.** Filets de rougets poêlés, tomates confites. Souris d'agneau cuite sept heures, jus aux truffes (December-April). Fondant au chocolat, sauce café. **Wines** Graves, Saint-Emilion.

XXX **Vieux Bordeaux** (Bordage), 27 r. Buhan ✆ 05 56 52 94 36, *Fax 05 56 44 25 11*, – ▤. AE ⓓ GB EY a
*closed 3 to 24 August, February Holidays, Saturday lunch, Sunday and Bank Holidays* – **Meals** 160/270 and a la carte 200/370
**Spec.** Blanc de bar à la concassée d'olives. Râble de lapin farci de pied de porc et d'escargots. Turron glacé, petites chocolatines à l'orange amère. **Wines** Côtes de Bourg, Pessac Léognan.

XXX **L'Alhambra,** 111 bis r. Judaïque ✆ 05 56 96 06 91, *Fax 05 56 98 00 52* – ▤. GB CX e
*closed 1 to 15 August, Saturday lunch and Sunday* – **Meals** 110 (lunch), 160/220 and a la carte 250/360.

XX **Didier Gélineau,** 26 r. Pas St-Georges ✆ 05 56 52 84 25, *Fax 05 56 51 93 25* – ▤. AE ⓓ GB JCB EX n
*closed 9 to 24 August, Saturday lunch and Sunday* – **Meals** (booking essential) 120/270.

XX **Chamade,** 20 r. Piliers de Tutelle ✆ 05 56 48 13 74, *Fax 05 56 79 29 67* – ▤. AE GB JCB DX d
*closed 24 July-12 August, 4 to 10 January, Sunday from 14 July-31 August and from January-March and Saturday lunch* – **Meals** 120/320.

XX **Rose des Vents,** 23 r. Ausonne ✆ 05 56 48 55 85, *Fax 05 56 48 55 85*, « 16C wine cellar » – ▤. AE GB EY r
*closed 1 to 21 August, Monday lunch, Sunday and Bank Holidays* – **Meals** 100/215.

XX **Buhan,** 28 r. Buhan ✆ 05 56 52 80 86, *Fax 05 56 52 80 86* – AE GB EY a
*closed 19 July-3 August, February Holidays, Sunday except lunch from September-June and Monday* – **Meals** 135/250.

XX **Café Régent,** 46 pl. Gambetta ✆ 05 56 44 16 20, *Fax 05 56 51 36 81*, , brasserie – ▤. AE GB DX s
Meals 125.

X **Croc-Loup,** 35 r. Loup ✆ 05 56 44 21 19 – GB DY n
*closed August, Sunday and Monday* – **Meals** 67 (lunch), 115/145 ₰.

X **Oiseau Bleu,** 65 cours Verdun ✆ 05 56 81 09 39, *Fax 05 56 81 09 39* – ▤. AE GB
*closed 3 to 23 August, Christmas-New Year, Saturday lunch and Sunday* – **Meals** 107 (lunch)/162.

X **Bistro du Sommelier,** 163 r. G. Bonnac ✆ 05 56 96 71 78, *Fax 05 56 24 52 36*, – GB CY u
*closed 10 to 16 August, Saturday lunch and Sunday* – **Meals** 125.

**at Parc des Expositions** *North of the town* – ✉ *33300 Bordeaux* :

**Sofitel Aquitania** Ⓜ, ✆ 05 56 69 66 66, *Fax 05 56 69 66 00*, , – |✱|, ⇔ rm, ▤ TV ☎ P – 🔺 25 - 400. AE ⓓ GB
***Le Flore*** : Meals 190 – ☕ 75 – **183 rm** 780/1000.

**Novotel-Bordeaux Lac** Ⓜ, ✆ 05 56 50 99 70, *Fax 05 56 43 00 66*, , , – |✱|, ⇔ rm, ▤ TV ☎ ♿ P – 🔺 200. AE ⓓ GB JCB
Meals a la carte approx. 150 – ☕ 55 – **176 rm** 450/490.

**Mercure Pont d'Aquitaine,** ✆ 05 56 43 36 72, *Fax 05 56 50 23 95*, , , , – |✱|, ⇔ rm, ▤ TV ☎ ♿ P – 🔺 80. AE ⓓ GB JCB
Meals (dinner only) 110 ₰ – ☕ 55 – **100 rm** 450/520.

**at Bouliac** *SE : 8 km – alt. 74 –* ✉ *33270* :

**St-James** (Amat) Ⓜ, pl. C. Hostein, near church ✆ 05 57 97 06 00, *Fax 05 56 20 92 58*, ≤ Bordeaux, , « Original contemporary decor », , – |✱|, ▤ rm, TV ☎ ♿ P – 🔺 25 - 40. AE ⓓ GB.
**Meals** 255/380 (buffet lunch on Sunday) and a la carte 330/450 - ***Le Bistroy*** ✆ 05 57 97 06 06 **Meals** à la carte 150/220 – ☕ 80 – **18 rm** 900/1550
**Spec.** Fondant d'aubergines au cumin, coulis de tomates au basilic. Homard breton rôti aux pommes de terre et gousses d'ail. Pigeon grillé aux épices et sa pastilla. **Wines** Entre-deux-Mers, Médoc.

**to the W :**

**at the airport** *11 km by A 630 : from the North, exit nº 11b, from the South, exit nº11 – ✉ 33700 Mérignac :*

**Mercure Aéroport** M, 1 av. Ch. Lindbergh ✆ 05 56 34 74 74, *Fax 05 56 34 30 84*, – rm, – 110. AE GB
**Meals** 120 – 55 – **148 rm** 685/725.

**Novotel Aéroport,** av. J. F. Kennedy ✆ 05 56 34 10 25, *Fax 05 56 55 99 64*, – rm, – 70. AE GB
**Meals** a la carte approx. 170 – 55 – **137 rm** 495/530.

**Eugénie-les-Bains** *40320 Landes 82 ① – pop. 467 alt. 65 – Spa (Feb.-Nov.).*
*Golf du Tursan ✆ 05 58 51 11 63 by D 11 and D 62 : 2 km.*
*Tourist Office, 147 r. René Vielle (Feb.-Nov.) ✆ 05 58 51 13 16, Fax 05 58 51 12 02.*
*Bordeaux 151.*

**Les Prés d'Eugénie** (Guérard) M, ✆ 05 58 05 06 07, *Fax 05 58 51 10 10*, « Elegantly decorated 19C mansion, park », – 60. AE GB.
*closed 1 to 17 December and 4 January-28 February* – (low-calorie menu for residents only) **- *rest. Michel Guérard*** (booking essential) *(closed Thursday lunch and Wednesday from 4 September-13 July except Bank Holidays)* **Meals** 590/750 and a la carte 520/710 – 120 – **17 rm** 1250/1650, 12 suites
**Spec.** Salade baroque aux crevettes et "croquignolles" d'araignée de mer. Poitrine de poulette fourrée d'herbes grillée au lard sur la braise. Gâteau mollet du Marquis de Béchamel, glace fondue à la rhubarbe. **Wines** Tursan blanc.
**Couvent des Herbes** M, park, « 18C convent » – AE GB. rest
**Meals** see ***Les Prés d'Eugénie*** and ***Michel Guérard*** – 120 – **5 rm** 1450/1650, 3 suites.

**Maison Rose** M (see also rest. Michel Guérard), ✆ 05 58 05 06 07, *Fax 05 58 51 10 10*, « Guesthouse ambience », – kitchenette AE GB.
*closed 1 to 17 December, 4 January-13 February* – **Meals** (residents only) – 60 – **32 rm** 460/580.

**Ferme aux Grives,** ✆ 05 58 51 19 08, *Fax 05 58 51 10 10*, « Old country inn », – GB
*closed 3 January-13 February, Monday dinner and Tuesday from 3 September-12 July except Bank Holidays* – **Meals** 185.

**CANNES** *06400 Alpes-Mar. 84 ⑨, 115 ㉟ ㊳ – pop. 68 676 alt. 2 – Casinos Carlton Casino* BYZ, *Palm Beach (temp. closed)* X, *Croisette* BZ.
**See :** *Site★★ – Seafront★★ : Boulevard★★* BCDZ *and Pointe de la Croisette★* X – *★ from the Mont Chevalier Tower* AZ **V** – *The Castre Museum★ (Musée de la Castre)* AZ – *Tour into the Hills★ (Chemin des Collines) NE : 4 km* V – *The Croix des Gardes* X **E** *★ W : 5 km then 15 mn.*
*of Cannes-Mougins ✆ 04 93 75 79 13 by ⑤ : 9 km ; of Cannes-Mandelieu ✆ 04 93 49 55 39 by ② : 6,5 km ; Royal Mougins Golf Club at Mougins ✆ 04 92 92 49 69 by ④ : 10 km ; Riviera Golf Club at Mandelieu ✆ 04 93 97 67 67 by ② : 8 km.*
*Tourist Office "SEM", Palais des Festivals ✆ 04 93 39 24 53, Fax 04 93 39 37 06 and railway station (first floor) ✆ 04 93 99 19 77, Fax 04 93 39 40 19 – A.C. 12 bis r. L. Blanc ✆ 04 93 39 38 94, Fax 04 93 38 30 65.*
*Paris 903 ⑤ – Aix-en-Provence 146 ⑤ – Grenoble 312 ⑤ – Marseilles 159 ⑤ – Nice 32 ⑤ – Toulon 121 ⑤.*

Plans on following pages

**Carlton Inter-Continental,** 58 bd Croisette ✆ 04 93 06 40 06, *Fax 04 93 06 40 25*, – rm, – 25 - 250. AE GB JCB CZ e
see ***Belle Otéro*** below **- *La Côte*** ✆ 04 93 06 40 23 *(15 June-15 September and closed lunch in July-August, Monday and Tuesday)* **Meals** 265 (lunch), 525/650 – ***Brasserie Carlton :*** **Meals** 255/320 – 145 – **300 rm** 2110/3915, 38 suites.

**Majestic,** 14 bd Croisette ✆ 04 92 98 77 00, *Fax 04 93 38 97 90*, – 400. AE GB JCB BZ n
*closed 15 November-23 December* - see ***Villa des Lys*** below – 120 – **239 rm** 2050/4300, 23 suites.

**Martinez,** 73 bd Croisette ✆ 04 92 98 73 00, *Fax 04 93 39 67 82*, – 600. AE GB JCB DZ n
see ***Palme d'Or*** below **- *Relais Martinez*** ✆ 04 92 98 74 12 **Meals** 165 (lunch) and a la carte 190/380 – 115 – **382 rm** 2000/4500, 12 suites.

**Noga Hilton** M, 50 bd Croisette ✆ 04 92 99 70 00, *Fax 04 92 99 70 11*, « Rooftop swimming pool and terrace ≤ Cannes », – rm, – 800. AE GB JCB CZ b
***La Scala :*** ✆ 04 92 99 70 93 *(closed Sunday dinner and Monday out of season)* **Meals** 210/295 – ***Grand Bleu*** brasserie - ✆ 04 92 99 70 92 **Meals** carte 290 à 390 – 115 – **196 rm** 1690/5590, 33 suites.

**Sofitel Méditerranée** M, 2 bd J. Hibert ✆ 04 92 99 73 00, *Fax 04 92 99 73 29*, « Rooftop swimming pool and restaurant ≤ bay of Cannes » – rm, – 100. AE GB JCB AZ n
*closed 22 November-12 December* – ***Méditerranée*** (7th floor) ✆ 04 92 99 73 02 **Meals** 230 – ***Chez Panisse*** ✆ 04 92 99 73 10 - Provencal decor **Meals** 150/180 – 100 – **141 rm** 1070/1790, 8 suites.

**Savoy** M, 5 r. F. Einesy ✆ 04 92 99 72 00, *Fax 04 93 68 25 59*, « Rooftop swimming pool and terrace », – rm, – 90. AE GB CZ u
*closed 20 November-20 December* – ***Roseraie*** ✆ 04 92 99 72 09 **Meals** 165 – 98 – **101 rm** 995/1455, 5 suites.

**Gray d'Albion** M, 38 r. Serbes ✆ 04 92 99 79 79, *Fax 04 93 99 26 10*, – rm, – 150. AE GB JCB BZ d
***Royal Gray*** ✆ 04 92 99 79 60 **Meals** 190/290 – 97 – **172 rm** 2150, 14 suites.

**Croisette Beach H.** M without rest, 13 r. Canada ✆ 04 93 94 50 50, *Fax 04 93 68 35 38* – rm, AE GB JCB DZ y
*closed 20 November-25 December* – 95 – **94 rm** 1090/1290.

**Belle Plage** M without rest, 6 r. J. Dollfus ✆ 04 93 06 25 50, *Fax 04 93 99 61 06*, ≤, « Rooftop terrace, ≤ sea » – AE GB JCB AZ u
*closed 15 November-25 January* – 80 – **48 rm** 960/1460.

**Amarante** M, 78 bd Carnot ✆ 04 93 39 22 23, *Fax 04 93 39 40 22*, – rm, – 25. AE GB JCB V e
**Meals** *(closed 1 to 21 December, Saturday and Sunday from September-March)* 130/250 b.i. – 60 – **71 rm** 630/790.

**Sun Riviera** M without rest, 138 r. d'Antibes ✆ 04 93 06 77 77, *Fax 04 93 38 31 10*, – rm, AE GB JCB CZ h
85 – **42 rm** 810/1800.

**Splendid** without rest, 4 r. F. Faure ✆ 04 93 99 53 11, *Fax 04 93 99 55 02*, ≤ harbour – kitchenette AE GB BZ a
50 – **64 rm** 590/950.

**Cristal** M, 15 rd-pt Duboys d'Angers ✆ 04 93 39 45 45, *Fax 04 93 38 64 66*, – rm, AE GB JCB CZ s
*closed 20 November-26 December* – **Meals** *(closed Sunday dinner and Monday)* 140/350 – 82 – **51 rm** 870/1900.

**Victoria** without rest, rd-pt Duboys d'Angers ✆ 04 93 99 36 36, *Fax 04 93 38 03 91* – AE GB JCB CZ x
*closed 17 November-27 December* – 70 – **25 rm** 750/1250.

**Fouquet's** without rest, 2 rd-pt Duboys d'Angers ✆ 04 93 38 75 81, *Fax 04 92 98 03 39* – AE GB JCB CZ y
*1 March-1 November* – 60 – **10 rm** 1100/1300.

**Paris** without rest, 34 bd Alsace ✆ 04 93 38 30 89, *Fax 04 93 39 04 61*, – – 25. AE GB JCB. CY a
*closed 15 November to 25 December* – 60 – **47 rm** 650/720, 3 suites.

**America** M without rest, 13 r. St-Honoré ✆ 04 93 06 75 75, *Fax 04 93 68 04 58* – AE GB JCB. BZ r
*closed 27 November-27 December* – 60 – **28 rm** 570/760.

**Mondial** without rest, 1 r. Tesseire ✆ 04 93 68 70 00, *Fax 04 93 99 39 11* – rm, AE GB CY e
65 – **58 rm** 650/780.

**Embassy** without rest, 6 r. Bône ✆ 04 93 38 79 02, *Fax 04 93 99 07 98* – AE GB JCB DY j
40 – **60 rm** 580/950.

**Villa de l'Olivier** without rest, 5 r. Tambourinaires ✆ 04 93 39 53 28, *Fax 04 93 39 55 85*, – P. AE GB. AZ e
52 – **24 rm** 525/715.

**Renoir** without rest, 7 r. Edith Cavell ✆ 04 92 99 62 62, *Fax 04 92 99 62 82* – kitchenette AE GB BY x
65 – **27 rm** 800/900.

**Beau Séjour,** 5 r. Fauvettes ✆ 04 93 39 63 00, *Fax 04 92 98 64 66*, – rm, AE GB AZ d
**Meals** 75/110 – 60 – **45 rm** 650/750.

## CANNES

André (R. du Cdt) .... CZ
Antibes (R. d') ....... BCY
Belges (R. des) ...... BZ 12
Chabaud (R.) ......... CY 22
Croisette (Bd de la) ... BDZ
Félix-Faure (R.) ....... ABZ
Foch (R. du Mar.) .... BY 44
Joffre (R. du Mar.) .... BY 60
Riouffe (R. Jean de) ... BY 98

Albert-Édouard (Jetée) . BZ
Alexandre-III (Bd) ..... X 2
Alsace (Bd) ......... BDY
Anc. Combattants d'Afrique du Nord (Av.) ...... AYZ 4
Bachaga Saïd Boualam (Av.) ..... AY 5
Beauséjour (Av.) ..... DYZ
Beau-Soleil (Bd) ...... X 10
Blanc (R. Louis) ...... AYZ
Broussailles (Av. des) . V 16
Buttura (R.) ......... BZ 17
Canada (R. du) ...... DZ
Carnot (Bd) ......... X
Carnot (Square) ...... V 20
Castre (Pl. de la) ..... AZ 21
Clemenceau (R. G.) ... AZ
Coteaux (Av. des) .... V
Croix-des-Gardes (Bd) . VX 29
Delaup (Bd) ......... AY 30
Dr-Pierre Gazagnaire (R.) . AZ 32
Dr-R. Picaud (Av.) .... X
Dollfus (R. Jean) ..... AZ 33
Etats-Unis (R. des) .... CZ 35
Faure (R. Félix) ....... ABZ
Favorite (Av. de la) ... X 38
Ferrage (Bd de la) .... ABY 40
Fiesole (Av.) ......... X 43
Gallieni (R. du Mar.) ... BY 48
Gaulle (Pl. Gén.-de) ... BZ 51
Gazagnaire (Bd Eugène) . X
Grasse (Av. de) ...... VX 53
Guynemer (Bd) ...... AY
Hespérides (Av. des) .. X 55
Hibert (Bd Jean) .... AZ
Hibert (R.) .......... AZ
Isola-Bella (Av. d') ... X
Jaurès (R. Jean) .... BCY
Juin (Av. Mar.) ..... DZ
Koenig (Av. Gén.) ... DY
Lacour (Bd Alexandre) . X 62
Latour-Maubourg (R.) . DZ
Lattre-de-T. (Av. de) . AY 63
Laubeuf (Quai Max) . AZ
Leader (Bd) ........ VX 64
Lérins (Av. de) ...... X 65
Lorraine (Bd. de) .... CDY
Macé (R.) .......... CZ 66
Madrid (Av. de) ..... DZ
Meynadier (R.) ..... ABY
Midi (Bd du) ........ X
Mimont (R. de) ...... BY
Mont-Chevalier (R. du) . AZ 72
Montfleury (Bd) ..... CDY 74
Monti (R. Marius) .... AY 75
Noailles (Av. J.-de) .. X
Observatoire (Bd de l') . X 84
Oxford (Bd d') ....... V 87
Pantiero (la) ........ ABZ
Paradis-Terrestre (Corniches du) .... V 88
Pasteur (R.) ......... DZ
Pastour (R. Louis) .... AY 90
Perier (Bd du) ....... V 92
Perrissol (R. Louis) ... AZ 93
Petit-Juas (Av. du) .... VX
Pins (Bd des) ........ X 95
Pompidou (Espl. G.) .. BZ
Prince-de-Galles (Av. du) X 97
République (Bd de la) . X
Riou (Bd du) ........ VX
Roi-Albert 1er (Av.) .. X
Rouguière (R.) ...... BY 100
St-Antoine (R.) ...... AZ 102
St-Nicolas (Av.) ...... BY 105
St-Pierre (Quai) ..... AZ
Sardou (R. Léandre) . X 108
Serbes (R. des) ..... BZ 110
Source (Bd de la) ... X 112
Stanislas (Pl.) ....... AY
Strasbourg (Bd de) .. CDY
Teisseire (R.) ....... CY 114
Tuby (Bd Victor) .... AYZ 115
Vallauris (Av. de) .... VX 116
Vallombrosa (Bd) ... AY 118
Vautrin (Bd Gén.) ... DZ
Vidal (R. du Cdt) .... CY 120
Wemyss (Av. Amiral Wester) . X 122

## LE CANNET

Aubarède (Ch. de l') . V 8
Bellevue (Pl.) ....... V 13
Bréguières (Ch. de) .. V 14
Cannes (R. des) ..... V 19
Carnot (Bd de) ...... V
Cheval (Av. Maurice) . V 23
Collines (Ch. des) ... V
Doumer (Bd Paul) ... V
Écoles (R. des) ..... V 34
Four-à-Chaux (Bd du) . V 45
Gambetta (Bd) ...... V 50
Gaulle (Av. Gén.-de) . V
Jeanpierre (Av. Maurice) . V 58
Mermoz (Av. Jean) .. V 67
Monod (Bd Jacques) . V 68
Mont-Joli (Av. du) ... V 73
N.-D.-des-Anges (Av.) . V 79
Olivet (Ch. de l') .... V 85
Olivetum (Av. d') .... V 86
Paris (R. de) ........ V 89
Pinède (Av. de la) ... V 94
Pompidou (Av. Georges) V 96
République (Bd de la) . V
Roosevelt (Av. Franklin) . V
St-Sauveur (R.) ..... V 106
Victor-Hugo (R.) ..... V 119
Victoria (Av.) ........ V

## VALLAURIS

Cannes (Av. de) .... V 18
Clemenceau (Av. G.) . V 25
Fournas (Av. du) .... V 46
Golfe (Av. du) ...... V 52
Isnard (Pl. Paul) ..... V 56
Rouvier (Bd Maurice) . V 102
Tapis-Vert (Av. du) .. V 113

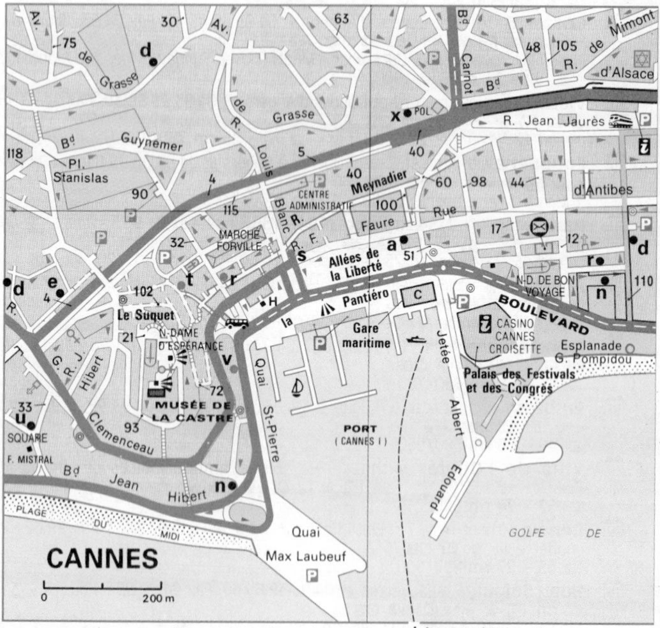

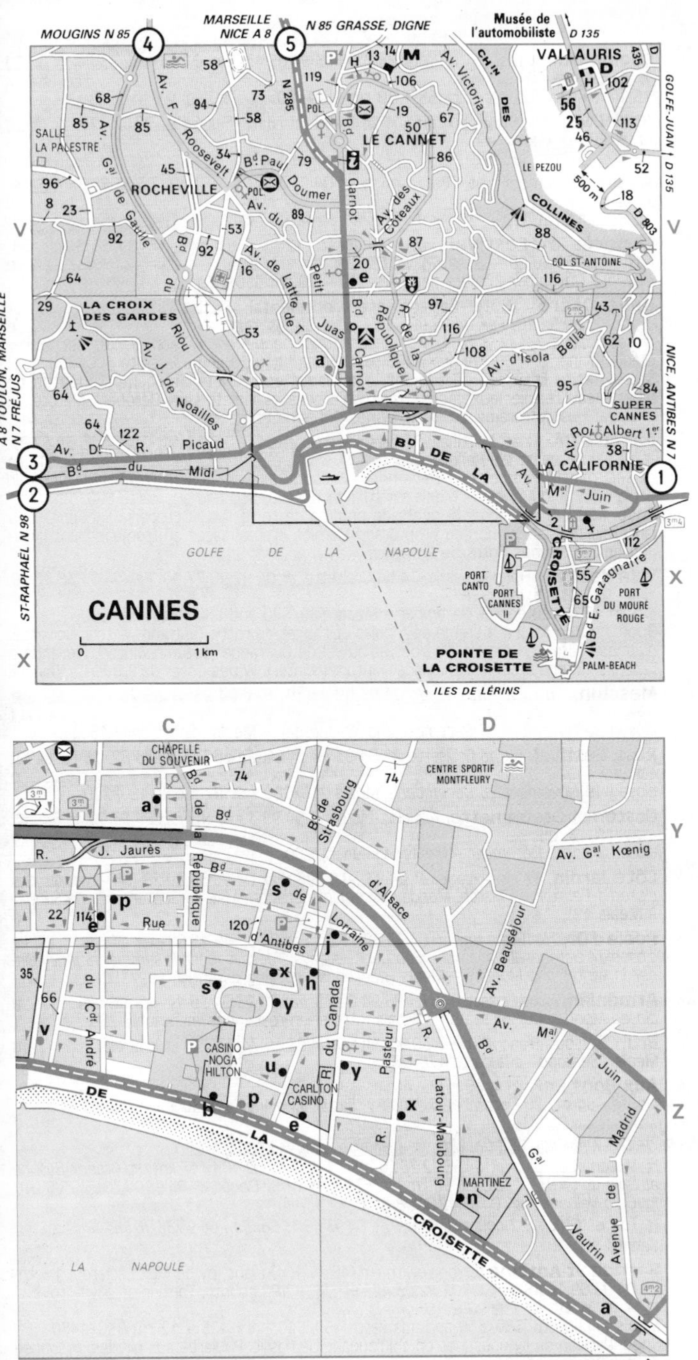
CANNES
MOUGINS N 85
MARSEILLE
NICE A 8
N 85 GRASSE, DIGNE
Musée de l'automobiliste
D 135
VALLAURIS
GOLFE-JUAN D 135
LE CANNET
ROCHEVILLE
SALLE LA PALESTRE
LE PEZOU
COLLINES
COL ST-ANTOINE
LA CROIX DES GARDES
SUPER CANNES
LA CALIFORNIE
NICE, ANTIBES N 7
A 8 TOULON, MARSEILLE N 7 FRÉJUS
ST-RAPHAËL N 98
GOLFE DE LA NAPOULE
PORT CANTO
PORT CANNES II
PORT DU MOURE ROUGE
POINTE DE LA CROISETTE
PALM-BEACH
ILES DE LÉRINS
0 1 km
CHAPELLE DU SOUVENIR
CENTRE SPORTIF MONTFLEURY
CASINO NOGA HILTON
CARLTON CASINO
MARTINEZ
LA NAPOULE
Pointe de la Croisette

**Régina** without rest, 31 r. Pasteur 04 93 94 05 43, *Fax 04 93 43 20 54* – AE GB. DZ x
*15 March-late October* – 55 – **18 rm** 550/680.

**Abrial** without rest, 24 bd Lorraine 04 93 38 78 82, *Fax 04 92 98 67 41* – AE GB JCB CY s
50 – **50 rm** 590/690.

**Albert 1er** without rest, 68 av. Grasse 04 93 39 24 04, *Fax 04 93 38 83 75* – GB AY d
35 – **11 rm** 350.

**Congrès et Festivals** without rest, 12 r. Teisseire 04 93 39 13 81, *Fax 04 93 39 56 28* – AE GB. CY p
*closed 1 November-27 December* – 40 – **20 rm** 330/650.

**Belle Otéro** - Hôtel Carlton Inter-Continental, 58 bd Croisette, 7th floor 04 92 99 51 10, *Fax 04 92 99 51 19* – AE GB JCB CZ e
*closed 7 June-7 July, 1 to 17 November, Sunday and Monday from September-June* – **Meals** (dinner only July-August) 290 b.i. (lunch), 390/620 and a la carte 500/750
**Spec.** Petite fricassée de supions, coquillages et rougets de roche. Poupeton de pigeonneau fermier aux cèpes, risotto d'artichauts violets (July-October). Marbré de chocolat, jus de caramel au rhum. **Wines** Côtes de Provence.

**Palme d'Or** - Hôtel Martinez, 73 bd Croisette 04 92 98 74 14, *Fax 04 93 39 67 82*, – AE GB JCB DZ n
*closed mid November-mid December, Tuesday except dinner from mid June-mid September and Monday* – **Meals** 295 b.i. (lunch), 350/580 and a la carte 500/620
**Spec.** Rougets de roche, beignets de pomme de terre (May-October). Pigeonneau du lauragais. Fraises des bois au sirop Grand Marnier, crème glacée au fromage blanc (May-September). **Wines** Côtes de Provence.

**Villa des Lys** - Hôtel Majestic, 14 bd Croisette 04 92 98 77 00, *Fax 04 93 38 97 90*, – AE GB JCB
*closed 15 November-23 December* – **Meals** 350/540 and a la carte 430/600
**Spec.** Potiron farci à la crème de moules et rouget de roche (autumn-winter). Noisettes d'agneau rôties en croûte d'herbes et au sel de Guérande (autumn-winter). Florentin à l'ananas Victoria braisé "Pina-Colada" (autumn-winter). **Wines** Côtes de Provence, Bandol.

**Mesclun,** 16 r. St-Antoine 04 93 99 45 19, *Fax 04 93 47 68 29* – AE GB JCB AZ t
*closed 20 November-20 December and Wednesday* – **Meals** (dinner only) 180.

**Rest. Festival,** 52 bd Croisette 04 93 38 04 81, *Fax 04 93 38 13 82*, – AE GB JCB CZ p
*closed 19 November-26 December* – **Meals** 215/280 - ***Grill*** : **Meals** 180/220 .

**Gaston et Gastounette,** 7 quai St-Pierre 04 93 39 47 92, *Fax 04 93 99 45 34*, – AE GB AZ v
*closed 1 to 20 December* – **Meals** 130 (lunch)/200.

**Côté Jardin,** 12 av. St-Louis 04 93 38 60 28, *Fax 04 93 38 60 28*, – AE GB
*closed 1 February-9 March, Monday except dinner from May-15 September and Sunday* – **Meals** 195. X a

**Poêle d'Or,** 23 r. États-Unis 04 93 39 77 65, *Fax 04 93 40 45 59* – AE GB CZ v
*closed 24 October-2 November, February Holidays, Tuesday lunch in summer, Sunday dinner in winter and Monday* – **Meals** (weekends : booking essential) 199/350.

**Arménien,** 82 bd Croisette 04 93 94 00 58, *Fax 04 93 94 56 12* – AE GB DZ a
*closed Monday out of season* – **Meals** - Armenian rest. - one menu only 250.

**Brun,** 2 r. Louis-Blanc 04 93 39 98 94, *Fax 04 93 39 74 27*, – AE GB AZ s
**Meals** - Seafood - a la carte 170/230.

**Aux Bons Enfants,** 80 r. Meynadier – AZ r
*closed August, 20 December-3 January, Saturday dinner and Sunday* – **Meals** 94.

## Grasse

*06130 Alpes-Mar. 84 ⑧, 114 ⑬, 115 ㉔ – pop. 41 388 alt. 250.*
*Victoria Golf Club 04 93 12 23 26 by D 4, D 3 and D 103 : 13 km ; Grande Bastide at Opio 04 93 77 70 08, E : 6 km by D 7 ; of St-Donat 04 93 09 76 60 : 5,5 km ; Opio-Valbonne 04 93 42 00 08 by D 4 : 11 km.*
*Tourist Office, 22 cours H. Cresp 04 93 36 03 56, Fax 04 93 36 86 36.*
*Cannes 17.*

**Bastide St-Antoine** (Chibois) with rm, 48 av. H. Dunant (by bd Mar. Leclerc) : 1,5 km 04 93 09 16 48, *Fax 04 92 42 03 42*, « 18C country farm in an olive-grove », – AE GB JCB
**Meals** 210 (lunch), 380/550 and a la carte 450/610 – 125 – **12 rm** 950/1450
**Spec.** Papillon de langoustines en chiffonnade de basilic. Poularde aux girolles, mitonnée de pois gourmands. Millefeuille de pommes sautées, sauce caramel.

**Juan-les-Pins** *06160 Alpes-Mar.* 84 ⑨, 115 ㉟ ㊴
*Tourist Office 51 bd Ch.-Guillaumont ✆ 04 92 90 53 05.*
*Cannes 8,5.*

**Juana and rest. La Terrasse**, la Pinède, av. G. Gallice ✆ 04 93 61 08 70, *Fax 04 93 61 76 60*, ≤, rm, – 25. AE GB
*Easter-late October* – **Meals** *(closed Wednesday except July-August and Bank Holidays)* 275 (lunch), 420/640 and a la carte 540/750 – 95 – **45 rm** 950/2050, 5 suites
**Spec.** Cannelloni de supions et palourdes à l'encre de seiche. Selle d'agneau de Pauillac cuite en terre d'argile de Vallauris. Fruits de saison cuits au parfum de vanille, mousseline briochée. **Wines** Bellet, côtes de Provence.

**La Napoule** *06210 Alpes-Mar.* 84 ⑧, 115 ㉞.
*of Mandelieu ✆ 04 93 49 55 39 ; Riviera Golf Club ✆ 04 92 97 67 67.*
*Cannes 9,5.*

**L'Oasis,** r. J. H. Carle ✆ 04 93 49 95 52, *Fax 04 93 49 64 13*, « Shaded and flowered patio » – AE GB
**Meals** 210 (lunch), 290/650 and a la carte 490/630
**Spec.** Asperges violettes du pays et morilles à l'oseille (spring). Risotto de daurade royale aux palourdes, thym et citron (summer). Selle de chevreuil en noisettes aux myrtilles, poires rôties à la cannelle (autumn and winter). **Wines** Côtes de Provence.

---

**LILLE** *59000 Nord* 51 ⑯, 111 ㉒ – *pop. 172 142 alt. 10.*

**See :** *Old Lille★★ : Old Stock Exchange★★ (Vieille Bourse)* EY, *Place du Général-de-Gaulle★* EY **66**, *Hospice Comtesse★ (panelled timber vault★★)* EY, *Rue de la Monnaie★* EY **120** – *Vauban's Citadel★* BV – *St-Sauveur district : Paris Gate★* EFZ, *≤★ from the top of the belfry of the Hôtel de Ville* FZ – *Fine Arts Museum★★★ (Musée des Beaux-Arts)* EZ – *Général de Gaulle's Birthplace (Maison natale)* EY.

*of Flandres (private) ✆ 03 20 72 20 74 : 4,5 km ; of Sart (private) ✆ 03 20 72 02 51 : 7 km ; of Brigode at Villeneuve d'Ascq ✆ 03 20 91 17 86 : 9 km ; of Bondues ✆ 03 20 23 20 62 : 9,5 km.*

*of Lille-Lesquin : ✆ 03 20 49 68 68 : 8 km.*

*✆ 08 36 35 35 35.*

*Tourist Office Palais Rihour ✆ 03 20 21 94 21, Fax 03 20 21 94 20 – Automobile Club du Nord, 8 r. Quennette ✆ 03 20 56 21 41, Fax 03 20 56 21 41.*

*Paris 221 ④ – Brussels 116 ② – Ghent 71 ② – Luxembourg 312 ④ – Strasbourg 525 ④*

Plans on following pages

**Carlton,** 3 r. Paris ✉ 59800 ✆ 03 20 13 33 13, *Fax 03 20 51 48 17* – rm, – 25 - 100. AE GB JCB EY u
***Clos Opéra*** (1st floor) *(closed Sunday dinner and Monday)* **Meals** (95)-135/195 – ***Brasserie Jean*** (basement) *(closed August, lunch Saturday and Sunday)* **Meals** 135 – 75 – **57 rm** 1025/1310, 3 suites.

**Alliance** M, 17 quai du Wault ✉ 59800 ✆ 03 20 30 62 62, *Fax 03 20 42 94 25*, « Former 17C convent » – rm, – 35 - 80. AE GB JCB. rest
**Meals** 110/160 – 70 – **80 rm** 655/900, 8 suites. BV d

**Novotel Centre** M, 116 r. Hôpital Militaire ✉ 59800 ✆ 03 20 30 65 26, *Fax 03 20 30 04 04* – rm, – 30 - 50. AE GB EY s
**Meals** a la carte approx. 170 – 57 – **102 rm** 555/620.

**Mercure Royal** M without rest, 2 bd Carnot ✉ 59800 ✆ 03 20 14 71 47, *Fax 03 20 14 71 48* – rm, – 25. AE GB EY h
55 – **102 rm** 450/580.

**Holiday Inn Express** M, 75 bis r. Gambetta ✆ 03 20 42 90 90, *Fax 03 20 51 14 24* – rm, – 25 - 100. AE GB JCB EZ e
**Meals** 98/160 – **98 rm** 420.

**Paix** without rest, 46 bis r. Paris ✉ 59800 ✆ 03 20 54 63 93, *Fax 03 20 63 98 97* – AE GB EY r
40 – **35 rm** 340/430.

**Treille** M without rest, 7 pl. L. de Bettignies ✉ 59800 ✆ 03 20 55 45 46, *Fax 03 20 51 51 69* – AE GB EY d
48 – **40 rm** 360/390.

**Lille Europe** M without rest, av. Le Corbusier ✆ 03 20 21 41 51, *Fax 03 20 21 41 59* – AE GB FY m
40 – **97 rm** 350.

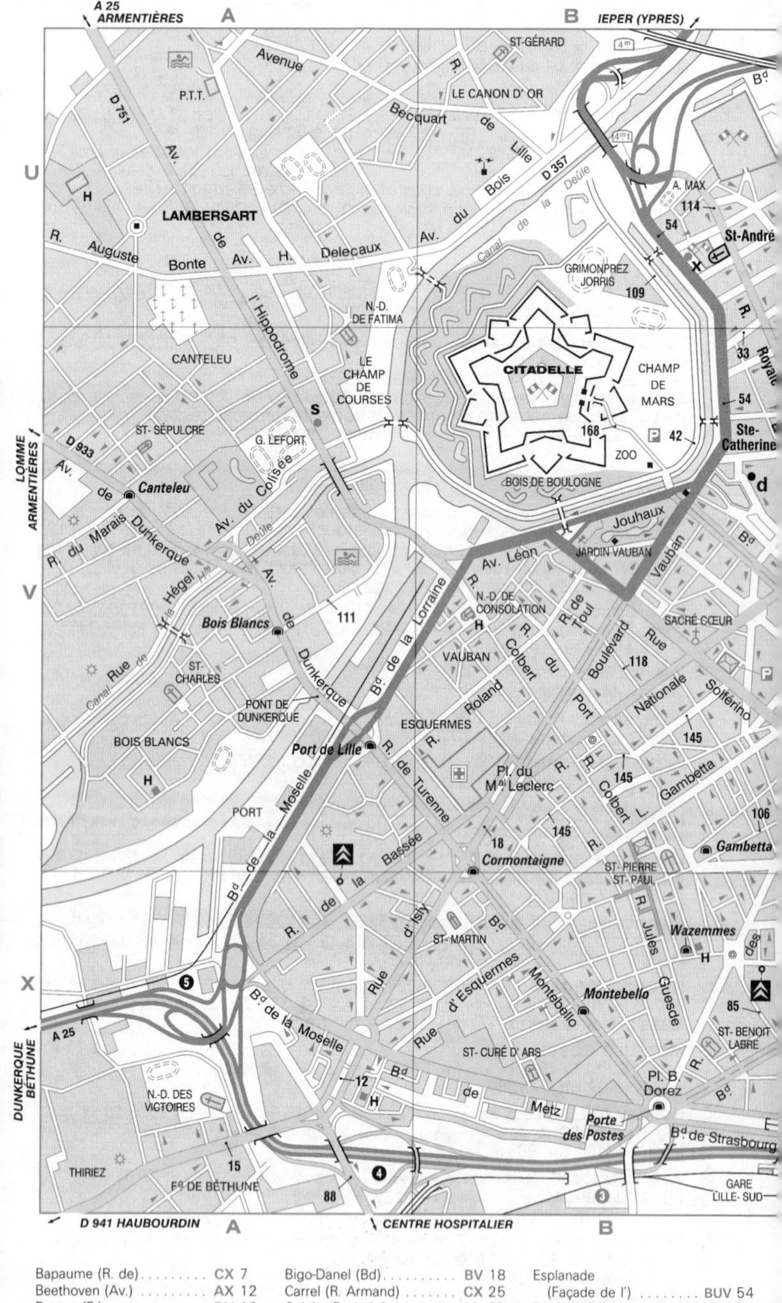
A 25
ARMENTIÈRES
A
B
IEPER (YPRES)
ST-GÉRARD
Avenue
R.
LE CANON D' OR
P.T.T.
D 751
Becquart
de
Lille
Av.
Bois
D 357
du
U
H
A. MAX
114
LAMBERSART
54
St-André
R.
Auguste
Bonte
de
Av.
H.
Delecaux
Av.
Canal
de
la
Deûle
GRIMONPREZ
JORRIS
109
l'Hippodrome
N.-D.
DE FATIMA
R.
33
Royale
CANTELEU
LE
CHAMP
DE
COURSES
CITADELLE
CHAMP
DE
MARS
54
S
ST- SÉPULCRE
168
42
Ste-
Catherine
LOMME
ARMENTIÈRES
D 933
G. LEFORT
ZOO
Av.
de
Canteleu
Av. du Colisée
BOIS DE BOULOGNE
d
R. du Marais
Dunkerque
Deûle
Jouhaux
Bd
Av.
Av. Léon
JARDIN VAUBAN
Vauban
V
Hégel
R.
N.-D. DE
CONSOLATION
R. de Toul
Bois Blancs
de
111
H
R.
SACRÉ CŒUR
Rue de
Canal
ST-
CHARLES
Dunkerque
Bd de la Lorraine
VAUBAN
Colbert
du
Port
Boulevard
Rue
118
PONT DE
DUNKERQUE
Roland
Nationale
Solférino
ESQUERMES
BOIS BLANCS
Port de Lille
R.
R. de Turenne
145
H
Pl. du
Mal Leclerc
R.
R.
Colbert
145
Gambetta
L.
PORT
Bd de la Moselle
145
R.
106
Gambetta
de la Bassée
18
Cormontaigne
ST-PIERRE
ST-PAUL
R.
R. Jules
Guesde
de
d'Isly
Bd
ST-MARTIN
Wazemmes
H
des
X
5
Rue
d'Esquermes
Montebello
Montebello
Bd de la Moselle
85
A 25
Rue
ST-CURÉ D' ARS
ST- BENOIT
LABRE
DUNKERQUE
BÉTHUNE
R.
Pl. B.
Dorez
Bd
N.-D. DES
VICTOIRES
12
H
Bd
de
Metz
Bd
Porte
des Postes
Bd de Strasbourg
15
THIRIEZ
4
Fg DE BÉTHUNE
88
3
GARE
LILLE- SUD
D 941 HAUBOURDIN
A
CENTRE HOSPITALIER
B

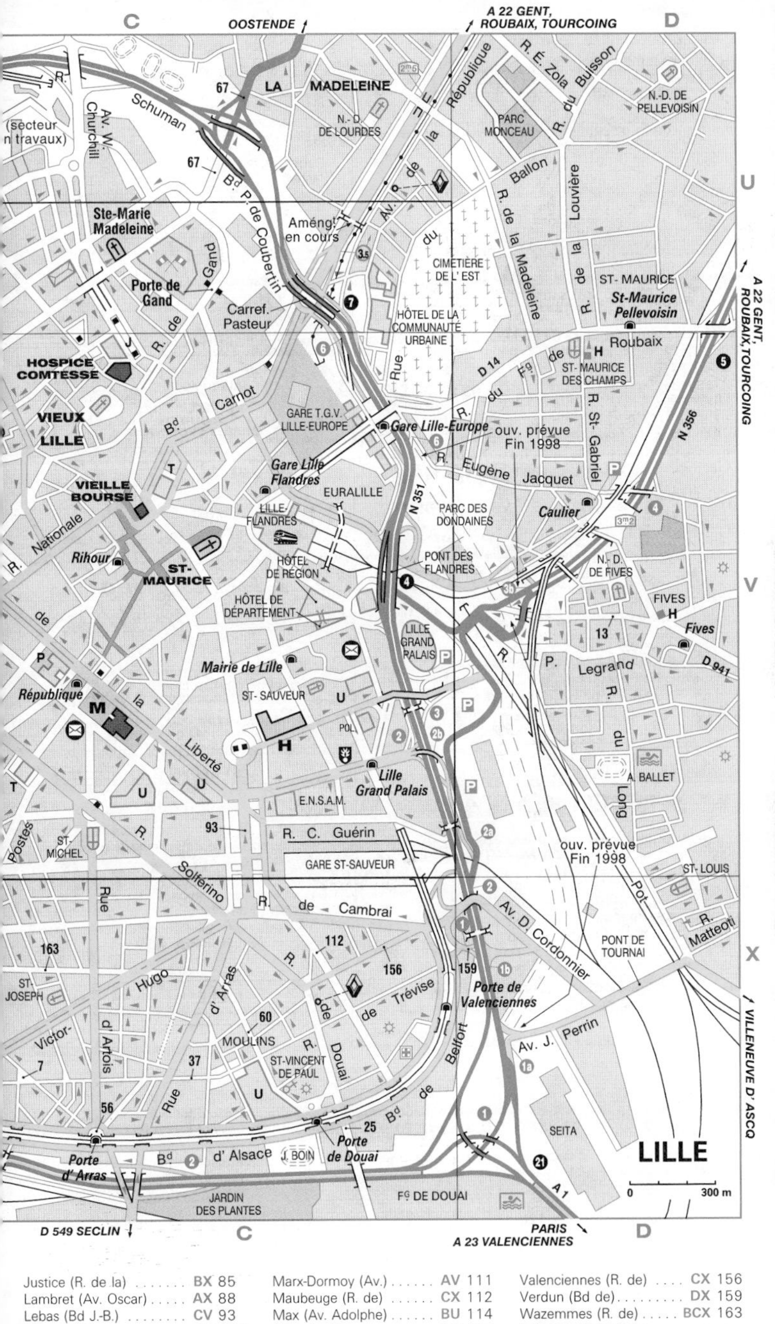
C
OOSTENDE
A 22 GENT, ROUBAIX, TOURCOING
D
U
V
X
LA MADELEINE
N.-D. DE LOURDES
PARC MONCEAU
N.-D. DE PELLEVOISIN
Schuman
Av. W. Churchill
(secteur en travaux)
Bd P. de Coubertin
R. de la République
Av. de la République
R. É. Zola
R. du Buisson
Ballon
R. de la Madeleine
Louvière
R. de la Louvière
Ste-Marie Madeleine
Porte de Gand
R. de Gand
Aménagt en cours
CIMETIÈRE DE L'EST
Carref. Pasteur
HÔTEL DE LA COMMUNAUTÉ URBAINE
ST-MAURICE
St-Maurice Pellevoisin
A 22 GENT, ROUBAIX, TOURCOING
HOSPICE COMTESSE
Rue du Ballon
Roubaix
D 14
R. du Fg de Roubaix
ST-MAURICE DES CHAMPS
VIEUX LILLE
Bd Carnot
GARE T.G.V. LILLE-EUROPE
Gare Lille-Europe
ouv. prévue Fin 1998
R. St-Gabriel
N 356
Gare Lille Flandres
R. Eugène Jacquet
VIEILLE BOURSE
EURALILLE
N 351
PARC DES DONDAINES
Caulier
LILLE-FLANDRES
R. Nationale
HÔTEL DE RÉGION
PONT DES FLANDRES
N.-D. DE FIVES
Rihour
ST-MAURICE
HÔTEL DE DÉPARTEMENT
FIVES
Fives
LILLE GRAND PALAIS
13
R. P. Legrand
D 941
Mairie de Lille
République
ST-SAUVEUR
R. de la Liberté
POL.
R. du Long Pot
Lille Grand Palais
A. BALLET
E.N.S.A.M.
ST-MICHEL
Postes
93
R. C. Guérin
GARE ST-SAUVEUR
ouv. prévue Fin 1998
ST-LOUIS
R. Solférino
R. de Cambrai
Av. D. Cordonnier
R. Matteoti
163
112
PONT DE TOURNAI
ST-JOSEPH
Hugo
R. d'Arras
156
159
Porte de Valenciennes
Rue d'Artois
R. de Trévise
VILLENEUVE D'ASCQ
Victor-
60
MOULINS
R. de Douai
Bd de Belfort
Av. J. Perrin
7
37
ST-VINCENT DE PAUL
Rue
56
25
Porte de Douai
SEITA
Porte d'Arras
Bd d'Alsace
J. BOIN
LILLE
A 1
0
300 m
JARDIN DES PLANTES
Fg DE DOUAI
D 549 SECLIN
C
PARIS A 23 VALENCIENNES
D

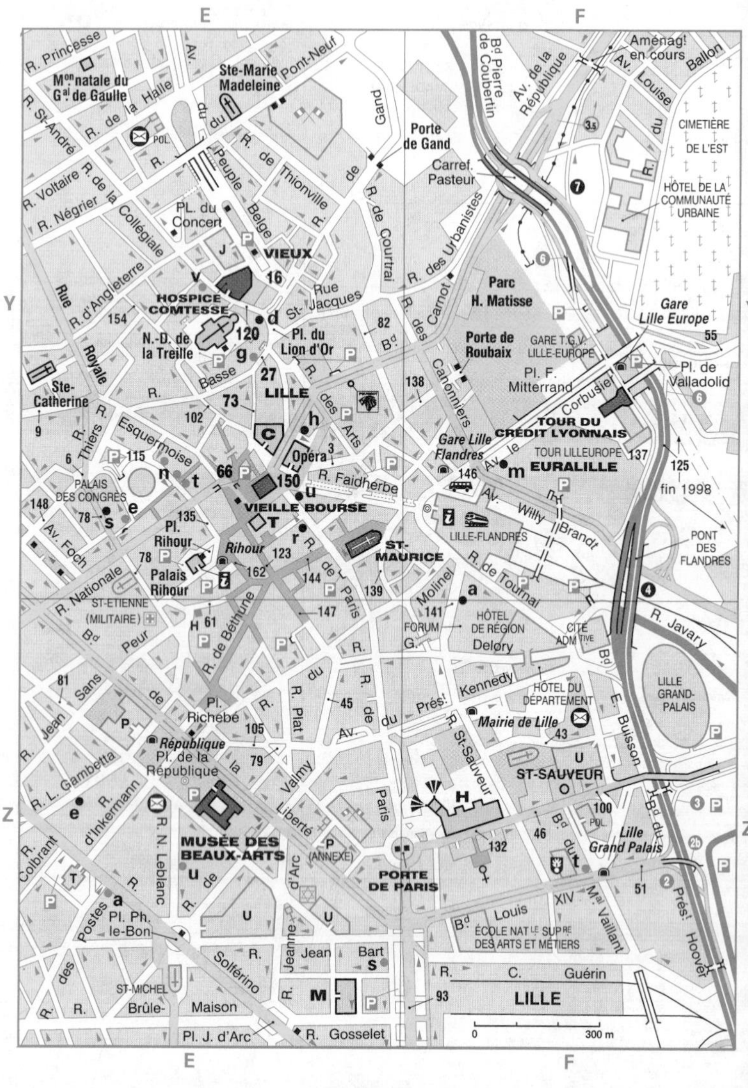


- Béthune (R. de) . . . . . . . . EYZ
- Esquermoise (R.) . . . . . . . . EY
- Faidherbe (R.) . . . . . . . . . EY
- Gambetta (R. Léon) . . . . . EZ
- Gaulle (Pl. Gén.-de) (Grand Place) . . . . . . . . EY 66
- Grande Chaussée (R. de la) EY 73
- Monnaie (R. de la) . . . . . . EY 120
- Nationale (R.) . . . . . . . . . EYZ
- Neuve (R.) . . . . . . . . . . . EY 123

- Anatole-France (R.) . . . . . . EY 3
- Arsenal (Pl. de l') . . . . . . . EY 6
- Barre (R. de la) . . . . . . . . . EY 9
- Bettignies (Pl. L. de) . . . . . EY 16
- Chats-Bossus (R. des) . . . . EY 27
- Debierre (R. Ch.) . . . . . . . . FZ 43
- Delesalle (R. E.) . . . . . . . . EZ 45
- Déportés (R. des) . . . . . . . FY 46
- Dr.-Calmette (Bd) . . . . . . . FY 51
- Faubourg de Roubaix . . . . . FY 55
- Fosses (R. des) . . . . . . . . . EYZ 61
- Hôpital-Militaire (R.) . . . . . EY 78
- Jacquart (Pl.) . . . . . . . . . . EZ 79
- Jacquemars-Giélée (R.) . . . . EZ 81
- Jardins (R. des) . . . . . . . . . EY 82
- Lebas (Bd J.-B.) . . . . . . . . . FZ 93
- Lefèvre (R. G.) . . . . . . . . . . FZ 100
- Lepelletier (R.) . . . . . . . . . EY 102
- Maillotte (R.) . . . . . . . . . . . EZ 105
- Mendès-France (Pl.) . . . . . . EY 115
- Pasteur (Bd. L.) . . . . . . . . . FY 125
- Philippe-le-Bon (Pl.) . . . . . . EZ 126
- Réduit (R. du) . . . . . . . . . . FZ 132
- Roisin (R. Jean) . . . . . . . . . EY 135
- Rotterdam (Parvis de) . . . . FY 137
- Roubaix (R. de) . . . . . . . . . EFY 138
- St-Génois (R.) . . . . . . . . . . EY 139
- St-Venant (Av. Ch.) . . . . . . FYZ 141
- Sec-Arembault (R. du) . . . . EY 144
- Suisses (Pl. des) . . . . . . . . FY 146
- Tanneurs (R. des) . . . . . . . EYZ 147
- Tenremonde (R.) . . . . . . . . EY 148
- Théâtre (Pl. du) . . . . . . . . . EY 150
- Trois-Mollettes (R. des) . . . EY 154
- Vieille Comédie (R. de la) . . EY 162

**Ibis Centre,** av. Ch. St-Venant ✉ 59800 ☎ 03 20 55 44 44, *Fax 03 20 31 06 25*, – |♦|, ⇸ rm, TV ☎ ♿ – 25 - 60. AE ⓓ GB FYZ a
Meals 95 – ☕ 35 – **151 rm** 360.

**Clarine,** 46 r. Fg d'Arras ☎ 03 20 53 53 40, *Fax 03 20 53 20 95* – |♦| TV ☎ – 40. AE ⓓ GB
Meals 98 – ☕ 32 – **80 rm** 280/350.

**A L'Huîtrière,** 3 r. Chats Bossus ✉ 59800 ☎ 03 20 55 43 41, *Fax 03 20 55 23 10*, « Original decoration with ceramics in the fish shop » – ▤. AE ⓓ GB EY g
*closed 20 July-20 August and dinner Sunday and Bank Holidays* – **Meals** 260 (lunch)/600 and a la carte 310/510
**Spec.** Huîtres et produits de la mer. Lotte rôtie à l'andouille et à la bière, ravioles au fromage de Roncq. Turbotin en croûte de pomme de terre, beurre crémeux de champignons et de truffes.

**Sébastopol,** 1 pl. Sébastopol ☎ 03 20 57 05 05, *Fax 03 20 40 11 31* – AE GB EZ a
*closed 9 to 17 August, Sunday in July-August and Saturday lunch* – **Meals** 160/265 and a la carte 290/400.

**Laiterie,** 138 av. Hippodrome at Lambersart NW : 2 km ✉ 59130 *Lambersart* ☎ 03 20 92 79 73, *Fax 03 20 22 16 19*, – P. AE GB AV s
*closed Sunday dinner and Monday* – **Meals** 160/270 and a la carte 300/430.

**Baan Thaï,** 22 bd J.-B. Lebas ☎ 03 20 86 06 01, *Fax 03 20 86 03 23* – AE ⓓ GB EZ s
*closed 20 July-17 August, Sunday dinner and Monday* – **Meals** - Thai rest. - 140 (lunch), 150/200.

**Clément Marot,** 16 r. Pas ✉ 59800 ☎ 03 20 57 01 10, *Fax 03 20 57 39 69* – ▤. AE ⓓ GB JCB EY n
*closed 1 to 25 August, Christmas-New Year, Monday dinner and Sunday* – **Meals** 135 (lunch), 185/235.

**Champlain,** 13 r. N. Leblanc ☎ 03 20 54 01 38, *Fax 03 20 40 07 28*, – AE ⓓ GB. EZ u
*closed 3 to 18 August, Saturday lunch and Sunday dinner* – **Meals** 145 b.i. (lunch), 165/360 b.i.

**Cour des Grands,** 61 r. Monnaie ✉ 59800 ☎ 03 20 06 83 61, *Fax 03 20 14 03 75* – AE ⓓ GB EY v
*closed 1 to 19 August, 1 to 10 January, Monday lunch, Saturday lunch and Sunday* – **Meals** (booking essential) 185/295.

**Cardinal,** 84 façade Esplanade ✉ 59800 ☎ 03 20 06 58 58, *Fax 03 20 51 42 59* – AE GB BV x
*closed 10 to 16 August and Sunday* – **Meals** 160/320 b.i.

**Varbet,** 2 r. Pas ✉ 59800 ☎ 03 20 54 81 40, *Fax 03 20 57 55 18* – AE ⓓ GB EY t
*closed 14 July-15 August, Christmas-New Year, Sunday, Monday and Bank Holidays* – **Meals** 165/400.

**Bistrot Tourangeau,** 61 bd Louis XIV ✉ 59800 ☎ 03 20 52 74 64, *Fax 03 20 85 06 39* – ▤. AE GB CV t
*closed Sunday* – **Meals** 149.

**Queen, Écume des Mers,** 10 r. Pas ✉ 59800 ☎ 03 20 54 95 40, *Fax 03 20 54 96 66* – ▤. AE GB JCB EY n
*closed 26 July-18 August, Sunday lunch in July and Sunday dinner* – **Meals** 130 (dinner) and a la carte 170/270.

**Coquille,** 60 r. St-Étienne ✉ 59800 ☎ 03 20 54 29 82, *Fax 03 20 54 29 82* – GB EY e
*closed 1 to 23 August, Saturday lunch and Sunday* – **Meals** 130 b.i. (lunch), 160/239.

**at Marcq-en-Baroeul** – *pop. 36 601 alt. 15 – ✉ 59700 :*

**Sofitel** M, av. Marne, by N 350 : 5 km ☎ 03 20 72 17 30, *Fax 03 20 89 92 34* – |♦|, ⇸ rm, ▤ TV ☎ ♿ P – 30 - 200. AE ⓓ GB JCB
***Europe*** : Meals 110 – ☕ 90 – **124 rm** 880.

**Septentrion,** parc du Château Vert Bois, by N 17 : 9 km ☎ 03 20 46 26 98, *Fax 03 20 46 38 33*, , « In a park with a lake » – P. AE ⓓ GB
*closed 2 to 24 August, February Holidays, Thursday dinner, Sunday dinner and Monday* – **Meals** 150/290 and a la carte 180/310.

**Épicurien,** 18 av. Flandre by N 350 : 4 km ☎ 03 20 45 82 15, *Fax 03 20 72 21 45*, – P. AE GB JCB
*closed Sunday dinner* – **Meals** 150/290 and a la carte 200/280.

**Aub. de la Garenne,** 17 chemin de Ghesles ☎ 03 20 46 20 20, *Fax 03 20 46 32 33*, , – P. AE GB
Meals 95/390 b.i.

**at Lille-Lesquin airport** *by A 1 : 8 km – ✉ 59810 Lesquin :*

**Mercure Aéroport** M, 03 20 87 46 46, *Fax 03 20 87 46 47*, – rm, – 25 - 700. AE GB JCB
***Grill La Flamme :*** **Meals** 151/205 – ***Poêlon*** *(closed weekends) (lunch only)* **Meals** 60/123 – 56 – **212 rm** 505/590.

**Novotel Aéroport,** 03 20 62 53 53, *Fax 03 20 97 36 12*, – rm, – 25 - 120. AE GB JCB
**Meals** a la carte approx. 160 – 56 – **92 rm** 480/505.

**Agena** without rest, ✉ 59155 *Faches-Thumesnil* 03 20 60 13 14, *Fax 03 20 97 31 79* – AE GB JCB
50 – **40 rm** 350/380.

**Septième Ciel,** niveau supérieur de l'aérogare 03 20 87 52 05, *Fax 03 20 87 52 05*, – AE GB JCB
*closed Sunday dinner* – **Meals** 165/230 - ***Zingue*** brasserie **Meals** a la carte approx 140.

**at Englos** *by A 25 : 10 km (exit Lomme) – alt. 46 – ✉ 59320 :*

**Novotel Englos,** 03 20 10 58 58, *Fax 03 20 10 58 59*, – rm, – 30 - 120. AE GB
**Meals** a la carte approx. 150 – 56 – **124 rm** 430/490.

**Béthune** *62400 P.-de-C.* 51 ⑭ – *pop. 24 556 alt. 34.*
*Tourist Office, 69 pl. Senis 03 21 57 25 47, Fax 03 21 68 26 29.*
*Lille 39.*

**Meurin,** 15 pl. République 03 21 68 88 88, *Fax 03 21 56 37 15* – AE GB JCB
*closed 1 to 20 August, Sunday dinner and Monday* – **Meals** 160/350 and a la carte 320/400.
**Spec.** Homard côtier au jus d'épices. Agneau de pays à la fleur de thym. Parfait glacé à la chicorée sirop au genièvre.

---

**LYONS** *69000 Rhône* 74 ⑪ ⑫ – *pop. 415 487 alt. 175.*

**See** : *Site★★★ (panorama★★ from Fourvière) – Fourvière hill : Notre-Dame Basilica* EX, *Museum of Gallo-Roman Civilization★★ (Claudian tablet★★★)* EY **M**[3], *Roman ruins* EY – *Old Lyons★★★ : Rue St-Jean★* FX, *St-Jean Cathedral★* FY, *Hôtel de Gadagne★ (Lyons Historical Museum★ and International Marionette Museum★)* EX **M**[1] – *Guignol de Lyon* FX **N** – *Central Lyons (Peninsula) : to the North, Place Bellecour* FY, *Hospital Museum (pharmacy★)* FY **M**[8], *Museum of Printing and Banking★★* FX **M**[6], *Place des Terreaux* FX, *Hôtel de Ville* FX, *Palais St-Pierre, Fine Arts Museum (Beaux-Arts)★★* FX **M**[4] – *to the South, St-Martin-d'Ainay Basilica (capitals★)* FY, *Weaving and Textile Museum★★★* FY **M**[2], *Decorative Arts Museum★★* FY **M**[5] – *La Croix-Rousse : Silkweavers' House* FV **M**[11], *Trois Gaules Amphitheatre* FV **E** – *Tête d'Or Park★* GHV – *Guimet Museum of Natural History★★* GV **M**[7] – *Historical Information Centre on the Resistance and the Deportation★* FZ **M**[9].

**Envir.** : *Rochetaillée : Henri Malartre Car Museum★★, 12 km to the North.*

*Verger-Lyon at St-Symphorien-d'Ozon 04 78 02 84 20, S : 14 km ; Lyon-Chassieu at Chassieu 04 78 90 84 77, E : 12 km by D 29 ; Salvagny (private) at the Tour of Salvagny 04 78 48 83 60 ; junction Lyon-Ouest : 8 km ; Golf Club of Lyon at Villette-d'Anthon 04 78 31 11 33.*

*of Lyon-Satolas 04 72 22 72 21 to the E : 27 km.*

*08 36 35 35 35.*

*Tourist Office pl. Bellecour 04 72 77 69 69, Fax 04 78 42 04 32 – A.C. du Rhône 7 r. Grolée 04 78 42 51 01, Fax 04 78 37 73 74.*

*Paris 462 – Geneva 151 – Grenoble 105 – Marseilles 313 – St-Étienne 60 – Turin 300.*

Plans on following pages

**Hotels**

**Town Centre (Bellecour-Terreaux) :**

**Sofitel** M, 20 quai Gailleton ✉ 69002 04 72 41 20 20, *Fax 04 72 40 05 50*, – rm, – 200. AE GB JCB FY p
***Les Trois Dômes*** (8th floor) 04 72 41 20 97 **Meals** 180/350 – ***Sofi Shop*** (ground floor) *04 72 41 20 80* **Meals** 130 – 90 – **138 rm** 1030/1530, 29 suites.

**Gd H. Concorde,** 11 r. Grolée ✉ 69002 04 72 40 45 45, *Fax 04 78 37 52 55* – rm, – 60. AE GB JCB. rest FX y
***Fiorelle*** : 04 78 42 99 84 *(closed 10 to 24 August, lunch Saturday and Sunday)* **Meals** 98/128 – 75 – **143 rm** 720/980.

**Royal,** 20 pl. Bellecour ✉ 69002 04 78 37 57 31, *Fax 04 78 37 01 36* – rm, AE GB JCB FY g
**Meals** *(closed Saturday)* 128/142 – 72 – **80 rm** 640/980.

## STREET INDEX TO LYON TOWN PLAN

Guillotière (Grande R. de la) GYZ
Jaurès (Av. J.) GY
La Part Dieu HXY
République (R. de la) FXY 73
Terme (Rue) FV 94
Victor-Hugo (Rue) FY 99
Vitton (Cours) HV

Annonciade (R. de l') FV 4
Antiquaille (R. de l') EY 5
Aubigny (R. d') HX
Barret (R. Croix) GZ
Basses-Vercheres (R. des) EY 6
Béchevelin (R.) GY
Belfort (R. de) FV
Belges (Bd des) GHV
Bellecour (Place) FY
Berliet (R. M.) HZ
Bernard (Quai Cl.) FY
Bert (R. P.) GHY
Berthelot (Av.) GHZ
Bloch (R. M.) GZ
Bonaparte (Pont) FY 7
Bonnel (R. de) GX
Bony (R.) EV
Boucle (Montée de la) FU
Brotteaux (Bd des) HVX
Bugeaud (R.) HX
Burdeau (Rue) FV 9
Canuts (Bd des) FUV
Carmélites (Montée des) FV 12
Carnot (Pl.) FY
Charlemagne (Cours) EZ
Charmettes (R. des) HVX
Chartreux (Pl. des) EV
Chartreux (R. des) EV
Chazière (Rue) EV
Chevreul (Rue) GYZ
Choulans (Chin de) EY
Churchill (Pt W.) GV 18
Condé (R. de) FY
Courmont (Quai J.) FX 19
Crepet (Rue) FZ
Créqui (R. de) GVY
Croix-Rousse (Bd de) EFV
Croix-Rousse (Grande R. de la) FV 21
Debrousse (Av.) EY
Deleuvre (R.) EUV
Dr-Gailleton (Quai) FY
Duguesclin (Rue) GVY
Duquesne (Rue) GV
Epargne (R. de l') HZ 25
Etroits (Quai des) EY
Farge (Bd Y.) FZ
Farges (R. des) EY 28
Faure (Av. F.) GHY
Favre (Bd J.) HX 30
Ferry (Pl. J.) HX 31
Flandin (R. M.) HXY
France (Bd A.) HV 34
Frères Lumière (Av. des) HZ
Fulchiron (Quai) EY
Gallieni (Pont) FY 37
Gambetta (Cours) GHY
Garibaldi (Rue) GVZ
Garillan (Montée de) EFX
Gaulle (Q. Ch. de) GHU
Gerland (R. de) GZ
Gerlier (R. Cardinal) EY 39
Gillet (Quai J.) EUV
Giraud (Cours Gén.) EV
Grande-Bretagne (Av. de) GV
Grenette (Rue) FX 40
Guillotière (Pt de la) FY 41
Hénon (Rue) EFV
Herbouville (Cours d') FV 42
Joffre (Quai Mar.) EY 46
Juin (Pt Alphonse) FX 48
Jutard (Pl. A.) GY
Koening (Pt Gén.) EV 49
La Fayette (Cours) GHX
La Fayette (Pont) GX 51
Lassagne (Quai A.) FV 54
Lassalle (R. Ph. de) EUV
Leclerc (Av.) EFZ
Leclerc (Pl. Gén.) GV
Liberté (Cours de la) GXY
Lortet (Rue) FZ
Lyautey (Pl. Mar.) GVX
Marchand (Pt Kitchener) EY 55
Marius Vivier Merle (Bd) HY 58
Marseille (R. de) GY
Montrochet (R. P.) EZ 60
Morand (Pont) FVX 61
Moulin (Quai J.) FX 62
Nadaud (R. G.) FZ
Peissel (R. F.) FU 65
Perrache (Quai) EZ
Pompidou (Av. G.) HY
Pradel (Pl. L.) FX 67
Pré Gaudry (Rue) FZ 69
Prés. Herriot (R. du) FX 70
Radisson (R. R.) EY
Rambaud (Quai) EYZ
Repos (R. du) GZ 71
Rolland (Quai R.) FX 76
Roosevelt (Cours F.) GVX
St-Antoine (Quai) FX 82
St-Barthélemy (Montée) EX 84
St-Jean (Rue) FX
St-Vincent (Quai) EFX
Sarrail (Quai Gén.) GX 87
Saxe (Av. Mar. de) GXY
Scize (Quai P.) EX
Sedallian (Quai P.) EU
Serbie (Quai de) GV
Servient (R.) GY
Stalingrad (Bd de) GHU
Stalingrad (Pl. de) GHY
Suchet (Cours) EFZ
Sully (Rue) GV
Tassigny (Pt de Lattre de) FV 93
Tchécoslovaques (Bd des) HZ
Terreaux (Pl. des) FX
Tête d'Or (Rue) GVX
Thiers (Av.) HVX
Tilsitt (Quai) FY
Trion (Pl. de) EY
Trion (R. de) EY
Université (Pont de l') FY 96
Université (R. de l') GY 97
Vauban (Rue) GHX
Verguin (Av.) HV
Viabert (R. de la) HX
Vienne (Rte de) GZ
Villette (R. de la) HY 100
Villon (Rue) HZ
Vitton (Cours) HV
Vivier (R. du) GZ 102
Wilson (Pont) FY 103
1re Div. Fr. Libre (Av.) EY 104

**Carlton** without rest, 4 r. Jussieu ✉ 69002 ✆ 04 78 42 56 51, *Fax 04 78 42 10 71* – lift, TV ☎. AE ① GB JCB FX b
☕ 59 – **83 rm** 440/830.

**Plaza République** Ⓜ without rest, 5 r. Stella ✉ 69002 ✆ 04 78 37 50 50, *Fax 04 78 42 33 34* – lift, ⇔ rm, TV ☎ ♿ – 35. AE ① GB JCB FY k
☕ 59 – **78 rm** 535/795.

**Beaux-Arts** without rest, 75 r. Prés. E. Herriot ✉ 69002 ✆ 04 78 38 09 50, *Fax 04 78 42 19 19* – lift, ⇔ rm, TV ☎. AE ① GB JCB FX t
☕ 59 – **75 rm** 440/640.

**Globe et Cécil** without rest, 21 r. Gasparin ✉ 69002 ✆ 04 78 42 58 95, *Fax 04 72 41 99 06* – lift TV ☎. AE ① GB JCB FY b
☕ 55 – **60 rm** 400/590.

**Résidence** without rest, 18 r. V. Hugo ✉ 69002 ✆ 04 78 42 63 28, *Fax 04 78 42 85 76* – lift TV ☎. AE ① GB FY s
☕ 35 – **65 rm** 300/330.

### Perrache :

**Château Perrache,** 12 cours Verdun ✉ 69002 ✆ 04 72 77 15 00, *Fax 04 78 37 06 56, « Art Nouveau decor »* – lift, ⇔ rm, TV ☎ ♿ – 250. AE ① GB EY a
***Les Belles Saisons*** : Meals 140/180 – ☕ 70 – **121 rm** 515/870.

**Charlemagne** Ⓜ, 23 cours Charlemagne ✉ 69002 ✆ 04 72 77 70 00, *Fax 04 78 42 94 84,* – lift TV ☎ – 120. AE ① GB EZ t
Meals *(closed weekends)* 90/150 – ☕ 52 – **116 rm** 395/545.

**Berlioz** without rest, 12 cours Charlemagne ✉ 69002 ✆ 04 78 42 30 31, *Fax 04 72 40 97 58* – lift TV ☎. AE ① GB JCB EZ z
☕ 35 – **38 rm** 313/346.

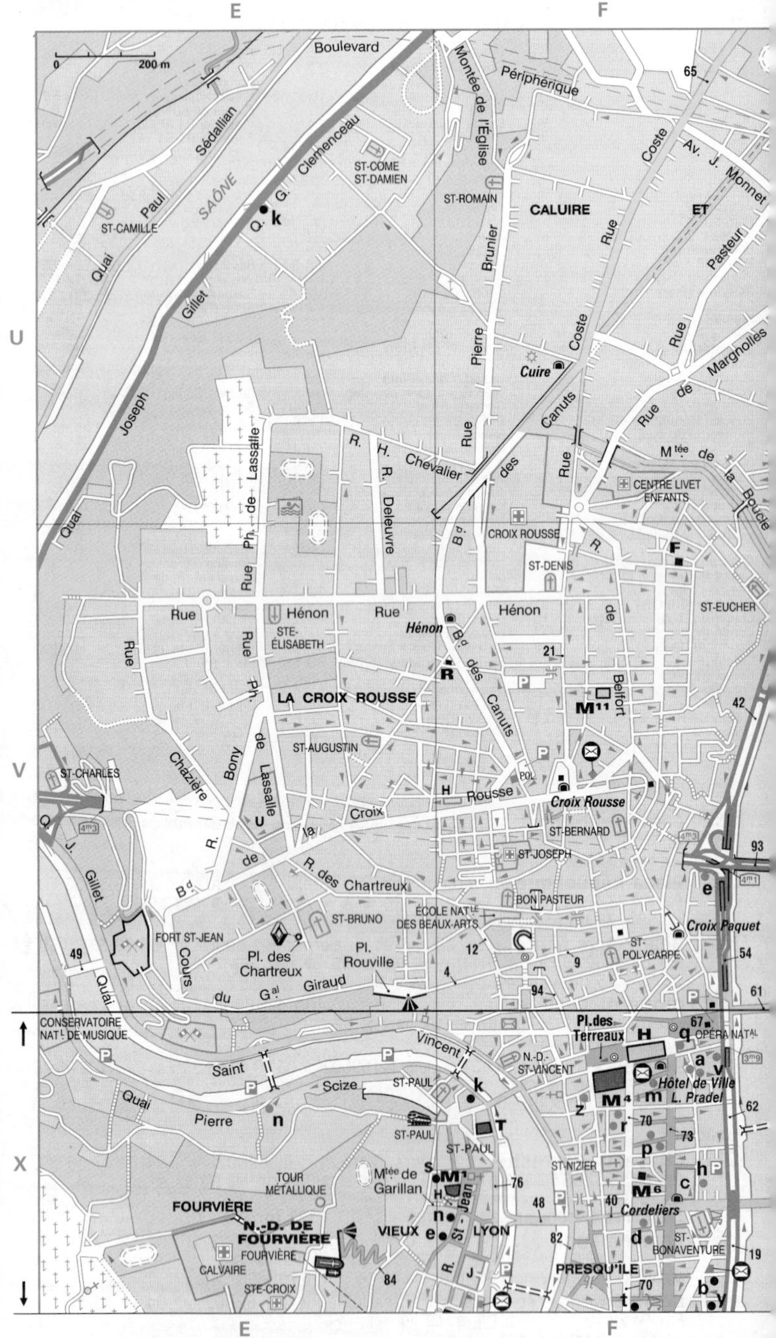
E
F
U
V
X
0
200 m
Boulevard
Périphérique
Montée de l'Église
65
Quai Paul Sédallian
SAÔNE
Q. G. Clemenceau
ST-COME
ST-DAMIEN
ST-ROMAIN
CALUIRE
ET
Rue Coste
Av. J. Monnet
Pasteur
Rue
k
ST-CAMILLE
Quai Joseph Gillet
Rue Pierre Brunier
Cuire
Rue de Margnolles
Rue des Canuts
Mtée de la Boucle
CENTRE LIVET
ENFANTS
R. H. Chevalier
R. Deleuvre
Rue Ph. de Lassalle
CROIX ROUSSE
ST-DENIS
F
R. de Belfort
Rue Hénon
Hénon
ST-EUCHER
STE-ÉLISABETH
Bd des Canuts
21
R
P
LA CROIX ROUSSE
M11
42
Rue Chazière
Rue Bony
ST-AUGUSTIN
ST-CHARLES
Q. J. Gillet
4m3
H
POL.
Rousse
Croix
la
de
R.
Croix Rousse
ST-BERNARD
U
ST-JOSEPH
93
4m1
R. des Chartreux
Bd
e
BON PASTEUR
ST-BRUNO
ÉCOLE NATLE
DES BEAUX-ARTS
Croix Paquet
FORT ST-JEAN
Pl. des
Chartreux
Pl.
Rouville
12
9
ST-POLYCARPE
54
49
Cours du Gal Giraud
4
94
61
Quai
CONSERVATOIRE
NATL DE MUSIQUE
Pl.des
Terreaux
H
q
67
OPÉRA NATAL
Vincent
Saint
N.-D.-
ST-VINCENT
a
v
3m9
Quai Pierre Scize
ST-PAUL
k
M4
Hôtel de Ville
L. Pradel
m
62
n
z
70
r
73
T
ST-PAUL
p
TOUR
MÉTALLIQUE
Mtée de
Garillan
s
M1
76
ST-NIZIER
h
c
FOURVIÈRE
H
M6
48
40
Cordeliers
N.-D. DE
FOURVIÈRE
VIEUX
n
e
R. St-Jean
LYON
82
d
ST-BONAVENTURE
19
FOURVIÈRE
CALVAIRE
84
J
PRESQU'ÎLE
70
b
STE-CROIX
t
y

G H

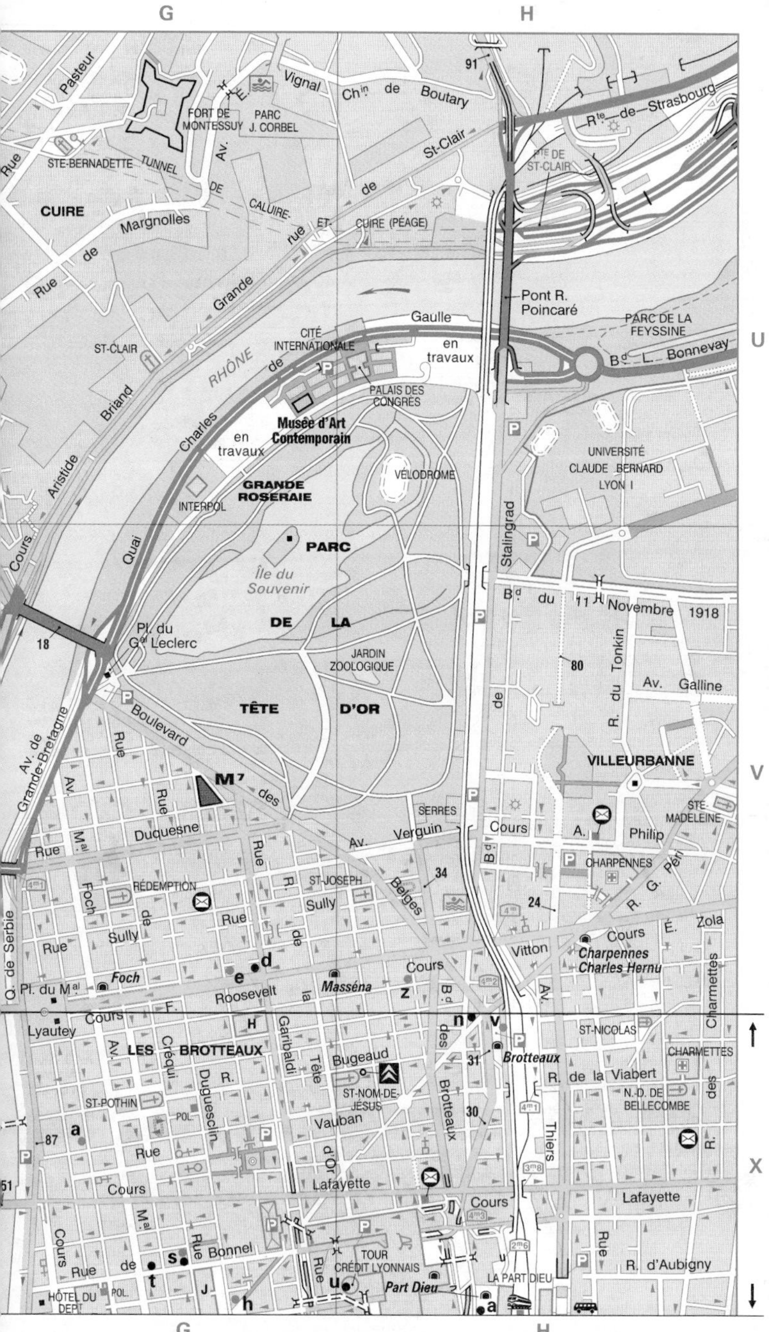
Pasteur
FORT DE MONTESSUY
PARC J. CORBEL
Vignal
Chin de Boutary
Rte de Strasbourg
Pte DE ST-CLAIR
STE-BERNADETTE
TUNNEL DE CALUIRE-ET-CUIRE (PÉAGE)
St-Clair
CUIRE
Rue de Margnolles
Grande rue de St-Clair
Pont R. Poincaré
PARC DE LA FEYSSINE
Gaulle
CITÉ INTERNATIONALE
en travaux
Bd L. Bonnevay
ST-CLAIR
RHÔNE
PALAIS DES CONGRÈS
Musée d'Art Contemporain
Cours Aristide Briand
Quai Charles de
INTERPOL
GRANDE ROSERAIE
VÉLODROME
UNIVERSITÉ CLAUDE BERNARD LYON I
PARC DE LA TÊTE D'OR
Île du Souvenir
Stalingrad
Bd du 11 Novembre 1918
Pl. du Gal Leclerc
JARDIN ZOOLOGIQUE
R. du Tonkin
Av. Galline
Boulevard des Belges
Av. de Grande-Bretagne
VILLEURBANNE
SERRES
Av. Verguin
Cours A. Philip
STE-MADELEINE
CHARPENNES
R. G. Péri
Rue Duquesne
RÉDEMPTION
ST-JOSEPH
Rue Sully
Av. Mal Foch
Rue de Sully
Rue de la Tête d'Or
Cours Vitton
Cours É. Zola
Charpennes Charles Hernu
Charmettes
Q. de Serbie
Pl. du Mal Lyautey
Foch
Masséna
Cours F. Roosevelt
Cours
LES BROTTEAUX
Av. Créqui
R. Duguesclin
Garibaldi
Bugeaud
ST-NOM-DE-JÉSUS
Bd des Brotteaux
Brotteaux
ST-NICOLAS
CHARMETTES
R. de la Viabert
N.D. DE BELLECOMBE
R. des
ST-POTHIN
POL.
Vauban
Thiers
Rue d'Or
Cours Lafayette
Lafayette
Rue Mal
Cours
Rue de Bonnel
TOUR CRÉDIT LYONNAIS
Part Dieu
LA PART DIEU
R. d'Aubigny
HÔTEL DU DÉPT
M7
91
18
80
34
24
31
30
87
51
U
V
X

G H

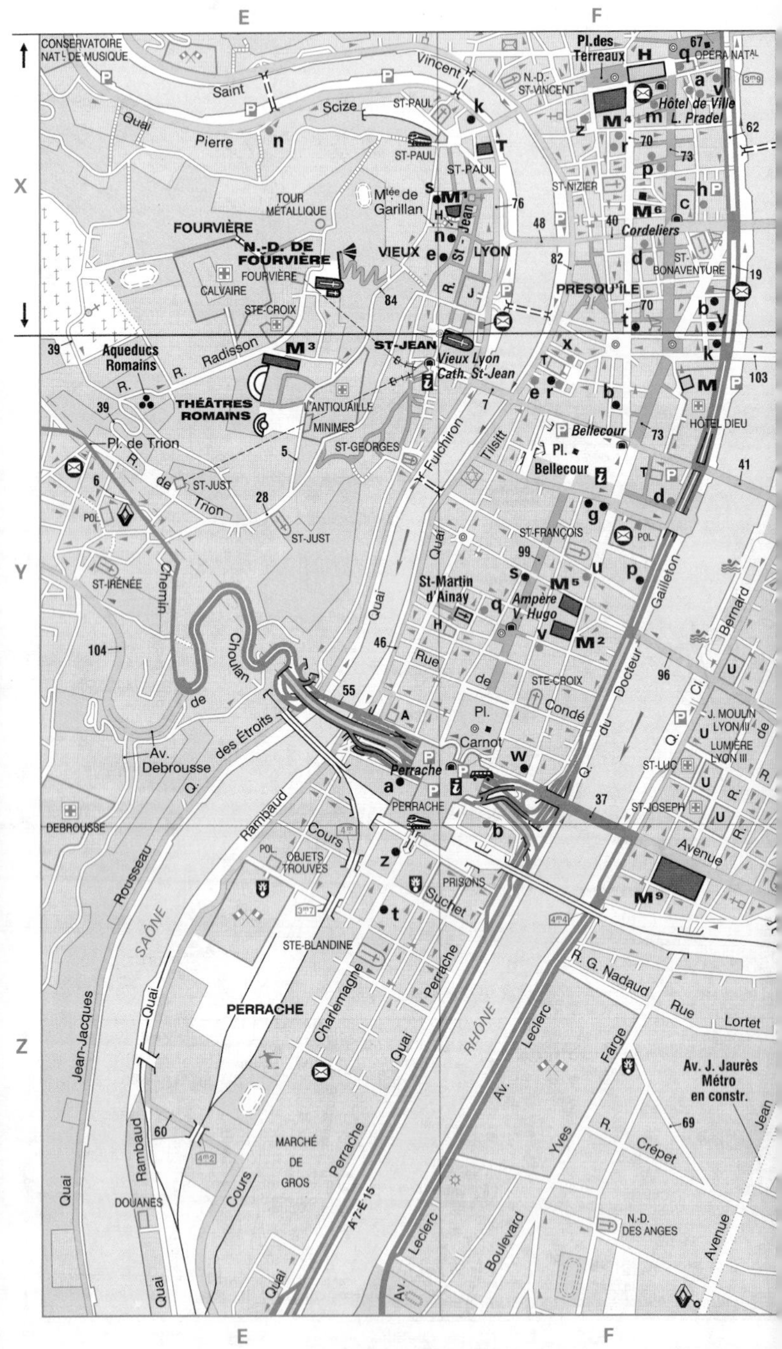

E
F
X
Y
Z
CONSERVATOIRE NAT. DE MUSIQUE
Pl. des Terreaux
OPÉRA NAT.
Hôtel de Ville L. Pradel
N.-D.-ST-VINCENT
ST-PAUL
ST-NIZIER
TOUR MÉTALLIQUE
Mtée de Garillan
FOURVIÈRE
N.-D. DE FOURVIÈRE
VIEUX
LYON
Cordeliers
ST-BONAVENTURE
CALVAIRE
STE-CROIX
PRESQU'ÎLE
Aqueducs Romains
ST-JEAN
Vieux Lyon Cath. St-Jean
THÉÂTRES ROMAINS
L'ANTIQUAILLE
MINIMES
ST-GEORGES
HÔTEL DIEU
Pl. de Trion
ST-JUST
Bellecour
Pl. Bellecour
ST-FRANÇOIS
ST-IRÉNÉE
St-Martin d'Ainay
Ampère V. Hugo
STE-CROIX
Pl. Carnot
J. MOULIN LYON III
LUMIÈRE LYON III
ST-LUC
Perrache
PERRACHE
ST-JOSEPH
Av. Debrousse
DEBROUSSE
OBJETS TROUVÉS
PRISONS
STE-BLANDINE
SAÔNE
RHÔNE
PERRACHE
Av. J. Jaurès Métro en constr.
MARCHÉ DE GROS
DOUANES
N.-D. DES ANGES
A 7-E 15

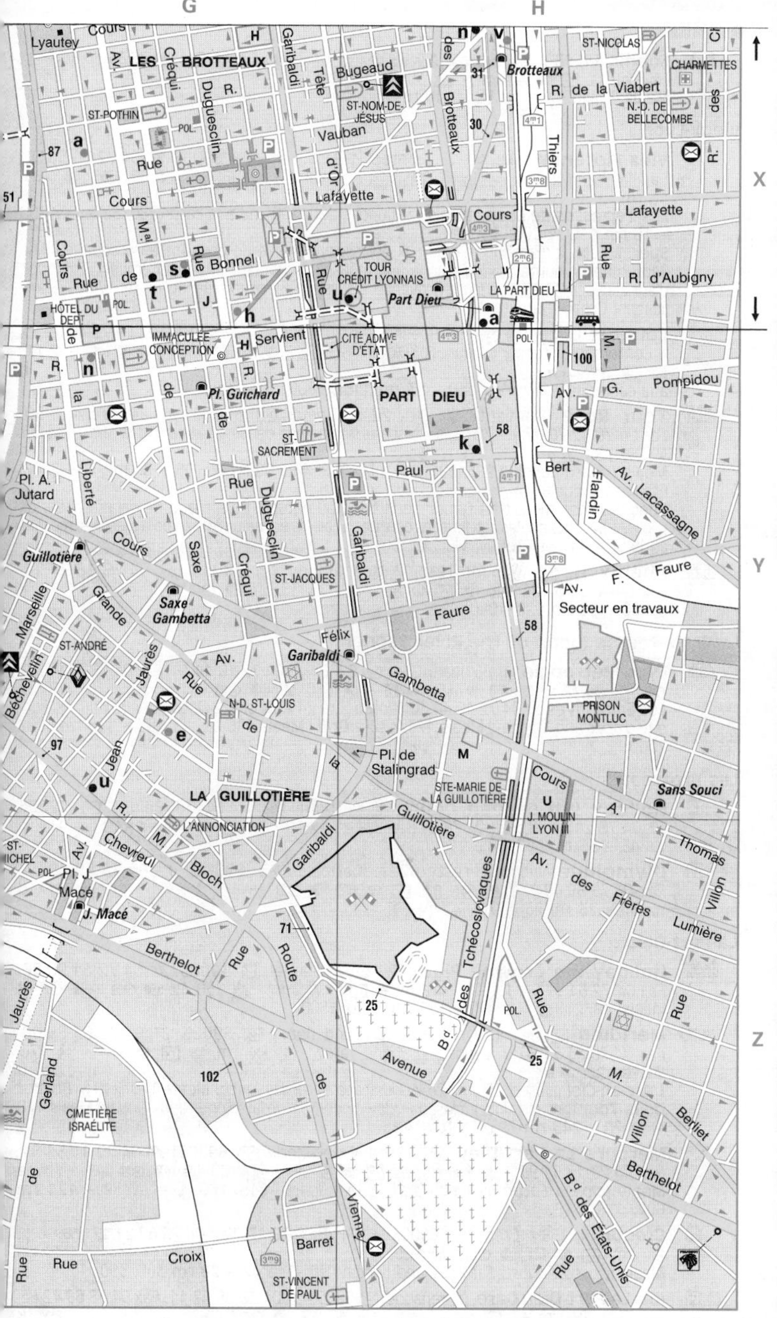
G
H
X
Y
Z
LES BROTTEAUX
Cours Lyautey
Av. Créqui
R. Duguesclin
Garibaldi
Tête d'Or
Bugeaud
Vauban
des Brotteaux
Brotteaux
ST-NICOLAS
CHARMETTES
R. de la Viabert
N.-D. DE BELLECOMBE
Thiers
ST-POTHIN
POL.
ST-NOM-DE-JÉSUS
Rue
Cours Lafayette
Lafayette
Cours
M.al
Rue de Bonnel
TOUR CRÉDIT LYONNAIS
Part Dieu
LA PART DIEU
Rue
R. d'Aubigny
HÔTEL DU DEPT
IMMACULÉE CONCEPTION
Servient
CITÉ ADM.VE D'ÉTAT
Av. G. Pompidou
R. de la Liberté
Pl. Guichard
R. de Créqui
PART DIEU
ST-SACREMENT
Paul Bert
Av. Flandin
Av. Lacassagne
Pl. A. Jutard
Rue Duguesclin
Garibaldi
Cours
Guillotière
Saxe
Créqui
ST-JACQUES
Av. F. Faure
Faure
Félix
Secteur en travaux
Saxe Gambetta
Grande
Marseille
ST-ANDRÉ
Jaurès
Av.
Rue
Garibaldi
Gambetta
PRISON MONTLUC
N.-D. ST-LOUIS
de la
Béchevelin
Jean
Pl. de Stalingrad
STE-MARIE DE LA GUILLOTIÈRE
Cours
Sans Souci
LA GUILLOTIÈRE
Guillotière
U
J. MOULIN LYON III
A. Thomas
L'ANNONCIATION
R. M. Bloch
Chevreul
ST-MICHEL
Pl. J. Macé
J. Macé
Garibaldi
Tchécoslovaques
Av. des Frères Lumière
Villon
Berthelot
Rue
Route de Vienne
Bd des
Rue
Rue
POL.
Avenue
M. Berliet
Villon
Berthelot
Bd des États-Unis
Jaurès
Gerland
CIMETIÈRE ISRAÉLITE
de
Rue
Rue
Croix
Barret
ST-VINCENT DE PAUL
Vienne
Rue
87
51
31
30
100
58
58
97
71
25
25
102
4m1
3m8
4m3
2m6
4m3
4m1
3m8
3m9
G
H

**at Vaise** :

**Saphir** M, 18 r. L. Loucheur ✉ 69009 ☎ 04 78 83 48 75, *Fax 04 78 83 30 81* – lift, rm, ☐ TV ☎ & – 50. AE GB
**Meals** 97/189 – 50 – **110 rm** 450/470.

**Vieux-Lyon** :

**Villa Florentine** M, 25 montée St-Barthélémy ✉ 69005 ☎ 04 72 56 56 56, *Fax 04 72 40 90 56*, ≤ Lyon, – lift ☐ TV ☎ & P. AE GB JCB. rm EFX s
***Les Terrasses de Lyon* : Meals** 170 (lunch), 290/400 and a la carte 380/520 – 100 – **16 rm** 1300/1900, 3 suites
**Spec.** Moelleux d'anchois mariné aux épices, symphonie de poissons en basquaise (May-September). Courgette fleur farcie à la mousse de homard (May-September). Couronne d'agneau des Alpes de Haute-Provence cloûtée aux anchois de Collioure. **Wines** Saint-Joseph, Crozes-Hermitage.

**Cour des Loges** M, 6 r. Boeuf ✉ 69005 ☎ 04 72 77 44 44, *Fax 04 72 40 93 61*, « Contemporary decor in houses of Old Lyons », – lift, rm, ☐ TV ☎ & – 40. AE GB JCB FX n
a la carte 260/340 – 110 – **53 rm** 1150/1800, 10 suites.

**Tour Rose** (Chavent) M, 22 r. Boeuf ✉ 69005 ☎ 04 78 37 25 90, *Fax 04 78 42 26 02*, « 17C house, tasteful silk themed decor » – lift ☐ TV ☎ – 35. AE GB JCB EFX e
**Meals** *(closed Sunday)* 295/595 and a la carte 440/580 – 95 – **8 rm** 1200/2800, 6 suites, 4 duplex
**Spec.** Saumon mi-cuit au fumoir servi tiède au naturel. Foie chaud de canard, filets de rougets barbets poêlés aux lentilles confites à l'ail. Ris de veau rôtis au pain d'épices, morilles au beurre. **Wines** Brouilly, Viognier.

**Phénix H.** M without rest, 7 quai Bondy ✉ 69005 ☎ 04 78 28 24 24, *Fax 04 78 28 62 86* – lift ☐ TV ☎ & – 35. AE GB FX k
60 – **36 rm** 620/1080.

**La Croix-Rousse (bank of the River Saône)** :

**Lyon Métropole** M, 85 quai J. Gillet ✉ 69004 ☎ 04 72 10 44 44, *Fax 04 78 39 99 20*, – lift ☐ TV ☎ & P – 350. AE GB EU k
***Les Eaux Vives*** ☎ *04 72 10 44 30 (closed 2 to 24 August, 22 December-3 January, Sunday dinner and Monday)* **Meals** 175/430 – ***Grill* : Meals** 130 b.i. – 80 – **118 rm** 590/2000.

**Les Brotteaux** :

**Holiday Inn Garden Court** M without rest, 114 bd Belges ✉ 69006 ☎ *04 78 24 44 68, Fax 04 78 24 82 36* – lift, rm, ☐ TV ☎. AE GB HX n
45 – **55 rm** 565/685.

**Olympique** without rest, 62 r. Garibaldi ✉ 69006 ☎ 04 78 89 48 04, *Fax 04 78 89 49 97* – lift, rm, TV ☎. AE GB GV d
31 – **23 rm** 230/270.

**La Part-Dieu** :

**Holiday Inn Crowne Plaza** M, 29 r. Bonnel ✉ 69003 ☎ 04 72 61 90 90, *Fax 04 72 61 17 54*, – lift, rm, ☐ TV ☎ & – 250. AE GB JCB GX t
**Meals** 105/200 – 90 – **155 rm** 1400/1500.

**Méridien** M, 129 r. Servient (32nd floor) ✉ 69003 ☎ 04 78 63 55 00, *Fax 04 78 63 55 20*, ≤ Lyons and Rhône Valley – lift, rm, ☐ TV ☎ – 170. AE GB JCB GX u
***L'Arc-en-Ciel*** *(closed 15 July-26 August and Saturday lunch)* **Meals** 170/210 – ***Bistrot de la Tour*** (ground floor) *(closed Friday dinner, Saturday dinner and Sunday)* **Meals** 110 – 70 – **245 rm** 795/1100.

**Mercure La Part-Dieu** M, 47 bd Vivier-Merle ✉ 69003 ☎ 04 72 13 51 51, *Fax 04 72 13 51 99* – lift, rm, ☐ TV ☎ & – 80. AE GB JCB HX a
**Meals** *(closed Saturday lunch and Sunday lunch)* 115/165 – 59 – **124 rm** 607.

**Créqui** M, 158 r. Créqui ✉ 69003 ☎ 04 78 60 20 47, *Fax 04 78 62 21 12*, – lift, rm, TV ☎. AE GB. rest GX s
**Meals** *(closed August, Saturday and Sunday)* 98 – 42 – **28 rm** 360/390.

**Ibis La Part-Dieu Gare**, pl. Renaudel ✉ 69003 ☎ 04 78 95 42 11, *Fax 04 78 60 42 85*, – lift, rm, ☐ TV ☎ & – 40. AE GB JCB HY k
**Meals** 95 – 35 – **144 rm** 345.

**La Guillotière** :

**Wilson** without rest, 6 r. Mazenod 69003 04 78 60 94 94, *Fax 04 78 62 72 01* – rm, . AE GB JCB
60 – **54 rm** 470/520.

**Ibis Université** without rest, 51 r. Université 69007 04 78 72 78 42, *Fax 04 78 69 24 36* – rm, . AE GB GY u
36 – **53 rm** 345.

**Gerland** :

**Mercure Gerland**, 70 av. Leclerc 69007 04 72 71 11 11, *Fax 04 72 71 11 00*, – rm, – 200. AE GB JCB
Meals 100 – 59 – **194 rm** 535/750.

**Montchat-Monplaisir** :

**Mercure Lumière**, 69 cours A. Thomas 04 78 53 76 76, *Fax 04 72 36 97 65* – rm, – 30. AE GB JCB
Meals *(closed 1 to 16 August and Saturday)* 100 (lunch)/140 – 57 – **78 rm** 480/540.

**Relais Mercure Park H.**, 4 r. Prof. Calmette 69008 04 78 74 11 20, *Fax 04 78 01 43 38*, – rm, . AE GB JCB
*closed 24 December-2 January* – **Meals** *(closed Sunday lunch, Friday dinner and Saturday)* 85/120 – 50 – **72 rm** 525/555.

**at Bron** – *pop. 39 683 alt. 204* – *69500* :

**Novotel Bron**, av. J. Monnet 04 72 15 65 65, *Fax 04 72 15 09 09*, , , – rm, – 25 - 800. AE GB
Meals a la carte approx. 180 – 55 – **189 rm** 525.

## Restaurants

**Paul Bocuse,** bridge of Collonges N : 12 km by the banks of River Saône (D 433, D 51 69660 *Collonges-au-Mont-d'Or* 04 72 42 90 90, *Fax 04 72 27 85 87*, « Fresco depicting great chefs » – . AE GB JCB
**Meals** 410 (lunch), 510/740 and a la carte 450/640
**Spec.** Soupe aux truffes. Rouget barbet en écailles de pommes de terre. Volaille de Bresse en vessie. **Wines** Saint-Véran, Brouilly.

**Léon de Lyon** (Lacombe), 1 r. Pleney 69001 04 78 28 11 33, *Fax 04 78 39 89 05* – . AE GB JCB FX r
*closed 9 to 18 August, Monday lunch and Sunday* – **Meals** 290 (lunch), 520/660 and a la carte 470/600
**Spec.** Cochon fermier, foie gras, oignons confits en "terrine rustique". Quenelles de brochet de la Dombes, sauce Nantua. Six petits desserts sur le thème de la praline de Saint-Genix. **Wines** Saint-Véran, Chiroubles.

**Pierre Orsi,** 3 pl. Kléber 69006 04 78 89 57 68, *Fax 04 72 44 93 34*, , « Elegant decor » – . AE GB JCB GV e
*closed Sunday except lunch in winter* – **Meals** 240 (lunch), 320/600 and a la carte 420/570
**Spec.** Ravioles de foie gras au jus de porto et truffes. Homard et rouget en barigoule. Pigeonneau rôti en cocotte aux gousses d'ail confites. **Wines** Mâcon-Clessé, Saint-Amour.

**Christian Têtedoie,** 54 quai Pierre Scize 69005 04 78 29 40 10, *Fax 04 72 07 05 65* – . AE GB EX n
*closed 1 to 24 August, Saturday lunch and Sunday except Bank Holidays* – **Meals** 165/295 and a la carte 250/360.

**Mère Brazier,** 12 r. Royale 69001 04 78 28 15 49, *Fax 04 78 28 63 63*, « Lyonnaise atmosphere » – AE GB. FV e
*closed 25 July-25 August, Saturday except dinner from August-May, Sunday and Bank Holidays* – **Meals** 170 (lunch), 250/300 and a la carte 210/310
**Spec.** Fond d'artichaut au foie gras de canard. Quenelle au gratin. Volaille de Bresse "demi-deuil". **Wines** Brouilly, Côtes du Rhône.

**Saint Alban,** 2 quai J. Moulin 69001 04 78 30 14 89, *Fax 04 72 00 88 82* – . AE GB FX v
*closed 20 July-20 August, February Holidays, Saturday lunch, Sunday and Bank Holidays* – **Meals** 155/320 and a la carte 240/330.

**Passage,** 8 r. Plâtre 69001 04 78 28 11 16, *Fax 04 72 00 84 34* – . AE GB FX r
*closed Saturday lunch, Sunday and Bank Holidays* – **Meals** 95 (lunch), 125/185.

**Aub. de l'Ile** (Ansanay-Alex), sur l'Ile Barbe 69009 04 78 83 99 49, *Fax 04 78 47 80 46* – . AE GB.
*closed 10 to 25 August, February Holidays, Sunday dinner and Monday* – **Meals** 160 (lunch), 190/390 and a la carte 310/480
**Spec.** Velouté de châtaignes aux "sot-l'y-laisse" et truffes (15 December-15 March). Omble chevalier à la peau croustillante et mousserons (15 March-15 June). Soufflé chaud à la pêche blanche (15 June-15 September). **Wines** Condrieu, Morgon.

XX **Gourmet de Sèze,** 129 r. Sèze ✉ 69006 ✆ 04 78 24 23 42, *Fax 04 78 24 66 81* – ▤. AE GB HV z
*closed 15 July-15 August, Sunday and Monday* – **Meals** (booking essential) 130 (lunch), 180/300 b.i.

XX **Fleur de Sel,** 3 r. Remparts d'Ainay ✉ 69002 ✆ 04 78 37 40 37, *Fax 04 78 37 26 37* – GB FY q
*closed mid July-mid August, Saturday and Sunday* – **Meals** 148 (lunch), 228/295.

XX **Thierry Gache,** 37 r. Thibaudière ✉ 69007 ✆ 04 78 72 81 77, *Fax 04 78 72 01 75* – ▤. AE GB GY e
*closed Monday dinner and Sunday* – **Meals** 99 b.i. (lunch)/265.

XX **Philippe B.,** 42 r. P. Corneille ✆ 04 78 52 19 13, *Fax 04 72 74 99 14* – AE GB GX a
*closed 1 to 24 August, Saturday lunch and Sunday* – **Meals** 135/210.

XX **L'Alexandrin,** 83 r. Moncey ✉ 69003 ✆ 04 72 61 15 69, *Fax 04 78 62 75 57* – ▤. AE GB GX h
*closed 1 to 4 May, 8 to 11 May, 2 to 24 August, 24 December-4 January, Sunday, Monday and Bank Holidays* – **Meals** 160/360.

XX **Le Nord,** 18 r. Neuve ✉ 69002 ✆ 04 72 10 69 69, *Fax 04 72 10 69 68*, 🏠 – ▤. AE GB JCB FX p
Meals brasserie 105/158 🍷.

XX **Tassée,** 20 r. Charité ✉ 69002 ✆ 04 72 77 79 00, *Fax 04 72 40 05 91* – ▤. AE ⓓ GB JCB FY u
*closed Saturday in July-August and Sunday* – **Meals** 110 (lunch), 130/260.

XX **Brasserie Georges,** 30 cours Verdun ✉ 69002 ✆ 04 72 56 54 54, *Fax 04 78 42 51 65*, 1925 brasserie – AE ⓓ GB JCB FZ b
**Meals** 85/150 🍷.

XX **Tante Alice,** 22 r. Remparts d'Ainay ✉ 69002 ✆ 04 78 37 49 83, *Fax 04 78 37 49 83* – ▤. AE GB FY v
*closed 25 July-25 August, Friday dinner and Saturday* – **Meals** 94/194 🍷.

XX **Chez Jean-François,** 2 pl. Célestins ✉ 69002 ✆ 04 78 42 08 26, *Fax 04 72 40 04 51* – ▤. AE GB JCB FY x
*closed 25 July-24 August. Sunday and Bank Holidays* – **Meals** (booking essential) 90/170 🍷.

XX **La Voûte - Chez Léa,** 11 pl. A. Gourju ✉ 69002 ✆ 04 78 42 01 33, *Fax 04 78 37 36 41* – ▤. AE ⓓ GB FY e
*closed Sunday* – **Meals** 115 b.i. (lunch), 133/176 🍷.

X **Assiette et Marée,** 49 r. Bourse ✉ 69002 ✆ 04 78 37 36 58, *Fax 04 78 38 20 35* – ▤. AE GB FX h
*closed Sunday* – **Meals** - Seafood - 100 b.i. (lunch)and a la carte 150/200.

X **Assiette et Marée,** 26 r. Servient ✉ 69003 ✆ 04 78 62 89 94, *Fax 04 78 38 20 35* – ▤. AE GB GY n
*closed 9 to 16 August, Saturday lunch and Sunday* – **Meals** - Seafood - a la carte 150/210.

X **L'Est,** Gare des Brotteaux, 14 pl. J. Ferry ✉ 69006 ✆ 04 37 24 25 26, *Fax 04 37 24 25 25*, 🏠 – ▤ HX v
Meals brasserie 105/158.

X **Francotte,** 8 pl. Célestins ✉ 69002 ✆ 04 78 37 38 64, *Fax 04 78 38 20 35* – ▤. AE GB FY r
*closed Sunday* – **Meals** a la carte 150/200.

X **Le Sud,** 11 pl. Antonin Poncet ✉ 69002 ✆ 04 72 77 80 00, *Fax 04 72 77 80 01*, 🏠 – ▤. AE GB FY d
Meals (booking essential) 105/158.

X **Les Muses de l'Opéra,** pl. Comédie, 7th floor of the Opera ✉ 69001 ✆ 04 72 00 45 58, *Fax 04 78 29 34 01*, ≤ Fourvière, 🏠, « Contemporary decor » – ▤. AE GB FX q
*closed Sunday* – **Meals** 129 (lunch)/159.

BOUCHONS : *Regional specialities and wine tasting in a Lyonnaise atmosphere*

X **Garet,** 7 r. Garet ✉ 69001 ✆ 04 78 28 16 94, *Fax 04 72 00 06 84* – ▤. AE GB FX a
*closed 15 July-16 August, 24 December-2 January, Saturday and Sunday* – **Meals** (booking essential) 95/118 🍷.

X **Meunière,** 11 r. Neuve ✉ 69001 ✆ 04 78 28 62 91 – AE ⓓ GB FX p
*closed 11 July-17 August, Sunday, Monday and Bank Holidays* – **Meals** (booking essential) 95 (lunch), 110/150.

X **Café des Fédérations,** 8 r. Major Martin ✉ 69001 ✆ 04 78 28 26 00 – ▤. GB FX z
*closed August, Saturday and Sunday* – **Meals** (booking essential) 118 (lunch)/148.

X **Daniel et Denise,** 156 r. Créqui ✉ 69003 ☎ 04 78 60 66 53, *Fax 04 78 60 66 53* – ▤. GB GX s
*closed August, Saturday and Sunday* – **Meals** a la carte 100/150.

X **Jura,** 25 r. Tupin ✉ 69002 ☎ 04 78 42 20 57 – GB FX d
*closed 1 to 24 August, February Holidays, Monday lunch from October-April, Saturday from May-September and Sunday* – **Meals** (booking essential) 98/200.

X **Au Petit Bouchon "chez Georges",** 8 r. Garet ✉ 69001 ☎ 04 78 28 30 46 – GB FX a
*closed August, Saturday and Sunday* – **Meals** 86/115 dinner a la carte approx. 170.

X **Chez Hugon,** 12 rue Pizay ✉ 69001 ☎ 04 78 28 10 94 – GB FX m
*closed August, Saturday and Sunday* – **Meals** (booking essential) 120/210 and a la carte 120/210.

## Environs

**to the NE :**

**at Rillieux-la-Pape** : *7 km by N 83 and N 84 – pop. 30 791 alt. 269 – ✉ 69140 :*

XXX **Larivoire** (Constantin), chemin des Iles ☎ 04 78 88 50 92, *Fax 04 78 88 35 22*, – P. AE GB
*closed 17 to 23 August, Monday lunch and Tuesday* – **Meals** 170/420 and a la carte 320/430
**Spec.** Brochet en deux façons, quenelles et filets sauce homardine. Gibier (season). Oeuf à la coque "vieux rhum et chocolat" (dessert). **Wines** Chardonnay du Bugey.

**to the E :**

**at the Satolas airport** : *27 km by A 43 – ✉ 69125 Lyon Satolas Airport :*

**Sofitel Lyon Aéroport** M without rest, 3rd floor ☎ 04 72 23 38 00, *Fax 04 72 23 98 00*, ≤ – |‡|, ⇆ rm, ▤ TV ☎ ♿. AE ⓓ GB JCB
90 – **120 rm** 880/920.

XXX **Grande Corbeille,** 1st floor ☎ 04 72 22 71 76, *Fax 04 72 22 71 72*, ≤ – ▤. AE ⓓ GB JCB – *closed August, Saturday and Sunday* – **Meals** 185 and a la carte 200/290.

X **Bouchon,** 1st floor ☎ 04 72 22 71 86, *Fax 04 72 22 71 72* – ▤. AE ⓓ GB JCB
**Meals** brasserie 105/160.

**to the NW :**

**Porte de Lyon** : *motorway junction A 6 N 6 Exit road signposted Limonest N : 10 km – ✉ 69570 Dardilly :*

**Novotel Lyon Nord** M, ☎ 04 72 17 29 29, *Fax 04 78 35 08 45*, – |‡|, ⇆ rm, ▤ TV ☎ P – 80. AE ⓓ GB
**Meals** 130 – 60 – **107 rm** 480/520.

**Relais Mercure Lyon Nord** M, ☎ 04 78 35 28 05, *Fax 04 78 47 47 15*, – |‡|, ⇆ rm, ▤ rest, TV ☎ P – 30 - 80. AE ⓓ GB JCB
**Meals** 95 b.i./125 – 52 – **115 rm** 435/460.

**Ibis Lyon Nord,** ☎ 04 78 66 02 20, *Fax 04 78 47 47 93*, – ⇆ rm, TV ☎ ♿ P – 30. AE ⓓ GB
**Meals** 95/150 – 38 – **64 rm** 335/365.

## Annecy *74000 H.-Savoie 74 ⑥ – pop. 49 644 alt. 448.*

**See** : *Old Annecy★★ : Descent from the Cross★ in church of St-Maurice, Palais de l'Isle★, rue Ste-Claire★, bridge over the Thiou ≤★ – Château★ – Jardins de l'Europe★.*

**Envir.** : *Tour of the lake★★★ 39 km (or 1 hour 30 min by boat).*

*18 of the lac d'Annecy ☎ 04 50 60 12 89 : 10 km ; 9 18 of Giez ☎ 04 50 44 48 41 ; 9 of Belvédère at St-Martin-Bellevue ☎ 04 50 60 31 78.*

*of Annecy-Haute Savoie : T.A.T. ☎ 04 50 27 30 30 by N 508 andD 14 : 4 km.*

*Tourist Office Clos Bonlieu 1 r. J. Jaurès ☎ 04 50 45 00 33, Fax 04 50 51 87 20 – A.C. 15 r. Préfecture ☎ 04 50 45 09 12, Fax 04 50 51 40 11.*

*Lyons 140.*

**at Veyrier-du-Lac** *E : 5,5 km – pop. 1 967 alt. 504 – ✉ 74290*

XXXXX **Aub. de l'Éridan** (Veyrat) M with rm, 13 Vieille rte des Pensières ☎ 04 50 60 24 00, *Fax 04 50 60 23 63*, ≤ lake, – |‡| ▤ TV ☎ ♿ P. AE ⓓ GB
*closed 15 December-15 January* – **Meals** *(closed Monday except July-August)* 385 (lunch), 595/995 and a la carte 660/970 – 235 – **11 rm** 1550/3250
**Spec.** Feuillantine d'escargots à l'achillée et pimprenelle. Féra du lac à la "benoîte urbaine". Gâteau de marrons au jus de truffes d'été (dessert). **Wines** Chignin, Mondeuse.

**Chagny** *71150 S.-et-L.* 69 ⑨ *– pop. 5 346 alt. 215.*

*Tourist Office 2 r. des Halles ✆ 03 85 87 25 95, Fax 03 85 87 14 44.*

*Lyons 145.*

**Lameloise** M, pl. d'Armes ✆ 03 85 87 08 85, *Fax 03 85 87 03 57,* « Old Burgundian house, tasteful decor » – AE GB JCB
*closed 23 December-28 January, Wednesday except dinner from 1 July-30 September and Thursday lunch* – **Meals** (booking essential) 390/600 and a la carte 410/560 – 95 – **17 rm** 700/1500
**Spec.** Ravioli d'escargots de Bourgogne au bouillon d'ail doux. Pigeonneau rôti à l'émietté de truffes. Griottines au chocolat noir sur marmelade d'orange. **Wines** Rully blanc, Chassagne-Montrachet.

**Fleurie** *69820 Rhône* 74 ① *– pop. 1 105 alt. 320.*

*Lyons 59.*

**Aub. du Cep,** pl. Église ✆ 04 74 04 10 77, *Fax 04 74 04 10 28* – . AE GB
*closed early December-mid January, Sunday dinner and Monday* – **Meals** (booking essential) 200/575 and a la carte 270/470
**Spec.** Cuisses de grenouilles rôties aux fines herbes. Volaille fermière mijotée au vin de Fleurie. Cassis du terroir beaujolais en sorbet et son coulis. **Wines** Beaujolais blanc, Fleurie.

**Mionnay** *01390 Ain* 74 ② *– pop. 1 103 alt. 276.*

*Lyons 23.*

**Alain Chapel** with rm, ✆ 04 78 91 82 02, *Fax 04 78 91 82 37,* , « Flowered garden » – P. AE GB
*closed January, Tuesday lunch and Monday except Bank Holidays* – **Meals** 380 b.i. (lunch), 595/795 and a la carte 510/650 – 90 – **13 rm** 750/800
**Spec.** Foie gras chaud au fenouil et hydromel. Rouget en crapaudine, farce croustillante (spring-summer). Poulette en vessie. **Wines** Mâcon-Clessé.

**Montrond-les-Bains** *42210 Loire* 73 ⑱ *– pop. 3 627 alt. 356 – Spa (April-November) – Casino.*

*Forez ✆ 04 77 30 86 85 at Craintilleux, S : 12 km by N 82 and D 16.*

*Syndicat d'Initiative 1 r. des Ecoles ✆ 04 77 94 64 74, Fax 04 77 54 51 96.*

*Lyons 62.*

**Host. La Poularde** (Etéocle), ✆ 04 77 54 40 06, *Fax 04 77 54 53 14* – – 30. AE GB JCB
*closed 2 to 15 January, Tuesday lunch and Monday except Bank Holidays* – **Meals** (Sunday : booking essential) 225/580 and a la carte 480/750 – 80 – **11 rm** 340/560, 3 duplex
**Spec.** Lobe de foie gras poché à la lie de vin. Ecrevisses et huîtres poêlées aux senteurs de noisettes. Pigeonneau amandine entre chair et peau. **Wines** Condrieu, Saint-Joseph.

**Roanne** *42300 Loire* 73 ⑦ *– pop. 41 756 alt. 265.*

*of Champlong at Villerest ✆ 04 77 69 70 60.*

*Roanne-Renaison ✆ 04 77 66 85 77 by D 9.*

*Tourist Office cours République ✆ 04 77 71 51 77, Fax 04 77 70 96 62 – A.C. 24-26 r. Rabelais ✆ 04 77 71 31 67.*

*Lyons 87.*

**Troisgros** M, pl. Gare ✆ 04 77 71 66 97, *Fax 04 77 70 39 77,* « Tasteful contemporary decor », – . AE GB JCB
*closed 1 to 15 August, February Holidays, Tuesday except lunch from May-October and Wednesday* – **Meals** (booking essential) 320 (lunch), 620/750 and a la carte 490/840 – 120 – **15 rm** 700/1400, 3 suites
**Spec.** "Pani" aux truffes noires à l'huile de noix. Sandre à la meunière, aux cèpes secs. Piccata de ris de veau dorée, tomates à la crème. **Wines** Bourgogne blanc, Saint-Joseph.

**St-Bonnet-le-Froid** *43290 H.-Loire* 76 ⑨ *– pop. 180 alt. 1 126.*

*Lyons 101.*

**Aub. des Cimes** (Marcon) M with rm, ✆ 04 71 59 93 72, *Fax 04 71 59 93 40,* , – rm, rest, P. AE GB
*Easter-15 November and closed Monday dinner and Tuesday* – **Meals** 160/580 and a la carte 310/440 – 100 – **12 rm** 620/800
**Spec.** Ragoût de lentilles vertes du Puy à l'œuf de caille fumé. Agneau noir du Velay cuit en croûte de foin. Menu "champignons" (spring and autumn). **Wines** Crozes-Hermitage blanc et rouge.

**Valence** *26000 Drôme* 77 ⑫ *– pop. 63 437 alt. 126.*

See : *House of the Heads (Maison des Têtes)★ – Interior★ of the cathedral – Champ de Mars ≤★ – Red chalk sketches by Hubert Robert★★ in the museum.*

*of Chanalets ✆ 04 75 55 16 23 ; of St-Didier ✆ 04 75 59 67 01, E : 14 km by D 119 ; of Bourget ✆ 04 75 59 48 18 at Montmeyran.*

*of Valence-Chabeuil ✆ 04 75 85 26 26.*

*Tourist Office Parvis de la Gare ✆ 04 75 44 90 44, Fax 04 75 44 90 41 – A.C. 33 bis av. F. Faure ✆ 04 75 43 61 07.*

*Lyons 101.*

**Pic,** 285 av. V. Hugo, Motorway exit signposted Valence-Sud ✆ 04 75 44 15 32, *Fax 04 75 40 96 03,* – AE GB JCB
*closed 3 to 19 August and Sunday dinner* – **Meals** (Sunday : booking essential) 290 (lunch), 480/660 and a la carte 690/800 – 90 – **12 rm** 850/1300, 3 suites
**Spec.** Multicolore de saumon et foie de canard poêlé au basilic. Filet de loup au caviar. Côtelettes d'agneau du Limousin rôti et sa truffe en feuille d'or (December-March).

**at Pont-de-l'Isère** *to the N by N 7 : 9 km – alt. 120 – ✉ 26600 :*

**Michel Chabran** with rm, N 7 ✆ 04 75 84 60 09, *Fax 04 75 84 59 65,* – AE GB
**Meals** 215 (lunch), 350/795 and a la carte 460/660 – 80 – **12 rm** 400/690
**Spec.** Salade de homard au museau de porc. Pigeonneau des Gandels rôti en cocotte, fondue de blettes à la crème. Millefeuille craquant aux fraises des bois, crème glacée à la pistache. **Wines** Saint-Péray, Crozes-Hermitage.

**Vienne** *38200 Isère* 74 ⑪ ⑫ *– pop. 29 449 alt. 160.*

See : *Site★ – St-Maurice cathedral★★ – Temple of Augustus and Livia★★ – Roman Theatre★ – Church★ and cloisters★ of St-André-le-Bas – Mont Pipet Esplanade ≤★ – Old church of St-Pierre★ : lapidary museum★ – Gallo-roman city★ of St-Romain-en-Gal – Sculpture group★ in the church of Ste-Colombe.*

*Tourist Office 3 cours Brillier ✆ 04 74 85 12 62, Fax 04 74 31 75 98.*

*Lyons 31.*

**Pyramide** (Henriroux), 14 bd F. Point ✆ 04 74 53 01 96, *Fax 04 74 85 69 73,* – – 25. AE GB JCB
**Meals** *(closed Thursday lunch and Wednesday from 15 September-15 June)* 280 b.i. (lunch), 440/640 and a la carte 500/670 – 90 – **20 rm** 650/970, 4 suites
**Spec.** Tian de homard et pipérade de rigatoni en salade d'herbes. Fine tarte à la semoule et aux cébettes, dos de rouget et chipirons poêlés. "Piano au chocolat en ut praliné". **Wines** Condrieu, Côtes-du-Rhône.

**Vonnas** *01540 Ain* 74 ② *– pop. 2 381 alt. 200.*

*Lyons 63.*

**Georges Blanc**, ✆ 04 74 50 90 90, *Fax 04 74 50 08 80,* « Elegant inn on the banks of the Veyle, flowered garden », – – 80. AE GB
*closed 4 January-12 February* – **Meals** *(closed Tuesday except dinner from 15 June-15 September and Monday except Bank Holidays)* (booking essential) 470/860 and a la carte 530/700 – 110 – **32 rm** 850/1800, 6 suites
**Spec.** Foie gras de canard confit en écorce d'épices. Aile de pigeon rôti servie dans un bouillon corsé. Panouille bressane glacée à la confiture de lait. **Wines** Mâcon-Azé, Chiroubles.

---

**MARSEILLES** *13000 B.-du-R.* 84 ⑬ *– pop. 800 550.*

See : *Site★★★ – N.-D.-de-la-Garde Basilica ★★★ – Old Port★★ – Fish market (quai des Belges* ET **5***) – Palais Longchamp★* GS *: Fine Arts Museum★, Natural History Museum★ – St-Victor Basilica★ : crypt★★* DU *– Old Major Cathedral★* DS **N** *– Pharo Park ≤★* DU *– Hôtel du département et Dôme-Nouvel Alcazar★ – Vieille Charité★★ (Mediterranean archeology)* DS **R** *– Museums : Grobet-Labadié★★* GS **M**[7]*, Cantini★* FU **M**[5]*, Vieux Marseille★* DT **M**[2]*, History of Marseilles★* ET **M**[1].

**Envir.** : *Corniche road★★ of Callelongue S : 13 km along the sea front.*

**Exc.** : *Château d'If★★ (★★★) 1 h 30.*

*of Marseilles-Aix ✆ 04 42 24 20 41 to the N : 22 km ; of Allauch-Fonvieille (private) ✆ 04 91 07 28 22 ; junction Marseilles-East : 15 km, by D 2 and D 4=A ; Country Club of la Salette ✆ 04 91 27 12 16 by A 50.*

*Marseilles-Provence : ✆ 04 42 78 21 00 to the N : 28 km.*

*✆ 08 36 35 35 35.*

*Tourist Office 4 Canebière, 13001 ✆ 04 91 13 89 00, Fax 04 91 13 89 20 and St-Charles railway station ✆ 04 91 50 59 18 – A.C. of Provence 149 bd Rabatau, 13010 ✆ 04 91 78 83 00, Fax 04 91 25 74 38.*

*Paris 772 – Lyons 312 – Nice 188 – Turin 407 – Toulon 64 – Toulouse 401.*

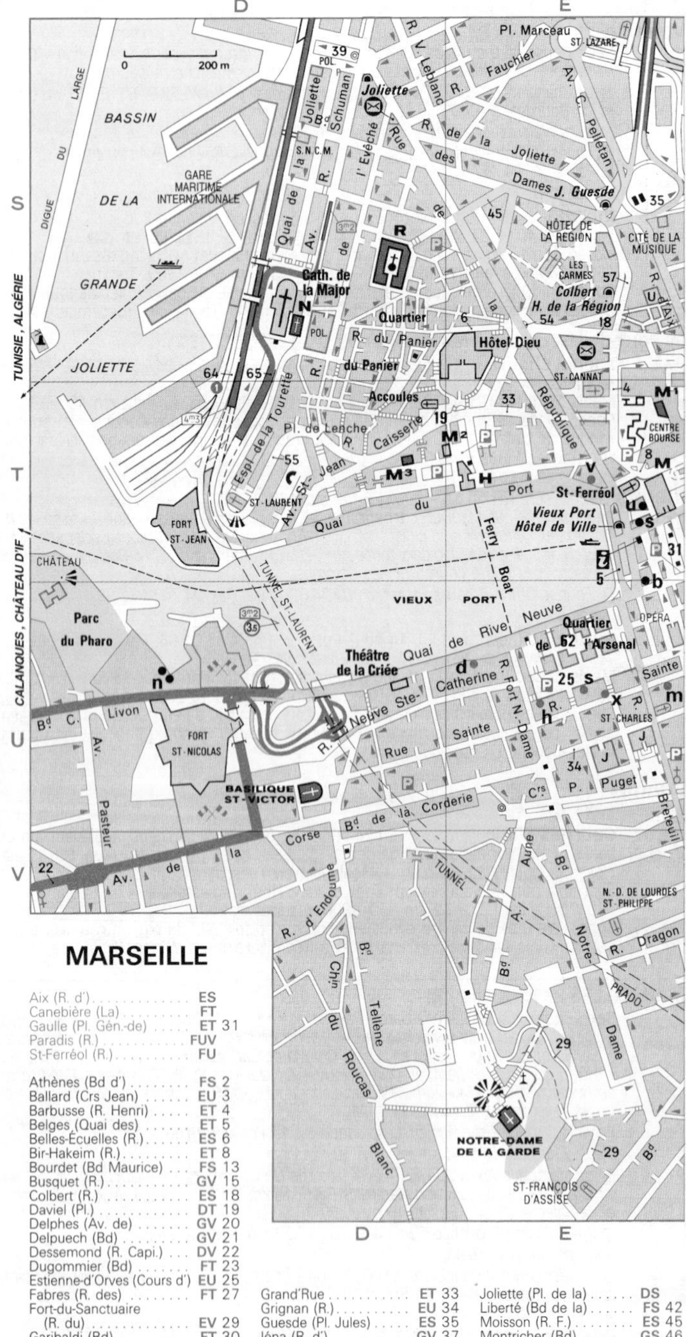


# MARSEILLE

Aix (R. d') . . . . . . . . . . . . ES
Canebière (La) . . . . . . . . . FT
Gaulle (Pl. Gén.-de) . . . . . ET 31
Paradis (R.) . . . . . . . . . . . FUV
St-Ferréol (R.) . . . . . . . . . FU

Athènes (Bd d') . . . . . . . . FS 2
Ballard (Crs Jean) . . . . . . EU 3
Barbusse (R. Henri) . . . . . ET 4
Belges (Quai des) . . . . . . ET 5
Belles-Écuelles (R.) . . . . . . ES 6
Bir-Hakeim (R.) . . . . . . . . ET 8
Bourdet (Bd Maurice) . . . FS 13
Busquet (R.) . . . . . . . . . . GV 15
Colbert (R.) . . . . . . . . . . . ES 18
Daviel (Pl.) . . . . . . . . . . . DT 19
Delphes (Av. de) . . . . . . . GV 20
Delpuech (Bd) . . . . . . . . . GV 21
Dessemond (R. Capi.) . . . DV 22
Dugommier (Bd) . . . . . . . FT 23
Estienne-d'Orves (Cours d') EU 25
Fabres (R. des) . . . . . . . . FT 27
Fort-du-Sanctuaire (R. du) . . . . . . . . . . . . . EV 29
Garibaldi (Bd) . . . . . . . . . FT 30

Grand'Rue . . . . . . . . . . . ET 33
Grignan (R.) . . . . . . . . . . EU 34
Guesde (Pl. Jules) . . . . . ES 35
Iéna (R. d') . . . . . . . . . . . GV 37

Joliette (Pl. de la) . . . . . . DS
Liberté (Bd de la) . . . . . . FS 42
Moisson (R. F.) . . . . . . . . ES 45
Montricher (Bd) . . . . . . . . GS 46

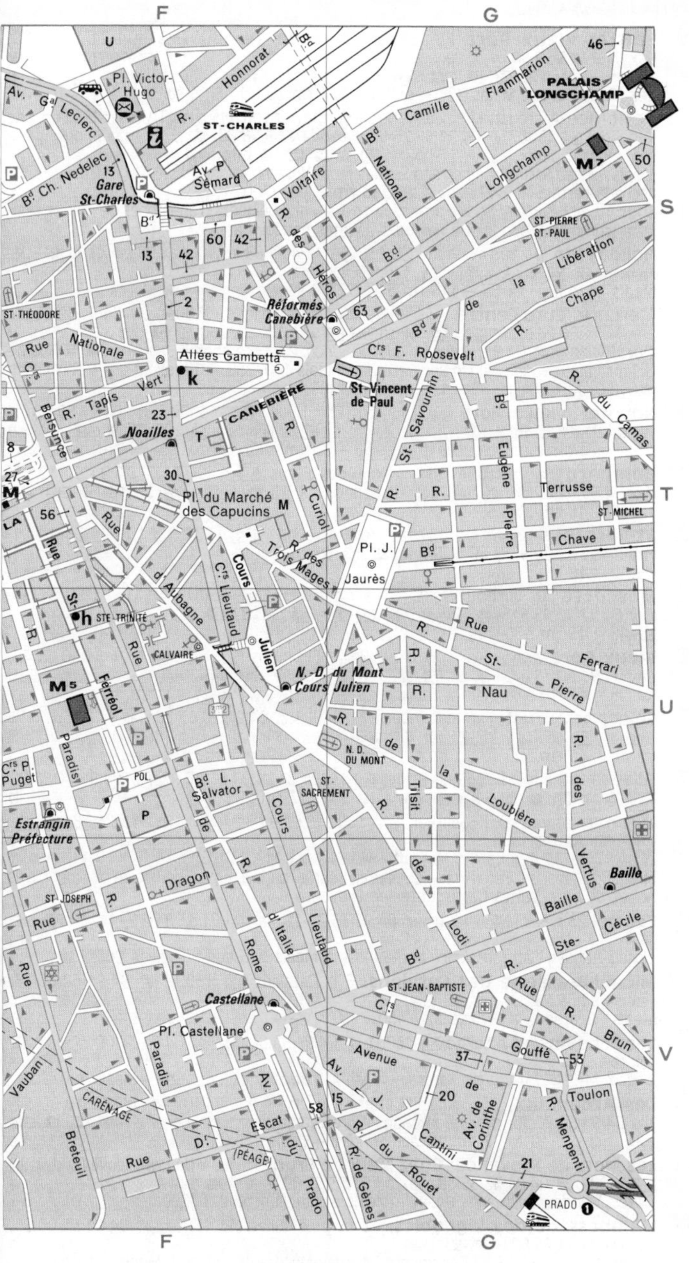


| | | | | | |
|---|---|---|---|---|---|
| Philipon (Bd) | **GS** 51 | St-Louis (Crs) | **FT** 56 | Thiars (Pl.) | **EU** 62 |
| Raynouard (Traverse) | **GV** 53 | Ste-Barbe (R.) | **ES** 57 | Thierry (Crs J.) | **GS** 63 |
| Sadi-Carnot (Pl.) | **ES** 54 | Ste-Philomène (R.) | **FV** 58 | Tourette (Quai) | **DS** 64 |
| St-Laurent (R.) | **DT** 55 | Sembat (R. Marcel) | **FS** 60 | Vaudoyer (Av.) | **DS** 65 |

**Sofitel Vieux Port** M, 36 bd Ch. Livon ✉ 13007 ☎ 04 91 15 59 00, *Fax 04 91 15 59 50*, ≤, « Panoramic restaurant ≤ old port », – |‡|, ⇔ rm, ▤ TV ☎ ♿ – 130. AE ⓓ GB JCB DU n
*Les Trois Forts :* **Meals** 225 – ☕ 85 – **127 rm** 790/1190, 3 suites.

**Petit Nice** (Passédat) M, anse de Maldormé (turn off when level with no 160 Corniche Kennedy) ✉ 13007 ☎ 04 91 59 25 92, *Fax 04 91 59 28 08*, « Villas overlooking the sea, elegant decor, ≤ », – |‡| ▤ TV ☎ P. AE ⓓ GB JCB
**Meals** *(closed Saturday lunch and Sunday from November-March)* 350 b.i. (lunch), 620/790 and a la carte 540/840 – ☕ 120 – **13 rm** 1200/2200
**Spec.** Compressé de "bouille abaisse port d'Orient". Beignets d'anémones de mer et tempura (summer). Loup "Lucie Passédat". **Wines** Bandol, Cassis.

**Holiday Inn** M, 103 av. Prado ✉ 13008 ☎ 04 91 83 10 10, *Fax 04 91 79 84 12* – |‡|, ⇔ rm, ▤ TV ☎ ♿ – 170. AE ⓓ GB JCB
**Meals** 90/135 – ☕ 55 – **115 rm** 510/650, 4 suites.

**Mercure Euro-Centre** M, r. Neuve St-Martin ✉ 13001 ☎ 04 91 39 20 00, *Fax 04 91 56 24 57*, ≤, – |‡|, ⇔ rm, ▤ TV ☎ ♿ P – 200. AE ⓓ GB JCB EST g
***Oursinade :*** ☎ *04 91 39 20 14 (closed lunch 20 December-5 January and 14 July - 8 September, Sunday lunch and Saturday)* **Meals** 140/250 – ***Oliveraie*** grill **Meals** (lunch only) 50/110 – ☕ 65 – **199 rm** 399/1085.

**Novotel Vieux Port** M, 36 bd Ch. Livon ✉ 13007 ☎ 04 91 59 22 22, *Fax 04 91 31 15 48*, ≤, – |‡|, ⇔ rm, ▤ TV ☎ ♿ – 200. AE ⓓ GB DU n
**Meals** a la carte approx. 170 – ☕ 55 – **90 rm** 550/630.

**Bompard** without rest, 2 r. Flots Bleus ✉ 13007 ☎ 04 91 52 10 93, *Fax 04 91 31 02 14*, – |‡| kitchenette ▤ TV ☎ ♿ P – 25. AE ⓓ GB JCB
☕ 50 – **46 rm** 500/550.

**St-Ferréol's** M without rest, 19 r. Pisançon ✉ 13001 ☎ 04 91 33 12 21, *Fax 04 91 54 29 97* – |‡| ▤ TV ☎. AE ⓓ GB JCB FU h
☕ 42 – **19 rm** 330/490.

**Mascotte** M without rest, 5 La Canebière ✉ 13001 ☎ 04 91 90 61 61, *Fax 04 91 90 95 61* – |‡|, ⇔ rm, ▤ TV ☎ – 30. AE ⓓ GB ET s
☕ 45 – **45 rm** 350/420.

**Vieux Port** without rest, 3 bis r. Reine Élisabeth ✉ 13001 ☎ 04 91 90 51 42, *Fax 04 91 90 76 24* – |‡| ▤ TV ☎ – 25. AE ⓓ GB JCB ET u
☕ 45 – **47 rm** 370.

**Sélect** without rest, 4 allées Gambetta ✉ 13001 ☎ 04 91 50 65 50, *Fax 04 91 50 45 56* – |‡| ▤ TV ☎ – 25. AE ⓓ GB JCB FS k
☕ 45 – **60 rm** 390.

**Alizé** M without rest, 35 quai Belges ✉ 13001 ☎ 04 91 33 66 97, *Fax 04 91 54 80 06*, ≤ – |‡| ▤ TV ☎. AE ⓓ GB JCB – ☕ 35 – **37 rm** 295/375. ETU b

**Miramar** (Minguella), 12 quai Port ✉ 13002 ☎ 04 91 91 10 40, *Fax 04 91 56 64 31*, – ▤. AE ⓓ GB JCB ET v
*closed 2 to 23 August and Sunday* – **Meals** a la carte 330/520
**Spec.** Bouillabaisse. Flan d'orties de mer au beurre rouge. Loup au beurre de pisala et olives noires de Nice. **Wines** Cassis, Côtes de Provence.

**Ferme,** 23 r. Sainte ✉ 13001 ☎ 04 91 33 21 12, *Fax 04 91 33 81 21* – ▤. AE ⓓ GB JCB EU m
*closed August, Saturday lunch and Sunday* – **Meals** 215 and a la carte 260/330.

**Michel-Brasserie des Catalans,** 6 r. Catalans ✉ 13007 ☎ 04 91 52 30 63, *Fax 04 91 59 23 05* – ▤. AE GB
**Meals** - Seafood - a la carte 270/430.

**Les Échevins,** 44 r. Sainte ✉ 13001 ☎ 04 91 33 08 08, *Fax 04 91 54 08 21* – ▤. AE ⓓ GB JCB EU x
*closed 14 July-15 August, Saturday lunch and Sunday except June* – **Meals** 110/310.

**Les Arcenaulx,** 25 cours d'Estienne d'Orves ✉ 13001 ☎ 04 91 59 80 30, *Fax 04 91 54 76 33*, « Bookshop and restaurant in original decor » – ▤. AE ⓓ GB JCB – *closed 10 to 17 August and Sunday* – **Meals** 135/280. EU s

**Les Mets de Provence "Chez Maurice Brun",** 18 quai de Rive Neuve (2nd floor) ✉ 13007 ☎ 04 91 33 35 38, *Fax 04 91 33 05 69* – ▤. GB EU d
*closed Monday lunch and Sunday* – **Meals** 200 b.i. (lunch), 220/290.

**L'Ambassade des Vignobles,** 42 pl. aux Huiles ✉ 13001 ☎ 04 91 33 00 25, *Fax 04 91 54 25 60* – ▤. AE GB EU h
*closed August, 24 to 30 December, Saturday lunch and Sunday* – **Meals** 120/250.

**René Alloin,** 9 pl. Amiral Muselier (by prom. G. Pompidou) ✉ 13008 ☎ 04 91 77 88 25, *Fax 04 91 77 76 84*, – ▤. AE GB
*closed Sunday lunch in August, Saturday lunch, dinner Sunday and Bank Holidays from September-July* – **Meals** 135 (lunch), 195/270.

**Les Baux-de-Provence** *13520 B.-du-R. 84 ① – pop. 457 alt. 185.*
See : *Site★★★ – Château ※★★ – Charloun Rieu monument ≤★ – Place St-Vincent★ – Rue du Trencat★ – Paravelle Tower ≤★ – Yves-Brayer museum★ (in Hôtel des Porcelet) – Shepherds' Festival★★ (Christmas midnight mass) – Cathédrale d'Images★ N : 1 km on the D 27 – ※★★★ of the village N : 2,5 km on the D 27.*
*9 ✆ 04 90 54 40 20, S : 2 km.*
*Tourist Office Ilôt "Post Tenebras Lux" ✆ 04 90 54 34 39, Fax 04 90 54 51 15.*
*Marseilles 83.*

**in the Vallon** :

XXXXX ✿✿ **Oustaù de Baumanière** (Charial) with rm, ✆ 04 90 54 33 07, *Fax 04 90 54 40 46*, ≤, « 16C period house tastefully decorated », – TV P. AE GB JCB
*closed 25 January-1 March, Thursday lunch and Wednesday from November-March* – **Meals** 480/740 and a la carte 460/760 – 115 – **7 rm** 1430, 4 suites2050
**Spec.** Ravioli de truffes. Filets de rougets au basilic. Gigot d'agneau en croûte. **Wines** Coteaux d'Aix-en-Provence-les Baux, Châteauneuf-du-Pape.
**Manoir** without rest, ≤, – TV P
*closed 15 January-1 March* – 115 – **5 rm** 1300, 4 suites2100.

XXX ✿ **Riboto de Taven** (Novi et Theme) with rm, ✆ 04 90 54 34 23, *Fax 04 90 54 38 88*, ≤, « Terrace and flowered garden near the rocks » – TV P. AE GB JCB
*closed 7 January-13 March, Tuesday dinner (out of season) and Wednesday* – **Meals** 200 b.i. (lunch), 300/450 and a la carte 310/460 – 80 – **3 rm** 1100
**Spec.** Caillettes provençales en courgette à fleur. Turbot à l'infusion de romarin. Tarte au fenouil caramélisé. **Wines** Coteaux d'Aix-en-Provence-Les Baux, Châteauneuf-du-Pape.

**road of Arles** *to the SW by D 78=F road :*

**Cabro d'Or**, à 1 km ✆ 04 90 54 33 21, *Fax 04 90 54 45 98*, ≤, « Flowered gardens », – rm, TV P – 60. AE GB JCB
*closed 11 November-20 December, Tuesday lunch and Monday from 15 October-31 March* – **Meals** 190 (lunch), 260/395 – 85 – **23 rm** 790/1150, 8 suites.

**Carry-le-Rouet** *13620 B.-du-R. 84 ⑫ – pop. 5 224 alt. 5.*
*Tourist Office av. A. Briand ✆ 04 42 13 20 36, Fax 04 42 44 52 03.*
*Marseilles 27.*

XXX ✿✿ **L'Escale** (Clor), prom. du Port ✆ 04 42 45 00 47, *Fax 04 42 44 72 69*, « Terrace overlooking the harbour, pleasant view », – AE GB
*1 February-late October and closed Sunday dinner from September-June and Monday except dinner in July-August* – **Meals** (Sunday : booking essential) 320 and a la carte 390/620
**Spec.** Poêlée de crevettes en chutney de curry. Cassoulet de baudroie aux cocos frais, coulis de crustacés (early July-late October). Homard rôti au beurre de corail. **Wines** Coteaux d'Aix-en-Provence, Bandol.

**Montpellier** *34000 Hérault 83 ⑦ – pop. 207 996 alt. 27.*
*of Montpellier-Méditerranée ✆ 04 67 20 85 00 to the SE : 7 km.*
*Tourist Office Triangle Comédie allée du Tourisme ✆ 04 67 58 67 58, Fax 04 67 58 67 59 and 78 av. du Pirée ✆ 04 67 22 06 16, Fax 04 67 22 38 10.*
*Marseilles 171.*

XXXX ✿✿✿ **Jardin des Sens** (Jacques et Laurent Pourcel) M with rm, 11 av. St-Lazare ✆ 04 67 79 63 38, *Fax 04 67 72 13 05*, « Elegant contemporary decor » – rest, P. AE GB JCB
*closed 1 to 15 January* – **Meals** *(closed Monday lunch and Sunday)* (booking essential) 210 (lunch), 370/580 and a la carte 420/560 – 90 – **13 rm** 650/1150
**Spec.** Petits encornets farcis de langoustines. Petite baudroie rôtie, tarte à la tomate. Côte de veau rôtie aux morilles. **Wines** Coteaux du Languedoc, Minervois.

---

**MONACO (Principality of)** 84 ⑩, 115 ㉗ ㉘ *– pop. 29 972 alt. 65 – Casino.*

**Monaco** *Capital of the Principality – ✉ 98000.*
See : *Tropical Garden★★ (Jardin exotique) : ≤★ – Observatory Caves★ (Grotte de l'Observatoire) – St-Martin Gardens★ – Early paintings of the Nice School★★ in Cathedral – Recumbent Christ★ in the Misericord Chapel – Place du Palais★ – Prince's Palace★ – Museums : oceanographic★★★ (aquarium★★, ≤★★ from the terrace), Prehistoric Anthropology★, Napoleon and Monaco History★, Royal collection of vintage cars★.*
*Urban racing circuit – A.C.M. 23 bd Albert-1er ✆ (00-377) 93 15 26 00, Fax (00-377) 93 25 80 08.*
*Paris 956 – Nice 21 – San Remo 44.*

**Monte-Carlo** *Fashionable resort of the Principality – Casinos Grand Casino, Monte-Carlo Sporting Club, Sun Casino.*

See : *Terrace★★ of the Grand Casino – Museum of Dolls and Automata★.*

*Monte-Carlo ✆ 04 93 41 09 11 to the S by N 7 : 11 km.*

*Tourist Office 2A bd Moulins ✆ (00-377) 92 16 61 66, Fax (00-377) 92 16 60 00.*

**Paris,** pl. Casino ✆ (00-377) 92 16 30 00, *Fax (00-377) 92 16 38 50*, ←, health centre, – rm, – 70. AE GB JCB. rest
*see* ***Louis XV*** *and* ***Grill*** *below* - ***Côté Jardin*** ✆ (00-377) 92 16 68 44 (lunch only) *(closed 4 July-30 August)* **Meals** 300 and a la carte 310/420 – ***Salle Empire*** ✆ (00-377) 92 16 29 52 *(4 July-30 August)* **Meals** a la carte 480/940 – 150 – **160 rm** 2300/3200, 40 suites.

**Hermitage,** square Beaumarchais ✆ (00-377) 92 16 40 00, *Fax (00-377) 92 16 38 52*, ←, health centre, « Dining room in baroque style », – – 80. AE GB JCB.
**Meals** 340/450 – 150 – **215 rm** 1850/2750, 16 suites.

**Loews** M, 12 av. Spélugues ✆ (00-377) 93 50 65 00, *Fax (00-377) 93 30 01 57*, ←, Casino and cabaret, – – 1 100. AE GB JCB. rest
***Truffe*** *(closed Monday and Tuesday)* **Meals** (dinner only) 380 – ***L'Argentin*** *(15 June-15 September)* **Meals** (dinner only) 365 – **Pistou** *(15 June-15 September)* **Meals** à la carte 250/370 – **Café de la Mer** *(15 June-15 September)* **Meals** a la carte 200/330 – 120 – **581 rm** 1550/1950, 38 suites.

**Métropole Palace** M, 4 av. Madone ✆ (00-377) 93 15 15 15, *Fax (00-377) 93 25 24 44*, « "Belle Epoque" decor », – rm, – 220. AE GB JCB. rest
***Le Jardin :*** **Meals** 225(lunch), 300/350 – 140 – **138 rm** 1400/2000, 12 suites.

**Méridien Beach Plaza** M, av. Princesse Grace, à la Plage du Larvotto ✆ (00-377) 93 30 98 80, *Fax (00-377) 93 50 23 14*, ←, « Attractive resort with », – – 500. AE GB JCB. rest
***Pergola*** - Italian rest. *(closed Sunday from 16 September to 30 June and Monday)* **Meals** (dinner only) 250/350 – ***Terrasse :*** **Meals** 190/250 – 125 – **295 rm** 1780/2835, 9 suites.

**Mirabeau** M, 1 av. Princesse Grace ✆ (00-377) 92 16 65 65, *Fax (00-377) 93 50 84 85*, ←, – rm, – 80. AE GB JCB. rest
*see* ***La Coupole*** *below* - ***Café Mirabeau*** at the swimming pool *(May-September)* **Meals** (lunch only) à la carte 240/300 – 140 – **99 rm** 1450/2400, 4 suites.

**Alexandra** without rest, 35 bd Princesse Charlotte ✆ (00-377) 93 50 63 13, *Fax (00-377) 92 16 06 48* – . AE GB JCB.
65 – **56 rm** 700/850.

**Balmoral,** 12 av. Costa ✆ (00-377) 93 50 62 37, *Fax (00-377) 93 15 08 69*, ← – , rm, . AE GB JCB.
**Meals** coffee shop *(closed November, Sunday dinner and Monday)* 150 – 80 – **66 rm** 450/1000, 6 suites.

XXXXX ✿✿✿ **Louis XV** - Hôtel de Paris, pl. Casino ✆ (00-377) 92 16 30 01, *Fax (00-377) 92 16 69 21* – P. AE GB JCB.
*closed 1 to 27 December, 2 to 17 February, Wednesday except dinner from 17 June-26 August and Tuesday* – **Meals** 480 (lunch), 810/920 and a la carte 650/950
**Spec.** Légumes des jardins de Provence mijotés à la truffe noire râpée, huile d'olive de Ligurie. Poitrine de pigeonneau, foie gras de canard et pommes de terre sur la braise. Le "Louis XV" au croustillant de pralin. **Wines** Côtes de Provence.

XXXX ✿ **Grill de l'Hôtel de Paris,** pl. Casino ✆ (00-377) 92 16 29 66, *Fax (00-377) 92 16 38 40*, « Rooftop restaurant with sliding roof and ← the Principality » – P. AE GB JCB.
*closed 4 January-4 February* – **Meals** a la carte 500/1 000
**Spec.** Grosses langoustines rôties, légumes au parfum de coriandre. Tronçon de turbot sur la braise, artichauts et asperges cuisinés à l'huile d'olive. Quartier d'agneau de lait rôti à la broche, petits légumes farcis (Spring). **Wines** Côtes de Provence.

XXXX ✿ **La Coupole** - Hôtel Mirabeau, 1 av. Princesse Grace ✆ (00-377) 92 16 65 65, *Fax (00-377) 93 50 84 85* – . AE GB JCB.
**Meals** 310/450 and a la carte 390/540
**Spec.** Cannelloni de chèvre frais, vianigrette de langoustines aux lardons de Parme (15 June-15 Sept.). Filets de petits rougets, compotée de tomates et fenouil au basilic. Cake au chocolat, crème fondante au safran, glace au "gianduja". **Wines** Côtes de Provence.

XXX **L'Hirondelle (Thermes Marins),** 2 av. Monte-Carlo ✆ (00-377) 92 16 49 47, *Fax (00-377) 92 16 49 49,* ≤ port and the Rock, ☂ – |‡| ▤. AE ⓓ GB JCB. ✂
*closed Sunday dinner* – **Meals** (booking essential) 285 and a la carte 330/380.

XXX **Saint Benoit,** 10 ter av. Costa ✆ (00-377) 93 25 02 34, *Fax (00-377) 93 30 52 64,* ≤ port and Monaco, ☂ – ▤. AE ⓓ GB JCB
*closed 20 December-4 January and Monday except dinner from July to Sept.* – **Meals** 168/235 and a la carte 250/420.

XX **Café de Paris,** pl. Casino ✆ (00-377) 92 16 20 20, *Fax (00-377) 92 16 38 58,* ☂, « 1900 brasserie decor » – ▤. AE ⓓ GB JCB. ✂
**Meals** a la carte 210/370.

X **Polpetta,** 2 r. Paradis ✆ (00-377) 93 50 67 84 – ▤. AE GB
*closed 15 to 30 October, 1 to 21 February, Saturday lunch and Tuesday* – **Meals** - Italian rest. - 150/250.

**at Monte-Carlo-Beach** *(06 Alpes-Mar.) at 2,5 km – ✉ 06190 Roquebrune-Cap-Martin :*

**Monte-Carlo Beach H.** M, av. Princesse Grace ✆ 04 93 28 66 66, *Fax 04 93 78 14 18,* ≤ sea and Monaco, ☂, « Extensive swimming complex », – |‡|, ▤ rm, TV ☎ ♿ P – 40. AE ⓓ GB JCB. ✂ rest
*3 April-4 October* – ***Salle à Manger*** (dinner only)(residents only) **Meals** a la carte 310/440 – ***Potinière*** (lunch only) *(29 May-14 September)* **Meals** a la carte 320/440 – **Rivage** (lunch only) **Meals** a la carte 220/340 – **Vigie** -buffet- *(26 June-31 August)* **Meals** (lunch only) 280 – ☕ 150 – **44 rm** 2400/2700.

---

**NICE** *06000 Alpes-Mar.* 84 ⑨ ⑩, 115 ㉖ ㉗ – *pop. 342 439 alt. 6 – Casino Ruhl* FZ.

**See** : *Site★★ – Promenade des Anglais★★* EFZ – *Old Nice★ : Château ≤★★* JZ, *Interior★ of church of St-Martin-St-Augustin* HY **D** – *Balustraded staircase★ of the Palais Lascaris* HZ **K**, *Interior★ of Ste-Réparate Cathedral* HZ **L**, *St-Jacques Church★* HZ **N**, *Decoration★ of St-Giaume's Chapel* HZ **R** – *Mosaic★ by Chagall in Law Faculty* DZ **U** – *Palais des Arts★* HJY – *Miséricorde Chapel★* HZ **S** – *Cimiez : Monastery★ (Masterpieces★★ of the early Nice School in the church)* HV **Q**, *Roman Ruins★* HV – *Parc Phoenix★ – Museums : Marc Chagall★★* GX, *Matisse★★* HV **M²**, *Fine Arts Museum★★* DZ **M**, *Masséna★* FZ **M¹** – *Modern and Contemporary Art★★* HY – *Carnival★★★ (before Shrove Tuesday).*

**Envir.** : *St-Michel Plateau ≤★★ 9,5 km.*

✈ *of Nice-Côte d'Azur ✆ 04 93 21 30 12 : 7 km –* 🚗 *✆ 08 36 35 35 35.*

ℹ *Tourist Office av. Thiers ✆ 04 93 87 07 07, Fax 04 93 16 85 16 ; 5 promenade des Anglais ✆ 04 93 87 60 60, Fax 04 93 82 07 99, Nice-Ferber (near the Airport) ✆ 04 93 83 32 64, Fax 04 93 72 08 27 and Airport, Terminal 1 ✆ 04 93 21 41 11 – Automobile-Club, 9 r. Massenet ✆ 04 93 87 18 17, Fax 04 93 88 90 00.*

*Paris 932 – Cannes 32 – Genova 194 – Lyons 472 – Marseilles 188 – Turin 220.*

Plans on following pages

**Négresco,** 37 promenade des Anglais ✆ 04 93 16 64 00, *Fax 04 93 88 35 68,* ≤, ☂, « 17C, 18C, Empire and Napoléon III furnishings » – |‡| ▤ TV ☎ 🚗 – 50 - 200. AE ⓓ GB JCB FZ k
see ***Chantecler*** below - ***Rotonde :*** **Meals** 170, Sunday a la carte – ☕ 130 – **122 rm** 1700/2450, 18 suites.

**Palais Maeterlinck** M, 6 km by Inferior Corniche ✉ 06300 ✆ 04 92 00 72 00, *Fax 04 92 04 18 10,* ≤, ☂, « Swimming pool, garden and terraces overlooking sea », – |‡| kitchenette ▤ TV ☎ ♿ 🚗 P – 25. AE ⓓ GB
*closed 5 January-13 March* – ***Mélisande*** ✆ 04 92 00 72 01 **Meals** 200 b.i. (lunch), 240/700 – ☕ 160 – **9 rm** 2000/2500, 13 suites3500/10000, 9 duplex.

**Radisson SAS** M, 223 promenade des Anglais ✉ 06200 ✆ 04 93 37 17 17, *Fax 04 93 71 21 71,* ☂, « Rooftop swimming pool ≤ bay », – |‡|, ⇔ rm, ▤ TV ☎ – 30 - 180. AE ⓓ GB JCB
***Les Mosaïques :*** **Meals** 155 (lunch), 195/250 – ***La Terrasse-Les Jardins*** grill *(June-September)* **Meals** 155 (lunch), 195/250 – ☕ 95 – **316 rm** 1000/1365, 12 suites.

**Méridien,** 1 promenade des Anglais ✆ 04 93 82 25 25, *Fax 04 93 16 08 90,* ☂, « Rooftop swimming pool, ≤ bay » – |‡|, ⇔ rm, ▤ TV ☎ – 25 - 200. AE ⓓ GB JCB FZ d
***Colonial Café :*** **Meals** a la carte 210/260 – ***La Terrasse*** *(1 May-15 October)* **Meals** 130/210 ⅄ – ☕ 95 – **314 rm** 1250/2850, 8 suites.

**Élysée Palace** M, 2. Sauvan ✆ 04 93 86 06 06, *Fax 04 93 44 50 40,* ☂, « Rooftop swimming pool ≤ Nice » – |‡| ▤ TV ☎ ♿ 🚗 – 45. AE ⓓ GB JCB EZ d
**Meals** 190 – ☕ 100 – **143 rm** 1150/1300.

**Plaza Concorde,** 12 av. Verdun ✆ 04 93 16 75 75, *Fax 04 93 88 61 11,* ≤, ☂, « Rooftop terrace » – |‡| ▤ TV ☎ – 260. AE ⓓ GB JCB GZ f
**Meals** 155/250 ⅄ – ☕ 80 – **173 rm** 1100/1500, 10 suites.

# NICE

Félix-Faure (Av.) . . . . . GZ 21
France (R. de) . . . . . . DFZ
Gambetta (Bd) . . . . . . EXZ
Gioffredo (R.) . . . . . . . . HY
Hôtel-des-Postes (R.) . . HY 30
Liberté (R. de la) . . . . . GZ 35
Masséna (Espace, Pl.) . . . . . . GZ
Masséna (R.) . . . . . . . FGZ 43
Médecin (Av. J.) . . . . FGY 44
Paradis (R.) . . . . . . . . . GZ 55
Pastorelli (R.) . . . . . . . . GY 58
République (Av. de la) . JXY 64

Alberti (R.) . . . . . . . . . GHY 2
Alsace-Lorraine (Jardin) EZ 3
Armée-du-Rhin (Pl.) . . . JX 5
Auriol (Pont V.) . . . . . . JV 7
Bellanda (Av.) . . . . . . . HV 10
Berlioz (R.) . . . . . . . . . FY 12
Bonaparte (R.) . . . . . . . JY 13
Carnot (Bd) . . . . . . . . . JZ 15
Desambrois (Av.) . . . GHX 18
Diables-Bleus (Av. des) . . . . . . . . . JX 19
Gallieni (Av.) . . . . . . . HJX 23
Gautier (Pl. P.) . . . . . . . HZ 25
Ile-de-Beauté (Pl. de l') . . . . . . . . . JZ 32
J.-Jaurès (Bd) . . . . . . . HYZ 33

Lunel (Quai) . . . . . . . . . . JZ 37
Meyerbeer (R.) . . . . . . . . FZ 45
Monastère (Av. et Pl. du) . . . . . . . HV 46
Moulin (Pl. J.) . . . . . . . . . HY 47
Parvis (de l'Europe) . . . . . . . JX 56
Passy (R. F.) . . . . . . . . . . EY 57

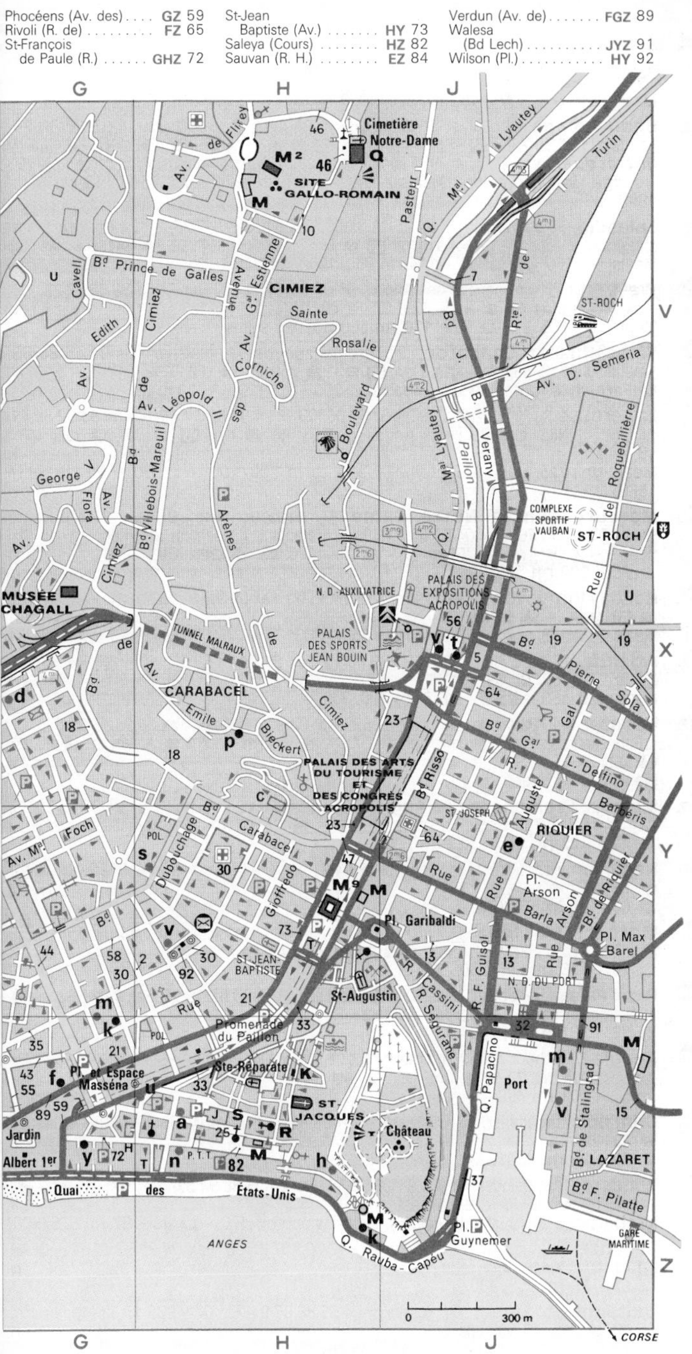
Cimetière
Notre-Dame
SITE GALLO-ROMAIN
CIMIEZ
ST-ROCH
COMPLEXE SPORTIF VAUBAN
MUSÉE CHAGALL
TUNNEL MALRAUX
CARABACEL
PALAIS DES EXPOSITIONS ACROPOLIS
PALAIS DES SPORTS JEAN BOUIN
PALAIS DES ARTS DU TOURISME ET DES CONGRÈS ACROPOLIS
RIQUIER
Pl. Garibaldi
Pl. Max Barel
St-Augustin
Promenade du Paillon
Pl. et Espace Masséna
Ste-Réparate
ST JACQUES
Château
Port
LAZARET
Jardin Albert 1er
Quai des États-Unis
ANGES
Q. Rauba-Capeu
Pl. Guynemer
GARE MARITIME
CORSE

**Sofitel** M, 2-4 parvis de l'Europe ✉ 06300 ℘ 04 92 00 80 00, *Fax 04 93 26 27 00*, « Panoramic rooftop swimming pool », – |‡|, ⇔ rm, ▤ TV ☎ ♿ – 🚗 – 30. AE ① GB JCB JX t
**Meals** 98 – 95 – **152 rm** 990/1090.

**Beau Rivage** M, 24 r. St-François-de-Paule ✉ 06300 ℘ 04 93 80 80 70, *Fax 04 93 80 55 77*, – |‡|, ⇔ rm, ▤ TV ☎ ♿ – 35. AE ① GB JCB GZ y
***Bistrot du Rivage*** *(October-April and closed Sunday dinner)* **Meals** *(98)*- a la carte 170/280 – ***Plage*** *(May-September)* **Meals** a la carte approx. 220 – 95 – **118 rm** 850/1800.

**Splendid,** 50 bd V. Hugo ℘ 04 93 16 41 00, *Fax 04 93 16 42 70*, « Rooftop swimming pool ≤ Nice » – |‡|, ⇔ rm, ▤ TV ☎ 🚗 – 30 - 100. AE ① GB JCB. ✻ rest
**Meals** 120/150 – 80 – **114 rm** 950/1250, 14 suites. FYZ g

**West End,** 31 promenade des Anglais ℘ 04 92 14 44 00, *Fax 04 93 88 85 07*, ≤, – |‡|, ⇔ rm, ▤ TV ☎ – 120. AE ① GB JCB FZ p
**Meals** 120/185 – 75 – **120 rm** 600/1350, 6 suites.

**Westminster Concorde,** 27 promenade des Anglais ℘ 04 92 14 86 86, *Fax 04 93 82 45 35*, – |‡|, ▤ rm, TV ☎ – 150. AE ① GB JCB. ✻ rest FZ m
***Le Farniente*** *(closed Sunday)* **Meals** *(150)*-200 – 100 – **102 rm** 950/1300.

**La Pérouse** , 11 quai Rauba-Capéu ✉ 06300 ℘ 04 93 62 34 63, *Fax 04 93 62 59 41*, , « ≤ Nice and Baie des Anges », – |‡|, ▤ rm, TV ☎. AE ① GB JCB. ✻ rest HZ k
**Meals** grill *(15 May-16 September)* a la carte 200/260 – 90 – **64 rm** 545/1380.

**Mercure Centre Notre Dame** M without rest, 28 av. Notre-Dame ℘ 04 93 13 36 36, *Fax 04 93 62 61 69*, ≤, « Hanging garden on 2nd floor, on 8th floor » – |‡|, ⇔ rm, ▤ TV ☎ ♿ – 25 - 120. AE ① GB JCB FXY q
75 – **200 rm** 595/795.

**Holiday Inn** M, 20 bd V. Hugo ℘ 04 93 16 55 00, *Fax 04 93 16 55 55*, – |‡|, ⇔ rm, ▤ TV ☎ ♿ – 90. AE ① GB JCB FY a
**Meals** 155/178 – 70 – **131 rm** 750/1200.

**Atlantic,** 12 bd V. Hugo ℘ 04 93 88 40 15, *Fax 04 93 88 68 60*, – |‡|, ⇔ rm, ▤ TV ☎ – 50. AE ① GB JCB FY d
**Meals** 120/150 – 80 – **123 rm** 750/900.

**Novotel,** 8-10 Parvis de l'Europe ✉ 06300 ℘ 04 93 13 30 93, *Fax 04 93 13 09 04*, « Panoramic rooftop swimming pool », – |‡|, ⇔ rm, ▤ TV ☎ ♿ 🚗 – 80. AE ① GB JCB JX v
**Meals** a la carte approx. 180 – 58 – **173 rm** 570/750.

**Mercure Promenade des Anglais** M without rest, 2 r. Halévy ℘ 04 93 82 30 88, *Fax 04 93 82 18 20* – |‡|, ⇔ rm, ▤ TV ☎ – 25. AE ① GB JCB FZ v
75 – **122 rm** 660/930.

**Napoléon** without rest, 6 r. Grimaldi ℘ 04 93 87 70 07, *Fax 04 93 16 17 80* – |‡| ▤ TV ☎. AE ① GB JCB FZ r
65 – **83 rm** 655/820.

**Mercure Masséna** M without rest, 58 r. Gioffredo ℘ 04 93 85 49 25, *Fax 04 93 62 43 27* – |‡|, ⇔ rm, ▤ TV ☎ 🚗. AE ① GB JCB GZ k
70 – **116 rm** 595/830.

**Petit Palais** without rest, 10 av. E. Bieckert ℘ 04 93 62 19 11, *Fax 04 93 62 53 60*, ≤ Nice and sea – |‡| TV ☎. AE ① GB JCB HX p
50 – **25 rm** 530/780.

**Apogia** M without rest, 26 r. Smolett ✉ 06300 ℘ 04 93 89 18 88, *Fax 04 93 89 16 06* – |‡|, ⇔ rm, ▤ TV ☎ ♿ 🚗. AE ① GB JCB JY e
55 – **101 rm** 490.

**Grimaldi** without rest, 15 r. Grimaldi ℘ 04 93 87 73 61, *Fax 04 93 88 30 05* – |‡| ▤ TV ☎. AE ① GB JCB FY s
50 – **24 rm** 450/800.

**Windsor,** 11 r. Dalpozzo ℘ 04 93 88 59 35, *Fax 04 93 88 94 57*, , , , – |‡|, ▤ rm, TV ☎. AE ① GB. ✻ rest FZ f
**Meals** (coffee shop) *(closed Sunday)* a la carte approx. 170 – 40 – **57 rm** 525/680.

**Régence** without rest, 21 r. Masséna ℘ 04 93 87 75 08, *Fax 04 93 82 41 31* – |‡| ▤ TV ☎. AE ① GB JCB FZ q
35 – **39 rm** 355/380.

**Lausanne** without rest, 36 r. Rossini ℘ 04 93 88 85 94, *Fax 04 93 88 15 88* – |‡|, ⇔ rm, ▤ TV ☎ 🚗. AE ① GB FY n
*closed 20 to 26 December* – 40 – **35 rm** 350/400.

XXXX ✿✿ **Chantecler** - Hôtel Négresco, 37 promenade des Anglais ✆ 04 93 16 64 00, *Fax 04 93 88 35 68* – ▤. AE ⓓ GB JCB FZ k
*closed 16 November-15 December* – **Meals** 280 b.i. (lunch), 415/590 and a la carte 460/680
**Spec.** Tatin de courgettes, beurre au miel, langoustines rôties (May-late August). Filets de rougets poêlés, panisses "façon socca". Pigeon au poêlon, ravioli d'abats poêlés, tranche de foie gras chaud. **Wines** Côtes de Provence.

XXX **L'Ane Rouge,** 7 quai Deux-Emmanuel ✉ 06300 ✆ 04 93 89 49 63, *Fax 04 93 89 49 63* – ▤. AE ⓓ GB JZ m
*closed 29 July-4 August, 7 to 21 January and Wednesday* – **Meals** 148/248 and a la carte 220/360.

XX **Boccaccio,** 7 r. Masséna ✆ 04 93 87 71 76, *Fax 04 93 82 09 06*, 🏠, « Carvel decor » – ▤. AE ⓓ GB JCB GZ f
**Meals** - Seafood - 140 (lunch)/200.

XX **Les Dents de la Mer,** 2 r. St-François-de-Paule ✉ 06300 ✆ 04 93 80 99 16, *Fax 04 93 85 05 78*, 🏠, « Unusual decor depicting a submerged galleon » – ▤. AE ⓓ GB
**Meals** - Seafood - 148/199. HZ n

XX **Flo,** 4 r. S. Guitry ✆ 04 93 13 38 38, *Fax 04 93 13 38 39*, brasserie, « Former theatre » – ▤. AE ⓓ GB GYZ m
**Meals** 112 b.i./153 b.i.

XX **Don Camillo,** 5 r. Ponchettes ✉ 06300 ✆ 04 93 85 67 95, *Fax 04 93 13 97 43* – ▤. AE GB HZ h
*closed Monday lunch and Sunday* – **Meals** - Niçoise and Italian specialities - 200/350.

XX **L'Univers de Christian Plumail,** 54 bd J. Jaurès ✉ 06300 ✆ 04 93 62 32 22, *Fax 04 93 62 55 69* – ▤. AE ⓓ GB JCB HZ u
*closed 15 July-1 August, Saturday lunch and Sunday except Bank Holidays* – **Meals** 170/290.

XX **Fleur de Sel,** 10 bd Dubouchage ✆ 04 93 13 45 45, 🏠 – ▤. AE GB HY s
*closed 20 December-20 January, Saturday and Sunday* – **Meals** 79/160 ♁.

XX **Les Épicuriens,** 6 pl. Wilson ✆ 04 93 80 85 00, *Fax 04 93 85 65 00*, 🏠 – ▤. GB HY v
*closed 2 to 23 August, Saturday lunch and Sunday* – **Meals** a la carte 190/300.

XX **Toque Blanche,** 40 r. Buffa ✆ 04 93 88 38 18, *Fax 04 93 88 38 18* – ▤. GB FZ n
*closed Sunday except lunch from September-June and Monday* – **Meals** 145/290.

X **Les Pêcheurs,** 18 quai des Docks ✆ 04 93 89 59 61, *Fax 04 93 55 47 50* – AE GB JZ v
*closed November-mid December, Thursday lunch from May-October, Tuesday dinner from December-April and Wednesday* – **Meals** - Seafood - 155.

X **Mireille,** 19 bd Raimbaldi ✆ 04 93 85 27 23 – ▤. GB GX d
*closed 8 June-12 July, 28 September-6 October, Monday and Tuesday* – **Meals** - One dish only : paella - 115/155.

X **Merenda,** 4 r. Terrasse ✉ 06300 – ▤ HZ a
*closed 13 to 26 April, 27 July-17 August, Christmas and February Holidays, Saturday, Sunday and Bank Holidays* – **Meals** - Niçoise specialities - (booking essential) a la carte 150/180.

**at the airport** : *7 km* – ✉ *06200 Nice* :

XXX **Ciel d'Azur,** aérogare 1, 2e étage ✆ 04 93 21 36 36, *Fax 04 93 21 35 31* – ▤. AE ⓓ GB JCB
**Meals** (lunch only) 170/300.

## St-Martin-du-Var *06670 Alpes-Mar. 84 ⑨, 115 ⑯ – pop. 1 869 alt. 110.*

*Nice 26.*

XXXX ✿✿ **Jean-François Issautier,** on Nice road (N 202) 3 km ✆ 04 93 08 10 65, *Fax 04 93 29 19 73* – ▤ P. AE ⓓ GB
*closed 12 to 20 October, 4 January-3 February, Sunday except lunch from 14 September-27 June and Monday* – **Meals** 260 b.i./530 and a la carte 390/570
**Spec.** Grosses crevettes en robe de pommes de terre. "Cul" d'agneau de Sisteron rôti rosé à la menthe. Gratin "chaud-froité" aux fruits du temps. **Wines** Côtes de Provence, Bellet.

## Vence *06140 Alpes-Mar. 84 ⑨, 115 ㉕ – pop. 15 330 alt. 325.*

ℹ *Tourist Office, pl. Grand-Jardin ✆ 04 93 58 06 38, Fax 04 93 58 91 81.*

*Nice 23.*

XXX ✿✿ **Jacques Maximin,** 689 chemin de La Gaude, by road of Cagnes : 3 km ✆ 04 93 58 90 75, *Fax 04 93 58 22 86*, 🏠, 🌳 – P. AE GB
*closed 12 January-12 February, Sunday dinner and Monday* – **Meals** (booking essential) 240 (lunch)/500 and a la carte 340/450
**Spec.** Rognonnade de lapereau au foie gras frais et à l'aubergine. Macaronade de rougets à la niçoise. Pigeonneau du Lauragais en tajine. **Wines** Bellet.

**STRASBOURG** *67000 B.-Rhin* 62 ⑩ *– pop. 252 338 alt. 143.*

See : *Cathedral★★★ : Astronomical clock★ – La Petite France★★ : rue du Bains-aux-Plantes★★* HJZ *– Barrage Vauban ※★★ – Ponts couverts★ – Place de la Cathédrale★* KZ **26** *: Maison Kammerzell★* KZ **e** *– Mausoleum★★ in St-Thomas Church* JZ *– Place Kléber★ – Hôtel de Ville★* KY **H** *– Orangery★ – Palais de l'Europe★ – Museum of Oeuvre N.-Dame★★* KZ **M¹** *– Boat trips on the Ill river and the canals★* KZ *– Museums★★ (decorative Arts, Fine Arts, Archeology) in the Palais Rohan★* KZ *– Alsatian Museum★★* KZ **M²** *– Historical Museum★* KZ **M³** *– Museum of Modern Art★* KZ **M⁴** *– Guided tours of the Port★ by boat.*

*9 9 9 at Illkirch-Graffenstaden (private) ✆ 03 88 66 17 22 ; 18 of the Wantzenau at Wantzenau (private) ✆ 03 88 96 37 73 ; N by D 468 : 12 km ; 18 of Kempferhof at Plobsheim ✆ 03 88 98 72 72, S by D 468 : 15 km.*

*of Strasbourg International : ✆ 03 88 64 67 67 by D 392 : 12 km* FR.

*✆ 08 36 35 35 35.*

*Tourist Office 17 pl. de la Cathédrale ✆ 03 88 52 28 28, Fax 03 88 52 28 29, pl. gare ✆ 03 88 32 51 49, Pont de l'Europe ✆ 03 88 61 39 23 – Automobile Club, 5 av. Paix ✆ 03 88 36 04 34, Fax 03 88 36 00 63.*

*Paris 490 – Basle 145 – Bonn 360 – Bordeaux 915 – Frankfurt 218 – Karlsruhe 81 – Lille 545 – Luxembourg 223 – Lyons 485 – Stuttgart 157.*

Plans on following pages

**Régent Petite France** M, 5 r. Moulins ✆ 03 88 76 43 43, *Fax 03 88 76 43 76*, ≤, « Former ice factory on the banks of River Ill - contemporary decor », – rm, – 30. AE GB JCB JZ z
*closed 25 December-4 January* – **Meals** *(closed Monday from June-September and week-ends from October-May)* 149 – 90 – **63 rm** 1090/1490, 5 suites, 4 duplex.

**Hilton,** av. Herrenschmidt ✆ 03 88 37 10 10, *Fax 03 88 36 83 27*, – rm, P – 25 - 300. AE GB JCB
***Jardin*** ✆ 03 88 35 72 61 **Meals** 111 (lunch), 140/187 – 93 – **241 rm** 950/1600, 5 suites.

**Sofitel** M, pl. St-Pierre-le-Jeune ✆ 03 88 15 49 00, *Fax 03 88 15 49 99*, , patio – rm, – 120. AE GB JY s
***L'Alsace Gourmande*** ✆ 03 88 15 49 10 **Meals** 155 – 95 – **153 rm** 1200/1400.

**Régent Contades** M without rest, 8 av. Liberté ✆ 03 88 15 05 05, *Fax 03 88 15 05 15*, « 19C mansion » – rm, . AE GB JCB LY f
90 – **45 rm** 820/1550.

**Beaucour** M without rest, 5 r. Bouchers ✆ 03 88 76 72 00, *Fax 03 88 76 72 60*, « Old Alsatian houses elegantly decorated » – – 30. AE GB KZ k
65 – **49 rm** 550/950.

**Holiday Inn,** 20 pl. Bordeaux ✆ 03 88 37 80 00, *Fax 03 88 37 07 04*, – rm, P – 450. AE GB JCB
**Meals** 150 – 85 – **170 rm** 980/1250.

**Maison Rouge** without rest, 4 r. Francs-Bourgeois ✆ 03 88 32 08 60, *Fax 03 88 22 43 73*, « Tasteful decor » – – 50. AE GB JZ g
65 – **140 rm** 540/590.

**Monopole-Métropole** without rest, 16 r. Kuhn ✆ 03 88 14 39 14, *Fax 03 88 32 82 55*, « Alsatian and contemporary decor » – rm, . AE GB JCB HY p
*closed Christmas-New Year* – 65 – **90 rm** 430/750.

**Europe** without rest, 38 r. Fossé des Tanneurs ✆ 03 88 32 17 88, *Fax 03 88 75 65 45*, « Half timbered Alsatian house, beautiful 1/50th copy of the Cathedral » – rm, – 30. AE GB JCB JZ v
*closed 23 to 29 December* – 48 – **60 rm** 380/560.

**France** without rest, 20 r. Jeu des Enfants ✆ 03 88 32 37 12, *Fax 03 88 22 48 08* – rm, – 30. AE GB JY v
65 – **66 rm** 500/710.

**Novotel Centre Halles** M, 4 quai Kléber ✆ 03 88 21 50 50, *Fax 03 88 21 50 51* – rm, – 80. AE GB JY k
**Meals** a la carte approx. 170 – 59 – **97 rm** 670.

**Mercure Centre** M without rest, 25 r. Thomann ✆ 03 88 75 77 88, *Fax 03 88 32 08 66* – rm, . AE GB JCB JY q
57 – **98 rm** 565/680.

**Grand Hôtel** without rest, 12 pl. Gare ✆ 03 88 52 84 84, *Fax 03 88 52 84 00* – . AE GB HY m
65 – **83 rm** 395/610.

**Cathédrale** without rest, 12 pl. Cathédrale 03 88 22 12 12, *Fax 03 88 23 28 00* – rm, . KZ n
48 – **32 rm** 450/790, 3 duplex.

**des Rohan** without rest, 17 r. Maroquin 03 88 32 85 11, *Fax 03 88 75 65 37* – , rm, . KZ u
52 – **36 rm** 410/795.

**Dragon** without rest, 2 r. Ecarlate 03 88 35 79 80, *Fax 03 88 25 78 95* – , rm, . JZ d
*closed 23 to 27 December* – 60 – **32 rm** 430/655.

**Dauphine** without rest, 30 r. 1e Armée 03 88 36 26 61, *Fax 03 88 35 50 07* – . 
*closed 23 December-2 January* – 45 – **45 rm** 395/580.

**Couvent du Franciscain** without rest, 18 r. Fg de Pierre 03 88 32 93 93, *Fax 03 88 75 68 46* – . JY e
*closed 24 December-4 January* – 44 – **43 rm** 300/320.

**Pax,** 24 r. Fg National 03 88 32 14 54, *Fax 03 88 32 01 16,* – , rm, – 25. – *closed 24 December-2 January* – **Meals** *(closed Sunday from 2 November-1 March)* 90/130 – 40 – **106 rm** 365/405. HYZ u

**Continental** without rest, 14 r. Maire Kuss 03 88 22 28 07, *Fax 03 88 32 22 25* – . HY s
*closed 23 December-2 January* – 36 – **48 rm** 297/340.

**Au Crocodile** (Jung), 10 r. Outre 03 88 32 13 02, *Fax 03 88 75 72 01,* « Elegant decor » – . KY x
*closed 12 July-3 August, 24 December-4 January, Sunday and Monday* – **Meals** 300 (lunch), 430/650 and a la carte 480/600
**Spec.** Lotte rôtie au fenouil confit et tomate safranée. Lobe de foie d'oie truffé cuit tel un "Baeckeoffe". Pêche blanche en gelée de verveine. **Wines** Riesling, Muscat d'Alsace.

**Buerehiesel** (Westermann), set in the Orangery Park 03 88 45 56 65, *Fax 03 88 61 32 00,* ≤, « Reconstructed authentic Alsatian farmhouse with conservatory » – 
*closed 10 to 26 August, 22 December-6 January, February Holidays, Tuesday and Wednesday* – **Meals** 290 (lunch), 380/710 and a la carte 500/700
**Spec.** Persillé de chevreuil au foie gras de canard (June-January). Schniederspaetle et cuisses de grenouilles poêlées au cerfeuil. Poulet de Bresse aux pommes de terre et artichauts cuit "comme un baeckeoffe" (spring-summer). **Wines** Riesling, Tokay-Pinot gris.

**Maison Kammerzell and H. Baumann** with rm, 16 pl. Cathédrale 03 88 32 42 14, *Fax 03 88 23 03 92,* « Attractive 16C Alsatian house » – , rm, – 80. KZ e
*accommodation : closed 17 February-10 March* – **Meals** 195/295 and a la carte 200/320 – 55 – **9 rm** 420/630.

**Vieille Enseigne** (Langs), 9 r. Tonneliers 03 88 32 58 50, *Fax 03 88 75 63 80* – . KZ f
*closed Saturday lunch and Sunday* – **Meals** 168/295 and a la carte 280/420
**Spec.** Terrine d'anguille fumée au raifort. Bar rôti au jus de bouillabaisse. Beignets croquants de chocolat au lait d'amande amère.

**Zimmer,** 8 r. Temple Neuf 03 88 32 35 01, *Fax 03 88 32 42 28* – . KY y
*closed 4 to 18 August, 24 December-5 January and Sunday* – **Meals** 180/280.

**Maison des Tanneurs dite "Gerwerstub",** 42 r. Bain aux Plantes 03 88 32 79 70, *Fax 03 88 22 17 26,* « Old Alsatian house on the banks of the River Ill » – JZ t
*closed 26 July-11 August, 28 December-18 January, Sunday and Monday* – **Meals** a la carte 210/320.

**Estaminet Schloegel,** 19 r. Krütenau 03 88 36 21 98, *Fax 03 88 36 21 98* – . – *closed 7 to 21 August, Saturday lunch and Sunday* – **Meals** 120 (lunch), 180/300 and a la carte 240/310 . LZ q

**Julien,** 22 quai Bateliers 03 88 36 01 54, *Fax 03 88 35 40 14* – . KZ x
*closed 1 to 23 August, 1 to 12 January, Sunday and Monday* – **Meals** 195 (lunch), 295/385 and a la carte 310/400
**Spec.** Escalopes de foie gras d'Alsace poêlées. Carré d'agneau rôti au thym. Feuilleté tiède de pommes, glace cannelle. **Wines** Klevener, Riesling.

**Au Bœuf Mode,** 2 pl. St-Thomas 03 88 32 39 03, *Fax 03 88 21 90 80,* – 
*closed Sunday* – **Meals** 95/155 . JZ k

**Pont des Vosges,** 15 quai Koch 03 88 36 47 75, *Fax 03 88 25 16 85,* – 
*closed Saturday lunch, Sunday and Bank Holidays* – **Meals** a la carte 190/300 . LY h

**Buffet de la Gare,** pl. Gare 03 88 32 68 28, *Fax 03 88 32 88 34* – HY r
**Meals** 68/150 .

# STRASBOURG

Division-Leclerc (R.) . . . . . JKZ
Gdes-Arcades (R. des) . . . JKY
Kléber (Place) . . . . . . . . . JY
Maire Kuss (R. du) . . . . . HY 120
Mésange (R. de la) . . . . . JKY 136
Nuée-Bleue (R. de la) . . . KY
Vieux-Marché-aux-
Poissons (R. du) . . . . . . KZ 229
22-Novembre (R. du) . . . HJY

Abreuvoir (R. de l') . . . . . LZ 3
Arc-en-Ciel (R. de l') . . . . KLY 7
Austerlitz (R. d') . . . . . . . . . KZ 10
Auvergne (Pont d') . . . . . . LY 12
Bateliers (R. des) . . . . . . . . LZ 14
Bonnes-Gens (R. des) . . . . JY 19
Boudier (R. du) . . . . . . . . . JZ 20
Castelnau (R. Gén. de) . . . KY 25
Cathédrale (Pl. de la) . . . . . KZ 26
Chaudron (R. du) . . . . . . . . KY 28
Cheveux (R. des) . . . . . . . . JZ 29
Corbeau (Pl. du) . . . . . . . . KZ 31
Cordiers (R. des) . . . . . . . . KZ 32
Courtine (R. de la) . . . . . . . LY 34
Dentelles (R. des) . . . . . . . JZ 36
Écarlate (R. de l') . . . . . . . . JZ 43
Escarpée (R.) . . . . . . . . . . . JZ 45
Étudiants (R. et Pl. des) . . KY 46
Faisan (Pont du) . . . . . . . JZ 47
Fossé-des-Tanneurs
(Rue du) . . . . . . . . . . . . JZ 57
Fossé-des-Treize (R. du) . KY 58
Francs-Bourgeois (R. des) JZ 60
Frey (Q. Charles) . . . . . . . JZ 63
Grande-Boucherie
(Pl. de la) . . . . . . . . . . . KZ 76
Gutenberg (R.) . . . . . . . . . JKZ 78
Haute-Montée (R.) . . . . . . JY 82
Homme-de-Fer (Pl. de l') . JY 90
Hôpital-Militaire (R. de l') . LZ 91
Humann (R.) . . . . . . . . . . . HZ 94
Ill (Quai de l') . . . . . . . . . . HZ 95

*Town plans: the names of main shopping streets are indicated in red at the beginning of the list of streets.*

Kellermann (Quai) . . . . . . JY 100
Krutenau (Rue de la) . . . . LZ 106
Kuss (Pont) . . . . . . . . . . . HY 108
Lamey (R. Auguste) . . . . LY 109
Lezay-Marnésia (Quai) . . . LY 114
Luther (R. Martin) . . . . . . JZ 117
Marché-aux-Cochons-de-Lait (Pl. du) . . . . . . . KZ 124
Marché-aux-Poissons (Pl. du) . . . . . . . . . . . . KZ 125
Marché-Gayot (Pl. du) . . . KYZ 126
Marché-Neuf (Pl. du) . . . . KYZ 127
Maroquin (R. du) . . . . . . . KZ 129
Mercière (R.) . . . . . . . . . . KZ 135
Monnaie (R. de la) . . . . . JZ 141
Munch (R.) . . . . . . . . . . . LZ 142
Noyer (R. du) . . . . . . . . . JY 147
Obernai (R. d') . . . . . . . . . HZ 150
Outre (R. de l') . . . . . . . . KY 153
Paix (Av. de la) . . . . . . . . KLY 154
Parchemin (R. du) . . . . . . KY 156
Pierre (R. du Fg-de) . . . . . JY 160
Pontonniers (R. des) . . . . LY 167
Récollets (R. des) . . . . . . KLY 172
St-Étienne (Quai) . . . . . . . LY 183
St-Michel (R.) . . . . . . . . . HZ 187
St-Nicolas (Pont) . . . . . . . KZ 189
St-Pierre-le-Jeune (Pl.) . . . JKY 190
Ste-Madeleine (Pont et R.) KLZ 192
Salzmann (R.) . . . . . . . . . JZ 193
Sanglier (R. du) . . . . . . . . KY 194
Saverne (Pont de) . . . . . . HY 195
Sébastopol (R. de) . . . . . . JY 202
Serruriers (R. des) . . . . . . JKZ 205
Temple-Neuf (Pl. du) . . . . KY 213
Temple-Neuf (R. du) . . . . KY 214
Théâtre (Pont du) . . . . . . KY 216
Thomann (R.) . . . . . . . . . . JY 217
Tonneliers (R. des) . . . . . KZ 220
Turckheim (Quai) . . . . . . . HZ 225
Vieil-Hôpital (R. du) . . . . . KZ 228
Vieux-Marché-aux-Vins (R. et Pl. du) . . . . . . . . JY 230
Vieux-Seigle (R. du) . . . . . JZ 231
Wasselonne (R. de) . . . . . HZ 238

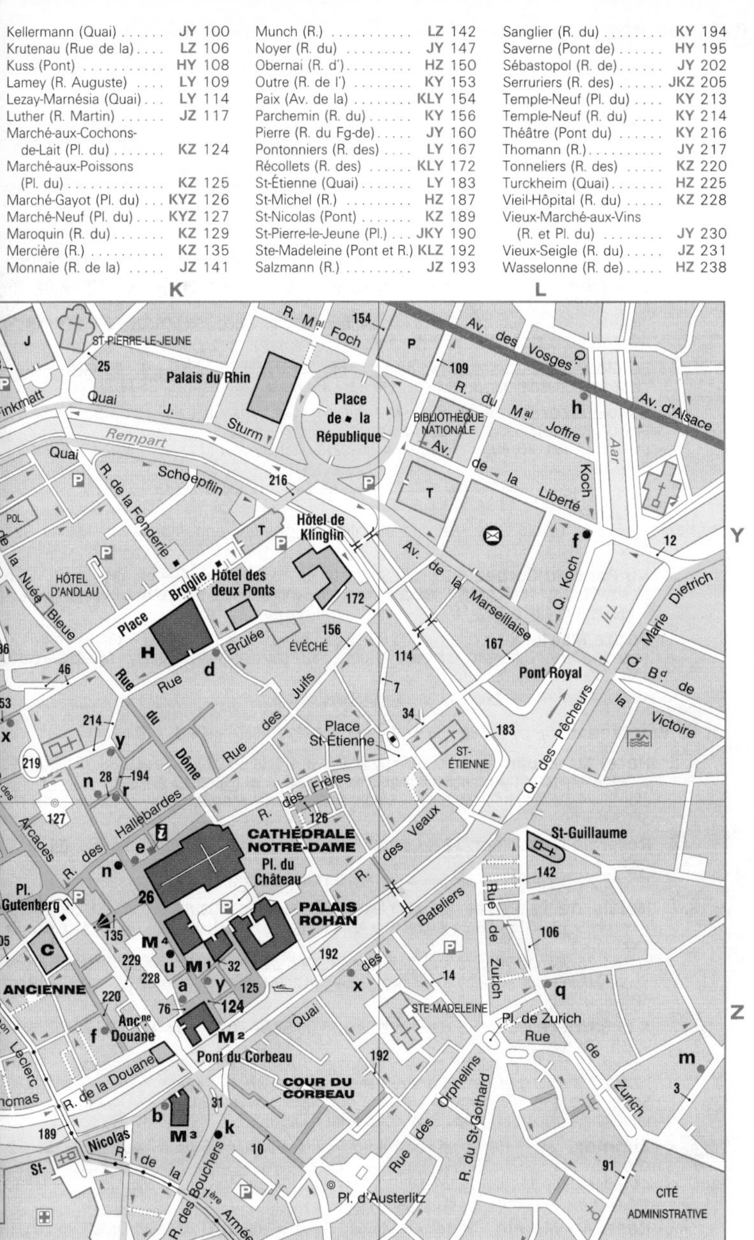


*For maximum information from town plans: consult the conventional signs key.*

**Ami Schutz,** 1 r. Ponts Couverts ☎ 03 88 32 76 98, *Fax 03 88 32 38 40,* – AE GB HZ r
**Meals** 175/195.

**Benjamin,** 3 r. Dentelles ☎ 03 88 75 16 67, *Fax 03 88 75 16 67* – AE GB JZ n
*closed 2 to 10 August, 25 December-3 January, Monday lunch and Sunday* – **Meals** 62 (lunch), 140/330 b.i.

**Au Rocher du Sapin,** 6 r. Noyer ☎ 03 88 32 39 65, *Fax 03 88 75 60 99,* , brasserie – GB JY f
*closed Sunday and Monday* – **Meals** 88/125.

WINSTUBS : *Regional specialities and wine tasting in a typical Alsatian atmosphere :*

**S'Burjerstuewel (Chez Yvonne),** 10 r. Sanglier ☎ 03 88 32 84 15, *Fax 03 88 23 00 18* – GB KYZ r
*closed 11 July-9 August, 23 to 31 December, Monday lunch and Sunday* – **Meals** (booking essential) a la carte 150/260.

**Le Clou,** 3 r. Chaudron ☎ 03 88 32 11 67, *Fax 03 88 75 72 83* – . AE GB KY n
*closed Wednesday lunch, Sunday and Bank Holidays* – **Meals** 125/230 b.i.

**S'Muensterstuewel,** 8 pl. Marché aux Cochons de Lait ☎ 03 88 32 17 63, *Fax 03 88 21 96 02,* – AE GB KZ y
*closed 27 July-18 August, February Holidays, Sunday and Monday* – **Meals** 128 (lunch), 165/320.

**Zum Strissel,** 5 pl. Gde Boucherie ☎ 03 88 32 14 73, *Fax 03 88 32 70 24,* rustic decor – . GB KZ a
*closed 4 to 31 July, February Holidays, Sunday and Monday* – **Meals** 62/126.

**Au Pont du Corbeau,** 21 quai St-Nicolas ☎ 03 88 35 60 68 – . GB KZ b
*closed 20 July-16 August, February Holidays, Sunday lunch, Saturday and Bank Holidays* – **Meals** a la carte 150/180.

**Petite Mairie,** 8 r. Brûlée ☎ 03 88 32 83 06, *Fax 03 88 32 83 06* – GB KY d
*closed 15 July-10 August, February Holidays, Saturday dinner and Sunday* – **Meals** a la carte 110/240.

## Environs

**at La Wantzenau** *NE by D 468 : 12 km – pop. 4 394 alt. 130 – ✉ 67610 :*

**Hôtel Au Moulin** , S : 1,5 km by D 468 ☎ 03 88 59 22 22, *Fax 03 88 59 22 00,* <, « Old watermill on a branch of the River Ill », – TV P. AE GB
*closed 24 December-2 January* – **Meals** see rest. ***Au Moulin*** below – 58 – **19 rm** 350/465.

**Roseraie** without rest, 32 r. Gare ☎ 03 88 96 63 44, *Fax 03 88 96 64 95* – TV P. GB
*closed 21 December-3 January* – 38 – **15 rm** 250/300.

**Relais de la Poste** M with rm, 21 r. Gén. de Gaulle ☎ 03 88 59 24 80, *Fax 03 88 59 24 89,* , « Attractive Alsatian decor » – , rest, TV P. AE GB
*closed 26 July-10 August and 3 January-27 February* – **Meals** *(closed Saturday lunch, Sunday dinner and Monday)* 175 (lunch), 225/395 and a la carte 270/430 – 50 – **19 rm** 300/650.

**A la Barrière** (Sutter), 3 rte Strasbourg ☎ 03 88 96 20 23, *Fax 03 88 96 25 59,* – P. AE GB JCB
*closed 10 to 31 August, February Holidays, Tuesday dinner and Wednesday* – **Meals** (Sunday : booking essential) 150/260 and a la carte 270/420
**Spec.** Streussel d'escargots. Lièvre à la royale (November-January). Millefeuille aux quetsches, glace pain d'épice (season). **Wines** Riesling.

**Zimmer,** 23 r. Héros ☎ 03 88 96 62 08, *Fax 03 88 96 37 40,* – AE GB
*closed 26 July-11 August, 24 January-10 February, Sunday dinner and Monday* – **Meals** 140 (lunch)/245 and a la carte 230/370.

**Rest. Au Moulin** - Hôtel Au Moulin, S : 1,5 km by D 468 ☎ 03 88 96 20 01, *Fax 03 88 59 22 00,* , « Floral garden » – P. AE GB
*closed 9 to 29 July, 31 December-16 January and dinner Sunday and Bank Holidays* – **Meals** 140/395.

**Les Semailles,** 10 r. Petit-Magmod ☎ 03 88 96 38 38, *Fax 03 88 96 38 38,* – GB.
*closed 15 August-10 September, Saturday lunch, Sunday dinner and Monday* – **Meals** 185/230.

**Baerenthal** *57 Moselle* 57 ⑱ *- pop. 723 alt. 220 - ✉ 57230 Bitche.*
*Strasbourg 64.*

**at Untermuhlthal** *SE : 4 km by D 87 - ✉ 57230 Baerenthal :*

XXX **L'Arnsbourg** (Klein), ✆ 03 87 06 50 85, *Fax 03 87 06 57 67*. – AE GB
✿✿ *closed 30 August-15 September, 3 January-3 February, Monday and Tuesday* – **Meals** (weekend booking essential) 189/410 and a la carte 330/470.
**Spec.** Foie gras d'oie et truffes fraiches en gelée (October-April). Grillade de foie gras de canard, salade d'herbes. Gibier (October-January). **Wines** Pinot blanc, Riesling.

**Illhaeusern** *68970 H.-Rhin* 62 ⑲ *- pop. 578 alt. 173.*
*Strasbourg 60.*

**Clairière** M without rest, rte Guémar ✆ 03 89 71 80 80, *Fax 03 89 71 86 22*, – rm, GB
*closed January and February* – 75 – **26 rm** 450/1100.

XXXXX **Auberge de l'Ill** (Haeberlin), ✆ 03 89 71 89 00, *Fax 03 89 71 82 83*, « Elegant instal-
✿✿✿ lation, on the banks of the River Ill, floral gardens » – AE GB
*closed 1 February-5 March, Monday except lunch in season and Tuesday* – **Meals** (booking essential) 530 (lunch), 630/740 and a la carte 460/690
**Spec.** Salade de langoustines, beignet et brandade de morue. Filet d'esturgeon, choucroute à la crème de caviar. Grande assiette d'oie non grasse sous toutes ses façons. **Wines** Riesling, Tokay-Pinot gris.
**H. des Berges** M, ✆ 03 89 71 87 87, *Fax 03 89 71 87 88*, , « Resembling a tobacco shed in the Ried country », – , rm, . AE GB
*closed Monday dinner and Tuesday* – **Meals** see ***Aub. de l'Ill*** – 130 – **11 rm** 1500/1750.

**Lembach** *67510 B.-Rhin* 57 ⑲ *- pop. 1 710 alt. 190.*
*Tourist Office 23 rte Bitche ✆ 03 88 94 43 16, Fax 03 88 94 20 04.*
*Strasbourg 55.*

XXXX **Aub. Cheval Blanc** (Mischler), 4 rte Wissembourg ✆ 03 88 94 41 86,
✿✿ *Fax 03 88 94 20 74*, « Old coaching inn », – AE GB
*closed 6 to 24 July, 1 to 26 February, Monday and Tuesday* – **Meals** 185/440 and a la carte 300/420
**Spec.** Foie gras d'oie poché au pinot noir et aux épices. Raviole ouverte de grenouilles aux herbes du Buttergate. Médaillons de dos de chevreuil à la moutarde de fruits rouges (15 May-28 February). **Wines** Riesling, Pinot blanc.

**Marlenheim** *67520 B.-Rhin* 62 ⑨ *- pop. 2 956 alt. 195.*
*Strasbourg 20.*

**Le Cerf** (Husser), ✆ 03 88 87 73 73, *Fax 03 88 87 68 08*, , « Flowered inn » – rest,
✿✿ AE GB JCB
*closed Tuesday and Wednesday* – **Meals** 250 b.i. (lunch), 295/550 and a la carte 360/500 – 65 – **17 rm** 285/850
**Spec.** Presskopf de tête de veau poêlée en croustille. Choucroute au cochon de lait et foie gras fumé. Aumônière aux griottines et glace au fromage blanc. **Wines** Pinot noir, Riesling.

---

## VALLEY OF THE LOIRE

**Tours** *37000 I.-et-L.* 64 ⑮ *- pop. 129 509 alt. 60.*

See : *Cathedral quarter★★ : Cathedral★★* CDY, *Fine Arts Museum★★* CDY, *Historial de Touraine★ (Château)* CY **M**[3], *The Psalette★* CY, *Place Grégoire de Tours★* DY 46 – *Old Tours★★ : Place Plumereau★* ABY, *Hôtel Gouin★* BY, *rue Briçonnet★* AY **12** – *St-Julien quarter★ : Craft Guilds Museum★★ (Musée du Compagnonnage)* BY, *Beaune-Semblançay Garden★* BY **B** – *St-Cosme Priory★ W : 3 km* V – *Museum of military transport and trains★* V **M**[6] – *Meslay Tithe Barn★ (Grange de Meslay) NE : 10 km par ②.*

*18 of Touraine ✆ 02 47 53 20 28 ; domaine de la Touche at Ballan-Miré : 14 km ; 18 of Ardrée ✆ 02 47 56 77 38 : 14 km.*

*of Tours-St-Symphorien : T.A.T ✆ 02 47 49 37 00, NE : 7 km.*

*Tourist Office 78 r. Bernard Palissy ✆ 02 47 70 37 37, Fax 02 47 61 14 22 – A.C. 4 pl. J. Jaurès ✆ 02 47 05 50 19, Fax 02 47 05 47 61.*

*Paris 234 – Angers 109 – Bordeaux 346 – Chartres 140 – Clermont-Ferrand 335 – Limoges 220 – Le Mans 80 – Orléans 115 – Rennes 219 – St-Étienne 474.*

Plans on following pages

# TOURS

| | | |
|---|---|---|
| Bordeaux (R. de) | CZ | |
| Commerce (R. du) | BY | 22 |
| Grammont (Av. de) | CZ | |
| Grand Passage | CZ | 50 |
| Halles (Pl. des) | AZ | |
| Halles (R. des) | BY | |
| Marceau (R.) | BYZ | |
| Nationale (R.) | BYZ | |
| Scellerie (R. de la) | BCY | |
| Amandiers (R. des) | CY | 4 |
| Berthelot (R.) | BCY | 7 |
| Bons Enfants (R. des) | BY | 8 |
| Boyer (R. Léon) | AZ | 10 |
| Briçonnet (R.) | AY | 13 |
| Carmes (Pl. des) | BY | 16 |
| Châteauneuf (Pl. de) | BY | 17 |
| Châteauneuf (R. de) | AY | 18 |
| Cœur-Navré (Passage du) | CY | 21 |
| Constantine (R. de) | BY | 24 |
| Corneille (R.) | CY | 25 |
| Courier (Rue Paul-Louis) | BY | 27 |
| Courteline (R. G.) | AY | 28 |

EUROPE on a single sheet Michelin Map no 970

Cygne (R. du) . . . . . . . . . . . CY 29
Descartes (R.) . . . . . . . . . . . BZ 33
Dolve (R. de la) . . . . . . . . . . BZ 35
Favre (R. Jules) . . . . . . . . . . BY 38
Fusillés (R. des) . . . . . . . . . . BY 41
Gambetta (R.) . . . . . . . . . . . BZ 43
Giraudeau (R.) . . . . . . . . . . . AZ 46
Grand-Marché (Pl. du) . . . . AY 49
Grégoire-de-Tours (Pl.) . . . . DY 52

Grosse-Tour (R. de la) . . . . . AY 55
Herbes (Carroi aux) . . . . . . AY 56
Lavoisier (R.) . . . . . . . . . . . CY 60
Marceau (R.) . . . . . . . . . . . . DY 61
Merville (R. du Prés.) . . . . . BY 65
Meusnier (R. Gén.) . . . . . . . DY 66
Monnaie (R. de la) . . . . . . . BY 68
Mûrier (R. du) . . . . . . . . . . . AY 71
Paix (R. de la) . . . . . . . . . . . BY 73

Petit-Cupidon (R. du) . . . . DY 77
Petit-St-Martin (R. du) . . . . AY 78
Petites-Boucheries
(Pl. des) . . . . . . . . . . . . . DY 80
Racine (R.) . . . . . . . . . . . . DY 84
Rapin (R.) . . . . . . . . . . . . . AZ 85
St-Pierre-le-Puellier (Pl.) . . ABY 93
Sully (R. de) . . . . . . . . . . . BZ 100
Victoire (Pl. de la) . . . . . . . AY 103

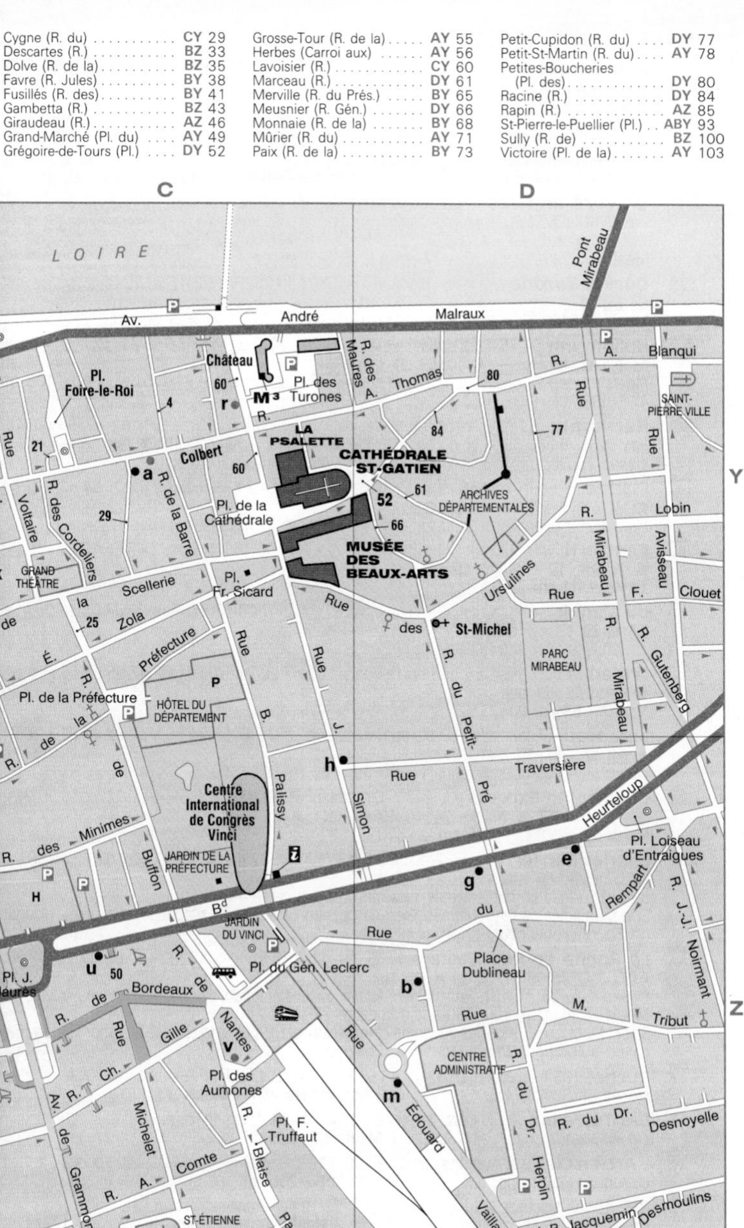

**Jean Bardet** [M], 57 r. Groison ✉ 37100 ☎ 02 47 41 41 11, *Fax 02 47 51 68 72*, €, « Flowered park, attractive kitchen garden », – 30. AE GB JCB
**Meals** *(closed Sunday dinner from November-March and Monday except dinner from April-October)* 250/750 and a la carte 450/810 – 120 – **16 rm** 750/1050, 5 suites
**Spec.** Pannequet de légumes, jus d'herbes tendres. Pintadeau fermier truffé du pays de Racan, parmentier de charlotte. Gibier (October-December). **Wines** Vouvray, Bourgueil.

**Univers and rest. La Touraine** [M], 5 bd Heurteloup ☎ 02 47 05 37 12, *Fax 02 47 61 51 80*, « Murals depicting famous past visitors » – rm, – 120. AE GB CZ u
**Meals** 140/170 – 70 – **77 rm** 690/830, 8 suites.

**Quality Turone** [M], 4 pl. Thiers ☎ 02 47 05 50 05, *Fax 02 47 20 22 07* – rm, – 70. AE GB
**Meals** 125/280 b.i. – 55 – **120 rm** 415/650.

**Holiday Inn** [M], 15 r. Ed. Vaillant ☎ 02 47 31 12 12, *Fax 02 47 38 53 35*, – rm, – 50. AE GB JCB DZ m
**Meals** *(closed Saturday, Sunday and lunch Bank Holidays)* 90 b.i./160 b.i. – 60 – **105 rm** 440/980.

**Harmonie** [M] without rest, 15 r. F. Joliot-Curie ☎ 02 47 66 01 48, *Fax 02 47 61 66 38* – kitchenette – 40. AE GB JCB DZ b
*closed 20 December-5 January* – 65 – **48 rm** 450/650, 6 suites.

**Clarine** without rest, 65 av. Grammont ☎ 02 47 64 71 78, *Fax 02 47 05 84 62* – – 35. AE GB
*closed 28 December-3 January* – 37 – **50 rm** 295/350.

**Central H.** without rest, 21 r. Berthelot ☎ 02 47 05 46 44, *Fax 02 47 66 10 26* – – 40. AE GB JCB CY k
45 – **41 rm** 380/590.

**du Manoir** without rest, 2 r. Traversière ☎ 02 47 05 37 37, *Fax 02 47 05 16 00* – AE GB CZ h
30 – **20 rm** 240/320.

**Criden** without rest, 65 bd Heurteloup ☎ 02 47 20 81 14, *Fax 02 47 05 61 65* – AE GB DZ g
40 – **33 rm** 275/315.

**Mirabeau** without rest, 89 bis bd Heurteloup ☎ 02 47 05 24 60, *Fax 02 47 05 31 09* – AE GB JCB DZ e
*closed 25 December-1 January* – 39 – **25 rm** 220/310.

**Holiday Inn Express** [M], 247 r. Giraudeau ☎ 02 47 37 00 36, *Fax 02 47 38 50 91* – rm, – 40. AE GB JCB
**Meals** 75 b.i./99 – **48 rm** 370.

**Charles Barrier,** 101 av. Tranchée ✉ 37100 ☎ 02 47 54 20 39, *Fax 02 47 41 80 95*, – AE GB
*closed Sunday dinner* – **Meals** 150/540 and a la carte 390/530
**Spec.** Ravioles de langoustines. Pied de cochon farci aux ris d'agneau et truffes. Nougat de Tours croquant au pralin de noisettes.

**La Roche Le Roy** (Couturier), 55 rte St-Avertin ✉ 37200 ☎ 02 47 27 22 00, *Fax 02 47 28 08 39*, – AE GB
*closed 1 to 25 August, February Holidays, Saturday lunch, Sunday dinner and Monday* – **Meals** 160 (lunch), 200/350 and a la carte 270/400
**Spec.** Matelote d'anguilles au vin de chinon (winter). Ris de veau braisé aux morilles. Soufflé chaud à l'orange. **Wines** Montlouis, Chinon.

**Ruche,** 105 r. Colbert ☎ 02 47 66 69 83, *Fax 02 47 20 41 76* – GB JCB CY a
*closed Christmas Holidays, Sunday dinner and Monday* – **Meals** 90/170.

**Les Tuffeaux,** 21 r. Lavoisier ☎ 02 47 47 19 89 – AE GB CY r
*closed Monday lunch and Sunday* – **Meals** 110/200.

**L'Arc-en-Ciel,** 2 pl. Aumônes ☎ 02 47 05 48 88, *Fax 02 47 66 94 05* – AE GB CZ f
*closed Sunday dinner and Monday* – **Meals** 88/230.

**Rif,** 12 av. Maginot ✉ 37100 ☎ 02 47 51 12 44 – GB
*closed August, Sunday dinner and Monday* – **Meals** North-African rest. a la carte 120/170.

**at Rochecorbon** *NE : 6 km by N 152 – alt. 58 – ✉ 37210 :*

**Les Hautes Roches** [M], 86 quai Loire ☎ 02 47 52 88 88, *Fax 02 47 52 81 30*, €, « Former troglodyte dwelling », – AE GB
*closed mid January-mid March* – **Meals** *(closed dinner Sunday and Monday out of season and Monday lunch except Bank Holidays)* 215/355 – 85 – **15 rm** 650/1350
**Spec.** Marbré de lapereau et foie gras en gelée d'herbes fraîches. Effeuillée de sandre, parmentière à la tome au Vouvray. Soufflé chaud au Grand-Marnier.

**Amboise** *37400 I.-et-L.* 64 ⑯ *– pop. 10 982 alt. 60.*

See : *Château★★ : ≤★★ from the terrace, ≤★★ from the Minimes tower – Clos-Lucé★ – Chanteloup Pagoda★ SW : 3 km par ④ by D431.*

*Tourist Office quai Gén.-de-Gaulle ✆ 02 47 57 09 28, Fax 02 47 57 14 35.*

*Tours 25.*

**Choiseul,** 36 quai Ch. Guinot ✆ 02 47 30 45 45, *Fax 02 47 30 46 10,* ≤, « Elegant installation, and flowered garden » – – 80. AE GB JCB
*closed 29 November-20 January* – **Meals** 190 (lunch), 280/500 and a la carte 340/480 – 130 – **28 rm** 600/1350

**Spec.** Gelée de ris de veau et écrevisses aux pousses de liseron d'eau (July-September). Peau croustillante de sandre poché, parmentier de coques au beurre de tilleul. Pêche au caramel d'abricots, liqueur de lait d'amande (June-September). **Wines** Montlouis, Bourgueil.

**Onzain** *41150 L.-et-Ch.* 64 ⑯ *– pop. 3 080 alt. 69.*

*Golf de la Carte at Chouzy-sur-Cisse, ✆ 02 54 20 49 99.*

*Tours 47.*

**Domaine des Hauts de Loire** M, NW : 3 km by D 1 and private lane ✆ 02 54 20 72 57, *Fax 02 54 20 77 32,* « Elegant hunting lodge in a park », – – 70. AE GB.
*closed 1 December-5 February* – **Meals** *(closed Tuesday lunch and Monday in March, November and February)* (booking essential) 310/395 and a la carte 310/560 – 88 – **25 rm** 950/1450, 10 suites

**Spec.** Salade d'anguille croustillante à la vinaigrette d'échalotes. Filet de boeuf poché au vin de Montlouis. Pigeonneau du Vendômois rôti, jus de presse à la livèche. **Wines** Touraine.

**Romorantin-Lanthenay** *41200 L.-et-Ch.* 64 ⑱ *– pop. 17 865 alt. 93.*

*Tourist Office 32 pl. Paix ✆ 02 54 76 43 89, Fax 02 54 76 96 24.*

*Tours 91.*

**Gd H. Lion d'Or** M, 69 r. Clemenceau ✆ 02 54 94 15 15, *Fax 02 54 88 24 87,* « Tasteful decor, flowered patio » – rest, – 50. AE GB
*closed mid February-mid March* – **Meals** (booking essential) 420/620 and a la carte 490/630 – 110 – **13 rm** 600/2000, 3 suites

**Spec.** Cuisses de grenouilles à la rocambole. Langoustines bretonnes rôties à la graine de paradis. Brioche caramélisée au sorbet d'angélique (May-October). **Wines** Pouilly Fumé, Bourgueil.

# Germany

## Deutschland

BERLIN – COLOGNE – DRESDEN
DÜSSELDORF – FRANKFURT ON MAIN
HAMBURG – HANOVER – LEIPZIG
MUNICH – STUTTGART

# PRACTICAL INFORMATION

## LOCAL CURRENCY

**Deutsche Mark:** *100 DEM = 55,88 USD ($) (Jan. 98)*

## TOURIST INFORMATION

**Deutsche Zentrale für Tourismus (DZT):**
*Beethovenstr. 69, 60325 Frankfurt, ☏ (069) 97 46 40, Fax (069) 75 19 03*

**Hotel booking service:**
*Allgemeine Deutsche Zimmerreservierung (ADZ)*
*Corneliusstr. 34, 60325 Frankfurt, ☏ (069) 74 07 67*
*Fax (069) 75 10 56*

**National Holiday in Germany:** *3 Octobre.*

## AIRLINES

**DEUTSCHE LUFTHANSA AG:** *Wilhelmshöher Allee 254, 34119 Kassel, ☏ (01803) 803803, Fax (0561) 9933115*

**AIR CANADA:** *60311 Frankfurt, Friedensstr. 7, ☏ (069) 27 11 51 11, Fax (069) 27 11 51 12*

**AIR FRANCE:** *60311 Frankfurt, Friedensstr. 11, ☏ (0180) 5 36 03 70, Fax (069) 23 05 81*

**AMERICAN AIRLINES:** *60329 Frankfurt, Wiesenhüttenplatz 26, ☏ (01803) 242 324, Fax (069) 230 461*

**BRITISH AIRWAYS:** *28320 Bremen, Sonneberger Str. 20, ☏ (0180) 340 340, Fax (0421) 55 75189*

**JAPAN AIRLINES:** *60311 Frankfurt, Roßmarkt 15, ☏ (0180) 22 28 700, Fax (069) 29 57 84*

**AUSTRIAN SWISSAIR SABENA:** *60329 Frankfurt, Am Hauptbahnhof 6, ☏ (0180) 52 58 520, Fax (0180) 52 21 591*

## FOREIGN EXCHANGE

*In banks, savings banks and at exchange offices.*
*Hours of opening from Monday to Friday 8.30am to 12.30pm and 2.30pm to 4pm except Thursday 2.30pm to 6pm.*

## SHOPPING

*In the index of street names, those printed in red are where the principal shops are found.*

## BREAKDOWN SERVICE

**ADAC:** *for the addresses see text of the towns mentioned*

**AvD:** *Lyoner Str. 16, 60528 Frankfurt-Niederrad, ☏ (069) 6 60 60, Fax (069) 660 67 89*
*In Germany the ADAC (emergency number (01802) 22 22 22), and the AvD (emergency number (0130) 99 09), make a special point of assisting foreign motorists. They have motor patrols covering main roads.*

## TIPPING

*In Germany, prices include service and taxes. You may choose to leave a tip if you wish but there is no obligation to do so.*

## SPEED LIMITS

*The speed limit, generally, in built up areas is 50 km/h - 31 mph and on all other roads it is 100 km/h - 62mph. On motorways and dual carriageways, the recommended speed limit is 130 km/h - 80 mph.*

## SEAT BELTS

*The wearing of seat belts is compulsory for drivers and all passengers.*

# BERLIN

L Berlin 416 418, I 23, 24 – 3 500 000 Ew – Höhe 40 m.

Frankfurt/Oder 105 – Hamburg 289 – Hannover 288 – Leipzig 183 – Rostock 222.

Berlin Tourismus Marketing GmbH – Information at Europa-Center (Budapester Straße), ✉ 10787 ☎ (030) 25 00 25, Fax (030) 25 00 24 24, and information in Brandenburer Tar (side-wing).

ADAC, Berlin-Wilmersdorf, ✉ 10717, Bundesallee 29-30, ☎ (030) 8 68 60, Fax (030) 86 16 025.

18 Berlin-Wannsee, Golfweg 22, ☎ (030) 8 06 70 60 – 9 Berlin-Gatow, Kladower Damm 182, ☎ (030) 3 65 76 60 – 18 9 Kallin (NW : 32 km), an der B273, ☎ (033230) 5 02 14 – 9 Mahlow (S : 20 km), Kiefernweg, ☎ (033379) 37 05 95 – 18 Potsdam (W : 38 km), Tremmener Landstraße, ☎ (033233) 8 02 44 – 18 18 Seddiner See (SW : 37 km), Fercher Weg, ☎ (033205) 6 49 04 – 18 Stolper Heide (N : 20 km), Frohnauer Weg 3, ☎ (03303) 54 90.

Berlin-Tegel EX, ☎ (030) 4 10 11
Berlin-Schönefeld (S : 25 km), ☎ (030) 6 09 10
Berlin-Tempelhof GZ, ☎ (030) 6 95 10
Deutsche Lufthansa City Center, Kurfürstendamm 220, ☎ (030) 88 75 38 00, Fax (030) 88 75 38 01

Berlin-Wannsee, Nibelungenstraße.
Exhibition Centre (Messegelände am Funkturm) BU, ☎ (030) 3 03 80, Fax (030) 30 38 23 25.

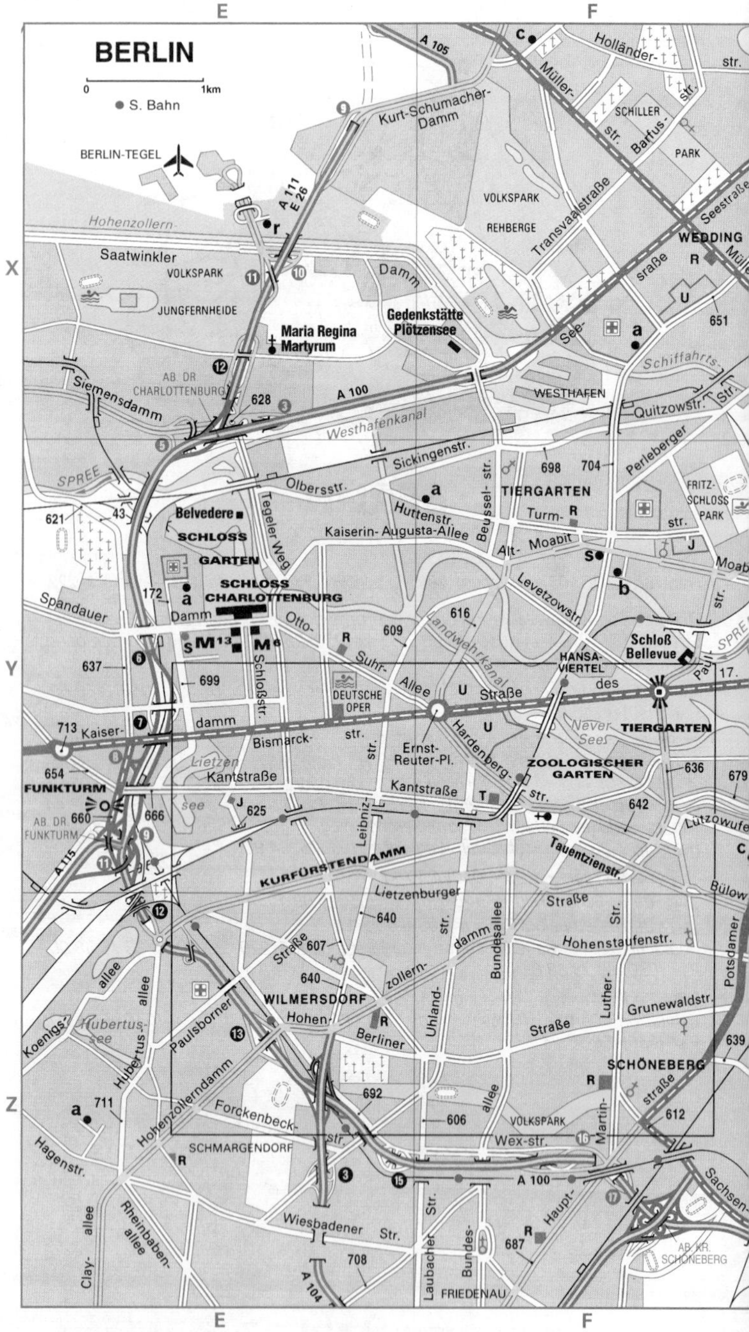
BERLIN
0
1km
S. Bahn
BERLIN-TEGEL
Hohenzollern-
Saatwinkler
VOLKSPARK
JUNGFERNHEIDE
Damm
Kurt-Schumacher-Damm
A 105
A 111
E 26
Maria Regina Martyrum
Gedenkstätte Plötzensee
VOLKSPARK
REHBERGE
Transvaalstraße
Müller-str.
Holländer-str.
SCHILLER PARK
Barfus-str.
Seestraße
WEDDING
See-straße
Schiffahrts-
WESTHAFEN
Westhafenkanal
Quitzowstr.
Perleberger
A 100
Siemensdamm
AB. DR. CHARLOTTENBURG
SPREE
Sickingenstr.
Olbersstr.
Tegeler Weg
Huttenstr.
TIERGARTEN
Beussel-str.
Turm-str.
FRITZ-SCHLOSS PARK
Belvedere
SCHLOSS GARTEN
Kaiserin-Augusta-Allee
Alt-Moabit
Levetzowstr.
SCHLOSS CHARLOTTENBURG
Spandauer Damm
Otto-Suhr-Allee
Landwehrkanal
Schloß Bellevue
HANSA-VIERTEL
Straße des 17.
TIERGARTEN
Neuer See
DEUTSCHE OPER
Schloßstr.
Kaiser-damm
Bismarck-str.
Ernst-Reuter-Pl.
Hardenberg-str.
ZOOLOGISCHER GARTEN
Lietzensee
Kantstraße
FUNKTURM
AB. DR. FUNKTURM
A 115
Leibniz-str.
KURFÜRSTENDAMM
Tauentzienstr.
Lützowufer
Lietzenburger Straße
Bülow
Hohenstaufenstr.
Hohenzollerndamm
Uhland-str.
Bundesallee
Potsdamer
WILMERSDORF
Hohen-
Berliner Straße
Grunewaldstr.
Luther-Str.
Koenigsallee
Hubertussee
Hubertusallee
Paulsborner
SCHÖNEBERG
Forckenbeck-str.
VOLKSPARK
Martin-Luther-straße
SCHMARGENDORF
Wex-str.
Hagenstr.
A 100
Haupt-
Sachsen-
Rheinbabenallee
Clay-allee
Wiesbadener Str.
Laubacher Str.
Bundes-allee
FRIEDENAU
AB. KR. SCHÖNEBERG
A 104
E
F
X
Y
Z
621
43
172
637
699
713
654
660
666
625
628
616
609
698
704
651
636
642
679
640
607
692
606
711
612
639
687
708

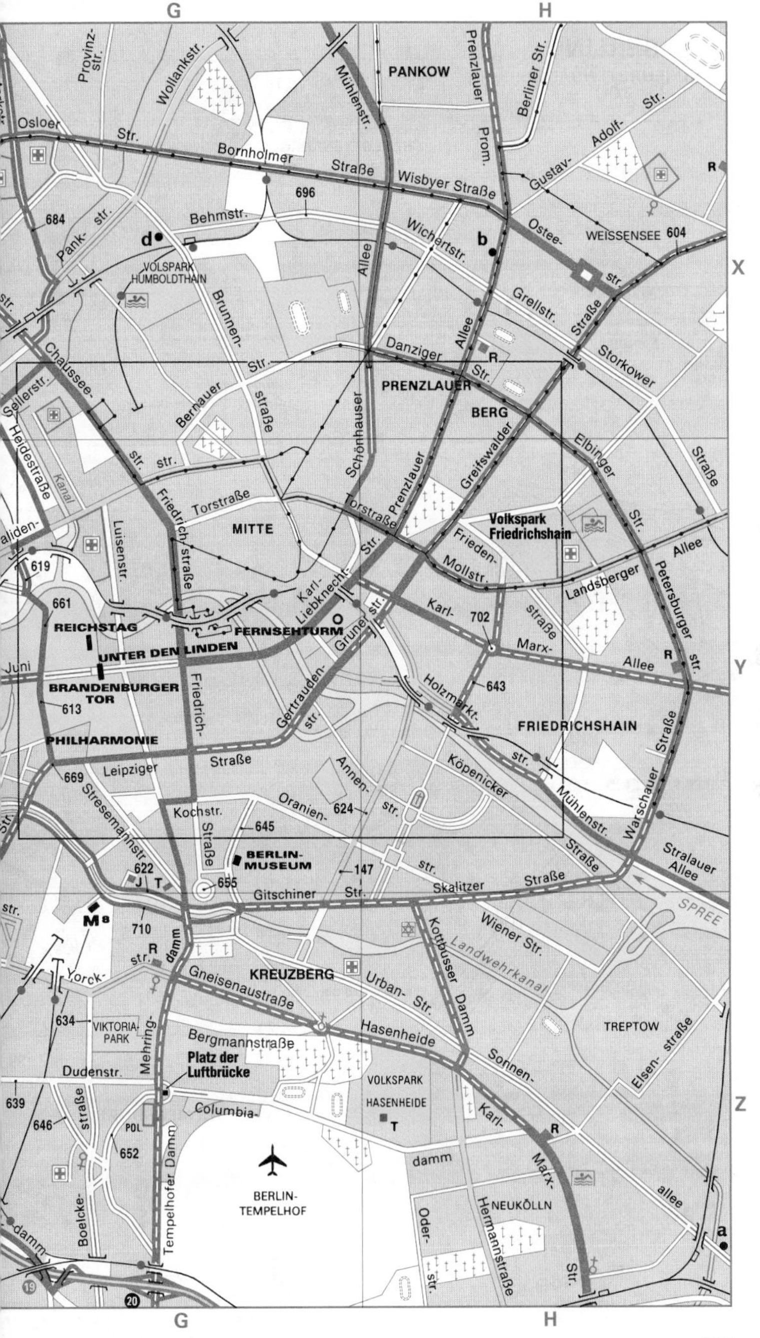
G
H
X
Y
Z
PANKOW
PRENZLAUER BERG
MITTE
WEISSENSEE
FRIEDRICHSHAIN
KREUZBERG
TREPTOW
NEUKÖLLN
VOLSPARK HUMBOLDTHAIN
Volkspark Friedrichshain
REICHSTAG
UNTER DEN LINDEN
BRANDENBURGER TOR
PHILHARMONIE
FERNSEHTURM
BERLIN-MUSEUM
VIKTORIA-PARK
Platz der Luftbrücke
VOLKSPARK HASENHEIDE
BERLIN-TEMPELHOF
SPREE
Landwehrkanal

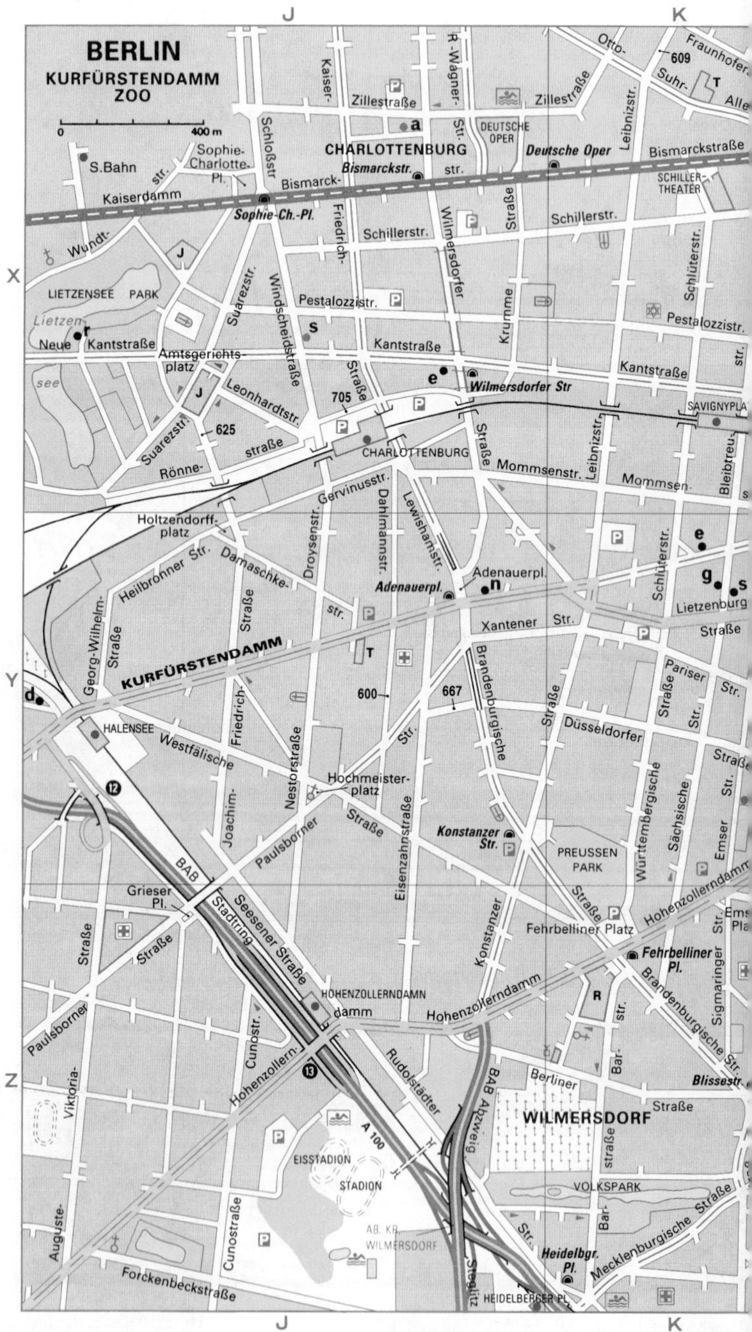
BERLIN
KURFÜRSTENDAMM
ZOO
0
400 m
J
K
X
Y
Z
CHARLOTTENBURG
Bismarckstr.
Deutsche Oper
DEUTSCHE OPER
SCHILLER-THEATER
Sophie-Ch.-Pl.
Wilmersdorfer Str
CHARLOTTENBURG
SAVIGNYPLATZ
Adenauerpl.
KURFÜRSTENDAMM
HALENSEE
Konstanzer Str.
PREUSSEN PARK
Fehrbelliner Platz
Fehrbelliner Pl.
HOHENZOLLERNDAMM
WILMERSDORF
VOLKSPARK
EISSTADION
STADION
AB. KR. WILMERSDORF
HEIDELBERGER PL.
Heidelbgr. Pl.
Blissestr.
LIETZENSEE PARK
Kantstraße
Kurfürstendamm
Hohenzollerndamm
Forckenbeckstraße

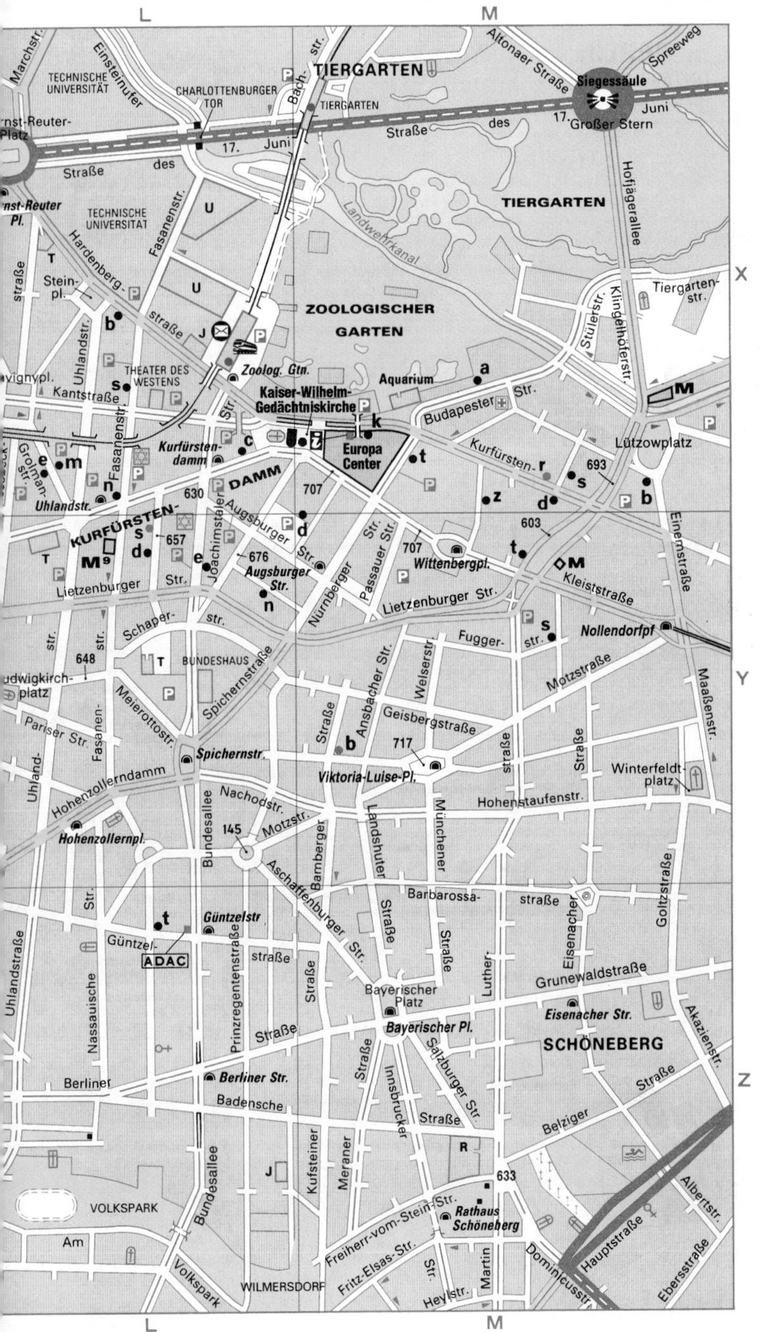

TIERGARTEN
Siegessäule
Großer Stern
ZOOLOGISCHER GARTEN
Aquarium
Kaiser-Wilhelm-Gedächtniskirche
Europa Center
KURFÜRSTENDAMM
TECHNISCHE UNIVERSITÄT
CHARLOTTENBURGER TOR
THEATER DES WESTENS
BUNDESHAUS
Zoolog. Gtn.
Wittenbergpl.
Nollendorfpl
Spichernstr.
Viktoria-Luise-Pl.
Hohenzollernpl.
Güntzelstr
Bayerischer Pl.
Eisenacher Str.
Berliner Str.
Rathaus Schöneberg
SCHÖNEBERG
VOLKSPARK
WILMERSDORF
ADAC
Lützowplatz
Winterfeldtplatz
Landwehrkanal
Straße des 17. Juni
Hardenbergstraße
Kantstraße
Budapester Str.
Kurfürstenstr.
Augsburger Str.
Lietzenburger Str.
Kleiststraße
Motzstraße
Hohenstaufenstr.
Grunewaldstraße
Hauptstraße
Bundesallee
L
M
X
Y
Z

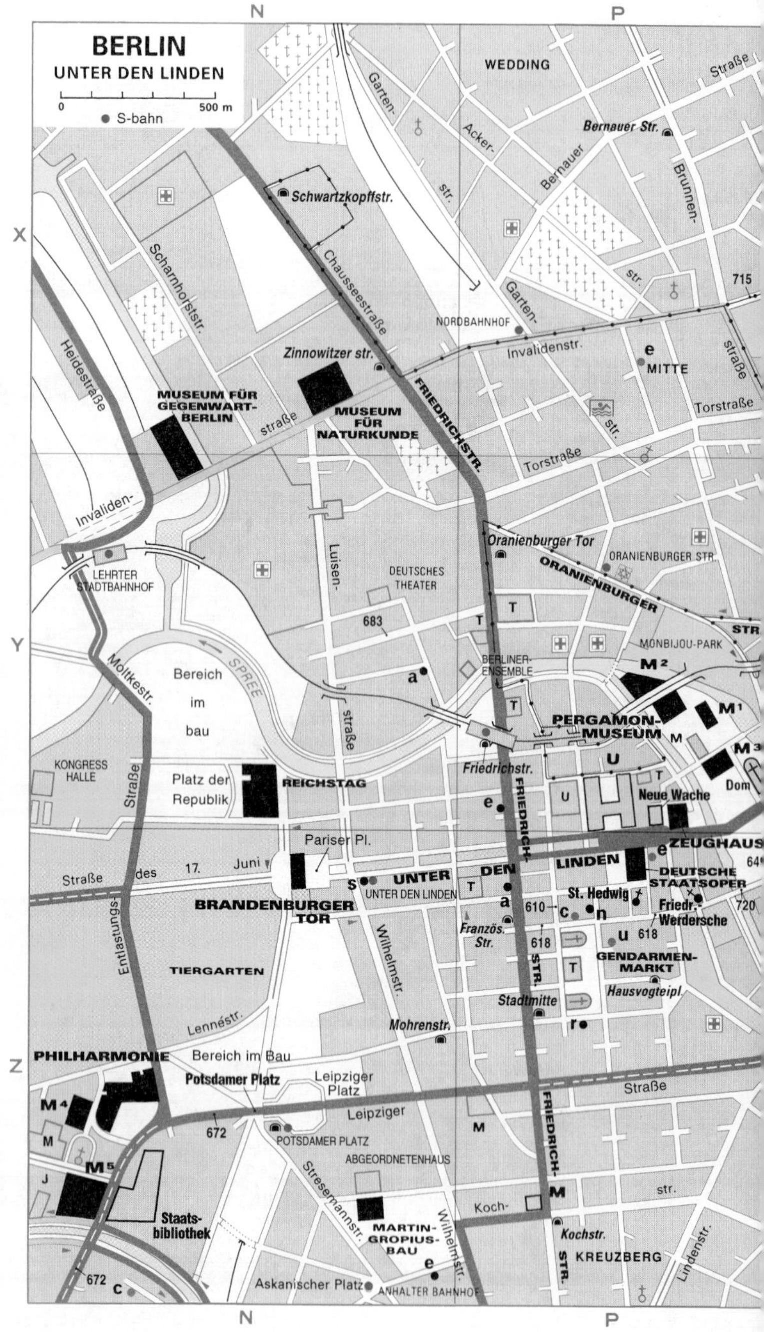
BERLIN
UNTER DEN LINDEN
0
500 m
S-bahn
N
P
X
Y
Z
WEDDING
MITTE
KREUZBERG
TIERGARTEN
Schwartzkopffstr.
Zinnowitzer str.
Oranienburger Tor
Friedrichstr.
Französ. Str.
Stadtmitte
Mohrenstr.
Potsdamer Platz
Kochstr.
Bernauer Str.
NORDBAHNHOF
LEHRTER STADTBAHNHOF
ORANIENBURGER STR.
UNTER DEN LINDEN
POTSDAMER PLATZ
ANHALTER BAHNHOF
MUSEUM FÜR GEGENWART-BERLIN
MUSEUM FÜR NATURKUNDE
DEUTSCHES THEATER
BERLINER-ENSEMBLE
MONBIJOU-PARK
PERGAMON-MUSEUM
REICHSTAG
BRANDENBURGER TOR
Neue Wache
ZEUGHAUS
DEUTSCHE STAATSOPER
St. Hedwig
Friedr.-Werdersche
GENDARMEN-MARKT
Hausvogteipl.
Dom
KONGRESS HALLE
Platz der Republik
Bereich im bau
Bereich im Bau
Pariser Pl.
PHILHARMONIE
Staats-bibliothek
ABGEORDNETENHAUS
MARTIN-GROPIUS-BAU
Askanischer Platz
Leipziger Platz
SPREE
Garten-str.
Acker-str.
Bernauer str.
Brunnen-str.
Garten-
Straße
Chausseestraße
FRIEDRICHSTR.
FRIEDRICH-STR.
Invalidenstr.
Invaliden-straße
Torstraße
Scharnhorststr.
Heidestraße
ORANIENBURGER STR
Luisen-straße
Moltkestr.
Straße
Straße des 17. Juni
UNTER DEN LINDEN
Wilhelmstr.
Entlastungs-
Lennéstr.
Leipziger Straße
Stresemannstr.
Koch-str.
Lindenstr.
715
683
610
618
720
672
a
e
c
n
u
r
S
T
U
M
J
M 1
M 2
M 3
M 4
M 5

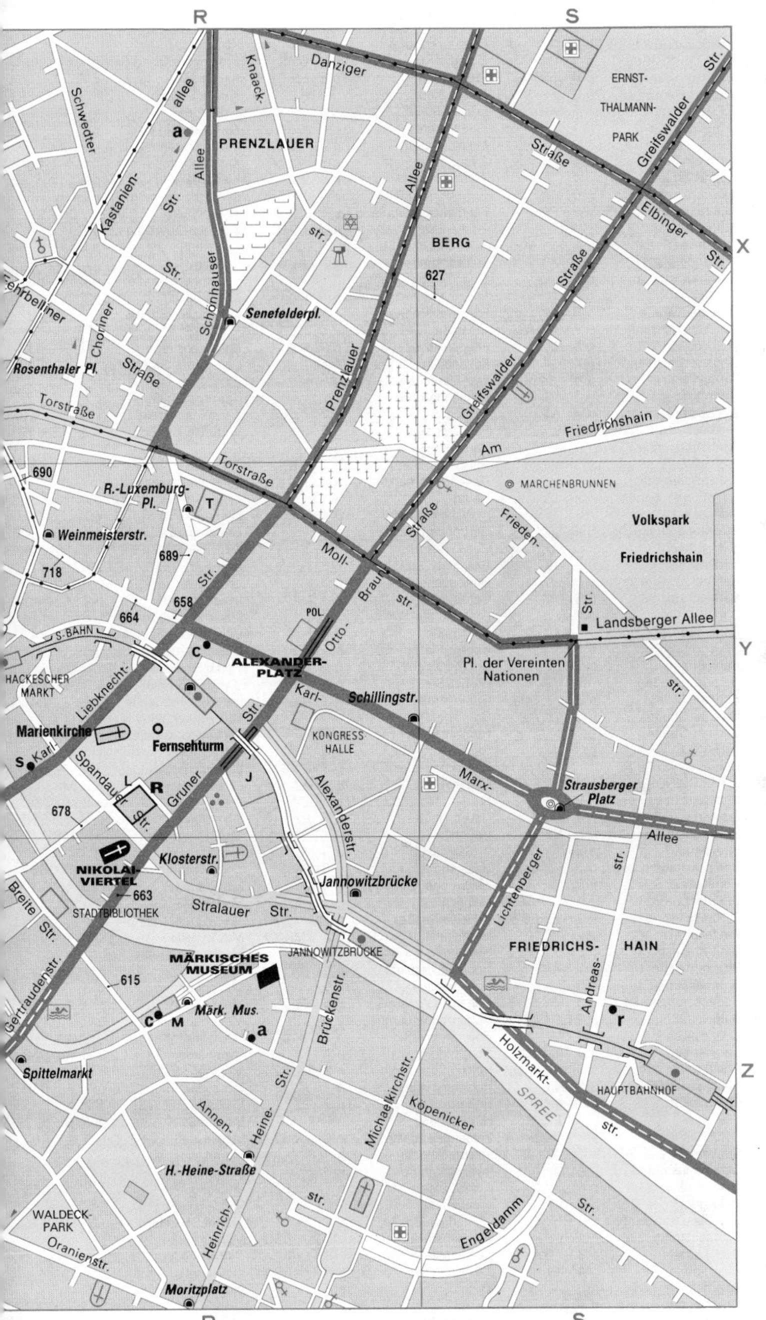
R
S
X
Y
Z
Danziger
Knaack-
ERNST-THALMANN-PARK
Greifswalder Str.
Straße
Elbinger Str.
PRENZLAUER
BERG
Schwedter
Kastanien-allee
Allee
Str.
Schönhauser
Senefelderpl.
Prenzlauer
Allee
627
Fehrbelliner
Choriner Straße
Rosenthaler Pl.
Torstraße
Greifswalder
Straße
Am Friedrichshain
MARCHENBRUNNEN
Volkspark Friedrichshain
Frieden-
690
R.-Luxemburg-Pl.
T
Weinmeisterstr.
689
718
Str.
Moll-
Braun-str.
Otto-
658
664
S-BAHN
POL.
Landsberger Allee
Pl. der Vereinten Nationen
HACKESCHER MARKT
Liebknecht-
C
ALEXANDERPLATZ
Karl-
Schillingstr.
Marienkirche
O
Fernsehturm
KONGRESS HALLE
Karl-
S
Spandauer Str.
L
R
Gruner Str.
J
Alexanderstr.
Marx-
Strausberger Platz
Allee
678
NIKOLAI-VIERTEL
Klosterstr.
Jannowitzbrücke
Lichtenberger
str.
663
STADTBIBLIOTHEK
Stralauer Str.
Breite Str.
FRIEDRICHS-HAIN
MÄRKISCHES MUSEUM
JANNOWITZBRÜCKE
615
Gertraudenstr.
C M Märk. Mus.
a
Brückenstr.
Andreas-
r
Holzmarkt-str.
Spittelmarkt
SPREE
HAUPTBAHNHOF
Annen-
Heine-Str.
Michaelkirchstr.
Köpenicker
H.-Heine-Straße
str.
Heinrich-
Str.
Engeldamm
WALDECK-PARK
Oranienstr.
Moritzplatz

Continued p. 9

## STREET INDEX TO BERLIN TOWN PLANS (Concluded)

# Sights

## MUSEUMS, GALLERIES, COLLECTIONS

*Museum Island (Museumsinsel)★★★* PY; *Pergamon-Museum; Collection of Antiquities (Antikensammlung)★★★, Altar of Pergamon (Pergamon-Altar)★★★, Gate to the Milet market (Markttor von Milet)★★ – Middle East Museum (Vorderasiatisches Museum)★ – Processional way and Gate of Ishtar (Prozessionsstraße und ischtartor)★★ – National Gallery (Alte Nationalgalerie)★★* **M¹** *– Bodemuseum* **M²**, *Egyptian Museum (Agyptisches Museum)★★, Gallery of Paintings (Gemälde-galerie)★ – Old Museum (Altes Museum)★★* **M³** *— Forum of Culture (Kulturforum)★★★* NZ *– Museum of Decorative Arts (Kunstgewerbe-museum)★★* DV **M¹³**, *Guelph Treasure (Welfenschatz)★★★, Lüneburg Treasure (Lüneburger Ratssilber)★★★ – New National Gallery (Neue Nationalgalerie)★★* NZ **M⁵** *– German Historiy Museum (Deutsches Historisches Museum; Zeughaus)* PY *– Friedrichswerdersche Church* PZ *(Schinkel-Museum)★ – Prussian State Library (Staatsbliothek preußischer Kulturbesitz)★* NZ *– Dahlem Museums (Museumszentrum Dahlem)★★★ by Clayalle* EZ *– Gallery of Paintings (Germäldegalerie)★★★, Museum of Ethnography (Museum für Völkerkunde)★★★ – Museum of Moslem Art (Museum für islamische Kunst)★★, Museum of Indian Art (Museum für indische Kunst)★★ – Sculpture Gallery (Skulpturengalerie)★★ – Museum for German Folklore (Museum für Deutsche Volkskunde)★ – Scholß Charlottenburg★★* EY: *Historical Rooms (Historische Räume)★★ Porcelain Room (Porzellan-Kabinett)★★, The Kronprinz's Silver (Kronprinzsilber)★★ – Knobelsdorff-wing (Knobelsdorff-Flügel)★★ Golden Gallery (Goldene Galerie)★★, Winter-kammer★, Gallery of Romanticism (Gallerie der Romantik)★★ – Museum of Pre- and Proto-History (Museum für Vor-und Frühgeschichte)★ – Collection Berggruen (Sammlung Berggruen)★★* **M¹³** *– Bröhan Museum★ – Egyptian Museum (Ägyptisches Museum)★★★* EY **M⁶** *– Schloßgarten★★ (Schinkel-Pavillon★, Belvedere★, Mausoleum★) – Museum of Contemporary Art (Museum für Gegenwart-Berlin)★★* NX *– Museum of Natural History (Museum für Naturkunde)★* NX *– Museum of Transport and Technology (Museum für Verkehr und Technik)★★* GZ **M⁸** *– Käthe-Kollwitz Museum★* LXY **M⁹** *– Brücke Museum★* BY **M³⁶** *– Brandenburg March Museum (Märkisches Museum)★* RZ

## PARKS, GARDENS, LAKES

*Tiergarten★★* MX *– Zoological Park (Zoologischer Garten)★★★* MX *– Wannsee★★ by Clay-Allee* EZ *(Volkspark Klein Glienicke★★) – Havel★★ – Peacook island (Pfaueninsel)★★ by Clay-Allee* EZ *– Tegeler See★★ by Müllerstraße* FX *– Großer Müggelsee★★ by Stralauer Allee* HYZ *– Grunewald★★ by Clay-Allee* EZ *(Jagdschloß Grunewald★* **M²⁸** *– Botanical Gardens (Botanischer Garten Dahlem)★★ by Rheinbabenallee* EZ

## HISTORIC BUILDINGS, STREETS, SQUARES

*Philharmonie★★★* NZ *– Martin-Gropius-Building★★* NZ *– Brandenburg Gate (Brandenburger Tor)★★* NZ *– Reichstag★* NY *– Unter den Linden★★* NPZ *– Gendarmenmarkt★★* PZ *German National Theatre (Schauspielhaus)★★, German Cathedral (Deutscher Dom)★, French Cathedral (Französischer Dom)★ – Arsenal (Zeughaus)★★* PY *– St-Nicholas District (Nikolaiviertel)★* RZ *– Friedrichstraße★* PYZ *– Oranienburger Straße★★* PY *– Kunfürstendamm★★* LXY *(Kaiser-Wilhelm-Gedächtniskirche★) – Olympic Stadium★ by Kaiserdamm* EY

## Town Centre : Charlottenburg, Mitte, Schöneberg, Tiergarten, Wilmersdorf

**Adlon** M, Unter den Linden 77, ✉ 10177, ☎ (030) 2 26 10, *Fax (030) 22612222*, Massage, – rm, – 300. AE VISA JCB. rest NZ s
Meals à la carte 67/90 – ***L'étoile*** *(closed Sunday - Monday)* **Meals** 100(lunch) 160(dinner) – **337 rm** 456/732 – 37 suites.

**Four Seasons** M, Charlottenstr. 49/at Gendarmenplatz, ✉ 10177, ☎ (030) 2 03 38, *Fax (030) 20336166*, Massage, – rm, – 75. AE VISA JCB. rest PZ n
***Seasons*** **: Meals** à la carte 55/90 – **204 rm** 427/759 – 42 suites.

**Kempinski Hotel Bristol Berlin**, Kurfürstendamm 27, ✉ 10719, ☎ (030) 88 43 40, *Fax (030) 8836075*, Massage, – rm, – 250. AE VISA JCB. rest LX n
***Kempinski-Restaurant*** *(closed Monday)* **Meals** à la carte 60/93 – ***Kempinski-Eck*** **: Meals** à la carte 47/80 – **301 rm** 372/594 – 29 suites.

**Grand Hotel Esplanade** M, Lützowufer 15, ✉ 10785, ☎ (030) 25 47 80, *Fax (030) 2651171*, (conference boat with own landing stage), « Modern hotel featuring contemporary art », Massage, – rm, – 260. AE VISA JCB. rest MX e
**Meals** see also ***Harlekin*** below – ***Eckkneipe*** **: Meals** à la carte 34/51 – **402 rm** 409/588 – 33 suites.

**Westin Grand Hotel**, Friedrichstr. 158, ✉ 10117, ☎ (030) 2 02 70, *Fax (030) 20273362*, Massage, – rm, – 100. AE VISA JCB PZ a
***Coelln*** (dinner only, outstanding wine list) **Meals** à la carte 58/90 – ***Goldene Gans*** *(dinner only)* **Meals** à la carte 41/70 – **Forellenquintett** (mainly seafood) **Meals** à la carte 39/53 – **358 rm** 354/553 – 20 suites.

**Palace**, Budapester Str. 42 (Europa-Centre), ✉ 10789, ☎ (030) 2 50 20, *Fax (030) 2626577*, free entrance to the thermal recreation centre – rm, – 260. AE VISA JCB. rest MX k
**Meals** see also ***First Floor*** below – ***Alt Nürnberg*** **: Meals** à la carte 37/53 – **321 rm** 279/592 – 18 suites.

**Inter-Continental**, Budapester Str. 2, ✉ 10787, ☎ (030) 2 60 20, *Fax (030) 26022600*, Massage, – rm, – 800. AE VISA MX a
**Meals** see also ***Zum Hugenotten*** below – ***L.A. Café*** **: Meals** à la carte 50/65 – **511 rm** 377/609 – 40 suites.

**Radisson SAS-Hotel Berlin**, Karl-Liebknecht-Str. 5, ✉ 10178, ☎ (030) 2 38 28, *Fax (030) 23827590*, Massage, – rm, – 360. AE VISA JCB. RY s
**Meals** à la carte 43/65 – **540 rm** 337/454 – 17 suites.

**Berlin**, Lützowplatz 17, ✉ 10785, ☎ (030) 2 60 50, *Fax (030) 26052715*, – rm, rest, – 400. AE VISA JCB. rest MX b
**Meals** 32 (buffet lunch) and à la carte 51/80 – **701 rm** 290/450 – 7 suites.

**Berlin Hilton** (with Kroneflügel), Mohrenstr. 30, ✉ 10117, ☎ (030) 2 02 30, *Fax (030) 20342699*, – rm, – 300. AE VISA JCB PZ r
***La Cupole*** *(dinner only, closed Sunday - Monday)* **Meals** à la carte 68/90 – ***Fellini*** (Italian rest.) *(dinner only)* **Meals** à la carte 45/87 – **Mark Brandenburg** (vegetarian menu available) **Meals** à la carte 45/70 – **502 rm** 377/559 – 12 suites.

**Steigenberger Berlin**, Los-Angeles-Platz 1, ✉ 10789, ☎ (030) 2 12 70, *Fax (030) 212117*, Massage, – rm, – 300. AE VISA JCB. rest MY d
***Park-Restaurant*** *(dinner only, closed Sunday - Monday)* **Meals** à la carte 54/78 – ***Berliner Stube*** **: Meals** à la carte 39/64 – **397 rm** 320/565 – 11 suites.

**Hliday Inn Crown Plaza** M, Nürnberger Str. 65, ✉ 10787, ☎ (030) 21 00 70, *Fax (030) 2132009*, Massage, – rm, – 120. AE VISA JCB. rest MX t
**Meals** à la carte 52/72 – **425 rm** 348/566 – 10 suites.

**Brandenburger Hof** M, Eislebener Str. 14, ✉ 10789, ☎ (030) 21 40 50, *Fax (030) 21405100*, « Modernized Wilhelminian mansion with Bauhaus furniture » – – 25. AE VISA JCB. rest LY n
***Die Quadriga*** (dinner only) *(closed Saturday - Sunday, 1 - 12 January and 13 July - 16 August)* **Meals** à la carte 72/110 – ***Der Wintergarten*** **: Meals** à la carte 46/73 – **86 rm** 275/445.

**Maritim Pro Arte**, Friedrichstr. 150, ✉ 10117, ☎ (030) 2 03 35, *Fax (030) 20334209*, rm, – 1050. AE VISA JCB PY e
***Galerie*** (buffet lunch only) **Meals** 47 – ***Atelier*** (dinner only) **Meals** à la carte 52/72 – **403 rm** 294/558 – 28 suites.

**Savoy**, Fasanenstr. 9, ✉ 10623, ☎ (030) 31 10 30, *Fax (030) 31103333*, – rm, – 50. AE VISA JCB LX s
**Meals** à la carte 48/80 – **125 rm** 277/455 – 18 suites.

**Mondial**, Kurfürstendamm 47, ✉ 10707, ☎ (030) 88 41 10, *Fax (030) 88411150*, Massage, – rm, – 50. AE VISA. rest KY e
**Meals** à la carte 47/69 – **75 rm** 190/480.

**President**, An der Urania 16, ✉ 10787, ☎ (030) 21 90 30, *Fax (030) 2141200*, – rm, – 40. AE VISA. rest MY t
**Meals** *(closed Sunday)* à la carte 42/67 – **188 rm** 235/357.

**Sorat Hotel Am Spreebogen**, Alt Moabit 99, ✉ 10559, ☎ (030) 39 92 00, *Fax (030) 39920999*, – rm, – 150. AE VISA JCB. rest FY b
**Meals** à la carte 47/60 – **221 rm** 220/430.

**Seehof**, Lietzensee-Ufer 11, ✉ 14057, ☎ (030) 32 00 20, *Fax (030) 32002251*, ≤, « Garden terrace », – rest, – 40. AE VISA. rest
**Meals** 43 (lunch) and à la carte 58/76 – **77 rm** 230/470. JX r

**art'otel Ermelerhaus**, Wallstr. 70, ✉ 10179, ☎ (030) 24 06 20, *Fax (030) 25062222*, « Reconstructed nobleman's house with modern hotel wing », – rm, rm, – 45. AE VISA RZ c
**Meals** *(closed Sunday - Monday)* (dinner only) à la carte 46/82 – **109 rm** Z 235/355.

**Luisenhof** without rest, Kopenicker Str. 92, ✉ 10179, ☎ (030) 2 41 59 06, *Fax (030) 2792983*, « Elegant installation » – – 30. AE VISA JCB
**27 rm** 210/360. RZ a

**Forum-Hotel Berlin**, Alexanderplatz, ✉ 10178, ☎ (030) 2 38 90, *Fax (030) 23894305*, – rm, – 240. AE VISA JCB. rest RY c
**Meals** à la carte 29/56 – **1006 rm** 235/325.

**Ambassador**, Bayreuther Str. 42, ✉ 10787, ☎ (030) 21 90 20, *Fax (030) 21902380*, Massage, – rm, rest, – 70. AE VISA JCB
**Meals** à la carte 34/65 – **199 rm** 230/310. MX z

**Berlin Excelsior Hotel**, Hardenbergstr. 14, ✉ 10623, ☎ (030) 3 15 50, *Fax (030) 31551002*, – rm, rest, – 60. AE VISA JCB. rest LX b
**Meals** à la carte 37/65 – **317 rm** 335/385.

**Hamburg**, Landgrafenstr. 4, ✉ 10787, ☎ (030) 26 47 70, *Fax (030) 2629394*, – rm, – 60. AE VISA JCB. rest MX s
**Meals** à la carte 44/68 – **240 rm** 225/320.

**Residenz**, Meinekestr. 9, ✉ 10719, ☎ (030) 88 44 30, *Fax (030) 8824726* – AE VISA. rest LY d
**Meals** à la carte 53/88 – **88 rm** 220/310.

**Bleibtreu-Hotel**, Bleibtreustr. 31, ✉ 10707, ☎ (030) 88 47 40, *Fax (030) 88474444*, « Modern interior », Massage, – rm, AE VISA JCB. rest KY s
**Meals** à la carte 46/68 – **60 rm** 275/441.

**Park Consul** without rest, Alt-Moabit 86a, ✉ 10555, ☎ (030) 39 07 80, *Fax (030) 39078900* – AE VISA FY s
**52 rm** 215/325.

**Sorat Art'otel**, Joachimstalerstr. 28, ✉ 10719, ☎ (030) 88 44 70, *Fax (030) 88447700*, « Modern hotel with exhibition of contemporary art » – – 65. AE VISA JCB. rest LY e
**Meals** *(closed Sunday)* à la carte 34/50 – **133 rm** 180/395.

**Sylter Hof**, Kurfürstenstr. 116, ✉ 10787, ☎ (030) 2 12 00, *Fax (030) 2142826* – – 80. AE VISA. rest MX d
**Meals** *(closed Sunday)* à la carte 26/41 – **160 rm** 186/322 – 18 suites.

**Hecker's Hotel**, Grolmanstr. 35, 10623, (030) 8 89 00, *Fax (030) 8890260* – rm, . – LX e
*Cassambalis (closed lunch Sunday and Monday)* **Meals** à la carte 44/72 – **72 rm** 250/390.

**Queens Hotel** without rest, Güntzelstr. 14, 10717, (030) 8 73 02 41, *Fax (030) 8619326* – – 40. LZ t
**108 rm** 199/342.

**Kanthotel** without rest, Kantstr. 111, 10627, (030) 32 30 20, *Fax (030) 3240952* – . JX e
**55 rm** 170/269.

**Concept Hotel**, Grolmanstr. 41, 10623, (030) 88 42 60, *Fax (030) 88426820*, , Massage, – , rm, – 85. LX m
**Meals** à la carte 34/59 – **106 rm** 220/350 – 5 suites.

**Holiday Inn Garden Court** without rest, Bleibtreustr. 25, 10707, (030) 88 09 30, *Fax (030) 88093939* – – 15. . KY g
**73 rm** 267/394.

**Albrechtshof**, Albrechtstr. 8, 10117, (030) 30 88 60, *Fax (030) 30886100*, – , rm, – 50. NY a
**Meals** à la carte 35/51 – **99 rm** 195/365 – 11 suites.

**Kronprinz** without rest (restored 1894 house), Kronprinzendamm 1, 10711, (030) 89 60 30, *Fax (030) 8931215* – – 25. JY d
**61 rm** 210/260.

**Schloßparkhotel** , Heubnerweg 2a, 14059, (030) 3 22 40 61, *Fax (030) 3258861*, , – – 50. EY a
**Meals** à la carte 36/60 – **39 rm** 189/244.

**Boulevard** without rest, Kurfürstendamm 12, 10719, (030) 88 42 50, *Fax (030) 88425450* – – 25. LX c
**57 rm** 198/320.

**Kurfürstendamm am Adenauerplatz** without rest, Kurfürstendamm 68, 10707, (030) 88 46 30, *Fax (030) 8825528* – – 30. JY n
**34 rm** 180/270 – 4 suites.

**Scandotel Castor** without rest, Fuggerstr. 8, 10777, (030) 21 30 30, *Fax (030) 21303160* – . . MY s
**78 rm** 198/235.

**Hugenotten** - Hotel Inter-Continental, Budapester Str. 2, 10787, (030) 26 02 12 63, *Fax (030) 260280760* – . MX a
*closed Sunday* – **Meals** (dinner only) (outstanding wine list) à la carte 83/100.

**First Floor** - Hotel Palace, Budapester Str. 42, 10789, (030) 25 02 10 20, *Fax (030) 25021160* – . MX k
*closed Saturday lunch and 20 July - 16 August* – **Meals** à la carte 91/112
**Spec.** Beeftea mit Kaviar und Crème fraîche. Gänsestopfleber "Berliner Art", Kartoffelpüree und Trüffeljus. Rücken vom Pauillac Lamm mit Aromaten gebraten.

**Harlekin** - Grand Hotel Esplanade, Lützowufer 15, 10785, (030) 25 47 88 58, *Fax (030) 2651171* – . . MX e
*closed Sunday - Monday, 2 to 9 January and 13 July - 11 August* – **Meals** (dinner only) à la carte 107/110
**Spec.** Gebackene Seezungengalantine mit Jakobsmuschel. Beluga Stör aus dem Korianderrauch auf Borschtschrisotto. Bresse Taube im Trüffeltempura mit Erdfruchtpanachée.

**Opernpalais-Königin Luise**, Unter den Linden 5, 10117, (030) 20 26 84 43, *Fax (030) 20044438* – 50. . PZ e
*closed Sunday - Monday* – **Meals** (dinner only, booking essential) à la carte 61/75.

**Bamberger Reiter**, Regensburger Str. 7, 10777, (030) 2 18 42 82, *Fax (030) 2142348*, – . MY b
*closed Sunday - Monday and 1 to 15 January* – **Meals** (dinner only, booking essential) 145/185 and à la carte 99/117 – ***Bistro :*** **Meals** à la carte 66/76
**Spec.** Provençalische Rotbarbenterrine. Geschmorte Milchlammschulter mit Powerarden. Haselnußsoufflé mit Karameleis.

**Vau**, Jägerstr. 55, 10117, (030) 2 02 97 30, *Fax (030) 20297311*, – . PZ u
*closed Sunday* – **Meals** 60 (lunch) and à la carte 86/108
**Spec.** Zweierlei vom Lamm. Taube mit Gänseleber und Artischocken. Topfensoufflé.

**Alt Luxemburg**, Windscheidtstr. 31, ✉ 10627, ☎ (030) 3 23 87 30, *Fax (030) 3274003* – ▤. AE ◑ E VISA JX s
*closed Sunday and 2 weeks July - August* – **Meals** (dinner only, booking essential) à la carte 95/135
**Spec.** Kartoffel-Zwiebelgalette mit Trüffelsauce. Seeteufel mit Senfkörnersauce und geschmorten Schalotten. Entenbrust mit gebratenen asiatischen Nudeln.

**Restaurant im Logenhaus**, Emser Str. 12, ✉ 10719, ☎ (030) 8 73 25 60, *Fax (030) 8612985* – AE ◑ E VISA KY t
*closed Sunday* – **Meals** (dinner only) 85/145 and à la carte.

**Ponte Vecchio** (Tuscan rest.), Spielhagenstr. 3, ✉ 10585, ☎ (030) 3 42 19 99, *Fax (030) 3324713* – ◑ JX a
*closed Tuesday and 4 weeks July - August* – **Meals** (dinner only, booking essential) à la carte 58/84.

**Ana e Bruno** (Italian rest.), Sophie-Charlotten-Str. 101, ✉ 14059, ☎ (030) 3 25 71 10, *Fax (030) 3226895* – AE. EY s
*closed Sunday and Monday, 1 week January and 3 weeks June - July* – **Meals** (dinner only, outstanding Italian wine list) à la carte 80/100.

**Borchardt**, Französische Str. 47, ✉ 10117, ☎ (030) 20 39 71 17, *Fax (030) 20397150*, « Courtyard-terrace » – VISA PZ c
**Meals** à la carte 55/79.

**Il Sorriso** (Italian rest.), Kurfürstenstr. 76, ✉ 10787, ☎ (030) 2 62 13 13, *Fax (030) 2650277*, – AE ◑ E VISA. MX r
*closed Sunday and 22 December - 5 January* – **Meals** (booking essential for dinner) à la carte 52/75.

**Peppino** (Italian rest.), Fasanenstr. 65, ✉ 10719, ☎ (030) 8 83 67 22, *Fax (030) 8836722*, – AE E LY v
*closed Sunday and 4 weeks July - August* – **Meals** à la carte 51/77.

**Maxwell**, Bergstr. 3 (Entrance in courtyard), ✉ 10115, ☎ (030) 2 80 71 21, *Fax (030) 2807121*, « Art nouveau facade ; courtyard-terrace » – AE ◑ E VISA PX e
**Meals** (booking essential) 29 (lunch) and à la carte 60/77.

**Am Karlsbad** (modern restaurant in bistro style), Am Karlsbad 11, ✉ 10785, ☎ (030) 2 64 53 49, *Fax (030) 2644240*, NZ c
*closed Saturday lunch and Sunday* – **Meals** 24 (lunch) and à la carte 48/78.

**at Berlin-Britz** *by Karl-Marx-Straße* HZ :

**Park Hotel Blub**, Buschkrugallee 60, ✉ 12359, ☎ (030) 60 00 36 00, *Fax (030) 60003777* – ⛭ – 50. AE ◑ E VISA
**Meals** (dinner only) à la carte 31/48 – **120 rm** 207/229.

**Buschkrugpark** without rest, Buschkrugallee 107, ✉ 12359, ☎ (030) 6 00 99 00, *Fax (030) 60099020* – AE ◑ E VISA
*closed 23 December - 1 January* – **25 rm** 197/259.

**at Berlin-Dahlem** *by Clayallee* EZ :

**Alter Krug**, Königin-Luise-Str. 52, ✉ 14195, ☎ (030) 8 32 50 89, *Fax (030) 8327749*, « Garden terrace » – Ⓟ. AE ◑ E VISA
*closed Sunday dinner and Monday* – **Meals** (weekdays dinner only) à la carte 47/82.

**at Berlin-Friedrichshain**

**Inn Side Residence-Hotel** Ⓜ, Lange Str. 31, ✉ 10243, ☎ (030) 29 30 30, *Fax (030) 29303199*, – rm, – 40. AE ◑ E VISA SZ r
**Meals** à la carte 33/64 – **133 rm** 235/415.

**at Berlin-Grunewald** :

**Schloßhotel Vier Jahreszeiten**, Brahmsstr. 6, ✉ 14193, ☎ (030) 89 58 40, *Fax (030) 89584800*, « Former Wilhelminian mansion », Massage, – rm, – Ⓟ – 40. AE ◑ E VISA JCB. rest EZ a
***Vivaldi*** *(dinner only, closed early January and 1 week August)* **Meals** à la carte 101/131 – ***Le Jardin*** : **Meals** à la carte 66/85 – **52 rm** 583/801 – 12 suites.

**Grand Slam**, Gottfried-von-Cramm-Weg 47, ✉ 14193, ☎ (030) 8 25 38 10, *Fax (030) 8266300*, – AE ◑ E VISA. by Königsallee EZ
*closed Sunday, Monday, 2 weeks January and 3 weeks July - August* – **Meals** (dinner only, booking essential) 135/175 à la carte 88/111
**Spec.** Blumenkohlmousse mit mariniertem Felchen. Dreierlei Lammkoteletts mit Auberginenconfit und Kräutercouscous. Gebratener weißer Pfirsich mit Lavendelblüteneis (June-July).

at Berlin-Kreuzberg :

**Stuttgarter Hof**, Anhalter Str. 9, ✉ 10963, ✆ (030) 26 48 30, *Fax (030) 26483900*, – |♦|, ⇔ rm, TV ☎ – 🅐 25. AE ⓓ E VISA JCB NZ e
Meals *(closed Sunday)* à la carte 29/50 – **110 rm** ☐ 185/370.

at Berlin-Lichtenberg *by Karl-Marx-Allee* HY :

**Abacus Tierpark Hotel** M, Franz-Mett-Str. 7, ✉ 10319, ✆ (030) 5 16 20, *Fax (030) 5162400* – |♦|, ⇔ rm, TV ☎ ✆ ♿ P – 🅐 300. AE ⓓ E VISA
Meals 32 (buffet only) – **278 rm** ☐ 190/280.

at Berlin-Lichterfelde *by Boelcke Straße* GZ :

**Villa Toscana** without rest, Bahnhofstr. 19, ✉ 12207, ✆ (030) 7 68 92 70, *Fax (030) 7734488*, « Villa with elegant installation » – |♦| TV ☎. AE ⓓ E VISA JCB.
**16 rm** ☐ 180/280.

at Berlin-Mariendorf *by Tempelhofer Damm* GZ :

**Landhaus Alpinia**, Säntisstr. 32, ✉ 12107, ✆ (030) 76 17 70 (Hotel) 7 41 99 98 (Rest.), *Fax (030) 7419835*, « Garden-terrace », – |♦|, ⇔ rm, TV ✆ – 🅐 20. AE E VISA
***Villa Rossini :*** **Meals** à la carte 42/72 – **58 rm** ☐ 178/380.

at Berlin-Neukölln :

**Estrel Residence** M, Sonnenallee 225, ✉ 12057, ✆ (030) 6 83 10, *Fax (030) 68312345*, beer garden, Massage, – |♦|, ⇔ rm, TV ✆ ♿ – 🅐 700. AE ⓓ E VISA. rest HZ a
***Portofino*** (Italian rest.) **Meals** à la carte 36/52 – ***Sans Souci :*** **Meals** à la carte 37/66 – **Sun Thai** (Thai rest.) **Meals** à la carte 29/50 – **1125 rm** ☐ 197/335 – 80 suites.

at Berlin-Prenzlauerberg :

**Sorat Hotel Gustavo** M without rest, Prenzlauer Allee 169, ✉ 10409, ✆ (030) 44 66 10, *Fax (030) 44661661* – |♦| ⇔ TV ☎ ✆ – 🅐 40. AE ⓓ E VISA JCB HX b
**122 rm** ☐ 185/310.

**Rosenbaum**, Oderberger Str. 61, ✉ 10435, ✆ (030) 4 48 46 10, *Fax (030) 4493077*, – E VISA RX a
*closed Sunday and 2 weeks January* – **Meals** (dinner only) à la carte 44/64.

at Berlin-Reinickendorf *by Sellerstr.* GX :

**Rheinsberg am See**, Finsterwalder Str. 64, ✉ 13435, ✆ (030) 4 02 10 02, *Fax (030) 4035057*, « Lakeside garden terrace », Massage, , , , – |♦|, ⇔ rm, TV ☎ ✆ P – 🅐 50. E VISA
Meals à la carte 34/78 – **81 rm** ☐ 185/235.

at Berlin-Rudow :

**Sorat Hotel u. Office** without rest, Rudower Str. 90, ✉ 12351, ✆ (030) 60 00 80, *Fax (030) 60008666*, – |♦| ⇔ ▤ TV ☎ ✆ – 🅐 60. AE ⓓ E VISA JCB by Karl-Marx-Straße HZ
**96 rm** ☐ 185/290.

at Berlin-Siemensstadt *by Siemensdamm* EX :

**Holiday Inn Berlin Esplanade** M, Rohrdamm 80, ✉ 13629, ✆ (030) 38 38 90, *Fax (030) 38389900*, , , – |♦|, ⇔ rm, ▤ TV ✆ ♿ – 🅐 170. AE ⓓ E VISA JCB. rest
Meals *(closed Saturday and Sunday dinner)* à la carte 54/70 – **336 rm** ☐ 258/416 – 4 suites.

**Novotel**, Ohmstr. 4, ✉ 13629, ✆ (030) 3 80 30, *Fax (030) 3819403*, – |♦|, ⇔ rm, TV ☎ ✆ ♿ – 🅐 200. AE ⓓ E VISA JCB
Meals à la carte 33/58 – **119 rm** ☐ 215/279.

at Berlin-Steglitz *by Hauptstr.* FZ :

**Steglitz International**, Albrechtstr. 2 (corner of Schloßstraße), ✉ 12165, ✆ (030) 79 00 50, *Fax (030) 79005550* – |♦|, ⇔ rm, ▤ rest, TV ♿ – 🅐 300. AE ⓓ E VISA
Meals à la carte 39/82 – **211 rm** ☐ 180/260 – 3 suites.

**at Berlin-Tegel :**

**Sorat-Hotel Humboldt-Mühle** M, An der Mühle 5, ✉ 13507, ✆ (030) 43 90 40, *Fax (030) 43904444*, , , – , rm, – 50. AE ① E VISA JCB by Müllerstraße FX
**Meals** à la carte 35/57 – **120 rm** 220/310.

**Novotel Berlin Airport**, Kurt-Schumacher-Damm 202 (by airport approach), ✉ 13405, ✆ (030) 4 10 60, *Fax (030) 4106700*, , , (heated) – , rm, – 150. AE ① E VISA EX r
**Meals** à la carte 44/64 – **184 rm** 217/269.

**at Berlin-Waidmannslust** *by Sellerstr.* GX :

**Rockendorf's Restaurant**, Düsterhauptstr. 1, ✉ 13469, ✆ (030) 4 02 30 99, *Fax (030) 4022742*, « Elegant installation » – . AE ① E VISA
*closed Sunday - Monday, 22 December - 6 January and July* – **Meals** *(booking essential)* 110/175 (lunch) 140/198 (dinner)
**Spec.** Cassoulet vom bretonischen Hummer. Soufflierte Taubenbrust auf Artischockenboden. Feigentarte mit Limonen.

---

**COLOGNE (KÖLN)** *Nordrhein-Westfalen* 417 N 4, 987 ㉕ ㉖ – *pop. 1 005 000 – alt. 65 m.*

See : *Cathedral (Dom)★★ (Magi's Shrine★★★, Gothic stained glass windows★ Cross of Gero (Gerokreuz)★, South chapel (Marienkapelle) : altarpiece★★★, stalls★, treasury★* GY – *Roman-Germanic Museum (Römisch-Germanisches Museum)★★ (Dionysos Mosaic★, Roman glassware collection★★)* GY **M**[1] – *Wallraf-Richartz-Museum and Museum Ludwig★★★ (Photo-Historama Agfa★)* GY **M**[2] – *Diocesan Museum (Diözesean Museum)★* GY **M**[3] – *Schnütgen-Museum★★* GZ **M**[4] – *Museum of East-Asian Art (Museum für Ostasiatische Kunst)★★ by Hahnenstraßeand Richard Wagner Straße* EV – *Museum for Applied Art (Museum für Angewandte Kunst)★* GYZ **M**[6] – *St. Maria Lyskirchen (frescoes★★)* FX – *St. Severin (interior★)* FX – *St. Pantaleon (rood screen★)* EX – *St. Kunibert (chancel : stained glass windows★)* FU – *St. Mary the Queen (St. Maria Königin) : wall of glass★ by Bonnerstraße* FX – *St. Aposteln (apse★)* EV **K** – *St. Ursula (treasury★)* FU – *St. Mary of the Capitol (St. Maria im Kapitol) (romanesque wooden church door★, trefoil chancel★)* GZ – *Imhoff-Stollwerrk-Museum★* FX – *Old Town Hall (Altes Rathaus)★* GZ – *Botanical garden Flora★ by Konrad-Adenauer-Ufer* FU.

*9 Köln-Marienburg, Schillingsrotter Weg, ✆ (0221) 38 40 53 ; 18 Bergisch Gladbach-Refrath (E : 17km), (02204) 6 31.*

*Köln-Bonn at Wahn (SE : 17 km) ✆ (02203) 4 01.*

*Köln-Deutz, Barmer Straße by Deutzer Brücke* FV.

*Exhibition Centre (Messegelände) by Deutzer Brücke* (FV), *✆ (0221) 82 11, Fax (0221) 8 21 25 74.*

*Tourist office (Verkehrsamt), Am Dom ✉ 50667, ✆ (0221) 2 21 33 45, Fax (0221) 2213320.*

**ADAC,** *Luxemburger Str. 169, ✉50963, ✆ (0221) 472747, Fax (0221) 4727452.*

*Düsseldorf 40 – Aachen 69 – Bonn 28 – Essen 68.*

Plans on following pages

**Excelsior Hotel Ernst**, Domplatz, ✉ 50667, ✆ (0221) 27 01, *Fax (0221) 135150* – , rm, – 80. AE ① E VISA GY a
**Meals** *see also* ***Hanse-Stube*** and ***Ambiance am Dom*** below – **160 rm** 310/635 – 8 suites.

**Maritim**, Heumarkt 20, ✉ 50667, ✆ (0221) 2 02 70, *Fax (0221) 2027826*, Massage , , – , rm, – 1300. AE ① E VISA JCB GZ m
***Bellevue*** « Terrace with ≤ Cologne » **Meals** à la carte 72/96 – ***La Gallerie*** *(dinner only closed Sunday - Monday and July to August)* **Meals** à la carte 56/73 – **Rôtisserie : Meals** 49 (buffet lunch only) – **454 rm** 281/564 – 28 suites.

**Hotel im Wasserturm** (former 19C water tower, elegant modern installation), Kaygasse 2, ✉ 50676, ✆ (0221) 2 00 80, *Fax (0221) 2008888*, , roof garden terrace with ≤ Cologne, – , rm, rest, – 25. AE ① E VISA JCB. rest FX c
**Meals** à la carte 71/93 – **90 rm** 449/578 – 42 suites.

**Dom-Hotel** , Domkloster 2a, ✉ 50667, ✆ (0221) 2 02 40, *Fax (0221)2024444*, « Terrace with ≤ » – , rm, – 60. AE ① E VISA JCB GY d
**Meals** à la carte 65/98 – **125 rm** 379/798.

**Dorint Kongress-Hotel**, Helenenstr. 14, ✉ 50667, ✆ (0221) 27 50, *Fax (0221) 2751301*, Massage, , – , rm, – 500. AE ① E VISA JCB. rest EV p
**Meals** à la carte 46/82 – ***Kabuki*** (Japanese rest.) *(closed Sunday)* **Meals** à la carte 42/64 – **285 rm** 293/411 – 15 suites.

**Renaissance Köln Hotel**, Magnusstr. 20, ✉ 50672, ℘ (0221) 2 03 40, *Fax (0221) 2034777*, Massage, – rm, 200. rest EV b
Meals à la carte 48/76 – **236 rm** 293/736.

**Holiday Inn Crowne Plaza**, Habsburger Ring 9, ✉ 50674, ℘ (0221) 2 09 50, *Fax (0221) 251206*, Massage, – rm, 230. rest by Hahnenstraße EV
Meals à la carte 47/68 – **299 rm** 324/658.

**Savoy** without rest, Turiner Str. 9, ✉ 50668, ℘ (0221) 1 62 30, *Fax (0221) 1623200*, – 70. FU s
*closed 24 December - 2 January* – **103 rm** 175/550.

**Consul**, Belfortstr. 9, ✉ 50668, ℘ (0221) 7 72 10, *Fax (0221) 7721259*, Massage, – rm, – 120. rest FU v
Meals à la carte 46/78 – **120 rm** 250/490.

**Mondial am Dom**, Kurt-Hackenberg-Platz 1, ✉ 50667, ℘ (0221) 2 06 30, *Fax (0221) 2063522*, – rm, – 180. GY f
Meals à la carte 55/75 – **205 rm** 253/452.

**Haus Lyskirchen**, Filzengraben 28, ✉ 50676, ℘ (0221) 2 09 70, *Fax (0221) 2097718*, – rm, rest, – 60. FX u
Meals *(closed Saturday lunch, Sunday and Bank Holidays)* à la carte 35/68 – **94 rm** 185/360.

**Euro Plaza Cologne**, Breslauer Platz 2, ✉ 50668, ℘ (0221) 1 65 10, *Fax (0221) 1651333* – rm, – 20. GY c
Meals à la carte 53/71 – **116 rm** 205/290 – 6 suites.

**Ascot** without rest, Hohenzollernring 95, ✉ 50672, ℘ (0221) 9 52 96 50, *Fax (0221) 952965100*, – EV a
*closed 23 December - 2 January* – **46 rm** 173/415.

**Flandrischer Hof** without rest, Flandrische Str. 3, ✉ 50674, ℘ (0221) 25 20 95, *Fax (0221) 251052* – – 20.
**143 rm** 120/380. by HahnenStraße EV

**Senats Hotel**, Unter Goldschmied 9, ✉ 50667, ℘ (0221) 2 06 20, *Fax (0221) 2062200* – – 200. rest GZ b
*closed 23 December - 3 January* – ***Falstaff*** *(closed Saturday lunch and Sunday)* **Meals** à la carte 40/65 – **59 rm** 160/440.

**Dorint Hotel**, Friesenstr. 44, ✉ 50670, ℘ (0221) 1 61 40, *Fax (0221) 1614100*, – rm, – 100. EV n
Meals *(closed Saturday and Sunday lunch)* à la carte 35/57 – **103 rm** 220/440.

**Viktoria** without rest, Worringer Str. 23, ✉ 50668, ℘ (0221) 9 73 17 20, *Fax (0221) 727067* – FU t
*closed 24 December - 1 January* – **47 rm** 175/460.

**Mercure Severinshof**, Severinstr. 199, ✉ 50676, ℘ (0221) 2 01 30, *Fax (0221) 2013666*, – rm, – 120. rest FX a
Meals à la carte 37/62 – **252 rm** 220/394 – 11 suites.

**Coellner Hof**, Hansaring 100, ✉ 50670, ℘ (0221) 12 20 75, *Fax (0221) 135235* – rm, rest, – 30. FU k
Meals *(closed Friday - Saturday)* (dinner only) à la carte 28/65 – **70 rm** 140/340.

**Hopper** M, Brüsseler Str. 26, ✉ 50674, ℘ (0221) 92 44 00, *Fax (0221) 924406*, « Modern hotel in a former monastery », – rm, – 20. by Hahnenstr. S j
*closed 19 December - 4 January* – **Meals** *(closed Saturday lunch)* à la carte 44/61 – **49 rm** 158/368.

**Cristall** without rest, Ursulaplatz 9, ✉ 50668, ℘ (0221) 1 63 00, *Fax (0221) 1630333*, « Modern interior » – FU r
**84 rm** 190/350.

**Euro Garden Cologne** without rest, Domstr. 10, ✉ 50668, ℘ (0221) 1 64 90, *Fax (0221) 1649333*, – – 30. FU a
**85 rm** 205/520.

**Königshof** without rest, Richartzstr. 14, ✉ 50667, ℘ (0221) 2 57 87 71, *Fax (0221) 2578762* – GY n
**82 rm** 155/395.

**Kommerzhotel** without rest, Breslauer Platz, ✉ 50668, ℘ (0221) 1 61 00, *Fax (0221) 1610122*, – GY r
**77 rm** 175/380.

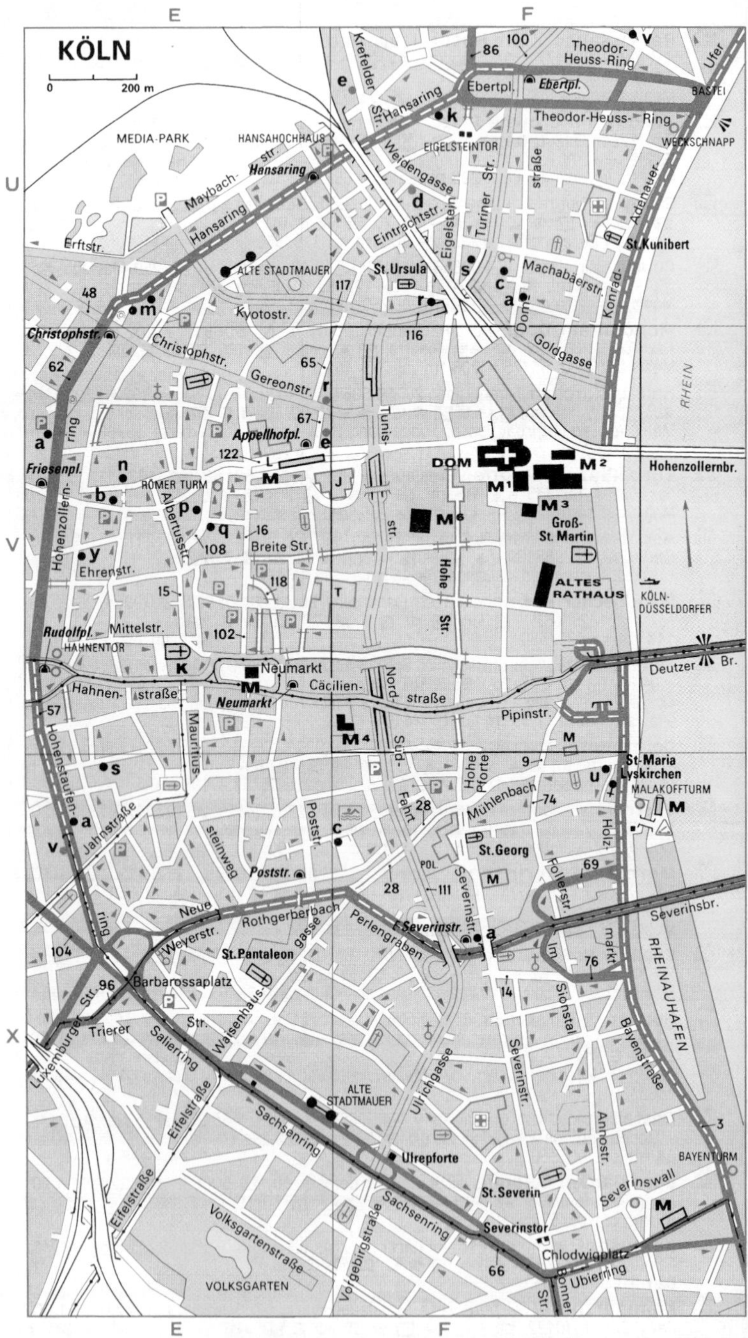
KÖLN
0
200 m
MEDIA-PARK
HANSAHOCHHAUS
Hansaring
Maybach-str.
Hansaring
Erftstr.
ALTE STADTMAUER
Kyotostr.
Christophstr.
Christophstr.
Gereonstr.
Appellhofpl.
Friesenpl.
RÖMER TURM
Albertusstr.
Breite Str.
Hohenzollern-ring
Ehrenstr.
Mittelstr.
Rudolfpl.
HAHNENTOR
Hahnen-straße
Neumarkt
Neumarkt
Cäcilien-straße
Hohenstaufen-ring
Mauritius-steinweg
Jahnstraße
Poststr.
Poststr.
Neue Weyerstr.
Rothgerberbach
St.Pantaleon
Waisenhaus-gasse
Barbarossaplatz
Luxemburger Str.
Trierer Str.
Salierring
Eifelstraße
Eifelstraße
ALTE STADTMAUER
Sachsenring
Sachsenring
Volksgartenstraße
VOLKSGARTEN
Vorgebirgstraße
Ulrichgasse
Ulrepforte
Severinstor
Chlodwigplatz
Ubierring
Bonner Str.
St.Severin
Severinstr.
Severinswall
BAYENTURM
Annostr.
Bayenstraße
RHEINAUHAFEN
Sionstal
Im Sionstal
Holz-markt
Severinsbr.
Severinstr.
Perlengraben
St.Georg
Follerstr.
Mühlenbach
Hohe Pforte
Nord-Süd-Fahrt
POL.
St.Maria Lyskirchen
MALAKOFFTURM
Pipinstr.
Deutzer Br.
KÖLN-DÜSSELDORFER
ALTES RATHAUS
Groß-St.Martin
Hohe Str.
Tunis-str.
DOM
Hohenzollernbr.
RHEIN
Goldgasse
Dom
Machabäerstr.
St.Ursula
Eigelstein
Eintrachtstr.
Weidengasse
Turiner Str.
straße
Konrad-Adenauer-Ufer
St.Kunibert
WECKSCHNAPP
EIGELSTEINTOR
Theodor-Heuss-Ring
Theodor-Heuss-Ring
Ebertpl.
Ebertpl.
BASTEI
Krefelder Str.
Hansaring
E
F
U
V
X

# KÖLN

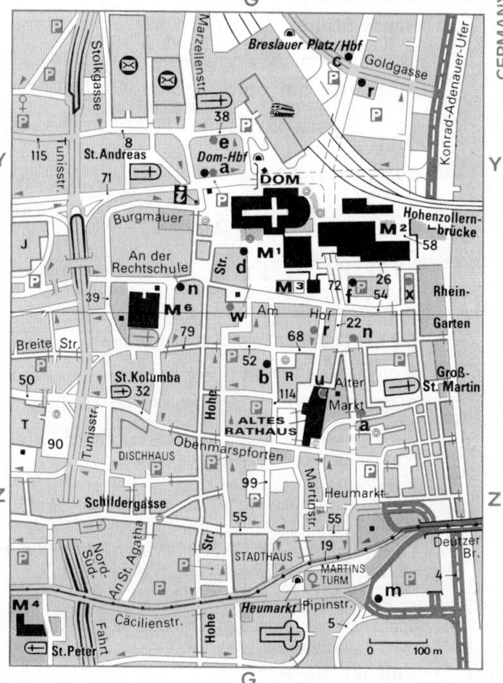


Breite Straße GZ
Ehrenstraße EV
Eigelstein FU
Gürzenichstraße GZ 55
Habsburgerring EV 57
Hahnenstraße EV
Hohenstaufenring EX
Hohenzollernring EV
Hohe Straße GYZ
Mittelstraße EV
Neumarkt EV
Richmodstraße EV 102
Schildergasse GZ
Severinstraße FX
Zeppelinstraße EV 118

Am Bayenturm FX 3
Am Leystapel GZ 4
Am Malzbüchel GZ 5
An den Dominikanern GY 8
An der Malzmühle FX 9
An St-Katharinen FX 14
Apostelnstraße EV 15
Auf dem Berlich EV 16
Augustinerstraße GZ 19
Bechergasse GZ 22
Bischofsgarten-Straße GY 26
Blaubach FX 28
Brückenstraße GZ 32
Dompropst-Ketzer-Straße GY 38
Drususgasse GY 39
Gladbacher Straße EU 48
Glockengasse GZ 50
Große Budengasse GZ 52
Große Neugasse GY 54
Heinrich-Böll-Platz GY 58
Kaiser-Wilhelm-Ring EV 62
Kardinal-Frings-Straße EV 65
Karolingerring FX 66
Kattenbug EV 67
Kleine Budengasse GZ 68
Kleine Witschgasse FX 69
Komödienstraße GY 71
Kurt-Hackenberg-Platz GY 72
Mathiasstraße FX 74
Mechtildisstraße FX 76
Minoritenstraße GZ 79
Neusser Straße FU 86
Offenbachplatz GZ 90
Pfälzer Straße EX 96
Quatermarkt GZ 99
Riehler Straße FU 100
Roonstraße EX 104
Sankt-Apern-Straße EV 108
Tel-Aviv-Straße FX 111
Unter Goldschmied GZ 114
Unter Sachsenhausen GY 115
Ursulaßße FU 116
Victoriastraße FU 117
Zeughausstraße EV 122

**Antik Hotel Bristol** without rest (antique furniture), Kaiser-Wilhelm-Ring 48, ✉ 50672, (0221) 12 01 95, *Fax (0221) 131495* – AE E VISA JCB
*closed 25 December - 1 January* – **44 rm** 165/330. EU m

**Esplanade** without rest, Hohenstaufenring 56, ✉ 50674, (0221) 9 21 55 70, *Fax (0221) 216822* – AE E VISA EX a
*closed 24 December - 2 January* – **33 rm** 165/360.

**Astor und Aparthotel Concorde** without rest, Friesenwall 68, ✉ 50672, (0221) 25 31 01, *Fax (0221) 253106* – AE E VISA. EV y
**51 rm** 185/360.

**Leonet** without rest, Rubensstr. 33, ✉ 50676, (0221) 23 60 16, *Fax (0221) 210893*, – 20. AE E VISA EX s
**78 rm** 148/325.

**Conti** without rest, Brüsseler Str. 40, ✉ 50674, (0221) 25 20 62, *Fax (0221) 252107* – AE E VISA by Hahnenstraße EV
*closed 22 to 28 December* – **43 rm** 130/390.

**Merian-Hotel** without rest, Allerheiligenstr. 1, ✉ 50668, (0221) 1 66 50, *Fax (0221) 1665200* – AE E VISA FU c
**32 rm** 120/375.

**Metropol** without rest, Hansaring 14, ✉ 50670, (0221) 13 33 77, *Fax (0221) 138307* – AE E VISA EU m
*closed 22 December - 2 January* – **26 rm** 145/320.

**Altstadt Hotel** without rest, Salzgasse 7, ✉ 50667, (0221) 2 57 78 51, *Fax (0221) 2577853*, – AE E VISA GZ p
*closed 20 December - 4 January* – **28 rm** 110/180.

XXXX **Hanse Stube** - (in Excelsior Hotel Ernst), Dompropst-Ketzer-Straße, ✉ 50667, ✆ (0221) 2 70 34 02 - ▤. AE ⓓ E VISA GY e
**Meals** 53 (lunch) and à la carte 88/120.

XXX **Ambiance am Dom** (in Excelsior Hotel Ernst), Trankgasse 1, ✉ 50667, ✆ (0221) 1 39 19 12 - AE ⓓ E VISA. ✻ GY a
*closed Saturday - Sunday, Bank Holidays and 3 weeks August* - **Meals** à la carte 81/104.

XXX **Börsen-Restaurant Maître**, Unter Sachsenhausen 10, ✉ 50667, ✆ (0221) 13 30 21, *Fax (0221) 133040*, ☂ - ▤. AE ⓓ E VISA. ✻ EV r
*closed Saturday lunch, Sunday, Bank Holidays and 4 weeks July - August* - **Meals** à la carte 63/90 - ***Börsenstube*** : **Meals** à la carte 48/76.

XXX **Grande Milano** (Italian rest.), Hohenstaufenring 37, ✉ 50674, ✆ (0221) 24 21 21, *Fax 244846* - AE ⓓ E VISA EX v
*closed Saturday lunch, Sunday and 3 weeks July - August* - **Meals** à la carte 63/96 - ***Pinot di Pinot*** : **Meals** à la carte 38/54.

XX **Em Krützche**, Am Frankenturm 1, ✉ 50667, ✆ (0221) 2 58 08 39, *Fax (0221) 253417*, ☂ - AE ⓓ E VISA GY x
*closed Monday* - **Meals** *(booking essential)* à la carte 53/85.

XX **Bizim** (Turkish rest.), Weidengasse 47, ✉ 50668, ✆ (0221) 13 15 81 - AE ⓓ E. ✻ FU d
*closed Sunday - Monday, 2 weeks February and 3 weeks July - August* - **Meals** (booking essential) à la carte 62/90.

XX **Ratskeller**, Rathausplatz 1 (entrance Alter Markt), ✉ 50667, ✆ (0221) 2 57 69 29, *Fax (0221) 2576946*, « Courtyard » - ▤ ♿ - 🏛 80. AE ⓓ E VISA GZ u
**Meals** à la carte 38/75.

X ✿ **Le Moissonnier** (Typical French bistro), Krefelder Str. 25, ✉ 50670, ✆ (0221) 72 94 79, *Fax (0221) 7325461* FU e
*closed Sunday - Monday, Bank Holidays dinner only* - **Meals** (booking essential) à la carte 56/83
**Spec.** Foie gras de canard. Charlotte de lapin aux calamars. Parfait de gingembre aux noix.

X **Daitokai** (Japanese rest.), Kattenbug 2, ✉ 50667, ✆ (0221) 12 00 48, *Fax (0221) 137503* - ▤. AE ⓓ E VISA JCB. ✻ EV e
**Meals** 58/98 and à la carte 50/63.

**Cologne brewery inns :**

X **Peters Brauhaus**, Mühlengasse 1, ✉ 50667, ✆ (0221) 2 57 39 50, *Fax (0221) 2573962*, ☂ - ✻ GZ n
**Meals** à la carte 28/45.

X **Gaffel-Haus**, Alter Markt 20, ✉ 50667, ✆ (0221) 2 57 76 92, *Fax (0221) 253879*, ☂. AE ⓓ E VISA GZ a
**Meals** à la carte 34/57.

X **Brauhaus Sion**, Unter Taschenmacher 5, ✉ 50667, ✆ (0221) 2 57 85 40, *Fax (0221) 2582081*, ☂ GZ r
**Meals** à la carte 27/48.

X ◎ **Früh am Dom**, Am Hof 12, ✉ 50667, ✆ (0221) 2 58 03 97, *Fax (0221) 256326*, beer garden GY w
**Meals** à la carte 27/53.

**at Cologne-Braunsfeld** *by Rudolfplatz* EV *and Aachener Str. :*

🏨 **Regent** without rest, Melatengürtel 15, ✉ 50933, ✆ (0221) 5 49 90, *Fax (0221) 5499998*, ≘s - 🛗 ✻ 📺 ✆ 🅟 - 🏛 80. AE ⓓ E VISA
*closed 22 December - 4 January* - **171 rm** ☕ 225/461 - 5 suites.

**at Cologne-Deutz** *by Deutzer Brücke* FV *:*

🏨 **Hyatt Regency**, Kennedy-Ufer 2a, ✉ 50679, ✆ (0221) 8 28 12 34, *Fax (0221) 8281370*, ≤, beer garden, Massage, 🏋, ≘s, 🏊 - 🛗, ✻ rm, ▤ 📺 ☎ ✆ ♿ 🚗 🅟 - 🏛 350. AE ⓓ E VISA JCB. ✻ rest
***Graugans*** *(Saturday and Sunday dinner only)* **Meals** à la carte 76/100 - ***Glashaus*** **: Meals** à la carte 55/74 - **307 rm** ☕ 343/701 - 18 suites.

XX **Der Messeturm**, Kennedy-Ufer (18th floor, 🛗), ✉ 50679, ✆ (0221) 88 10 08, *Fax (0221) 818575*, ≤ Cologne - ▤ - 🏛 30. AE ⓓ E VISA. ✻
*closed Saturday lunch* - **Meals** à la carte 52/93.

**at Cologne-Ehrenfeld** *by Rudolfplatz* EV *and Aachener Str. :*

**Imperial**, Barthelstr. 93, ✉ 50823, ☎ (0221) 51 70 57, *Fax (0221) 520993*, – |‡|, rm, rest, ☎. AE E VISA. rest
**Meals** *(closed Saturday - Sunday)* (dinner only) à la carte 39/63 – **36 rm** 198/350.

**at Cologne-Junkersdorf** *by Rudolfplatz* EV *and Aachener Str. :*

**Brenner'scher Hof**, Wilhelm-von-Capitaine-Str. 15, ✉ 50858, ☎ (0221) 9 48 60 00, *Fax (0221) 94860010*, « Installation in country house style » – |‡| ☎ – 50. AE E VISA
**Meals** *(closed Monday)* à la carte 63/84 – **40 rm** 235/425 – 6 suites.

**at Cologne-Lindenthal** *by Rudolfplatz* EV *and B 264 :*

**Queens Hotel**, Dürener Str. 287, ✉ 50935, ☎ (0221) 4 67 60, *Fax (0221) 433765*, « Garden terrace » – |‡|, rm, rest, ☎ P – 350. AE E VISA
**Meals** à la carte 52/78 – **147 rm** 285/375.

**at Cologne-Marienburg** *by Bonner Straße* FX *:*

**Marienburger Bonotel**, Bonner Str. 478, ✉ 50968, ☎ (0221) 3 70 20, *Fax (0221) 3702132*, – |‡|, rm, ☎ P – 40. AE E VISA
**Meals** (dinner only) à la carte 46/64 – **93 rm** 180/415 – 4 suites.

**at Cologne-Marsdorf** *by Rudolfplatz* EV *and B 264 :*

**Novotel Köln-West**, Horbeller Str. 1, ✉ 50858, ☎ (02234) 51 40, *Fax (02234) 514106*, beer garden, (heated), – |‡|, rm, rest, ☎ P – 120. AE E VISA. rest
**Meals** à la carte 43/69 – **199 rm** 199/270.

**at Cologne-Merheim** *by Deutzer Brücke* FV *:*

**Goldener Pflug**, Olpener Str. 421, ✉ 51109, ☎ (0221) 89 61 24, *Fax (0221) 8908176* – P. AE E VISA
*closed Saturday lunch, Sunday and Bank Holidays* – **Meals** 65 (lunch) and à la carte 90/134
**Spec.** Ragout vom Kalbsbries mit Blätterteig. Ganzer Hummer mit Dicken Bohnen (2. Pers.). Das Beste vom Reh mit Pfeffersauce.

**at Cologne-Müngersdorf** *by Rudolfplatz* EV *and B 55 :*

**Landhaus Kuckuck**, Olympiaweg 2, ✉ 50933, ☎ (0221) 4 91 23 23, *Fax (0221) 4972847*, – 120. AE E VISA
*closed Monday and 3 - 13 February* – **Meals** (booking essential) à la carte 65/85.

**at Cologne-Porz-Grengel** *SE : 15 km by A 59 :*

**Holiday Inn**, Waldstr. 255, ✉ 51147, ☎ (02203) 56 10, *Fax (02203) 5619*, – |‡|, rm, P – 90. AE E VISA JCB
**Meals** à la carte 53/80 – **177 rm** 330/560.

**at Cologne - Rodenkirchen** *by Bayen Straße* FX *:*

**Atrium Rheinhotel** without rest, Karlstr. 2, ✉ 50996, ☎ (0221) 93 57 20, *Fax (0221) 93572222*, – |‡| ☎. AE E VISA by Am Bayenturm FX
**67 rm** 193/378.

**BERGISCH GLADBACH** *Nordrhein-Westfalen* 417 N 5, 987 ㉖ – *pop. 104 000 – alt. 86 m.*
*Köln 17.*

XXXX ✿✿✿ **Restaurant Dieter Müller** - Schloßhotel Lerbach, Lerbacher Weg, ✉ 51465, ✆ (02202) 20 40, *Fax (02202) 20490* – P. AE O E VISA JCB. *closed Sunday - Monday and 1 to 15 January 3 weeks July - August* – **Meals** 148/198 and à la carte 118/136
**Spec.** Gänseleberterrine im Sauternesgelee. St. Petersfisch auf Blattspinat mit Thunfischsauce. Crépinette von der Taube mit gebackener Blutwurstscheibe und Trüffelsauce.

**Laasphe, Bad** *Nordrhein-Westfalen* 417 N 9, 987 ㉖ – *pop. 16 000 – alt. 335 m.*
*Köln 144.*

**at Bad Laasphe-Hesselbach** *SW : 10 km :*

XXX ✿✿ **L'ecole**, Hesselbacher Str. 23, ✉ 57334, ✆ (02752) 53 42, *Fax (02752) 6900*, « Elegant installation » – P. AE E
*closed Monday - Tuesday and January* – **Meals** (weekdays dinner only)(booking essential) 125/155 and à la carte 80/113
**Spec.** Gebratene Gänseleber mit glacierten Apfelspalten. Das Beste vom Reh auf Spitzkohl mit Preiselbeerapfel. Moccacharlotte mit Mascarponesauce.

**Wittlich** *Rheinland - Pfalz* 417 Q 4, 987 ㉕ ㉖ – *pop. 17 300 – alt. 155 m.*
*Köln 130.*

**at Dreis** *SW : 8 km :*

XXXX ✿✿ **Waldhotel Sonnora** with rm, Auf dem Eichelfeld, ✉ 54518, ✆ (06578) 4 06, *Fax (06578) 1402*, ≤, « Garden » – TV ☎ P. AE E VISA.
*closed January* – **Meals** *(closed Monday and Tuesday)* (booking essential) 145/175 and à la carte 100/145 – **20 rm** ☐ 100/300
**Spec.** Hummermedaillons in gelierter Tomatenessenz. Kaisergranat im Kartoffelmantel fritiert. Stubenkükenroulade mit Trüffel gespickt.

---

**DRESDEN** L *Sachsen* 418 M 25, 987 ⑲, 984 ㉔ – *pop. 480 000 – alt. 105 m.*

**See** : *Zwinger★★★ (Wall Pavilion★★, Nymphs' Bath★★, Porcelain Collection★★, Mathematical-Physical Salon★★, Armoury★★)* AY – *Semper Opera★★* AY – *Former court church★★ (Hofkirche)* BY – *Palace (Schloß) : royal houses★ (Fürstenzug-Mosaik), Long Passage★ (Langer Gang)* BY – *Albertinum : Picture Gallery Old Masters★★★ (Gemäldegalerie Alte Meister), Picture Gallery New Masters★★★ (Gemäldegalerie Neue Meister), Green Vault★★★ (Grünes Gewölbe)* BY – *Prager Straße★* ABZ – *Museum of History of Dresden★ (Museum für Geschichte der Stadt Dresden)* BY **L** – *Church of the Cross★ (Kreuzkirche)* BY – *Japanese Palace★ (Japanisches Palais)(garden ≤★)* ABX – *Museum of Folk Art★ (Museum für Volkskunst)* BX **M²** – *Great Garden★ (Großer Garten)* CDZ – *Russian-Orthodox Church★ (Russisch-orthodoxe Kirche) (by Leningrader Str.* BZ *)* – *Brühl's Terrace ≤★ (Brühlsche Terrasse)* BY – *Equestrian statue of Augustus the Strong ★ (Reiterstandbild Augusts des Starken)* BX **E** – *Pfunds dairy (Pfunds Molkerei) (interior★) Bautzener Straße 97* CX.

**Envir.** : *Schloß (palace) Moritzburg★ (NW : 14 km by Hansastr.* BX*) – Schloß (palace) Pillnitz★ (SE : 15 km by Bautzener Str.* CX *) – Saxon Swiss★★★ (Sächsische Schweiz) : Bastei★★★, Festung (fortress) Königstein★★ ≤★★, Großsedlitz : Baroque Garden★.*

*18 Possendorf (S : 13 km) ✆ (035206) 33 76 51 11 ; 18 Herzogswaldeb (SW : 19 km) ✆ (0172) 3 57 68 88.*

*✈ Dresden-Klotzsche (N : 13 km), ✆ (0351) 58 31 41. City Office, Rampische Str. 2, ✆ (0351) 4 95 60 13.*

*ℹ Dresden-Information, Prager Str. 10, ✉ 01069, ✆ (0351) 4 95 50 25, Fax (0351) 4951276.*

*ℹ Tourist-Information, Neustädter Narkt, ✉ 01097, ✆ (0351) 49 19 20.*

**ADAC**, *Schandauer Str. 46, ✉ 01277, ✆ (0351) 3 45 80, Fax (0351) 30214.*

*Berlin 198 – Chemnitz 70 – Görlitz 98 – Leipzig 111 – Praha 152.*

Plans on following pages

**Kempinski Hotel Taschenbergpalais** M, Am Taschenberg 3, ✉ 01067, ✆ (0351) 4 91 20, *Fax (0351) 4912812*, « Modern hotel in 18C baroque palace », Massage, Fа, ≘s, ☐ – ‖, ⇔ rm, ☐ TV ✆ ♿ – 🚗 – 🏛 320. AE O E VISA JCB
**Meals** à la carte 59/80 – **213 rm** ☐ 427/629 – 19 suites. BY a

**Radisson SAS Gewandhaushotel** M, Ringstr. 1, ✉ 01067, ✆ (0351) 4 94 90, *Fax (0351) 4949490*, Fа, ≘s, ☐ – ‖, ⇔ rm, ☐ TV ✆ ♿ P – 🏛 60. AE O E VISA JCB BY s
**Meals** à la carte 55/81 – **97 rm** ☐ 324/463.

**Bellevue**, Große Meißner Str. 15, ✉ 01097, ✆ (0351) 8 12 00, *Fax (0351) 8120609*, ≤, « Courtyard terraces », Fа, ≘s, ☐ – ‖, ⇔ rm, ☐ TV ♿ 🚗 P – 🏛 260. AE O E VISA JCB BX a
**Meals** à la carte 45/91 – **339 rm** ☐ 255/490 – 16 suites.

**Dresden Hilton**, An der Frauenkirche 5, ✉ 01067, ☎ (0351) 8 64 20, *Fax (0351) 8642725*, – rm, – 350. AE VISA JCB BY e
***Rossini*** (Italian rest.) *(closed July - August)* **Meals** à la carte 52/74 – ***Grüner Baum*** *(closed Friday dinner, Saturday and Sunday lunch)* : **Meals** (buffet only) 45/49 – **333 rm** 436/527 – 4 suites.

**Dorint Hotel** M, Grunauer Str. 14, ✉ 01069, ☎ (0351) 4 91 50, *Fax (0351) 4915100*, – – 160. AE E VISA JCB CYZ n
**Meals** à la carte 40/65 – **244 rm** 225/290.

**Bülow Residenz**, Rähnitzgasse 19, ✉ 01097, ☎ (0351) 8 00 30, *Fax (0351) 8003100*, « Courtyard terrace » – – 25. AE E VISA. rest BX c
**Meals** (dinner only) (booking essential) à la carte 73/96 – **31 rm** 315/650
**Spec.** Gebratener Steinbutt mit Steinpilzrisotto. Rehmedallions mit weißer Pfeffersauce und Selleriepüree. Crépinette vom Lamm mit Pestojus.

**Bayerischer Hof**, Antonstr. 35, ✉ 01097, ☎ (0351) 82 93 70, *Fax (0351) 8014860*, – rm, – 40. AE E VISA JCB. rest BX r
*closed 22 December - 5 January* – **Meals** *(closed Sunday)* (dinner only) à la carte 31/52 – **50 rm** 180/260 – 5 suites.

**art'otel**, Ostra-Allee 33, ✉ 01067, ☎ (0351) 4 92 20, *Fax (0351) 4922777*, « Modern interior », – rm, – 280. AE E VISA AY s
**Meals** à la carte 45/62 – **174 rm** 225/450.

**Holiday Inn** M, Stauffenbergsallee 25, ✉ 01099, ☎ (0351) 8 15 10, *Fax (0351) 8151333*, – rm, rest, – 120. AE E VISA. by Königsbrücker Straße BX
**Meals** à la carte 50/78 – **120 rm** 180/240.

**Elbflorenz** M without rest, Rosenstr. 36, ✉ 01067, ☎ (0351) 8 64 00, *Fax (0351) 8640100*, – – 150. AE E VISA AZ v
**209 rm** 180/240.

**Am Terrassenufer**, Terrassenufer 12, ✉ 01069, ☎ (0351) 4 40 95 00, *Fax (0351) 4409600*, – rm, – 20. AE E VISA CY a
**Meals** à la carte 27/49 – **196 rm** 240/370 – 6 suites.

**Astron** M, Hansastr. 37, ✉ 01097, ☎ (0351) 8 42 40, *Fax (0351) 8424200*, – rm, – 220. AE E VISA JCB
**Meals** à la carte 36/55 – **269 rm** 210/290. by Hansastraße BX

**Ramada** M, Melanchthonstr. 2, ✉ 01099, ☎ (0351) 8 06 10 (Hotel) 8 03 60 33 (Rest.), *Fax (0351) 8061444* – rm, – 25. AE E VISA JCB CX a
***Am Glacis*** *(dinner only)* **Meals** à la carte 40/54 – ***Bistro*** *(lunch only)* **Meals** à la carte 28/46 – **132 rm** 169/213 – 6 suites.

**Verde** M, Buchenstr. 10, ✉ 01097, ☎ (0351) 8 11 10, *Fax (0351) 8111333*, – rm, – 15. AE E VISA JCB by Königsbrücker Str. BX
**Meals** à la carte 27/46 – **77 rm** 180/230 – 9 suites.

**Transmar Leonardo** M, Bamberger Str. 12, ✉ 01187, ☎ (0351) 4 66 00, *Fax (0351) 4660100*, – rm, – 50. AE E VISA
**Meals** *(closed Saturday lunch)* à la carte 30/60 – **94 rm** 194/344. V v

**Mercure Newa**, St Petersburger Str. 34, ✉ 01069, ☎ (0351) 4 81 41 09, *Fax (0351) 4955137*, – rm, – 180. AE E VISA. rest BZ n
**Meals** à la carte 39/61 – **315 rm** 200/252.

**Windsor**, Roßmäßlerstr. 13, ✉ 01139, ☎ (0351) 8 49 01 41, *Fax (0351) 8490144* – AE E VISA by Leipziger Straße AX
**Meals** *(closed Sunday and Monday)* (dinner only) à la carte 27/42 – **25 rm** 160/250.

**Martha Hospiz** without rest, Nieritzstr. 11, ✉ 01097, ☎ (0351) 8 17 60, *Fax (0351) 8176222* – AE E VISA. BX s
*closed 23 to 27 December* – **50 rm** 140/230.

**Tulip Inn**, Fritz-Reuter-Str. 21, ✉ 01097, ☎ (0351) 8 04 69 02, *Fax (0351) 8046901*, – rm, – 15. AE E VISA. rest by Hansastr. BX
**Meals** à la carte 33/53 – **76 rm** 180/230.

**Novalis** M without rest, Bärnsdorfer Str. 185, ✉ 01127, ☎ (0351) 8 21 30, *Fax (0351) 8213180*, – – 40. AE E VISA
**85 rm** 160/195. by Hansastraße BX

**Wenotel** without rest, Schlachthofring 24, ✉ 01067, ☎ (0351) 4 97 60, *Fax (0351) 4976100* – – 20. AE E VISA by Pieschener Allee AX
**82 rm** 114/140.

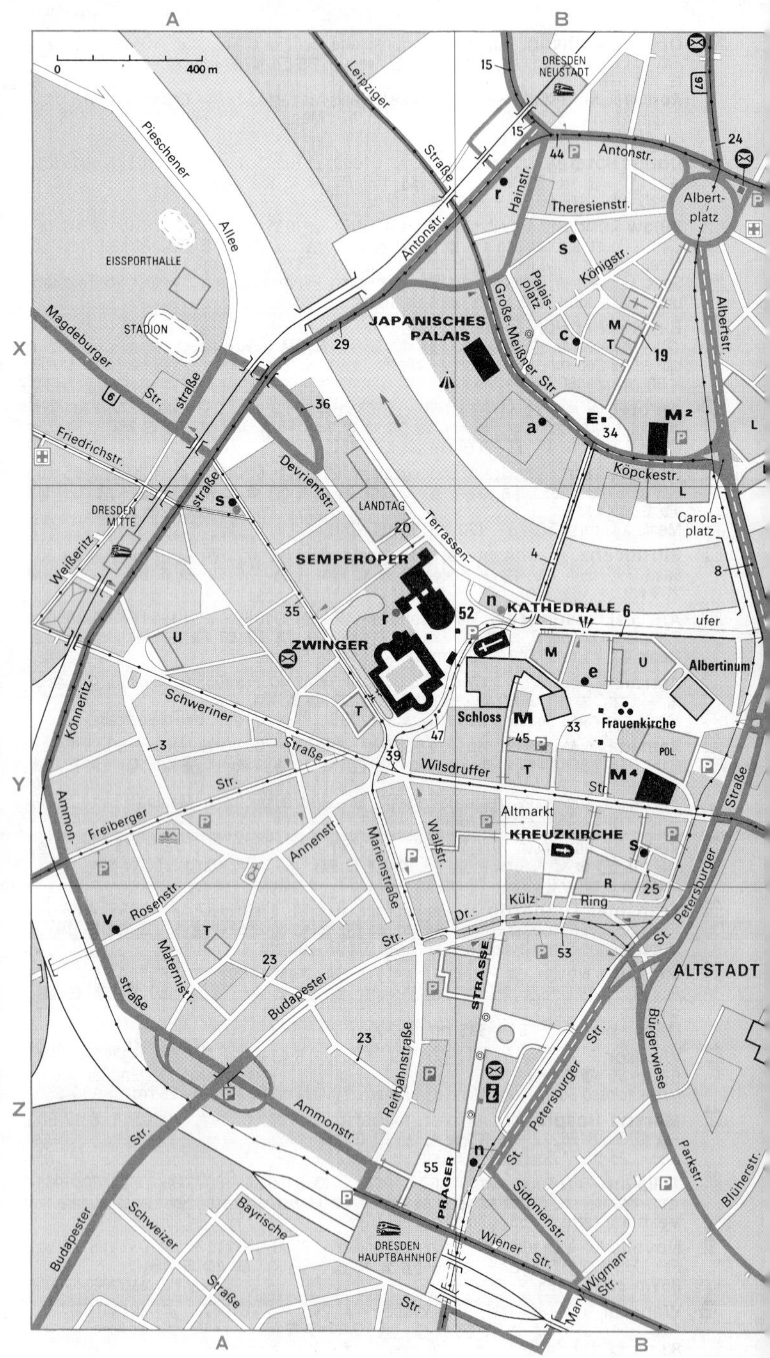
A
B
0
400 m
DRESDEN NEUSTADT
Leipziger Straße
Pieschener Allee
EISSPORTHALLE
STADION
Magdeburger straße
Antonstr.
Hainstr.
Theresienstr.
Albertplatz
Königstr.
Palaisplatz
Große Meißner Str.
JAPANISCHES PALAIS
Albertstr.
Köpckestr.
Carolaplatz
Friedrichstr.
DRESDEN MITTE
Weißeritzstr.
Devrientstr.
LANDTAG
Terrassenufer
SEMPEROPER
KATHEDRALE
ZWINGER
Schloss
Frauenkirche
Albertinum
POL.
Schweriner Straße
Wilsdruffer Str.
Freiberger Str.
Könneritzstr.
Ammonstraße
Annenstr.
Marienstraße
Wallstr.
Altmarkt
KREUZKIRCHE
Dr.-Külz-Ring
St. Petersburger Straße
ALTSTADT
Rosenstr.
Maternistr.
Budapester Str.
Reitbahnstraße
PRAGER STRASSE
Bürgerwiese
Parkstr.
Blüherstr.
Sidonienstr.
Ammonstr.
Schweizer Straße
Bayrische Str.
DRESDEN HAUPTBAHNHOF
Wiener Str.
Mary-Wigman-Str.
X
Y
Z

# DRESDEN

| | |
|---|---|
| Albertbrücke | CX 2 |
| Alfred-Althus-Str. | AY 3 |
| Augustusbrücke | BY 4 |
| Brühlsche Terrasse | BY 6 |
| Carolabrücke | BY 8 |
| Elsasser Str. | CDY 13 |
| Hansastr | BX 15 |
| Hauptstr. | BX 19 |
| Holländische Str. | AY 20 |
| Josephinenstr. | AZ 23 |
| Königsbrücker Str. | BX 24 |
| Kreuzstr. | BYZ 25 |
| Lessingstr. | CX 27 |
| Marienbrücke | AX 29 |
| Neumarkt | BY 33 |
| Neustädter-Markt | BX 34 |
| Ostra-Allee | AY 35 |
| Ostra-Ufer | AX 36 |
| Postplatz | AY 39 |
| Reichpietschufer | CX 40 |
| Rothenburger Straße | CX 42 |
| Sachsenallee | CY 43 |
| Schlesischer Pl. | BX 44 |
| Schloßstr. | BY 45 |
| Sophienstr | AY 47 |
| Steinstr. | CY 49 |
| Theaterplatz | BY 52 |
| Waisenhausstr | BZ 53 |
| Wiener Pl. | AZ 55 |

**Italienisches Dörfchen**, Theaterplatz 3, ✉ 01067, ✆ (0351) 49 81 60, *Fax (0351) 4981688*, beer garden, « Terrace with ≤ » – AE ① E VISA BY n
***Erlwein :*** (dinner only) *(closed Sunday - Monday, 2 weeks January and 3 weeks July - August)* **Meals** à la carte 77/118 – ***Weinzimmer :*** **Meals** à la carte 43/60 – ***Kurfürstenzimmer :*** **Meals** à la carte 35/50.

**Opernrestaurant**, Theatherplatz 2 (1st floor), ✉ 01067, ✆ (0351) 4 91 15 21, *Fax (0351) 4956097*, – AE ① E VISA JCB AY r
*closed Monday and 20 July - 10 August* – **Meals** (weekdays dinner only) à la carte 40/70.

**Ars Vivendi**, Bürgerstr. 14, ✉ 01127, ✆ (0351) 8 40 09 69, *Fax (0351) 8400969*, – AE E VISA by Leipziger Str. AX
**Meals** (dinner only)(booking essential) 48/120 and à la carte.

**Fischgalerie**, Maxstr. 2, ✉ 01067, ✆ 4 90 35 06, *Fax 4903508*, – AE E VISA JCB
*closed Saturday lunch, Sunday and Monday lunch* – **Meals** (only fishdishes), (booking essential) à la carte 49/76. AY s

**König Albert** (bistro style restaurant), Königstr. 28, ✉ 01097, ✆ (0351) 8 04 48 83, *Fax (0351) 8042958*, – AE E VISA JCB. BX e
*closed Saturday lunch and Sunday* – **Meals** à la carte 44/68.

**at Dresden-Blasewitz :**

**Am Blauen Wunder**, Loschwitzer Str. 48, ✉ 01309, ✆ (0351) 3 36 60, *Fax (0351) 3366299*, – ☎ – 25. AE E VISA
*closed 23 to 30 December* – **Meals** *(closed Sunday and 2 to 23 August)* (Italian rest.) à la carte 44/72 – **37 rm** 190/260. by Blasewitzer Straße DY

**at Dresden-Cotta :**

**Cotta-Hotel** M, Mobschatzer Str. 17, ✉ 01157, ✆ (0351) 4 28 60, *Fax (0351) 4286333*, – rm, ☎ – 45. AE ① E VISA JCB. rest by Freiberger Straße and Emerich-Ambros-Ufer AY
**Meals** à la carte 27/47 – **44 rm** 170/255.

**Residenz Alt Dresden**, Mobschatzerstr. 29, ✉ 01157, ✆ (0351) 4 28 10, *Fax (0351) 4281988*, – rm, ☎ P – 100. AE ① E VISA JCB by Freiberger Straße an Emerich-Ambros-Ufer AY
**Meals** à la carte 40/61 – **124 rm** 170/210.

**Mercure Elbpromenade** M, Hamburger Str. 64, ✉ 01157, ✆ (0351) 4 25 20, *Fax (0351) 4252420* – rm, ☎ P – 50. AE ① E VISA JCB
**Meals** à la carte 32/51 – **103 rm** 170/232. by Magdeburger Straße AX

**In Dresden-Kemnitz :**

**Romantik-Hotel Pattis** M, Merbitzer Str. 53, ✉ 01157, ✆ (0351) 4 25 50, *Fax (0351) 4255255*, « Health, fitness and beauty centre ; small park », – rm, rest, P – 35. AE ① E VISA by Magdeburger Straße AX
***Gourment-Restaurant*** *(closed Sunday), (dinner only)* **Meals** à la carte 74/92 – ***Erholung :*** **Meals** à la carte 41/58 – **47 rm** 190/320 – 3 suites.

**at Dresden-Klotzsche :**

**Airport Hotel** M, Karl-Marx-Str. 25, ✉ 01109, ✆ (0351) 8 83 30, *Fax (0351) 8833333*, – rm, rest, ☎ P – 45. AE ① E VISA JCB
**Meals** à la carte 31/60 – **100 rm** 245/315 – 7 suites. by Königsbrücker Straße BX

**at Dresden-Laubegast** *E : 9 km by Striesener Straße* DY *:*

**Treff Resident Hotel Dresden** M, Brünner Str. 11, ✉ 01279, ✆ (0351) 2 56 20, *Fax (0351) 2562800* – rm, ☎ P – 45. AE ① E VISA. rest
**Meals** *(dinner only)* à la carte 31/52 – **125 rm** 135/235.

**at Dresden-Leubnitz-Neuostra** *by Parkstr.* BCZ *and Teplitzer Str. :*

**Treff Hotel Dresden** M, Wilhelm-Franke-Str. 90, ✉ 01219, ✆ (0351) 4 78 20, *Fax (0351) 4782550*, – rm, ☎ P – 370. AE ① E VISA JCB
**Meals** à la carte 37/55 – **262 rm** 209/273.

**In Dresden-Loschwitz :**

**Schloß Eckberg** (with separate hotel wing), Bautzner Str. 134, ✉ 01099, ✆ (0351) 8 09 90, *Fax (0351) 8099199*, ≤ Dresden and Elbe, « New Gothic Mansion ; extensive parkland », Massage, – rm, ☎ P – 70. AE ① E VISA JCB. rest U d
*closed 2 to 25 January* – **Meals** 39 (lunch) and à la carte 49/85 – **84 rm** 203/396.

**at Dresden-Niedersedlitz** *SE : 10 km by Parkstraße* BZ :

**Ambiente** without rest, Meusegaster Str. 23, ✉ 01259, ☎ (0351) 20 78 80, *Fax (0351) 2078836* – TV. E VISA
**20 rm** 158/265.

**at Dresden-Reick** *by Parkstraße (B 172)* BCZ :

**Coventry**, Hüßestr. 1, ✉ 01237, ☎ (0351) 2 82 60, *Fax (0351) 2816310*, – rm, TV – 25. AE E VISA
**Meals** *(closed Monday)* à la carte 28/46 – **53 rm** 175/250.

**at Dresden-Weißer Hirsch** *by Bautzner Straße* CDX :

**Villa Emma** M, Stechgrundstr. 2 (corner of Bautzner Landstr.), ✉ 01324, ☎ (0351) 8 32 10, *Fax (0351) 8321445*, « Modernized Art Deco villa », Massage, – rm, TV. AE E VISA
**Meals** (dinner only) (booking essential) à la carte 49/68 – **21 rm** 210/450.

**at Radebeul** *NW : 7 km by Leipziger Straße* AX :

**Steigenberger Parkhotel** M, Nizzastr. 55, ✉ 01445, ☎ (0351) 8 32 10, *Fax (0351) 8321445*, Massage, – rm, TV – 170. AE E VISA JCB. rest
***La Vigna :*** **Meals** à la carte 48/74 – ***Bistro Rienzi :*** **Meals** à la carte 39/56 – **200 rm** 245/400 – 11 suites.

---

**DÜSSELDORF** L *Nordrhein-Westfalen* 417 M 4, 987 ㉕ ㉖ – *pop. 570 000 – alt. 40 m.*

**See** : *Königsallee*★ EZ – *Hofgarten*★ DEY *und Schloß Jägerhof (Goethemuseum*★ EY **M**[1]) – *Hetjensmuseum*★ DZ **M**[4] – *Land Economic Museum (Landesmuseum Volk u. Wirtschaft)*★ DY **M**[5] – *Museum of Art (Kunstmuseum)*★ DY **M**[2] – *Collection of Art (Kunstsammlung NRW)*★ DY **M**[3] – *Löbbecke-Museum und Aquazoo*★ *by Kaiserswerther Str.* AU.

**Envir.** : *Chateau of Benrath (Schloß Benrath) (Park*★*) S : 10 km by Siegburger Str.* CX.

*18 Ratingen-Hösel, NE : 16 km, ☎ (02102) 6 86 29 ; 18 Gut Rommeljans, NE : 12 km, ☎ (02102) 8 10 92 ; 18 Düsseldorf-Hubbelrath, E : 12 km, ☎ (02104) 7 21 78 ; 9 Düsseldorf-Hafen, Auf der Lausward, ☎ (0211) 39 65 98*

*18 Düsseldorf-Schmidtberg, NE : 12 km, ☎ (02104) 7 70 60.*

*Düsseldorf-Lohausen (N : 8 km), ☎ (0211) 42 10.*

*Hauptbahnhof.*

*Exhibition Centre (Messegelände), ☎ (0211) 4 56 01, Fax (0211) 4560668.*

*Tourist office, Konrad-Adenauer-Platz, ✉ 40210, ☎ (0211) 17 20 20, Fax (0211) 161071.*

**ADAC,** *Himmelgeister Str. 63, ✉ 40225, ☎ (0211) 472747.*

*Berlin 552 – Amsterdam 225 – Essen 31 – Köln 40 – Rotterdam 237.*

Plans on following pages

**Breidenbacher Hof**, Heinrich-Heine-Allee 36, ✉ 40213, ☎ (0211) 1 30 30, *Fax (0211) 1303830*, – rm, TV – 60. AE E VISA JCB. EY a
***Grill Royal*** *(Saturday, Sunday and Bank Holidays dinner only)* **Meals** à la carte 80/124 – ***Breidenbacher Eck :*** **Meals** à la carte 54/80 – ***Trader Vic's*** *(dinner only)* **Meals** à la carte 56/92 – **129 rm** 480/850 – 7 suites.

**Steigenberger Parkhotel**, Corneliusplatz 1, ✉ 40213, ☎ (0211) 1 38 10, *Fax (0211) 131679*, – rm, rest, TV – 200. AE E VISA JCB. rest
**Meals** à la carte 64/97 – **135 rm** 340/590 – 9 suites. EY p

**Nikko**, Immermannstr. 41, ✉ 40210, ☎ (0211) 83 40, *Fax (0211) 161216*, – rm, TV – 300. AE E VISA JCB. rest BV g
***Benkay*** (Japanese rest.) **Meals** à la carte 65/90 – ***Brasserie Nikkolette :*** **Meals** à la carte 37/60 – **301 rm** 340/560 – 5 suites.

**Queens Hotel** M, Ludwig-Erhard-Allee 3, ✉ 40227, ☎ (0211) 7 77 10, *Fax (0211) 7771777*, – rm, TV – 50. AE E VISA JCB. rest
**Meals** à la carte 34/50 – **120 rm** 299/628 – 5 suites. BV s

**Holiday Inn**, Graf-Adolf-Platz 10, ✉ 40213, ☎ (0211) 3 84 80, *Fax (0211) 3848390*, – rm, rm, TV – 50. AE E VISA JCB EZ t
**Meals** à la carte 50/70 – **177 rm** 375/675.

**Majestic** without rest, Cantadorstr. 4, ✉ 40211, ☎ (0211) 36 70 30 (hotel) 35 72 92 (rest.), *Fax (0211) 3670399*, – TV – 30. AE E VISA JCB.
*closed 21 December - 5 January* – **52 rm** 245/460. BV a

**Günnewig Hotel Esplanade** without rest, Fürstenplatz 17, ✉ 40215, ☎ (0211) 38 68 50, *Fax (0211) 374032*, – TV – 40. AE E VISA JCB BX s
**81 rm** 179/468.

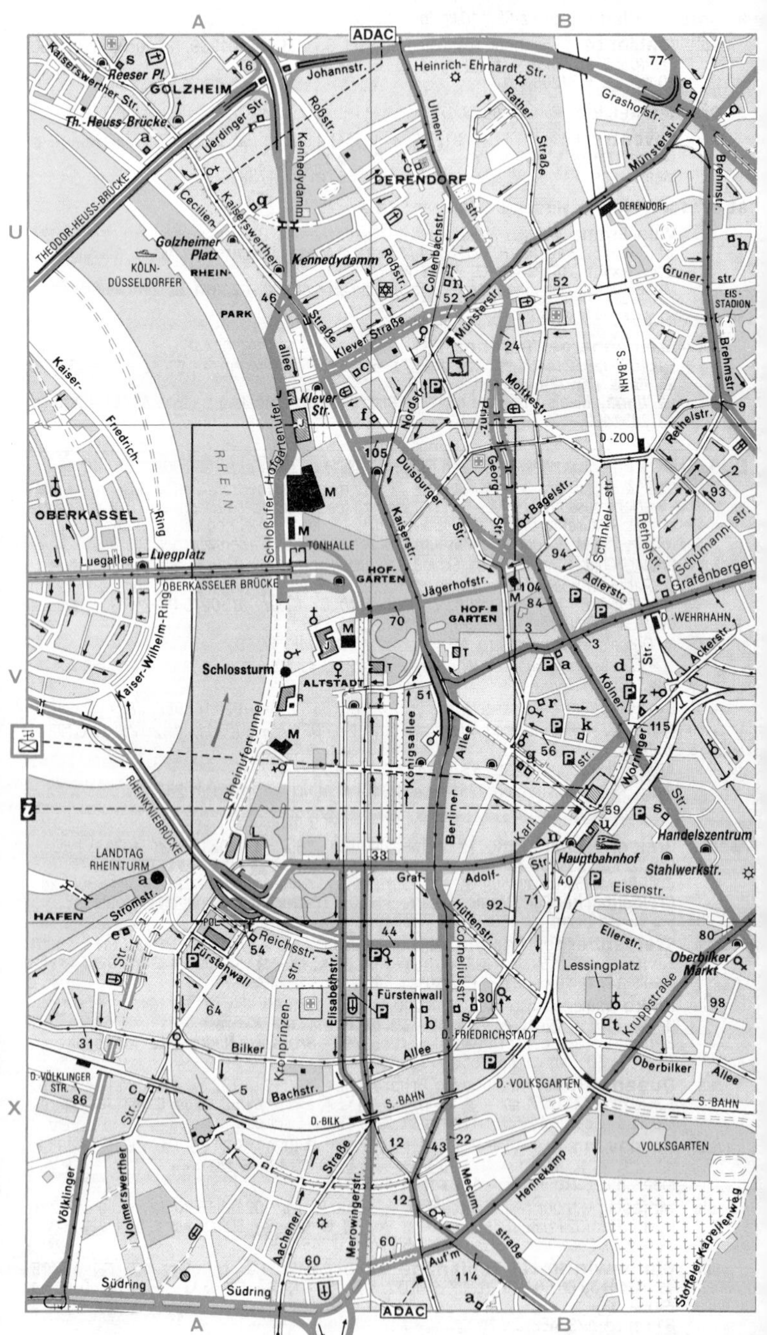
A
B
ADAC
U
V
X
GOLZHEIM
DERENDORF
OBERKASSEL
ALTSTADT
HOFGARTEN
HAFEN
Kaiserswerther Str.
Reeser Pl.
Th.-Heuss-Brücke
THEODOR-HEUSS-BRÜCKE
Johannstr.
Heinrich-Ehrhardt Str.
Grashofstr.
Münsterstr.
Brehmstr.
Uerdinger Str.
Kennedydamm
Roßstr.
Ulmenstr.
Rather Straße
Cecilienallee
Golzheimer Platz
KÖLN-DÜSSELDORFER
RHEINPARK
Collenbachstr.
Klever Straße
Klever Str.
Nordstr.
Moltkestr.
Prinz-Georg-Str.
Duisburger Str.
Kaiserstr.
Bagelstr.
Schinkelstr.
Rethelstr.
Schumannstr.
Grafenberger
Grunerstr.
EIS-STADION
S-BAHN
D-ZOO
DERENDORF
Kaiser-Friedrich-Ring
Luegallee
Luegplatz
OBERKASSELER BRÜCKE
Kaiser-Wilhelm-Ring
Schloßufer
Hofgartenufer
RHEIN
TONHALLE
Jägerhofstr.
Adlerstr.
D.-WEHRHAHN
Ackerstr.
Schlossturm
Königsallee
Berliner Allee
Kölner Str.
Worringer Str.
Rheinufertunnel
RHEINKNIEBRÜCKE
LANDTAG RHEINTURM
Stromstr.
Karlstr.
Hauptbahnhof
Handelszentrum
Stahlwerkstr.
Graf-Adolf-Str.
Hüttenstr.
Eisenstr.
Ellerstr.
Lessingplatz
Oberbilker Markt
Kruppstraße
Reichsstr.
Fürstenwall
Elisabethstr.
Kronprinzenstr.
Corneliusstr.
D.-FRIEDRICHSTADT
Bilker Allee
Bachstr.
D.-VOLKSGARTEN
Oberbilker Allee
S-BAHN
D.-VÖLKLINGER STR.
D.-BILK
VOLKSGARTEN
Völklinger
Volmerswerther Str.
Aachener Straße
Merowingerstr.
Mecumstraße
Hennekamp
Stoffeler Kapellenweg
Südring
Auf'm Hennekamp
POL
M
J
T
R
L

# STREET INDEX

## DÜSSELDORF

# DÜSSELDORF

| Street | Grid | No. |
|---|---|---|
| Am Wehrhahn | EY | 3 |
| Berliner Allee | EZ | |
| Flinger Str. | DY | 28 |
| Graf-Adolf-Str. | EZ | |
| Königsallee | EZ | |
| Schadowstraße | EY | 91 |
| Blumenstraße | EZ | 7 |
| Bolkerstraße | DY | 8 |
| Citadellstraße | DZ | 13 |
| Corneliusstraße | EZ | 15 |
| Elberfelder Str. | EY | 21 |
| Ernst-Reuter-Platz | EZ | 23 |
| Fischerstraße | EY | 27 |
| Friedrich-Ebert-Straße | EZ | 29 |
| Grabbeplatz | DY | 32 |
| Heinrich-Heine-Allee | EY | 42 |
| Hofgartenrampe | DY | 45 |
| Jan-Wellem-Platz | EY | 51 |
| Marktplatz | DY | 68 |
| Martin-Luther-Platz | EZ | 69 |
| Maximilian-Weyhe-Allee | EY | 70 |
| Mühlenstraße | DY | 73 |
| Ratinger Str. | DY | 88 |
| Schadowplatz | EY | 90 |
| Schneider-Wibbel-Gasse | DY | 95 |
| Schulstraße | DZ | 96 |
| Schwanenmarkt | DZ | 98 |
| Tonhallenstraße | EY | 101 |
| Vagedesstraße | EY | 104 |
| Venloer Str. | EY | 105 |

**Madison I** without rest, Graf-Adolf-Str. 94, 40210, (0211) 1 68 50, *Fax (0211) 1685328*, - - 40. BV n
**100 rm** 175/285.

**Eden**, Adersstr. 29, 40215, (0211) 3 89 70, *Fax (0211) 3897777* - rm, - 80. EZ m
**Meals** *(closed Saturday lunch and Sunday except exhibitions)* à la carte 44/64 - **120 rm** 218/506.

**Dorint Hotel**, Stresemannplatz 1, 40210, (0211) 3 55 40, *Fax (0211) 354120* - rm, - 50. rest EZ j
**Meals** à la carte 42/60 - **162 rm** 219/443 - 3 suites.

**Madison II** without rest, Graf-Adolf-Str. 47, 40210, (0211) 38 80 30, *Fax (0211) 3880388* - EZ e
*closed July and 20 December - 8 January* - **24 rm** 150/260.

**Hotel An der Kö** without rest, Talstr. 9, 40217, (0211) 37 10 48, *Fax (0211) 370835* - EZ n
**45 rm** 158/420.

**Astoria** without rest, Jahnstr. 72, 40215, (0211) 38 51 30, *Fax (0211) 372089* - BX b
*closed 22 December - 8 January* - **26 rm** 149/380 - 4 suites.

**Rema-Hotel Concorde** without rest, Graf-Adolf-Str. 60, 40210, (0211) 36 98 25, *Fax (0211) 354604* - EZ f
**84 rm** 170/390.

**Carat Hotel** without rest, Benrather Str. 7a, 40213, (0211) 1 30 50, *Fax (0211) 322214*, - - 20. DZ r
**73 rm** 220/275.

**Rema-Hotel Monopol** without rest, Oststr. 135, 40210, (0211) 8 42 08, *Fax (0211) 328843* - EZ d
**51 rm** 170/390.

**Günnewig Hotel Uebachs** without rest, Leopoldstr. 5, 40211, (0211) 17 37 10, *Fax (0211) 358064* - - 30. BV r
**82 rm** 179/390.

**Cornelius** without rest, Corneliusstr. 82, 40215, (0211) 38 65 60, *Fax (0211) 382050*, - - 30. BX s
*closed 20 December - 7 January* - **52 rm** 140/190.

**Orangerie** without rest, Bäckergasse 1, 40213à la car4, (0211) 86 68 00, *Fax (0211) 8668099* - - 30. DZ n
**27 rm** 195/295.

**Residenz** without rest, Worringer Str. 88, 40211, (0211) 36 08 54, *Fax (0211) 364676* - BV z
**34 rm** 148/350.

**Ibis Hauptbahnhof** without rest, Konrad-Adenauer-Platz 14, 40210, (0211) 1 67 20, *Fax (0211) 1672101* - - 20. BV u
**166 rm** 148/213.

**Schumacher** without rest, Worringer Str. 55, 40211, (211) 36 78 50, *Fax (0211) 3678570*, - BV d
**29 rm** 150/380.

**Victorian**, Königstr. 3a (1st floor), 40212, (0211) 8 65 50 22, *Fax (0211) 8655013* - EZ c
*closed Sunday and Bank Holidays* - **Meals** (booking essential, outstanding wine list) 55 (lunch) and à la carte 84/120 - ***Bistro im Victorian*** *(closed Sunday July and August)* **Meals** à la carte 39/72
**Spec.** Gänselberterrine mit weißen Feigen in Sauternes mariniert. Krebsschwänze á la nage (May-Aug.). Epigramm vom Angusfilet.

**Weinhaus Tante Anna** (former 16C house-chapel), Andreasstr. 2, 40213, (0211) 13 11 63, *Fax (0211) 132974*, « Antique pictures and furniture » - DY c
*closed Sunday except exhibitions* - **Meals** (dinner only, booking essential, outstanding wine list) à la carte 55/85.

**La Terrazza** (Italian rest.), Königsallee 30 (Kö-Centre, 2nd floor, ), 40212, (0211) 32 75 40, *Fax (0211) 320975* - EZ v
*closed Sunday and Bank Holidays except exhibitions* - **Meals** à la carte 64/92.

**Calvados**, Hohe Str. 33, 40213, (0211) 32 84 96, *Fax (0211) 327877*, - DZ a
*closed Sunday* - **Meals** à la carte 48/78.

**Nippon Kan** (Japanese rest.), Immermannstr. 35, ✉ 40210, ☎ (0211) 17 34 70, *Fax (0211) 3613625* – AE ⓓ E VISA JCB. ✻ BV g
*closed Easter and Christmas* – **Meals** (booking essential) à la carte 43/110.

**Daitokai** (Japanese rest.), Mutter-Ey-Str. 1, ✉ 40213, ☎ (0211) 32 50 54, *Fax (0211) 325056* – ▤. AE ⓓ E VISA JCB. ✻ DY z
*closed Monday April - October except exhibitions* – **Meals** 49/78 and à la carte.

**Brewery-inns** :

**Zum Schiffchen**, Hafenstr. 5, ✉ 40213, ☎ (0211) 13 24 21, *Fax (0211) 134596*, ☂ – AE ⓓ E VISA JCB DZ f
*closed Christmas - New Year, Sunday and Bank Holidays* – **Meals** à la carte 38/68.

**Im Goldenen Ring**, Burgplatz 21, ✉ 40213, ☎ (0211) 13 31 61, *Fax (0211) 324780*, beer garden – AE ⓓ E VISA DY n
*closed Christmas* – **Meals** à la carte 30/60.

**at Düsseldorf-Angermund** *N : 15 km by Danziger Straße* AU :

**Haus Litzbrück**, Bahnhofstr. 33, ✉ 40489, ☎ (0203) 99 79 60, *Fax (0203) 9979653*, « Garden terrace », ≘s, ☒, ☂ – TV ☎ ⇔ P – 🏛 30. AE ⓓ E VISA
**Meals** à la carte 50/77 – **21 rm** ☐ 145/285.

**at Düsseldorf-Bilk** :

**Grand Hotel** without rest, Varnhagenstr. 37, ✉ 40225, ☎ (0211) 31 08 00, *Fax (0211) 316667*, ≘s – |♦| ⇹ TV ☎ ♿ ⇔ – 🏛 30. AE ⓓ E VISA JCB BX a
**70 rm** ☐ 315/365.

**Aida** without rest, Ubierstr. 36, ✉ 40223, ☎ (0211) 1 59 90, *Fax (0211) 1599103*, ≘s – |♦| TV ☎ ♿ P – 🏛 30. AE ⓓ E VISA JCB. ✻ by Aachener Str. AX
**93 rm** ☐ 158/298.

**at Düsseldorf-Derendorf** *by Prinz-Georg-Str.* BU :

**Villa Viktoria** without rest, Blumenthalstr. 12, ✉ 40476, ☎ (0211) 46 90 00, *Fax (0211) 46900601*, « Elegant modern installation », ≘s, ☂ – |♦| ⇹ TV ⇔. AE ⓓ E VISA JCB
*closed 24 December - 1 January* – **40 suites** ☐ 377/909.

**Lindner Hotel Rhein Residence** Ⓜ, Kaiserswerther Str. 20, ✉ 40477, ☎ (0211) 4 99 90, *Fax (0211) 4999499*, ☂, Massage, ⅟♿, ≘s – |♦|, ⇹ rm, TV ☎ – 🏛 18. AE ⓓ E VISA JCB ABU f
Meals à la carte 42/74 – **126 rm** ☐ 272/519.

**Gildors Hotel** without rest (with guesthouse), Collenbachstr. 51, ✉ 40476, ☎ (0211) 48 80 05, *Fax (0211) 444844* – |♦| TV ☎ ⇔. AE ⓓ E VISA BU n
**50 rm** ☐ 175/350.

**Cascade** without rest, Kaiserswerther Str. 59, ✉ 40477, ☎ (0211) 49 22 00, *Fax (0211) 4922022* – |♦| ⇹ TV ☎ ⇔. AE ⓓ E VISA AU c
**29 rm** ☐ 155/320.

**at Düsseldorf-Düsseltal** :

**Haus am Zoo** ⛯ without rest, Sybelstr. 21, ✉ 40239, ☎ (0211) 62 63 33, *Fax (0211) 626536*, « Garden », ≘s, ☒ (heated) – |♦| TV ☎ ⇔. AE E VISA. ✻ BU h
**23 rm** ☐ 180/350.

**at Düsseldorf-Golzheim** *by Fischerstr.* BV :

**Radisson SAS Hotel**, Karl-Arnold-Platz 5, ✉ 40474, ☎ (0211) 4 55 30, *Fax (0211) 4553110*, ☂, Massage, ≘s, ☒ – |♦|, ⇹ rm, ▤ TV ☎ ♿ ⇔ P – 🏛 400. AE ⓓ E VISA JCB. ✻ rest AU q
Meals à la carte 48/76 – **309 rm** ☐ 383/732 – 15 suites.

**Düsseldorf Hilton**, Georg-Glock-Str. 20, ✉ 40474, ☎ (0211) 4 37 70, *Fax (0211) 4377650*, ☂, Massage, ≘s, ☒, ☂ – |♦|, ⇹ rm, ▤ TV ☎ ♿ ⇔ P – 🏛 900. AE ⓓ E VISA JCB AU r
Meals à la carte 54/88 – **372 rm** ☐ 362/729 – 9 suites.

**Rosati** (Italian rest.), Felix-Klein-Str. 1, ✉ 40474, ☎ (0211) 4 36 05 03, *Fax (0211) 452963*, ☂ – P. AE ⓓ E VISA JCB. ✻ AU s
*closed Saturday lunch and Sunday except exhibitions* – **Meals** (booking essential) à la carte 63/85.

✿ **An'ne Bell**, Rotterdamer Str. 11, ✉ 40474, ☎ (0211) 4 37 08 88, *Fax (0211) 4380369*, ☂, beer garden – AE E AU a
*closed Saturday lunch, Thursday October to April, early January, 6 to 12 April and 2 weeks October* – **Meals** 68/125 and à la carte 68/129
**Spec.** Blumenkohlragout mit Kartoffeln und Kaviar. Gebratener Loup de mer mit Hummercanneloni. Frischkäsemousse und Passionsfruchtsorbet.

**at Düsseldorf-Kaiserswerth** by *Kaiserswerther Str.* AU :

**Im Schiffchen**, Kaiserswerther Markt 9 (1st floor), ✉ 40489, ✆ (0211) 40 10 50, *Fax (0211) 403667* – AE ⓓ E VISA.
*closed Sunday - Monday* – **Meals** (dinner only, booking essential) 179/198 and à la carte 119/135
**Spec.** Beuchelle vom Bresse Kaninchen. Risotto vom Pauillac Lamm mit Haselnußjus. Warmer Passionsfruchtauflauf mit Schokoladensorbet.

**Aalschokker**, Kaiserswerther Markt 9 (ground floor), ✉ 40489, ✆ (0211) 40 39 48, *Fax (0211) 403667* – AE ⓓ E VISA.
*closed Sunday - Monday* – **Meals** (dinner only, booking essential) à la carte 80/107
**Spec.** Kartoffel mit Sylter Royal gefüllt in Kaviar-Sud. "Himmel und Erde" mit gebratener Gänseleber. Schwarzwälder Kirschtorte "neue Art".

**at Düsseldorf-Lörick** by *Luegallee* AV :

**Fischerhaus**, Bonifatiusstr. 35, ✉ 40547, ✆ (0211) 59 79 79, *Fax (0211) 5979759* – TV ☎ P. AE ⓓ E VISA
Meals *see* ***Hummerstübchen*** below – **40 rm** 179/380.

**Hummerstübchen** - Hotel Fischerhaus, Bonifatiusstr. 35, ✉ 40547, ✆ (0211) 59 44 02, *Fax (0211) 5979759* – P. AE ⓓ E VISA
*closed Sunday, Monday and 1 to 10 January* – **Meals** (dinner only, booking essential) 139/169 and à la carte 101/131
**Spec.** Hummer-Menu. Hummersuppe mit Champagner. Kalbsfilet mit gebackenem Ziegenkäse auf Sprossengemüse.

**at Düsseldorf-Lohausen** by *Danziger Str.* AU :

**Arabella Airport Hotel**, at airport, ✉ 40474, ✆ (0211) 4 17 30, *Fax (0211) 4173707* – lift, rm, TV – 180. AE ⓓ E VISA JCB. rest
**Meals** à la carte 49/63 – **184 rm** 306/372.

**at Düsseldorf-Mörsenbroich** by *Rethelstr.* DV :

**Düsseldorf-Renaissance-Hotel**, Nördlicher Zubringer 6, ✉ 40470, ✆ (0211) 6 21 60, *Fax (0211) 6216666*, Massage, – lift, rm, TV – 260. AE ⓓ E VISA JCB BU e
**Meals** à la carte 56/82 – **245 rm** 320/600 – 3 suites.

**at Düsseldorf-Oberkassel** by *Luegallee* AV :

**Lindner-Hotel-Rheinstern**, Emanuel-Leutze-Str. 17, ✉ 40547, ✆ (0211) 5 99 70, *Fax (0211) 5997339*, – lift, rm, TV P – 240. AE ⓓ E VISA JCB. rest
**Meals** 39 buffet lunch and à la carte 50/78 – **254 rm** 212/629.

**Ramada**, Am Seestern 16, ✉ 40547, ✆ (0211) 59 59 59, *Fax (0211) 593569*, – lift, rm, TV P – 120. AE ⓓ E VISA JCB
**Meals** à la carte 45/72 – **222 rm** 257/646.

**Hanseat** without rest, Belsenstr. 6, ✉ 40545, ✆ (0211) 57 50 69, *Fax (0211) 589662*, « Elegant installation » – TV ☎. AE ⓓ E VISA
*closed Christmas - New Year* – **37 rm** 180/350.

**De' Medici** (Italian rest.), Amboßstr. 3, ✉ 40547, ✆ (0211) 59 41 51, *Fax (0211) 592612* – AE ⓓ E VISA JCB
*closed Saturday lunch, Sunday and Bank Holidays except exhibitions* – **Meals** (booking essential) à la carte 48/82.

**Edo** (Japanese restaurants : Teppan, Robata and Tatami), Am Seestern 3, ✉ 40547, ✆ (0211) 59 10 82, *Fax (0211) 591394*, « Japanese garden » – P. AE ⓓ E VISA JCB.
*closed Saturday lunch, Sunday and Bank Holidays except exhibitions* – **Meals** à la carte 90/150.

**at Düsseldorf-Unterbilk** :

**Sorat** M (elegant modern installation), Volmerswerther Str. 35, ✉ 40221, ✆ (0211) 3 02 20, *Fax (0211) 3022555*, – lift, rm, TV ☎ – 160. AE ⓓ E VISA JCB AX c
**Meals** à la carte 44/62 – **160 rm** 198/461.

**Savini**, Stromstr. 47, ✉ 40221, ✆ (0211) 39 39 31, *Fax (0211) 391719*, – AE ⓓ
*closed Saturday lunch and Sunday except exhibitions* – **Meals** (booking essential) (outstanding winelist) à la carte 62/93. AX e

**Rheinturm Top 180** (revolving restaurant at 172 m), Stromstr. 20, ✉ 40221, ✆ (0211) 8 48 58, *Fax (0211) 325619*, Düsseldorf and Rhein (lift, charge) – – 40. AE ⓓ E VISA JCB. AV a
**Meals** à la carte 56/87.

**at Düsseldorf-Unterrath** *by Ulmenstraße* BU :

**Lindner Hotel Airport** M, Unterrather Str. 108, ✉ 40468, ☎ (0211) 9 51 60, *Fax (0211) 9516516*, – rm, – 140. AE VISA JCB. rest
**Meals** à la carte 47/70 – **201 rm** 287/520.

**at Meerbusch-Büderich** *by Luegallee* AV – ☎ *02132* :

**Landsknecht** with rm, Poststr. 70, ✉ 40667, ☎ (02132) 9 33 90, *Fax (02132) 10978*, – rm, . AE VISA.
*closed Saturday lunch and Monday* – **Meals** (outstanding wine list) à la carte 55/90 – **9 rm** 168/280.

**Landhaus Mönchenwerth**, Niederlöricker Str. 56 (at the boat landing stage), ✉ 40667, ☎ (02132) 7 79 31, *Fax (02132) 71899*, ≤, « Garden terrace » – . AE VISA JCB.
*closed Saturday and Monday lunch* – **Meals** (outstanding wine list) à la carte 56/87.

**Lindenhof**, Dorfstr. 48, ✉ 40667, ☎ (02132) 26 64, *Fax (02132) 10196*, AE
*closed Monday* – **Meals** (booking essential) à la carte 49/64.

**In Meerbusch - Langst-Kirst** *NW : 14 km by Luegallee* AV *and Neusser Straße* :

**Rheinhotel Vier Jahreszeiten** M, Zur Rheinfähre 14, ✉ 40668, ☎ (02150) 91 40, *Fax (02150) 914900*, beer garden, – rm, – 120. AE VISA
***Bellevue*** *(weekdays dinner only)* **Meals** à la carte 56/86 – ***Orangerie*** *(lunch only)* **Meals** à la carte 43/65 – **78 rm** 190/370 – 3 suites.

## Essen

*Nordrhein-Westfalen* 417 L 5, 987 ⑭ – *pop. 670 000 – alt. 120 m.*
*Düsseldorf 31.*

**at Essen-Kettwig** S : *11 km* :

**Résidence** with rm, Auf der Forst 1, ✉ 45219, ☎ (02054) 89 11, *Fax (02054) 82501*, – . AE VISA
*closed 1 to 8 January and 3 weeks July - August* – **Meals** *(closed Sunday - Monday)* (dinner only, booking essential) (outstanding wine list) 125/175 and à la carte 92/142 – ***Benedikt*** (Euro-Asian rest.) **Meals** 148/185 – **18 rm** 188/387
**Spec.** Hummer mit Dicken Bohnen in Thymianrahm. Roulade vom Entrecôte mit Gänseleberkartoffel. Quarksoufflé mit Beerenkompott und Zitronengrassorbet.

## Grevenbroich

*Nordrhein-Westfalen* 417 M 3, 987 ㉕ – *pop. 62 000 – alt. 60 m.*
*Düsseldorf 28.*

**Zur Traube** with rm, Bahnstr. 47, ✉ 41515, ☎ (02181) 6 87 67, *Fax (02181) 61122* – . VISA. rm
*closed 5 to 14 April, 19 July - 4 August and 20 December - 22 January* – **Meals** *(closed Sunday and Monday)* (booking essential, outstanding wine list) 78 (lunch) and à la carte 94/154 – **6 rm** 220/360
**Spec.** Mousse vom Perlhuhn im Entenlebermantel. Maultaschen mit Langustinen und Steinbutt im Trüffelsud. Warme Ananastorte mit Mandeleis.

---

## FRANKFURT ON MAIN

*Hessen* 417 P 10, 987 ㉗ – *pop. 660 000 – alt. 91 m.*

See : *Zoo*★★★ FX – *Goethe's House (Goethehaus)*★ GZ – *Cathedral (Dom)*★ *(Gothic Tower*★★, *Choir-stalls*★, *Museum*★*)* HZ – *Tropical Garden (Palmengarten)*★ CV – *Senckenberg-Museum*★ *(Palaeontology department*★★*)* CV **M**[9] – *Städel Museum (Städelsches Museum and Städtische Galerie)*★★ GZ – *Museum of Applied Arts (Museum für Kunsthandwerk)*★ HZ – *German Cinema Museum*★ GZ **M**[7] – *Henninger Turm* ★ FX – *Museum of Modern Art (Museum für moderne Kunst)*★ HY **M**[10].

*Frankfurt-Niederrad, by Kennedy-Allee* CDX, ☎ *(069) 6 66 23 17.*

*Rhein-Main (SW : 12 km),* ☎ *(069) 6 90 25 95.*

*at Neu-Isenburg (S : 7 km).*

*Exhibition Centre (Messegelände) (CX),* ☎ *(069) 7 57 50, Fax (069) 75756433.*

*Tourist Information, Main Station (Hauptbahnhof),* ✉ *60329,* ☎ *(069) 21 23 88 49, Fax (069) 21240512.*

*Tourist Information, im Römer,* ✉ *60311,* ☎ *(069) 21 23 87 08.*

**ADAC,** *Schumannstr. 4,* ✉ *60325,* ☎ *(069) 74 38 00, Fax (069) 749254.*

**ADAC,** *Schillerstr. 12,* ✉ *60313,* ☎ *(069) 74 38 03 35, Fax (069) 283597.*

*Berlin 537 – Wiesbaden 41 – Bonn 178 – Nürnberg 226 – Stuttgart 204.*

**Steigenberger Frankfurter Hof**, Bethmannstr. 33, ✉ 60311, ☎ (069) 2 15 02, *Fax (069) 215900*, Massage – |♦|, ⇔ rm, ▤ TV ☎ – 🏛 120. AE ⓓ E VISA JCB. ✻ rest GZ e
Meals see ***Restaurant Francais*** *below* – ***Frankfurter Stubb*** (booking essential) *(closed Saturday, Sunday, Bank Holidays and 4 weeks July - August)* **Meals** à la carte 39/66 – ***Oscar's*** *(closed 4 weeks July - August)* **Meals** à la carte 44/75 – **332 rm** ☐ 407/694 – 20 suites.

**Hessischer Hof**, Friedrich-Ebert-Anlage 40, ✉ 60325, ☎ (069) 7 54 00, *Fax (069) 7540924*, « Rest. with collection of Sèvres porcelain » – |♦|, ⇔ rm, ▤ TV ☎ 🚗 P – 🏛 120. AE ⓓ E VISA JCB. ✻ rest CX p
**Meals** 49 (lunch) and à la carte 72/93 – **117 rm** ☐ 390/660 – 11 suites.

**Arabella Grand Hotel**, Konrad-Adenauer-Str. 7, ✉ 60313, ☎ (069) 2 98 10, *Fax (069) 2981810*, Massage, Fø, ≘s, 🏊 – |♦|, ⇔ rm, ▤ TV 🚗 – 🏛 300. AE ⓓ E VISA JCB. ✻ rest HY c
***Premiere*** *(dinner only, closed 4 weeks July - August)* **Meals** 90/136 and à la carte 76/107 – ***Brasserie*** *(lunch only)* **Meals** à la carte 47/89 – **378 rm** ☐ 417/749 – 11 suites.

**Martim Hotel Frankfurt** M, Theodor-Heuss-Allee 3, ✉ 60486, ☎ (069) 7 57 80, *Fax (069) 75781000*, Massage, Fø, ≘s, 🏊 – |♦|, ⇔ rm, ▤ TV ☎ ♿ 🚗 – 🏛 1900. AE ⓓ E VISA JCB. ✻ rest CVX c
***Classico*** *(closed Saturday and Sunday lunch)* **Meals** à la carte 57/86 – ***Ambiente*** *(closed Friday)* **Meals** 50 (buffet lunch only) – **543 rm** ☐ 365/704 – 24 suites.

**Intercontinental Frankfurt**, Wilhelm-Leuschner-Str. 43, ✉ 60329, ☎ (069) 2 60 50, *Fax (069) 252467*, Fø, ≘s, 🏊 – |♦|, ⇔ rm, ▤ TV ☎ ♿ – 🏛 500. AE ⓓ E VISA JCB GZ a
Meals à la carte 56/82 – ***Kyoto*** (Japanese rest.) *(closed Saturday lunch and Sunday)* **Meals** à la carte 36/72 – **465 rm** ☐ 412/689 – 49 suites.

**Frankfurt Marriott Hotel**, Hamburger Allee 2, ✉ 60486, ☎ (069) 7 95 50, *Fax (069) 79552432*, ≤ Frankfurt, Massage, Fø, ≘s – |♦|, ⇔ rm, ▤ TV ☎ 🚗 – 🏛 600. AE ⓓ E VISA JCB. ✻ rest CV a
**Meals** à la carte 38/92 – **588 rm** ☐ 316/565 – 17 suites.

**Le Meridien Parkhotel**, Wiesenhüttenplatz 28, ✉ 60329, ☎ (069) 2 69 70, *Fax (069) 2697884*, Fø, ≘s – |♦|, ⇔ rm, ▤ TV ☎ ♿ 🚗 P – 🏛 160. AE ⓓ E VISA JCB CX k
**Meals** à la carte 49/82 – **296 rm** ☐ 346/714 – 11 suites.

**Alexander am Zoo** M, without rest, Waldschmidtstr. 59, ✉ 60316, ☎ (069) 94 96 00, *Fax (069) 94960720*, ≘s – |♦| ⇔ TV ☎ 🚗 – 🏛 30. AE ⓓ E VISA. ✻ FV c
**59 rm** ☐ 210/390 – 9 suites.

**Palmenhof**, Bockenheimer Landstr. 89, ✉ 60325, ☎ (069) 7 53 00 60, *Fax (069) 75300666* – |♦| TV ☎ 🚗. AE ⓓ E VISA JCB CV m
*closed 23 December - 2 January* – **Meals** *(closed Saturday, Sunday and Bank Hollidays)* à la carte 60/77 – **47 rm** ☐ 195/305.

**An der Messe** without rest, Westendstr. 104, ✉ 60325, ☎ (069) 74 79 79, *Fax (069) 748349* – |♦| TV 🚗. AE ⓓ E VISA CV e
**46 rm** ☐ 210/480.

**Sofitel**, Savignystr. 14, ✉ 60325, ☎ (069) 7 53 30, *Fax (069) 7533175* – |♦|, ⇔ rm, TV – 🏛 80. AE ⓓ E VISA JCB. ✻ rest CX f
**Meals** à la carte 46/87 – **155 rm** ☐ 390/480.

**Forum Hotel** M without rest, Wilhelm-Leuschner-Str. 34, ✉ 60329, ☎ (069) 2 60 60, *Fax (069) 260602925* – |♦|, ⇔ rm, ▤ TV ☎. AE ⓓ E VISA JCB CZ z
**301 rm** ☐ 327/589.

**Mercure**, Voltastr. 29, ✉ 60486, ☎ (069) 7 92 60, *Fax (069) 79261606*, ≘s – |♦|, ⇔ rm, TV ☎ ☎ 🚗 – 🏛 80. AE ⓓ E VISA JCB by Th.-Heuss-Allee CV
**Meals** à la carte 38/75 – **346 rm** ☐ 203/430 – 12 suites.

**Holiday Inn**, Wiesenhüttenstr. 42, ✉ 60329, ☎ (069) 27 39 60, *Fax (069) 27396795*, Massage, ≘s, 🏊 – |♦|, ⇔ rm, ▤ rest, TV ☎ – 🏛 100. AE ⓓ E VISA JCB CX s
**Meals** à la carte 46/67 – **144 rm** ☐ 260/335.

**Imperial**, Sophienstr. 40, ✉ 60487, ☎ (069) 7 93 00 30, *Fax (069) 79300388* – |♦|, ⇔ rm, ▤ TV ☎ 🚗 P. AE ⓓ E VISA JCB CV t
**Meals** *(closed Sunday)* (dinner only) à la carte 44/66 – **60 rm** ☐ 190/480.

**Victoria Hotel** without rest, Elbestr. 24, ✉ 60329, ☎ (069) 27 30 60, *Fax (069) 27306100* – |♦| ⇔ TV ☎ ☎. AE ⓓ E VISA JCB CDX t
**75 rm** ☐ 160/390.

**Bauer Hotel Domicil** without rest, Karlstr. 14, ✉ 60329, ☎ (069) 27 11 10, *Fax (069) 253266* – |♦| TV ☎. AE ⓓ E VISA JCB CX d
*closed Christmas - New Year* – **70 rm** ☐ 166/309.

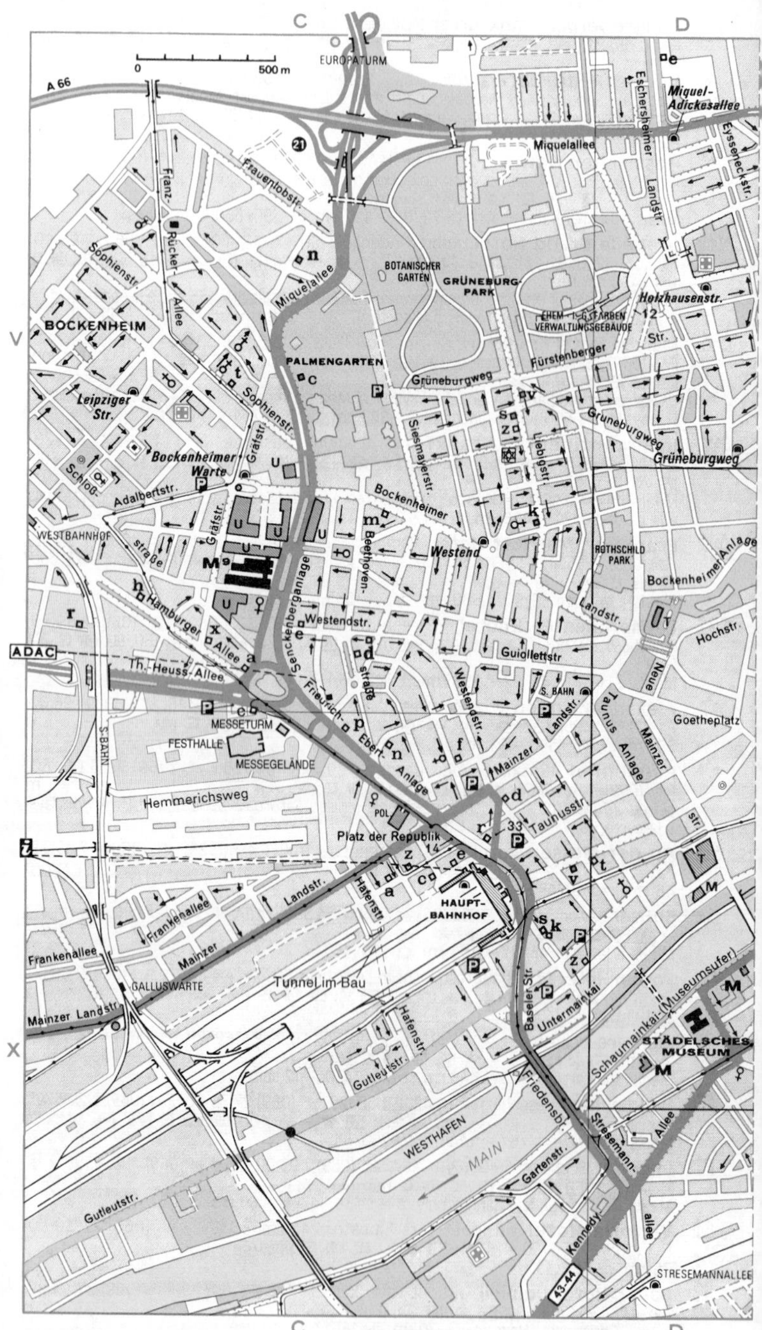
C
D
EUROPATURM
A 66
0
500 m
Miquel-Adickesallee
Miquelallee
Eschersheimer Landstr.
Eysseneckstr.
Franz-Rücker-Allee
Frauenlobstr.
Sophienstr.
Miquelallee
BOTANISCHER GARTEN
GRÜNEBURG-PARK
Holzhausenstr.
EHEM. I.G.FARBEN VERWALTUNGSGEBÄUDE
BOCKENHEIM
PALMENGARTEN
Fürstenberger Str.
Grüneburgweg
Leipziger Str.
Sophienstr.
Siesmayerstr.
Liebigstr.
Grüneburgweg
Bockenheimer Warte
Gräfstr.
Schloß-
Adalbertstr.
Bockenheimer
WESTBAHNHOF
straße
Gräfstr.
Beethoven-
Westend
ROTHSCHILD PARK
Bockenheimer Anlage
Senckenberganlage
Hamburger Allee
Westendstr.
Landstr.
Hochstr.
ADAC
Th.-Heuss-Allee
straße
Guiollettstr
Neue Mainzer
Friedrich-Ebert-Anlage
S. BAHN
Landstr.
Taunus Anlage
Goetheplatz
MESSETURM
FESTHALLE
MESSEGELÄNDE
Westendstr.
Mainzer
S-BAHN
Hemmerichsweg
POL
Taunusstr.
str.
Platz der Republik
HAUPT-BAHNHOF
Frankenallee
Landstr.
Hafenstr.
Frankenallee
Mainzer
GALLUSWARTE
Tunnel im Bau
Baseler Str.
Untermainkai
Schaumainkai (Museumsufer)
Mainzer Landstr.
STÄDELSCHES MUSEUM
X
Hafenstr.
Gutleutstr.
Friedensbr.
Stresemann-Allee
WESTHAFEN
MAIN
Gartenstr.
Gutleutstr.
Kennedy-
allee
STRESEMANNALLEE
43-44
C
D

# FRANKFURT AM MAIN

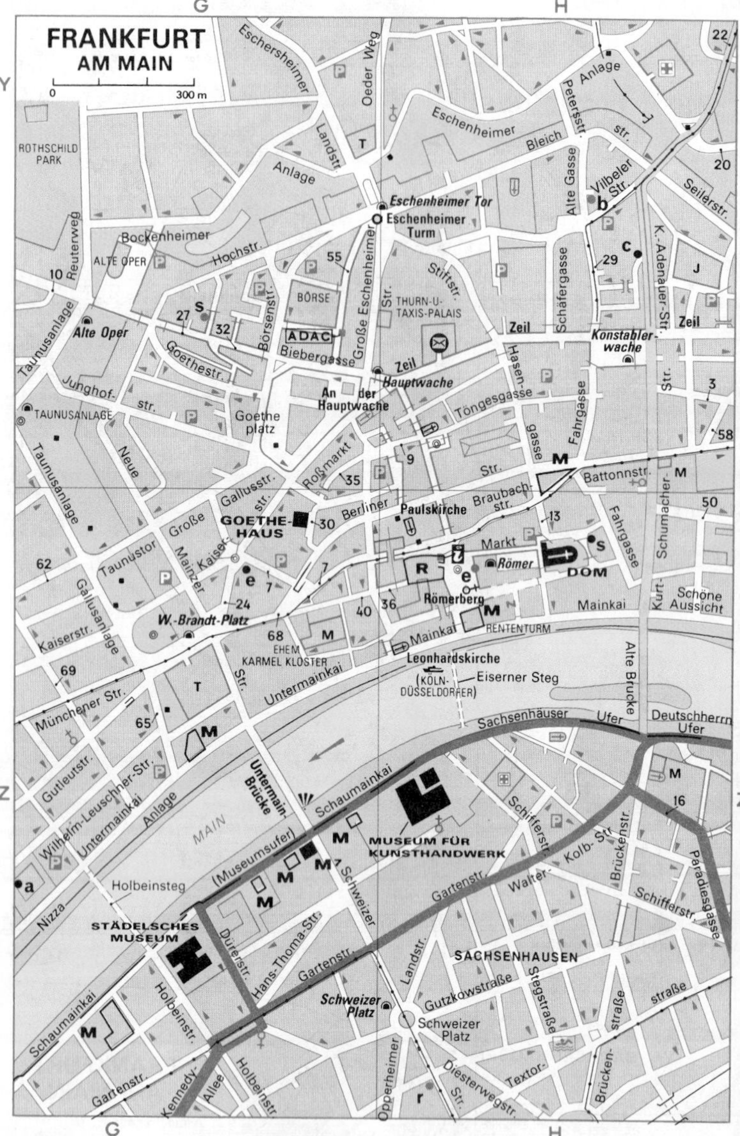


An der Hauptwache . . . GHY
Goethestraße . . . GY
Gr. Bockenheimer Straße . . . GY 27
Kaiserstraße . . . GZ
Münchener Straße . . . GZ
Roßmarkt . . . GY
Schillerstraße . . . GY 55
Zeil . . . HY

Allerheiligenstraße . . . HY 3

Bethmannstraße . . . GZ 7
Bleidenstraße . . . HY 9
Bockenheimer Landstr. . . . GY 10
Domstraße . . . HZ 13
Elisabethenstraße . . . HZ 16
Friedberger Anlage . . . HY 20
Friedberger Landstr. . . . HY 22
Friedensstraße . . . GZ 24
Große Friedberger Str. . . . HY 29

Großer Hirschgraben . . . GZ 30
Kalbächer Gasse . . . GY 32
Kleiner Hirchgraben . . . GY 35
Limpurgergasse . . . HZ 36
Münzgasse . . . GZ 40
Rechneigrabenstr. . . . HZ 50
Stoltzestraße . . . HY 58
Taunusstraße . . . GZ 62
Untermainanlage . . . GZ 65
Weißfrauenstraße . . . GZ 68
Weserstraße . . . GZ 69

**Rema-Hotel Bristol** without rest, Ludwigstr. 13, ✉ 60327, ☎ (069) 24 23 90, *Fax (069) 251539* – 25. CX a
**145 rm** 170/390.

**InterCityHotel**, Poststr. 8, ✉ 60329, ☎ (069) 27 39 10, *Fax (069) 27391999* – rm, – 80. rest CX e
**Meals** *(closed Saturday lunch and Sunday)* à la carte 38/61 – **384 rm** 230/395.

**Novotel Frankfurt City West**, Lise-Meitner-Str. 2, ✉ 60486, ☎ (069) 79 30 30, *Fax (069) 79303930*, – rm, – 140. CV r
**Meals** à la carte 36/63 – **235 rm** 200/304.

**Die Villa** without rest, Emil-Sulzbach-Str. 14, ✉ 60486, ☎ (069) 9 79 90 70, *Fax (069) 97990711* – . CV x
*closed 20 December - 2 January* – **22 rm** 273/496.

**Atrium** without rest, Beethovenstr. 30, ✉ 60325, ☎ (069) 97 56 70, *Fax (069) 97567100* – . CV d
*closed 20 December - 2 January and Easter* – **45 rm** 199/455.

**Manhattan** without rest, Düsseldorfer Str. 10, ✉ 60329, ☎ (069) 23 47 48, *Fax (069) 234532* – . CX r
**60 rm** 160/390.

**Liebig-Hotel** without rest, Liebigstr. 45, ✉ 60323, ☎ (069) 72 75 51, *Fax (069) 727555* – . CV z
**19 rm** 203/356.

**Am Dom** without rest, Kannengießergasse 3, ✉ 60311, ☎ (069) 28 21 41, *Fax (069) 283237* – . HZ s
**30 rm** 155/300.

**Topas** without rest, Niddastr. 88, ✉ 60329, ☎ (069) 23 08 52, *Fax (069) 237228* – . CX z
**31 rm** 110/310.

**Cristall** without rest, Ottostr. 3, ✉ 60329, ☎ (069) 23 03 51, *Fax (069) 253368* – . CX c
**30 rm** 110/310.

**Restaurant Français** - Hotel Steigenberger Frankfurter Hof, Bethmannstr. 33, ✉ 60311, ☎ (069) 2 15 02 – . GZ e
*closed Saturday lunch, Sunday - Monday and Bank Holidays except exhibitions and late July - mid August* – **Meals** (booking essential) à la carte 63/125
**Spec.** Warme Gänseleberterrine mit Granatapfeljus. Geschmortes Rindfleisch "en Daube" mit schwarzem Trüffel. Variation von der Bitterschokolade mit Gewürzorangenkompott.

**Humperdinck**, Grüneburgweg 95, ✉ 60323, ☎ (069) 72 21 22, *Fax (069) 97203155*, – CV v
*closed Saturday lunch, Sunday and Bank Holidays, 3 weeks July - August and Christmas - early January* – **Meals** 49 (lunch) and à la carte 81/127
**Spec.** Gebackene Kartoffelschalen mit Langostinos und Kaviar. Waller mit Kalbskopf und Liebstöckel. Geräucherte Gänsestopfleber mit Steinpilzen (Sept.- Nov.).

**Union Club Restaurant**, Am Leonhardsbrunnen 12, ✉ 60487, ☎ (069) 70 30 33, *Fax (069) 7073820*, – CV n
*closed Sunday dinner, Saturday and 25 December - 5 January* – **Meals** (booking essential) à la carte 71/86.

**Tigerpalast-Restaurant**, Heiligkreuzgasse 20, ✉ 60313, ☎ (069) 92 00 22 25, *Fax (069) 92002217* (with variety theatre) – . FV s
*closed Monday and August* – **Meals** (dinner only) à la carte 70/95
**Spec.** Ravioli gefüllt mit Kalbsbäckchen. Gebratene Brust und gefüllte Keule vom Schwarzfederhuhn. Lauwarme Topfentarte mit Sauerrahmeis.

**Villa Leonhardi**, Zeppelinallee 18, ✉ 60325, ☎ (069) 74 25 35, *Fax (069) 740476*, « Terrace in park » – . CV c
*closed Saturday lunch, Sunday, Bank Holidays and 23 December - early January* – **Meals** à la carte 72/88.

**Aubergine**, Alte Gasse 14, ✉ 60313, ☎ (069) 9 20 07 80, *Fax (069) 9200786* – HY b
*closed Saturday lunch, Sunday (except exhibitions) and 3 weeks July - August* – **Meals** (booking essential) (outstanding wine list) à la carte 70/89.

**Tse-Yang** (Chinese rest.), Kaiserstr. 67, ✉ 60329, ☎ (069) 23 25 41, *Fax (069) 237825* – . rm CX v
*closed Sunday except exhibitions* – **Meals** à la carte 44/80.

**Gallo Nero** (Italian rest.), Kaiserhofstr. 7, ✉ 60313, ☎ (069) 28 48 40, *Fax (069) 291645*, – GY s
*closed Sunday except exhibitions* – **Meals** à la carte 63/93.

**Gargantua**, Liebigstr. 47, 60323, (069) 72 07 18, *Fax (069) 720717*, - AE E VISA CV s
*closed Saturday lunch, Sunday and late December - early January* – **Meals** (booking essential) 49 (lunch) and à la carte 82/108.

**Ernos Bistro** (French rest.), Liebigstr. 15, 60323, (069) 72 19 97, *Fax (069) 173838*, - AE E VISA CV k
*closed Saturday and Sunday except exhibitions, 18 July - 9 August and 23 December - 4 January* – **Meals** (booking essential) 50 (lunch) à la carte 91/112
**Spec.** Rotbarbe mit Calamari-Risotto. Entencassoulet nach Art des Hauses. Schokoladenvariation.

**Frankfurter Äppelwoilokale** *(mainly light meals only)* :

**Das Rad**, Leonhardsgasse 2 (Seckbach), 60389, (069) 47 91 28, *Fax (069) 472942*, by Im Prüfling and Seckbacher Landstraße FV
*closed Monday November-March and Tuesday* – **Meals** (weekdays open from 5.00 pm, Sunday and Bank Holidays from 3.00 pm) à la carte 25/47.

**Römerbembel**, Römerberg 22, 60311, (069) 28 83 83, *Fax (069) 557644*,
**Meals** à la carte 25/35. HZ e

**Klaane Sachsehäuser**, Neuer Wall 11 (Sachsenhausen), 60594, (069) 61 59 83, *Fax (069) 622141*, FX n
*closed Sunday* – **Meals** (open from 4 pm) à la carte 21/42.

**Zum gemalten Haus**, Schweizer Str. 67 (Sachsenhausen), 60594, (069) 614559, *Fax (069) 6031457*, EX c
*closed Monday - Tuesday, late December - early January and late July - mid August* – **Meals** à la carte 20/27.

**at Frankfurt-Bergen-Enkheim** *by Wittelsbacherallee* FV *06109* :

**Amadeus**, Röntgenstr. 5, 60338, (06109) 37 00, *Fax (06109) 370720* – , rm, - 80. AE E VISA JCB
**Meals** *(closed Saturday)* à la carte 43/60 – **160 rm** 195/345.

**at Frankfurt-Griesheim** *by Th.-Heuss-Allee* CV :

**Ramada**, Oeserstr. 180, 65933, (069) 3 90 50, *Fax (069) 3808218*, , - , rm, rest, - 220. AE E VISA JCB
**Meals** à la carte 36/57 – **236 rm** 224/425.

**at Frankfurt-Höchst** *W : 10 km by Mainzer Landstraße* CX :

**Lindner Congress Hotel** M, Alt Erlenbach 44, 60437, (069) 3 30 02 00, *Fax (069) 33002999*, , - , rm, - 200. AE E VISA JCB. rest
**Meals** à la carte 46/78 – **285 rm** 281/504.

**at Frankfurt-Nieder-Erlenbach** *by Friedberger Landstr.* FV *and Homburger Landstr. N : 14 km* :

**Erlenbach 33**, Alt Erlenbach 33, 60437, (06101) 4 80 98, *Fax (06101) 48783* – AE E VISA
*closed Thursday and 3 weeks July - August* – **Meals** (weekdays dinner only) à la carte 46/68.

**at Frankfurt-Niederrad** *by Kennedy-Allee* CDX :

**Queens Hotel**, Isenburger Schneise 40, 60528, (069) 6 78 40, *Fax (069) 6784190*, - , rm, - 450. AE E VISA JCB
**Meals** à la carte 58/74 – **295 rm** 321/592.

**Arabella Congress Hotel**, Lyoner Str. 44, 60528, (069) 6 63 30, *Fax (069) 6633666*, , - , rm, - 300. AE E VISA
**Meals** à la carte 42/72 – **396 rm** 246/360 – 4 suites.

**Dorint** M, Hahnstr. 9, 60528, (069) 66 30 60, *Fax (069) 66306600*, , - , rm, - 180. AE E VISA JCB. rest
**Meals** à la carte 42/66 – **191 rm** 294/528.

**Weidemann**, Kelsterbacher Str. 66, 60528, (069) 67 59 96, *Fax (069) 673928*, - . AE E VISA by Gartenstraße CX
*closed Saturday lunch, Sunday and Bank Holidays* – **Meals** (booking essential) 53 (lunch) and à la carte 77/115.

**at Frankfurt-Nordweststadt** *by Miquelallee* CV :

**Ramada Hotel Nordwest Zentrum** M without rest, Walter-Möller-Platz, 60439, (069) 58 09 30, *Fax (069) 582447* – - 20. AE E VISA JCB – **93 rm** 179/222.

**at Frankfurt-Rödelheim** *NW : 6 km by Theodor-Heuss-Allee* CV *and Ludwig-Landmann-Str :*

XX ✿ **Osteria Enoteca** (Italian rest.), Arnoldshainer Str. 2 (corner Lorcher Str.), ✉ 60489, ☎ (069) 7 89 22 16, – AE E VISA.
*closed Saturday lunch, Sunday and late December - early January* – **Meals** (booking essential) 47/105 and à la carte 77/96
**Spec.** Carpaccio vom Loup de mer mit Nussöl und Limetten mariniert. Presskopf vom Octopus mit Sauerampfer-Kerbelvinaigrette. Zicklein aus dem Ofen.

**at Frankfurt-Sachsenhausen :**

**Holiday Inn Crowne Plaza**, Mailänder Str. 1, ✉ 60598, ☎ (069) 6 80 20, *Fax (069) 6802333*, – rm, – 220. AE E VISA JCB. rest by Darmstädter Landstr. (B 3) FX
**Meals** 40 and à la carte 40/75 – **404 rm** 299/640.

XX **Bistrot 77**, Ziegelhüttenweg 1, ✉ 60598, ☎ (069) 61 40 40, *Fax (069) 615998*, – AE E VISA EX a
*closed Saturday lunch, Sunday and Christmas - early January* – **Meals** (outstanding wine list) 48 (lunch) and à la carte 75/103.

**at Eschborn** *NW : 12 km by A66 :*

**Novotel**, Philipp-Helfmann-Str. 10, ✉ 65760, ☎ (06196) 90 10, *Fax (06196) 482114*, (heated), – rm, – 200. AE E VISA
**Meals** à la carte 37/65 – **227 rm** 200/260. by A 66 CV

**at Neu-Isenburg - Gravenbruch** *SE : 11 km by Darmstädter Landstr.* FX *and B 459 :*

**Gravenbruch-Kempinski-Frankfurt**, ✉ 63263, ☎ (06102) 50 50, *Fax (06102) 505900*, « Park », Massage, (heated), – rm, – 350. AE E VISA JCB. rest
**Meals** 49 (lunch) and à la carte 60/88 – **285 rm** 289/590 – 21 suites.

**near Rhein-Main airport** *SW : 12 km by Kennedy-Allee* CX *:*

**Sheraton**, at the airport (Terminal1), ✉ 60549, ☎ (069) 6 97 70, *Fax (069) 69772209*, Massage, – rm, – 900. AE E VISA JCB. rest
***Papillon*** (outstanding wine list) *(closed Saturday lunch, Sunday and Bank Holidays)* **Meals** 65 (lunch) and à la carte 89/126 – ***Maxwell's Bistro :*** **Meals** à la carte 50/84 – **Taverne** *(closed Saturday - Sunday lunch)* **Meals** à la carte 54/82 – **1050 rm** 465/745 – 30 suites.

## Eltville *Hessen* 417 P 8 – *pop. 16 500 – alt. 90 m.*

*Frankfurt am Main 55.*

**at Eltville-Hattenheim** *W : 4 km :*

XXXX ✿✿ **Marcobrunn**, Hauptstr. 43 (at Hotel Schloss Reinhartshausen), ✉ 65346, ☎ (06123) 67 64 32, *Fax (06123) 676400*, « Terrace in park » – . AE E VISA.
*closed Monday - Tuesday, 1 January - 5 February, Wednesday to Friday dinner only* – **Meals** (booking essential) 95/185 and à la carte 81/136
**Spec.** Kalbsfuß mit Trüffel und Kartoffeln gefüllt auf Langustinen-Spragelragout. Carpaccio von Hummer und Steinpilzen mit Muskat-Kürbissalat (Sept.). Bresse Taube mit Oliven in der Artischocke geschmort und Rosmarinjus.

## Maintal *Hessen* 417 P 10 – *pop. 40 000 – alt. 95 m.*

*Frankfurt am Main 13.*

**at Maintal-Dörnigheim :**

XXX ✿ **Hessler** with rm, Am Bootshafen 4, ✉ 63477, ☎ (06181) 4 30 30, *Fax (06181) 430333* – . AE E VISA
*closed 3 weeks July* – **Meals** *(closed Sunday - Monday)* (booking essential, outstanding wine list) 108/175 and à la carte 94/111 – **7 rm** 180/290
**Spec.** Getrüffelte Taube im Strudelteig mit Trüffeljus. Gemüselasagne gefüllt mit Fisch und Meeresfrüchten. Marinierter Seeteufel mit schwarzem Kokosreis und Erdnussbutter.

## Mannheim *Baden-Württemberg* 417 419 R 9, 987 ㉗ – *pop. 324 000 – alt. 95 m.*

*Frankfurt am Main 79.*

XXX ✿✿ **Da Gianni** (Italian rest.), R 7, 34 (Friedrichsring), ✉ 68161, ☎ (0621) 2 03 26 – . AE E.
*closed Monday, Bank Holidays and 3 weeks July - August* – **Meals** (booking essential) 149 and à la carte 92/120
**Spec.** Variation von Antipasti. Petersfisch mit Gemüseministrone. Perlhuhn im Salzmantel.

**Stromberg Kreis Kreuznach** *Rheinland-Pfalz* 417 Q 7, 987 ㉖ – *pop.* 3 000 – *alt.* 235 *m.*
*Frankfurt am Main 82.*

XXXX ✿✿ **Le Val d'Or in Lafer's Stromburg** ⑤ with rm, Schloßberg (E : 1,5km), ✉ 55442, ✆ (06724) 9 31 00, *Fax (06724) 931090*, ≤, beer garden – TV ☎ P – 100. AE ⓓ E VISA
**Meals** *(Tuesday - Friday dinner only, closed Monday)* 159/189 and à la carte 100/129 – ***Turmstube* : Meals** à la carte 52/76 – **13 rm** ⊐ 180/390
**Spec.** Variation von der Gänsestopfleber. Lammcarré in der Olivenkruste mit Pinienkernjus. Dessert-Impressionen.

**Wertheim** *Baden-Württemberg* 417 419 Q 12, 987 ㉗ – *pop.* 21 700 – *alt.* 142 *m.*
*Frankfurt am Main 87.*

**at Wertheim-Bettingen** *E : 10 km :*

✿✿ **Schweizer Stuben** ⑤, Geiselbrunnweg 11, ✉ 97877, ✆ (09342) 30 70, *Fax (09342) 307155*, « Hotel in a park », Massage, (heated), (indoor) – TV P – 30. AE ⓓ E VISA
**Meals** *(closed Tuesday and January)* (weekdays dinner only) (booking essential) 145/210 and à la carte 88/169 – **33 rm** ⊐ 225/496 – 3 suites
**Spec.** Entenstopfleberterrine mit Gelee von Muscat de Beaumes-de-Venise. Rotbarbenfilet mit Sauce à la bourride. Zicklein in Sarriette mit Olivenölsauce.

*Ask your bookseller for the catalogue of* ***Michelin publications.***

---

**HAMBURG** L *Stadtstaat Hamburg* 415 416 F 14, 987 ⑤ – *pop.* 1 650 000 – *alt.* 10 *m.*

See : *Jungfernstieg*★ GY – *Außenalster*★★★ *(trip by boat*★★★*)* GHXY – *Hagenbeck Zoo (Tierpark Hagenbeck)*★★ *by Schröderstiftstr.* EX – *Television Tower (Fernsehturm)*★ *(*★★*)* EX – *Fine Arts Museum (Kunsthalle)*★★ HY **M1** – *St. Michael's church (St. Michaelis)*★ *(tower* ★*)* EFZ – *Stintfang (≤*★*)* EZ – *Port (Hafen)*★★ EZ – *Decorative Arts and Crafts Museum (Museum für Kunst und Gewerbe)*★ HY **M2** – *Historical Museum (Museum für Hamburgische Geschichte)*★ EYZ **M3** – *Post-Museum*★ FY **M4** – *Planten un Blomen Park*★ EFX – *Museum of Ethnography (Hamburgisches Museum für Völkerkunde)*★ *by Rothenbaumchaussee* FX.

**Envir.** : *Altona and Northern Germany Museum (Norddeutsches Landesmuseum)*★★ *by Reeperbahn* EZ – *Altona Balcony (Altonaer Balkon)* ≤★ *by Reeperbahn* EZ – *Elbchaussee*★ *by Reeperbahn* EZ.

18 *Hamburg-Blankenese, In de Bargen 59 (W : 17 km),* ✆ *(040) 81 21 77 ;* 18 *Ammersbek (NE : 15 km),* ✆ *(040) 6 05 13 37 ;* 18 *Hamburg-Wendlohe (N : 14 km),* ✆ *(040) 5 50 50 14 ;* 18 *Wentorf, Golfstr. 2 (SE : 21 km),* ✆ *(040) 72 97 80 66.*

*Hamburg-Fuhlsbüttel (N : 15 km),* ✆ *(040) 50 80.*

*Hamburg-Altona, Sternschanze.*

*Exhibition Centre (Messegelände) (*EFX*),* ✆ *(040) 3 56 90.*

*Tourist – Information im Hauptbahnhof (entrance Kirchenallee),* ✉ *20095,* ✆ *(040) 30 05 13 00, Fax (040) 30051333.*

*Tourist-Information, Harbour, Landungsbrücke 4-5,* ✉ *20459,* ✆ *(040) 30 05 12 00.*

**ADAC**, *Amsinckstr. 39,* ✉ *20097,* ✆ *(040) 23 91 90, Fax (040) 23919271.*

*Berlin 289 – Bremen 120 – Hannover 151.*

Plans on following pages

**Town centre :**

**Vier Jahreszeiten**, Neuer Jungfernstieg 9, ✉ 20354, ✆ (040) 3 49 40, *Fax (040) 3494602*, ≤ Binnenalster – |♦|, ⇔ rm, TV – 80. AE ⓓ E VISA JCB. GY v
**Meals** see also ***Rest. Haerlin*** below – ***Jahreszeiten Grill* :** **Meals** à la carte 57/103 – ***Condi*** *(lunch only, closed Sunday and July - August)* **Meals** à la carte 37/69 – **158 rm** ⊐ 413/1000 – 12 suites.

**Kempinski Hotel Atlantic Hamburg** ⑤, An der Alster 72, ✉ 20099, ✆ (040) 2 88 80, *Fax (040) 247129*, ≤ Außenalster, Massage, – |♦|, ⇔ rm, TV – 300. AE ⓓ E VISA JCB. rest HY a
**Meals** à la carte 65/104 – ***Atlantic-Mühle*** *(dinner only)* **Meals** à la carte 48/75 – **254 rm** ⊐ 399/598 – 13 suites.

**Steigenberger Hamburg** M, Heiligengeistbrücke 4, ✉ 20459, ✆ (040) 36 80 60, *Fax (040) 36806777* – |♦|, ⇔ rm, TV – 180. AE ⓓ E VISA JCB FZ s
***Calla*** *(dinner only, closed Sunday - Monday and July - August)* **Meals** à la carte 54/88 – ***Bistro am Fleet* : Meals** à la carte 44/57 – **234 rm** ⊐ 308/588 – 4 suites.

**Marriott Hotel**, ABC-Str. 52, 20354, (040) 3 50 50, *Fax (040) 35051777*, Massage, – rm, – 160. AE VISA JCB FY b
**Meals** 28 (buffet lunch) and à la carte 45/69 – **277 rm** 330/555 – 4 suites.

**Renaissance Hamburg Hotel**, Große Bleichen, 20354, (040) 34 91 80, *Fax (040) 34918431*, Massage, – rm, – 110. AE VISA JCB. rest FY e
**Meals** à la carte 53/85 – **205 rm** 303/635 – 3 suites.

**Radisson SAS Plaza Hotel**, Marseiller Str. 2, 20355, (040) 3 50 20, *Fax (040) 35023530*, Hamburg, – rm, – 320. AE VISA JCB. rest FX a
***Vierländer Stuben* : Meals** à la carte 36/56 – ***Trader Vic's*** *(dinner only, closed July)* **Meals** à la carte 50/84 – **560 rm** 314/460 – 26 suites.

**Holiday Inn Crowne Plaza**, Graumannsweg 10, 22087, (040) 22 80 60, *Fax (040) 2208704*, Massage, – rm, – 120. AE VISA JCB. rest by Lange Reihe HX
***Lord Nelson*** *(closed Sunday dinner)* **Meals** à la carte 50/81 – ***King George Pub* : Meals** à la carte 34/51 – **285 rm** 308/456.

**Europäischer Hof**, Kirchenallee 45, 20099, (040) 24 82 48, *Fax (040) 24824799*, Massage, Squash – rm, rest, – 150. AE VISA HY e
**Meals** à la carte 43/70 – **320 rm** 190/430.

**Maritim Hotel Reichshof**, Kirchenallee 34, 20099, (040) 24 83 30, *Fax (040) 24833588*, – rm, – 160. AE VISA JCB. rest
**Meals** à la carte 64/87 – **303 rm** 239/398 – 6 suites. HY d

**Prem**, An der Alster 9, 20099, (040) 24 17 26, *Fax (040) 2803851*, « Antique furnishings, garden », – . AE VISA JCB HX c
***La mer*** *(closed Saturday and Sunday lunch)* **Meals** à la carte 79/101 – **53 rm** 220/455 – 3 suites.

**Residenz Hafen Hamburg**, Seewartenstr. 7, 20459, (040) 31 11 90, *Fax (040) 314505*, – – 60. AE VISA EZ y
**Meals** see ***Hotel Hafen Hamburg*** – **125 rm** 206/282.

**Berlin**, Borgfelder Str. 1, 20537, (040) 25 16 40, *Fax (040) 25164413*, – , rm, rest, – 30. AE VISA JCB
**Meals** à la carte 45/60 – **93 rm** 180/225. by Kurt-Schumacher-Allee HY

**Senator**, Lange Reihe 18, 20099, (040) 24 12 03, *Fax (040) 2803717* – , rm, – 30. AE VISA JCB. rest HY u
**Meals** (residents only)(dinner only) – **56 rm** 185/285.

**Novotel City Süd**, Amsinckstr. 53, 20097, (040) 23 63 80, *Fax (040) 234230*, – , rm, – 50. AE VISA by Amsinckstraße HZ
**Meals** à la carte 40/60 – **185 rm** 202/302.

**Hafen Hamburg**, Seewartenstr. 9, 20459, (040) 31 11 30, *Fax (040) 31113751*, – – 70. AE VISA. rest EZ y
**Meals** à la carte 46/80 – **239 rm** 182/222.

**Bellevue**, An der Alster 14, 20099, (040) 28 44 40, *Fax (040) 28444222* – , rm, – 40. AE VISA HX d
**Meals** à la carte 48/63 – **93 rm** 170/330.

**St. Raphael**, Adenauerallee 41, 20097, (040) 24 82 00, *Fax (040) 24820333*, – , rm, – 40. AE VISA JCB. rest by Adenauerallee HY
**Meals** *(closed Saturday and Sunday lunch)* à la carte 38/60 – **130 rm** 190/300.

**Baseler Hof**, Esplanade 11, 20354, (040) 35 90 60, *Fax (040) 35906918* – – 30. AE VISA. GY x
*closed 23 to 29 December* – **Meals** *(closed Saturday and Sunday lunch, 28 June - 19 July)* 22 (lunch) and à la carte 49/71 – **149 rm** 150/225.

**Alster-Hof** without rest, Esplanade 12, 20354, (040) 35 00 70, *Fax (040) 35007514* – . AE VISA GY x
*closed 24 December - 2 January* – **118 rm** 145/220 – 3 suites.

**Aussen-Alster-Hotel** (Italian rest.), Schmilinskystr. 11, 20099, (040) 24 15 57, *Fax (040) 2803231*, – , rm, . AE VISA JCB HX e
*closed 24 to 27 December* – **Meals** *(closed Saturday lunch and Sunday)* à la carte 48/65 – **27 rm** 180/310.

**Eden** without rest, Ellmenreichstr. 20, 20099, (040) 24 84 80, *Fax (040) 241521* – . AE VISA HY r
**63 rm** 135/220.

**Wedina** without rest, Gurlittstr. 23, 20099, (040) 24 30 11, *Fax (040) 2803894*, – . AE VISA HY b
**28 rm** 155/240.

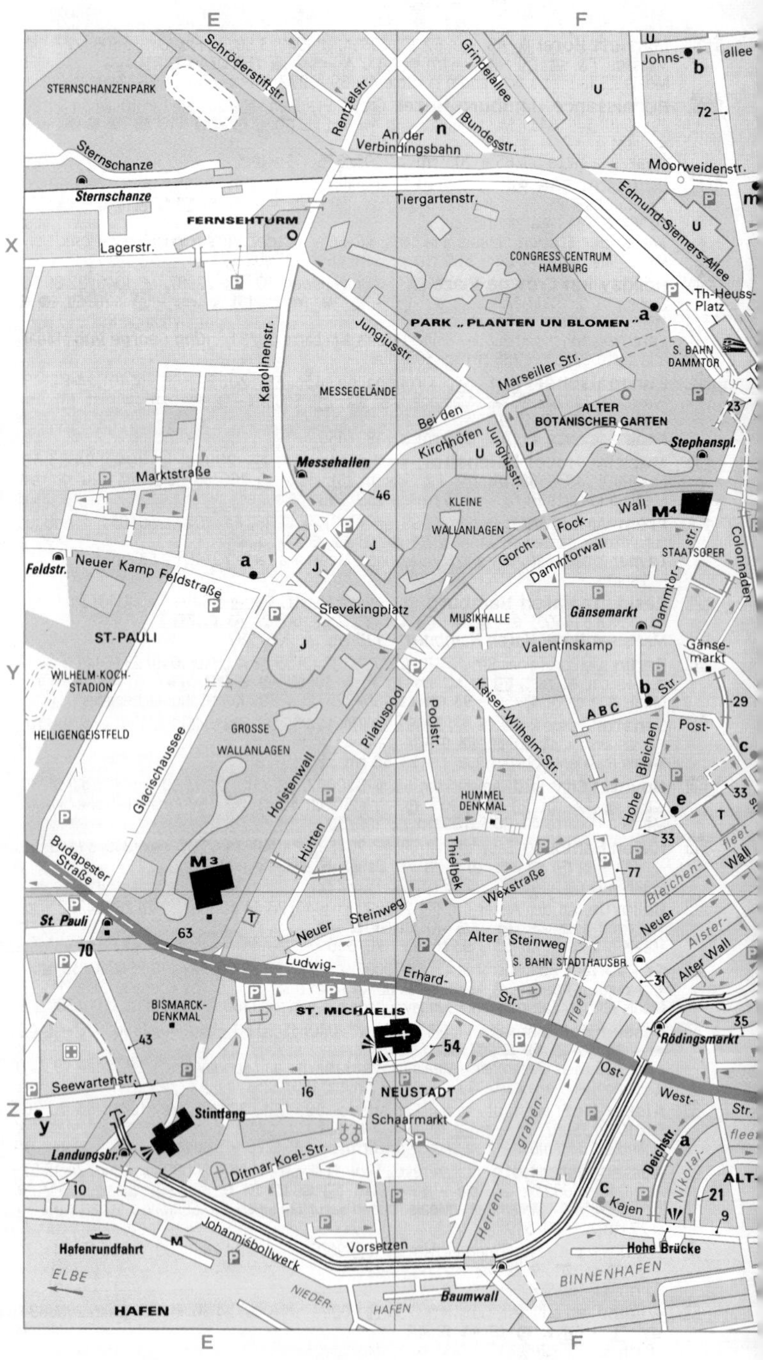
E
F
STERNSCHANZENPARK
Schröderstiftstr.
Rentzelstr.
Grindelallee
Bundesstr.
An der Verbindungsbahn
Johns-
allee
Sternschanze
Sternschanze
Moorweidenstr.
Edmund-Siemers-Allee
Tiergartenstr.
FERNSEHTURM
Lagerstr.
CONGRESS CENTRUM HAMBURG
Th.-Heuss-Platz
PARK „PLANTEN UN BLOMEN"
Jungiusstr.
Karolinenstr.
MESSEGELÄNDE
Marseiller Str.
S. BAHN DAMMTOR
ALTER BOTANISCHER GARTEN
Bei den Kirchhöfen
Stephanspl.
Messehallen
Marktstraße
KLEINE WALLANLAGEN
Gorch-Fock-Wall
Dammtorwall
Dammtorstr.
STAATSOPER
Colonnaden
Feldstr.
Neuer Kamp
Feldstraße
Sievekingplatz
MUSIKHALLE
Gänsemarkt
Valentinskamp
Gänsemarkt
ST-PAULI
WILHELM-KOCH-STADION
HEILIGENGEISTFELD
Glacischaussee
GROSSE WALLANLAGEN
Holstenwall
Pilatuspool
Poolstr.
Kaiser-Wilhelm-Str.
ABC Str.
Post-
Hohe Bleichen
HUMMEL DENKMAL
Hütten
Thielbek
Wexstraße
Bleichenfleet
Neuer Wall
Budapester Straße
St. Pauli
Neuer Steinweg
Alter Steinweg
S. BAHN STADTHAUSBR.
Alsterfleet
Alter Wall
Ludwig-Erhard-Str.
BISMARCK-DENKMAL
ST. MICHAELIS
Rödingsmarkt
Ost-West-Str.
NEUSTADT
Seewartenstr.
Stintfang
Schaarmarkt
Herrengraben-fleet
Deichstr.
Nikolaifleet
Landungsbr.
Ditmar-Koel-Str.
Kajen
ALT-
Johannisbollwerk
Vorsetzen
Hohe Brücke
Hafenrundfahrt
BINNENHAFEN
ELBE
NIEDERHAFEN
Baumwall
HAFEN
X
Y
Z
M³
M⁴
46
63
70
72
23
29
33
77
31
35
54
43
16
10
21
9

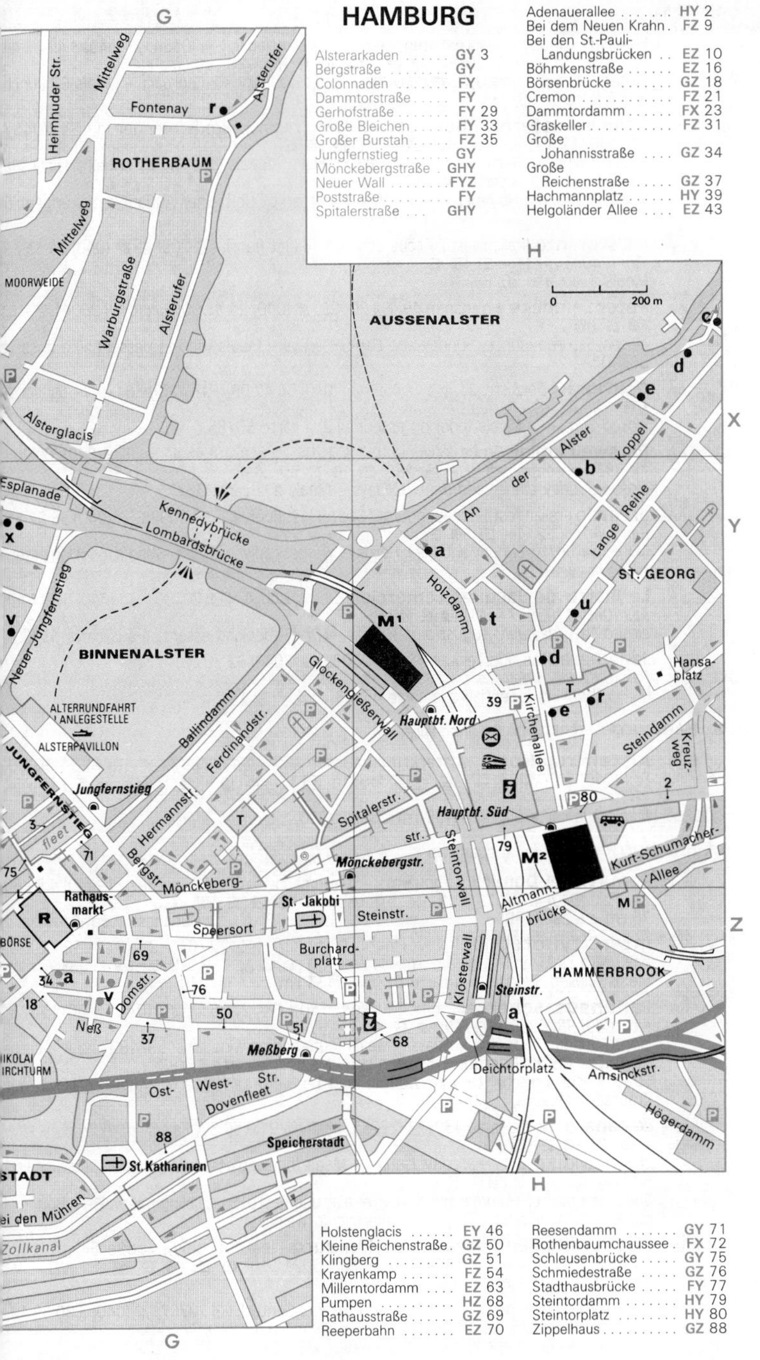
HAMBURG
Alsterarkaden . . . . . . GY 3
Bergstraße . . . . . . . . GY
Colonnaden . . . . . . . FY
Dammtorstraße . . . . . FY
Gerhofstraße . . . . . . . FY 29
Große Bleichen . . . . . FY 33
Großer Burstah . . . . . FZ 35
Jungfernstieg . . . . . . . GY
Mönckebergstraße . GHY
Neuer Wall . . . . . . . . FYZ
Poststraße . . . . . . . . . FY
Spitalerstraße . . . GHY
Adenauerallee . . . . . . . HY 2
Bei dem Neuen Krahn . FZ 9
Bei den St.-Pauli-Landungsbrücken . . EZ 10
Böhmkenstraße . . . . . . EZ 16
Börsenbrücke . . . . . . . GZ 18
Cremon . . . . . . . . . . . . FZ 21
Dammtordamm . . . . . . FX 23
Graskeller . . . . . . . . . . FZ 31
Große Johannisstraße . . . . GZ 34
Große Reichenstraße . . . . . GZ 37
Hachmannplatz . . . . . . HY 39
Helgoländer Allee . . . . EZ 43
G
H
X
Y
Z
0
200 m
Heimhuder Str.
Mittelweg
Fontenay
Alsterufer
ROTHERBAUM
MOORWEIDE
Warburgstraße
Alsterglacis
AUSSENALSTER
Esplanade
Kennedybrücke
Lombardsbrücke
An der Alster
Koppel
Lange Reihe
ST. GEORG
Holzdamm
Neuer Jungfernstieg
BINNENALSTER
ALTERRUNDFAHRT ANLEGESTELLE
ALSTERPAVILLON
JUNGFERNSTIEG
Jungfernstieg
Ballindamm
Ferdinandstr.
Glockengießerwall
Hauptbf. Nord
Kirchenallee
Hansaplatz
Steindamm
Kreuzweg
Hermannstr.
Spitalerstr.
Hauptbf. Süd
Steintorwall
Kurt-Schumacher-Allee
Bergstr.
Mönckeberg-str.
Mönckebergstr.
Rathausmarkt
St. Jakobi
Steinstr.
Altmannbrücke
BÖRSE
Speersort
Burchardplatz
Klosterwall
HAMMERBROOK
Domstr.
Steinstr.
Neß
Meßberg
Deichtorplatz
Amsinckstr.
NIKOLAI KIRCHTURM
Ost-West-Str.
Dovenfleet
Högerdamm
Speicherstadt
St. Katharinen
STADT
Bei den Mühren
Zollkanal
Holstenglacis . . . . . . EY 46
Kleine Reichenstraße . GZ 50
Klingberg . . . . . . . . . GZ 51
Krayenkamp . . . . . . . FZ 54
Millerntordamm . . . . EZ 63
Pumpen . . . . . . . . . . HZ 68
Rathausstraße . . . . . . GZ 69
Reeperbahn . . . . . . . EZ 70
Reesendamm . . . . . . . GY 71
Rothenbaumchaussee . FX 72
Schleusenbrücke . . . . GY 75
Schmiedestraße . . . . . GZ 76
Stadthausbrücke . . . . . FY 77
Steintordamm . . . . . . . HY 79
Steintorplatz . . . . . . . . HY 80
Zippelhaus . . . . . . . . . GZ 88

**Haerlin** - Hotel Vier Jahreszeiten, Neuer Jungfernstieg 9, ✉ 20354, ☎ (040) 3 49 46 41, *Fax (049) 3494602*, ≤ Binnenalster – AE ⓓ E VISA JCB. ✻ GY v
*closed Sunday - Monday, Saturday lunch and 2 January - 2 February* – **Meals** 62 (lunch) and à la carte 88/135.

**Cölln's Austernstuben** (private dining rooms), Brodschrangen 1, ✉ 20457, ☎ (040) 32 60 59, *Fax (040) 326059* – AE ⓓ E GZ v
*closed Saturday lunch, Sunday and Bank Holidays* – **Meals** (booking essential) (mainly seafood) 89/146 à la carte 74/115
**Spec.** Gratin von Hummer. "Feines vom Fischmarkt". Holsteiner Auflauf mit Orangenblüteneis.

**il Ristorante** (Italian rest.), Große Bleichen 16 (1st floor), ✉ 20354, ☎ (040) 34 33 35, *Fax (040) 345748* – AE ⓓ E FY c
**Meals** à la carte 56/83.

**Peter Lembcke**, Holzdamm 49, ✉ 20099, ☎ (040) 24 32 90, *Fax (040) 2804123* – AE ⓓ E VISA HY t
*closed Saturday lunch, Sunday and Bank Holidays* – **Meals** (booking essential) à la carte 56/102.

**Deichgraf**, Deichstr. 23, ✉ 20459, ☎ (040) 36 42 08, *Fax (040) 364268* – AE ⓓ E VISA FZ a
*closed Sunday* – **Meals** (booking essential) à la carte 50/85.

**Ratsweinkeller**, Große Johannisstr. 2, ✉ 20457, ☎ (040) 36 41 53, *Fax (040) 372201*, « 1896 Hanseatic rest. » – 🏛 280. AE ⓓ E VISA JCB GZ R
*closed Sunday dinner and Bank Holidays* – **Meals** à la carte 36/75.

**al Pincio** (Italian rest.), Schauenburger Str. 59 (1st floor, |‡|), ✉ 20095, ☎ (040) 36 52 55, *Fax (040) 362244* – AE ⓓ E. ✻ GZ a
*closed Saturday, Sunday and Bank Holidays, 4 weeks July - August* – **Meals** (booking essential) à la carte 54/80.

**Le Bistro de Jacques Lemercier**, Dornbusch 4, ✉ 20095, ☎ (040) 32 14 14, *Fax (040) 4105857* – AE ⓓ E VISA GZ v
*closed Saturday July-August and Sunday* – **Meals** (booking essential) à la carte 43/62.

**Jena Paradies**, Klosterwall 23, ✉ 20095, ☎ (040) 32 70 08, *Fax (040) 327598* HZ a
**Meals** (booking essential) à la carte 45/65.

**at Hamburg-Alsterdorf** *by Grindelallee* FX :

**Alsterkrug-Hotel**, Alsterkrugchaussee 277, ✉ 22297, ☎ (040) 51 30 30, *Fax (040) 51303403*, 🏠, ≘s – |‡|, ⇔ rm, TV ☎ 🚗 P – 🏛 50. AE ⓓ E VISA JCB. ✻
**Meals** à la carte 51/64 – **105 rm** ☕ 210/290.

**at Hamburg-Altona** *by Reeperbahn* EZ :

**Rema-Hotel Domicil** without rest, Stresemannstr. 62, ✉ 22769, ☎ (040) 4 31 60 26, *Fax (040) 4397579* – |‡| ⇔ TV ☎ 🚗. AE ⓓ E VISA JCB
**75 rm** ☕ 290/390. by Budapester Straße EY

**InterCityHotel**, Paul-Nevermann-Platz 17, ✉ 22765, ☎ (040) 38 03 40, *Fax (040) 38034999* – |‡|, ⇔ rm, ▤ rest, TV ☎ ☎ ♿ – 🏛 70. AE ⓓ E VISA
**Meals** *(closed Sunday)* à la carte 31/56 – **133 rm** ☕ 190/270.

**Landhaus Scherrer**, Elbchaussee 130, ✉ 22763, ☎ (040) 8 80 13 25, *Fax (040) 8806260* – P. AE ⓓ E
*closed Sunday and Bank Holidays* – **Meals** (outstanding wine list) 159/189 and à la carte 80/132 – ***Bistro-Restaurant*** *(lunch only)* **Meals** à la carte 66/87
**Spec.** Milchlammschnitte vom Wagen. Wan-Tan vom Kaisergranat. Angelschellfisch mit Kräuter-Senfsauce.

**Le canard**, Elbchaussee 139, ✉ 22763, ☎ (040) 8 80 50 57, *Fax (040) 472413*, ≤, 🏠 – P. AE ⓓ E VISA. ✻
*closed Sunday and 1 week early January* – **Meals** (booking essential) (outstanding wine list) 60 (lunch) and à la carte 103/149
**Spec.** Marinierter Hummer mit Kartoffelsalat und Pesto. Seesaibling mit weißem Bohnenpüree und Ingwersauce. Topfensoufflé mit Rotweineis.

**Fischereihafen-Restaurant Hamburg** (seafood only), Große Elbstr. 143, ✉ 22767, ☎ (040) 38 18 16, *Fax (040) 3893021*, ≤ – P. AE ⓓ E VISA
**Meals** (booking essential) à la carte 49/111.

**Rive Bistro**, Van-der Smissen-Str. 1 (Kreuzfahrt-Center), ✉ 22767, ☎ (040) 3 80 59 19, *Fax (040) 3894775*, ≤, 🏠 – AE
**Meals** (booking essential) à la carte 45/84.

**at Hamburg-Bahrenfeld** *by Budapester Str.* EY :

**Novotel Hamburg West**, Albert-Einstein-Ring 2, 22761, (040) 89 95 20, *Fax 040) 89952333*, – , rm, – 50.
**Meals** à la carte 35/64 – **137 rm** 191/229 – 4 suites.

**Tafelhaus**, Holstenkamp 71, 22525, (040) 89 27 60, *Fax (040) 8993324*, –
*closed Saturday lunch, Sunday, Monday, 3 weeks January, late July - mid August and 1 week over Easter* – **Meals** (booking essential) 58 (lunch) and à la carte 79/83
**Spec.** Topinambursuppe mit Hummer. Seezunge im Steinpilzsud. Kalbsstelze aus dem Ofen mit Trüffel.

**at Hamburg-Barmbek** *by An der Alster* HX :

**Rema-Hotel Meridian** without rest, Holsteinischer Kamp 59, 22081, (040) 2 91 80 40, *Fax (040) 2983336*, , – – 30.
**68 rm** 290/390.

**at Hamburg-Billbrook** *by Amsinckstr.* HZ *and Billstr.* :

**Böttcherhof**, Wöhlerstr. 2, 22113, (040) 73 18 70, *Fax (040) 73187899*, , – , rm, – 140. rest
**Meals** à la carte 42/73 – **155 rm** 210/290.

**at Hamburg-Billstedt** *by Kurt Schumacher-Allee and B 5* HY :

**Panorama** without rest, Billstedter Hauptstr. 44, 22111, (040) 73 35 90, *Fax (040) 73359950*, – – 150.
*closed 23 to 28 December* – **111 rm** 180/275 – 7 suites.

**at Hamburg-City Nord** *by Grindelallee* FX :

**Queens Hotel**, Mexicoring 1, 22297, (040) 63 29 40, *Fax (040) 6322472*, , – , rm, – 120. rest
**Meals** à la carte 47/65 – **182 rm** 259/328.

**at Hamburg-Duvenstedt** *by Grindelallee* FX :

**Le Relais de France**, Poppenbütteler Chaussee 3, 22397, (040) 6 07 07 50, *Fax (040) 6072673*, – .
*closed Sunday and Monday* – **Meals** (dinner only, booking essential) à la carte 67/84 – ***Bistro*** *(also lunch)* **Meals** à la carte 57/68.

**at Hamburg-Eimsbüttel** *by Schröderstiftstraße* EX :

**Norge**, Schäferkampsallee 49, 20357, (040) 44 11 50, *Fax (040) 44115577* – , rm, rest, – 80.
**Meals** *(closed Sunday dinner)* à la carte 43/67 – **130 rm** 199/328.

**at Hamburg-Eppendorf** *by Grindelallee* FX :

**Anna e Sebastiano** (Italian rest.), Lehmweg 30, 20251, (040) 4 22 25 95, *Fax (040) 4208008* – .
*closed Sunday and Monday, 23 December - 16 January and 3 weeks June - July* – **Meals** (dinner only, booking essential) 100/120 and à la carte 83/93
**Spec.** Risotto mit Steinpilzen (May-Oct.). Gedünsteter Stör mit Kartoffeln und Spargel in Sardellenbutter. Kleine Charlotte von Passionsfrucht und Schockolade.

**Il Gabbiano** (Italian rest.), Eppendorfer Landstr. 145, 20251, (040) 4 80 21 59, *Fax (040) 4807921*, –
*closed Saturday lunch, Sunday and 3 weeks July* – **Meals** (booking essential) à la carte 56/87.

**Sellmer** (mainly seafood), Ludolfstr. 50, 20249, 47 30 57, *Fax 4601569* – .
**Meals** à la carte 51/104.

**at Hamburg-Flottbek** *by Stresemannstraße* AU :

**Landhaus Flottbek**, Baron-Voght-Str. 179, 22607, (040) 8 22 74 10, *Fax (040) 82274151*, , « Hotel in former farmhouses ; elegant rustic installation », , – – 30. S m
**Meals** à la carte 50/80 – **25 rm** 175/255.

**at Hamburg-Fuhlsbüttel** *by Grindelallee* FX :

**Airport Hotel**, Flughafenstr. 47, 22415, (040) 53 10 20, *Fax (040) 53102222*, , – , rm, rest, – 140.
**Meals** à la carte 49/74 – **159 rm** 262/399 – 10 suites.

**top air**, Paul-Bäumer-Platz 1 (at the airport, terminal 4, level 3), 22335, (040) 50 75 33 24, *Fax (040) 50751842* – R h
*closed Saturday* – **Meals** à la carte 61/90.

**at Hamburg-Hamm** *by Kurt-Schumacher-Allee* HY :

**Hamburg International**, Hammer Landstr. 200, 20537, (040) 21 14 01, *Fax (040) 211409* – 20. rest
Meals (dinner only) à la carte 39/74 – **112 rm** 130/290.

**at Hamburg-Harburg** *2100 S : 15 km by Amsinckstr.* HZ :

**Lindtner**, Heimfelder Str. 123, 21075, (040) 79 00 90, *Fax (040) 79009482*, « Elegant modern installation ; collection of contemporary art » – rm, – 450. rest
***Lilium*** : Meals 35 (lunch) and à la carte 56/75 – ***Hofgarten*** : Meals à la carte 49/82 – **108 rm** 245/355 – 7 suites.

**Panorama**, Harburger Ring 8, 21073, (040) 76 69 50, *Fax (040) 76695183* – rm, – 110.
Meals *(closed Sunday dinner)* à la carte 38/65 – **98 rm** 180/210.

**Marinas**, Schellerdamm 26, 21079, (040) 7 65 38 28, *Fax (040) 7651491*, –
*closed Saturday lunch and Sunday* – **Meals** (booking essential for dinner) 44 (lunch) and à la carte 55/81
**Spec.** Bouillabaise von Nordseefischen. Seeteufel auf Weinkraut mit eingelegtem Kürbis. Gekochter Steinbutt mit Meerrettich.

**at Hamburg-Harvestehude** :

**Inter-Continental**, Fontenay 10, 20354, (040) 41 41 50, *Fax (040) 41415186*, Hamburg and Alster, , Massage, – rm, – 350. rest GX r
***Fontenay-Grill*** *(dinner only)* **Meals** à la carte 65/117 – ***Orangerie*** : **Meals** 49 (lunch buffet) and à la carte 59/69 – **286 rm** 314/518 – 12 suites.

**Garden Hotels Pöseldorf** without rest, Magdalenenstr. 60, 20148, (040) 41 40 40, *Fax (040) 4140420*, « Elegant modern installation » – by Mittelweg GX
**60 rm** 200/450.

**Abtei**, Abteistr. 14, 20149, (040) 44 29 05, *Fax (040) 449820*, – rest, rest by Rothenbaumchaussee FX
**Meals** *(closed Sunday - Monday, 1 week January and July)* (dinner only, booking essential) 128/167 – **11 rm** 260/450
**Spec.** Pot au feu von Kalbskopf und Kalbsbries mit Steinpilzen. Chartreuse von Spargel mit Langostinos und Steinbutt. Pochiertes Deichlammrückenfilet und Hummer in Safran-Knoblauchsauce.

**Smolka**, Isestr. 98, 20149, (040) 48 09 80, *Fax (040) 4809811* – rm, rest by Rothenbaumchaussee FX
**Meals** *(closed Sunday and Bank Holidays)* (dinner only) à la carte 48/70 – **40 rm** 170/320.

**at Hamburg-Langenhorn** *N : 8 km by B 433* :

**Dorint-Hotel-Airport**, Langenhorner Chaussee 183, 22415, (040) 53 20 90, *Fax (040) 53209600*, – rm, – 80. rest
**Meals** à la carte 41/72 – **147 rm** 243/408.

**Zum Wattkorn**, Tangstedter Landstr. 230, 22417, (040) 5 20 37 97, *Fax (040) 5209044*, –
*closed Monday* – **Meals** à la carte 53/80.

**at Hamburg-Lemsahl-Mellingstedt** *by An der Alster NE : 16 km* :

**Mariott Hotel Treudelberg**, Lemsahler Landstr. 45, 22397, (040) 60 82 20, *Fax (040) 60822444*, , Massage, – rm, – 150. rest
**Meals** à la carte 56/79 – **135 rm** 240/500.

**Ristorante Dante** (Italian rest.), An der Alsterschleife 3, 22399, (040) 6 02 00 43, *Fax (040) 6022826*, –
*closed Monday, Tuesday to Friday dinner only* – **Meals** (booking essential) à la carte 50/73.

**at Hamburg-Nienstedten** *W : 13 km by Reeperbahn* EZ :

**Louis C. Jacob**, Elbchaussee 401, 22609, (040) 82 25 50, *Fax (040) 82255444*, Hafen and Elbe, « Elbe-side setting ; lime-tree terrace », – rm, – 140. rest
**Meals** à la carte 65/100 – ***Kleines Jacob*** *(closed Sunday, dinner only)* **Meals** à la carte 49/68 – **86 rm** 319/764 – 8 suites.

**at Hamburg-Rothenburgsort** *by Amsinkstr.* HZ :

**Forum Hotel**, Billwerder Neuer Deich 14, ✉ 20539, ☎ (040) 78 84 00, *Fax (040) 78841000*, ←, 🏖, Fö, ≋, 🏊 – 🛗 ⇹ 📺 ☏ ♿ 🚗 🅿 – 👥 90. AE ⓓ E VISA JCB. ✈ rest
**Meals** à la carte 46/63 – **385 rm** ☕ 198/310 – 12 suites.

**at Hamburg-Rotherbaum :**

**Elysee** ♨, Rothenbaumchaussee 10, ✉ 20148, ☎ (040) 41 41 20, *Fax (040) 41412733*, 🏖, Massage, ≋, 🏊 – 🛗, ⇹ rm, ▤ 📺 ♿ 🚗 – 👥 350. AE ⓓ E VISA JCB
***Piazza Romana :*** **Meals** à la carte 53/84 – ***Brasserie :*** **Meals** à la carte 41/55 – **305 rm** ☕ 276/492 – 4 suites. FX m

**Vorbach** without rest, Johnsallee 63, ✉ 20146, ☎ (040) 44 18 20, *Fax (040) 44182888* – 🛗 ⇹ 📺 ☎ 🚗 – 👥 20. AE E VISA FX b
**115 rm** ☕ 170/280.

**at Hamburg-St. Pauli :**

**Astron Suite-Hotel** without rest, Feldstr. 54, ✉ 20357, ☎ (040) 43 23 20, *Fax (040) 43232300*, ≋ – 🛗 ⇹ 📺 ☎ ☏ ♿ 🚗 – 👥 15. AE ⓓ E VISA JCB EY a
**119 rm** ☕ 250/360.

**at Hamburg-Stellingen** *by Grindelallee* FX :

**Holiday Inn**, Kieler Str. 333, ✉ 22525, ☎ (040) 54 74 00, *Fax (040) 54740100*, ≋ – 🛗, ⇹ rm, 📺 ☎ ☏ 🚗 🅿 – 👥 25. AE ⓓ E VISA JCB
**Meals** à la carte 37/50 – **105 rm** ☕ 231/252.

**Helgoland**, Kieler Str. 177, ✉ 22525, ☎ (040) 85 70 01, *Fax (040) 8511445* – 🛗, ⇹ rm, 📺 ☎ 🚗 🅿 – 👥 150. AE ⓓ E VISA JCB. ✈
**Meals** *(closed Sunday)* (dinner only) à la carte 38/53 – **110 rm** ☕ 160/230.

**at Hamburg-Stillhorn** *by Amsinckstr.* HZ :

**Forte Hotel Hamburg**, Stillhorner Weg 40, ✉ 21109, ☎ (040) 75 01 50, *Fax (040) 75015444*, Fö, ≋, 🏊 – 🛗, ⇹ rm, ▤ rest, 📺 ☏ ♿ 🅿 – 👥 160. AE ⓓ E VISA. ✈ rest
**Meals** à la carte 42/76 – **148 rm** ☕ 199/269.

**at Hamburg-Uhlenhorst** *by An der Alster* HX :

**Nippon** (Japanese installation and rest.), Hofweg 75, ✉ 22085, ☎ (040) 2 27 11 40, *Fax (040) 22711490* – 🛗 📺 ☎ 🚗 – 👥 20. AE ⓓ E VISA. ✈
**Meals** *(closed Monday)* (dinner only) à la carte 45/68 – **42 rm** ☕ 195/303.

---

## HANOVER (HANNOVER) 🄻 *Niedersachsen* 415 416 417 418 I 13, 987 ⑯ – *pop. 510 000 – alt. 55 m.*

**See :** *Herrenhausen Gardens (Herrenhäuser Gärten)★★ (Großer Garten★★, Berggarten★)* CV – *Kestner-Museum★* DY **M¹** – *Market Church (Marktkirche) (Altarpiece★★)* DY – *Museum of Lower Saxony (Niedersächsisches Landesmuseum) (Prehistorical department★)* EZ **M²** – *Museum of Arts (Kunstmuseum) (Collection Sprengel★)* EZ.

⛳ *Garbsen, Am Blauen See (W : 14 km),* ☎ *(05137) 7 30 68 ;* ⛳ *Isernhagen, Gut Lohne,* ☎ *(05139) 29 98 ;* ⛳ *Langenhagen, Hainhaus 22 (N : 12 km),* ☎ *(0511) 73 93 00.*

✈ *Hanover-Langenhagen (N : 11 km),* ☎ *(0511) 9 77 12 23.*

🚗 *Raschplatz* (EX).

*Exhibition Centre (Messegelände) (by Bischofsholer Damm* FY *and Messe Schnellweg),* ☎ *(0511) 8 90, Fax (0511) 8931216.*

🄸 *Tourist office, Ernst-August-Platz 2,* ✉ *30159,* ☎ *(0511) 30 14 0, Fax 301414.*

**ADAC,** *Nordmann Passage,* ✉ *30175,* ☎ *(0511) 12250, Fax (0511) 8500333.*

*Berlin 288 – Bremen 123 – Hamburg 151.*

Plans on following pages

**Kastens Hotel Luisenhof**, Luisenstr. 1, ✉ 30159, ☎ (0511) 3 04 40, *Fax (0511) 3044807* – 🛗, ⇹ rm, ▤ rest, 📺 ☏ ♿ 🚗 🅿 – 👥 100. AE ⓓ E VISA JCB. ✈ rest EX b
**Meals** *(closed Sunday July - August)* 35 (lunch) and à la carte 52/83 – **158 rm** ☕ 209/598 – 5 suites.

**Maritim Grand Hotel**, Friedrichswall 11, ✉ 30159, ☎ (0511) 3 67 70, *Fax (0511) 325195* – 🛗, ⇹ rm, ▤ rest, 📺 ♿ – 👥 250. AE ⓓ E VISA JCB DY a
***L'Adresse - Brasserie :*** **Meals** à la carte 54/78 – ***Wilhelm-Busch-Stube :*** *(dinner only, closed Sunday, Bank Holidays and mid July - mid August)* **Meals** à la carte 36/53 – **285 rm** ☕ 255/588 – 15 suites.

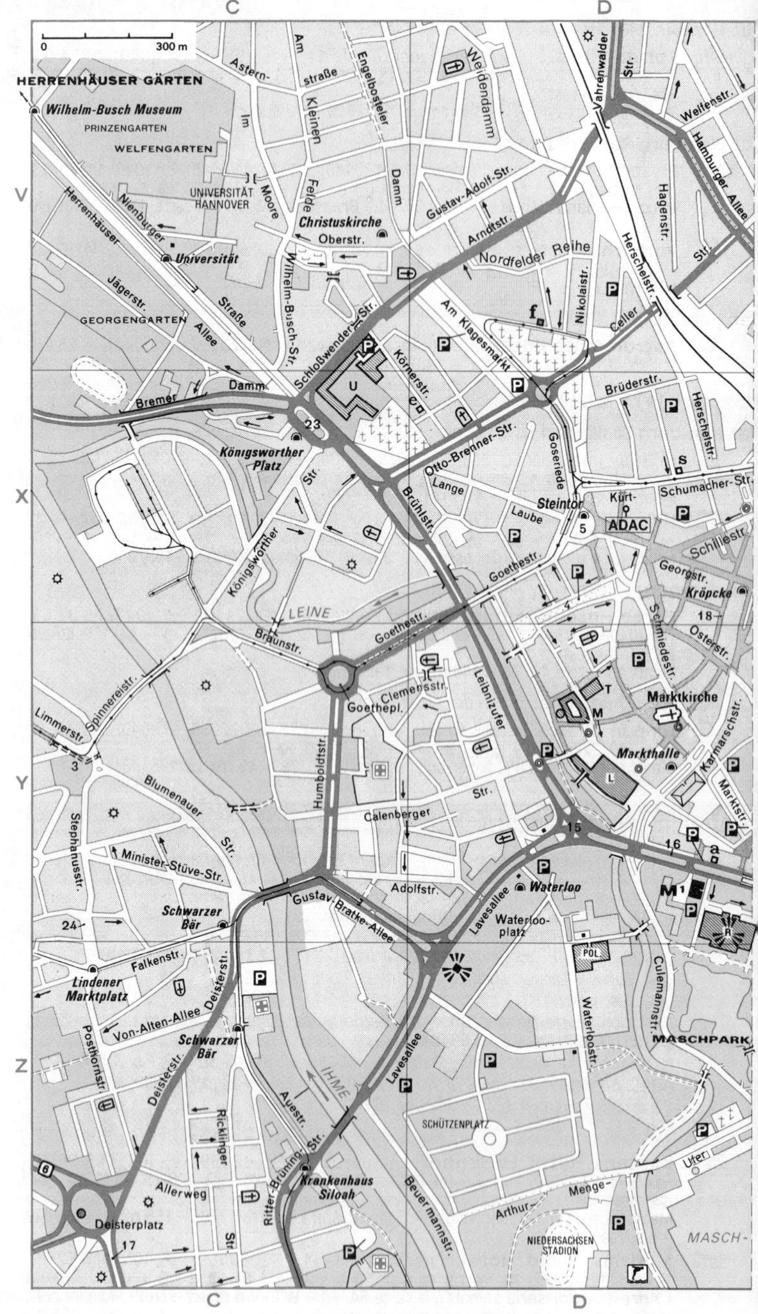
C
D
V
X
Y
Z
0
300 m
HERRENHÄUSER GÄRTEN
Wilhelm-Busch Museum
PRINZENGARTEN
WELFENGARTEN
UNIVERSITÄT HANNOVER
Universität
GEORGENGARTEN
Christuskirche
Königsworther Platz
LEINE
Goethepl.
Steintor
ADAC
Kröpcke
Marktkirche
Markthalle
Waterloo
Waterlooplatz
Schwarzer Bär
Lindener Marktplatz
Krankenhaus Siloah
Deisterplatz
SCHÜTZENPLATZ
NIEDERSACHSEN STADION
MASCHPARK
MASCH-
IHME
POL.

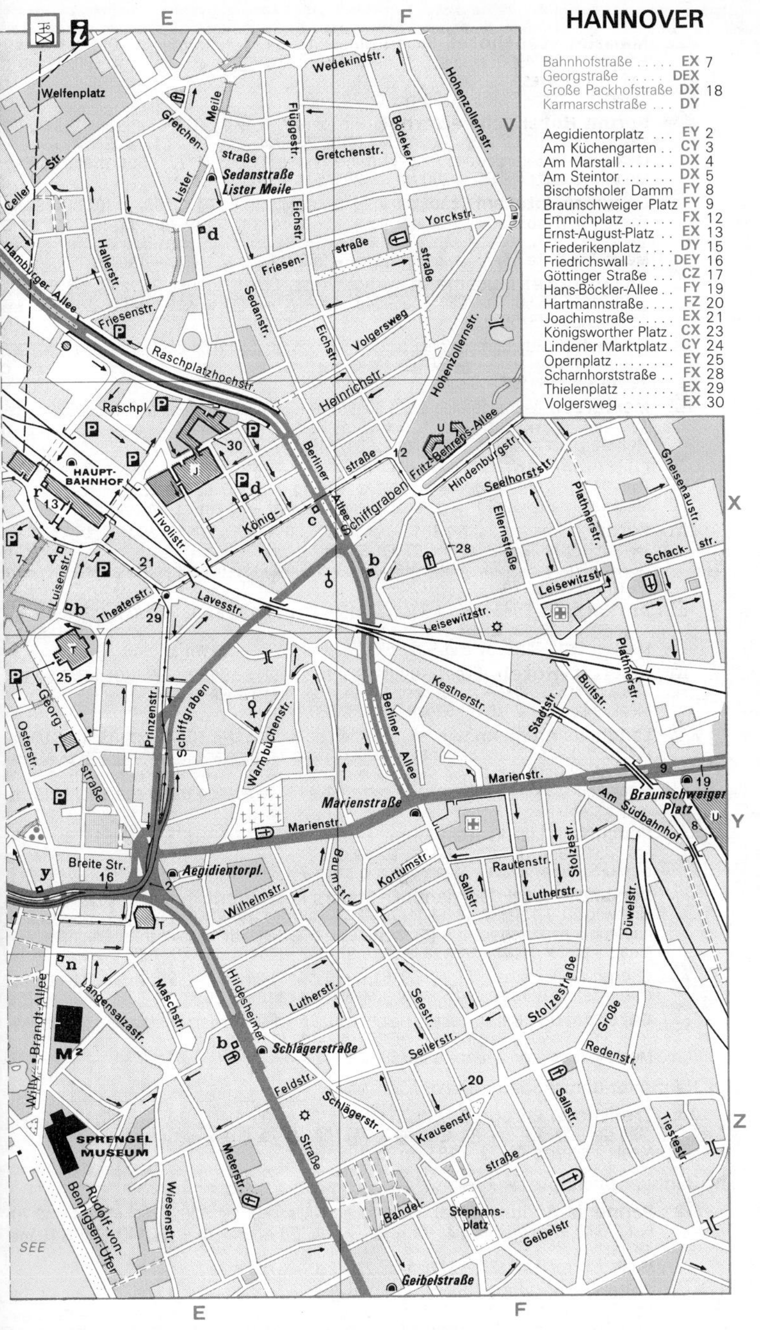
HANNOVER
Bahnhofstraße . . . . . EX 7
Georgstraße . . . . . DEX
Große Packhofstraße DX 18
Karmarschstraße . . . DY
Aegidientorplatz . . . EY 2
Am Küchengarten . . CY 3
Am Marstall . . . . . . . DX 4
Am Steintor . . . . . . . DX 5
Bischofsholer Damm FY 8
Braunschweiger Platz FY 9
Emmichplatz . . . . . . FX 12
Ernst-August-Platz . . EX 13
Friederikenplatz . . . . DY 15
Friedrichswall . . . . . DEY 16
Göttinger Straße . . . CZ 17
Hans-Böckler-Allee . . FY 19
Hartmannstraße . . . . FZ 20
Joachimstraße . . . . . EX 21
Königsworther Platz . CX 23
Lindener Marktplatz . CY 24
Opernplatz . . . . . . . . EY 25
Scharnhorststraße . . FX 28
Thielenplatz . . . . . . . EX 29
Volgersweg . . . . . . . EX 30
E
F
V
X
Y
Z
Welfenplatz
Celler Str.
Gretchen-straße
Meile
Lister Meile
Sedanstraße Lister Meile
Wedekindstr.
Flüggestr.
Gretchenstr.
Bödeker-straße
Hohenzollernstr.
Eichstr.
Yorckstr.
Friesen-straße
Hallerstr.
Hamburger Allee
Friesenstr.
Sedanstr.
Volgersweg
Raschplatzhochstr.
Heinrichstr.
Raschpl.
HAUPT-BAHNHOF
Berliner Allee
Fritz-Behrens-Allee
Hindenburgstr.
Seelhorststr.
Schiffgraben
König-straße
Tivolistr.
Ellernstraße
Plathnerstr.
Gneisenaustr.
Schack-str.
Leisewitzstr.
Luisenstr.
Theaterstr.
Lavesstr.
Kestnerstr.
Bultstr.
Stadtstr.
Georgstraße
Osterstr.
Prinzenstr.
Warmbüchenstr.
Marienstr.
Marienstraße
Braunschweiger Platz
Am Südbahnhof
Breite Str.
Aegidientorpl.
Wilhelmstr.
Baumstr.
Kortumstr.
Sallstr.
Rautenstr.
Lutherstr.
Stolzestr.
Düwelstr.
Langensalzastr.
Maschstr.
Hildesheimer Straße
Seestr.
Stolzestraße
Große Redenstr.
Willy-Brandt-Allee
M²
Schlägerstraße
Seilerstr.
Feldstr.
Schlägerstr.
Krausenstr.
Sallstr.
Tiestestr.
SPRENGEL MUSEUM
Meterstr.
Bandel-straße
Stephans-platz
Geibelstr
Rudolf-von-Bennigsen-Ufer
Wiesenstr.
SEE
Geibelstraße

**Maritim Stadthotel**, Hildesheimer Str. 34, ✉ 30169, ☎ (0511) 9 89 40, *Fax (0511) 9894900*, – rm, – 380. AE E VISA JCB. rest EZ b
Meals à la carte 56/83 – **293 rm** 245/598.

**Forum Hotel Schweizerhof**, Hinüberstr. 6, ✉ 30175, ☎ (0511) 3 49 50, *Fax (0511) 3495123* – rm, – 280. AE E VISA JCB
Meals *(closed Saturday and Sunday)* (dinner only) à la carte 41/72 – ***Gourmet's Buffet*** : Meals à la carte 48/77 – **200 rm** 293/521 – 3 suites. EX d

**Congress-Hotel am Stadtpark** M, Clausewitzstr. 6, ✉ 30175, ☎ (0511) 2 80 50, *Fax (0511) 814652*, Massage, – rm, – 1300. AE E VISA by Hans-Böckler Allee FY
Meals à la carte 33/75 *(also diet menu)* – **252 rm** 170/480 – 4 suites.

**Grand Hotel Mussmann** without rest, Ernst-August-Platz 7, ✉ 30159, ☎ (0511) 3 65 60, *Fax (0511) 3656145*, – – 50. AE E VISA
**137 rm** 178/598. EX v

**Königshof** without rest, Königstr. 12, ✉ 30175, ☎ (0511) 31 20 71, *Fax (0511) 312079* – – 30. AE E VISA EX c
**79 rm** 158/398 – 3 suites.

**Mercure**, Willy-Brandt-Allee 3, ✉ 30169, ☎ (0511) 8 00 80, *Fax (0511) 8093704*, – rm, – 130. AE E VISA EZ n
Meals à la carte 38/73 – **145 rm** 217/485.

**Loccumer Hof**, Kurt-Schumacher-Str. 16, ✉ 30159, ☎ (0511) 1 26 40, *Fax (0511) 131192* – rm, – 40. AE E VISA DX s
Meals à la carte 42/71 *(vegetarian menu available)* – **87 rm** 145/400.

**Körner**, Körnerstr. 24, ✉ 30159, ☎ (0511) 1 63 60, *Fax (0511) 18048*, – rm, – 50. AE E VISA DX e
*closed Christmas - New Year* – **Meals** *(closed Sunday)* 22 (lunch) and à la carte 43/63 – **75 rm** 140/240.

**Am Rathaus**, Friedrichswall 21, ✉ 30159, ☎ (0511) 32 62 68, *Fax (0511) 328868*, – . AE E VISA EY y
Meals *(closed Saturday and Sunday)* à la carte 33/66 – **40 rm** 140/395.

**InterCityHotel**, Ernst-August-Platz 1, ✉ 30159, ☎ (0511) 3 02 60, *Fax (0511) 3026499* – rest, – 100. AE E VISA EX r
Meals à la carte 29/55 – **57 rm** 125/380.

**Landhaus Ammann** with rm, Hildesheimer Str. 185, ✉ 30173, ☎ (0511) 83 08 18, *Fax (0511) 8437749*, « Elegant installation, patio with terrace », – – 100. AE E VISA JCB. rest by Hildesheimer Str. EFZ
Meals (outstanding wine list) à la carte 84/117 *(vegetarian menu available)* – **15 rm** 265/450.

**Feuchter's Lila Kranz** with rm, Berliner Str. 33, ✉ 30175, ☎ (0511) 85 89 21, *Fax (0511) 854383*, – . AE VISA FX b
*closed Saturday lunch* – **Meals** and à la carte 71/89 – **5 rm** 180/320.

**Romantik Hotel Georgenhof - Stern's Restaurant** with rm, Herrenhäuser Kirchweg 20, ✉ 30167, ☎ (0511) 70 22 44, *Fax (0511) 708559*, « Lower Saxony country house in a park, terrace » – . AE E VISA by Engelbosteler Damm CV
Meals (outstanding wine list) à la carte 87/130 – **14 rm** 170/450.

**Clichy**, Weißekreuzstr. 31, ✉ 30161, ☎ (0511) 31 24 47, *Fax (0511) 318283* – AE VISA
*closed Saturday lunch and Sunday* – **Meals** à la carte 63/96. EV d

**Gattopardo** (Italian rest.), Hainhölzer Str. 1 / corner Postkamp, ✉ 30159, ☎ (0511) 1 43 75, *Fax (0511) 318283*, – AE E DV f
Meals (dinner only) à la carte 48/68.

**at Hannover-Bemerode** *by Bischofsholer Damm* FY :

**Treff Hotel Europa**, Bergstr. 2, ✉ 30539, ☎ (0511) 9 52 80, *Fax (0511) 9528488*, – rm, – 300. AE E VISA. rest
Meals à la carte 40/72 – **183 rm** 195/595.

**at Hanover-Buchholz** *by Bödekerstr.* FV :

**Pannonia Atrium Hotel**, Karl-Wiechert-Allee 68, ✉ 30625, ☎ (0511) 5 40 70, *Fax (0511) 572878*, – rm, – 140. AE E VISA. rest
Meals à la carte 40/77 – **222rm** 220/290 – 6 suites.

**Gallo Nero**, Groß Buchholzer Kirchweg 72 b, ✉ 30655, ☎ (0511) 5 46 34 34, *Fax (0511) 548283*, « 18C farmhouse with contemporary interior design » – . E VISA
*closed Sunday, 1 week January and 3 weeks July - August* – **Meals** (outstanding Italian wine and grappa list) 58/88 and à la carte.

**at Hanover-Döhren :**

**Wichmann**, Hildesheimer Str. 230, ✉ 30519, ✆ (0511) 83 16 71, *Fax (0511) 8379811*, « Courtyard » – by Hildesheimer Str. EFZ
Meals à la carte 71/102.

**Die Insel**, Rudolf-von-Bennigsen-Ufer 81, ✉ 30519, ✆ (0511) 83 12 14, *Fax (0511) 831322*, ≤, – P. VISA by Rudolf-von Benningsen-Ufer EZ
*closed Monday* – Meals (booking essential) à la carte 49/93.

**at Hanover-Flughafen (Airport)** *by Vahrenwalder Str DV : 11 km :*

**Maritim Airport Hotel** M, Flughafenstr. 5, ✉ 30669, ✆ (0511) 9 73 70, *Fax (0711) 9737590*, – rm, – 850. AE D E VISA JCB. rest
Meals (buffet only) 45/49 – ***Bistro Bottaccio*** *(closed Sunday and Monday)* **Meals** à la carte 46/81 – **528 rm** 259/618 – 30 suites.

**Holiday Inn Crowne Plaza**, Petzelstr. 60, ✉ 30855 *Langenhagen*, ✆ (0511) 7 70 70, *Fax (0511) 737781*, – rm, P – 150. AE D E VISA JCB
**Meals** 37 (buffet lunch) and à la carte 54/79 – **210 rm** 260/560.

**at Hanover-Kirchrode** *by Hans-Böckler Allee FY :*

**Queens Hotel**, Tiergartenstr. 117, ✉ 30559, ✆ (0511) 5 10 30, *Fax (0511) 526924*, – rm, P – 160. AE D E VISA
**Meals** à la carte 42/75 – **176 rm** 236/520 – 3 suites.

**at Hanover-Kleefeld** *by Hans-Böckler Allee FY :*

**Kleefelder Hof** without rest, Kleestr. 3a, ✉ 30625, ✆ (0511) 5 30 80, *Fax (0511) 5308333* – P – 20. AE D E VISA JCB
**86 rm** 165/250.

**at Hanover-Lahe** *by Hohenzollernstraße FV :*

**Holiday Inn**, Oldenburger Allee 1, ✉ 30659, ✆ (0511) 6 15 50, *Fax (0511) 6155555*, – rm, P – 280. AE D E VISA
**Meals** à la carte 36/66 – **150 rm** 205/267.

**at Hannover-List** *by Hohenzollernstr. FV :*

**Seidler Hotel Pelikan** M, Podbielskistr. 145, ✉ 30177, ✆ (0511) 9 09 30, *Fax (0511) 9093555*, « Hotel with modern interior in a former factory », – rm, P – 150. AE D E VISA JCB
***Signatur* : Meals** à la carte 43/66 – ***Edo* :** (Japanese rest.) *(dinner only, closed Sunday)* **Meals** 65/130 – **138 rm** 250/530 – 8 suites.

**Dorint** M, Podbielskistr. 21, ✉ 30163, ✆ (0511) 3 90 40, *Fax (0511) 3904100*, – rm, – 250. AE D E VISA
**Meals** à la carte 39/79 – **206 rm** 229/575.

**at Hanover-Messe (near Exhibition Centre)** *by Hans-Böckler Allee FY :*

**Parkhotel Kronsberg**, Laatzener Str. 18 (at Exhibition Centre), ✉ 30539, ✆ (0511) 8 74 00, *Fax (0511) 867112*, – rm, rest, P – 200. AE D E VISA
**Meals** *(closed 26 December - 4 January)* à la carte 46/71 – **169 rm** 190/480.

**at Hanover-Roderbruch** *by Hans-Böckler Allee FY E : 7 km :*

**Novotel**, Feodor-Lynen-Str. 1, ✉ 30625, ✆ (0511) 9 56 60, *Fax (0511) 9566333*, (heated) – rm, P – 100. AE D E VISA
**Meals** à la carte 47/72 – **112 rm** 187/350.

**Ibis**, Feodor-Lynen-Str. 1, ✉ 30625, ✆ (0511) 9 56 70, *Fax (0511) 576128* – rm, P – 30. AE D E VISA
**Meals** (dinner only) 26 – **96 rm** 133/210.

**at Hanover-Vahrenwald** *by Vahrenwalder Str. DV N : 4km :*

**Fora**, Großer Kolonnenweg 19, ✉ 30163, ✆ (0511) 6 70 60, *Fax (0511) 6706111*, – rm, rest, – 100. AE D E VISA JCB
**Meals** à la carte 37/56 – **142 rm** 195/255.

**at Laatzen** *by Hildesheimer Str. EFZ S : 9 km :*

**Copthorne** M, Würzburger Str. 21, ✉ 30880, ✆ (0511) 9 83 60, *Fax (0511) 9836666*, – rm, P – 280. AE D E VISA JCB
**Meals** à la carte 37/69 – **222 rm** 272/530.

**Treff-Hotel Britannia Hannover**, Karlsruher Str. 26, ✉ 30880, ✆ (0511) 8 78 20, *Fax (0511) 863466*, (indoor) golf simulator – rm, P – 150. AE D E VISA. rest
**Meals** à la carte 40/72 – **100 rm** 195/595.

**at Ronnenberg-Benthe** *by Bornumer Str.* CZ *and B 65, SW : 10 km :*

**Benther Berg**, Vogelsangstr. 18, ✉ 30952, ☎ (05108) 6 40 60, *Fax (05108) 640650*, – rest, – 60.
**Meals** à la carte 69/93 – **70 rm** 145/240.

**Nenndorf, Bad** *Niedersachsen* 415 417 I 12, 987 ⑯ – *pop. 10 000 – alt. 70 m – Heilbad.*
*Hannover 33.*

**at Bad Nenndorf-Riepen** *NW : 4,5 km by B 65 :*

**La Forge** - Schmiedegasthaus Gehrke, Riepener Str. 21, ✉ 31542, ☎ (05725) 50 55, *Fax (05725) 7282* – .
*closed Monday - Tuesday, 2 weeks January and 3 weeks July - August* – **Meals** (dinner only)(booking essential) 105/150
**Spec.** Steckrübenröllchen mit Langostinos und Kümmelschaum. Schaumburger Milchzicklein (March-April). Karamelisierte Ziegenquarkcrème mit Essig-Brombeeren.

---

**LEIPZIG** *Sachsen* 418 *L 21,* 987 ⑰, 984 ⑱ – *pop. 480 000 – alt. 113 m.*
**See :** *Old Town Hall★ (Altes Rathaus)* BY – *Old Stock Exchange★ (Naschmarkt)* BY – *Museum of Fine Arts★ (Museum der Bildenden Künste)* BZ.
*Leipzig-Halle (NW : 13 km by Gerberstr. und Eutritzscher Straße* BY*), ☎ (0341)22 40.*
*Exhibition Grounds (Neue Messe), Messe-Allee 1 (by Eutritzscher Straße* BY*), ✉ 04356, ☎ (0341) 67 80, Fax (0341) 67 88 67 62.*
*Tourist-Information, Sachsenplatz 1, ✉ 04109, ☎ (0341) 7 10 40.*
**ADAC,** *Augustusplatz 6, ✉ 04109, ☎ (0351) 44 78 80, Fax (0341) 2110540.*
*Berlin 180 – Dresden 109 – Erfurt 126.*

Plans on following pages

**Kempinski Hotel Fürstenhof** M, Tröndlinring 8, ✉ 04105, ☎ (0341) 14 00, *Fax (0341) 1403700*, « 1770 Patrician palace », Massage, – – 60. BY c
**Meals** à la carte 46/98 – **92 rm** 380/610 – 4 suites.

**Inter-Continental**, Gerberstr. 15, ✉ 04105, ☎ (0341) 98 80, *Fax (0341) 9881229*, beer garden, Massage, – rm, – 450. rest BY a
**Meals** à la carte 56/79 – **447 rm** 294/453 – 18 suites.

**Renaissance** M, Querstr. 12, ✉ 04103, ☎ (0341) 1 29 20, *Fax (0341) 1292800*, – rm, – 350. DY a
**Meals** à la carte 41/58 – **356 rm** 266/422.

**Dorint Hotel Leipzig** M, Stephanstr. 6, ✉ 04103, ☎ (0341) 9 77 90, *Fax (0341) 9779100*, beer garden, – rm, – 150. DZ n
**Meals** à la carte 46/72 – **177 rm** 220/300.

**Parkhotel-SeaSide** M, Richard-Wagner-Str. 7, ✉ 04109, ☎ (0341) 9 85 20, *Fax (0341) 9852750*, – rm, rest, – 80. rest
**Meals** *(closed Sunday and July - 15 August)* à la carte 42/68 – **288 rm** 195/268 – 9 suites. CY s

**Michaelis** M, Paul-Gruner-Str. 44, ✉ 04107, ☎ (0341) 2 67 80, *Fax (0341) 2678100*, – rm, – 45. by Peterssteinweg BZ
**Meals** à la carte 41/55 – **60 rm** 160/195.

**Ramada** without rest, Gutenbergplatz 1, ✉ 04103, ☎ (0341) 1 29 30, *Fax (0341) 1293444* – – 20. DZ s
**122 rm** 143/216.

**Markgraf** without rest, Körnerstr.36, ✉ 04107, ☎ (0341) 30 30 30, *Fax (0341) 3030399* – . by Peterssteinweg BZ
**54 rm** 125/275.

**Novotel**, Goethestr. 11, ✉ 04109, ☎ (0341) 9 95 80, *Fax (0341) 9958200*, – rm, – 100. CY n
**Meals** à la carte 34/65 – **200 rm** 189/219.

**Mercure Leipzig**, Augustusplatz 5, ✉ 04109, ☎ (0341) 2 14 60, *Fax (0341) 9604916* – rm, – 100. CZ f
**Meals** à la carte 34/57 – **283 rm** 150/210 – 10 suites.

**Deutscher Hof** M, Waldstr. 31, ✉ 04105, ☎ (0341) 7 11 00, *Fax (0341) 7110222* – . by Gustav-Adolf-Str. AY
**Meals** *(closed Sunday except exhibitions)* (dinner only) à la carte 32/65 – **39 rm** 150/195.

**Holiday Inn Garden Court**, Rudolf-Breitscheid-Str. 3, ✉ 04105, ℘ (0341) 1 25 10, *Fax (0341) 1251100*, – rm, AE VISA JCB CY g
Meals à la carte 28/51 – **121 rm** 190/270 – 6 suites.

**Leipziger Hof** M, Hedwigstr. 3, ✉ 04315, ℘ (0341) 6 97 40, *Fax (0341) 6974150*, « Permanent exhibition of paintings », – rm, – 20. AE VISA by Eisenbahnstraße DY
Meals *(closed Saturday - Sunday)* (dinner only) à la carte 31/45 – **73 rm** 155/240.

**Rema Hotel Vier Jahreszeiten** M without rest, Rudolf Breitscheidstr. 23, ✉ 04105, ℘ (0341) 9 85 10, *Fax (0341) 985122* – AE VISA JCB CY b
67 rm 150/330.

**Ibis** without rest, Brühl 69, ✉ 04109, ℘ (0341) 2 18 60, *Fax (0341) 2186222* – AE VISA CY a
**126 rm** 139/154.

**Kaiser Maximilian**, Neumarkt 9, ✉ 04105, ℘ (0341) 9 98 69 00, *Fax (0341) 9986901*, – AE BZ a
Meals à la carte 47/74.

**Stadtpfeiffer**, Augustusplatz 8 (Neues Gewandhaus), ✉ 04109, ℘ (0341) 9 60 51 86, *Fax (0341) 2113594*, – AE VISA CZ
*closed Sunday* – **Meals** (outstanding wine list) à la carte 42/72.

**Apels Garten** Kolonnadenstr. 2, ✉ 04109, ℘ (0341) 9 60 77 77, *Fax (0341) 9607777*, – 30. AE VISA AZ q
*closed dinner Sunday and Bank Holidays* – **Meals** à la carte 25/51.

**Medici** (Italian rest.), Nikolaikirchhof 5, ✉ 04109, ℘ (0341) 2 11 38 78, *Fax (0341) 9262200* – AE VISA CY c
*closed Sunday and 23 December - 4 January* – **Meals** à la carte 55/71.

**Auerbachs Keller** (16C historical wine tavern), Grimmaische Str. 2 (Mädler-Passage), ✉ 04109, ℘ (0341) 21 61 00, *Fax (0341) 2161011* – AE VISA BYZ
**Meals** à la carte 53/74 – ***Großer Keller*** **: Meals** à la carte 36/66.

**Thüringer Hof**, Burgstr. 19, ✉ 04109, ℘ (0341) 9 94 49 99, *Fax (0341) 9944933*, , « Restored 15C tavern » – AE VISA BZ s
**Meals** à la carte 31/59.

**Mövenpick**, Naschmarkt 1, ✉ 04109, ℘ (0341) 2 11 77 22, *Fax (0341) 2114810*, – . AE VISA BY r
**Meals** à la carte 31/60.

**at Leipzig-Eutritzsch** *by Eutritzscher Str.* BY :

**Prodomo**, Gräfestr. 15a, ✉ 04129, ℘ (0341) 9 03 50, *Fax (0341) 9035113* – , rm, . AE VISA
**Meals** (dinner only) à la carte 32/53 – **80 rm** 95/155.

**at Leipzig-Gohlis** *by Pfaffendorfer Str.* BY :

**De Saxe**, Gohliser Str. 25, ✉ 01455, ℘ (0341) 5 93 80, *Fax (0341) 5938299* – , rm, . AE VISA
**Meals** à la carte 31/49 – ***Bistro*** **: Meals** à la carte 29/39 – **33 rm** 150/195.

**at Leipzig-Grosszschocher** *by Käthe-Kollwitz-Str.* AZ *and Erich-Zeigner-Allee* :

**Windorf**, Gerhard-Ellrodt-Str. 21, ✉ 04249, ℘ (0341) 4 27 70, *Fax (0341) 4277222*, – , rm, – 50. AE VISA
**Meals** à la carte 31/50 – **98 rm** 145/185.

**at Leipzig-Leutzsch** *by Friedrich-Ebert-Str.* AY :

**Lindner Hotel** M, Hans-Driesch-Str. 27, ✉ 04179, ℘ (0341) 4 47 80, *Fax (0341) 4478478*, , , – , rm, – 120. AE VISA JCB. rest
**Meals** à la carte 49/77 – **185 rm** 212/359 – 15 suites.

**at Leipzig-Lindenau** *by Jahn-Allee* AY :

**Lindenau** M, Georg-Schwarz-Str. 33, ✉ 04177, ℘ (0341) 4 48 03 10, *Fax (0341) 4480300*, – , rm, – 25. AE VISA JCB
**Meals** (dinner only) à la carte 35/47 – **52 rm** 135/190.

**at Leipzig-Möckern** *by Eutritzscher Str.* BY :

**Silencium** M without rest, Georg-Schumann-Str. 268, ✉ 04159, ℘ (0341) 9 01 29 90, *Fax (0341) 9012991* – – 40. AE VISA
*closed 24 December - 6 January* – **34 rm** 114/169.

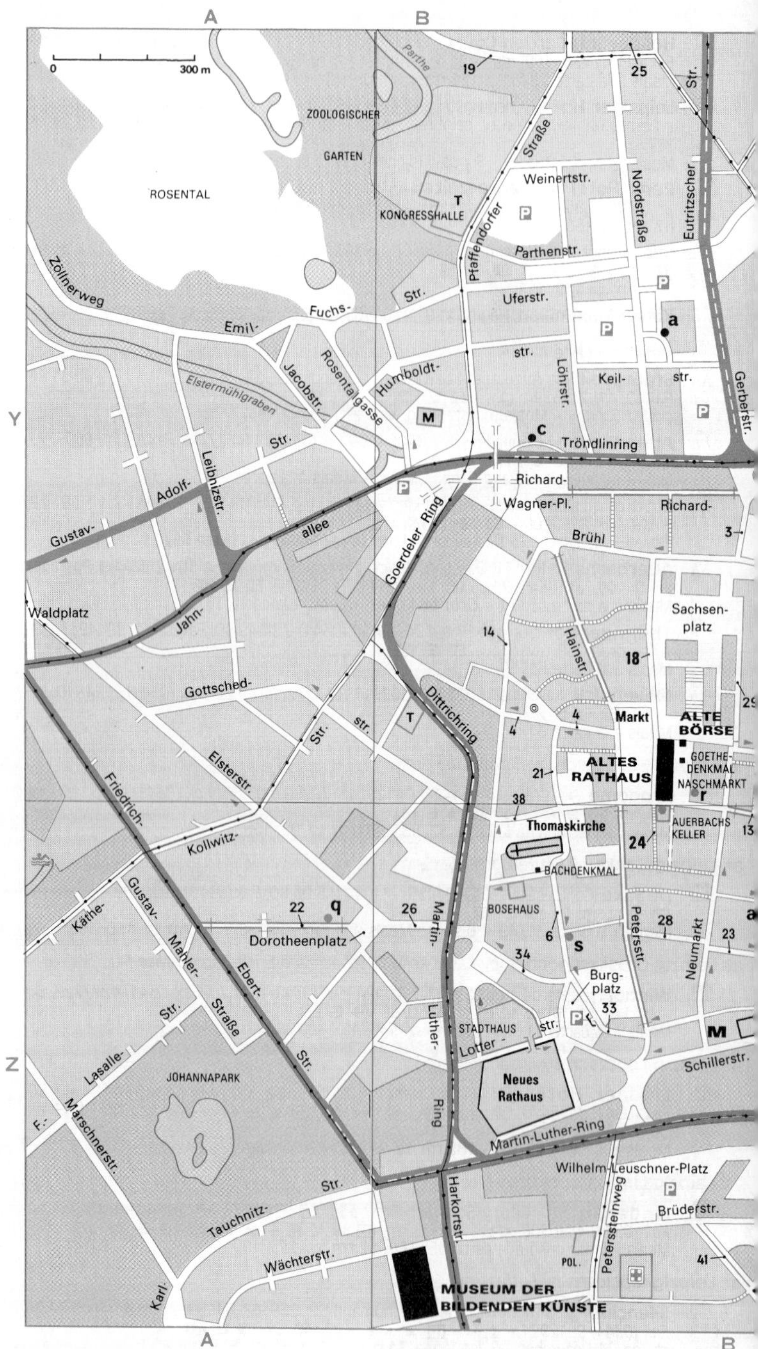
A
B
0
300 m
ZOOLOGISCHER
GARTEN
ROSENTAL
KONGRESSHALLE
Parthe
19
25
Pfaffendorfer
Straße
Weinertstr.
Nordstraße
Eutritzscher
Str.
Parthenstr.
Uferstr.
Zöllnerweg
Emil-
Fuchs-
Str.
a
Löhrstr.
Keil-
str.
Gerberstr.
Jacobstr.
Rosentalgasse
Humboldt-
Elstermühlgraben
Y
c
Tröndlinring
Str.
Leibnizstr.
Adolf-
Gustav-
allee
Goerdeler Ring
Richard-
Wagner-Pl.
Richard-
Brühl
3
Waldplatz
Jahn-
Sachsen-
platz
14
Hainstr.
18
Gottsched-
Dittrichring
str.
Str.
4
4
Markt
ALTE
BÖRSE
GOETHE-
DENKMAL
NASCHMARKT
21
ALTES
RATHAUS
r
Elsterstr.
Friedrich-
38
Thomaskirche
AUERBACHS
KELLER
24
13
Kollwitz-
BACHDENKMAL
Käthe-
Gustav-
22
q
26
Martin-
BOSEHAUS
Petersstr.
28
23
Dorotheenplatz
6
s
Neumarkt
Mahler-
Ebert-
34
Burg-
platz
Str.
Straße
33
Luther-
STADTHAUS
str.
M
Lotter-
Z
Lasalle-
Str.
Schillerstr.
JOHANNAPARK
Neues
Rathaus
F.-
Marschnerstr.
Ring
Martin-Luther-Ring
Wilhelm-Leuschner-Platz
Str.
Harkortstr.
Peterssteinweg
Brüderstr.
Tauchnitz-
Wächterstr.
POL.
41
Karl-
MUSEUM DER
BILDENDEN KÜNSTE
A
B

# LEIPZIG

| Street | Grid | No. |
|---|---|---|
| Althner Straße | DY | 2 |
| Am Hallischen Tor | BY | 3 |
| Barfußgäßchen | BY | 4 |
| Dörrienstraße | DY | 8 |
| Grimmaischer Steinweg | CZ | 12 |
| Grimmaische Str. | BCYZ | 13 |
| Große Fleischer gasse | BY | 14 |
| Katharinenstraße | BY | 18 |
| Kickerlingsberg | BY | 19 |
| Klostergasse | BY | 21 |
| Kolonnadenstr. | AZ | 22 |
| Kupfergasse | BZ | 23 |
| Mädlerpassage | BZ | 24 |
| Nordplatz | BY | 25 |
| Otto-Schill-Str. | BZ | 26 |
| Preußergäßchen | BZ | 28 |
| Reichsstraße | BY | 29 |
| Reudnitzer Str. | DY | 32 |
| Schloßgasse | BZ | 33 |
| Schulstraße | BZ | 34 |
| Schützenstraße | DY | 37 |
| Thomaskirchhof | BYZ | 38 |
| Universitätsstr. | CZ | 39 |
| Windmühlenstr. | BCZ | 41 |
| Wintergartenstr. | CY | 42 |

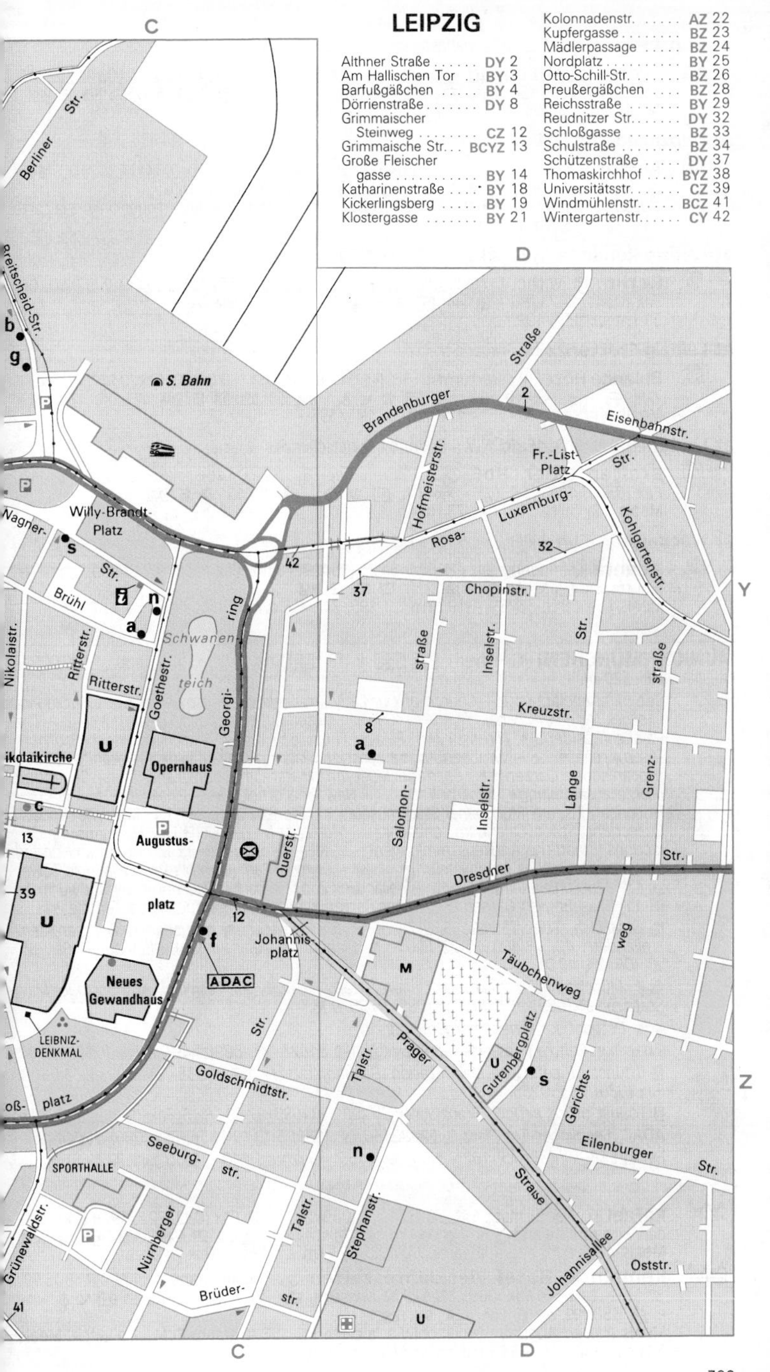

**at Leipzig-Paunsdorf** *by Eisenbahnstraße* DY :

**Treff Hotel Leipzig** M, Schongauer Str. 39, ✉ 04329, ☎ (0341) 25 40, *Fax (0341) 2541550*, – rm, – 600. AE E VISA
**Meals** à la carte 37/65 – **291 rm** 129/339.

**at Leipzig-Portitz** *by Berliner Str.* CY :

**Accento**, Tauchaer Str. 260, ✉ 04349, ☎ (0341) 9 26 20, *Fax (0341) 9262100*, – rm, rest, – 60. AE E VISA JCB
*closed Christmas - 4 January* – **Meals** *(closed Saturday and Sunday)* (dinner only) à la carte 26/52 – **115 rm** 179/279.

**at Leipzig-Reudnitz** *by Dresdner Str.* DZ *and Breite Str.* :

**Berlin** M without rest, Riebeckstr. 30, ✉ 04317, ☎ (0341) 2 67 30 00, *Fax (0341) 2673280* – – 10. AE E VISA JCB
**51 rm** 139/199.

**at Leipzig-Stötteritz** *by Prager Str.* DZ :

**Balance Hotel**, Wasserturmstr. 33, ✉ 04299, ☎ (0341) 8 67 90, *Fax (0341) 8679444*, – rm, rest, – 35. AE E VISA JCB. rest
**Meals** à la carte 32/55 – **126 rm** 195/395 – 16 suites.

**at Lindenthal-Breitenfeld** *NW : 8 km, by Euritzscher Str.* BX :

**Breitenfelder Hof**, Lindenallee 8, ✉ 04466, ☎ (0341) 4 65 10, *Fax (0341) 4651133*, – rm, – 20. AE E VISA
**Meals** à la carte 30/50 – **73 rm** 175/225.

**at Wachau** *SO : 8 km, by Prager Straße* DZ :

**Atlanta** M, Südring 21, ✉ 04445, ☎ (034297) 8 40, *Fax (034297) 84999*, – rm, – 220. AE E VISA
**Meals** à la carte 36/59 – **191 rm** 195/245 – 6 suites.

---

**MUNICH (MÜNCHEN)** L *Bayern* 419 420 V 18, 987 ㊵, 426 G 4 – *pop. 1 300 000 – alt. 520 m.*

**See** : *Marienplatz*★ KZ – *Church of Our Lady (Frauenkirche)*★ *(tower* ※★*)* KZ – *Old Pinakothek (Alte Pinakothek)*★★★ KY – *German Museum (Deutsches Museum)*★★★ LZ – *The Palace (Residenz)*★ *(Treasury*★★ *Palace Theatre*★*)* KY – *Church of Asam Brothers (Asamkirche)*★ KZ – *Nymphenburg*★★ *(Castle*★, *Park*★, *Amalienburg*★★, *Botanical Garden (Botanischer Garten)*★★, *Carriage Museum (Marstallmuseum) and China-Collection (Porzellansammlung*★*) by Arnulfstr.* EV – *New Pinakothek (Neue Pinakothek)*★ KY – *City Historical Museum (Münchener Stadtmuseum)*★ *(Moorish Dancers*★★*)* KZ **M7** – *Villa Lenbach Collections (Städt. Galerie im Lenbachhaus) (Portraits by Lenbach*★*)* JY **M4** – *Antique Collections (Staatliche Antikensammlungen)*★ JY **M3** – *Glyptothek*★ JY **M2** – *German Hunting Museum (Deutsches Jagdmuseum)*★ KZ **M1** – *Olympic Park (Olympia-Park) (Olympic Tower* ※★★★*) by Schleißheimer Str.* FU – *Hellabrunn Zoo (Tierpark Hellabrunn)*★ *by Lindwurmstr. (B 11)* EX – *English Garden (Englischer Garten)*★ *(view from Monopteros Temple* ★*)* LY.

18 *Straßlach, Tölzer Straße (S : 17 km), ☎ (08170) 4 50 ;* 9 *München-Thalkirchen, Zentralländstr. 40, ☎ (089) 7 23 13 04 ;* 18 *Eichenried (NE : 24 km), Münchener Str. 55, ☎ (08123) 10 05.*

✈ *München (NE : 29 km) by Ungererstraße* HU, *City Air Terminal, Arnulfstraße (Main Station), ☎ (089) 9 75 00, Fax (089) 97557906.*

*Ostbahnhof, Friedenstraße* (HX).

*Exhibition Centre (Messegelände)* (by ③), ✉ *81823, ☎ (089) 9 49 01, Fax (089) 94909.*

**i** *Tourist office in the Main Station, Bahnhofsplatz 2, ✉ 80335, ☎ (089) 2 33 03 00, Fax (089) 23330233.*

**i** *Tourist-office, airport "Franz-Josef-Strauß", ☎ (089) 97 59 28 15, Fax (089) 975292813.*

**ADAC**, *Sendlinger-Tor-Platz 9, ✉ 80336, ☎ (089) 5 40 19 44 56, Fax (089) 5504449.*

*Berlin 586 – Innsbruck 162 – Nürnberg 165 – Salzburg 140 – Stuttgart 222.*

Plans on following pages

**Rafael** M, Neuturmstr. 1, ✉ 80331, ☎ (089) 29 09 80, *Fax (089) 222539*, « Roof garden with terrace and » – rm, – 50. AE E VISA JCB. rest
**Meals** 48 (lunch) and à la carte 74/102 – **73 rm** 485/800 – 7 suites. KZ s

**Kempinski Hotel Vier Jahreszeiten**, Maximilianstr. 17, ✉ 80539, ☎ (089) 2 12 50, *Fax (089) 21252000*, Massage, – rm, – 350. AE E VISA JCB. rest LZ a
**Meals** *(closed August)* (dinner only) à la carte 65/106 – ***Bistro-Eck*** *(also lunch)* **Meals** à la carte 45/71 – **316 rm** 453/865 – 48 suites.

**Bayerischer Hof**, Promenadeplatz 6, 80333, (089) 2 12 00, *Fax (089) 2120906*, Massage, – rm, – 600. AE VISA JCB
***Garden-Restaurant*** *(booking essential)* **Meals** à la carte 72/116 – ***Trader Vic's*** *(dinner only)* **Meals** à la carte 50/80 – ***Palais Keller*:** **Meals** à la carte 31/54 – **396 rm** 328/605 – 45 suites. KY y

**Königshof**, Karlsplatz 25, 80335, (089) 55 13 60, *Fax (089) 55136113* – rm, – 80. AE VISA JCB. rest JY s
**Meals** (booking essential) (outstanding wine list) à la carte 83/126 – **90 rm** 328/614 – 9 suites.

**Park Hilton**, Am Tucherpark 7, 80538, (089) 3 84 50, *Fax (089) 38451845*, beer garden, Massage, – rm, – 750. AE VISA JCB HU n
**Meals** see also ***Hilton Grill*** *below* – ***Tse Yang*** (Chinese rest.) *(closed Monday)* **Meals** à la carte 47/88 – ***Isar Terrassen*:** **Meals** à la carte 51/79 – **477 rm** 333/618 – 21 suites.

**Excelsior**, Schützenstr. 11, 80335, (089) 55 13 70, *Fax (089) 55137121* – rm, AE VISA JCB. rest JY z
***Vinothek*** **:** **Meals** à la carte 45/57 – **113 rm** 247/424 – 4 suites.

**Maritim** M, Goethestr. 7, 80336, (089) 55 23 50, *Fax (089) 55235900*, – rm, – 250. AE VISA JCB. rest JZ j
**Meals** à la carte 53/86 – **339 rm** 288/520 – 5 suites.

**Arabella Westpark Hotel**, Garmischer Str. 2, 80339, (089) 5 19 60, *Fax (089) 5196649*, – rm, rest, – 80. AE VISA JCB by Leopoldstr. GU
*closed 19 December - 6 January* – **Meals** 42 (buffet lunch) and à la carte 44/72 – **258 rm** 225/466 – 6 suites.

**Eden-Hotel-Wolff**, Arnulfstr. 4, 80335, (089) 55 11 50, *Fax (089) 55115555* – rm, – 140. AE VISA JCB JY p
**Meals** à la carte 34/65 – **211 rm** 218/450.

**King's Hotel** without rest, Dachauer Str. 13, 80335, (089) 55 18 70, *Fax (089) 55187300* – – 30. AE VISA JCB JY f
**96 rm** 210/295 – 5 suites.

**Trustee Parkhotel** without rest, Parkstr. 31 (approach in Gollierstraße), 80339, (089) 51 99 50, *Fax (089) 51995420* – – 30. AE VISA JCB EX r
*closed 23 - 28 December* – **35 rm** 245/476 – 6 suites.

**Exquisit** without rest, Pettenkoferstr. 3, 80336, (089) 5 51 99 00, *Fax (089) 55199499*, – – 30. AE VISA JZ s
**50 rm** 195/320 – 5 suites.

**Platzl**, Platzl 1 (entrance in Sparkassenstraße), 80331, (089) 23 70 30, *Fax (089) 23703800*, – rm, – 50. AE VISA
***Pfistermühle*** *(closed Saturday lunch, Sunday and mid July - mid August)* **Meals** à la carte 42/78 – **167 rm** 235/430. KZ z

**Krone** without rest, Theresienhöhe 8, 80339, (089) 50 40 52, *Fax (089) 506706* – – 15. VISA EX a
**30 rm** 110/330.

**Arabella-Central-Hotel** without rest, Schwanthalerstr. 111, 80339, (089) 51 08 30, *Fax (089) 51083249*, – – 30. AE VISA
*closed 21 December - 7 January* – **102 rm** 216/422. EX s

**Europa**, Dachauer Str. 115, 80335, (089) 54 24 20, *Fax (089) 54242500*, – rm, – 60. AE VISA FU c
***Isola Bella*** (Italian rest.) **Meals** à la carte 30/56 – **180 rm** 180/350 – 7 suites.

**Erzgießerei-Europe**, Erzgießereistr. 15, 80335, (089) 12 68 20, *Fax (089) 1236198*, – rm, – 50. AE VISA JY a
**Meals** *(closed Sunday lunch and Saturday)* à la carte 33/58 – **106 rm** 170/300.

**Ambiente** without rest, Schillerstr. 12, 80336, (089) 54 51 70, *Fax (089) 54517200* – . AE VISA JCB JZ m
**46 rm** 182/250.

**Domus** without rest, St.-Anna-Str. 31, 80538, (089) 22 17 04, *Fax (089) 2285359* – . AE VISA LY b
*closed 23 to 28 December* – **45 rm** 198/290.

**Carathotel** M without rest, Lindwurmstr. 13, 80337, (089) 23 03 80, *Fax (089) 23038199* – . AE VISA JZ f
**70 rm** 205/320.

**Drei Löwen** without rest, Schillerstr. 8, 80336, (089) 55 10 40, *Fax (089) 55104905* – – 15. AE VISA JCB JZ m
**82 rm** 182/315.

## STREET INDEX



Continued on following pages

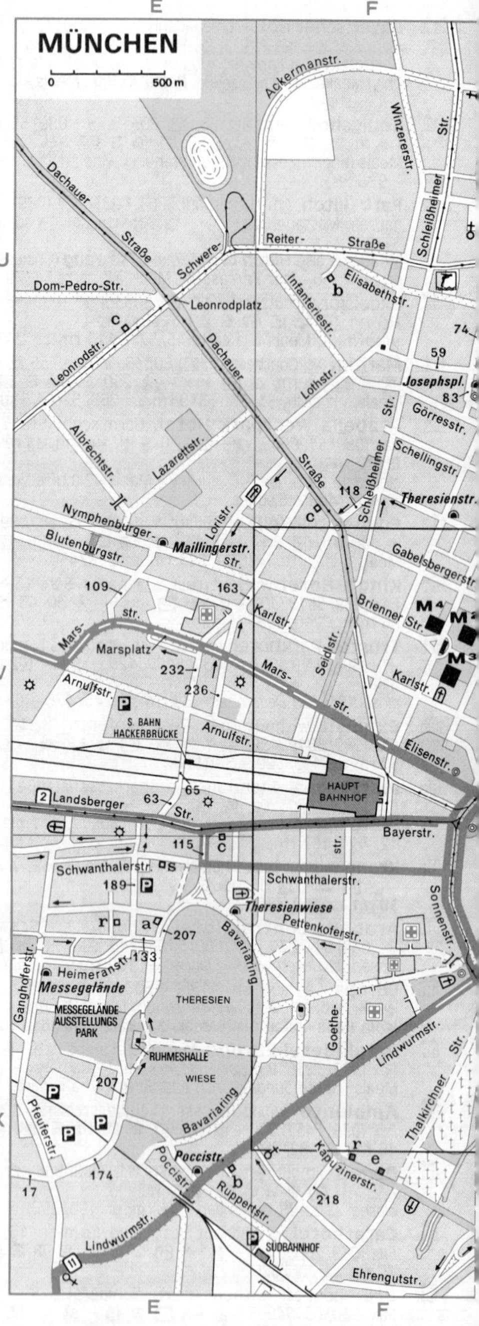

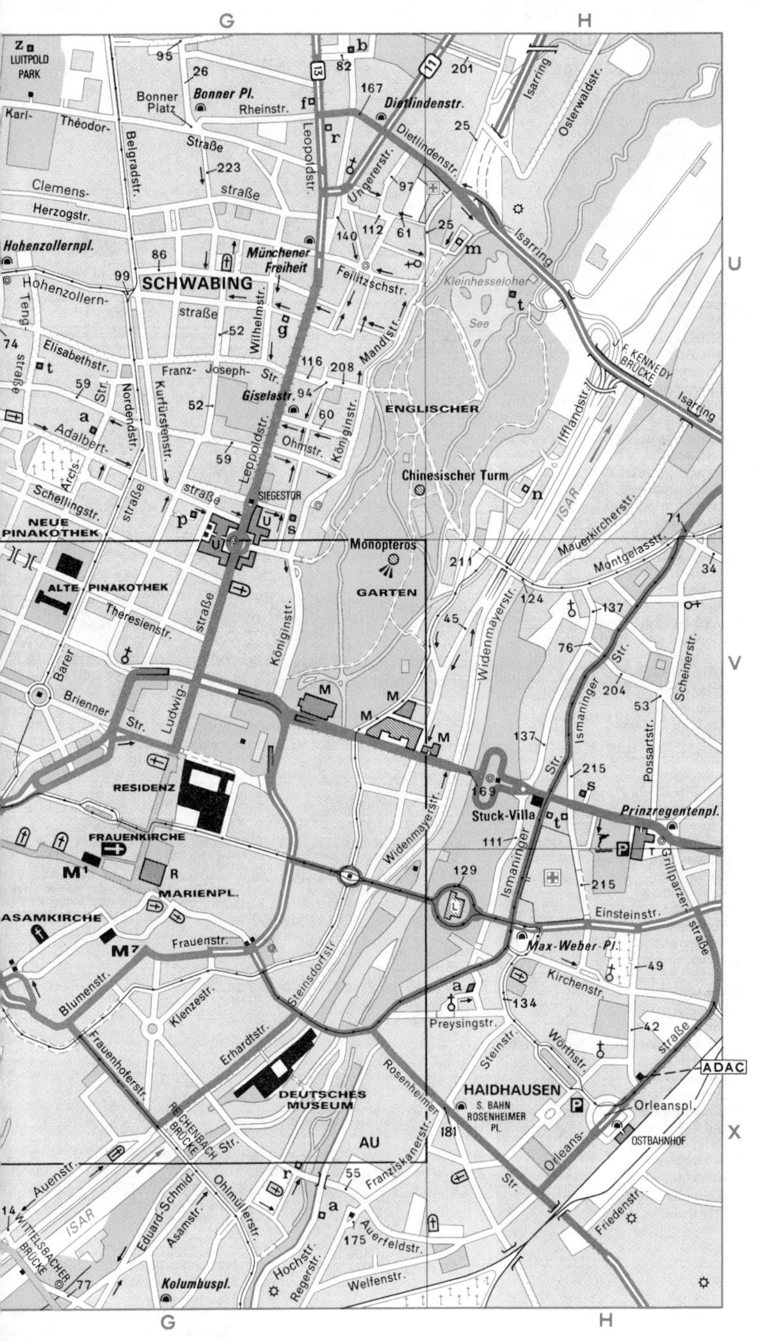
G
H
U
V
X
LUITPOLD PARK
Bonner Pl.
Bonner Platz
Rheinstr.
Dietlindenstr.
Karl-
Theodor-
Straße
Clemens-
straße
Herzogstr.
Belgradstr.
Leopoldstr.
Ungererstr.
Hohenzollernpl.
Münchener Freiheit
SCHWABING
Hohenzollern-
straße
Feilitzschstr.
Kleinhesseloher See
Isarring
Osterwaldstr.
Wilhelmstr.
Mandlstr.
Elisabethstr.
Franz-Joseph-Str.
Giselastr.
ENGLISCHER
GARTEN
J.F. KENNEDY BRÜCKE
Adalbert-
Ohmstr.
Königinstr.
Chinesischer Turm
Ifflandstr.
Kurfürstenstr.
Nordendstr.
Schellingstr.
SIEGESTOR
Monopteros
NEUE PINAKOTHEK
ALTE PINAKOTHEK
Theresienstr.
Mauerkircherstr.
Montgelasstr.
ISAR
Barer Str.
Brienner Str.
Ludwigstraße
Widenmayerstr.
Ismaninger Str.
Possartstr.
Scheinerstr.
RESIDENZ
Stuck-Villa
Prinzregentenpl.
FRAUENKIRCHE
MARIENPL.
Einsteinstr.
Grillparzerstraße
ASAMKIRCHE
Frauenstr.
Max-Weber-Pl.
Kirchenstr.
Blumenstr.
Klenzestr.
Steinsdorfstr.
Preysingstr.
Wörthstr.
Steinstr.
Frauenhoferstr.
Erhardtstr.
DEUTSCHES MUSEUM
Rosenheimer Str.
HAIDHAUSEN
S. BAHN ROSENHEIMER PL.
ADAC
Orleanspl.
Orleans-
OSTBAHNHOF
REICHENBACH BRÜCKE
AU
Auenstr.
Franziskanerstr.
Ohlmüllerstr.
Eduard-Schmid-
Asamstr.
WITTELSBACHER BRÜCKE
Hochstr.
Regerstr.
Auerfeldstr.
Welfenstr.
Friedenstr.
Kolumbuspl.

## STREET INDEX



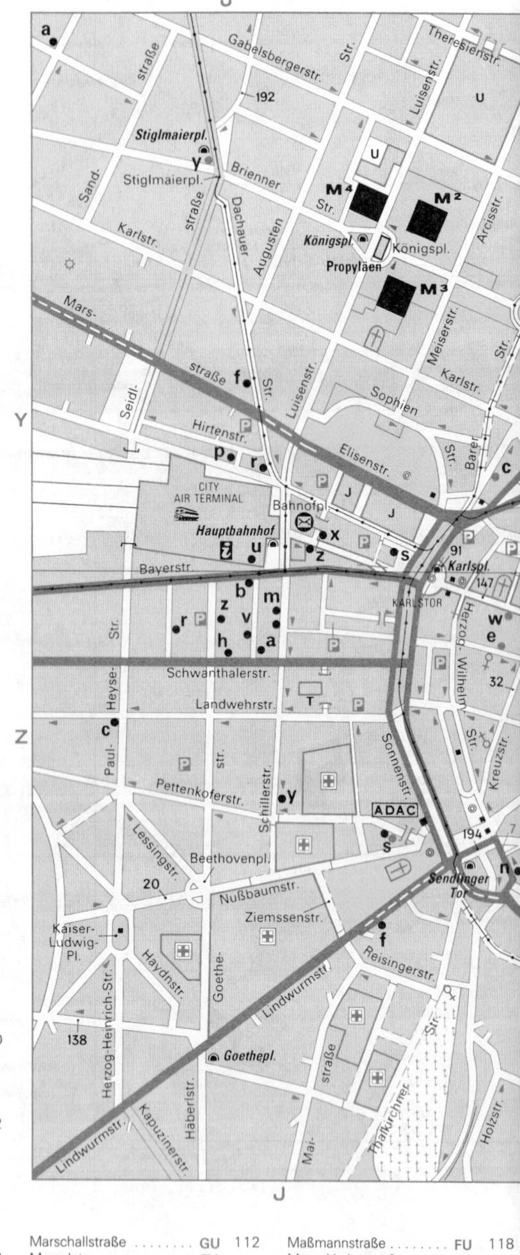

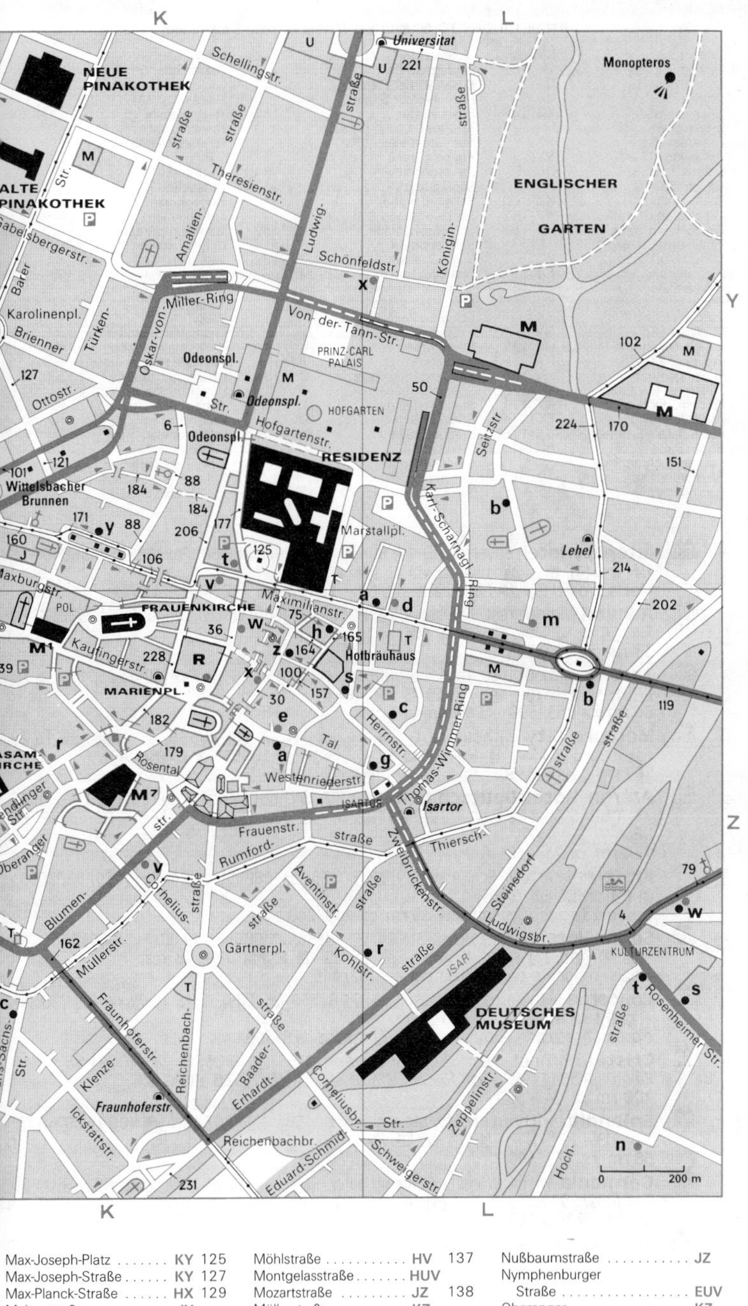




Continued on following page

## STREET INDEX TO MÜNCHEN TOWN PLANS (Concluded)

| Street | Plan | No. |
|---|---|---|
| Odeonsplatz | KY | |
| Oettingenstraße | LY | 151 |
| Ohlmüllerstraße | GX | |
| Ohmstraße | GU | |
| Orlandostraße | KZ | 157 |
| Orleansplatz | HX | |
| Orleansstraße | HX | |
| Oskar-von-Miller-Ring | KY | |
| Osterwaldstraße | HU | |
| Ottostraße | KY | |
| Pacellistraße | KY | 160 |
| Papa-Schmid-Straße | KZ | 162 |
| Pappenheimstraße | EV | 163 |
| Paul-Heyse-Straße | JZ | |
| Pettenkoferstraße | JZ | |
| Pfeuferstraße | EX | |
| Pfisterstraße | KZ | 164 |
| Platzl | KZ | 165 |
| Poccistraße | EX | |
| Possartstraße | HV | |
| Potsdamer Straße | GU | 167 |
| Preysingstraße | HX | |
| Prinzregentenbrücke | HV | 169 |
| Prinzregentenstraße | LY | 170 |
| Promenadeplatz | KY | 171 |
| Radlkoferstraße | EX | 174 |
| Regerplatz | GX | 175 |
| Regerstraße | GX | |
| Reichenbachbrücke | KZ | |
| Reichenbachstraße | KZ | |
| Reisingerstraße | JZ | |
| Rheinstraße | GU | |
| Rindermarkt | KZ | 179 |
| Rosenheimer Platz | HX | 181 |
| Rosenheimer Straße | LZ | |
| Rosenstraße | KZ | 182 |
| Rosental | KZ | |
| Rumfordstraße | KZ | |
| Ruppertstraße | EFX | |
| Salvatorstraße | KY | 184 |
| Sandstraße | JY | |
| Scheinerstraße | HV | |
| Schellingstraße | KY | |
| Schießstättstraße | EX | 189 |
| Schillerstraße | JZ | |
| Schleißheimer Str. | JY | 192 |
| Schönfeldstraße | KLY | |
| Schwanthalerstraße | JZ | |
| Schweigerstraße | LZ | |
| Schwere-Reiter-Straße | EFU | |
| Seidlstraße | JY | |
| Seitzstraße | LY | |
| Sendlinger-Tor-Platz | JZ | 194 |
| Sophienstraße | JY | |
| Steinsdorfstraße | LZ | |
| Steinstraße | HX | |
| Stengelstraße | HU | 201 |
| Sternstraße | LZ | 202 |
| Sternwartstraße | HV | 204 |
| Stiglmaierplatz | JY | |
| Tal | KZ | |
| Tengstraße | GU | |
| Thalkirchner Straße | JZ | |
| Theresienhöhe | EX | 207 |
| Theresienstraße | JK | |
| Thiemestraße | GU | 208 |
| Thierschstraße | LZ | |
| Thomas-Wimmer-Ring | LZ | |
| Tivolistraße | HV | 211 |
| Triftstraße | LY | 214 |
| Trogerstraße | HVX | 215 |
| Türkenstraße | KY | |
| Tumblingerstraße | FX | 218 |
| Ungererstraße | GU | |
| Veterinärstraße | LY | 221 |
| Viktoriastraße | GU | 223 |
| Von-der-Tann-Straße | KLY | |
| Wagmüllerstraße | LY | 224 |
| Welfenstraße | GX | |
| Westenriederstraße | KZ | |
| Widenmayerstraße | GHV | |
| Wilhelmstraße | GU | |
| Winzererstraße | FU | |
| Wittelsbacherbrücke | GX | |
| Wittelsbacherstraße | KZ | 231 |
| Wörthstraße | HX | |
| Wredestraße | EV | 232 |
| Zeppelinstraße | LZ | |
| Ziemssenstraße | JZ | |
| Zirkus-Krone-Straße | EV | 236 |
| Zweibrückenstraße | LZ | |

**InterCityHotel**, Bayerstr. 10, ✉ 80335, (089) 54 55 60, *Fax (089) 54556610* – rm, – 100. AE VISA JCB — JY u
Meals *(closed Sunday)* à la carte 41/62 – **193 rm** 198/398 – 4 suites.

**Admiral** without rest, Kohlstr. 9, ✉ 80469, (089) 21 63 50, *Fax (089) 293674* – . AE VISA — LZ r
**33 rm** 230/345.

**Torbräu** without rest, Tal 41, ✉ 80331, (089) 22 50 16, *Fax (089) 225019* – – 15. AE VISA JCB — LZ g
**86 rm** 255/390 – 3 suites.

**Mercure City** without rest, Senefelder Str. 9, ✉ 80336, (089) 55 13 20, *Fax (089) 596444* – – 50. AE VISA JCB — JZ v
**167 rm** 188/350.

**Astron Hotel Deutscher Kaiser** M without rest, Arnulfstr. 2, ✉ 80335, (089) 5 45 30, *Fax (089) 54532255* – – 80. AE VISA JCB — JY r
**174 rm** 253/386.

**Kraft** without rest, Schillerstr. 49, ✉ 80336, (089) 59 48 23, *Fax (089) 5503856* – . AE VISA — JZ y
*closed 23 to 26 December* – **35 rm** 140/240.

**Sol Inn Hotel** M, Paul-Heyse-Str. 24, ✉ 80336, (089) 51 49 00, *Fax (089) 51490701* – rm, – 35. AE VISA JCB. rest — JZ c
Meals (residents only) – **182 rm** 182/416.

**Concorde** without rest, Herrnstr. 38, ✉ 80539, (089) 22 45 15, *Fax (089) 2283282* – . AE VISA — LZ c
*closed Christmas - early January* – **71 rm** 175/300.

**Cristal** without rest, Schwanthalerstr. 5, ✉ 80336, (089) 55 11 10, *Fax (089) 55111992* – rm, – 75. AE VISA — JZ h
**100 rm** 240/350.

**Splendid** without rest, Maximilianstr. 54, ✉ 80538, (089) 29 66 06, *Fax (089) 2913176* – . AE VISA JCB — LZ b
**38 rm** 178/346.

**Germania** without rest, Schwanthaler Str. 28, ✉ 80336, (089) 59 04 60, *Fax (089) 591171* – . AE VISA JCB — JZ a
**96 rm** 160/280.

**Schlicker** without rest, Tal 8, ✉ 80331, (089) 22 79 41, *Fax (089) 296059* – . AE VISA — KZ a
*closed 20 December - 7 January* – **69 rm** 130/360.

**Brack** without rest, Lindwurmstr. 153, ✉ 80337, (089) 7 47 25 50, *Fax (089) 74725599* – . AE VISA JCB — EX b
**50 rm** 150/298.

**Europäischer Hof** without rest, Bayerstr. 31, ✉ 80335, ℘ (089) 55 15 10, *Fax (089) 55151222* – |$| ⇄ TV ☎ ⇔ P – 🏛 20. AE ⓓ E VISA JCB JZ b
158 rm ☐ 178/370.

**Olympic** without rest, Hans-Sachs-Str. 4, ✉ 80469, ℘ (089) 23 18 90, *Fax (089) 23189199* – TV ☎ ⇔. AE ⓓ E VISA KZ c
32 rm ☐ 230/280.

**Acanthus** without rest, An der Hauptfeuerwache 14, ✉ 80331, ℘ (089) 23 18 80, *Fax (089) 2607364* – |$| TV ☎ ⇔. AE E VISA JZ n
36 rm ☐ 155/290.

XXXX ✿ **Hilton Grill** - Hotel Park Hilton, Am Tucherpark 7, ✉ 80538, ℘ (089) 3 84 52 61, *Fax (089) 38451845* – ▤. AE ⓓ E VISA JCB. ⌘ HU n
*closed Saturday lunch, Monday, 2 to 18 January, Easter and late July - mid August* – **Meals** 53 (lunch) and à la carte 74/103
**Spec.** Gebratnes Doradenfilet mit Pestonudeln. Wachtelkotelett mit Gänsestopfleber und geschmortem Wirsing. Rehmedallions mit Feigen und Roquefort überbacken.

XX ✿ **Gasthaus Glockenbach** (former old Bavarian pub), Kapuzinerstr. 29, ✉ 80337, ℘ (089) 53 40 43, *Fax (089) 534043* – E VISA FX e
*closed Saturday lunch, Sunday - Monday, Bank Holidays and 2 weeks August* – **Meals** (booking essential) 40 (lunch) and à la carte 81/105
**Spec.** Gambas-Kartoffeltarte mit grüner Sauce. Gebratenes Bresse Geflügel in zwei Gängen serviert. Tarte Tatin von der Birne mit Schokoladensorbet.

XX **Böswirth an der Oper**, Falkenturmstr. 10, ✉ 80331, ℘ (089) 29 79 09, *Fax (089) 297909* – AE E VISA KZ h
*closed Sunday - Monday lunch, Bank Holidays and 2 weeks May - June* – **Meals** 39 (lunch) and à la carte 64/91.

XX **Zum Bürgerhaus**, Pettenkoferstr. 1, ✉ 80336, ℘ (089) 59 79 09, *Fax (089) 595657*, « Bavarian farmhouse furniture ; courtyard terrace » – AE E VISA JZ s
*closed Saturday lunch, Sunday and Bank Holidays* – **Meals** (booking essential) à la carte 44/73.

XX **Halali**, Schönfeldstr. 22, ✉ 80539, ℘ (089) 28 59 09, *Fax (089) 282786* – AE E VISA LY x
*closed Saturday and Sunday lunch, Bank Holidays, 2 weeks August* – **Meals** (booking essential) 35 (lunch) and à la carte 51/73.

XX **Chesa**, Wurzerstr. 18, ✉ 80539, ℘ (089) 29 71 14, *Fax (089) 2285698*, ⛱ – AE ⓓ VISA LZ d
*closed Sunday* – **Meals** (booking essential) 26 lunch and à la carte 43/72.

XX **Galleria** (Italian rest.), Ledererstr. 2 (corner of Sparkassenstr.), ✉ 80331, ℘ (089) 29 79 95, *Fax (089) 2913653* – AE ⓓ E VISA KZ x
*closed Sunday and 1 to 7 January* – **Meals** (booking essential) à la carte 60/76.

XX **Lenbach**, Ottostr. 6, ✉ 80333, ℘ (089) 5 49 13 00, *Fax (089) 54913015*, ⛱, « Mansion with modern interior » – AE ⓓ E VISA JY c
**Meals** à la carte 38/65.

X ⚭ **Straubinger Hof** (Bavarian inn), Blumenstr. 5, ✉ 80331, ℘ (089) 2 60 84 44, *Fax (089) 2608917*, beer garden – AE E VISA. ⌘ KZ c
*closed Sunday and Bank Holidays* – **Meals** à la carte 24/55.

**Brewery - inns :**

X **Spatenhaus-Bräustuben**, Residenzstr. 12, ✉ 80333, ℘ (089) 2 90 70 60, *Fax (089) 2913054*, ⛱, « Furnished in traditional Alpine style » – AE ⓓ E VISA
**Meals** à la carte 42/74. KY t

X **Weisses Bräuhaus**, Tal 7, ✉ 80331, ℘ (089) 29 98 75, *Fax (089) 29013875*, ⛱ – 🏛 30. AE KZ e
**Meals** à la carte 27/48.

X **Augustiner Gaststätten**, Neuhauser Str. 27, ✉ 80331, ℘ (089) 23 18 32 57, *Fax (089) 2605379*, « Beer garden » – AE ⓓ E VISA JZ w
**Meals** à la carte 25/59.

X **Altes Hackerhaus**, Sendlinger Str. 14, ✉ 80331, ℘ (089) 2 60 50 26, *Fax (089) 2605027*, ⛱ – AE ⓓ E VISA JCB KZ r
**Meals** à la carte 30/67.

X **Franziskaner Fuchsenstuben**, Perusastr. 5, ✉ 80333, ℘ (089) 2 31 81 20, *Fax (089) 23181244*, ⛱ – AE ⓓ E VISA JCB KY v
**Meals** à la carte 33/66.

X **Paulaner Bräuhaus**, Kapuzinerplatz 5, ✉ 80337, ℘ (089) 5 44 61 10, *Fax (089) 54461118*, beer garden – E FX r
**Meals** à la carte 32/62.

## at Munich-Allach by *Arnulfstr.* EV :

**Lutter** without rest, Eversbuschstr. 109, ✉ 80999, ☎ (089) 8 92 67 80, *Fax (089) 89267810* – TV ☎ P. AE E VISA
*closed 21 December - 4 January* – **22 rm** ☐ 110/200.

## at Munich-Bogenhausen :

**Palace**, Trogerstr. 21, ✉ 81675, ☎ (089) 41 97 10, *Fax (089) 41971819*, « Elegant installation with period furniture », ☐, – |♦|, ✱ rm, TV ☎ ⇔ – 🏃 40. AE ⊙ E VISA JCB
**Meals** à la carte 40/70 – **71 rm** ☐ 381/572 – 6 suites. HV t

**Arabella-Hotel**, Arabellastr. 5, ✉ 81925, ☎ (089) 9 23 20, *Fax (089) 92324449*, ≤ Munich, ☂, Massage, ⚒, ☐, ☐ – |♦|, ✱ rm, ▤ rest, TV ☎ ♿ ⇔ P – 🏃 280. AE ⊙ E VISA. ✱ rest by Isarring HU
**Meals** à la carte 43/66 – **467 rm** ☐ 250/450 – 39 suites.

**Prinzregent** without rest, Ismaninger Str. 42, ✉ 81675, ☎ (089) 41 60 50, *Fax (089) 41605466*, ☐ – |♦| ✱ TV ⇔ – 🏃 35. AE ⊙ E VISA JCB HV t
*23 December - 7 January* – **64 rm** ☐ 290/400.

**Rothof** without rest, Denniger Str. 114, ✉ 81925, ☎ (089) 91 50 61, *Fax (089) 915066*, ☐ – |♦| ✱ TV ⇔. AE ⊙ E VISA by Einsteinstr. HX
*closed 23 December - 7 January* – **37 rm** ☐ 198/390.

**Queens Hotel München**, Effnerstr. 99, ✉ 81925, ☎ (089) 92 79 80, *Fax (089) 983813* – |♦|, ✱ rm, TV ☎ ⇔ P – 🏃 200. AE ⊙ E VISA. ✱ rest
**Meals** à la carte 33/76 – **152 rm** ☐ 262/574. by Ismaninger Str. HV

**Bogenhauser Hof** (1825 former hunting lodge), Ismaninger Str. 85, ✉ 81675, ☎ (089) 98 55 86, *Fax (089) 9810221*, « Garden terrace » – AE ⊙ VISA HV c
*closed Sunday, Bank Holidays and Christmas - 12 January* – **Meals** (booking essential) à la carte 64/103.

**Acquarello** (Italian rest.), Mühlbaurstr. 36, ✉ 81677, ☎ (089) 4 70 48 48, *Fax (089) 476464*, ☂ – AE E. ✱ by Mühlbaurstr HV
*closed Saturday and Sunday lunch* – **Meals** à la carte 60/79.

**Käfer Schänke**, Schumannstr. 1 (corner to Prinzregentenstraße), ✉ 81675, ☎ (089) 4 16 82 47, *Fax (089) 4168623*, ☂, « Several rooms with elegant rustic installation » – AE ⊙ E VISA HV s
*closed Sunday and Bank Holidays* – **Meals** (booking essential) 43 (lunch) and à la carte 58/103.

**Prielhof**, Oberföhringer Str. 44, ✉ 81925, ☎ (089) 98 53 53, *Fax (089) 9827289*, ☂ – ⊙ E VISA. ✱ by Ismaninger Str. HV
*closed Saturday lunch, Sunday, Bank Holidays and 23 December - 6 January* – **Meals** (booking essential) à la carte 52/74.

## at Munich-Denning by *Denninger Str.* HV :

**Casale** (Italian rest.), Ostpreußenstr. 42, ✉ 81927, ☎ (089) 93 62 68, *Fax (089) 9306722*, ☂ – P. AE ⊙ E VISA
**Meals** à la carte 51/72.

## at Munich-Haidhausen :

**City Hilton** M, Rosenheimer Str. 15, ✉ 81667, ☎ (089) 4 80 40, *Fax (089) 48044804*, ☂ – |♦|, ✱ rm, ▤ TV ♿ ⇔ – 🏃 180. AE ⊙ E VISA JCB. ✱ rest LZ s
**Meals** 53 (buffet) and à la carte 54/76 – **479 rm** ☐ 383/616 – 4 suites.

**Preysing**, Preysingstr. 1, ✉ 81667, ☎ (089) 45 84 50, *Fax (089) 45845444*, ☐, ☐ – |♦| ▤ ⇔ – 🏃 40. AE ⊙ E VISA LZ w
*closed 23 December - 6 January* – **Meals** see ***Preysing-Keller*** *below* – **76 rm** ☐ 169/298 – 5 suites.

**Forum Hotel München**, Hochstr. 3, ✉ 81669, ☎ (089) 4 80 30, *Fax (089) 4488277*, Massage, ☐, ☐ – |♦|, ✱ rm, ▤ TV ☎ – 🏃 350. AE ⊙ E VISA JCB LZ t
**Meals** à la carte 51/83 – **582 rm** ☐ 300/410 – 12 suites.

**Preysing-Keller** - Hotel Preysing, Innere-Wiener-Str. 6, ✉ 81667, ☎ (089) 45 84 52 60, *Fax (089) 45845444* – ▤. AE ⊙ E VISA LZ w
*closed Sunday, Bank Holidays and 23 December - 6 January* – **Meals** (dinner only) (outstanding wine list) 89/125 and à la carte 65/101
**Spec.** Sautierter Rochenfügel mit Pinienkernvinaigrette. Stubenküken im weißen Trüffelölsud mit Topinambur. Terrine von Grapfruit und Orangen mit Sauerrahmeis.

**Massimiliano**, Rablstr. 10, ✉ 81699, ☎ (089) 4 48 44 77, *Fax (089) 4484405*, ☂ – P. ⊙ E VISA LZ n
*closed Saturday lunch* – **Meals** 39 (lunch) and à la carte 67/103
**Spec.** Seeteufel mit Pommery-Senfsauce. Bresse Taube mit Gänseleber und glasiertem Weißkraut. Marmorietes Grießsoufflé (2 Pers.).

**Rue Des Halles** (Bistro), Steinstr. 18, ✉ 81667, ☎ (089) 48 56 75, *Fax (089) 43987378* – E VISA HX a
**Meals** (dinner only, booking essential) à la carte 54/76.

at **Munich-Laim** *by Landsberger Str. (B 2)* EV :

**Park Hotel Laim** without rest, Zschokkestr. 55, ✉ 80686, ☎ (089) 57 93 60, *Fax (089) 57936100*, – 30.
**68 rm** 180/270.

at **Munich-Neu Perlach** *by Rosenheimer Str.* HX :

**Mercure**, Karl-Marx-Ring 87, ✉ 81735, ☎ (089) 6 32 70, *Fax (089) 6327407*, – rm, rest, – 100.
Meals 37 (buffet lunch) and à la carte 38/62 – **184 rm** 195/350 – 3 suites.

**Villa Waldperlach** without rest, Putzbrunner Str. 250 (Waldperlach), ✉ 81739, ☎ (089) 6 60 03 00, *Fax (089) 66003066* – .
**21 rm** 150/250.

at **Munich-Pasing** *by Landsberger Straße* EV :

**Zur Goldenen Gans**, Planegger Str.31, ✉ 81241, ☎ (089) 83 70 33, *Fax (089) 8204680*, « Bavarian Inn with cosy atmosphere » – .
*closed Sunday and Bank Holidays* – Meals 25 (lunch) and à la carte 45/71.

at **Munich-Schwabing** :

**Marriott-Hotel**, Berliner Str. 93, ✉ 80805, ☎ (089) 36 00 20, *Fax (089) 36002200*, Massage, – rm, – 320. rest by Ungererstr. (B 11) HU
Meals à la carte 39/73 – **348 rm** 393/556 – 16 suites.

**Holiday Inn Crowne Plaza**, Leopoldstr. 194, ✉ 80804, ☎ (089) 38 17 90, *Fax (089) 38179888*, Massage, – rm, – 320. by Leopoldstr. GU
Meals à la carte 51/87 – **365 rm** 324/608.

**Ramada Parkhotel**, Theodor-Dombart-Str. 4 (corner of Berliner Straße), ✉ 80805, ☎ (089) 36 09 90, *Fax (089) 36099684*, – rm, – 40. by Ungererstr. (B 11) HU
Meals à la carte 43/64 – **260 rm** 249/548 – 80 suites.

**Arabella - Olympiapark-Hotel**, Helene-Mayer-Ring 12, ✉ 80809, ☎ (089) 35 75 10, *Fax (089) 3543730* – rm, – 30.
*closed 20 December - 6 January* – **Meals** (residents only) – **105 rm** 301/422. by Schleißheimer Str. FU

**Vitalis**, Kathi-Kobus-Str. 24, ✉ 80797, ☎ (089) 12 00 80, *Fax (089) 1298382* – rm, – 60. rest FU b
Meals à la carte 28/51 – **102 rm** 260/310.

**Cosmopolitan** without rest, Hohenzollernstr. 5, ✉ 80801, ☎ (089) 38 38 10, *Fax (089) 38381111* – . GU g
**71 rm** 155/220.

**Mercure** without rest, Leopoldstr. 120, ✉ 80802, ☎ (089) 39 05 50, *Fax (089) 349344* – . GU r
**65 rm** 172/294.

**Leopold**, Leopoldstr. 119, ✉ 80804, ☎ (089) 36 70 61, *Fax (089) 36043150*, – . GU f
*closed 23 December - 1 January* – **Meals** à la carte 27/63 – **75 rm** 165/275.

**Tantris**, Johann-Fichte-Str. 7, ✉ 80805, ☎ (089) 3 61 95 90, *Fax (089) 3618469*, – . GU b
*closed Sunday, Monday, Bank Holidays and 1 week January* – **Meals** (booking essential) 218 and à la carte 88/138
**Spec.** Auberginen-Sardellenterrine mit Langustinen im Fenchelblatt. Lauwarmer Thunfisch auf Polenta mit Curry-Koriandermarinade. Mousse und Sorbet von Holunderblüten mit eingelegtem Pfirsich.

**Savoy** (Italian rest.), Tengstr. 20, ✉ 80798, ☎ (089) 2 71 14 45 – GU t
*closed Sunday* – **Meals** (booking essential for dinner) à la carte 43/69.

**Spago** (Italian rest.), Neureutherstr. 15, ✉ 80799, ☎ (089) 2 71 24 06, *Fax (089) 2780442*, – GU a
*dinner only Saturday, Sunday and Bank Holidays* – **Meals** à la carte 53/72.

**Seehaus**, Kleinhesselohe 3, ✉ 80802, ☎ 3 81 61 30, *Fax 341803*, ≤, « Lakeside setting terrace » – . HU t
Meals à la carte 37/69.

**Bistro Terrine**, Amalienstr. 89 (Amalien-Passage), ✉ 80799, ☎ (089) 28 17 80, *Fax (089) 2809316*, – AE E VISA GU q
*closed Saturday and Monday lunch, Sunday and Bank Holidays* – **Meals** (booking essential for dinner) 43 (lunch) and à la carte 47/70
**Spec.** Gebratenes Zanderfilet mit Petersilienpüree. Geschmorte Rinderschulter mit Serviettenknödel und Pilzen. Topfennockerln mit Aprikosenkompott.

**Bamberger Haus**, Brunnenstr. 2 (at Luitpoldpark), ✉ 80804, ☎ (089) 3 08 89 66, *Fax (089) 3003304*, « 18C palace ; terrace » – P. AE E VISA GU z
**Meals** à la carte 28/55.

**at Munich-Sendling** *by Lindwurmstr. (B 11)* EX :

**Holiday Inn München - Süd**, Kistlerhofstr. 142, ✉ 81379, ☎ (089) 78 00 20, *Fax (089) 78002672*, beer garden, Massage, – rm, – 90. AE D E VISA JCB
*closed 23 December - 6 January* – **Meals** à la carte 40/69 – **320 rm** 287/444 – 7 suites.

**Ambassador Parkhotel** (Italian rest.), Plinganserstr. 102, ✉ 81369, ☎ (089) 72 48 90, *Fax (089) 72489100*, beer garden – . AE D E VISA
*closed 24 December - 6 January* – **Meals** *(closed Saturday lunch)* à la carte 38/66 – **42 rm** 175/325.

**K u. K Hotel am Harras** without rest, Albert-Rosshaupter-Str. 4, ✉ 81369, ☎ (089) 77 00 51, *Fax (089) 7212820* – rm, . AE D E VISA JCB
**120 rm** 199/340.

**at Munich-Untermenzing** *by Arnulfstr.* EV :

**Romantik-Hotel Insel Mühle**, von-Kahr-Str. 87, ✉ 80999, ☎ (089) 8 10 10, *Fax (089) 8120571*, , beer garden, « Converted 16C riverside mill », – P – 40. D E VISA
**Meals** *(closed Sunday and Bank Holidays)* à la carte 49/72 – **37 rm** 185/350.

**at Unterhaching** *by Kapuzinerstr.* GX :

**Schrenkhof** without rest, Leonhardsweg 6, ✉ 82008, ☎ (089) 6 10 09 10, *Fax (089) 61009150*, « Bavarian farmhouse furniture », – P – 40. AE D E VISA
*closed 20 December - early January and Easter* – **25 rm** 185/315.

**Holiday Inn Garden Court** M, Inselkamer Str. 7, ✉ 82008, ☎ (089) 66 69 10, *Fax (089) 66691600*, beer garden, – rm, P – 230. AE D E VISA JCB
**Meals** à la carte 36/77 – **282 rm** 225/420 – 6 suites.

**at Aschheim** *NE : 13 km by Riem* :

**Schreiberhof**, Erdinger Str. 2, ✉ 85609, ☎ (089) 90 00 60, *Fax (089) 90006459*, , Massage, – rm, P – 90. AE D E VISA
*closed Christmas - early January* – ***Alte Gaststube*** : Meals à la carte 48/78 – **87 rm** 235/325.

**at Grünwald** *S : 13 km by Wittelsbacher Brücke* GX – ✆ *089* :

**Tannenhof** without rest, Marktplatz 3, ✉ 82031, ☎ (089) 6 41 89 60, *Fax (089) 6415608*, « Period house with elegant interior » – P. AE D E VISA.
*closed 20 December - 6 January* – **21 rm** 150/240.

**at airport Franz-Josef-Strauß** *NE : 37km by A 9 and A 92* :

**Kempinski Airport München** M, Terminalstraße/Mitte 20, ✉ 85356 *München*, ☎ (089) 9 78 20, *Fax (089) 97822610*, – rm, – 280. AE D E VISA JCB. rest
**Meals** à la carte 58/90 – **389 rm** 441/472 – 17 suites.

**Il Mondo** (Italian rest.), Bereich B - Ebene 07, ✉ 85356 *München*, ☎ (089) 97 59 32 22, *Fax (089) 97593106* – P. AE D E VISA – **Meals** à la carte 45/76.

**Zirbelstube**, Zentralgebäude - Ebene 04, ✉ 85356 *Munich*, ☎ (089) 97 59 31 11, *Fax (089) 97593106*, « Original pine interior » – P. AE D E VISA
**Meals** à la carte 36/55.

## Aschau im Chiemgau *Bayern* 420 W 20, 987 ⑩ – *pop. 5 200 – alt. 615 m.*

*München 82.*

**Residenz Heinz Winkler**, Kirchplatz 1, ✉ 83229, ☎ (08052) 1 79 90, *Fax (08052) 179966*, ≤ Kampenwand, , « Elegant hotel and renovated 17C inn », Massage, – rm, P. AE D E VISA JCB. rest
**Meals** *(closed Monday lunch)* 168/215 and à la carte 85/138 – **32 rm** 220/460
**Spec.** Terrine vom Wildlachs und Kaviar mit Sauerrahm. Hummermedaillons mit Safransauce und schwarzen Nudeln. Souffliertes Rehfilet mit Pertersilienmousseline auf weißer Pfeffersauce.

**STUTTGART** L Baden-Württemberg 419 T 11, 987 ㊳ – pop. 559 000 – alt. 245 m.

GERMANY

**See** : *Linden Museum* ★★ KY **M**[1] – *Park Wilhelma*★ HT *and Killesberg-Park*★ GT – *Television Tower (Fernsehturm)* ★ HX – *Stuttgart Gallery (Otto-Dix-Collection*★*)* LY **M**[4] – *Swabian Brewery Museum (Schwäb. Brauereimuseum)*★ *by Böblinger Straße* FX – *Old Castle (Altes Schloß) (Renaissance courtyard*★*)* – *Württemberg Regional Museum*★ *(Sacred Statuary*★★*)* LY **M**[3] – *State Gallery*★ *(Old Masters Collection*★★*)* LY **M**[2] – *Collegiate church (Stiftskirche) (Commemorative monuments of dukes*★*)* KY **A** – *State Musem of Natural History (Staatl. Museum für Naturkunde)*★ HT **M**[5] – *Daimler-Benz Museum*★ JV **M**[6] – *Porsche Museum*★ *by Heilbronner Straße* GT – *Schloß Solitude*★ *by Rotenwaldstraße* FX.

**Envir.** : *Bad Cannstatt Spa Park (Kurpark)*★ *E : 4 km* JT.

*Kornwestheim, Aldinger Str. (N : 11 km),* ✆ *(07141) 87 13 19 ; Mönsheim (NW : 30 km by A 8),* ✆ *(07044) 69 09.*

*Stuttgart-Echterdingen, by Obere Weinsteige (B 27)* GX, ✆ **(0711)** *94 80, City Air Terminal, Stuttgart, Lautenschlagerstr. 14 (LY),* ✆ *(0711) 20 12 68.*

*Exhibition Centre (Messegelände Killesberg) (GT),* ✆ *(0711) 2 58 90, Fax (0711) 2589440.*

*Tourist-Info, Königstr. 1a,* ✉ *70173,* ✆ *(0711) 2 22 82 40, Fax (0711) 2228253.*

**ADAC,** *Am Neckartor 2,* ✉ *70190,* ✆ *(0711) 2 80 00, Fax (0711) 2800167.*

*Berlin 630 – Frankfurt am Main 204 – Karlsruhe 88 – München 222 – Strasbourg 156.*

Plans on following pages

**Steigenberger Graf Zeppelin** M, Arnulf-Klett-Platz 7, ✉ 70173, ✆ (0711) 2 04 80, *Fax (0711) 2048542*, Massage, ≘s, ▣ – ▮, ⇹ rm, ▤ TV ✆ ⇔ – 🏛 300. AE ① E VISA JCB. ✗ rest LY v
***Graf Zeppelin*** *(dinnner only, closed Sunday - Monday and 18 July - 31. August)* **Meals** à la carte 72/106 – ***Zeppelin Stüble*** **: Meals** à la carte 41/69 – **195 rm** ⊒ 355/505.

**Maritim** M, Forststr. 2, ✉ 70174, ✆ (0711) 94 20, *Fax (0711) 9421000*, Massage, 🏋, ≘s, ▣ – ▮, ⇹ rm, ▤ TV ✆ ♿ ⇔ – 🏛 800. AE ① E VISA JCB. ✗ rest FV r
**Meals** à la carte 58/88 – **555 rm** ⊒ 257/496 – 50 suites.

**Inter-Continental**, Willy-Brandt-Str. 30, ✉ 70173, ✆ (0711) 2 02 00, *Fax (0711) 202012*, Massage, 🏋, ≘s, ▣ – ▮, ⇹ rm, ▤ TV ✆ ♿ ⇔ – 🏛 350. AE ① E VISA JCB. ✗ rm HV t
**Meals** à la carte 48/70 – **276 rm** ⊒ 359/503 – 24 suites.

**Am Schloßgarten**, Schillerstr. 23, ✉ 70173, ✆ (0711) 2 02 60, *Fax (0711) 2026888*, « Terrace with ≤ » – ▮, ⇹ rm, TV ⇔ – 🏛 100. AE ① E VISA. ✗ rest LY u
**Meals** à la carte 64/96 – **116 rm** ⊒ 255/425.

**Royal**, Sophienstr. 35, ✉ 70178, ✆ (0711) 62 50 50, *Fax (0711) 628809* – ▮, ⇹ rm, ▤ rest, TV ☎ ⇔ P – 🏛 70. AE ① E VISA JCB KZ b
**Meals** *(closed Sunday and Bank Holidays)* à la carte 28/73 – **100 rm** ⊒ 185/490 – 3 suites.

**Parkhotel**, Villastr. 21, ✉ 70190, ✆ (0711) 2 80 10, *Fax (0711) 2864353*, 🏠 – ▮, ⇹ rm, TV ☎ ⇔ P – 🏛 80. AE ① E VISA. ✗ HU r
**Meals** *(closed Saturday and Sunday)* 35/75 and à la carte 53/79 – **72 rm** ⊒ 195/330.

**Rema-Hotel-Ruff** without rest, Friedhofstr. 21, ✉ 70191, ✆ (0711) 2 58 70, *Fax (0711) 2587404*, ≘s, ▣ – ▮ ⇹ TV ☎ ⇔ P – 🏛 15. AE ① E VISA JCB GU a
**90 rm** ⊒ 170/390.

**Rega Hotel**, Ludwigstr. 18, ✉ 70176, ✆ (089) 61 93 40, *Fax (089) 6193477* – ▮ TV ☎ ⇔ – 🏛 20. AE ① E VISA FV a
**Meals** *(closed Sunday dinner)* à la carte 29/55 – **60 rm** ⊒ 175/235.

**InterCityHotel** M without rest, Arnulf-Klett-Platz 2, ✉ 70173, ✆ (0711) 2 25 00, *Fax (0711) 2250499* – ▮ ⇹ TV ☎ ✆ – 🏛 25. AE ① E VISA LY p
**112 rm** ⊒ 200/300.

**Unger** without rest, Kronenstr. 17, ✉ 70173, ✆ (0711) 2 09 90, *Fax (0711) 2099100* – ▮ ⇹ TV ☎ ✆ ⇔ – 🏛 20. AE ① E VISA LY a
**97 rm** ⊒ 189/349.

**Bergmeister** without rest, Rotenbergstr. 16, ✉ 70190, ✆ (0711) 28 33 63, *Fax (0711) 283719*, ≘s – ▮ ⇹ TV ☎ ⇔. AE ① E VISA JCB HV r
**47 rm** ⊒ 129/210.

**Kronen-Hotel** without rest, Kronenstr. 48, ✉ 70174, ✆ (0711) 2 25 10, *Fax (0711) 2251404*, ≘s – ▮ ⇹ TV ☎ ⇔ – 🏛 20. AE ① E VISA JCB KY m
*closed 22 December - 7 January* – **83 rm** ⊒ 160/330.

**Wörtz zur Weinsteige**, Hohenheimer Str. 30, ✉ 70184, ✆ (0711) 2 36 70 00, *Fax (0711) 2367007*, « Garden terrace » – ⇹ rm, TV ☎ P. AE ① E VISA JCB LZ p
*closed 20 December - 7 January* – **Meals** *(closed Sunday, Monday and Bank Holidays)* à la carte 29/89 – **25 rm** ⊒ 140/280.

# STUTTGART

Alexanderstraße . HV 2
Am Neckartor . . HU 4
Augustenstraße . FV 7
Berliner Platz . . . . . . . . GV 8
Bismarckstraße . . FV 9
Blumenstraße . . . GV 10
Bolzstraße . . . . . GV 15
Botnanger Straße . . . . . . FV 16
Brückenstraße . . HT 17
Charlottenplatz . . GV 20
Charlottenstraße . GV 21
Dillmannstraße . . FV 22
Dobelstraße . . . . GV 23
Eberhardstraße . . GV 25

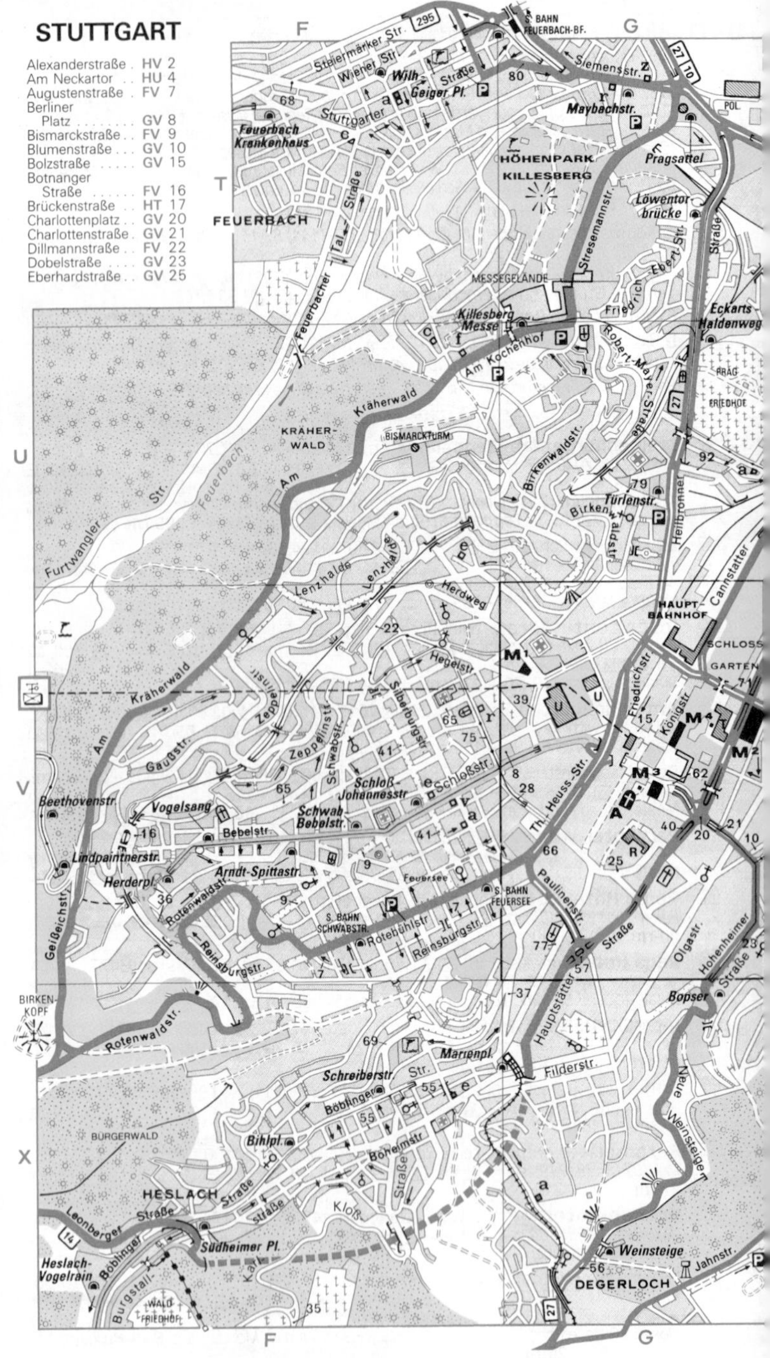

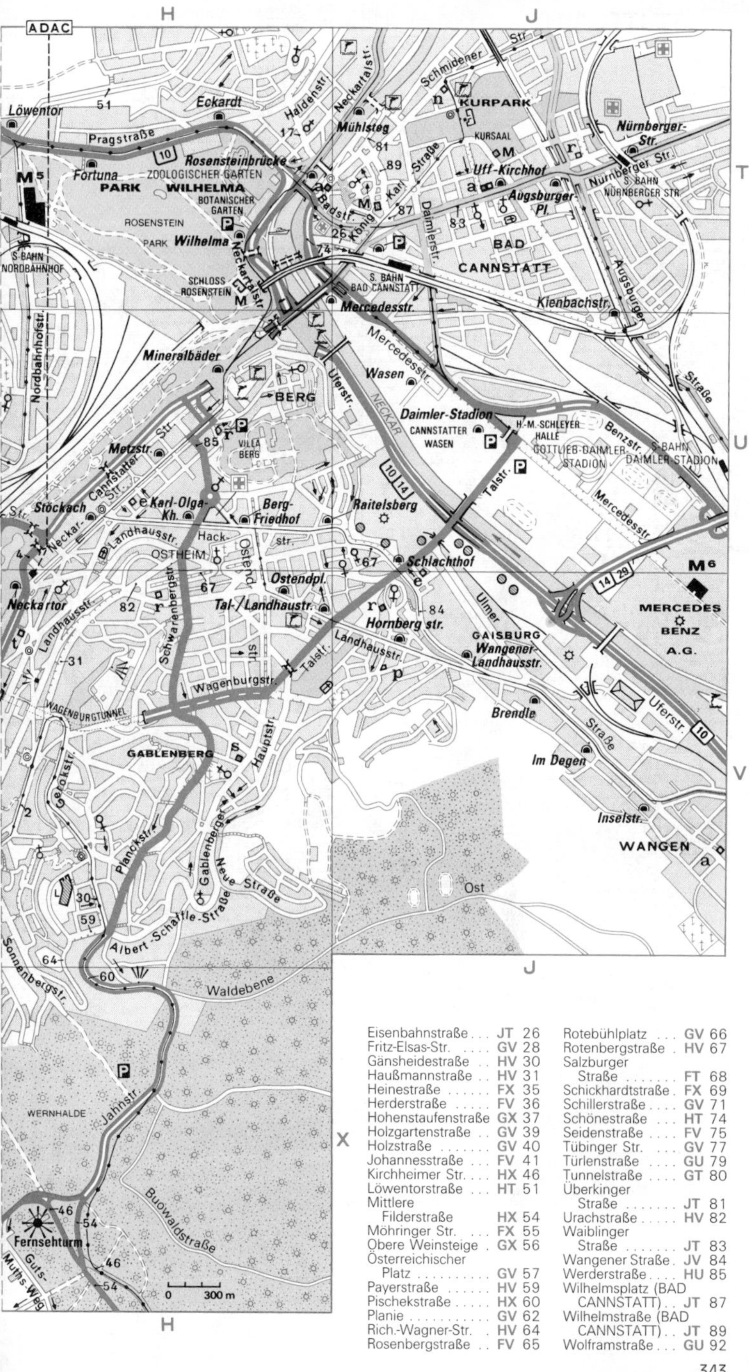


| | | |
|---|---|---|
| Eisenbahnstraße | JT | 26 |
| Fritz-Elsas-Str. | GV | 28 |
| Gänsheidestraße | HV | 30 |
| Haußmannstraße | HV | 31 |
| Heinestraße | FX | 35 |
| Herderstraße | FV | 36 |
| Hohenstaufenstraße | GX | 37 |
| Holzgartenstraße | GV | 39 |
| Holzstraße | GV | 40 |
| Johannesstraße | FV | 41 |
| Kirchheimer Str. | HX | 46 |
| Löwentorstraße | HT | 51 |
| Mittlere Filderstraße | HX | 54 |
| Möhringer Str. | FX | 55 |
| Obere Weinsteige | GX | 56 |
| Österreichischer Platz | GV | 57 |
| Payerstraße | HV | 59 |
| Pischekstraße | HX | 60 |
| Planie | GV | 62 |
| Rich.-Wagner-Str. | HV | 64 |
| Rosenbergstraße | FV | 65 |
| Rotebühlplatz | GV | 66 |
| Rotenbergstraße | HV | 67 |
| Salzburger Straße | FT | 68 |
| Schickhardtstraße | FX | 69 |
| Schillerstraße | GV | 71 |
| Schönestraße | HT | 74 |
| Seidenstraße | FV | 75 |
| Tübinger Str. | GV | 77 |
| Türlenstraße | GU | 79 |
| Tunnelstraße | GT | 80 |
| Überkinger Straße | JT | 81 |
| Urachstraße | HV | 82 |
| Waiblinger Straße | JT | 83 |
| Wangener Straße | JV | 84 |
| Werderstraße | HU | 85 |
| Wilhelmsplatz (BAD CANNSTATT) | JT | 87 |
| Wilhelmstraße (BAD CANNSTATT) | JT | 89 |
| Wolframstraße | GU | 92 |

# STUTTGART

Charlottenplatz ........ LZ 20
Eberhardstraße ........ KLZ 25
Königstraße ........ KLYZ
Schulstraße ........ KZ 75
Theodor- Heuss- Str. ........ KYZ 80

Arnulf-Klett-Platz ........ LY 6
Augustenstraße ........ KZ 7
Blumenstraße ........ LZ 10
Bolzstraße ........ LY 15
Calwer Str. ........ KYZ 18
Dorotheenstraße ........ LZ 24
Friedrichsplatz ........ KY 27
Hauptstätter Str. ........ KZ 30
Hegelplatz ........ KY 32
Heilbronner Str. ........ LY 34
Holzstraße ........ LZ 40
Karlsplatz ........ LY 43
Karlstraße ........ LZ 44
Katharinenplatz ........ LZ 45
Kirchstraße ........ LZ 46
Konrad- Adenauer- Str. ........ LY 47
Kronenstraße ........ KLY 48
Kronprinzstraße ........ KYZ 49
Leonhardsplatz ........ LZ 50
Marktplatz ........ KLZ 52
Marktstraße ........ LZ 53
Österreichischer Platz ........ KZ 57
Pfarrstraße ........ LZ 61
Rotebühlplatz ........ KZ 66
Rotebühlstraße ........ KZ 70
Schloßplatz ........ LY 72
Silberburgstraße ........ KZ 76
Sophienstraße ........ KZ 78
Torstraße ........ KZ 82
Wilhelmsplatz ........ LZ 86
Wilhelmstraße ........ LZ 88
Willi- Bleicher- Str. ........ KY 91

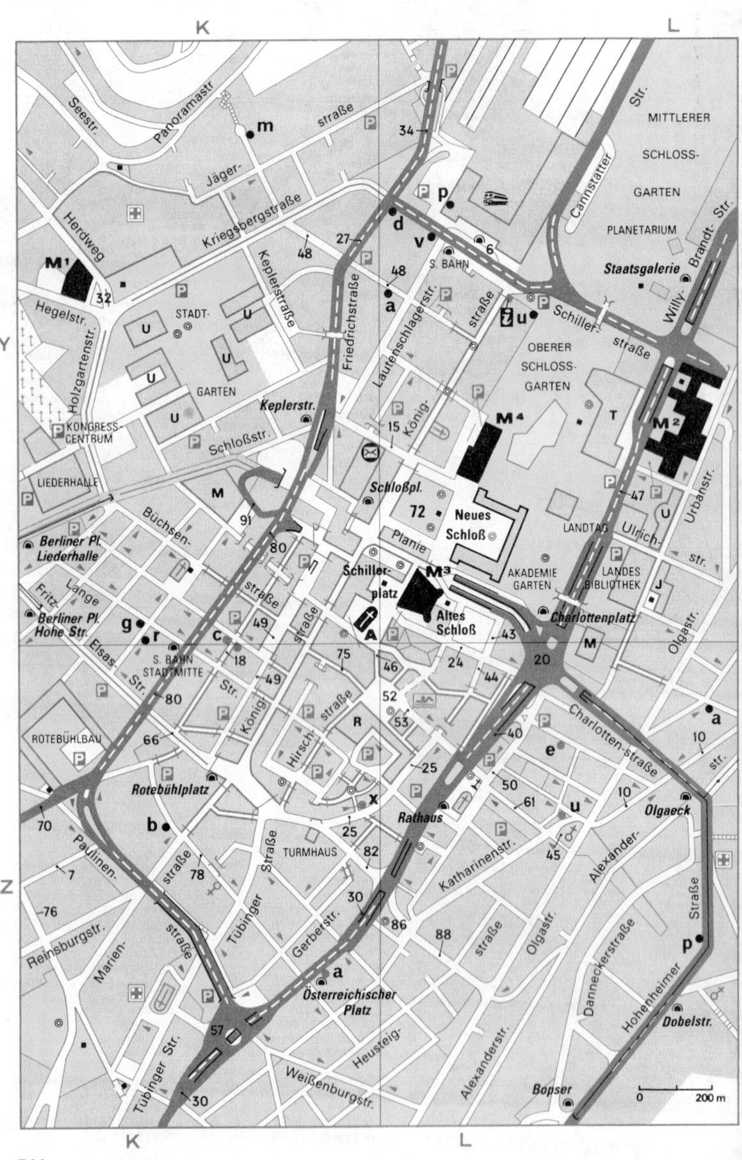

**Azenberg**, Seestr. 114, ✉ 70174, ℘ (0711) 22 10 51, *Fax (0711) 297426*, – rm, . rest FU e
**Meals** (dinner only) (residents only) – **58 rm** 120/260.

**Wartburg**, Lange Str. 49, ✉ 70174, ℘ (0711) 2 04 50, *Fax (0711) 2045450* – rm, rest, – 60. KY g
*closed Easter and 22 December - 2 January* – **Meals** *(closed Saturday, Sunday and Bank Holidays)* (lunch only) à la carte 36/55 – **81 rm** 155/265.

**Rema-Hotel Astoria** without rest, Hospitalstr. 29, ✉ 70174, ℘ (0711) 29 93 01, *Fax (0711) 299307* – – 20. KY r
**57 rm** 170/390.

**Rieker** without rest, Friedrichstr. 3, ✉ 70174, ℘ (0711) 22 13 11, *Fax (0711) 293894* – . LY d
**66 rm** 178/238.

**City-Hotel** without rest, Uhlandstr. 18, ✉ 70182, ℘ (0711) 21 08 10, *Fax (0711) 2369772* – . . LZ a
**31 rm** 150/210.

**Bellevue**, Schurwaldstr. 45, ✉ 70186, ℘ (0711) 48 07 60, *Fax (0711) 4807631* – . JV p
**Meals** *(closed Tuesday - Wednesday)* 23 (lunch) and à la carte 37/62 – **12 rm** 90/150.

**Delice**, Hauptstätter Str. 61, ✉ 70178, ℘ (0711) 6 40 32 22, « Vaulted cellar with contemporary art » – KZ a
*closed Saturday, Sunday and Bank Holidays* – **Meals** (dinner only, booking essential, outstanding wine list) 125 and à la carte 73/104
**Spec.** Nudeln mit Asetra Kaviar. Taubenbrüstchen im Strudelteig auf Taubenlebersauce. Topfenknödel mit Pflaumenröster.

**Da Franco** (Italian rest.), Calwer Str. 23 (1st floor), ✉ 70173, ℘ (0711) 29 15 81, *Fax (0711) 294549* – . KYZ c
*closed Monday and August* – **Meals** à la carte 47/76.

**La nuova Trattoria da Franco** (Italian rest.), Calwer Str. 32 (1st floor), ✉ 70173, ℘ (0711) 29 47 44, *Fax (0711) 294549*, – KYZ c
**Meals** à la carte 43/67.

**Gaisburger Pastetchen**, Hornbergstr. 24, ✉ 70188, ℘ (0711) 48 48 55, *Fax (0711) 487565* JV r
*closed Sunday and Bank Holidays* – **Meals** (dinner only) à la carte 66/92.

**Alter Fritz am Killesberg**, Feuerbacher Weg 101, ✉ 70192, ℘ (0711) 13 56 50, *Fax (0711) 1356565*, – . FU c
*closed 2 weeks December - January and August* – **Meals** *(closed Monday and Bank Holidays)* (dinner only) à la carte 58/81 – **10 rm** 130/215.

**Goldener Adler**, Böheimstr. 38, ✉ 70178, ℘ (0711) 6 40 17 62, *Fax (0711) 6492405* – . FX e
*closed Tuesday and Saturday lunch, Monday and 4 weeks August - September* – **Meals** à la carte 42/89.

**La Scala** (Italian rest.), Friedrichstr. 41 (1st floor, ), ✉ 70174, ℘ (0711) 29 06 07, *Fax (0711) 2991640* – . KY e
*closed Sunday and 3 weeks August - September* – **Meals** à la carte 43/67.

**Swabian wine taverns (Weinstuben)** *(mainly light meals only)* :

**Kachelofen**, Eberhardstr. 10 (entrance in Töpferstraße), ✉ 70173, ℘ (0711) 24 23 78, KZ x
*closed Sunday* – **Meals** (open from 5pm) à la carte 47/65.

**Weinstube Schellenturm**, Weberstr. 72, ✉ 70182, ℘ (0711) 2 36 48 88, *Fax (0711) 2262699*, – . LZ u
*closed Sunday and Bank Holidays* – **Meals** (dinner only) à la carte 36/59.

**Weinstube Träuble**, Gablenberger Hauptstr. 66, ✉ 70186, ℘ (0711) 46 54 28, – HV s
*closed Sunday, Bank Holidays and late August - mid September* – **Meals** *(dinner only)* only cold and warm light meals.

**Weinstube Klösterle**, Marktstr. 71 (Bad Cannstatt), ✉ 70372, ℘ (0711) 56 89 62, « Former monastery, rustic interior » – HT a
*closed Sunday, Bank Holidays and 2 weeks July - August* – **Meals** *(open from 4 pm)* à la carte 39/61.

**Weinhaus Stetter**, Rosenstr. 32, ✉ 70182, ℘ (0711) 24 01 63, *Fax (0711) 240193*, LZ e
*open Monday to Friday from 3 pm, closed Saturday 3 pm, Sunday, Bank Holidays and 24 December - 8 January* – **Meals** (outstanding wine list) à la carte 24/35.

**at Stuttgart-Botnang** *by Botnanger Str.* FV :

**Hirsch**, Eltinger Str. 2, ✉ 70195, ✆ (0711) 69 29 17, *Fax (0711) 6990788*, beer garden – 140. AE E VISA
Meals *(closed Sunday dinner and Monday)* à la carte 39/70 – **44 rm** 96/150.

**at Stuttgart-Büsnau** *by Rotenwaldstraße* FX :

**Relexa Waldhotel Schatten**, Magstadter Straße (Solitudering), ✉ 70569, ✆ (0711) 6 86 70, *Fax (0711) 6867999*, – rm, – 80. AE E VISA. rest
***La fenêtre*** *(closed Sunday - Monday)* **Meals** à la carte 68/90 – ***Kaminrestaurant*** **: Meals** à la carte 45/75 – **136 rm** 195/690 – 7 suites.

**at Stuttgart-Bad Cannstatt** :

**Pannonia Hotel** M, Teinacher Str. 20, ✉ 70372, ✆ (0711) 9 54 00, *Fax (0711) 9540630*, – rm, rest, – 120. AE E VISA JCB JT n
**Meals** à la carte 46/78 – **156 rm** 175/295 – 5 suites.

**Krehl's Linde**, Obere Waiblinger Str. 113, ✉ 70374, ✆ (0711) 52 75 67, *Fax (0711) 5286370*, – JT r
*closed 3 weeks July - August* – **Meals** *(closed Sunday - Monday)* à la carte 43/88 – **18 rm** 100/220.

**at Stuttgart-Degerloch** :

**Waldhotel Degerloch**, Guts-Muths-Weg 18, ✉ 70597, ✆ (0711) 76 50 17, *Fax (0711) 7653762*, – – 100. AE E VISA JCB
**Meals** à la carte 45/75 – **50 rm** 175/260. by Guts-Muths-Weg HX

**Wielandshöhe**, Alte Weinsteige 71, ✉ 70597, ✆ (0711) 6 40 88 48, *Fax (0711) 6409408*, « Beautiful situation ≤ Stuttgart » – AE E VISA GX a
*closed Sunday and Monday* – **Meals** (booking essential) 118/178 and à la carte 86/139
**Spec.** Hummer mit Basilikum-Kartoffelsalat. Fränkischer Bauernhahn. Marquise von Bitterschokolade.

**Skyline-Restaurant** (in TV-tower at 144 m, ), Jahnstr. 120, ✉ 70597, ✆ (0711) 24 61 04, *Fax (0711) 2360633*, Stuttgart and surroundings – . AE E VISA
*closed Monday* – **Meals** (booking essential for dinner) à la carte 65/97.

**Das Fässle**, Löwenstr. 51, ✉ 70597, ✆ (0711) 76 01 00, *Fax (0711) 764432*, – AE E VISA by Jahnstraße GX
*closed Sunday* – **Meals** à la carte 49/74.

**at Stuttgart-Fasanenhof** *by Obere Weinsteige (B 27)* GX :

**Mercure** M, Eichwiesenring 1, ✉ 70567, ✆ (0711) 7 26 60, *Fax (0711) 7266444*, – rm, – 120. AE E VISA
**Meals** à la carte 45/77 – **148 rm** 207/294.

**Fora Hotel** M, Vor dem Lauch 20 (Businesspark), ✉ 70567, ✆ (0711) 7 25 50, *Fax (0711) 7255666*, – rm, rest, – 80. AE E VISA JCB
**Meals** à la carte 38/60 – **101 rm** 190/238.

**at Stuttgart-Feuerbach** :

**Messehotel Europe** M without rest, Siemensstr. 33, ✉ 70469, ✆ (0711) 81 48 30, *Fax (0711) 8148348* – . AE E VISA GT r
**114 rm** 180/310.

**Kongresshotel Europe**, Siemensstr. 26, ✉ 70469, ✆ (0711) 81 00 40, *Fax (0711) 854082*, – rm, – 130. AE E VISA GT z
**Meals** *(closed Saturday and Sunday lunch)* à la carte 46/75 – **145 rm** 130/275.

**Weinsberg** (Rest. Bistro style), Grazer Str. 32, ✉ 70469, ✆ (0711) 13 54 60, *Fax (0711) 1354666*, – rm, – 30. AE E VISA FT a
**Meals** *(closed Saturday dinner and Sunday)* à la carte 30/75 – **37 rm** 175/215.

**at Stuttgart-Flughafen (Airport)** *S : 15 km by Obere Weinsteige (B 27)* GX :

**Airport Mövenpick-Hotel**, Randstr. 7, ✉ 70629, ✆ (0711) 7 90 70, *Fax (0711) 793585*, – rm, – 45. AE E VISA JCB
**Meals** à la carte 37/68 – **230 rm** 289/534.

**top air**, Randstraße (in the airport) Terminal 1, ✉ 70621, ✆ (0711) 9 48 21 37, *Fax (0711) 7979210* – – 170. AE E VISA
*closed Saturday lunch and 3 weeks August* – **Meals** 75/150 and à la carte 72/126
**Spec.** Variation von der Gänseleber. Lasagne von Steinbutt und Hummer mit Rotweinbuttersauce. Milchkalbskotelett mit Artischocken-Tomatenragout und Trüffelsauce.

**at Stuttgart-Hoheheim** *by Mittlere Filderstraße* HX :

**Speisemeisterei**, Am Schloß Hohenheim, ✉ 70599, ✆ (0711) 4 56 00 37, *Fax (0711) 4560038*, – P
*closed Sonday dinner, Monday and 1 to 15 January* – **Meals** (weekdays dinner only, booking essential) 125/148 and à la carte 86/124
**Spec.** Törtchen von der Perigord-Gänseleber mit Traubensauce. Steinbuttfilet mit Hummerschaum im Lauchmantel. Kotelett und Torte vom Salzwiesenlamm mit gebackenen Kräutern.

**at Stuttgart-Möhringen** *SW : 7 km by Obere Weinsteige* GX :

**Copthorne Hotel** M (with Stuttgart International), Plieninger Str. 100, ✉ 70567, ✆ (0711) 7 21 10 50, *Fax (0711) 7212931*, (direct entrance to the recreation centre Schwaben Quelle) – rm, – 80. AE E VISA JCB
**Meals** à la carte 40/78 – **454 rm** 287/528.

**Fora Hotel Garni**, Filderbahnstr. 43, ✉ 70567, ✆ (0711) 71 60 80, *Fax (0711) 7160850* – . AE E VISA JCB
*closed late December - early January* – **41 rm** 160/208.

**Landgasthof Riedsee** with rm, Elfenstr. 120, ✉ 70567, ✆ (0711) 71 24 84, *Fax (0711) 7189764*, « Lakeside garden terrace » – P. AE E VISA
*closed Monday* – **Meals** à la carte 41/71 – **12 rm** 85/130.

**at Stuttgart-Obertürkheim** *by Augsburger Straße* JU :

**Brita Hotel**, Augsburger Str. 671, ✉ 70329, ✆ (0711) 32 02 30, *Fax (0711) 324440* – rm, rest, – 80. AE E VISA
*closed 24 December - 1 January* – **Meals** *(closed Saturday - Sunday)* à la carte 32/55 – **70 rm** 143/268.

**at Stuttgart-Plieningen** *S : 14 km by Mittlere Filderstraße* HX :

**Romantik Hotel Traube**, Brabandtgasse 2, ✉ 70599, ✆ 45 89 20, *Fax 4589220*, « Rustic restaurant with cosy atmosphere » – P. AE E VISA
*closed 23 December - 3 January* – **Meals** *(closed Sunday - Monday)* (booking essential) à la carte 58/95 – **20 rm** 155/280.

**at Stuttgart-Stammheim** *by Heilbronner Straße* GT :

**Novotel-Nord**, Korntaler Str. 207, ✉ 70439, ✆ (0711) 98 06 20, *Fax (0711) 803673*, (heated) – rm, P – 200. AE E VISA
**Meals** à la carte 31/61 – **117 rm** 165/219.

**at Stuttgart-Vaihingen** *by Böblinger Str.* FX :

**Dorint-Hotel Fontana** M, Vollmöllerstr. 5, ✉ 70563, ✆ (0711) 73 00, *Fax (0711) 7302525*, Massage, – rm, – 250. AE E VISA JCB. rest
**Meals** à la carte 39/82 – **252 rm** 293/395 – 5 suites.

**at Stuttgart-Weilimdorf** *by B 295* FT :

**Holiday Inn** M, Mittlerer Pfad 27, ✉ 70499, ✆ (0711) 98 88 80, *Fax (0711) 988889*, beer garden, – rm, – 200. AE E VISA JCB
**Meals** à la carte 39/65 – **325 rm** 232/400 – 7 suites.

**at Stuttgart-Zuffenhausen** *by Heilbronner Straße* GT :

**Fora Hotel Residence**, Schützenbühlstr. 16, ✉ 70435, ✆ (0711) 8 20 01 00, *Fax (0711) 8200101*, – rm, rest, – 60. AE E VISA JCB
**Meals** *(closed Friday - Saturday)* (dinner only) à la carte 42/57 – **120 rm** 175/225.

**at Fellbach** *NE : 8 km by Nürnberger Straße (B 14)* JT – 0711 :

**Classic Congress Hotel**, Tainer Str. 7, ✉ 70734, ✆ (0711) 5 85 90, *Fax (0711) 5859304*, « Changing exhibition of pictures », – rm, P – 60. AE E VISA
*closed 23 December - 6 January* – **Meals** see ***Alt Württemberg*** *below* – **148 rm** 195/350.

**Alt Württemberg**, Tainer Str. 7 (Schwabenlandhalle), ✉ 70734, ✆ (0711) 5 85 94 11, *Fax (0711) 581927*, – P. AE E VISA JCB
**Meals** à la carte 52/87.

**Aldinger's Weinstube Germania** with rm, Schmerstr. 6, ✉ 70734, ✆ (0711) 58 20 37, *Fax (0711) 582077*, – .
*closed 2 weeks February - March and 3 weeks July - August* – **Meals** *(closed Sunday, Monday and Bank Holidays)* (booking essential) à la carte 40/70 – **7 rm** 75/140.

**at Gerlingen** *W : 10 km by Rotenwaldstraße* FX – ✆ *07156 :*

**Krone**, Hauptstr. 28, ✉ 70839, ✆ (07156) 4 31 10, *Fax (07156) 4311100*, – rm, – 120. AE E VISA
**Meals** *(closed Sunday, Monday, Bank Holidays, Easter and Christmas)* (booking essential) à la carte 38/83 *(vegetarian menu available)* – **56 rm** 142/249.

**at Korntal-Münchingen** *NW : 9 km, by Heilbronner Str.* GT *:*

**Mercure**, Siemensstr. 50, ✉ 70825, ✆ (07150) 1 30, *Fax (07150) 13266*, , beer garden, , – , rm, – 160. AE E VISA
**Meals** à la carte 53/75 – **200 rm** 164/220.

**at Leinfelden-Echterdingen** *S : 11 km by Obere Weinsteige (B 27)* GX *:*

**Filderland** without rest, Tübinger Str. 16 (Echterdingen), ✉ 70771, ✆ (0711) 9 49 46, *Fax (0711) 9494888* – – 20. AE E VISA.
*closed 24 December - 2 January* – **48 rm** 135/190.

## Baiersbronn *Baden-Württemberg* 419 U 9, 987 ㊳ – *pop. 16 000 – alt. 550 m.*

*Stuttgart 100.*

XXXXX ✿✿✿ **Schwarzwaldstube** (French rest.), Tonbachstr. 237 (at Hotel Traube Tonbach), ✉ 72270, ✆ (07442) 49 26 65, *Fax (0742) 492692*, ← – . AE E VISA
*closed Monday, Tuesday, 12 January - 3 February and 3 to 25 August* – **Meals** (booking essential) 165/208 and à la carte 101/149
**Spec.** Salat von gegerillten Gemüsen und Jakobsmuscheln mit Olivenmarinade. Gefüllte Entenbrust mit Trüffel, Wirsing und Entenleber auf Rotweinjus. Soufflé von weißer und dunkler Schokolade mit Kompott von Zitrusfrüchten.

XXXXX ✿✿ **Restaurant Bareiss**, Gärtenbühlweg 14 (at Hotel Bareiss), ✉ 72270, ✆ (07224) 4 70, *Fax (07224) 47320*, ← – . AE E VISA
*closed Monday, Tuesday, June - 2 July and 23 November - 24 December* – **Meals** (booking essential) (outstanding wine list) 148/189 and à la carte 98/122
**Spec.** Mosaik von der Gänseleber und Trüffel. Loup de mer auf der Haut gebraten mit Artischocken. Glacierter Rehbockrücken mit Datteln.

## Haigerloch *Baden-Württemberg* 419 U 10, 987 ㊳ – *pop. 11 000 – alt. 425 m.*

*Stuttgart 70.*

XXX ✿✿ **Schwanen** with rm, Marktplatz 5 (Unterstadt), ✉ 72401, ✆ (07474) 75 75, *Fax (07474) 7576*, , « Restored 17C baroque house » – . AE E. rest
**Meals** *(closed Monday)* (Tuesday-Friday dinner only) 98/164 and à la carte 84/117 – **23 Z** 120/220
**Spec.** Gänsestopfleberterrine mit Kaninchenconfit. Zweierlei vom Lamm mit Bohnengemüse und eingelegten Sherrytomaten. Topfensoufflé mit Früchtecoulis und Passionsfruchtsorbet.

# *Greece*

## *Elláda*

ATHENS

# PRACTICAL INFORMATION

## LOCAL CURRENCY

**Greek Drachma:** *100 GRD = 0,36 USD ($) (Jan. 98)*

## TOURIST INFORMATION

**National Tourist Organisation (EOT):** *2 Karageorgi Servias (Sindagma), ✆ (01) 322 25 45 (information), 6 Amerikis ✆ (01) 331 04 37. Hotel reservation: Hellenic Chamber of Hotels, 24 Stadiou, ✆ (01) 323 71 93. Fax (01) 322 54 49, also at East Airport ✆ (01) 961 27 22 - Tourist Police: 4 Stadiou ✆ 171.*

**National Holidays in Greece:** *25 March and 28 October.*

## FOREIGN EXCHANGE

*Banks are usually open on weekdays from 8am to 2pm. A branch of the National Bank of Greece is open daily from 8am to 2pm (from 9am to 1pm at weekends) at 2 Karageorgi Servias (Sindagma). East Airport offices operate a 24-hour service.*

## AIRLINES

**OLYMPIC AIRWAYS:** *96 Singrou 117 41 Athens, ✆ (01) 926 73 33/926 91 11-3, 2 Kotopouli (Omonia), ✆ (01) 926 72 16-9, reservations only ✆ (01) 966 66 66.*
*All following Companies are located in Sindagma area:*

**AIR FRANCE:** *18 Vouliagmenis, Glyfada (01) 166 75 Athens, ✆ (01) 960 11 00.*
**BRITISH AIRWAYS:** *10 Othonos (01) 105 57 Athens, ✆ (01) 325 06 01.*
**JAPAN AIRLINES:** *22 Voulis 105 63 Athens, ✆ (01) 324 82 11-2.*
**LUFTHANSA:** *11 Vas. Sofias 106 71 Athens, ✆ (01) 369 2200.*
**SABENA:** *41 c, Vouliagmenis, Glyfada ✆ (01) 960 00 21-4.*
**SWISSAIR:** *4 Othonos, (lst floor) 105 57 Athens, ✆ (01) 323 5811-7.*

## TRANSPORT IN ATHENS

**Taxis:** *may be hailed in the street even when already engaged; it is always advisable to pay by the meter.*

**Bus:** *good for sightseeing and practical for short distances: 100 GRD.*

**Metro:** *one single line crossing the city from North (Kifissia) to South (Pireas): 100 GRD.*

## POSTAL SERVICES

**General Post Office:** *100 Eolou (Omonia) with poste restante, and also at Sindagma.*
**Telephone (OTE):** *15 Stadiou and 85 Patission (all services).*

## SHOPPING IN ATHENS

*In summer, shops are usually open from 8am to 1.30pm, and 5.30 to 8.30pm. They close on Sunday, and at 2.30pm on Monday, Wednesday and Saturday. In winter they open from 9am to 5pm on Monday and Wednesday, from 10am to 7pm on Tuesday, Thursday and Friday, from 8.30am to 3.30pm on Saturday. Department Stores in Patission and Eolou are open fron 8.30 am to 8 pm on weekdays and 3 pm on Saturdays. The main shopping streets are to be found in Sindagma, Kolonaki, Monastiraki and Omonia areas. Flea Market (generally open on Sunday) and Greek Handicraft in Plaka and Monastiraki.*

## TIPPING

*Service is generally included in the bills but it is usual to tip employees.*

## SPEED LIMITS

*The speed limit in built up areas is 50 km/h (31 mph); on motorways the maximum permitted speed is 100 km/h (62 mph) and 80 km/h (50 mph) on others roads.*

## SEAT BELTS

*The wearing of seat belts is compulsory for drivers and front seat passengers.*

## BREAKDOWN SERVICE

*The ELPA (Automobile and Touring Club of Greece, ✆ (01) 74 88 800) operate a 24 hour breakdown service: phone 174.*

# ATHENS

(ATHÍNA) *Atikí* 980 ㉚ – *Pop. 3 076 786 (Athens and Piraeus area).*

*Igoumenítsa 581 – Pátra 215 – Thessaloníki 479.*

*Tourist Information (EOT), 2 Amerikis ☎ (01) 322 31 11, Information center, 2 Karageorgi Servias (Sindagma) ☎ (01) 322 25 45 and East Airport ☎ (01) 961 27 22. ELPA (Automobile and Touring Club of Greece), 2 Messogion ☎ (01) 748 88 00.*

18 *Glifáda (near airport) ☎ (01) 894 68 20, Fax (01) 894 37 21.*

*S : 15 km, East Airport ☎ (01) 969 41 11 (International Airport – All companies except Olympic Airways), West Airport ☎ (01) 966 66 66 (Elinikó Airport – Olympic Airways only).*

*1 Karolou ☎ (01) 524 06 01.*

## SIGHTS

*Views of Athens: Lycabettos (Likavitós) ✳★★★* DX – *Philopappos Hill (Lófos Filopápou) ≤★★★* AY.

## ANCIENT ATHENS

*Acropolis★★★ (Akrópoli)* ABY – *Theseion★★ (Thissío)* AY *and Agora★ (Arhéa Agorá)* AY – *Theatre of Dionysos★★ (Théatro Dionissou)* BY *and Odeon of Herod Atticus★ (Odío Iródou Atikoú)* AY – *Olympieion★★ (Naós Olimbíou Diós)* BY *and Hadrian's Arch★ (Píli Adrianoú)* BY – *Tower of the Winds★* BY **G** *in the Roman Forum (Romaïkí Agorá).*

## OLD ATHENS AND THE TURKISH PERIOD

*Pláka★★ : Old Metropolitan★★* BY **A²** – *Monastiráki★ (Old Bazaar) : Kapnikaréa (Church)* BY **A⁶**, *Odós Pandróssou★* BY **29**, *Monastiráki Square★* BY.

## MODERN ATHENS

*Sindagma Square★* CY : *Greek guard on sentry duty – Academy, University and Library Buildings★ (Akadimía* CX, *Panepistímio* CX, *Ethnikí Vivliothíki* BX) – *National Garden★ (Ethnikós Kípos)* CY.

## MUSEUMS

*National Archaelogical Museum★★★ (Ethnikó Arheologikó Moussío)* BX – *Acropolis Museum★★★* BY **M¹** – *Museum of Cycladic and Ancient Greek Art★★* DY **M¹⁵** – *Byzantine Museum★★ (Vizandinó Moussío)* DY – *Benaki Museum★★ (Moussío Benáki, private collection of antiquities and traditional art)* CDY – *Museum of Traditional Greek Art★* BY **M²** – *National Historical Museum★* BY **M⁷** – *Jewish Museum of Greece★* BY **M¹⁶** – *National Gallery and Soutzos Museum★ (painting and sculpture)* DY **M⁸**.

## EXCURSIONS

*Cape Sounion★★★ (Soúnio) SE : 71 km* BY – *Kessariani Monastery★★, E : 9 km* DY – *Daphne Monastery★★ (Dafní) NW : 10 km* AX – *Aigina Island★ (Égina) : Temple of Aphaia★★, 3 hours return.*

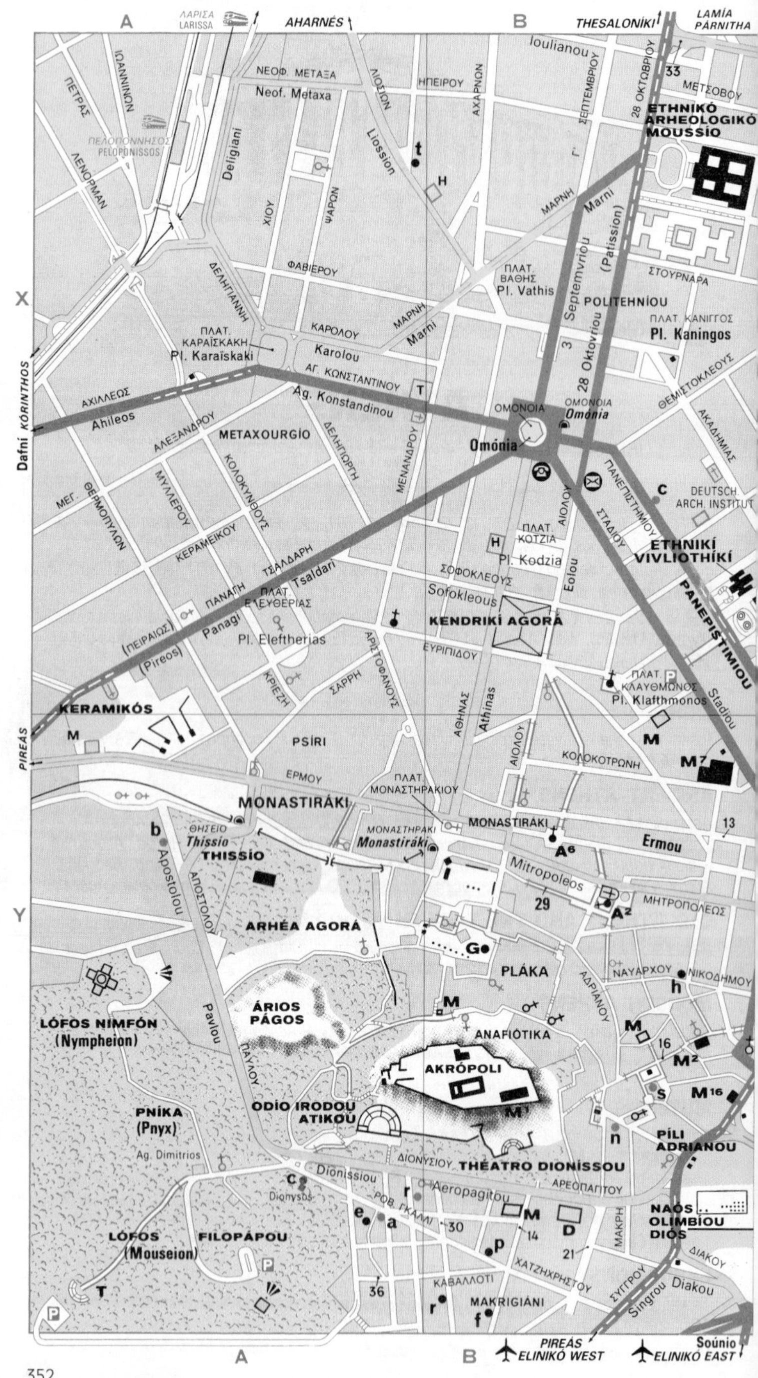

A
B
ΛΑΡΙΣΑ LARISSA
AHARNÉS
THESALONÍKI
LAMÍA PÁRNITHA
ΠΕΛΟΠΟΝΝΗΣΟΣ PELOPONISSOS
Ioulianou
ΝΕΟΦ. ΜΕΤΑΞΑ
Neof. Metaxa
ΗΠΕΙΡΟΥ
33
ΜΕΤΣΟΒΟΥ
ETHNIKÓ ARHEOLOGIKÓ MOUSSÍO
Liossion
Deligiani
Marni
(Patission)
ΦΑΒΙΕΡΟΥ
ΠΛΑΤ. ΒΑΘΗΣ
Pl. Vathis
POLITEHNÍOU
ΣΤΟΥΡΝΑΡΑ
ΠΛΑΤ. ΚΑΝΙΓΓΟΣ
Pl. Kaningos
X
ΚΑΡΟΛΟΥ
Karolou
ΠΛΑΤ. ΚΑΡΑΪΣΚΑΚΗ
Pl. Karaïskaki
ΑΓ. ΚΩΝΣΤΑΝΤΙΝΟΥ
Ag. Konstandinou
28 Oktovriou
3 Septemvriou
ΘΕΜΙΣΤΟΚΛΕΟΥΣ
ΑΚΑΔΗΜΙΑΣ
ΟΜΟΝΟΙΑ
Omónia
KÓRINTHOS
Dafní
ΑΧΙΛΛΕΩΣ
Ahileos
ΑΛΕΞΑΝΔΡΟΥ
METAXOURGÍO
ΜΕΝΑΝΔΡΟΥ
ΠΑΝΕΠΙΣΤΗΜΙΟΥ
ΣΤΑΔΙΟΥ
DEUTSCH. ARCH. INSTITUT
ΜΕΓ. ΘΕΡΜΟΠΥΛΩΝ
ΜΥΛΛΕΡΟΥ
ΚΟΛΟΚΥΝΘΟΥΣ
ΚΕΡΑΜΕΙΚΟΥ
ΠΛΑΤ. ΚΟΤΖΙΑ
Pl. Kodzia
ETHNIKÍ VIVLIOTHÍKÍ
ΣΟΦΟΚΛΕΟΥΣ
Sofokleous
Eolou
ΤΣΑΛΔΑΡΗ
Tsaldari
ΠΑΝΑΓΗ
Panagi
ΠΛΑΤ. ΕΛΕΥΘΕΡΙΑΣ
Pl. Eleftherias
(ΠΕΙΡΑΙΩΣ)
(Pireos)
KENDRIKÍ AGORÁ
ΕΥΡΙΠΙΔΟΥ
PANEPISTIMIOU
ΠΛΑΤ. ΚΛΑΥΘΜΩΝΟΣ
Pl. Klafthmonos
Stadiou
ΑΡΙΣΤΟΦΑΝΟΥΣ
ΣΑΡΡΗ
ΚΡΙΕΖΗ
ΑΘΗΝΑΣ
Athinas
KERAMIKÓS
PSÍRI
ΑΙΟΛΟΥ
ΚΟΛΟΚΟΤΡΩΝΗ
PIREÁS
ΕΡΜΟΥ
ΠΛΑΤ. ΜΟΝΑΣΤΗΡΑΚΙΟΥ
MONASTIRÁKI
ΘΗΣΕΙΟ
Thissío
THISSÍO
ΜΟΝΑΣΤΗΡΑΚΙ
Monastiráki
13
Ermou
Mitropoleos
29
ΜΗΤΡΟΠΟΛΕΩΣ
Apostolou
ΑΠΟΣΤΟΛΟΥ
Y
ARHÉA AGORÁ
PLÁKA
ΝΑΥΑΡΧΟΥ
ΝΙΚΟΔΗΜΟΥ
ΑΔΡΙΑΝΟΥ
ÁRIOS PÁGOS
ANAFIÓTIKA
LÓFOS NIMFÓN (Nympheion)
Pavlou
ΠΑΥΛΟΥ
AKRÓPOLI
16
PNÍKA (Pnyx)
ODÍO IRODOU ATIKOÚ
PÍLI ADRIANOU
Ag. Dimitrios
ΔΙΟΝΥΣΙΟΥ
THÉATRO DIONÍSSOU
Dionissiou
Dionysos
Aeropagitou
ΑΡΕΟΠΑΓΙΤΟΥ
ΡΟΒ. ΓΚΑΛΛΙ
30
ΜΑΚΡΗ
NAÓS OLIMBÍOU DIÓS
LÓFOS (Mouseion)
FILOPÁPOU
14
21
ΧΑΤΖΗΧΡΗΣΤΟΥ
ΔΙΑΚΟΥ
ΣΥΓΓΡΟΥ
Singrou
Diakou
36
ΚΑΒΑΛΛΟΤΙ
MAKRIGIÁNI
PIREÁS ELINIKÓ WEST
ELINIKÓ EAST
Soúnio

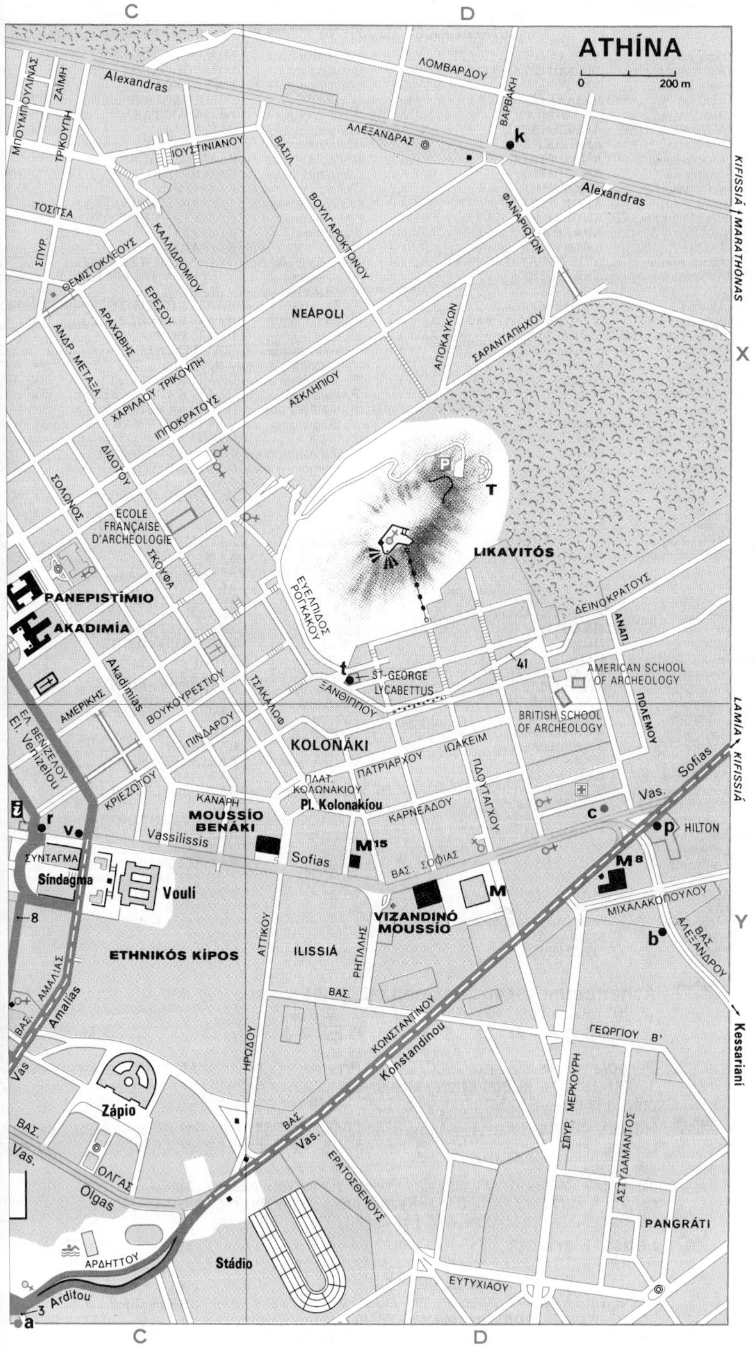
ATHÍNA
0
200 m
C
D
X
Y
Alexandras
ΛΟΜΒΑΡΔΟΥ
ΑΛΕΞΑΝΔΡΑΣ
ΒΑΡΒΑΚΗ
ΙΟΥΣΤΙΝΙΑΝΟΥ
ΤΟΣΙΤΣΑ
ΚΑΛΛΙΔΡΟΜΙΟΥ
ΒΟΥΛΓΑΡΟΚΤΟΝΟΥ
ΦΑΝΑΡΙΩΤΩΝ
ΘΕΜΙΣΤΟΚΛΕΟΥΣ
ΕΡΕΣΟΥ
NEÁPOLI
ΑΠΟΚΑΥΚΩΝ
ΣΑΡΑΝΤΑΠΗΧΟΥ
ΧΑΡΙΛΑΟΥ ΤΡΙΚΟΥΠΗ
ΙΠΠΟΚΡΑΤΟΥΣ
ΑΣΚΛΗΠΙΟΥ
ΣΟΛΩΝΟΣ
ECOLE FRANÇAISE D'ARCHEOLOGIE
LIKAVITÓS
PANEPISTÍMIO
AKADIMÍA
ΔΕΙΝΟΚΡΑΤΟΥΣ
ST-GEORGE LYCABETTUS
AMERICAN SCHOOL OF ARCHEOLOGY
BRITISH SCHOOL OF ARCHEOLOGY
KOLONÁKI
Pl. Kolonakíou
MOUSSÍO BENÁKI
Vassilissis
Sofias
ΒΑΣ. ΣΟΦΙΑΣ
HILTON
Síndagma
Voulí
VIZANDINÓ MOUSSÍO
ΜΙΧΑΛΑΚΟΠΟΥΛΟΥ
ETHNIKÓS KÍPOS
ILISSIÁ
ΓΕΩΡΓΙΟΥ Β'
Konstandinou
Zápio
Vas. Olgas
ΑΡΔΗΤΤΟΥ
Stádio
ΕΡΑΤΟΣΘΕΝΟΥΣ
ΕΥΤΥΧΙΔΟΥ
PANGRÁTI
Arditou
KIFISSIÁ MARATHÓNAS
LAMÍA KIFISSIÁ
Kessarianí

## STREET INDEX TO ATHÍNA TOWN PLAN

| Street | Greek | Grid | No. |
|---|---|---|---|
| Adrianou | ΑΔΡΙΑΝΟΥ | BY | |
| Ag. Konstandinou | ΑΓ. ΚΩΝΣΤΑΝΤΙΝΟΥ | AX | |
| Aharnon | ΑΧΑΡΝΩΝ | BX | |
| Ahilleos | ΑΧΙΛΛΕΩΣ | AX | |
| Akadimias | ΑΚΑΔΙΜΙΑΣ | BCX | |
| Alexandras | ΑΛΕΞΑΝΔΡΑΣ | CDX | |
| Amerikis | ΑΜΕΡΙΚΗΣ | CXY | |
| Anapavseos | ΑΝΑΠΑΥΣΕΩΣ | CY | 3 |
| Anapiron Polemou | ΑΝΑΠΗΡΩΝ ΠΟΛΕΜΟΥ | DXY | |
| Apokafkon | ΑΠΟΚΑΥΚΩΝ | DX | |
| Apostolou Pavlou | ΑΠΟΣΤΟΛΟΥ ΠΑΥΛΟΥ | AY | |
| Arahovis | ΑΡΑΧΩΒΗΣ | CX | |
| Arditou | ΑΡΔΗΤΤΟΥ | CY | |
| Aristofanous | ΑΡΙΣΤΟΦΑΝΟΥΣ | AX | |
| Asklipiou | ΑΣΚΛΗΠΙΟΥ | DX | |
| Ath. Diakou | ΑΘ. ΔΙΑΚΟΥ | BY | |
| Athinas | ΑΘΗΝΑΣ | BXY | |
| Bouboulinas | ΜΠΟΥΜΠΟΥΛΙΝΑΣ | CX | |
| Deligiani | ΔΕΛΗΓΙΑΝΝΗ | AX | |
| Deligiorgi | ΔΕΛΗΓΙΩΡΓΗ | AX | |
| Didotou | ΔΙΔΟΤΟΥ | CX | |
| Dionissiou Areopagitou | ΔΙΟΝΥΣΙΟΥ ΑΡΕΟΠΑΓΙΤΟΥ | ABY | |
| El. Venizelou | ΕΛ ΒΕΝΙΖΕΛΟΥ | CXY | |
| Eolou | ΑΙΟΛΟΥ | BXY | |
| Eratosthenous | ΕΡΑΤΟΣΘΕΝΟΥΣ | DY | |
| Ermou | ΕΡΜΟΥ | ABY | |
| Evelpidos Rongakou | ΕΥΕΛΠΙΔΟΣ ΡΟΓΚΑΚΟΥ | DX | |
| Fanarioton | ΘΑΝΑΡΙΩΤΩΝ | DX | |
| Favierou | ΘΑΒΙΕΡΟΥ | AX | |
| Filelinon | ΘΙΛΕΛΛΗΝΩΝ | BCY | 8 |
| Hadzihristou | ΧΑΤΖΗΧΡΗΣΤΟΥ | BY | |
| Harilaou Trikoupi | ΧΑΡΙΛΑΟΥ ΤΡΙΚΟΥΠΗ | CX | |
| Hiou | ΧΙΟΥ | AX | |
| Ioulianou | ΙΟΥΛΙΑΝΟΥ | AX | |
| Ioustinianou | ΙΟΥΣΤΙΝΙΑΝΟΥ | CX | |
| Ipirou | ΗΠΕΙΡΟΥ | ABX | |
| Ipokratous | ΙΠΠΟΚΡΑΤΟΥΣ | CX | |
| Irodou Atikou | ΗΡΩΔΟΥ ΑΤΤΙΚΟΥ | DY | |
| Kalidromiou | ΚΑΛΛΙΔΡΟΜΙΟΥ | CX | |
| Kanari | ΚΑΝΑΡΗ | CY | |
| Karageorgi Servias | ΚΑΡΑΓΙΩΡΓΗ ΣΕΡΒΙΑΣ | BY | 13 |
| Karneadou | ΚΑΡΝΕΑΔΟΥ | DY | |
| Karolou | ΚΑΡΟΛΟΥ | AX | |
| Kavaloti | ΚΑΒΑΛΛΟΤΙ | BY | |
| Keramikou | ΚΕΡΑΜΕΙΚΟΥ | AX | |
| Kidathineon | ΚΥΔΑΘΗΝΑΙΩΝ | BY | 16 |
| Kolokinthous | ΚΟΛΟΚΥΝΘΟΥΣ | AX | |
| Kolokotroni | ΚΟΛΟΚΟΤΡΩΝΗ | BY | |
| Kriezotou | ΚΡΙΕΖΩΤΟΥ | CY | |
| Liossion | ΛΙΟΣΙΩΝ | AX | |
| Lomvardou | ΛΟΜΒΑΡΔΟΥ | DX | |
| Makri | ΜΑΚΡΗ | BY | |
| Makrigiani | ΜΑΚΡΥΓΙΑΝΝΗ | BY | 21 |
| Marni | ΜΑΡΝΗ | ABX | |
| Meg. Alexandrou | ΜΕΓ. ΑΛΕΞΑΝΔΡΟΥ | AX | |
| Menandrou | ΜΕΝΑΝΔΡΟΥ | AX | |
| Metsovou | ΜΕΤΣΟΒΟΥ | BX | |
| Mihalakopoulou | ΜΙΧΑΛΑΚΟΠΟΥΛΟΥ | DY | |
| Mitropoleos | ΜΗΤΡΟΠΟΛΕΩΣ | BY | |
| Navarhou Nikodimou | ΝΑΥΑΡΧΟΥ ΝΙΚΟΔΗΜΟΥ | BY | |
| Neof. Metaxa | ΝΕΟΦ. ΜΕΤΑΞΑ | AX | |
| Omonia | ΟΜΟΝΟΙΑ | BX | |
| Pandrossou | ΠΑΝΔΡΟΣΟΥ | BY | 29 |
| Panepistimiou | ΠΑΝΕΠΙΣΤΗΜΙΟΥ | BX | |
| Parthenonos | ΠΑΡΘΕΝΩΝΟΣ | BY | 30 |
| Patission (28 Oktovriou) | ΠΑΤΗΣΙΩΝ (28 ΟΚΤΩΒΡΙΟΥ) | BX | |
| Patr. Ioakim | ΠΑΤΡ. ΙΩΑΚΕΙΜ | DY | |
| Pindarou | ΠΙΝΔΑΡΟΥ | CY | |
| Pireos (Panagi Tsaldari) | ΠΕΙΡΑΙΩΣ (ΠΑΝΑΓΗ ΤΣΑΛΔΑΡΗ) | AX | |
| Pl. Anexartissias (Vathis) | ΠΛΑΤ. ΑΝΕΞΑΡΤΗΣΙΑΣ (ΒΑΘΗΣ) | BX | |
| Pl. Egiptou | ΠΛΑΤ. ΑΙΓΥΠΤΟΥ | BX | 33 |
| Pl. Eleftherias | ΠΛΑΤ. ΕΛΕΥΘΕΡΙΑΣ | AX | |
| Pl. Eth. Andistasseos (Kodzia) | ΠΛΑΤ. ΕΘΝ. ΑΝΤΙΣΤΑΣΕΩΣ (ΚΟΤΖΙΑ) | BX | |
| Pl. Kaningos | ΠΛΑΤ. ΚΑΝΙΓΓΟΣ | BX | |
| Pl. Karaïskaki | ΠΛΑΤ. ΚΑΡΑΙΣΚΑΚΗ | AX | |
| Pl. Klafthmonos | ΠΛΑΤ. ΛΑΥΘΕΡΙΑΖ | BX | |
| Pl. Kolonakiou | ΠΛΑΤ. ΚΟΛΩΝΑΚΙΟΥ | DY | |
| Pl. Monastirakiou | ΠΛΑΤ. ΜΟΝΑΣΤΗΡΑΚΙΟΥ | ABY | |
| Ploutarhou | ΠΛΟΥΤΑΡΧΟΥ | DX | |
| Psaron | ΨΑΡΩΝ | AX | |
| Radzieri | ΡΑΤΖΙΕΡΗ | AY | 36 |
| Rigilis | ΡΗΓΙΛΛΗΣ | DY | |
| Rovertou Gali | ΡΟΒΕΡΤΟΥ ΓΚΑΛΛΙ | AY | |
| Sarandapihou | ΣΑΡΑΝΤΑΠΗΧΟΥ | DX | |
| Sindagma | ΣΥΝΤΑΓΜΑ | CY | |
| Singrou | ΣΥΓΓΡΟΥ | BY | |
| Skoufa | ΣΚΟΥΦΑ | CX | |
| Sofokleous | ΣΟΦΟΚΛΕΟΥΣ | ABX | |
| Solonos | ΣΟΛΩΝΟΣ | CX | |
| Spir. Merkouri | ΣΗΥΡ. ΜΕΡΚΟΥΡΗ | DY | |
| Spir. Trikoupi | ΣΗΥΡ. ΤΡΙΚΟΥΠΗ | CX | |
| Stadiou | ΣΤΑΔΙΟΥ | BXY | |
| Stournara | ΣΤΟΥΡΝΑΡΑ | BX | |
| Themistokleous | ΘΕΜΙΣΤΟΚΛΕΟΥΣ | BCX | |
| Thermopilon | ΘΕΡΜΟΠΥΛΩΝ | AX | |
| Tossitsa | ΤΟΣΙΤΖΑ | CX | |
| Tsakalof | ΤΣΑΚΑΛΩΦ | DXY | |
| Varvaki | ΒΑΡΒΑΚΗ | DX | |
| Vas. Alexandrou | ΒΑΣ. ΑΛΕΞΑΝΔΡΟΥ | DY | |
| Vas. Amalias | ΒΑΣ. ΑΜΑΛΙΑΣ | CY | |
| Vas. Georgiou B' | ΒΑΣ. ΓΕΩΡΓΙΟΥ Β | DY | |
| Vas. Konstandinou | ΒΑΣ. ΚΩΝΣΤΑΝΤΙΝΟΥ | DY | |
| Vas. Olgas | ΒΑΣ. ΟΛΓΑΣ | CY | |
| Vas. Sofias | ΒΑΣ. ΣΟΦΙΑΣ | CDY | |
| Vassiliou Voulgaroktonou | ΒΑΣΙΛΕΙΟΥ ΒΟΥΛΓΑΡΟΚΤΟΝΟΥ | DX | |
| Voukourestiou | ΒΟΥΚΟΥΡΕΣΤΙΟΥ | CXY | |
| Xanthipou | ΞΑΝΘΙΠΠΟΥ | DXY | |
| Xenokratous | ΞΕΝΟΚΠΑΤΟΥΣ | DX | 41 |
| Zaïmi | ΖΑΙΜΗ | CX | |
| 3 Septemvriou | Γ'ΣΕΠΤΕΜΒΡΙΟΥ | BX | |

**Athenaeum Inter-Continental,** 89-93 Singrou, ✉ 117 45, *SW : 2 ¾ km* ☎ (01) 9206 000, *Fax (01) 9243 000,* « Première rooftop restaurant with ≤ Athens », heated – lift, rm, TV ☎ – 2000. AE VISA JCB.
***Pergola*** **: Meals** a la carte 7900/9900 – ***Première*** (9th floor) **: Meals** (buffet dinner only) 12000/15000 – ***Kublai Khan*** **: Meals** - Mongolian and Chinese - *(closed Sunday)* (dinner only) a la carte 8600/11100 – ☕ 3800 – **510 rm** 68000/105000, 44 suites.

**Hilton,** 46 Vas. Sofias, ✉ 115 28, ☎ (01) 7250 201, *Fax (01) 7253 110,* « Roof terrace with ≤ Athens », heated – lift, rm, TV ☎ – 1000. AE VISA JCB
DY p
***Ta Nissia*** **: Meals** (dinner only) 23000 and a la carte – ***Kellari*** **: Meals** - Taverna - (dinner only) a la carte 9900/12400 – ***Byzantine*** **: Meals** (buffet lunch) 6900 and a la carte 9900/12700 – ☕ 4500 – **434 rm** 73960/95870, 19 suites.

**Ledra Marriott,** 115 Singrou, ✉ 117 45, SW : 3 km ☎ (01) 9347 711, *Fax (01) 9358 603,* « Rooftop terrace with and Athens » – lift, rm, TV ☎ – 500. AE VISA.
***Kona Kai*** **: Meals** - Polynesian and Japanese - *(closed Sunday)* (dinner only) 8500/17000 and a la carte – ***Zephyros*** **: Meals** 6000/11500 and a la carte – ☕ 4550 – **244 rm** 49000, 15 suites.

**Grande Bretagne,** 1 Vas. Georgiou A, Sindagma Sq., 105 63, (01) 3330 000, *Fax (01) 3328 064* – 500. AE VISA JCB. rest CY v
***G B Corner :*** **Meals** (buffet lunch) 7500/10600 and a la carte – 4300 – **341 rm** 75000/105000, 23 suites.

**Divani Palace Acropolis,** 19-25 Parthenonos, 117 42, (01) 9222 945, *Fax (01) 9214 993,* « Ancient ruins of Themistocles wall in basement », – 300. AE E VISA JCB. BY r
***Aspassia :*** **Meals** 6500 and a la carte – ***Roof Garden :*** **Meals** *(closed Tuesday and November-April)* (live music) (buffet dinner only) 9500 – **244 rm** 39000/60000, 7 suites.

**Divani Caravel,** 2 Vas. Alexandrou, 116 10, (01) 7253 725, *Fax (01) 7253 770,* « Rooftop with Athens », rm, – 1300. AE E VISA JCB. DY b
***Amalia :*** **Meals** 5600 and a la carte – 4500 – **423 rm** 40000/55000, 48 suites.

**Le NJV Meridien,** 2 Vas. Georgiou A, Sindagma Sq., 105 64, (01) 325 5301, *Fax (01) 323 5856* – rm, – 250. AE E VISA JCB. CY r
***Marco Polo :*** **Meals** 8000 and a la carte – 4200 – **152 rm** 62000/95000, 25 suites.

**Novotel,** 4-6 Mihail Voda, 104 39, (01) 8250 422, *Fax (01) 8837 816,* « Roof garden with and Athens » – 600. AE E VISA JCB AX t
**Meals** 4500/7000 and a la carte – 3500 – **190 rm** 32000/36000, 5 suites.

**St. George Lycabettus,** 2 Kleomenous, 106 75, (01) 7290 712, *Fax (01) 7290 439,* « Athens from rooftop restaurant », – 150. AE E VISA JCB. DX t
***Grand Balcon :*** **Meals** *(closed Sunday and Monday)* (dinner only) 7000/15000 and a la carte – ***Mediterraneo :*** **Meals** (buffet lunch) 5000/10000 and a la carte – **150 rm** 43900/77000, 7 suites.

**Holiday Inn,** 50 Mihalakopoulou, 115 28, (01) 7248 322, *Fax (01) 7248 187,* – rm, – 600. AE E VISA JCB. DY
**Meals** 6000/6500 and a la carte – 4000 – **188 rm** 32000, 3 suites.

**Zafolia,** 87-89 Alexandras, 114 74, (01) 6449 002, *Fax (01) 6442 042,* « Rooftop terrace with and Athens » – – 200. AE E VISA JCB. DX k
**Meals** 4400/4700 and a la carte – **183 rm** 21500/26500, 8 suites.

**Electra,** 5 Ermou, 105 63, (01) 3223 223, *Fax (01) 3220 310* – rm, AE E VISA. BY e
**Meals** 4900 and a la carte – **110 rm** 33100/40400.

**Herodion,** 4 Rovertou Galli, 117 42, (01) 9236 832, *Fax (01) 9235 851,* « Roof garden with Acropolis » – – 50. AE E VISA JCB. BY p
**Meals** 5000 and a la carte – **90 rm** 30500/39900.

**Electra Palace,** 18 Nikodimou, 105 57, (01) 3241 401, *Fax (01) 3241 875,* « Terrace with and Athens » – rm, – 200. AE E VISA.
**Meals** 4900 and a la carte – **101 rm** 33100/40400, 5 suites. BY h

**Philippos** without rest., 3 Mitseon, 117 42, (01) 9223 611, *Fax (01) 9223 615* – AE E VISA JCB. BY f
**48 rm** 22300/28000.

**Acropolis View** without rest., 10 Wemster, off Rovertou Galli, 117 42, (01) 9217 303, *Fax (01) 9230 705,* « Roof terrace with Acropolis » – AE E VISA AY e
**32 rm** 17600/23100.

**Boschetto,** Evangelismou, off Vas. Sofias, 106 76, (01) 7210 893, *Fax (01) 7223 598,* « Summerhouse in small park » – AE VISA DY c
*closed Saturday lunch, Sunday, Easter, 1 to 20 August, 25 December and 1 January* – **Meals** - Italian - 4000/16500 and a la carte.

**Bajazzo** (Feuerbach), 1 Tyrteou &corner of Anapavseos, 116 36, (01) 9213 012, *Fax (01) 9213 013,* – AE VISA CY a
*closed Sunday* – **Meals** (booking essential) (dinner only) 8000/15000 and a la carte 13700/20300
**Spec.** Tranche of sea bass on a French mustard sauce. Goat's rack fillet on a Greek coffee foam. Fillet of deer on a bitter chocolate sauce.

**Symbosio,** 46 Erehthiou, 117 42, (01) 9225 321, *Fax (01) 9232 780,* « Attractive conservatory, » – AE E VISA JCB AY r
*closed Sunday and 2 weeks August* – **Meals** (booking essential) (dinner only) a la carte 11600/14000.

**Pil-Poul,** 51 Apostolou Pavlou, 118 51, (01) 3423 665, *Fax (01) 3413 046,* « Former mansion with Acropolis and Athens from rooftop terrace » – AE E VISA AY b
*closed Sunday* – **Meals** (dinner only) 13000/16000 and a la carte.

XX **Dionysos,** 43 Rovertou Galli, Lofos Filopapou, ✉ 117 42, ☎ (01) 9233 182, *Fax (01) 9221 998,* ☂, « ≤ Acropolis » – ▤. AE ⓓ E VISA JCB AY c
**Meals** 4800/9000 and a la carte.

XX **Daphne's,** 4 Lysikratous, Plaka, ✉ 105 58, ☎ (01) 3227 971, *Fax (01) 3227 971,* ☂, « Frescoes depicting ancient Greek myths ; attractive inner courtyard » – ▤. AE ⓓ VISA BY n
**Meals** (booking essential) (dinner only) a la carte 11400/15700.

XX **Ideal,** 46 Panepistimiou, (El. Venizelou), ✉ 106 78, ☎ (01) 330 3000, *Fax (01) 330 3003* – ▤. AE ⓓ E VISA JCB BX c
*closed Sunday, Easter Monday and 25 December* – **Meals** a la carte 5110/8980.

XX **Dioscuri,** 16 Dimitriou Vassiliou, N. Psihiko, ✉ 154 51, *NE : 7 km by Kifissia Rd turning at A.B. supermarket* ☎ (01) 6713 997, *Fax (01) 6745 560,* ☂ – ▤. AE ⓓ E VISA
**Meals** 6000/8500 and a la carte.

X **Kidathineon,** 1 Filomoussou Pl., Eterias, ✉ 105 58, ☎ (01) 3234 281, ☂ – AE ⓓ E VISA JCB BY s
**Meals** (buffet lunch) 2640/4400 and a la carte.

X **Strofi,** 25 Rovertou Galli, ✉ 117 42, ☎ (01) 9214 130, ☂, « ≤ Acropolis from rooftop terrace » – ▤. ⓓ E VISA AY a
*closed Sunday, 4 days Easter and 1 week Christmas* – **Meals** (dinner only) 5000/6500 and a la carte.

## Environs

**at Kifissia** *NE : 15 km by Vas. Sofias* – DY :

**Pentelikon** ⛰, 66 Diligianni, Kefalari, ✉ 145 62, off Harilaou Trikoupi, follow signs to Politia ☎ (01) 6230 650, *Fax (01) 8010 314,* ☂, 🏊, 🌳 – |‡| ▤ 📺 ☎ Ⓟ – 🏛 150. AE ⓓ E VISA. ✈
***Vardis :* Meals** - French - *(closed Sunday)* (dinner only) a la carte 10200/16800 – ***La Terrasse :* Meals** a la carte 6550/10850 – ☕ 4600 – **33 rm** 74000/88000, 6 suites.

XXX **Varoulko,** 14 Deligiorgi, off Omiridou Skilitsi, ✉ 185 33, ☎ (01) 4112 043 – ▤. AE ⓓ VISA
*closed Sunday, August and Christmas* – **Meals** - Seafood - (booking essential) (dinner only) 6450/8250 and a la carte 6450/8250.

**at Pireas** *SW : 10 km by Singrou* – BY :

XX **Aglamer,** 54-56 Akti Koumoundourou, Mikrolimano, ✉ 185 33, ☎ (01) 4115 511, *Fax (01) 4181 951,* ≤ Harbour, ☂ – ▤. AE ⓓ E VISA
*closed Good Friday and 1 January* – **Meals** - Seafood - 7200/12800 and a la carte.

X **Durambeis,** 29 Athinas Dilaveri, ✉ 185 33, ☎ (01) 4122 092, ☂ – AE VISA
*closed Easter* – **Meals** - Seafood - a la carte 8800/11000.

# *Hungary*

## *Magyarország*

BUDAPEST

# PRACTICAL INFORMATION

## LOCAL CURRENCY

**Forint:** *100 HUF = 0.50 US $ (Jan. 98)*

**National Holidays in Hungary:** *15 March, 20 August, and 23 October.*

## PRICES

*Prices may change if goods and service costs in Hungary are revised and it is therefore always advisable to confirm rates with the hotelier when making a reservation.*

## FOREIGN EXCHANGE

*It is strongly advised against changing money other than in banks, exchange offices or authorised offices such as large hotels, tourist offices, etc... Banks are usually open on weekdays from 8.30am to 4pm.*

## HOTEL RESERVATIONS

*In case of difficulties in finding a room through our hotel selection, it is always possible to apply to IBUSZ Hotel Service, Apáczai ut. 1, Budapest 5th ☎ (01) 118 57 76, Fax (01) 117 90 99. This office offers a 24-hour assistance to the visitor.*

## POSTAL SERVICES

*Main Post offices are open from 8am to 7pm on weekdays and 8am to 3pm on Saturdays.*

**General Post Office:** *Városház ut. 18, Budapest 5th, ☎ (01) 118 48 11.*

## SHOPPING IN BUDAPEST

*In the index of street names, those printed in red are where the principal shops are found. Typical goods to be bought include embroidery, lace, china, leather goods, paprika, salami, Tokay, palinka, foie-gras... Shops are generally open from 10am to 6pm on weekdays (7pm on Thursday) and 9am to 1pm on Saturday.*

## TIPPING

*Hotel, restaurant and café bills often do not include service in the total charge. In these cases it is usual to leave the staff a gratuity which will vary depending upon the service given.*

## CAR HIRE

*The international car hire companies have branches in Budapest. Your hotel porter should be able to give details and help you with your arrangements.*

## BREAKDOWN SERVICE

*A breakdown service is operated by SARGA ANGYAL (Yellow Angel), ☎ (01) 252 80 00.*

## SPEED LIMIT

*On motorways, the maximum permitted speed is 120 km/h – 74 mph, 100 km/h – 62 mph on main roads, 80 km/h – 50 mph on others roads and 50 km/h – 31 mph in built up areas.*

## SEAT BELTS

*In Hungary, the wearing of seat belts is compulsory for drivers and front seat passengers.*

## TRANSPORT

*The three metro lines (yellow, red and blue) and the trams and buses make up an extensive public transport network. Tickets must be purchased in advance. Daily, weekly and monthly passes are available.*

# BUDAPEST

*Hungary* 970 N 6 – *Pop. 1 909 000.*

*Munich 678 – Prague 533 – Venice 740 – Vienna 243 – Zagreb 350*

*Tourinform, Sütő u. 2, ✉ H 1052 ☎ (01) 117 98 00 – IBUSZ Head Office, Ferenciek tér 5, Budapest 5th ☎ (01) 118 68 66.*

✈ *Ferihegy SE : 16 km by Üllői* FX, *☎ (01) 296 96 96 (information), Bus to airport : from International Bus station, Erzsébet tér, Station 6 Budapest 5th and Airport Minibus Service LRI – MALEV, Roosevelt tér 2, Budapest 5th ☎ (01) 267 29 11*

## Views of Budapest

*St. Gellert Monument and Citadel (Szt. Gellért-szobor, Citadella)* <★★★ EX – *Fishermen's Bastion (Halászbástya)* <★★ DU.

## BUDA

*Matthias Church★★ (Mátyás-templom)* DU – *Attractive Streets★★ (Tancsics Mihaly utca – Fortuna utca – Uri utca)* CDU – *Royal Palace★★ (Budavári palota)* DV – *Hungarian National Gallery★★ (Magyar Nemzeti Galéria)* DV **M¹** – *Budapest Historical Museum★ (Budapesti Történeti Múzeum)* DV **M¹** – *Vienna Gate★ (Bécsi kapu)* CU – *War History Museum★ (Hadtörténety Múzeum)* CU.

## PEST

*Parliament Building★★★ (Országház)* EU – *Museum of Fine Arts★★★ (Szepmüveszeti Múzeum)* BY **M³** – *Hungarian National Museum★★ (Magyar Nemzeti Múzeum)* FVX – *Museum of Applied Arts★★ (Iparmüvészeti Múzeum)* BZ **M⁵** – *Szechenyi Thermal Baths★★ (Széchenyi Gyógyés Strandfürdö)* BY **F²** – *Hungarian State Opera House★ (Magyar Állami Operaház)* FU – *Liszt Conservatory : foyer★ (Liszt Ferenc Zenemüvészeti Föiskola)* FU – *Chinese Art Museum★ (Kína Muzéum)* BYZ **M⁶** – *St. Stephen's Basilica★ (Szt. István-bazilika)* EU – *City Parish Church★ (Belvárosi plébániatemplom)* EV – *University Church★ (Egyetemi Templom)* FX – *Franciscan Church★ (Ferences templom)* FV – *Municipal Concert Hall★ (Vigadó)* EV – *Town Hall★ (Fövárosi Tanács)* EFV – *Paris Arcade★ (Párizsi udvar)* EV – *Vaci Street★ (Váci utca)* EV – *Hungaria Restaurant★ (Hungaria Ettermek)* BZ **N** – *Budapest West Station★ (Nyugati pályaudvar)* AY – *Millenary Monument★ (Millenniumi emlékmu)* BY **D** – *City Park★ (Városliget)* BYZ – *Vajdahunyad Castle★ (Vajdahunyad vára)* BY **B** – *Hungarian Transport Museum★ (Magyar Közlekedesi Múzeum)* BY **M⁷**.

## ADDITIONAL SIGHTS

*Chain Bridge★★ (Széchenyi Lánchíd)* DEV – *Margaret Island★ (Margitsziget)* AY – *Aquincum Museum★ (Aquincumi Muzéum) N : 12 km by Szentendrei út* AY – *Gellert Thermal Baths★ (Gellért gyógyfürdö)* EX – *St. Ann's Church★ (Szent Anna templom)* DU.

**Envir.**: *Szentendre★ N : 20 km – Visegrad N : 42 km : Citadel, view★★*

**Kempinski H. Corvinus**, Erzsébet tér 7-8, 1051, (01) 266 1000, *Fax (01) 266 2000*, – rm, – 450. rest EV a
***Corvinus*** **: Meals** *(closed Saturday lunch and Sunday)* 3900/5500 and a la carte – ***Bistro Jardin*** **: Meals** a la carte 3450/6100 – 3300 – **345 rm** 42000/58800, 22 suites.

**Hilton**, Hess András tér 1-3, 1014, (01) 214 3000, *Fax (01) 156 0285*, Danube and Buda, « Remains of a 13C Dominican church » – rm, – 600. DU a
***Dominican*** **: Meals** 5000/10000 and a la carte – ***Kalocsa*** **: Meals** *(closed Sunday and January-March)* (dinner only) a la carte 5600/6600 – 3600 – **294 rm** 47500/69500, 28 suites.

**Marriott**, Apáczai Csere János útca 4, 1052, (01) 266 7000, *Fax (01) 266 5000*, Danube and Buda, – rm, – 650. EV r
***Csarda*** **: Meals** *(closed Sunday)* (dinner only) a la carte 4500/7300 – ***Duna Grill*** **: Meals** a la carte 4000/5500 – 3100 – **349 rm** 46200/50400, 13 suites.

**Atrium Hyatt**, Roosevelt tér 2, 1051, (01) 266 1234, *Fax (01) 266 9101*, – rm, – 350. rest
***Old Timer*** **: Meals** (dinner only) 3200/5500 and a la carte – ***Atrium Terrace*** **: Meals** 2200/4500 and a la carte – ***Clark Brasserie*** **: Meals** 1600/2500 and a la carte – 2800 – **328 rm** 36800/42000, 27 suites. EV e

**Inter-Continental,** Apáczai Csere János útca 12-14, 1052, (01) 327 6333, *Fax (01) 327 6357*, Danube and Buda, – rm, – 300. rest EV n
***Silhouette*** **: Meals** 4000/6000 and a la carte – ***Grill*** **: Meals** 2800 and a la carte – 3100 – **383 rm** 33600/46200, 15 suites.

**Aquincum Corinthia**, Árpád Fejedelem útja 94, 1036, (01) 250 3360, *Fax (01) 250 4672*, Therapy centre, – rm, – 280. AY d
***Ambrosia*** **: Meals** (dinner only) 4200 and a la carte – ***Apicius*** **: Meals** 3200/3700 and a la carte – **304 rm** 30500/35700, 8 suites.

**Radisson SAS Béke,** Teréz körut 43, 1067, (01) 301 1600, *Fax (01) 301 1615*, – rm, – 200. FU a
***Shakespeare*** **: Meals** 3600/10600 and a la carte – ***Szondi*** **: Meals** 3600/10600 and dinner a la carte – 2400 – **239 rm** 31700/40600, 8 suites.

**Danubius Grand H.**, Margitsziget, 1138, (01) 311 1000, *Fax (01) 153 3029*, Direct entrance to Thermal Hotel, – rm, – 85. AY b
**Meals** 3600 and a la carte – **154 rm** 31700/37700, 10 suites.

**Thermal H. Helia**, Kárpát útca 62-64, 1133, (01) 270 3277, *Fax (01) 270 2262*, Therapy centre, – rm, – 400. AY c
**Meals** (buffet only) 4800 – **254 rm** 33500/43100, 8 suites.

**Gellert,** Gellért tér 1, 1111, (01) 185 2200, *Fax (01) 166 6631*, « Art Nouveau decor », Direct entrance to the Therapeutic baths, heated, – rm, – 400. EX n
**Meals** 2800/8000 and a la carte – **220 rm** 29900/46700, 13 suites.

**K + K Hotel Opera**, Révay útca 24, 1065, (01) 269 0222, *Fax (01) 269 0230*, « Stylish modern interior design », – rm, – 80. rest FU f
**Meals** (dinner only) a la carte 4500/5800 – **198 rm** 27900/34700, 7 suites.

**Mercure Buda**, Krisztina körut 41-43, 1013, (01) 156 6333, *Fax (01) 155 6964*, – rm, – 180. CV f
**Meals** 1500/2200 and a la carte – **388 rm** 20000/24200, 6 suites.

**Mercure Korona**, Kecskeméti útca 14, 1053, (01) 117 4111, *Fax (01) 118 3867*, – rm, – 130.
**Meals** 2100/12600 and a la carte – **423 rm** 21000/23100, 10 suites. FX s

**Astoria,** Kossuth Lajos útca 19-21, 1053, (01) 117 3411, *Fax (01) 118 6798*, « Art Nouveau decor » – rm, – 80. FV q
**Meals** 2700 and a la carte – **125 rm** 22200/29400, 5 suites.

**Park H. Flamenco,** Tas Vezér útca 7, 1113, (01) 372 2000, *Fax (01) 165 8007*, – rm, – 160. AZ p
*closed 14 to 16 August* – **Meals** 2500/3500 and a la carte – **348 rm** 26400/32300.

**Novotel,** Alkotás útca 63-67, 1123, (01) 209 1990, *Fax (01) 166 5636*, – rm, – 1200. rest CX h
**Meals** 1100/1900 and a la carte – **321 rm** 23000/27800, 3 suites.

# BUDAPEST

Bécsi u. . . . . . . . . . . . . . EV
Deák Ferenc u. . . . . . . . . EV 8
Haris Köz . . . . . . . . . . . . . EV 21
Párizsi u. . . . . . . . . . . . . EV 53
Petöfi
Sándor u. . . . . . . . . . . . EV 55
Régi posta u. . . . . . . . . . EV 58
Váci u. . . . . . . . . . . . . . . EFV
Vörösmarty Tér . . . . . . . . EV

Apáczai Csere
János u. . . . . . . . . . . . . EV 2
Árpád Fejedelem
útja . . . . . . . . . . . . . . . AY 3
Bárczy István u. . . . . . . . . EV 4
Batthyány u. . . . . . . . . . . CDU 5
Erzsébet Krt . . . . . . . . . . . BZ 10
Fehérvári út. . . . . . . . . . . AZ 11
Ferenciek Tér . . . . . . . . . . EFV 12
Ferenc Krt. . . . . . . . . . . . BZ 14
Fortuna u. . . . . . . . . . . . . CDU 15
Fö u. . . . . . . . . . . . . . . . . DUV 17
Gerlóczy u. . . . . . . . . . . . FV 19
Groza Péter
Rakpart . . . . . . . . . . . . . EVX 20
Hattyú u. . . . . . . . . . . . . CU 22
Hunfalvy u. . . . . . . . . . . . CDU 24
Irányi u. . . . . . . . . . . . . . EX 26
Irinyi József u. . . . . . . . . . AZ 27
Istenhegyi út . . . . . . . . . . CV 28
Kálmán Imre u. . . . . . . . . . EU 29
Karinthy Frigyes út. . . . . . AZ 31
Karolina út. . . . . . . . . . . . AZ 32
Károlyi Mihály u. . . . . . . . FVX 33
Kecskeméti u. . . . . . . . . . FX 35
Kosciuszko
Tádé u. . . . . . . . . . . . . . CV 37
Kuny Domokos u. . . . . . . . CV 39
Lajos u. . . . . . . . . . . . . . . AY 40
Logodi u. . . . . . . . . . . . . . CU 42
Magyar u. . . . . . . . . . . . . FVX 44
Nagyenyed u. . . . . . . . . . . CV 46
Nagyszölös u. . . . . . . . . . . AZ 47
Naphegy u. . . . . . . . . . . . CDV 48
Országház u. . . . . . . . . . . CDU 50
Pacsirtamezö u. . . . . . . . . AY 52
Reáltanoda u. . . . . . . . . . FV 57
Rumbach
Sebestyén u. . . . . . . . . . FV 60
Schönherz
Zoltán u. . . . . . . . . . . . . AZ 61
Szabó Ilonka u. . . . . . . . . CDU 63
Szentendrei út. . . . . . . . . AY 65
Szerb u. . . . . . . . . . . . . . . FX 66
Szt. István Krt. . . . . . . . . AY 67
Szilágyi Erzsébetfasor . . . . CU 69
Tábor u. . . . . . . . . . . . . . CDV 70
Táncsics Mihály u. . . . . . . CDU 71
Városház u. . . . . . . . . . . . EFV 73
Vörösvári út. . . . . . . . . . . AY 75

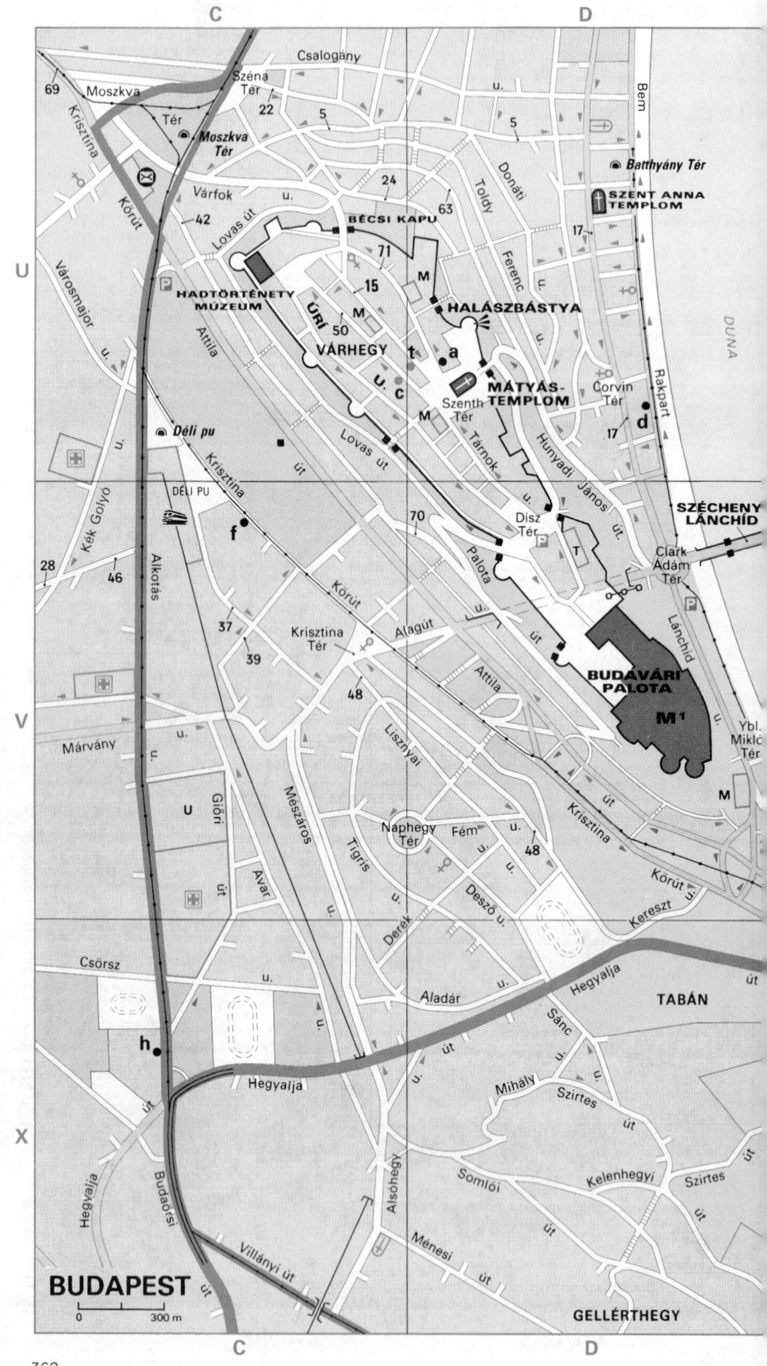
C
D
U
V
X
BUDAPEST
0
300 m
Csalogány
Széna Tér
Moszkva Tér
Moszkva Tér
Krisztina Körút
Várfok u.
Lovas út
BÉCSI KAPU
HADTÖRTÉNETY MÚZEUM
ÚRI U.
VÁRHEGY
HALÁSZBÁSTYA
MÁTYÁS-TEMPLOM
Szenth Tér
Tárnok
Toldy
Donáti
Ferenc u.
Batthyány Tér
SZENT ANNA TEMPLOM
Bem
DUNA
Rakpart
Corvin Tér
Hunyadi János út
SZÉCHENY LÁNCHÍD
Clark Ádám Tér
Lánchíd u.
Dísz Tér
Palota út
BUDAVÁRI PALOTA
Ybl. Mikló Tér
Városmajor u.
Attila út
Déli pu
DÉLI PU
Kék Golyó u.
Alkotás u.
Krisztina Tér
Alagút
Attila út
Lisznyai
Márvány u.
Győri út
Avar
Mészáros u.
Tigris u.
Naphegy Tér
Fém u.
Desző u.
Derék u.
Krisztina Körút
Kereszt
Csörsz u.
Aladár u.
Hegyalja út
Hegyalja
TABÁN
Sánc u.
Mihály
Szirtes út
Somlói út
Kelenhegyi
Szirtes út
Alsóhegy
Ménesi út
Hegyalja
Budaörsi út
Villányi út
GELLÉRTHEGY
a
t
c
d
f
h
M
T
U

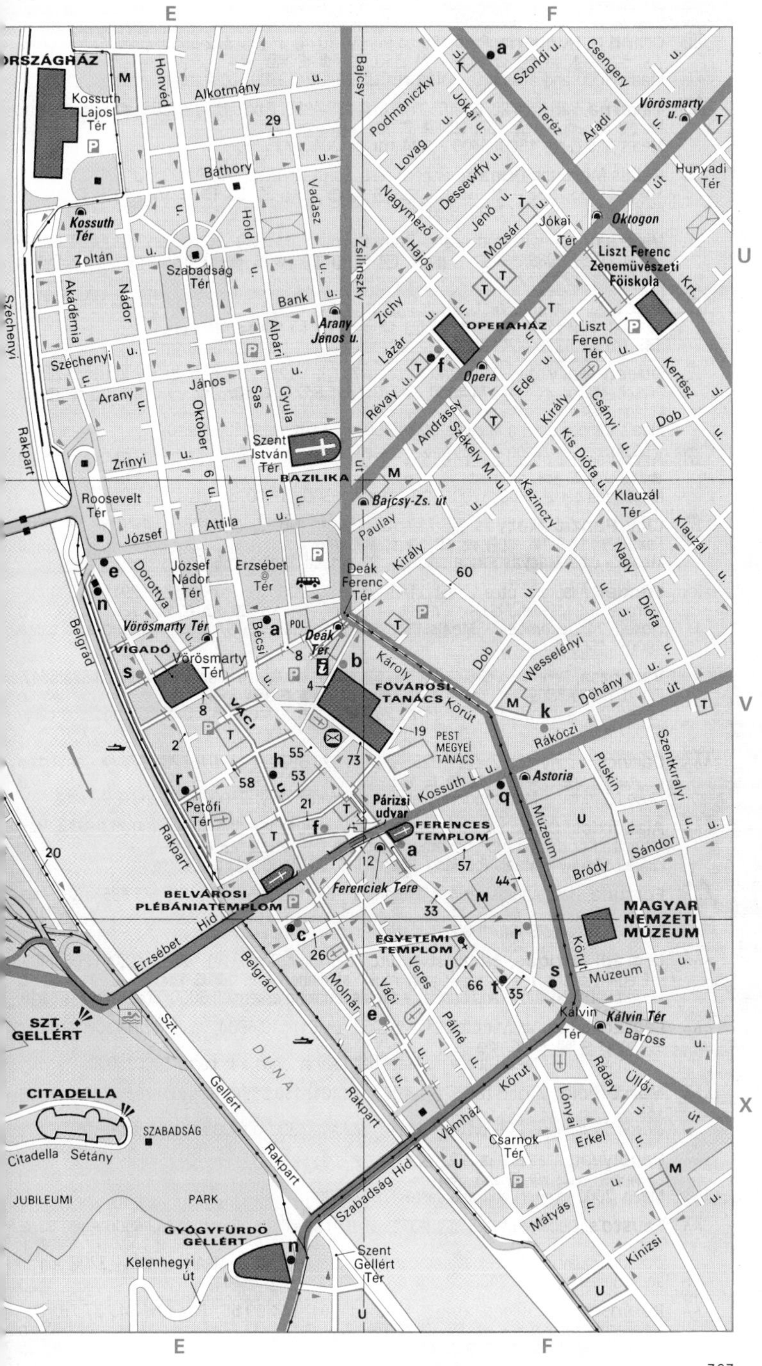
E
F
ORSZÁGHÁZ
Kossuth Lajos Tér
Kossuth Tér
Alkotmány
Báthory
Szabadság Tér
Zoltán
Akadémia
Nádor
Széchenyi
Arany
Zrínyi
Roosevelt Tér
József
Attila
Dorottya
József Nádor Tér
Erzsébet Tér
Deák Ferenc Tér
Vörösmarty Tér
VIGADÓ
Vörösmarty Tér
Bécsi
Deák Tér
FŐVÁROSI TANÁCS
PEST MEGYEI TANÁCS
VÁCI
Petőfi Tér
Párizsi udvar
FERENCES TEMPLOM
Ferenciek Tere
BELVÁROSI PLÉBÁNIATEMPLOM
EGYETEMI TEMPLOM
MAGYAR NEMZETI MÚZEUM
Kálvin Tér
Erzsébet Híd
SZT. GELLÉRT
CITADELLA
Citadella Sétány
SZABADSÁG
JUBILEUMI
PARK
GYÓGYFÜRDŐ GELLÉRT
Kelenhegyi út
Szent Gellért Tér
Szabadság Híd
DUNA
Szt. Gellért Rakpart
Belgrád Rakpart
Rakpart
Vámház Körut
Csarnok Tér
Szent István Tér
BAZILIKA
Bajcsy-Zs. út
Bajcsy Zsilinszky út
Arany János u.
OPERAHÁZ
Opera
Andrássy
Oktogon
Liszt Ferenc Zeneművészeti Főiskola
Liszt Ferenc Tér
Vörösmarty u.
Hunyadi Tér
Teréz
Aradi
Szondi u.
Csengery
Podmaniczky
Lovag
Jókai
Dessewffy u.
Nagymező
Hajós
Zichy
Lázár
Révay
Mozsár
Jenő
Jókai Tér
Király
Kis Diófa u.
Csányi
Kertész
Dob
Kazinczy
Székely M. u.
Klauzál Tér
Klauzál
Paulay
Wesselényi
Dohány
Rákóczi
Astoria
Kossuth L. u.
Múzeum Körut
Puskin
Szentkirályi
Bródy
Sándor
Múzeum
Baross
Ráday
Üllői út
Lónyai
Erkel
Mátyás
Kinizsi
Molnár
Váci
Veres Pálné u.
Károly Körút
Honvéd
Hold
Vadász
Bank
Alpári
Gyula
Sas
Október 6 u.
Nagy Diófa
Ede
U
V
X

**Grand H. Hungaria,** Rákóczi útca 90, ✉ 1074, ℘ (01) 322 9050, *Fax (01) 351 0675,* – 350. AE E VISA JCB BZ f
**Meals** 3000 and a la carte – **491 rm** 26400/32300, 20 suites.

**Taverna,** Váci útca 20, ✉ 1052, ℘ (01) 138 4999, *Fax (01) 118 7188,* rm, – 160. AE E VISA JCB. rest EV h
**Meals** a la carte 1500/5300 – **224 rm** 20400/26200.

**Relais Mercure Duna** M without rest., Soroksári útca 12, ✉ 1095, ℘ (01) 215 7414, *Fax (01) 215 7522* – rm, – 50. AE E VISA JCB. BZ b
**124 rm** 14700/17900, 6 suites.

**Victoria** M without rest., Bem Rakpart 11, ✉ 1011, ℘ (01) 457 8080, *Fax (01) 457 8088,* AE E VISA JCB. rest DU d
**27 rm** 19500/20500.

**Liget** M without rest., Dózsa György útca 106, ✉ 1068, ℘ (01) 269 5300, *Fax (01) 269 5329,* AE E VISA JCB BY e
**139 rm** 17700/20800.

**Queen Mary**, Béla Király útca 47, ✉ 1121, Zugliget, W : 9 km by Szilágyi Erzsébetfasor ℘ (01) 274 4000, *Fax (01) 395 8377,* rest, AE E VISA.
**Meals** (dinner only) a la carte 900/2700 – **22 rm** 10500/12100.

**Art,** Királyi Pál útca 12, ✉ 1053, ℘ (01) 266 2166, *Fax (01) 266 2170,* AE E VISA. rest FX t
**Meals** a la carte 1400/3200 – **29 rm** 16300/20400, 3 suites.

**City Panzió Mátyás** M, Március 15 tér, No. 8, ✉ 1056, ℘ (01) 138 4711, *Fax (01) 117 9086* – AE E VISA JCB EX c
**Meals** – (see ***Mátyás Pince*** below) – **27 rm** 13100/16600, 2 suites.

**Gundel,** Állatkerti útca 2, ✉ 1146, ℘ (01) 321 3550, *Fax (01) 342 2917,* « Summer terrace », Gypsy and classical music at dinner – AE E VISA JCB BY d
*closed 24 December* – **Meals** (booking essential) 4000/16000 b.i. and a la carte 4800/11500.

**Vadrózsa,** Pentelei Molnár útca 15, ✉ 1025, *via-Rómer Flóris útca* ℘ (01) 326 5817, *Fax (01) 326 5809,* « Summer terrace » – AE E VISA JCB AY e
*closed last 2 weeks July and 23 to 26 December* – **Meals** 6200/10600 and a la carte 5300/10600.

**Garvics,** Urömi Köz 2, ✉ 1025, ℘ (01) 326 3878, *Fax (01) 326 3876,* « Converted vaulted chapel » – AE E VISA AY a
*closed Sunday* – **Meals** (booking essential) (dinner only) 2500/8000 and a la carte.

**Alabárdos,** Országház útca 2, ✉ 1014, ℘ (01) 156 0851, *Fax (01) 214 3814,* « Vaulted Gothic interior, covered courtyard » – AE E VISA JCB CU c
*closed Sunday* – **Meals** (booking essential) 3700/7400 and a la carte.

**Fortuna,** Hess András tér 4, ✉ 1014, ℘ (01) 175 6857, *Fax (01) 175 6857,* – AE E VISA JCB CDU t
**Meals** a la carte 5000/10000.

**Légrádi Antique,** Bárczy István útca 3-5 (first floor), ✉ 1052, ℘ (01) 266 4993, « Elegant decor, antiques », Gypsy music at dinner – AE E VISA EV b
*closed Saturday lunch and Sunday* – **Meals** (booking essential) 3000/8000 and a la carte.

**Légrádi &Tsa,** Magyar útca 23, ✉ 1053, ℘ (01) 118 6804, Vaulted cellar, Gypsy music at dinner – AE E VISA FX r
*closed Sunday* – **Meals** (booking essential) (dinner only) a la carte 3400/5000.

**Marco Polo,** Vigadó tér 3, ✉ 1051, ℘ (01) 138 3354, *Fax (01) 266 2727* – E VISA
*closed 15 January-15 February* – **Meals** - Italian - 3800/11300 and a la carte. EV s

**Bagolyvár,** Allatkerti útca 2, ✉ 1146, ℘ (01) 343 0217, *Fax (01) 342 2917,* Music at dinner – AE E VISA JCB BY d
**Meals** 2000 (dinner) and a la carte 1700/3800.

**Fausto's,** Dohány útca 5, ✉ 1072, ℘ (01) 269 6806, *Fax (01) 269 6806* – AE E VISA FV k
*closed Sunday, first week January and first 2 weeks July* – **Meals** - Italian - 2200 (lunch) and a la carte 3500/7000.

**Robinson,** Városligeti tó, ✉ 1146, ℘ (01) 343 09 55, *Fax (01) 343 37 76,* « Lakeside setting » – AE E VISA JCB BY a
**Meals** 3400/4200 and a la carte.

XX **Belcanto,** Dalszínház útca 8, ✉ 1061, ☎ (01) 269 2786, *Fax (01) 111 2091,* « Classical and operatic recitals » – AE ⓓ E VISA JCB FU f
*closed Sunday lunch and 24 December* – **Meals** (booking essential) 2500/10000 and a la carte.

XX **Kárpátia,** Ferenciek tere 7-8, ✉ 1053, ☎ (01) 117 3596, *Fax (01) 118 0591,* « Part of former Franciscan monastery », Gypsy music at dinner – AE ⓓ E VISA JCB FV a
**Meals** 1700/2000 and a la carte.

XX **Mátyás Pince,** Március 15 tér, No. 7, ✉ 1056, ☎ (01) 118 1693, *Fax (01) 118 1650,* « Vaulted cellar, murals », Gypsy music – ▤. AE ⓓ E VISA JCB EX c
**Meals** 2500 and a la carte.

## LOCAL ATMOSPHERE

X **Aranymókus,** Istenhegyi útca 25, ✉ 1126, ☎ (01) 155 6728, *Fax (01) 155 6728,* ⛱ – AE ⓓ E VISA JCB via Nagyenyed útca CV
**Meals** a la carte 2000/6000.

X **Náncsi Néni,** Ördögárok útca 80, Pesthidegkut, ✉ 1029, NW : 12 km by Szilágyi Erzsébetfasor ☎ (01) 397 2742, ⛱, Accordion music at dinner except Saturday – AE E VISA JCB
**Meals** a la carte 1400/3800.

X **Kisbuda Gyöngye,** Kenyeres útca 34, ✉ 1034, ☎ (01) 368 6402, *Fax (01) 368 9227,* Music at dinner – ▤. AE ⓓ E VISA AY f
*closed Sunday* – **Meals** (booking essential) 1500/7000 and a la carte 4500/7500.

X **Apostolok,** Kígyó útca 4, ✉ 1052, ☎ (01) 267 0290, *Fax (01) 118 3559,* « Old chapel decor, wood carvings » – ▤. AE ⓓ E VISA JCB EV f
**Meals** 1500/2500 and a la carte.

X **Fatâl,** Váci útca 67, ✉ 1056, entrance on Pintér útca ☎ (01) 266 2607, Vaulted basement FX e
**Meals** a la carte 1600/2700.

**at the Motorway** *M 1/M 7, South 12 km* – BZ – ✉ *Budapest :*

**Forte Agip** Ⓜ, Agip útca 2, ✉ 2040, ☎ (023) 415 500, *Fax (023) 415 505,* ⛱, ≘s – |♦|, ⇆ rm, ▤ TV ☎ ♿ 🚗 Ⓟ – 🏛 350. AE ⓓ E VISA JCB. ✂ rest
**Meals** (buffet lunch) 1950/4000 and a la carte – **160 rm** ☐ 16700/20900, 3 suites.

# *Republic of*
# *Ireland*

## *Eire*

**DUBLIN**

The town plans in the Republic of Ireland Section of this Guide are based upon the Ordnance Survey of Ireland by permission of the Government of the Republic, Permit number 6537.

# PRACTICAL INFORMATION

## LOCAL CURRENCY

**Punt (Irish Pound):** *1 IEP = 1,43 USD ($) (Jan. 98)*

## TOURIST INFORMATION

*The telephone number and address of the Tourist Information office is given in the text under* ℹ.

**National Holiday in the Republic of Ireland:** *17 March.*

## FOREIGN EXCHANGE

*Banks are open between 10am and 4pm on weekdays only.*

*Banks in Dublin stay open to 5pm on Thursdays and banks at Dublin and Shannon airports are open on Saturdays and Sundays.*

## SHOPPING IN DUBLIN

*In the index of street names, those printed in red are where the principal shops are found.*

## CAR HIRE

*The international car hire companies have branches in each major city. Your hotel porter should be able to give details and help you with your arrangements.*

## TIPPING

*Many hotels and restaurants include a service charge but where this is not the case an amount equivalent to between 10 and 15 per cent of the bill is customary. Additionally doormen, baggage porters and cloakroom attendants are generally given a gratuity.*

*Taxi drivers are tipped between 10 and 15 per cent of the amount shown on the meter in addition to the fare.*

## SPEED LIMITS

*The maximum permitted speed in the Republic is 60 mph (97 km/h) except where a lower speed limit is indicated.*

## SEAT BELTS

*The wearing of seat belts is compulsory if fitted for drivers and front seat passengers. Additionally, children under 12 are not allowed in front seats unless in a suitable safety restraint.*

## ANIMALS

*It is forbidden to bring domestic animals (dogs, cats...) into the Republic of Ireland.*

# DUBLIN

(Baile Átha Cliath) *Dublin* 923 N 7 - *pop. 859 976.*

*Belfast 103 - Cork 154 - Londonderry 146.*

*Baggot Street Bridge, D2 - Arrivals Hall, Dublin Airport - Taltaght, D24.*

*Elm Park, G & S.C., Nutley House, Donnybrook ✆ (01) 269 3438 - Milltown, Lower Churchtown Rd, ✆ (01) 497 6090,* EV *- Royal Dublin, North Bull Island, Dollymont, ✆ (01) 833 6346 NE : by R 105 - Forrest Little, Cloghran ✆ (01) 840 1183 - Lucan, Celbridge Rd, Lucan ✆ (01) 628 0246.*

*Dublin Airport ✆ (01) 844 4900, N : 5 ½ m. by N 1 - Terminal : Busaras (Central Bus Station) Store St.*

*to Holyhead (Irish Ferries) 2 daily (3 h 15 mn) - to Holyhead (Stena Line) daily (4 h) - to the Isle of Man (Douglas) (Isle of Man Steam Packet Co Ltd.) (4 h 30 mn).*

**See**: *City★★★ - Trinity College★★★ (Library★★★)* JY *- Chester Beatty Library★★★* FV *- Phoenix Park★★★ - Dublin Castle★★* HY *- Christ Church Cathedral★★* HY *- St. Patrick's Cathedral★★* HZ *- Marsh's Library★★* HZ *- National Museum★★ (Treasury★★),* KZ *- National Gallery★★* KZ *- Merrion Square★★* KZ *- Rotunda Hospital Chapel★★* JX *- Kilmainham Hospital★★ - Kilmainham Gaol Museum★★ - National Botanic Gardens★★ - N° 29★* KZ **D** *- Liffey Bridge★* JY *- Taylors' Hall★* HY *- City Hall★* HY *- St. Audoen's Gate★* HY **B** *- St. Stephen's Green★* JZ *- Grafton Street★* JZ *- Powerscourt Centre★* JY *- Civic Museum★* JY **M1** *- Bank of Ireland★* JYZ *- O'Connell Street★ (Anna Livia Fountain★),* JX *- St. Michan's Church★* HY **E** *- Hush Lane Municipal Gallery of Modern Art★* JX **M4** *- Pro-Cathedral★* JX *- Garden of Remembrance★* JX *- Custom House★* KX *- Bluecoat School★ - Guinness Museum★ - Marino Casino★ - Zoological Gardens★ - Newman House★* JZ.

**Envir.**: *Powerscourt★★ (Waterfall★★★), S : 14 m by N 11 and R 117* EV *- Russborough House★★★, SW : 22 m by N 81 - Rathfarnham Castle★, S : 3 m by N 81 and R 115 8 T.*

## DUBLIN

### SOUTH EAST BUILT UP AREA

Ailesbury Road . . . . . . . . . FV 4
Baggot Street Upper . . . . . EU 7
Beech Hill Avenue . . . . . . FV 10
Beechwood Road . . . . . . . EV 12
Belgrave Road . . . . . . . . . . DV 13
Bloomfield Avenue . . . . . . DU 18
Brighton Road . . . . . . . . . . DV 22
Camder Street . . . . . . . . . . DU 28
Castlewood Avenue . . . . . DV 31
Charlemont Street . . . . . . . DU 34
Charlotte Street . . . . . . . . . DU 36
Chelmsford Road . . . . . . . EV 37
Church Avenue . . . . . . . . . FU 39
Clyde Road . . . . . . . . . . . . EFU 43
Eastmoreland Place . . . . . . EU 61
Elgin Road . . . . . . . . . . . . EFU 64
Harrington Street . . . . . . DU 73
Herbert Place . . . . . . . . . EU 76
Irishtown Road . . . . . . . . FU 82
Lansdowne Road . . . . . . FU 90
Lea Road . . . . . . . . . . . . . GU 91
Leeson Street Lower . . . . EU 93
Leinster Road West . . . . . DV 96
Londonbridge Road . . . . FU 97
Maxwell Road . . . . . . . . . DV 102

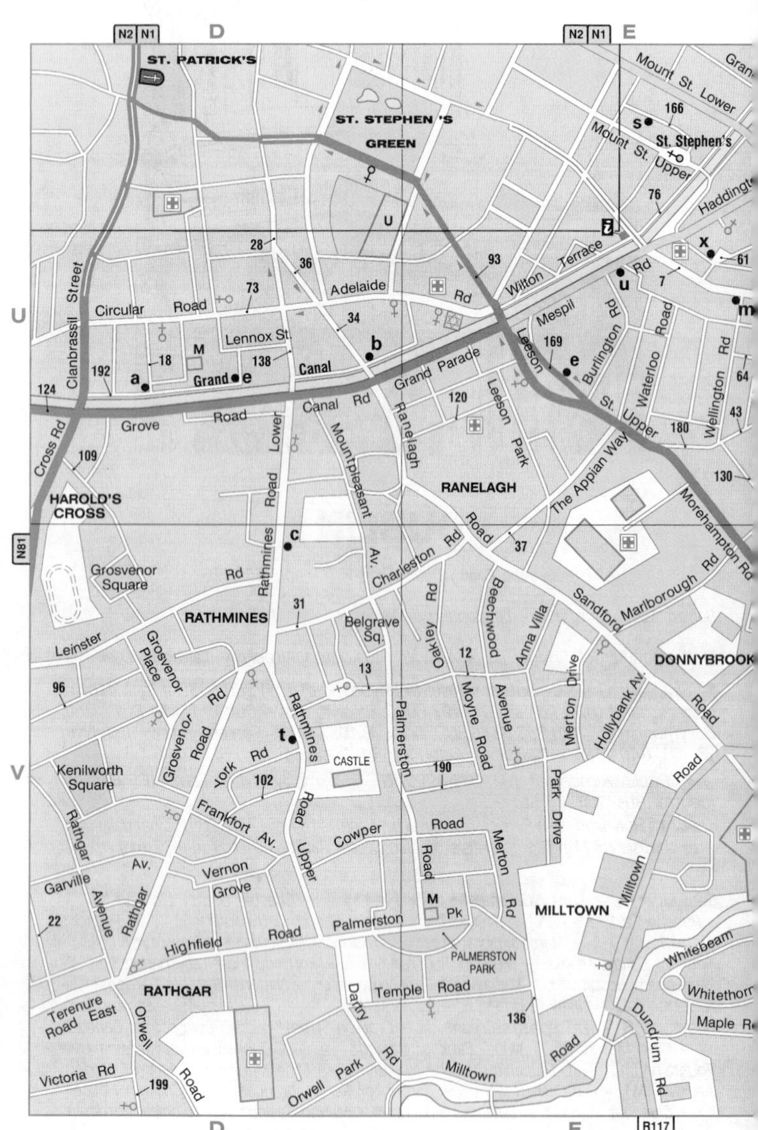


*Your recommendation is self-evident if you always walk into a hotel Guide in hand.*

| | | |
|---|---|---|
| Merlyn Park | GV | 105 |
| Mount Drummond Avenue | DU | 109 |
| Newbridge Avenue | FU | 115 |
| Newgrove Avenue | GU | 117 |
| Northbrook Road | EU | 120 |
| Nutgrove Park | FV | 121 |
| Parnell Road | DU | 124 |
| Pembroke Park | EU | 130 |
| Raglan Road | FU | 133 |
| Richmond Avenue South | EV | 136 |
| Richmond Street South | DU | 138 |
| St Alban's Park | GV | 142 |
| St John's Road East | GV | 145 |
| Seafort Avenue | GU | 153 |
| Sean Moore Road | GU | 154 |
| Serpentine Avenue | FU | 156 |
| Simmonscourt Road | FU | 160 |
| South Lotts Road | FU | 163 |
| Stephen's Lane | EU | 166 |
| Sussex Road | EU | 169 |
| Trimbleston Avenue | GV | 175 |
| Victoria Avenue | FV | 177 |
| Wellington Place | EU | 180 |
| Windsor Road | EV | 190 |
| Windsor Terrace | DU | 192 |
| Wynnsward Drive | FV | 198 |
| Zion Road | DV | 199 |

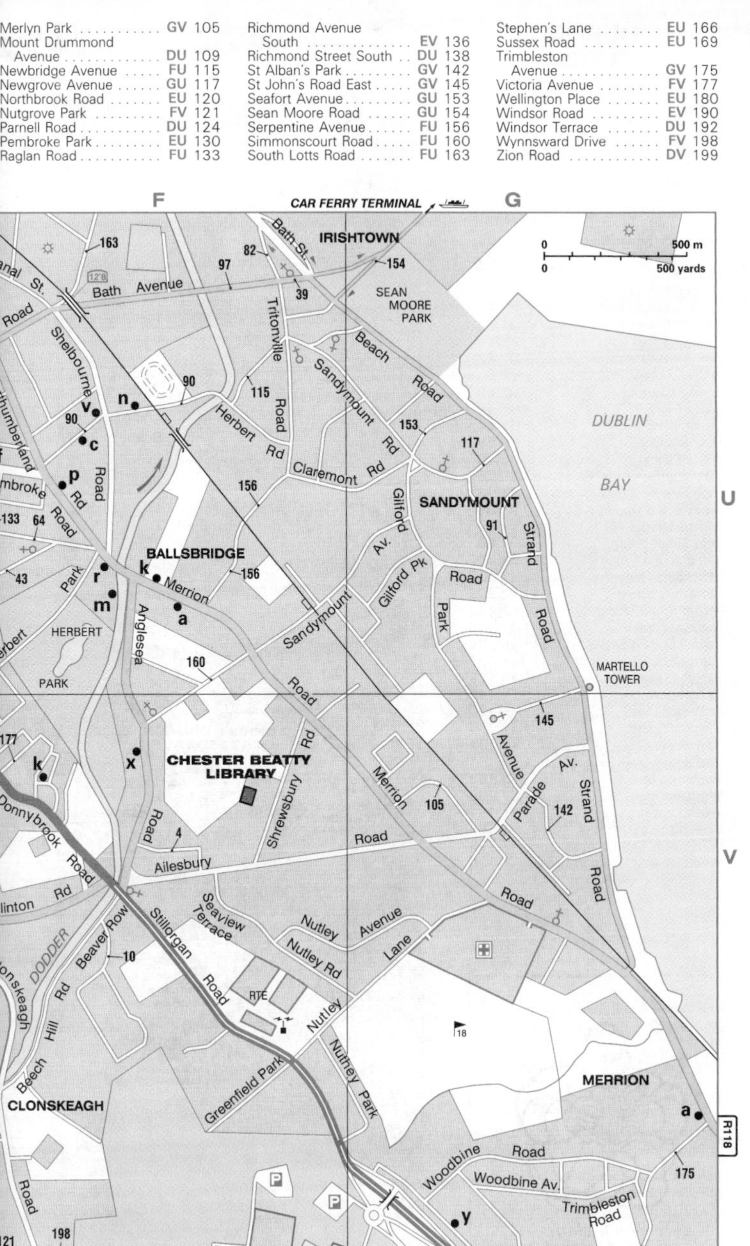


*If you find you cannot take up a hotel booking you have made, please let the hotel know immediately.*

# DUBLIN
## CENTRE

| Street | Grid | No. |
|---|---|---|
| Anne Street South | JYZ | 6 |
| Dawson Street | JYZ | |
| Duke Street | JY | 58 |
| Grafton Street | JYZ | |
| Henry Street | JX | |
| Ilac Centre | HJX | |
| Irish Life Mall Centre | JKX | |
| O'Connell Street | JX | |

| Street | Grid | No. |
|---|---|---|
| Brunswick Street North | HX | 24 |
| Buckingham Street | KX | 25 |
| Bull Alley | HZ | 27 |
| Chancery Street | HY | 33 |
| Clanbrassil Street | HZ | 40 |
| College Green | JY | 45 |
| College Street | JY | 46 |
| Cornmarket | HY | 49 |
| D'Olier Street | JY | 51 |
| Earlsfort Terrace | JZ | 60 |
| Essex Quay | HY | 66 |
| Fishamble Street | HY | 67 |
| George's Quay | KY | 69 |
| Golden Lane | HZ | 70 |
| Henrietta Street | HX | 75 |
| High Street | HY | 78 |
| Kevin Street Upper | HZ | 85 |
| Kildare Street | JKZ | 87 |
| King Street South | JZ | 88 |
| Marlborough Street | JX | 100 |
| Merchants Quay | HY | 103 |
| Montague Street | JZ | 106 |
| Mount Street Upper | KZ | 112 |
| Nicholas Street | HY | 118 |
| Parnell Square East | JX | 126 |
| Parnell Square North | JX | 127 |
| Parnell Square West | HJX | 129 |
| St Mary's Abbey Street | HY | 148 |
| St Patrick Close | HZ | 150 |
| Stephen Street | HJY | 165 |
| Tara Street | KY | 171 |
| Wellington Quay | HJY | 181 |
| Werburgh Street | HY | 183 |
| Westland Row | KY | 186 |
| Westmoreland Street | JY | 187 |
| Wexford Street | HZ | 189 |
| Winetavern Street | HY | 193 |
| Wood Quay | HY | 196 |

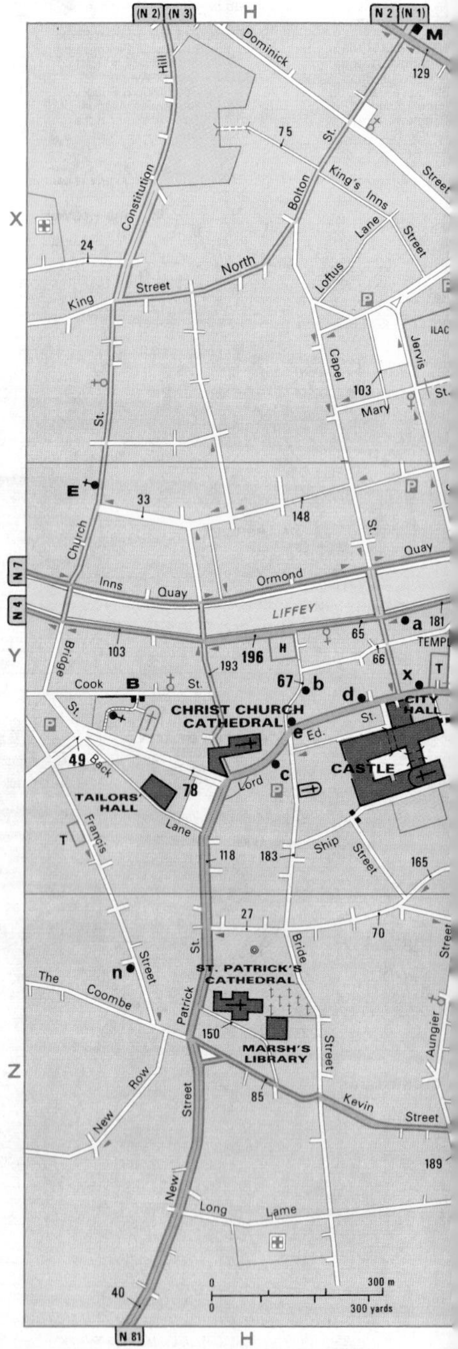

*Town plans:*
*roads most used by traffic*
*and those on which guide-*
*listed hotels and restaurants*
*stand are fully drawn;*
*the beginning only*
*of lesser roads is indicated.*

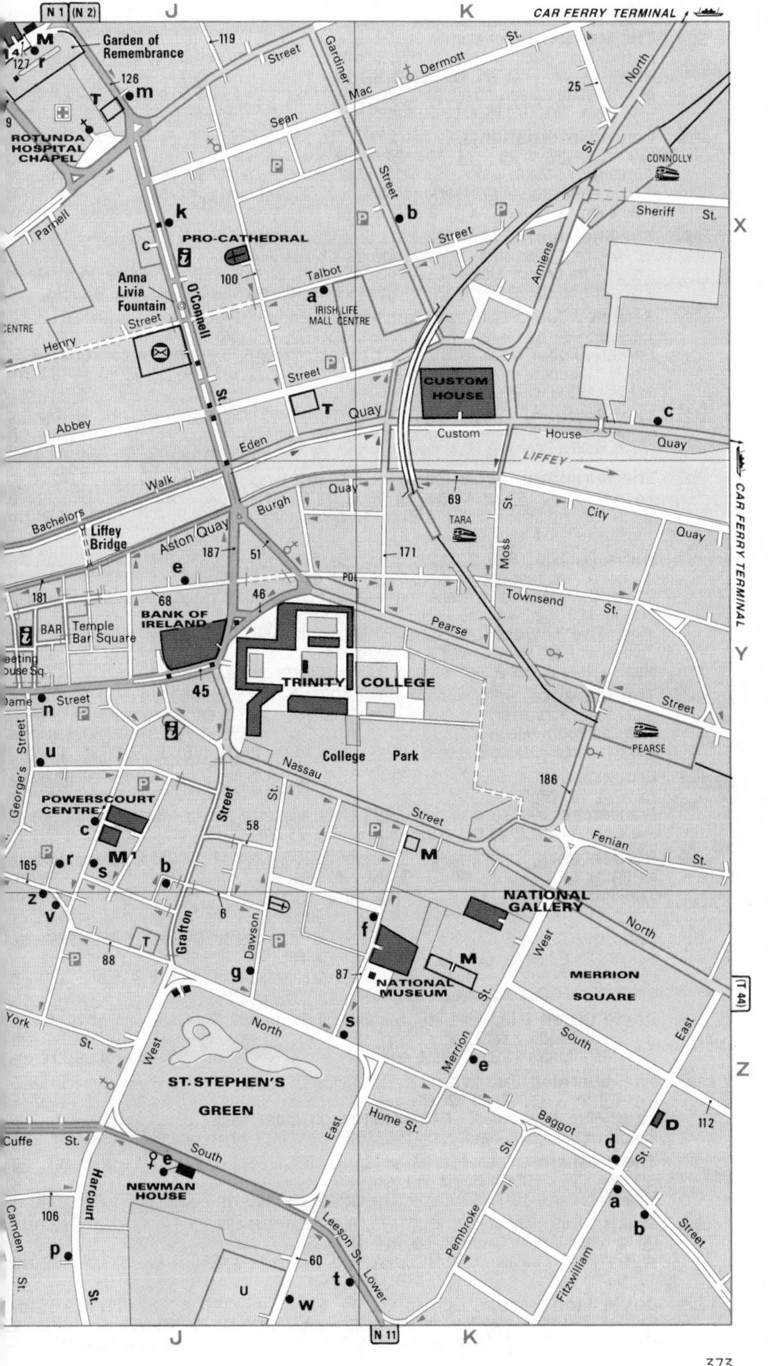

J
K
CAR FERRY TERMINAL
N 1
N 2
Garden of Remembrance
ROTUNDA HOSPITAL CHAPEL
PRO-CATHEDRAL
Anna Livia Fountain
O'Connell St.
Henry Street
Talbot Street
IRISH LIFE MALL CENTRE
Sean Mac Dermott St.
Gardiner Street
CONNOLLY
Sheriff St.
Amiens Street
CUSTOM HOUSE
Abbey Street
Eden Quay
Custom House Quay
LIFFEY
Bachelors Walk
Liffey Bridge
Aston Quay
Burgh Quay
City Quay
TARA
Moss St.
Townsend St.
Pearse Street
PEARSE
BANK OF IRELAND
Temple Bar Square
TRINITY COLLEGE
College Park
Dame Street
George's Street
POWERSCOURT CENTRE
Nassau Street
Grafton Street
Dawson St.
Fenian St.
NATIONAL GALLERY
NATIONAL MUSEUM
MERRION SQUARE
Merrion St.
Merrion Square North
Merrion Square South
Merrion Square West
Merrion Square East
St. Stephen's Green North
York St.
ST. STEPHEN'S GREEN
Hume St.
Baggot St.
Cuffe St.
NEWMAN HOUSE
Harcourt St.
Camden St.
Leeson St. Lower
Pembroke St.
Fitzwilliam St.
X
Y
Z
T 44
N 11

**The Merrion,** Upper Merrion St., D2, ℘ (01) 603 0600, *Fax (01) 603 0700*, « Carefully restored Georgian town houses, collection of contemporary Irish art », – rm, – 45. KZ e
***Mornington :*** Meals 16.00/23.00 **st.** and a la carte 21.45/35.50 **st.** 8.00 – 13.00 – **135 rm** 190.00/255.00 **t.**, 10 suites – SB.

**Conrad International,** Earlsfort Terr., D2, ℘ (01) 676 5555, *Fax (01) 676 5424* – rm, – 310. 
***Alexandra :*** Meals *(closed Saturday lunch and Sunday)* 17.50/29.50 **t.** and a la carte 7.00 – ***Plurabelle Brasserie :*** Meals 15.00/17.50 **t.** and a la carte 7.00 – 12.00 – **182 rm** 185.00/210.00 **t.**, 9 suites. JZ w

**The Shelbourne,** 27 St. Stephen's Green, D2, ℘ (01) 676 6471, *Fax (01) 661 6006* – rm, – 400. JZ s
***No. 27 The Green :*** Meals 17.50/26.50 **t.** and a la carte 8.50 – ***The Side Door :*** Meals a la carte 10.50/20.20 **t.** 7.50 – 13.50 – **181 rm** 169.00/225.00 **t.**, 9 suites.

**Berkeley Court,** Lansdowne Rd, Ballsbridge, D4, ℘ (01) 660 1711, *Fax (01) 661 7238*, – rm, rest, – 450. FU c
***Berkeley Room :*** Meals 17.75/27.50 **t.** and a la carte 6.75 – ***Conservatory Grill :*** Meals 12.00 **t.** (lunch) and a la carte 17.75/28.35 **t.** 6.75 – 11.00 – **182 rm** 145.00/185.00 **t.**, 6 suites – SB.

**The Westbury,** Grafton St., D2, ℘ (01) 679 1122, *Fax (01) 679 7078* – rm, rest, – 150. JY b
Meals 16.50/28.50 **t.** and a la carte 5.90 – 9.95 – **195 rm** 185.00/205.00 **t.**, 8 suites.

**The Burlington,** Upper Leeson St., D4, ℘ (01) 660 5222, *Fax (01) 660 3172* – rm, rest, – 1000. EU e
Meals (carving lunch) 12.00/18.00 **t.** and dinner a la carte 7.45 – 10.50 – **531 rm** 138.00/160.00 **t.**, 4 suites.

**Jurys,** Pembroke Rd, Ballsbridge, D4, ℘ (01) 660 5000, *Fax (01) 660 5540*, heated – rm, rest, – 850. FU p
***Raglans :*** Meals 24.00 **t.** (dinner) and a la carte 21.50/30.70 **t.** 6.00 – 9.25 – **290 rm** 140.00/180.00 **t.**, 4 suites – SB.

**The Towers,** Lansdowne Rd, D4, ℘ (01) 667 0033, *Fax (01) 660 5540*, , heated – rm, .
Meals – (see ***Jurys H.*** above) – 9.25 – **100 rm** 180.00/210.00 **t.**, 4 suites – SB.

**The Clarence,** 6-8 Wellington Quay, D2, ℘ (01) 670 9000, *Fax (01) 670 7800*, « Contemporary interior design » – – 60. HY a
***The Tea Room :*** Meals *(closed lunch Saturday, Sunday and Bank Holidays)* 17.50 **st.** (lunch) and a la carte 20.00/35.00 **st.** 15.00 – 13.00 – **45 rm** 175.00/190.00 **st.**, 4 suites.

**Brooks,** Drury St., D2, ℘ (01) 670 4000, *Fax (01) 670 4455* – rm, – 70. JY r
***Francesca's :*** Meals (dinner only) 17.95 **t.** and a la carte 7.25 – ***Brasserie 59 :*** Meals a la carte 14.00/23.45 **t.** 5.95 – 10.50 – **75 rm** 125.00/195.00 **t.**

**Herbert Park,** Ballsbridge, D4, ℘ (01) 667 2200, *Fax (01) 667 2595*, – rm, – 100. FU m
***The Park :*** Meals 11.50/23.50 **t.** and a la carte 6.50 – 10.50 – **149 rm** 135.00/175.00 **t.**, 4 suites – SB.

**Red Cow,** Naas Rd, D22, SW : 5 m. on N 7 ℘ (01) 459 3650, *Fax (01) 459 1588* – rm, – 700.
*closed 25 December* – **Meals** 12.50/19.75 **t.** and dinner a la carte 7.50 – **120 rm** 75.00/150.00 **t.**, 3 suites – SB.

**Doyle Green Isle,** Naas Rd, D22, SW : 7 ¾ m. off N7 (eastbound carriageway) ℘ (01) 459 3406, *Fax (01) 459 2178* – rm, – 250. – **Meals** 13.95/18.95 **t.** and a la carte 6.00 – 7.50 – **90 rm** 89.00 **t.**

**The Hibernian,** Eastmoreland Pl., Ballsbridge, D4, ℘ (01) 668 7666, *Fax (01) 660 2655* – . EU x
*closed 24 to 27 December* – ***Patrick Kavanagh Room :*** Meals *(closed Saturday lunch and Sunday dinner to non-residents)* 14.95/25.95 **t.** 7.00 – **40 rm** 110.00/160.00 **st.** – SB.

**The Gresham,** O'Connell St., D1, ℘ (01) 874 6881, *Fax (01) 878 7175* – rest, – 250. JX k
Meals a la carte 19.00/39.00 7.00 – 15.00 – **198 rm** 200.00 **t.**, 6 suites – SB.

**Stakis,** Charlemont Pl., D2, ℘ (01) 402 9988, *Fax (01) 402 9966* – rm, rest, – 400. DU b
***Waterfront :*** Meals 16.00/18.00 **st.** and a la carte 5.50 – 11.00 – **189 rm** 135.00/155.00 **st.** – SB.

**Doyle Montrose,** Stillorgan Rd, D4, SE : 4 m. by N 11 ℘ (01) 269 3311, *Fax (01) 269 1164* – rm, – 70. GV y
Meals 10.50/18.50 **t.** and a la carte 6.70 – 6.50 – **179 rm** 85.00/130.00 **t.**

**Doyle Tara,** Merrion Rd, D4, SE : 4 m. on T 44 ☎ (01) 269 4666, *Fax (01) 269 1027* – |‡|, ▤ rest, TV ☎ ♿ P – 🏛 300. MC AE D VISA JCB. ✻ GV a
**Meals** (carving lunch) 8.40/15.50 **t.** and a la carte 🍷 5.20 – ☕ 6.75 – **113 rm** 85.00/105.00 **t.**

**Russell Court,** 21-25 Harcourt St., D2, ☎ (01) 478 4066, *Fax (01) 478 1576* – |‡| TV ☎ P – 🏛 150. MC AE D VISA. ✻ JZ p
*closed 24 to 26 December* – **Meals** 10.95/18.50 **st.** and a la carte – ☕ 5.25 – **41 rm** 65.00/87.00 **t.**, 6 suites – SB.

**Buswells,** Molesworth St., D2, ☎ (01) 614 6500, *Fax (01) 676 2090* – |‡|, ⊁ rm, TV ☎ ♿ P – 🏛 80. MC AE D VISA. ✻ KZ f
***Trumans :*** **Meals** *(closed Sunday)* 12.95/24.50 **st.** and a la carte 🍷 6.00 – ***Grill :*** **Meals** (carving lunch)/dinner a la carte 9.40/24.50 **st.** 🍷 6.00 – **67 rm** ☕ 97.00/155.00 **st.**, 2 suites.

**Cassidys,** Cavendish Row, Upper O'Connell St., D1, ☎ (01) 878 0555, *Fax (01) 878 0687* – |‡|, ⊁ rm, TV ☎. MC AE D VISA. ✻ JX m
*closed 24 to 26 December* – **Meals** (bar lunch)/dinner a la carte 14.95/17.95 **t.** 🍷 5.25 – **67 rm** ☕ 68.00/95.00 **t.**, 1 suite – SB.

**Butlers Town House,** 44 Lansdowne Rd, Ballsbridge, D4, ☎ (01) 667 4022, *Fax (01) 667 3960* – ▤ TV ☎ P. MC AE D VISA. ✻ FU v
*closed 24 to 27 December* – **Meals** (room service only) 🍷 7.50 – **19 rm** ☕ 90.00/129.00 **st.**

**Jurys Custom House Inn,** Custom House Quay, D1, ☎ (01) 607 5000, *Fax (01) 829 0400,* 🏋 – |‡|, ⊁ rm, TV ☎ ♿ – 🏛 100. MC AE D VISA. ✻ KX c
*closed 24 to 26 December* – **Meals** *(closed lunch Saturday and Sunday)* (buffet lunch)/dinner 14.50 **st.** and a la carte 🍷 5.25 – ☕ 6.00 – **234 rm** 57.00 **st.**

**Doyle Skylon,** Upper Drumcondra Rd, D9, N : 2 ½ m. on N 1 ☎ (01) 837 9121, *Fax (01) 837 2778* – |‡|, ⊁ rm, ▤ rest, TV ☎ ♿ P. MC AE D VISA. ✻
**Meals** 9.50/14.00 **t.** and a la carte 🍷 5.20 – ☕ 6.50 – **88 rm** 85.00/105.00 **t.**

**Stephen's Hall,** Earlsfort Centre, 14-17 Lower Leeson St., D2, ☎ (01) 661 0585, *Fax (01) 661 0606* – |‡| ⊁ TV ☎ 🚗. MC AE D VISA. ✻ JZ t
*restricted service 24 December-2 January* – **Meals** – (see ***Morels at Stephen's Hall*** below) – ☕ 8.00 – **3 rm** 105.00/150.00 **st.**, **34 suites** 150.00 **st.**

**Temple Bar,** Fleet St., D2, ☎ (01) 677 3333, *Fax (01) 677 3088* – |‡|, ⊁ rm, TV ☎ P – 🏛 30. MC AE D VISA. ✻ JY e
*closed 25 December* – **Meals** *(closed lunch Saturday and Sunday)* 9.75/15.00 **t.** and a la carte 🍷 6.50 – **108 rm** ☕ 95.00/125.00 **t.** – SB.

**Bewley's Principal,** 19-20 Fleet St., D2, ☎ (01) 670 8122, *Fax (01) 670 8103* – |‡|, ⊁ rm, TV ☎. MC AE D VISA. ✻ JY d
*closed 24 to 26 December* – **Meals** *(closed Sunday dinner)* a la carte 12.00/19.00 **st.** 🍷 6.00 – ☕ 6.00 – **70 rm** 75.00/95.00 **st.** – SB.

**Ariel House** without rest., 52 Lansdowne Rd, Ballsbridge, D4, ☎ (01) 668 5512, *Fax (01) 668 5845,* 🌳 – ⊁ TV ☎ P. MC VISA. ✻ FU n
*closed 24 December-12 January* – ☕ 8.60 – **28 rm** 68.00/169.00 **st.**

**George Frederic Handel,** 16-18 Fishamble St., Christchurch, D2, ☎ (01) 670 9400, *Fax (01) 670 9410* – |‡|, ⊁ rm, ▤ rest, TV ☎ ♿. MC AE D VISA. ✻ HY b
**Meals** a la carte 10.00/25.00 **st.** – **39 rm** ☕ 95.00/160.00 **st.**

**Rathmines Plaza,** Lower Rathmines Rd, Rathmines, D6, ☎ (01) 496 6966, *Fax (01) 491 0603* – |‡| TV ☎ ♿ P. MC AE D VISA. ✻ DV c
*closed 24 to 26 December* – **Meals** (carving lunch) 6.00/11.00 **st.** and dinner a la carte 🍷 3.00 – ☕ 7.50 – **54 rm** 70.00/90.00 **st.** – SB.

**Grafton Plaza,** Johnsons Pl., D2, ☎ (01) 475 0888, *Fax (01) 475 0908* – |‡| TV ☎ ♿. MC AE D VISA. ✻ JZ v
*closed 25 and 26 December* – **Meals** *(closed Sunday lunch and Good Friday)* (bar lunch)/dinner a la carte 11.00/21.50 **st.** 🍷 7.00 – ☕ 7.50 – **75 rm** 95.00/115.00.

**Jurys Christchurch Inn,** Christchurch Pl., D8, ☎ (01) 454 0000, *Fax (01) 454 0012* – |‡|, ⊁ rm, ▤ rest, TV ☎ ♿ P. MC AE D VISA. ✻ HY c
*closed 24 to 26 December* – **Meals** (carving lunch Monday to Saturday)/dinner 15.00 **t.** and a la carte 🍷 6.00 – ☕ 6.50 – **182 rm** 57.00 **t.**

**Mespil,** 50-60 Mespil Rd, D4, ☎ (01) 667 1222, *Fax (01) 667 1244* – |‡|, ⊁ rm, ▤ rest, TV ☎ P – 🏛 50. MC AE D VISA. ✻ EU u
*closed 24 to 26 December* – **Meals** (carving lunch)/dinner 16.95 **st.** and a la carte 🍷 5.90 – ☕ 8.00 – **153 rm** 75.00/95.00 **st.**

**Drury Court,** 28-30 Lower Stephens St., D2, ℘ (01) 475 1988, *Fax (01) 478 5730* – . . – JYZ z
*closed 25 December* – **Meals** 15.00 **st.** (dinner) and a la carte 9.85/16.50 **st.** 5.95 – **32 rm** 87.00/139.00 **st.** – SB.

**Central,** 1-5 Exchequer St., D2, ℘ (01) 679 7302, *Fax (01) 679 7303* – – 80. . JY u
**Meals** *(closed 25 December)* (bar lunch)/dinner 12.50 **t.** and a la carte 4.75 – 7.50 – **68 rm** 95.00/135.00 **st.**, 2 suites – SB.

**Adams Trinity,** 28 Dame St., D2, ℘ (01) 670 7100, *Fax (01) 670 7101* – . JY n
*closed 25 and 26 December* – **Meals** 10.95 **st.** and a la carte 6.00 – **28 rm** 82.00/132.00 **st.** – SB.

**Parliament,** Lord Edward St., D2, ℘ (01) 670 8777, *Fax (01) 670 8787* – , rm, rest, . . HY d
**Meals** (bar lunch)/dinner 14.95 **st.** and a la carte 5.25 – 6.75 – **63 rm** 100.00/140.00.

**Bewley's,** Newlands Cross, D22, SW : 7 m. by N 7 on R 113 ℘ (01) 464 0140, *Fax (01) 464 0900* – , rm, . .
*closed 25 and 26 December* – **Meals** (carving lunch) a la carte 11.15/19.90 **st.** 6.25 – 4.25 – **165 rm** 49.00 **st.**

**Kylemore Park,** Kylemore Rd, D12, SW : 4 ¾ m. by N 7 ℘ (01) 460 1055, *Fax (01) 460 1880*, , – – 400. .
*closed 25 December* – **Meals** (carving lunch)/dinner a la carte 12.00/22.00 **t.** 4.50 – **72 rm** 55.00/79.00 **st.** – SB.

**Patrick Guilbaud,** 21 Upper Merrion St., D2, ℘ (01) 676 4192, *Fax (01) 661 0052* – . KZ e
*closed Sunday, Monday, 25 to 29 December and 1 week January* – **Meals** a la carte 38.00/55.00 **st.** 13.00
**Spec.** Poached Connemara lobster, green apple juice. Roast saddle of Wicklow lamb with honey roast apricots. Hot rhubarb soufflé.

**The Commons,** Newman House, 85-86 St. Stephen's Green, D2, ℘ (01) 478 0530, *Fax (01) 478 0551*, « Contemporary collection of James Joyce inspired Irish Art » – JZ e
*closed Saturday lunch, Sunday, 2 weeks Christmas and Bank Holidays* – **Meals** 20.00/35.00 **st.** and a la carte 8.50.

**Le Coq Hardi,** 35 Pembroke Rd, D4, ℘ (01) 668 9070, *Fax (01) 668 9887* – . EU m
*closed Saturday lunch, Sunday, 2 weeks August, 10 days Christmas and Bank Holidays* – **Meals** 19.00/34.00 **t.** and a la carte 8.10.

**Thornton's** (Thornton), 1 Portobello Rd, D8, ℘ (01) 454 9067, *Fax (01) 453 2947* – . DU e
*closed Sunday, Monday and 2 weeks January* – **Meals** (booking essential) (dinner only and Friday lunch) 18.95 **t.** (lunch) and a la carte 34.95/41.30 **t.** 8.50
**Spec.** Langoustine bisque with truffle sabayon. Suckling pig with trotter, Maxim potatoes and poitin jus. Nougat pyramid with glazed fruit and orange sauce.

**Chapter One,** The Dublin Writers Museum, 18-19 Parnell Sq., D1, ℘ (01) 873 2266, *Fax (01) 873 2330* – . JX r
*closed Saturday lunch, Monday dinner, Sunday and 24 December-6 January* – **Meals** 13.50 **t.** (lunch) and dinner a la carte 22.00/27.00 **t.** 8.50.

**L'Ecrivain,** 109 Lower Baggot St., D2, ℘ (01) 661 1919, *Fax (01) 661 0617*, – . KZ b
*closed Saturday lunch, Sunday, 25-26 December and Bank Holidays* – **Meals** (booking essential) 15.50/25.00 **t.** and dinner a la carte approx. 31.50 **t.** 7.00.

**Peacock Alley** (Gallagher), 47 South William St., ℘ (01) 677 0708, *Fax (01) 671 8854* – JY s
*closed 25 December and Bank Holidays* – **Meals** (booking essential) 14.95 **t.** (lunch) and a la carte 22.40/40.40 **t.** 8.00
**Spec.** Ravioli of lobster with lemon grass vinaigrette and lobster cream. Daube of beef with rosemary mashed potato and madeira cream. Warm chocolate fondant with pistachio ice cream.

**Ernie's,** Mulberry Gdns., off Morehampton Rd, Donnybrook, D4, ℘ (01) 269 3300, *Fax (01) 269 3260*, « Contemporary Irish Art collection » – . FV k
*closed Saturday lunch, Sunday, Monday and 24 December-1 January* – **Meals** 13.95/25.00 **t.** and a la carte 26.20/36.15 **t.** 8.00.

**Les Frères Jacques,** 74 Dame St., D2, ℘ (01) 679 4555, *Fax (01) 679 4725* – HY x
*closed Saturday lunch, Sunday, 24 December-2 January and Bank Holidays* – **Meals** - French - 13.50/20.00 **t.** and a la carte 5.50.

XX **Morels at Stephen's Hall,** 14-17 Lower Leeson St., D2, ☏ (01) 662 2480, *Fax (01) 662 8595* – ▤. MC AE ① VISA JZ t
*closed Saturday lunch, Sunday, 5 days Christmas and Bank Holidays* – **Meals** (booking essential) 12.50/23.00 **t.** and a la carte 7.00.

XX **Locks,** 1 Windsor Terr., Portobello, D8, ☏ (01) 4543391, *Fax (01) 4538352* – MC AE ① VISA DU a
*closed Saturday lunch, Sunday, last week July-first week August, 1 week Christmas and Bank Holidays* – **Meals** 14.95/25.00 **t.** and a la carte 6.00.

XX **Old Dublin,** 90-91 Francis St., D8, ☏ (01) 4542028, *Fax (01) 4541406* – MC AE ① VISA HZ n
*closed Saturday lunch, Sunday, 25 December and Bank Holidays* – **Meals** - Russian-Scandinavian - 12.50/21.00 **t.** and dinner a la carte 8.25.

XX **La Stampa,** 35 Dawson St., D2, ☏ (01) 677 8611, *Fax (01) 677 3336,* « 19C former ballroom » – ▤. MC AE ① VISA JZ g
*closed lunch Saturday and Sunday, Good Friday and 25-26 December* – **Meals** 12.50 (lunch) and dinner a la carte 21.45/31.40 **t.** 8.00.

XX **Popjoys,** 4 Rathfarnham Rd, Terenure, D6, S : 3 m. on N 81 ☏ (01) 492 9346, *Fax (01) 492 9293* – ▤. MC AE ① VISA
*closed Saturday lunch, Good Friday and 1 week Christmas* – **Meals** 11.95/21.00 **t.** and a la carte 6.75.

XX **L'Epee d'Or,** 112 Lower Baggot St., D2, ☏ (01) 662 5511, *Fax (01) 676 7488* – MC AE ① VISA KZ a
*closed Saturday lunch, Sunday, 25 December and Bank Holidays* – **Meals** 13.50/24.00 **t.** and a la carte 5.75.

XX **Zen,** 89 Upper Rathmines Rd, D6, ☏ (01) 4979428 – ▤. MC AE ① VISA DV t
*closed lunch Monday to Wednesday, Saturday and 25 to 28 December* – **Meals** - Chinese (Szechuan) - 8.50 (lunch) and a la carte 12.50/21.00.

XX **Number 10** (at Longfield's H.), 10 Lower Fitzwilliam St., D2, ☏ (01) 676 1060, *Fax (01) 676 1542* – MC AE ① VISA KZ d
*closed lunch Saturday, Sunday and Bank Holidays and 24 to 27 December* – **Meals** 15.00/27.50 **st.** 8.00.

XX **Coopers Cafe,** The Sweepstakes Centre, Ballsbridge, D4, ☏ (01) 660 1525, *Fax (01) 660 1537* – ▤. MC AE ① VISA FU k
*closed 25 and 26 December* – **Meals** 9.95 **t.** and a la carte 18.80/25.35 **t.** 6.00.

XX **Fitzers Café,** RDS, Merrion Rd, Ballsbridge, D4, ☏ (01) 667 1301, *Fax (01) 667 1303* – Ⓟ. MC AE ① VISA FU a
*closed Sunday dinner and 4 days Christmas* – **Meals** (booking essential) 11.25 **t.** (lunch) and a la carte 18.25/29.75 **t.** 7.95.

X **Roly's Bistro,** 7 Ballsbridge Terr., Ballsbridge, D4, ☏ (01) 668 2611, *Fax (01) 660 8535* – ▤. MC AE ① VISA FU r
*closed 25-26 December and Bank Holidays* – **Meals** (booking essential) 11.50 **t.** (lunch) and a la carte 18.00/23.25 **t.** 5.25.

X **Cooke's Café,** 14 South William St., D2, ☏ (01) 679 0536, *Fax (01) 679 0546,* – ▤. MC AE ① VISA JY c
*closed 25-26 December and Bank Holidays* – **Meals** 14.95 **t.** and a la carte 10.00.

X **Dobbin's,** 15 Stephen's Lane, off Lower Mount St., D2, ☏ (01) 676 4679, *Fax (01) 661 3331,* – ▤ Ⓟ. MC AE ① VISA EU s
*closed Saturday lunch, Monday dinner, Sunday, 1 week Christmas, 1 January and Bank Holidays* – **Meals** - Bistro - (booking essential) 15.50/27.00 **st.** and a la carte 6.25.

**at Tallaght** *SW : 7 ½ m. by N 81* – DV – ✉ *Dublin* :

**Abberley Court,** Belgard Rd, D24, ☏ (01) 459 6000, *Fax (01) 462 1000* – , rm, – 250. MC AE ① VISA.
*closed 25 December* – **Meals** *(closed lunch Saturday and Bank Holidays)* 12.95 **st.** (lunch) and dinner a la carte 12.00/18.90 **st.** 5.00 – **40 rm** 79.00/98.00 **st.** – SB.

**at Saggart** *SW : 9 ¼ m. off N 7* – HY – ✉ *Dublin* :

**Citywest,** ☏ (01) 458 8566, *Fax (01) 458 8565,* 18, , park – Ⓟ – 300. MC AE ① VISA.
**Meals** 12.50/22.00 **t.** 5.25 – **50 rm** 75.00/180.00 **t.** – SB.

# Italy

## Italia

ROME – FLORENCE – MILAN – NAPLES
PALERMO – TAORMINA – TURIN – VENICE

# PRACTICAL INFORMATION

## LOCAL CURRENCY

**Italian Lire:** *1000 ITL = 0,57 USD ($) (Jan. 98)*

## TOURIST INFORMATION

**Welcome Office** *(Ente Provinciale per il Turismo):*
*– Via Parigi 11 - 00185 ROMA (closed Sunday), ☏ (06) 488991, Fax (06) 488 99 250*
*– Via Marconi 1 - 20123 MILANO, ☏ (02) 72 52 43 00, Fax (02) 72 52 43 50*
*See also telephone number and address of other Tourist Information offices in the text of the towns under* **ℹ**.
*American Express:*
*– Piazza di Spagna 38 - 00187 ROMA, ☏ (06) 67641, Fax (06) 67 64 24 99*
*– Via Brera 3 - 20121 MILANO, ☏ (02) 72 00 36 96, Fax (02) 86 10 28*

**National Holiday in Italy:** *25 April.*

## AIRLINES

**ALITALIA:** *Via Bissolati 20 - 00187 ROMA, ☏ (06) 65621, Fax (06) 656 28 282*
*Via Albricci 5 - 20122 MILANO, ☏ (02) 24992700, Fax (02) 805 67 57*

**AIR FRANCE:** *Via Sardegna 40 - 00187 ROMA, ☏ (06) 48791555, Fax (06) 483803*
*Piazza Cavour 2 - 20121 MILANO, ☏ (02) 760731, Fax (02) 760 73 333*

**DELTA AIRLINES:** *Viale Liberazione 18 - 20124 MILANO, ☏ (02) 67 07 00 47, Fax (02) 67 07 31 82*

**TWA:** *Via Barberini 59 - 00187 ROMA, ☏ (06) 47241, Fax (06) 474 61 25*
*Corso Europa 11 - 20122 MILANO, ☏ (02) 77961, Fax (02) 76 01 45 83*

## FOREIGN EXCHANGE

*Money can be changed at the Banca d'Italia, other banks and authorised exchange offices (Banks close at 1.30pm and at weekends).*

## POSTAL SERVICES

**Local post offices:** *open Monday to Saturday 8.30am to 2.00pm*

**General Post Office** *(open 24 hours only for telegrams):*
*– Piazza San Silvestro 00187 ROMA – Piazza Cordusio 20123 MILANO*

## SHOPPING

*In the index of street names, those printed in red are where the principal shops are found. In Rome, the main shopping streets are: Via del Babuino, Via Condotti, Via Frattina, Via Vittorio Veneto; in Milan: Via Dante, Via Manzoni, Via Monte Napoleone, Corso Vittorio Emanuele, Via della Spiga.*

## BREAKDOWN SERVICE

*Certain garages in the centre and outskirts of towns operate a 24 hour breakdown service. If you break down the police are usually able to help by indicating the nearest one.*
*A free car breakdown service (a tax is levied) is operated by the A.C.I. for foreign motorists carrying the fuel card (Carta Carburante). The A.C.I. also offers telephone information in English (24 hours a day) for road and weather conditions and tourist events: (06) 4477.*

## TIPPING

*As well as the service charge, it is the custom to tip employees. The amount can vary depending upon the region and the service given.*

## SPEED LIMITS

*On motorways, the maximum permitted speed is 130 km/h - 80 mph for vehicles over 1000 cc, 110 km/h - 68 mph for all other vehicles. On other roads, the speed limit is 90 km/h - 56 mph.*

# ROME

(ROMA) *00100* 988 ㉖ 430 Q 19 38 – *Pop. 2 645 322 – alt. 20.*

*Distances from Rome are indicated in the text of the other towns listed in this Guide.*

*via Parigi 5 ✉ 00185 ☎ (06) 48 89 92 53, Fax (06) 481 93 16 ; at Termini Station ☎ (06) 4871270 ; at Fiumicino Airport ☎ (06) 65956074.*

A.C.I. *via Cristoforo Colombo 261 ✉ 00147 ☎ (06) 514 971 and via Marsala 8 ✉ 00185 ☎ (06) 49981, Telex 610686, Fax (06) 499 82 34.*

18 *Parco de' Medici (closed Tuesday) ✉ 00148 Roma SW : 4,5 km ☎ (06) 655 34 77 – Fax (06) 655 33 44.*

18 *(closed Monday) at Acquasanta ✉ 00178 Roma SE : 12 km. ☎ (06) 78 34 07, Fax (06) 78 34 62 19.*

18 *and* 18 *Marco Simone (closed Tuesday) at Guidonia Montecelio ✉ 00012 Roma W : 7 km ☎ (0774) 366 469, Fax (0774) 366 476.*

18 9 *Arco di Costantino (closed Tuesday) ✉ 00188 Roma N : 15 km ☎ (06) 33 62 44 40, Fax (06) 33 61 29 19*

9 *and* 18 *(closed Monday) at Olgiata ✉ 00123 Roma NW : 19 km ☎ (06) 308 89 141, Fax (06) 308 89 968.*

9 *Fioranello (closed Wednesday) at Santa Maria delle Mole ✉ 00040 Roma SE : 19 km ☎ (06) 713 80 80, Fax (06) 713 82 12.*

*Ciampino SW : 15 km ☎ 794941 and Leonardo da Vinci di Fiumicino SE : 26 km ☎ (06) 65951 – Alitalia, via Bissolati 13 ✉ 00187 ☎ (06) 46881 and via della Magliana 886 ✉ 00148 ☎ (06) 65643.*

*Termini ☎ (06) 4775 – Tiburtina ☎ (06) 47301.*

## SIGHTS

*Rome's most famous sights are listed after town plans. For a more complete visit use the Michelin Green Guide to Rome.*

## ROMA
**NORTH CENTRE**

Traffic restricted
in the town centre



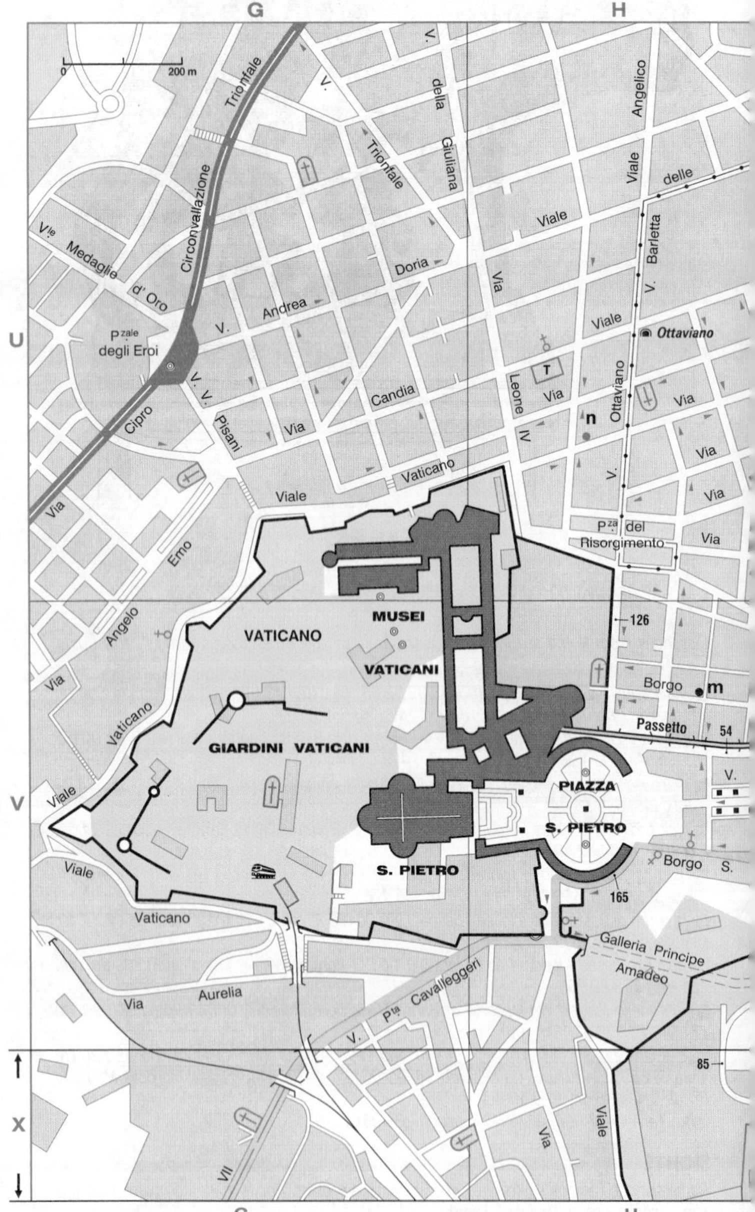

Governo Vecchio (Via d.) . . . . . . . . . . . . . **KVX** 88
Lucania (Via) . . . . . . . . . . **PU** 94
Monte Brianzo (Via di) . . . **LV** 108
Nenni (Ponte P.) . . . . . . . . **KU** 111
Porta Angelica (Via di) . . . **HV** 126
Prinicpe A. Savoia Aosta (Ponte . . . . . . . . **JV** 135
Quirinale (Via d.) . . . . . . . . . . . . . **OV** 138
Regina Margherita (Ponte) . . . . . . . . . . . . . **KU** 139
Regolo (Via A.) . . . . . . . . **JU** 141
Rinascimento (Corso d.) . . . . . . . . . . **LVX** 142
Rotonda (Via) . . . . . . . . . **MX** 147
S. Angelo (Borgo) . . . . . . **JV** 151
S. Chiara (Via) . . . . . . . . . . **MX** 153

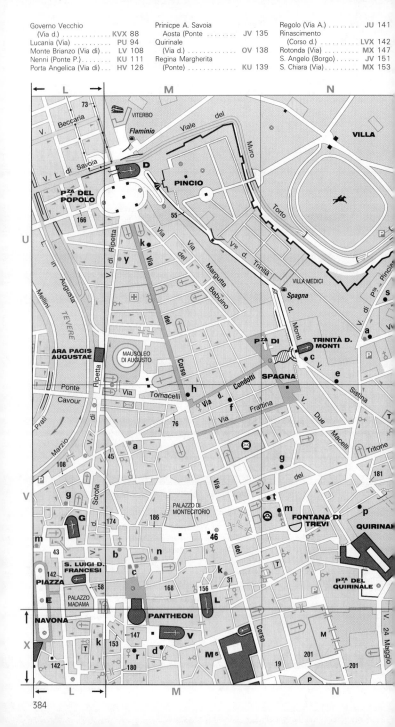

# ROMA
## SOUTH CENTRE

Traffic restricted
in the town centre



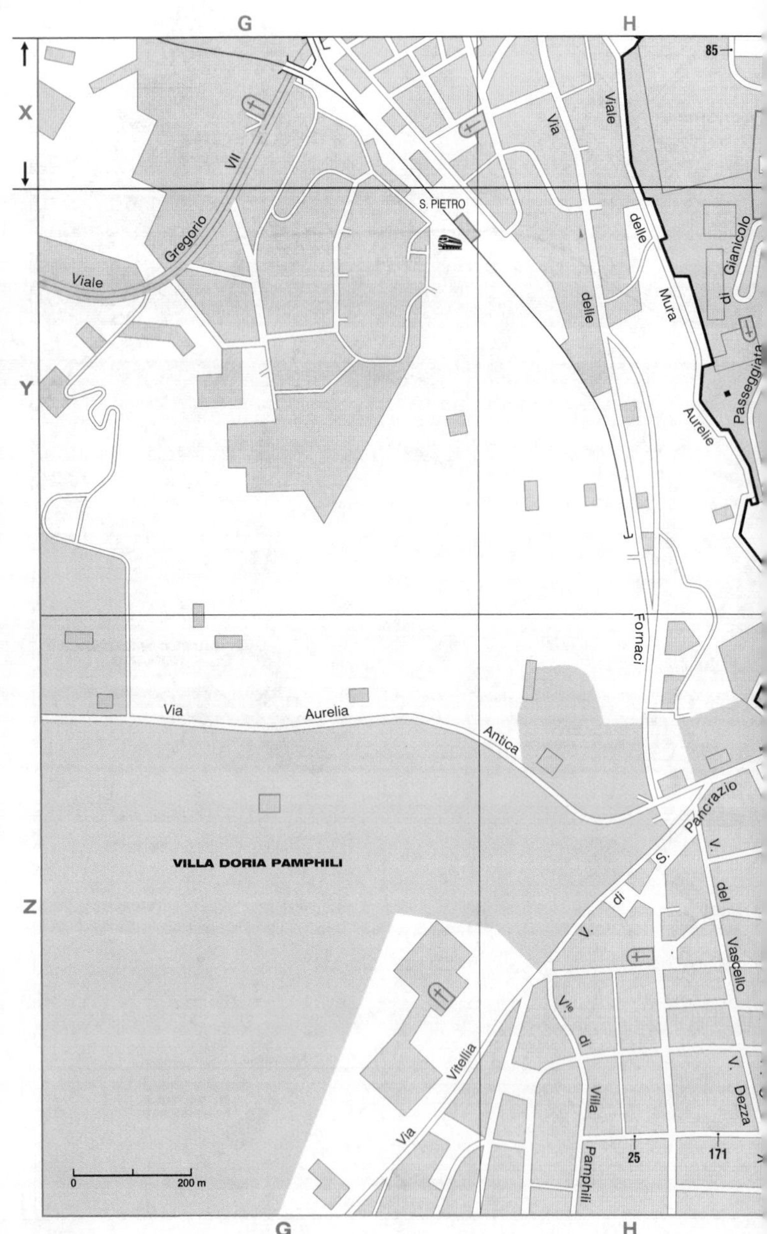

Campo dei Fiori (Piazza) . . . . . . . . . . . . . KY 28
Cappellari (Via d.) . . . . . . . KX 30
Consolazione (Via d.) . . . . . . . . . . . . . . NY 49
Fabriciq (Ponte) . . . . . . . . . MY 64
Florida (Via) . . . . . . . . . . . . MY 75
Foro Olitorio (Via d.) . . . . . MY 78
Garibaldi (Ponte) . . . . . . . . LY 81
Gianicolo (Via d.) . . . . . . . . HX 85
Governo Vecchio (Via d.) . . . . . . . . . . . . . KVX 88
Greca (Via d.) . . . . . . . . . MZ 90
Jugario (Vico) . . . . . . . . . MY 91
Lungaretta (Via d.) . . . . . KZ 96
Mascherone (Via d.) . . . . . . . . . . . . KY 103
Massina (Via A.) . . . . . . . JZ 105

Monserrato (Via) . . . . . . . . . . . . . . . . KY 106
Paglia (Via d.) . . . . . . . . . . KZ 114
Pierleoni (Lungotevere d.) . . . . . . MZ 117
Plebiscito (Via d.) . . . . . . . MY 121
Porta Lavernale (Via) . . . . MZ 127
Porta Portese (Via di) . . . . LZ 129
Portico d'Ottavia (Via) . . . . . . . . . . . . . . MY 130
Portuense (Lungotevere) . . . . . . . . LZ 132
Publicii (Clivo d.) . . . . . . . . . . . NZ 136
Rinascimento (Corso d.) . . . . . . . . . . LVX 142
Rotonda (Via) . . . . . . . . . . MX 147
Saffi (Viale A.) . . . . . . . . . JKZ 150

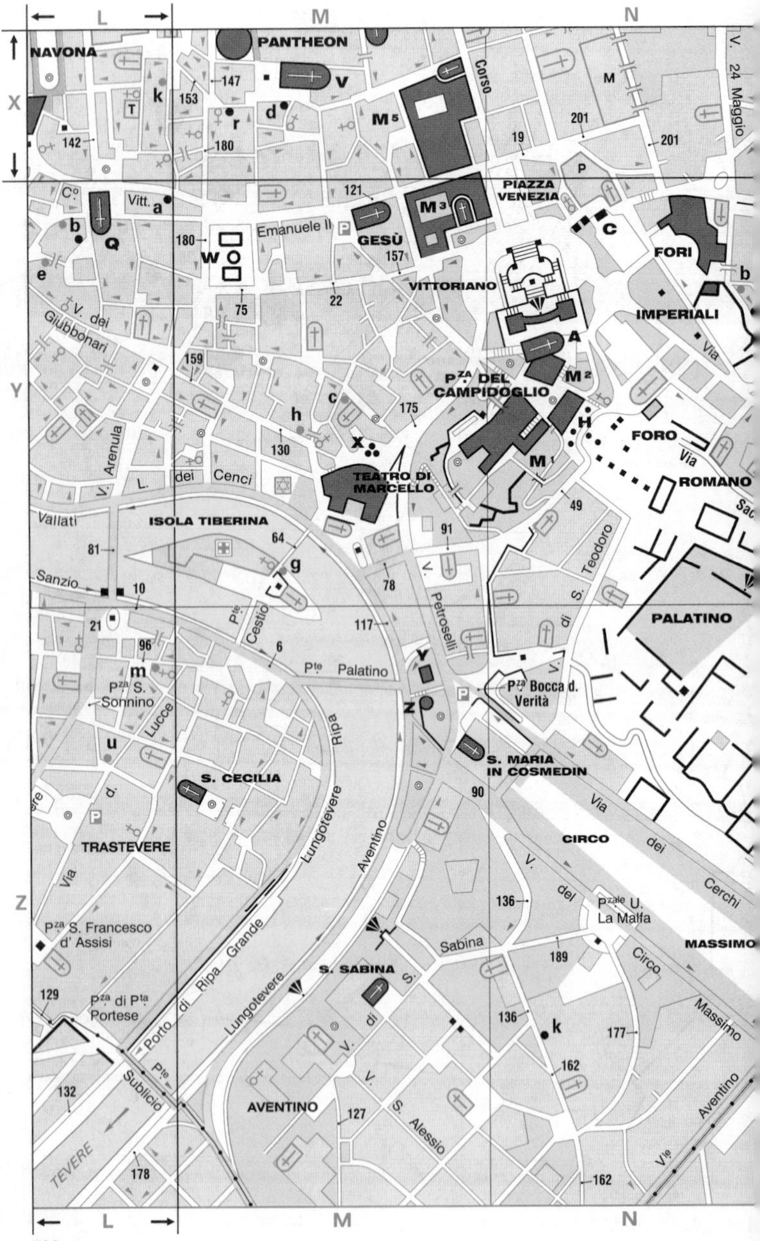

S. Chiara (Via) . . . . . . . . . **MX** 153
S. Marco (Via) . . . . . . . . . **MY** 157
S. Maria del Pianto (Via) . . . . . . . . . . . . . . . **MY** 159
S. Maria Maggiore (Via) . **PX** 160
S. Prisca (Via di) . . . . . . . . **NZ** 162
Sprovieri (Via F. S.) . . . . . **HZ** 171
Teatro di Marcello (Via d.) . . . . . . . . . . . . . **MY** 175
Terme Deciane (Via d.) . . **NZ** 177
Testaccio (Lungotevere) . . . . . . . . **LZ** 178
Torre Argentina (Via) . . . . . . . . . . . . . . **MXY** 180
Valle Murcia (Via di) . . . . **NZ** 189
Venezian (Via G.) . . . . . . **KZ** 192
4 Novembre (Via) . . . . . . **NX** 201
30 Aprile (Viale) . . . . . . . **JZ** 202

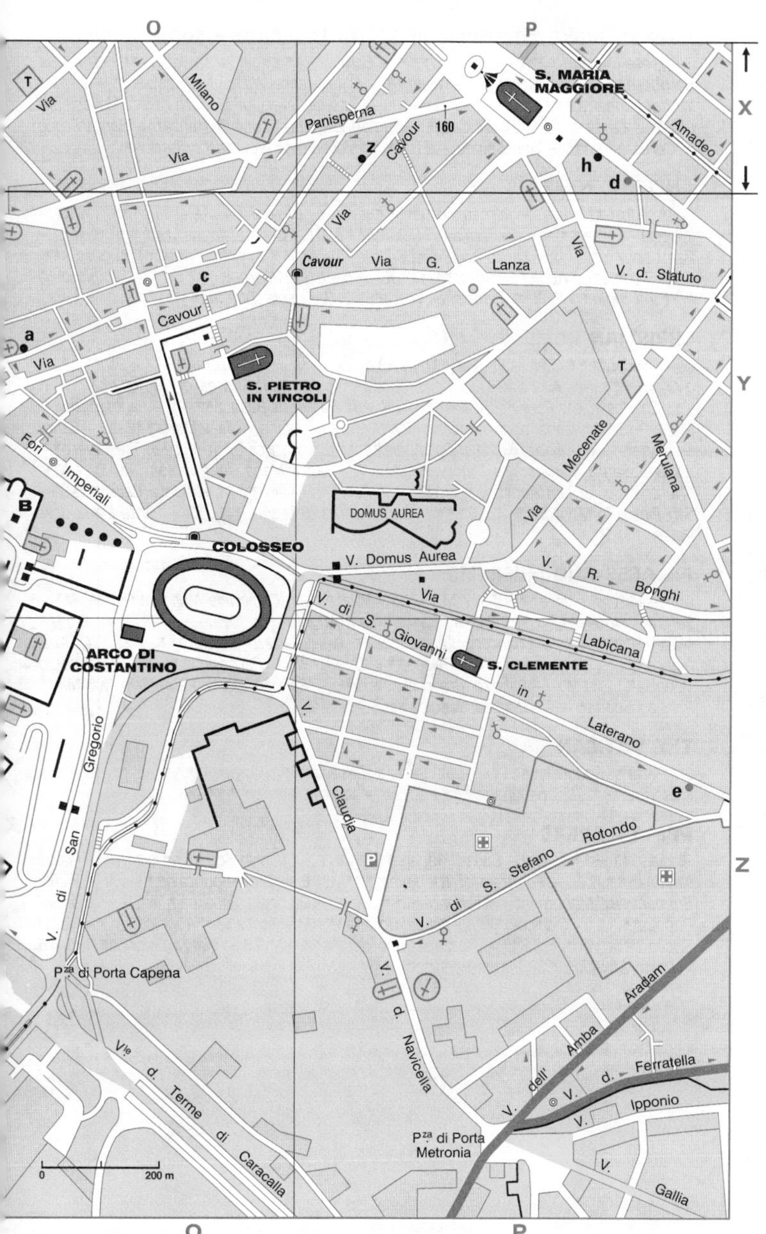

# Sights

## How to make the most of a trip to Rome – some ideas :

*Borghese Museum*★★★ – *Villa Giulia*★★★ – *Catacombs*★★★ – *Santa Sabina*★★ MZ – *Villa Borghese*★★ NOU – *Baths of Caracalla*★★ – *St Lawrence Without the Walls*★★ – *St Paul Without the Walls*★★ – *Old Appian Way*★★ – *National Gallery of Modern Art*★ – *Mausoleum of Caius Cestius*★ – *St Paul's Gate*★ – *San'Agnese and Santa Costanza*★ – *Santa Croce in Gerusalemme*★ – *San Saba*★ – *E.U.R.*★ – *Museum of Roman Civilisation*★.

### ANCIENT ROME

*Colosseum*★★★ OYZ – *Roman Forum*★★★ NOY – *Basilica of Maxentius*★★★ OY **B** – *Imperial Fora*★★★ NY – *Trajan's Column*★★★ NY **C** – *Palatine Hill*★★★ NOYZ – *Pantheon*★★★ MVX – *Largo Argentina Sacred Precinct*★★ MY **W** – *Altar of Augustus*★★ LU – *Temple of Apollo Sosianus*★★ MY **X** – *Theatre of Marcellus*★★ MY – *Tempio della Fortuna Virile*★ MZ **Y** – *Tempio di Vesta*★ MZ **Z** – *Isola Tiberina*★ MY.

### CHRISTIAN ROME

*Gesù Church*★★★ MY – *St Mary Major*★★★ PX – *St John Lateran*★★★ – *Santa Maria d'Aracoeli*★★ NY **A** – *San Luigi dei Francesi*★★ LV – *Sant'Andrea al Quirinale*★★ OV **F** – *St Charles at the Four Fountains*★★ OV **K** – *St Clement's Basilica*★★ PZ – *Sant'Ignazio*★★ MV **L** – *Santa Maria degli Angeli*★★ PV **N** – *Santa Maria della Vittoria*★★ PV – *Santa Susanna*★★ OV – *Santa Maria in Cosmedin*★★ MNZ – *Basilica of St Mary in Trastevere*★★ KZ **S** – *Santa Maria sopra Minerva*★★ MX **V** – *Santa Maria del Popolo*★ MU **D** – *New Church*★ KX – *Sant'Agostino*★ LV **G** – *St Peter in Chains*★ OY – *Santa Cecilia*★ MZ – *San Pietro in Montorio*★ JZ ⩽★★★ – *Sant'Andrea della Valle*★ LY **Q** – *Santa Maria della Pace*★ KV **R**.

### PALACES AND MUSEUMS

*Conservators' Palace*★★★ MNY **M**[1] – *New Palace*★★★ *(Capitoline Museum*★★*)* NY **M**[1] – *Senate House*★★★ NY **H** – *Castel Sant'Angelo*★★★ JKV – *National Roman Museum*★★★ PV – *Chancery Palace*★★ KX **A** – *Palazzo Farnese*★★ KY – *Quirinal Palace*★★ NOV – *Barberini Palace*★★ OV – *Villa Farnesina*★★ KY – *Palazzo Venezia*★ MY **M**[3] – *Palazzo Braschi*★ KX **M**[4] – *Palazzo Doria Pamphili*★ MX **M**[5] – *Palazzo Spada*★ KY – *Museo Napoleanico*★ KV.

### THE VATICAN

*St Peter's Square*★★★ HV – *St Peter's Basilica*★★★ *(Dome* ⩽★★★*)* GV – *Vatican Museums*★★★ *(Sistine Chapel*★★★*)* GHUV – *Vatican Gardens*★★★ GV.

### PRETTY AREAS

*Pincian Hill* ⩽★★★ MU – *Capitol Square*★★★ MNY – *Spanish Square*★★★ MNU – *Piazza Navona*★★★ LVX – *Fountain of the Rivers*★★★ LV **E** – *Trevi Fountain*★★★ NV – *Victor Emmanuel II Monument (Vittoriano)* ⩽★★ MNY – *Quirinale Square*★★ NV – *Piazza del Popolo*★★ MU – *Gianicolo*★ JY – *Via dei Coronari*★ KV – *Ponte Sant'Angelo*★ JKV – *Piazza Bocca della Verità*★ MNZ – *Piazza Campo dei Fiori*★ KY **28** – *Piazza Colonna*★ MV **46** – *Porta Maggiore*★ – *Piazza Venezia*★ MNY.

**Historical Centre** corso Vittorio Emanuele, piazza Venezia, Pantheon e Quirinale, piazza di Spagna, piazza Navona :

**Hassler,** piazza Trinità dei Monti 6 ✉ 00187 ☎ (06)699340, *Fax (06)6789991*, ← City from roof-garden rest. – |♦| ▤ TV ☎ – 🅰 70. AE ◑ E VISA JCB. ✂ NU c
**Meals** a la carte 145/205000 – ☕ 52000 – **85 rm** 480/980000, 15 suites.

**Holiday Inn Minerva** M, piazza della Minerva 69 ✉ 00186 ☎ (06)69941888, *Fax (06)6794165*, « Terrace with ← » – |♦|, ✂ rm, ▤ TV ☎ ♿ – 🅰 120. AE ⑤ ◑ E VISA JCB. ✂ MX d
**Meals** a la carte 75/145000 – ☕ 45000 – **118 rm** 550/750000, 3 suites.

**De la Ville Inter-Continental,** via Sistina 69 ✉ 00187 ☎ (06)67331, *Fax (06)6784213*, ☂ – |♦| ▤ TV ☎ – 🅰 70. AE ⑤ ◑ E VISA JCB. ✂ NU e
**Meals** a la carte 100/165000 – **169 rm** ☕ 590/730000, 23 suites.

**D'Inghilterra,** via Bocca di Leone 14 ✉ 00187 ☎ (06)69981, *Fax (06)69922243*, « Former boarding house traditional furnishings » – |♦| ▤ TV ☎. AE ⑤ ◑ E VISA. ✂
**Meals** a la carte 80/100000 – ☕ 33000 – **95 cam** 415/595000, 10 suites. MV f

**Dei Borgognoni** without rest., via del Bufalo 126 ✉ 00187 ☎ (06)69941505, *Fax (06)69941501* – |♦| ▤ TV ☎ 🚗 – 🅰 70. AE ⑤ ◑ E VISA JCB. ✂ NV g
☕ 20000 – **50 rm** 420/480000.

**Plaza** without rest., via del Corso 126 ✉ 00186 ☎ (06)69921111, *Fax (06)69941575*, « Floral terrace with ← » – |♦| ▤ TV ☎ – 🅰 60. AE ⑤ ◑ E VISA JCB. ✂ MV h
☕ 26000 – **195 rm** 390/580000, 10 suites.

**Valadier,** via della Fontanella 15 ✉ 00187 ☎ (06)3611998 and rest. ☎ (06)3610880, *Fax (06)3201558*, ☂ – |♦| ▤ TV ☎ – 🅰 35. AE ⑤ ◑ E VISA JCB. ✂ MU k
**Meals** ***Valentino*** Rest. a la carte 35/75000 – **38 rm** ☕ 390/490000, 4 suites.

**Delle Nazioni,** via Poli 7 ✉ 00187 ☎ (06)6792441, *Fax (06)6782400* – |♦| ▤ TV ☎ 🚗 – 🅰 50. AE ⑤ ◑ E VISA JCB. ✂ NV m
**Meals** (see rest. **Le Grondici** below) – ☕ 25000 – **83 rm** 320/400000.

**White** M without rest., via Arcione 77 ✉ 00187 ☎ (06)6991242, *Fax (06)6788451* – |♦| ▤ TV ☎ – 🅰 40. AE ⑤ ◑ E VISA JCB. ✂ NV p
**40 rm** ☕ 320/400000.

**Santa Chiara** without rest., via Santa Chiara 21 ✉ 00186 ☎ (06)6872979, *Fax (06)6873144* – |♦| ▤ TV ☎ – 🅰 40. AE ⑤ ◑ E VISA JCB. ✂ MX r
**93 rm** ☕ 260/330000, 3 suites.

**Della Torre Argentina** without rest., corso Vittorio Emanuele 102 ✉ 00186 ☎ (06)6833886, *Fax (06)68801641* – |♦| ▤ TV ☎. AE ⑤ ◑ E VISA JCB. ✂ LY a
**52 rm** ☕ 220/315000, suite.

**Tritone** without rest., via del Tritone 210 ✉ 00187 ☎ (06)69922575, *Fax (06)6782624* – |♦| ▤ TV ☎. AE ⑤ ◑ E VISA JCB NV t
**43 rm** ☕ 270/320000.

**Teatro di Pompeo** without rest., largo del Pallaro 8 ✉ 00186 ☎ (06)6830170, *Fax (06)68805531*, « Vaults of Pompeius' theatre » – |♦| ▤ TV ☎ – 🅰 30. AE ⑤ ◑ E VISA. ✂ LY b
**12 rm** ☕ 210/280000.

**El Toulà,** via della Lupa 29/b ✉ 00186 ☎ (06)6873498, *Fax (06)6871115*, Elegant rest. – ▤. AE ⑤ ◑ E VISA JCB. ✂ MV a
*closed Sunday, Monday lunch, August and 24 to 26 December* – **Meals** (booking essential) a la carte 85/130000 (15 %).

**Enoteca Capranica,** piazza Capranica 100 ✉ 00186 ☎ (06)69940992, *Fax (06)69940989* – ▤. AE ⑤ ◑ VISA JCB. ✂ MV n
*closed Saturday lunch and Sunday* – **Meals** (booking essential for dinner) 35000 b.i. (lunch only) and a la carte 60/85000.

**Camponeschi,** piazza Farnese 50 ✉ 00186 ☎ (06)6874927, *Fax (06)6865244*, « Summer service with ← Farnese palace » – ▤. AE ⑤ ◑ E VISA KY c
*closed Sunday and 13 to 22 August* – **Meals** (dinner only) (booking essential) a la carte 100/140000 (13 %).

**Vecchia Roma,** via della Tribuna di Campitelli 18 ✉ 00186 ☎ (06)6864604, ☂, Elegant rest. – ▤. AE ◑ MY c
*closed Wednesday and 10 to 25 August* – **Meals** Roman and seafood rest. a la carte 65/105000.

**Quinzi Gabrieli,** via delle Coppelle 6 ✉ 00186 ☎ (06)6879389, *Fax (06)6874940* – AE ⑤ ◑ E VISA. ✂ MV b
*closed Sunday and August* – **Meals** (dinner only) (booking essential) seafood a la carte 100/130000
**Spec.** Carpaccio di pesce ai sapori mediterranei. Spaghetti all'aragosta. Scorfano "all'acqua pazza".

**La Rosetta,** via della Rosetta 9 ✉ 00187 ☎ (06)6861002, *Fax (06)6872852* – ▤. AE ⑤ ⊙ E VISA JCB MV c
*closed Saturday lunch, Sunday and 5 to 25 August* – **Meals** (booking essential) seafood a la carte 95/140000.

**Le Grondici,** via del Mortaro 14 ✉ 00187 ☎ (06)6795761 – ▤. AE ⑤ ⊙ E VISA. ✂ NV m
*closed Sunday* – **Meals** a la carte 55/85000.

**Il Convivio,** via dell'Orso 44 ✉ 00186 ☎ (06)6869432, *Fax (06)6869432* – ▤. AE ⑤ ⊙ E VISA JCB. ✂ LV g
*closed Sunday and Monday lunch* – **Meals** (booking essential) a la carte 95/140000
**Spec.** Seppioline ripiene di patate e rosmarino in salsa all'aglio dolce. Tagliolini con pomodoro verde, bottarga ed erba cipollina. Coscia di faraona con porcini e salsa alla senape.

**Eau Vive,** via Monterone 85 ✉ 00186 ☎ (06)68801095, *Fax (06)68802571*, Catholic missionaries, « 16C building » – ⊭ ▤. AE ⑤ E VISA. ✂ LX k
*closed Sunday and August* – **Meals** (booking essential for dinner) French and exotic cuisine 25/30000 and a la carte 30/65000.

**Taverna Giulia,** vicolo dell'Oro 23 ✉ 00186 ☎ (06)6869768, *Fax (06)6893720* – ▤. AE ⑤ ⊙ E VISA JCB. ✂ JV r
*closed Sunday and August* – **Meals** (booking essential for dinner) Ligurian rest. a la carte 50/75000.

**Passetto,** via Zanardelli 14 ✉ 00186 ☎ (06)68806569, *Fax (06)68806569* – AE ⑤ ⊙ E VISA JCB. ✂ LV m
**Meals** a la carte 70/150000.

**Da Pancrazio,** piazza del Biscione 92 ✉ 00186 ☎ (06)6861246, *Fax (06)6861246*, « Inn rebuilt on the remains of Pompeius' theatre » – ⊭. AE ⑤ ⊙ E VISA JCB. ✂ LY e
*closed Wednesday, 1 to 20 August and Christmas* – **Meals** a la carte 50/95000.

**Da Giggetto,** via del Portico d'Ottavia 21/a ✉ 00186 ☎ (06)6861105, ☂ – AE ⑤ ⊙ E VISA. ✂ MY h
*closed Monday and 21 July-3 August* – **Meals** Typical Roman trattoria a la carte 50/75000.

**Il Falchetto,** via del Montecatini 12/14 ✉ 00186 ☎ (06)6791160, Rustic trattoria – AE ⑤ ⊙ E VISA MV k
*closed Friday and 5 to 20 August* – **Meals** a la carte 45/65000.

**La Buca di Ripetta,** via di Ripetta 36 ✉ 00186 ☎ (06)3219391, Habituès trattoria – ▤. AE ⑤ ⊙ VISA. ✂ MU y
*closed Sunday dinner, Monday and August* – **Meals** a la carte 40/60000.

**Termini Railway Station** via Vittorio Veneto, via Nazionale, Viminale, Santa Maria Maggiore, Porta Pia :

**Excelsior,** via Vittorio Veneto 125 ✉ 00187 ☎ (06)47081, *Fax (06)4826205* – |‡|, ⊭ rm, ▤ TV ☎ – 🏛 600. AE ⑤ ⊙ E VISA JCB. ✂ OU d
**Meals** a la carte 115/205000 – ☐ 32000 – **282 rm** 480/740000, 45 suites.

**Le Grand Hotel,** via Vittorio Emanuele Orlando 3 ✉ 00185 ☎ (06)47091, *Fax (06)4747307* – |‡| ▤ TV ☎ – 🏛 300. AE ⑤ ⊙ E VISA JCB. ✂ PV c
**Meals** a la carte 125/175000 – ☐ 35500 – **134 rm** 480/750000, 36 suites.

**Eden,** via Ludovisi 49 ✉ 00187 ☎ (06)478121, *Fax (06)4821584*, ≤, Fø – |‡| ⊭ ▤ TV ☎ – 🏛 100. AE ⑤ ⊙ E VISA JCB. ✂ NU a
**Meals** (see rest. **La Terrazza** below) – ☐ 55000 – **92 rm** 495/850000, 11 suites.

**Majestic,** via Vittorio Veneto 50 ✉ 00187 ☎ (06)486841, *Fax (06)4880984* – |‡| ▤ TV ☎ ♿ – 🏛 150. AE ⑤ ⊙ E VISA JCB. ✂ OU e
**Meals** a la carte 75/125000 – **83 rm** ☐ 530/720000, 10 suites.

**Bernini Bristol,** piazza Barberini 23 ✉ 00187 ☎ (06)4883051, *Fax (06)4824266* – |‡|, ⊭ rm, ▤ TV ☎ – 🏛 100. AE ⑤ ⊙ E VISA JCB. ✂ rest OV f
**Meals** a la carte 85/115000 – ☐ 33000 – **115 rm** 440/615000, 10 suites.

**Ambasciatori Palace,** via Vittorio Veneto 62 ✉ 00187 ☎ (06)47493, *Fax (06)4743601*, ≘ – |‡| ▤ TV ☎ ♿ – 🏛 200. AE ⑤ ⊙ E VISA JCB. ✂ rest
**Meals** *(closed Saturday dinner and Sunday)* a la carte 75/115000 – ☐ 27000 – **110 rm** 400/600000, 8 suites. OU g

**Regina Baglioni,** via Vittorio Veneto 72 ✉ 00187 ☎ (06)476851, *Fax (06)485483* – |‡|, ⊭ rm, ▤ ☎ ♿ – 🏛 40. AE ⑤ ⊙ E VISA. ✂ OU m
**Meals** *(closed Sunday)* a la carte 65/85000 – **130 rm** ☐ 420/590000, 7 suites.

**Jolly Vittorio Veneto,** corso d'Italia 1 ✉ 00198 ☎ (06)8495, *Fax (06)8841104* – |‡|, ⊭ rm, ▤ TV ☎ ♿ – 🏛 400. AE ⑤ ⊙ E VISA. ✂ rest OU k
**Meals** *(closed Sunday dinner and August)* a la carte 85/130000 – **200 rm** ☐ 375/460000, 3 suites.

**Quirinale,** via Nazionale 7 ✉ 00184 ☎ (06)4707, *Fax (06)4820099*, « Summer service rest. in the garden » – |‡| ▤ TV ☎ ♿ – 🏛 250. AE ⑤ ⊙ E VISA JCB. ✂ PV h
**Meals** a la carte 60/110000 – **198 rm** ☐ 330/440000, 3 suites.

**Grand Hotel Palace,** via Veneto 70 ✉ 00187 ☎ (06)478719, *Fax (06)47871800* – ... 200. AE VISA. OU c
Meals a la carte 40/80000 – **91 rm** ☐ 470/580000, 4 suites.

**Artemide** M, via Nazionale 22 ✉ 00184 ☎ (06)489911, *Fax (06)48991700* – ... rm, ... 110. AE VISA JCB. OV b
Meals 45/80000 – **80 rm** ☐ 350/490000, 4 suites.

**Mecenate Palace Hotel,** via Carlo Alberto 3 ✉ 00185 ☎ (06)44702024, *Fax (06)4461354* – ... 30. AE VISA JCB. PX h
Meals *(closed Sunday)* a la carte 60/100000 – **59 rm** ☐ 380/500000, 3 suites.

**Starhotel Metropole,** via Principe Amedeo 3 ✉ 00185 ☎ (06)4774, *Fax (06)4740413* – ... 200. AE VISA JCB. rest PV p
Meals 65/95000 – **265 rm** ☐ 385/480000.

**Londra e Cargill,** piazza Sallustio 18 ✉ 00187 ☎ (06)473871, *Fax (06)4746674* – ... 200. AE VISA JCB. PU q
Meals *(closed Saturday, Sunday lunch and August)* a la carte 55/85000 – **104 rm** ☐ 320/395000, 6 suites.

**Victoria,** via Campania 41 ✉ 00187 ☎ (06)473931, *Fax (06)4871890*, « Terrace roof-garden » – ... 30. AE VISA. rest OU v
Meals a la carte 45/70000 – **108 rm** ☐ 250/350000.

**Mediterraneo,** via Cavour 15 ✉ 00184 ☎ (06)4884051, *Fax (06)4744105* – ... 90. VISA JCB. PV n
Meals *(closed Saturday)* (dinner only) 40/50000 – **251 rm** ☐ 360/480000, 11 suites.

**Imperiale,** via Vittorio Veneto 24 ✉ 00187 ☎ (06)4826351, *Fax (06)4826351* – ... AE VISA. OV s
Meals 85000 – **95 rm** ☐ 440/620000.

**Genova** without rest., via Cavour 33 ✉ 00184 ☎ (06)476951, *Fax (06)4827580* – ... AE VISA JCB. PV r
**91 rm** ☐ 400/420000.

**Universo,** via Principe Amedeo 5 ✉ 00185 ☎ (06)476811, *Fax (06)4745125* – ... 300. AE VISA JCB PV p
Meals 55000 – **198 rm** ☐ 275/390000.

**Sofitel,** via Lombardia 47 ✉ 00187 ☎ (06)478021 and rest. ☎ (06)4818965, *Fax (06)4821019* – ..., rm, ... 90. AE VISA JCB. NU s
Meals a la carte 55/85000 – **117 rm** ☐ 380/520000.

**La Residenza** without rest., via Emilia 22 ✉ 00187 ☎ (06)4880789, *Fax (06)485721* – ... AE VISA OU t
**28 rm** ☐ 140/295000.

**Massimo D'Azeglio,** via Cavour 18 ✉ 00184 ☎ (06)4870270, *Fax (06)4827386* – ... 200. VISA JCB. PV n
Meals *(closed Sunday)* 40/50000 – **200 rm** ☐ 330/440000.

**Eliseo** without rest., via di Porta Pinciana 30 ✉ 00187 ☎ (06)4870456, *Fax (06)4819629* – ... 25. AE VISA JCB. OU u
**51 rm** ☐ 250/400000, 7 suites.

**Britannia** without rest., via Napoli 64 ✉ 00184 ☎ (06)4883153, *Fax (06)4882343* – ... AE VISA JCB PV y
**32 rm** ☐ 250/350000.

**Napoleon,** piazza Vittorio Emanuele 105 ✉ 00185 ☎ (06)4467264, *Fax (06)4467282* – ... 80. AE VISA. by via Cavour PVX
Meals *(dinner only)* a la carte 40/60000 – **79 rm** ☐ 230/330000.

**Rex** without rest., via Torino 149 ✉ 00184 ☎ (06)4824828, *Fax (06)4882743* – ... 50. AE VISA JCB PV w
**44 rm** ☐ 285/370000, 2 suites.

**Barocco** without rest., via della Purificazione 4 angolo piazza Barberini ✉ 00187 ☎ (06)4872001, *Fax (06)485994* – ... AE VISA JCB. OV a
**28 rm** ☐ 320/420000.

**Commodore** without rest., via Torino 1 ✉ 00184 ☎ (06)485656, *Fax (06)4747562* – ... 30. AE VISA. PV e
**60 rm** ☐ 280/415000.

**Diana,** via Principe Amedeo 4 ✉ 00185 ☎ (06)4827541, *Fax (06)486998* – ... 25. AE VISA JCB. PV d
Meals 40000 – **183 rm** ☐ 220/310000, 2 suites.

**Turner** without rest., via Nomentana 29 ✉ 00161 ☎ (06)44250077, *Fax (06)44250165* – ... AE VISA JCB. PU x
**37 rm** ☐ 255/310000.

XXXX ✿ **La Terrazza** - Hotel Eden, via Ludovisi 49 ✉ 00187 ☎ (06)478121, *Fax (06)4821584*, « Roof-garden with ≤ town » – ▤. AE ⓢ ⓓ E VISA JCB. ✂ NU a
**Meals** a la carte 90/145000
**Spec.** Fiori di zucchina ripieni di taleggio, ricotta ed olive nere (autumn-winter). Penne piccanti con melanzane, pomodori di Pachino ed origano fresco (spring-summer). Filetto di rombo al forno con limone e capperi.

XXXX ✿ **Sans Souci,** via Sicilia 20/24 ✉ 00187 ☎ (06)4821814, *Fax (06)4821771*, Elegant rest., late night dinners – ▤. AE ⓢ ⓓ E VISA JCB. ✂ OU a
*closed Monday and 10 to 23 August* – **Meals** (dinner only) (booking essential) a la carte 95/150000
**Spec.** Terrina di foie gras con gelatina al Sauternes. Tortelli farciti di tartufo bianco e nero cremolati. Fricassea d'astice ed animelle.

XXX **Harry's Bar,** via Vittorio Veneto 150 ✉ 00187 ☎ (06)4742103, *Fax (06)4883117*, ☂ – ▤. AE ⓢ ⓓ E VISA JCB. ✂ OU b
*closed Sunday and 10 to 17 August* – **Meals** (booking essential) a la carte 70/115000.

XXX **Grappolo d'Oro,** via Palestro 4/10 ✉ 00185 ☎ (06)4941441, *Fax (06)4452350* – ▤. AE ⓢ ⓓ E VISA JCB PU c
*closed Sunday and August* – **Meals** 35/50000 (lunch) and a la carte 45/65000.

XX **Agata e Romeo,** via Carlo Alberto 45 ✉ 00185 ☎ (06)4466115, *Fax (06)4465842* – ▤. AE ⓢ ⓓ E VISA JCB. ✂ PX d
*closed Sunday, August and 6 to 12 January* – **Meals** (booking essential) a la carte 80/140000.

XX **Edoardo,** via Lucullo 2 ✉ 00187 ☎ (06)486428, *Fax (06)486428* – ▤. AE ⓢ ⓓ E VISA. ✂
*closed Sunday and August* – **Meals** a la carte 45/95000. OU h

XX **Giovanni,** via Marche 64 ✉ 00187 ☎ (06)4821834, *Fax (06)4817366*, Habitués rest. – ▤. AE ⓢ ⓓ E VISA OU a
*closed Friday dinner, Saturday and August* – **Meals** a la carte 55/90000.

XX **Cicilardone Monte Caruso,** via Farini 12 ✉ 00185 ☎ (06)483549 – AE ⓢ ⓓ E VISA. ✂ PV k
*closed Sunday, Monday lunch and August* – **Meals** a la carte 50/75000.

XX **Girarrosto Toscano,** via Campania 29 ✉ 00187 ☎ (06)4823835, *Fax (06)4821899* – ▤. AE ⓢ ⓓ E VISA JCB. ✂ OU n
*closed Wednesday* – **Meals** a la carte 70/100000.

XX **Dai Toscani,** via Forlì 41 ✉ 00161 ☎ (06)44231302 – ▤. AE ⓢ E VISA
*closed Sunday and August* – **Meals** Tuscan rest. a la carte 50/65000.
by via 20 Settembre PU

XX **Mangrovia,** via Milazzo 6/a ✉ 00185 ☎ (06)4452755, *Fax (06)4959204* – ▤. AE ⓢ ⓓ VISA JCB. ✂ by via Volturno PV
**Meals** seafood a la carte 60/80000.

XX **Tullio,** via San Nicola da Tolentino 26 ✉ 00187 ☎ (06)4745560, *Fax (06)4818564*, Tuscan trattoria with spit – ▤. AE ⓢ ⓓ E VISA JCB. ✂ OV f
*closed Sunday and August* – **Meals** a la carte 55/85000.

XX **Papà Baccus,** via Toscana 36 ✉ 00187 ☎ (06)42742808, *Fax (06)42742808* – ▤. AE ⓢ ⓓ E VISA JCB. ✂ OU w
*closed Saturday lunch, Sunday, 10 to 20 August and 1 to 10 January* – **Meals** (booking essential) Tuscan and seafood specialities 60000 and a la carte 65/90000.

XX **Hostaria da Vincenzo,** via Castelfidardo 6 ✉ 00185 ☎ (06)484596, *Fax (06)4870092* – ▤. AE ⓢ ⓓ E VISA JCB PU e
*closed Sunday and August* – **Meals** a la carte 45/75000.

XX **Peppone,** via Emilia 60 ✉ 00187 ☎ (06)483976, *Fax (06)483976*, Traditional rest. – AE ⓢ E VISA. ✂ OU r
*closed Saturday in August and Sunday* – **Meals** a la carte 45/75000 (15 %).

X **Il Dito e la Luna,** via dei Sabelli 51 ✉ 00185 ☎ (06)4940726, « Pleasant bistro atmosphere » – ✂ by via Labicana PZ
*closed Sunday and August* – **Meals** (dinner only) (booking essential) a la carte 40/50000.

X **Trimani il Wine Bar,** via Cernaia 37/b ✉ 00185 ☎ (06)4469630, *Fax (06)4468351*, Wine bar serving quick meals – ▤. AE ⓢ ⓓ E VISA JCB PU m
*closed Sunday and 10 to 23 August* – **Meals** a la carte 45/65000.

**Ancient Rome** Colosseo, Fori Imperiali, Aventino, Terme di Caracalla, Porta San Paolo, Monte Testaccio :

🏨 **Forum,** via Tor de' Conti 25 ✉ 00184 ☎ (06)6792446, *Fax (06)6786479*, « Roof-garden rest. with ≤ Imperial Forum » – |♦| ▤ TV ☎ 🚗 – 🏛 100. AE ⓢ ⓓ E VISA JCB. ✂ OY a
**Meals** *(closed Sunday)* a la carte 80/130000 – **81 rm** ☐ 320/465000.

**Borromeo** without rest., via Cavour 117 ✉ 00184 ☎ (06)485856, *Fax (06)4882541* – . PX z
**28 rm** 225/290000, suite.

**Piccadilly** without rest., via Magna Grecia 122 ✉ 00183 ☎ (06)77207017, *Fax (06)70476686* – VISA. by via Gallia PZ
**55 rm** 170/240000.

**Duca d'Alba** without rest., via Leonina 12/14 ✉ 00184 ☎ (06)484471, *Fax (06)4884840* – VISA JCB OY c
15000 – **24 rm** 160/200000.

**Domus Aventina** without rest., via Santa Prisca 11/b ✉ 00153 ☎ (06)5746135, *Fax (06)57300044* – VISA JCB. NZ k
**26 rm** 200/300000.

**Nerva** without rest., via Tor de' Conti 3/4/4 a ✉ 00184 ☎ (06)6781835, *Fax (06)69922204* – VISA NY h
**19 rm** 220/325000.

**Checchino dal 1887,** via Monte Testaccio 30 ✉ 00153 ☎ (06)5746318, *Fax (06)5743816*, Historical building – VISA.
*closed August, 24 December-3 January, Sunday dinner and Monday, also Sunday lunch June-September* – **Meals** (booking essential) Roman rest. a la carte 60/100000 by lungotevere Aventino MZ
**Spec.** Rigatoni con la pajata. Abbacchio alla cacciatora. Garofolato di bue (stracotto ai chiodi di garofano).

**Charly's Sauciere,** via di San Giovanni in Laterano 270 ✉ 00184 ☎ (06)70495666, *Fax (06)70494700* – . VISA JCB PZ e
*closed 5 to 20 August, Sunday and lunch Saturday-Monday* – **Meals** (booking essential) French-Swiss rest. a la carte 60/80000.

**Mario's Hostaria,** piazza del Grillo 9 ✉ 00184 ☎ (06)6793725, – . VISA. NY b
*closed Saturday lunch and Sunday* – **Meals** (booking essential) a la carte 50/80000.

**St. Peter's Basilica (Vatican City)** Gianicolo, Monte Mario, Stadio Olimpico :

**Cavalieri Hilton** M, via Cadlolo 101 ✉ 00136 ☎ (06)35091, *Fax (06)35092241*, ≤ city, , « Terraces-solarium and park with », – – 2100. VISA JCB. rest by via Trionfale GU
**Meals** a la carte 80/130000 see also rest. ***La Pergola*** – 39000 – **359 rm** 545/695000, 17 suites.

**Jolly Leonardo da Vinci,** via dei Gracchi 324 ✉ 00192 ☎ (06)32499, *Fax (06)3610138* – , rm, – 220. VISA JCB. rest
**Meals** 65000 – **256 rm** 360/410000, 2 suites. KU a

**Visconti Palace** without rest., via Federico Cesi 37 ✉ 00193 ☎ (06)3684, *Fax (06)3200551* – – 150. VISA JCB. KU b
**234 rm** 310/400000, 13 suites.

**Dei Mellini** M without rest., via Muzio Clementi 81 ✉ 00193 ☎ (06)324771, *Fax (06)32477801* – – 70. VISA. KU f
**67 rm** 370/410000, 13 suites

**Atlante Star,** via Vitelleschi 34 ✉ 00193 ☎ (06)6873233, *Fax (06)6872300* – – 50. VISA JCB JV c
**Meals** (see rest. ***Les Etoiles*** below) – **61 rm** 390/580000, 3 suites.

**Farnese** without rest., via Alessandro Farnese 30 ✉ 00192 ☎ (06)3212553, *Fax (06)3215129* – . VISA. KU e
**22 rm** 270/380000.

**Giulio Cesare** without rest., via degli Scipioni 287 ✉ 00192 ☎ (06)3210751, *Fax (06)3211736*, – – 40. VISA JCB. KU d
**90 rm** 310/410000.

**Sant'Anna** without rest., borgo Pio 133 ✉ 00193 ☎ (06)68801602, *Fax (06)68308717* – . VISA JCB HV m
**20 rm** 210/270000.

**Clodio** without rest., via di Santa Lucia 10 ✉ 00195 ☎ (06)3721122, *Fax (06)37350745* – – 60. VISA JCB. by via Trionfale GU
**114 rm** 200/290000.

**La Pergola** - Hotel Cavalieri Hilton, via Cadlolo 101 ✉ 00136 ☎ (06)35091, ≤ town, Elegant rest., « Summer service on terrace » – VISA JCB.
*closed Sunday, Monday and January* – **Meals** (dinner only) 120/175000 and a la carte 160/180000 by via Trionfale GU
**Spec.** Panachè di pesce all'olio di basilico. Lasagnetta ai gamberi e radicchio rosso. Filetto di San Pietro in crosta di zucchine e patate.

**Les Etoiles** - Hotel Atlante Star, via dei Bastioni 1 ✉ 00193 ☎ (06)6893434, « Roof-garden and summer service on terrace with ≤ St. Peter's Basilica » – ▤. AE Ⓢ ⓞ E VISA JCB. ❊ JV c
**Meals** 75/125000 (lunch) 95/180000 (dinner) and a la carte 115/165000.

**Il Simposio-di Costantini,** piazza Cavour 16 ✉ 00193 ☎ (06)3211502, *Fax (06)3213210*, Wine bar and rest. – ▤. AE Ⓢ ⓞ E VISA KU c
*closed Saturday lunch, Sunday and 10 to 25 August* – **Meals** (booking essential) a la carte 45/70000.

**Da Enzo,** via Ennio Quirino Visconti 39/41 ✉ 00193 ☎ (06)3215743 – ▤. AE Ⓢ ⓞ E VISA JCB. ❊ KU m
*closed Sunday and August* – **Meals** a la carte 50/80000.

Dal Toscano-al Girarrosto, via Germanico 58 ✉ 00192 ☎ (06)39725717, Habitués rest. – ▤ HU n
**Meals** Tuscan specialities.

**Taverna Angelica,** piazza delle Vaschette 14/a ✉ 00193 ☎ (06)6874514, After theatre restaurant, open until late – ▤. AE Ⓢ E VISA. ❊ JV t
*closed Sunday, Monday lunch, 10 to 30 August and 23 December-3 January* – **Meals** (booking essential) a la carte 55/85000.

**Parioli** via Flaminia, Villa Borghese, Villa Glori, via Nomentana, via Salaria :

**Lord Byron** ⛱, via De Notaris 5 ✉ 00197 ☎ (06)3220404, *Fax (06)3220405* – ⬍ ▤ TV ☎. AE Ⓢ ⓞ E VISA JCB. ❊ by lungotevere A. da Brescia KU
**Meals** (see rest. ***Relais le Jardin*** below) – **28 rm** ☕ 500/620000, 9 suites.

**Aldrovandi Palace Hotel,** via Aldrovandi 15 ✉ 00197 ☎ (06)3223993, *Fax (06)3221435*, « Small shaded park with ⛲ », Fб – ⬍ ⇔ ▤ TV ☎ Ⓟ – 🏛 350. AE Ⓢ ⓞ E VISA JCB. ❊ by via Flaminia LU
**Meals** (see rest. ***Relais La Piscine*** below) – **125 rm** ☕ 600/650000, 10 suites.

**Parco dei Principi,** via Gerolamo Frescobaldi 5 ✉ 00198 ☎ (06)854421, *Fax (06)8845104*, ≤, ⛱, « Small botanical park with ⛲ » – ⬍ ▤ TV ☎ 🚗 – 🏛 1000. AE Ⓢ ⓞ E VISA JCB. ❊ by via Pinciana OU
**Meals** 80/95000 – **165 rm** ☕ 450/650000, 15 suites.

Albani, via Adda 45 ✉ 00198 ☎ (06)84991, *Fax (06)8499399* – ⬍ ▤ TV ☎ 🚗 – 🏛 80
**155 rm.** by via Salaria PU

**Polo** without rest., piazza Gastaldi 4 ✉ 00197 ☎ (06)3221041, *Fax (06)3221359* – ⬍ ▤ TV ☎ – 🏛 70. AE Ⓢ ⓞ E VISA by lungotevere A. da Brescia KU
**66 rm** ☕ 350/405000.

**Borromini** without rest., via Lisbona 7 ✉ 00198 ☎ (06)8841321, *Fax (06)8417550* – ⬍ ▤ TV ☎ 🚗 – 🏛 100 by via Pinciana OU
☕ 22000 – **75 rm** 325/360000.

**Degli Aranci,** via Oriani 11 ✉ 00197 ☎ (06)8070202, *Fax (06)8070704* – ⬍ ▤ TV ☎ – 🏛 40. AE Ⓢ ⓞ E VISA. ❊ by lungotevere A. da Brescia KU
**Meals** 35000 – **54 rm** ☕ 250/360000.

**Villa Glori** without rest., via Celentano 11 ✉ 00196 ☎ (06)3227658, *Fax (06)3219495* – ⬍ ▤ TV ☎. AE Ⓢ ⓞ E VISA JCB. ❊ by lungotevere in Augusta KLU
**38 rm** ☕ 240/320000.

**Villa Florence** without rest., via Nomentana 28 ✉ 00161 ☎ (06)4403036, *Fax (06)4402709*, « In a late 19C Patrician villa with a collection of Roman marble remains » – ⬍ ▤ TV ☎ Ⓟ. AE Ⓢ ⓞ E VISA. ❊ by via 20 Settembre PU
**33 rm** ☕ 220/270000.

**Relais le Jardin** - Hotel Lord Byron, via De Notaris 5 ✉ 00197 ☎ (06)3220404, *Fax (06)3220405*, Elegant rest. – ▤. AE Ⓢ ⓞ E VISA JCB. ❊
*closed Sunday and August* – **Meals** (booking essential) a la carte 85/155000
**Spec.** Parmigiana di verdure in crosta con salsa al basilico. Medaglioni di pescatrice arrostiti al forno con patate e carciofi alla mentuccia (winter-spring). Semifreddo di formaggi magri e pistacchio con salsa al miele. by lungotevere A. da Brescia KU

**Relais la Piscine** - Hotel Aldrovandi Palace, via Mangili 6 ✉ 00197 ☎ (06)3216126, « Outdoor summer service » – ⇔ ▤ Ⓟ. AE Ⓢ ⓞ E VISA JCB. ❊
**Meals** 60/90000 (lunch) 80/110000 (dinner) and a la carte 85/115000.
by lungotevere A. da Brescia KU

**Al Ceppo,** via Panama 2 ✉ 00198 ☎ (06)8551379, *Fax (06)85301370* – AE Ⓢ ⓞ E VISA by via Salaria PU
*closed Monday and 8 to 30 August* – **Meals** (booking essential for dinner) a la carte 55/75000.

**Coriolano,** via Ancona 14 ✉ 00198 ☎ (06)44249863, Elegant trattoria – ▤. AE Ⓢ ⓞ E VISA PU d
*closed 5 to 30 August* – **Meals** (booking essential) a la carte 65/100000 (15 %).

XX **Il Caminetto,** viale dei Parioli 89 ✉ 00197 ✆ (06)8083946, 🏠 – ▤. AE ⑤ ⓓ E VISA. ✻ by lungotevere A. da Brescia KU
**Meals** a la carte 50/70000.

XX **La Scala,** viale dei Parioli 79/d ✉ 00197 ✆ (06)8083978, 🏠 – ▤. AE ⑤ ⓓ E VISA. ✻ by lungotevere A. da Brescia KU
*closed Wednesday and 6 to 21 August* – **Meals** a la carte 40/60000.

XX **Al Fogher,** via Tevere 13/b ✉ 00198 ✆ (06)8417032, Rustic rest. – ▤. AE ⑤ ⓓ E VISA JCB. ✻ PU b
*closed Saturday lunch, Sunday and August* – **Meals** Venetian specialities a la carte 60/70000.

XX **Al Chianti,** via Ancona 17 ✉ 00198 ✆ (06)44291534, Tuscan trattoria with taverna – ▤. AE ⑤ ⓓ E VISA PU d
*closed Sunday and 6 to 22 August* – **Meals** (booking essential) 40000 and a la carte 40/60000.

X **Al Bersagliere-da Raffone,** via Ancona 43 ✉ 00198 ✆ (06)44249846, Traditional rustic rest. – ▤. AE ⑤ ⓓ E VISA PU d
*closed Saturday and 5 to 20 August* – **Meals** a la carte 40/65000.

**Trastevere area** (typical district) :

XXX **Alberto Ciarla,** piazza San Cosimato 40 ✉ 00153 ✆ (06)5818668, *Fax (06)5884377*, 🏠 – ▤. AE ⑤ ⓓ VISA JCB. ✻ KZ k
*closed Sunday* – **Meals** (dinner only) (booking essential) seafood 75/110000.

XX **Corsetti-il Galeone,** piazza San Cosimato 27 ✉ 00153 ✆ (06)5816311, *Fax (06)5896255*, 🏠, « Typical atmosphere » – ▤. AE ⑤ ⓓ E VISA JCB KZ m
**Meals** Roman and seafood rest. a la carte 50/80000.

XX **Sora Lella,** via di Ponte Quattro Capi 16 (Isola Tiberina) ✉ 00186 ✆ (06)6861601, *Fax (06)6861601* – ▤. AE ⑤ ⓓ E VISA. ✻ MY g
*closed Sunday and August* – **Meals** Traditional Roman rest. a la carte 60/85000.

XX **Galeassi,** piazza di Santa Maria in Trastevere 3 ✉ 00153 ✆ (06)5803775, 🏠 – AE ⑤ ⓓ E VISA. ✻ KZ q
*closed Monday and 20 December-20 January* – **Meals** Roman and seafood rest. a la carte 55/80000.

XX **Paris,** piazza San Callisto 7/a ✉ 00153 ✆ (06)5815378, 🏠 – ▤. AE ⑤ ⓓ E VISA. ✻ KZ r
*closed Sunday dinner, Monday and August* – **Meals** a la carte 60/95000.

XX **Checco er Carettiere,** via Benedetta 10 ✉ 00153 ✆ (06)5817018, 🏠 – ▤. AE ⑤ ⓓ E VISA JCB KY t
*closed Sunday dinner, Monday and 11 to 18 August* – **Meals** Roman and seafood rest. a la carte 60/80000.

XX **Pastarellaro,** via di San Crisogono 33 ✉ 00153 ✆ (06)5810871 – ▤. AE ⑤ ⓓ E VISA. ✻ LZ u
*closed Wednesday and August* – **Meals** Roman and seafood rest. a la carte 60/85000 (12 %).

XX **Taverna Trilussa,** via del Politeama 23 ✉ 00153 ✆ (06)5818918, *Fax (06)5811064*, 🏠 – ▤. AE ⑤ ⓓ VISA KY v
*closed Sunday dinner, Monday and 30 July-28 August* – **Meals** Typical Roman rest. a la carte 40/60000.

X **Gino in Trastevere,** via della Lungaretta 85 ✉ 00153 ✆ (06)5803403 – ▤. AE ⑤ ⓓ E VISA. ✻ LZ m
*closed Wednesday* – **Meals** (dinner only except holidays)Roman rest. and pizzeria a la carte 35/55000.

**North western area** via Flaminia, via Cassia, Balduina, Prima Valle, via Aurelia :

🏨 **Jolly Hotel Midas,** via Aurelia 800 (al km ; 8) ✉ 00165 ✆ (06)66396, *Fax (06)66418457*, ⛱, 🌳, 🎾 – |♦|, ⇹ rm, ▤ TV ☎ P – 🏛 650. AE ⑤ ⓓ E VISA. ✻ rest by via Aurelia GV
**Meals** a la carte 60/90000 – **340 rm** ☕ 225/270000, 5 suites.

🏨 **Forte Agip,** via Aurelia al km 8 ✉ 00165 ✆ (06)66411200, *Fax (06)66414437*, 🏠, ⛱, 🌳 – |♦|, ⇹ rm, ▤ TV ☎ P – 🏛 150. AE ⑤ ⓓ E VISA JCB. ✻
**Meals** a la carte 55/90000 – **213 rm** ☕ 230/320000. by via Aurelia GV

🏨 **Colony Flaminio** without rest., via Monterosi 18 ✉ 00191 ✆ (06)36301843, *Fax (06)36309495* – |♦| ▤ TV ☎ P – 🏛 90. AE ⑤ ⓓ E VISA JCB
**72 rm** ☕ 185/225000, suite. by via Po OPU

XX **L'Ortica,** via Flaminia Vecchia 573 ✉ 00191 ☎ (06)3338709, *Fax (06)3338709,* – AE ⓢ E VISA JCB by via Po OPU
*closed Sunday dinner* – **Meals** (dinner only) Napolitan rest. a la carte 60/95000.

XX **Da Benito,** via Flaminia Nuova 230/232 ✉ 00191 ☎ (06)36307851, *Fax (06)36306079* – ▤ P. AE ⓢ ◑ E VISA by via Po OPU
*closed Sunday and 10 to 31 August* – **Meals** a la carte 45/80000.

**North eastern area** via Salaria, via Nomentana, via Tiburtina :

**Eurogarden** without rest., raccordo anulare Salaria-Flaminia uscita n. 7 ✉ 00138 ☎ (06)8804507, *Fax (06)8804417,* – ▤ TV ☎ P. AE ⓢ ◑ E VISA. by via Salaria PU
**48 rm** 170/200000.

**Southern western area** via Aurelia Antica, E.U.R., Città Giardino, via della Magliana, Portuense :

**Sheraton** M, viale del Pattinaggio 100/102 ✉ 00144 ☎ (06)5453, *Fax (06)5940689,* – ▤ TV ☎ P – 1800. AE ⓢ ◑ E VISA JCB. by viale Aventino NZ
**Meals** a la carte 65/100000 – **600 rm** 450/545000, 22 suites.

**Sheraton Golf,** viale Parco de Medici 22 ✉ 00148 ☎ (06)658588, *Fax (06)65858742,* – rm, ▤ TV ☎ P – 500. AE ⓢ ◑ E VISA JCB.
**Meals** 75/90000 – **248 rm** 290/330000, 14 suites. by viale Trastevere KZ

**Villa Pamphili,** via della Nocetta 105 ✉ 00164 ☎ (06)5862, *Fax (06)66157747,* (covered in winter), – rm, ▤ TV ☎ P – 500. AE ⓢ ◑ E VISA. by via Garibaldi JZ
**Meals** a la carte 60/85000 – **238 rm** 340/405000, 10 suites.

**Holiday Inn St. Peter's,** via Aurelia Antica 415 ✉ 00165 ☎ (06)6642, *Fax (06)6637190,* – rm, ▤ TV ☎ P – 220. AE ⓢ ◑ E VISA JCB. by via Garibaldi JZ
**Meals** a la carte 50/80000 – 25000 – **321 rm** 335/455000.

**Holiday Inn-Parco dei Medici,** viale Castello della Magliana 65 ✉ 00148 ☎ (06)65581, *Fax (06)6557005,* – rm, ▤ TV ☎ P – 650. AE ⓢ ◑ E VISA JCB. by viale Trastevere KZ
**Meals** a la carte 70/90000 – **317 rm** 300/450000.

**Shangri Là-Corsetti,** viale Algeria 141 ✉ 00144 ☎ (06)5916441, *Fax (06)5413813,* heated, – ▤ TV ☎ P – 80. AE ⓢ ◑ E VISA. by viale Aventino NZ
**Meals** (see rest. ***Shangri Là-Corsetti*** below) – **52 rm** 285/350000, 11 suites.

XXX **Shangri-Là Corsetti,** viale Algeria 141 ✉ 00144 ☎ (06)5918861, – ▤ P. AE ⓢ ◑ E VISA JCB by viale Aventino NZ
*closed August* – **Meals** seafood a la carte 50/90000.

XX **Vecchia America-Corsetti,** piazza Marconi 32 ✉ 00144 ☎ (06)5926601, *Fax (06)5922284,* Typical rest. and ale house – AE ⓢ ◑ E VISA
**Meals** a la carte 45/80000. by viale Aventino NZ

XX **La Maielletta,** via Aurelia Antica 270 ✉ 00165 ☎ (06)39366595, *Fax (06)39366595* – P. AE ⓢ ◑ E VISA JCB. by via Cipro GU
*closed Monday* – **Meals** Abruzzi rest. a la carte 30/45000.

XX **Pietro al Forte,** via Del Capasso 56/64 ✉ 00164 ☎ (06)66158531, *Fax (06)66165101,* Rest. and pizzeria – AE ⓢ ◑ E VISA. by via Aurelia GV
*closed Monday* – **Meals** a la carte 35/60000.

## Outskirts of Rome

**on national road 6 - Casilina :**

**Myosotis,** località Torre Gaia, piazza Pupinia 2 ✉ 00133 ☎ (06)2054470, *Fax (06)2053671,* heated, – ▤ TV ☎ P – 35. AE ⓢ ◑ E VISA JCB by via Merulana PY
**Meals** (see rest. ***Villa Marsili*** below) – **18 rm** 150/180000.

**Città 2000** without rest., via della Tenuta di Torrenova 60/68 ✉ 00133 ☎ (06)2025540, *Fax (06)2025539* – ▤ TV ☎ P – 30. AE ⓢ ◑ E VISA JCB
**80 rm** 90/110000. by via Merulana PY

XX **Villa Marsili,** via Casilina 1604 ✉ 00133 ☎ (06)2050200, *Fax (06)2055176,* « Outdoor summer service » – ▤ P. AE ⓢ ◑ E VISA JCB by via Merulana PY
**Meals** a la carte 35/60000.

**at Ciampino** *SE : 15 km :*

XX **Da Giacobbe,** via Appia Nuova 1681 ✉ 00179 Ciampino ☎ (06)79340131, – ▤ P. AE ⓢ ◑ E VISA. by via Labicana PZ
*closed Sunday dinner, Monday and 10 to 30 August* – **Meals** (booking essential) a la carte 40/60000.

**Baschi** 05023 Terni 988 ㉕, 430 N 18 – pop. 2 703 alt. 165.
Roma 118 – Orvieto 10 – Terni 70 – Viterbo 46.

XXX ✿✿ **Vissani,** N : 12 ; km ✉ 05020 Civitella del Lago ✆ (0744)950396, Fax (0744)950396 – ⊭ ▤ P. AE S ◑ E VISA JCB. ✻
*closed Sunday dinner, Wednesday and Thursday lunch* – **Meals** (booking essential) 130/190000 (lunch) 160/190000 (dinner) and a la carte 145/265000
**Spec.** Aragosta alle bacche di senape e trippa di maiale. Cervo con salsa "parigina" e scalogni caramellati. Soufflè di torrone con salsa al cioccolato e miele.

---

**FLORENCE** (FIRENZE) *50100* P 988 ⑮, 429 430 K 15 *G. Tuscan – pop. 380 058 alt. 49.*
**See** : *Cathedral*** (Duomo)* Y : *east end***, dome*** (✻**), Campanile**** YB : *✻** Baptistry**** YC : *doors***, mosaics***, Cathedral Museum*** Y **M**[1] – *Piazza della Signoria*** Z – *Loggia della Signoria*** Z **D** : *Perseus*** by B. Cellini Palazzo Vecchio**** Z **H** – *Uffizi Gallery**** Z – *Bargello Palace and Museum**** Z – *San Lorenzo**** Y : *Church**, Laurentian Library**, Medici Tombs*** in Medicee Chapels** – Medici-Riccardi Palace*** Y : *Chapel***, Luca Giordano Gallery** – Church of Santa Maria Novella*** Y : *frescoes*** by Ghirlandaio – Ponte Vecchio*** Z – *Pitti Palace*** DV : *Palatine Gallery***, Silver Museum**, Works** by Macchiaioli in Modern Art Gallery* – Boboli Garden** DV : *✻** from the Citadel Belvedere Porcelain Museum** DV – *Monastery and Museum of St. Mark*** ET : *works*** by Beato Angelico – Academy Gallery*** ET : *Michelangelo gallery*** Piazza della Santissima Annunziata** ET **168** : *frescoes* in the church, portico** with corners decorated with terracotta Medallions** in the Foundling Hospital* – Church of Santa Croce*** EU : *Pazzi Chapel**, Excursion to the hills** : ✻*** from Michelangiolo Square* EFV, *Church of San Miniato al Monte*** EFV – *Strozzi Palace*** Z – *Rucellai Palace*** Z – *Santa Maria del Carmine*** DUV – *Last Supper of Foligno** DT – *Last Supper of San Salvi** BS **G** – *Orsanmichele** ZN : *tabernacle** by Orcagna – La Badia* Z : *campanile*, delicate relief sculpture in marble**, tombs*, Virgin appearing to St. Bernard* by Filippino Lippi – Sassetti Chapel** and the Chapel of the Annunciation* in the Holy Trinity Church* Z – *Church of the Holy Spirit** DUV – *Last Supper* of Sant'Apollonia* ET – *All Saints' Church* DU : *Last Supper* by Ghirlandaio, Davanzanti Palace** Z **M**[2] – *New Market Loggia** Z **K** – *Museums : Archaeological** (Chimera from Arezzo** Françoise Vase**)* ET – *Science** Z **M**[6] – *Marino Marini** Z **M**[7] – *Bardini** EV – *La Specola** DV – *Casa Buonarroti** EU **M**[3] – *Semi-precious Stone Workshop** ET **M**[4].
**Envir.** : *Medicee Villas* : villa della Petraia*, villa di Castello*, villa di Poggio a Caiano** by via P. Toselli* CT : *17 km Galluzzo Carthusian Monastery** by via Senese* CV.
18 *Dell'Ugolino (closed Monday), to Grassina ✉ 50015 ✆ (055)2301009, Fax (055)23011411, S : 12 km* BS.
✈ *Amerigo Vespucci NW : 4 km by via P. Toselli* CT *✆ (055)373498 – Alitalia, lungarno Acciaiuoli 10/12 r, ✉ 50123 ✆ (055)27889, Fax (055)2788.*
i *via Cavour 1 r ✉ 50129 ✆ (055)290832, Fax (055)2760383.*
**A.C.I.** *viale Amendola 36 ✉ 50121 ✆ (055)24861.*
*Roma 277 – Bologna 105 – Milano 298.*

Plans on following pages

**Excelsior,** piazza Ognissanti 3 ✉ 50123 ✆ (055)264201, *Fax (055)210278* – ♦ ▤ TV ☎ – 🏛 300. AE S ◑ E VISA JCB. ✻ rest DU b
**Meals** a la carte 105/150000 – ☐ 57500 – **146 rm** 690/825000, 7 suites.

**Grand Hotel,** piazza Ognissanti 1 ✉ 50123 ✆ (055)288781, *Fax (055)217400* – ♦ ▤ TV ☎ ♿ 🚗 – 🏛 220. AE S ◑ E VISA JCB. ✻ rest DU a
**Meals** a la carte 110/155000 – ☐ 33000 – **90 rm** 530/870000, 17 suites.

**Villa Medici,** via Il Prato 42 ✉ 50123 ✆ (055)2381331, *Fax (055)2381336*, ⛱, ⛲, 🌳 – ♦ ▤ TV ☎ – 🏛 90. AE S ◑ E VISA JCB. ✻ rest CT c
**Meals** a la carte 70/110000 – ☐ 33000 – **89 rm** 480/750000, 14 suites.

**Regency,** piazza Massimo D'Azeglio 3 ✉ 50121 ✆ (055)245247, *Fax (055)2346735*, 🌳 – ♦ ▤ TV ☎ 🚗. AE S ◑ E VISA JCB. ✻ rest FU a
**Meals** ***Relais le Jardin*** Rest. (*closed Sunday*) (booking essential) a la carte 70/110000 – **30 rm** ☐ 500/620000, 5 suites.

**Helvetia e Bristol,** via dei Pescioni 2 ✉ 50123 ✆ (055)287814, *Fax (055)288353* – ♦ ▤ TV ☎. AE S ◑ E VISA. ✻ Z b
**Meals** a la carte 65/110000 – ☐ 34500 – **34 rm** 400/595000, 15 suites.

**Albani,** via Fiume 12 ✉ 50123 ✆ (055)26030, *Fax (055)211045* – ♦ ▤ TV ☎ – 🏛 40. AE S ◑ E VISA JCB. ✻ DT a
**Meals** a la carte 60/90000 – **75 rm** ☐ 430/460000, 4 suites.

**Brunelleschi,** piazza Santa Elisabetta 3 ✉ 50122 ✆ (055)290311, *Fax (055)219653*, ≤, « Small private museum in a Byzantine tower » – ♦, ⊭ rm, ▤ TV ☎ – 🏛 100. AE S ◑ E VISA JCB. ✻ Z c
**Meals** (residents only) a la carte 70/100000 – **88 rm** ☐ 360/480000, 8 suites.

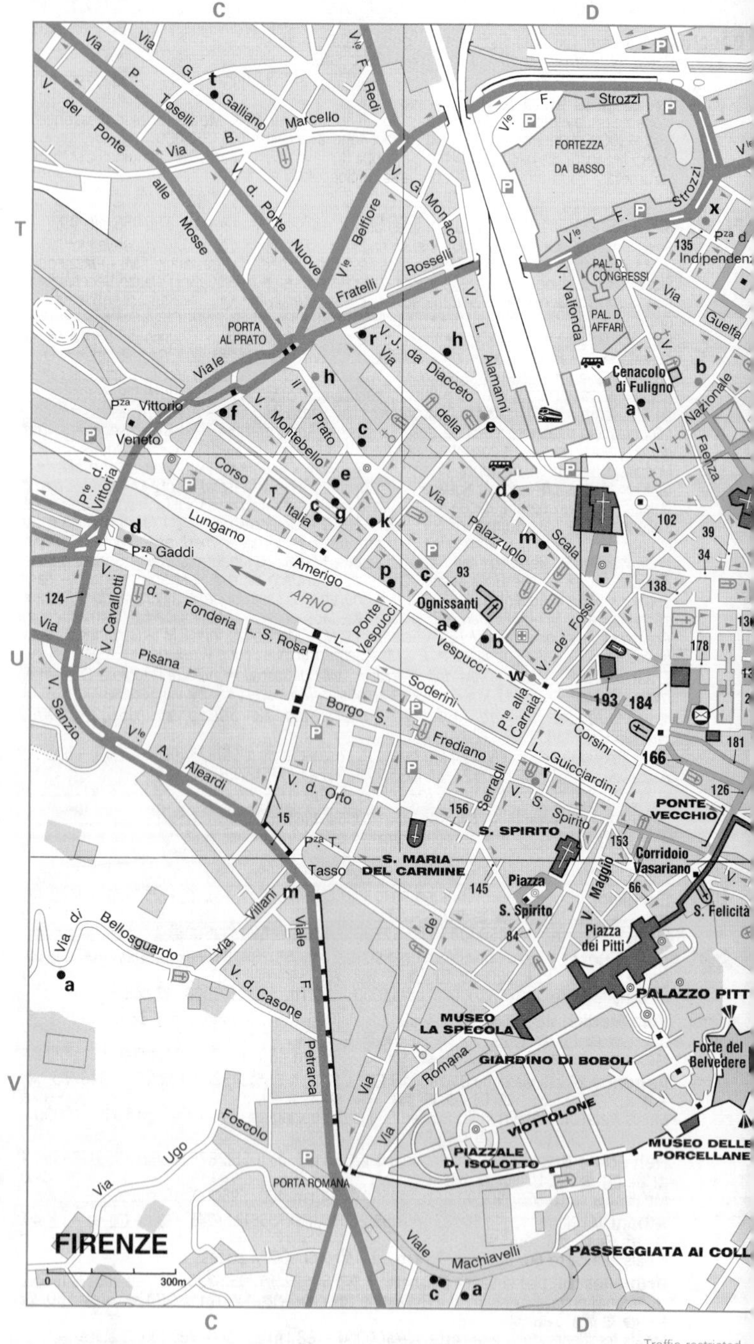
FIRENZE
FORTEZZA DA BASSO
PORTA AL PRATO
Cenacolo di Fuligno
Ognissanti
ARNO
PONTE VECCHIO
S. SPIRITO
S. MARIA DEL CARMINE
Corridoio Vasariano
Piazza S. Spirito
Piazza dei Pitti
PALAZZO PITT
MUSEO LA SPECOLA
GIARDINO DI BOBOLI
Forte del Belvedere
VIOTTOLONE
PIAZZALE D. ISOLOTTO
MUSEO DELLE PORCELLANE
PORTA ROMANA
PASSEGGIATA AI COLL
Traffic restricted

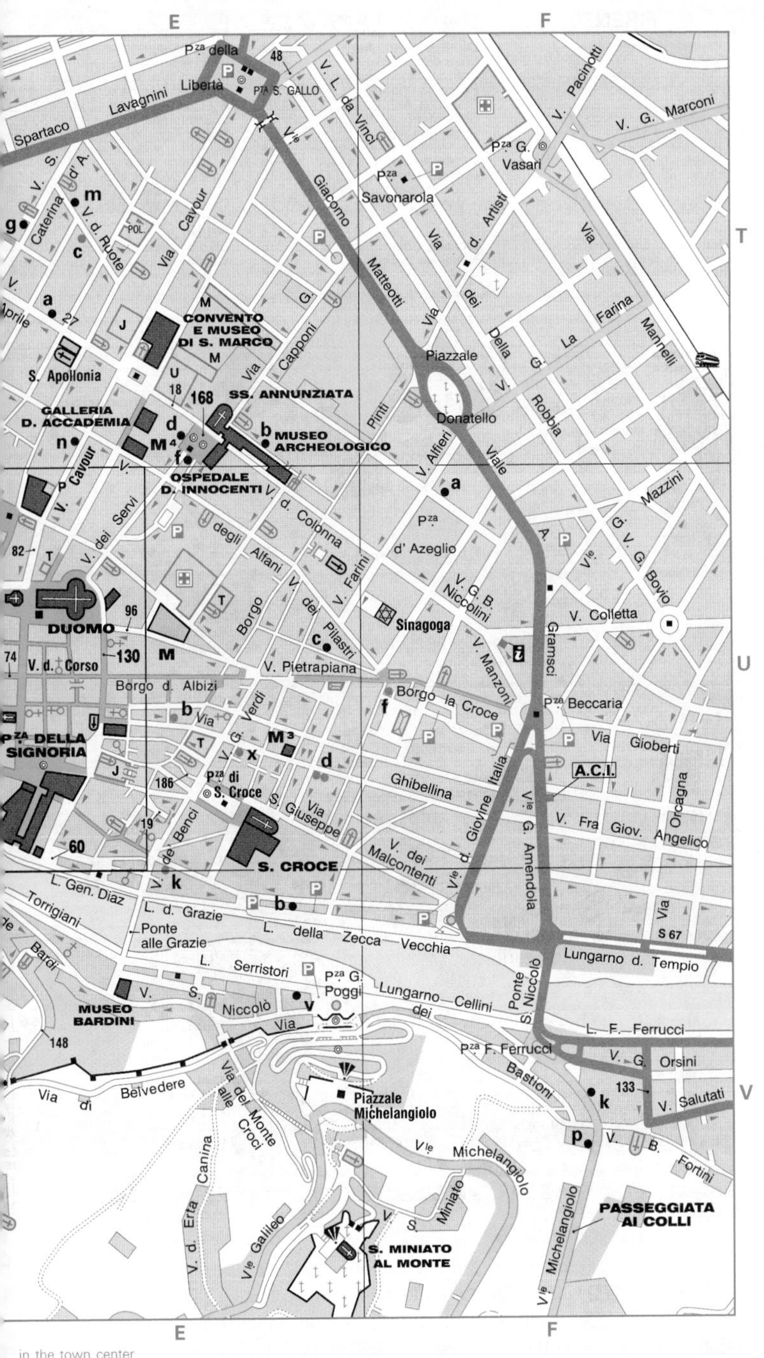


in the town center

# FIRENZE

Calimala . . . . . . . . . . . . . . Z 24
Calzaiuoli (Via dei) . . . . . . YZ
Por S. Maria (Via) . . . . . . Z 126
Porta Rossa (Via) . . . . . . . Z
Roma (Via) . . . . . . . . . . . . YZ
S. Jacopo (Borgo) . . . . . . Z
Strozzi (Via degli) . . . . . . . Z
Tornabuoni (Via) . . . . . . . Z
Vecchio (Ponte) . . . . . . . . Z

Agli (Via degli) . . . . . . . . . Y 3
Albizi (Vorgo degli) . . . . . Z 7
Antinori (Piazza degli) . . . Y 10
Archibusieri (Lungarno) . . Z 12
Avelli (Via degli) . . . . . . . . Y 16
Brunelleschi (Via de) . . . . YZ 22
Canto de' Nelli (Via del) . . T 27
Castellani (Via de') . . . . . . Z 31
Dante Alighieri (Via) . . . . . Z 42
Davanzati (Piazza) . . . . . . Z 43
Faenza (Via) . . . . . . . . . . . Y 51
Fiordalisa (Via del) . . . . . . Z 52
Fossi (Via de') . . . . . . . . . . Y 54
Ghibellina (Via) . . . . . . . . . Z 57
Gondi (Via dei) . . . . . . . . . Z 61
Guicciardini (Lungarno) . . Z 64
Lambertesca (Via) . . . . . . Z 69
Leoni (Via dei) . . . . . . . . . Z 70
Madonna degli Aldobrandini (Piazza di) . . . . . . . . . . . Y 75
Magazzini (Via dei) . . . . . Z 76
Melarancio (Via del) . . . . . Y 85
Monalda (Via) . . . . . . . . . Z 88
Nazionale (Via) . . . . . . . . . Y 90
Oriulo (Via d.) . . . . . . . . . . Y 96
Orsanmichele (Via) . . . . . Z 99
Parte Guelfa (Piazza di) . . . . . . . . . . Z 106
Pellicena (Via) . . . . . . . . . Z 109
Pescioni (Via de') . . . . . . YZ 111
Rondinelli (Via de') . . . . . Y 138
S. Giovanni (Piazza) . . . . Y 150
S. Spinto (Via) . . . . . . . . . Z 162
S. Trinità (Piazza) . . . . . . Z 163
Sassetti (Via de') . . . . . . . Z 171
Spada (Via della) . . . . . . . Z 173
Speziali (Via degli) . . . . . 174
Strozzi (Piazza) . . . . . . . . Z 177
Tavolini (Via dei) . . . . . . . 180
Terme (Via delle) . . . . . . . 181
Trebbio (Via del) . . . . . . . Y 187
Uffizi (Piazzale degli) . . . . 188
Vacchereccia (Via) . . . . . Z 189
Vigna Nuova (Via della) . Z 193

Traffic restricted in the town centre

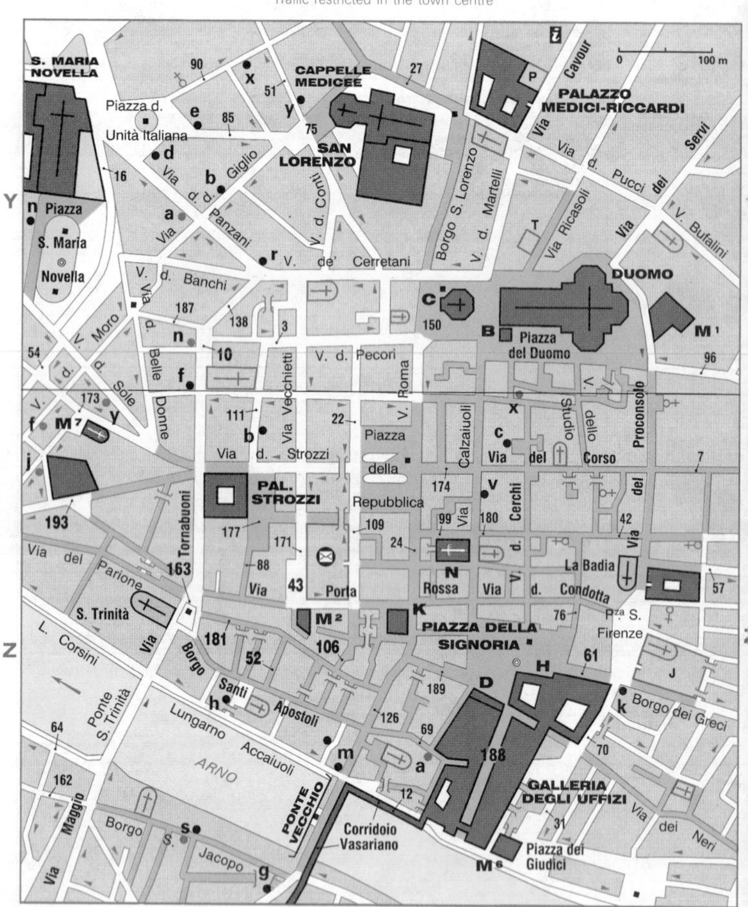


*For the quickest route use the* MICHELIN *Main Road Maps:*
970 Europe, 974 Poland, 976 Czech Republic-Slovak Republic, 980 Greece, 984 Germany, 985 Scandinavia-Finland, 986 Great Britain and Ireland, 987 Germany-Austria-Benelux, 988 Italy, 989 France *and* 990 Spain-Portugal.

## STREET INDEX TO FIRENZE TOWN PLAN

**Gd H. Minerva**, piazza Santa Maria Novella 16 ✉ 50123 ℰ (055)284555, *Fax (055)268281*, – – 90. – rest Y n
**Meals** 50/65000 – **93 rm** 350/480000, 6 suites.

**Astoria Palazzo Gaddi**, via del Giglio 9 ✉ 50123 ℰ (055)2398095, *Fax (055)214632* – – 130. Y b
**Meals** *(closed Sunday)* a la carte 50/65000 – **96 rm** 340/470000, 6 suites.

**Plaza Hotel Lucchesi**, lungarno della Zecca Vecchia 38 ✉ 50122 ℰ (055)26236, *Fax (055)2480921*, – rm, – 160. rest EV b
**Meals** *(closed Sunday)* (residents only) a la carte 70/100000 – **87 rm** 350/500000, 10 suites.

**Grand Hotel Baglioni**, piazza Unità Italiana 6 ✉ 50123 ℰ (055)23580, *Fax (055)2358895*, « Roof-garden rest. with town » – – 200. rest Y d
**Meals** a la carte 65/105000 – **190 rm** 320/430000, 5 suites.

**Sofitel**, via de' Cerretani 10 ✉ 50123 ℰ (055)2381301, *Fax (055)2381312* – rm, rest Y r
**Meals** a la carte 65/100000 – **84 rm** 450/490000.

**Majestic**, via del Melarancio 1 ✉ 50123 ℰ (055)264021, *Fax (055)268428* – – 80. rest Y e
**Meals** 50/55000 – **102 rm** 350/495000, suite.

**Continental** without rest., lungarno Acciaiuoli 2 ✉ 50123 ℰ (055)282392, *Fax (055)283139*, « Floral terrace with » – Z m
**47 rm** 325/450000, suite.

**Bernini Palace** without rest., piazza San Firenze 29 ✉ 50122 ℰ (055)288621, *Fax (055)268272* – – 40. Z k
**83 rm** 320/460000, 3 suites.

**Berchielli** without rest., piazza del Limbo 6 r ✉ 50123 ℰ (055)264061, *Fax (055)218636*, – – 100. Z h
**73 rm** 320/440000, 3 suites.

**Montebello Splendid**, via Montebello 60 ✉ 50123 ℰ (055)2398051, *Fax (055)211867*, – – 100. CU e
**Meals** *(closed Sunday)* a la carte 55/95000 – **53 rm** 340/500000, suite.

**Rivoli** without rest., via della Scala 33 ✉ 50123 ℰ (055)282853, *Fax (055)294041*, – – 100. DU m
**65 rm** 320/420000.

**De la Ville**, piazza Antinori 1 ✉ 50123 ℰ (055)2381805, *Fax (055)2381809* – – 60. rest Y f
**Meals** (residents only) a la carte 55/70000 – **71 rm** 360/490000, 4 suites.

**Augustus** without rest., piazzetta dell'Oro 5 ✉ 50123 ℰ (055)27263, *Fax (055)268557* – Z m
**53 rm** 340/420000, 8 suites.

**J and J** without rest., via di Mezzo 20 ✉ 50121 ℰ (055)2345005, *Fax (055)240282* – EU c
**14 rm** 500000, 5 suites.

**Lungarno** without rest., borgo Sant'Jacopo 14 ✉ 50125 ℰ (055)264211, *Fax (055)268437*, , « Collection of modern pictures » – – 30. Z s
30000 – **57 rm** 420/450000, 6 suites.

**Holiday Inn**, viale Europa 205 ✉ 50126 ℰ (055)6531841, *Fax (055)6531806*, , – , rm, – 120. rest BS e
**Meals** 40000 and ***La Tegolaia*** Rest. a la carte 40/65000 – 25000 – **92 rm** 310/335000.

**Londra**, via Jacopo da Diacceto 18 ✉ 50123 ℰ (055)2382791, *Fax (055)210682*, – – 200. rest DT h
**Meals** a la carte 60/95000 – **158 rm** 300/400000.

**Starhotel Michelangelo**, viale Fratelli Rosselli 2 ✉ 50123 ℰ (055)2784, *Fax (055)2382232* – – 250. rest CT f
**Meals** (residents only) 65/95000 – **137 rm** 330/480000.

**Executive** without rest., via Curtatone 5 ✉ 50123 ℰ (055)217451, *Fax (055)268346* – – 50. CU k
**38 rm** 310/420000.

**Kraft** without rest., via Solferino 2 ✉ 50123 ☎ (055)284273, *Fax (055)2398267*, « Roof garden rest. with ≤ », 🏊 – |≑| ▤ TV ☎ – 🏃 50. AE ⓘ ⓞ E VISA CU g
**77 rm** ☕ 310/460000.

**Principe** without rest., lungarno Vespucci 34 ✉ 50123 ☎ (055)284848, *Fax (055)283458*, ≤, 🌳 – |≑| ▤ TV ☎. AE ⓘ ⓞ E VISA JCB. ✗ CU p
**18 rm** ☕ 300/410000, 2 suites.

**Malaspina** without rest., piazza dell'Indipendenza 24 ✉ 50129 ☎ (055)489869, *Fax (055)474809* – |≑| ▤ TV ☎ ♿. AE ⓘ ⓞ E VISA. ✗ ET g
**31 rm** ☕ 185/280000.

**Il Guelfo Bianco** without rest., via Cavour 29 ✉ 50129 ☎ (055)288330, *Fax (055)295203* – |≑| ▤ TV ☎ ♿. AE ⓘ E VISA. ✗ ET n
**29 rm** ☕ 200/275000.

**Grifone** without rest., via Pilati 22 ✉ 50136 ☎ (055)661367, *Fax (055)677628* – |≑| ▤ TV ☎ P. AE ⓘ ⓞ E VISA
**50 rm** ☕ 170/240000, 9 suites.

**Palazzo Benci** without rest., piazza Madonna degli Aldobrandini 3 ✉ 50123 ☎ (055)2382821, *Fax (055)288308* – |≑| ▤ TV ☎ – 🏃 30. AE ⓘ ⓞ E VISA JCB. ✗ Y y
**35 rm** ☕ 180/270000.

**Royal** without rest., via delle Ruote 52 ✉ 50129 ☎ (055)483287, *Fax (055)490976*, « Garden » – |≑| ▤ TV ☎ P. AE ⓘ ⓞ E VISA ET m
**39 rm** ☕ 165/280000.

**Villa Azalee** without rest., viale Fratelli Rosselli 44 ✉ 50123 ☎ (055)214242, *Fax (055)268264*, 🌳 – ▤ TV ☎. AE ⓘ ⓞ E VISA CT r
**24 rm** ☕ 170/250000.

**Calzaiuoli** without rest., via Calzaiuoli 6 ✉ 50122 ☎ (055)212456, *Fax (055)268310* – |≑| ▤ TV ☎ ♿. AE ⓘ ⓞ E VISA ZV
**45 rm** ☕ 210/270000.

**Select** without rest., via Giuseppe Galliano 24 ✉ 50144 ☎ (055)330342, *Fax (055)351506* – |≑| ▤ TV ☎. AE ⓘ ⓞ E VISA JCB CT t
☕ 10000 – **36 rm** 150/250000.

**David** without rest., viale Michelangiolo 1 ✉ 50125 ☎ (055)6811695, *Fax (055)680602*, 🌳 – |≑| ▤ TV ☎ P. AE ⓘ ⓞ E VISA. ✗ FV k
**24 rm** ☕ 135/230000.

**Villa Liberty** without rest., viale Michelangiolo 40 ✉ 50125 ☎ (055)6810581, *Fax (055)6812595*, 🌳 – |≑| ▤ TV ☎ P. AE ⓘ ⓞ E VISA JCB FV p
**14 rm** ☕ 195/260000, 2 suites.

**Morandi alla Crocetta** without rest., via Laura 50 ✉ 50121 ☎ (055)2344747, *Fax (055)2480954* – ▤ TV ☎. AE ⓘ ⓞ E VISA ET b
☕ 18000 – **10 rm** 150/250000.

**Laurus** without rest., via de' Cerretani 8 ✉ 50123 ☎ (055)2381752, *Fax (055)268308* – |≑| ▤ TV ☎. AE ⓘ ⓞ E VISA. ✗ Y k
**59 rm** ☕ 250/350000.

**De Rose Palace Hotel** without rest., via Solferino 5 ✉ 50123 ☎ (055)2396818, *Fax (055)268249* – |≑| ▤ TV ☎. AE ⓘ ⓞ E VISA JCB CU c
**18 rm** ☕ 230/360000

**Pitti Palace** without rest., via Barbadori 2 ✉ 50125 ☎ (055)2398711, *Fax (055)2398867* – |≑| ▤ TV ☎. AE ⓘ ⓞ E VISA Z g
☕ 20000 – **72 rm** 190/270000.

**Loggiato dei Serviti** without rest., piazza SS. Annunziata 3 ✉ 50122 ☎ (055)289592, *Fax (055)289595*, « 16C building » – |≑| ▤ TV ☎. AE ⓘ ⓞ E VISA JCB ET d
**25 rm** ☕ 205/310000, 4 suites.

**City** without rest., via Sant'Antonino 18 ✉ 50123 ☎ (055)211543, *Fax (055)295451* – |≑| ▤ TV ☎. AE ⓘ ⓞ E VISA JCB Y x
**18 rm** ☕ 195/260000.

**Cellai** without rest., via 27 Aprile 14 ✉ 50129 ☎ (055)489291, *Fax (055)470387* – ▤ TV ☎. AE ⓘ ⓞ E VISA JCB ET a
**47 rm** ☕ 195/265000.

**Alba** without rest., via della Scala 22 ✉ 50123 ☎ (055)282610, *Fax (055)288358* – |≑| ▤ TV ☎. AE ⓘ ⓞ E VISA. ✗ DU d
**24 rm** ☕ 195/270000.

**Sanremo** without rest., lungarno Serristori 13 ✉ 50125 ☎ (055)2342823, *Fax (055)2342269* – |≑| ▤ TV ☎. AE ⓘ ⓞ E VISA EV v
*closed 15 January-15 February* – **20 rm** ☕ 160/220000.

XXXXX ✿✿ **Enoteca Pinchiorri,** via Ghibellina 87 ✉ 50122 ✆ (055)242777, *Fax (055)244983,* « Summer service in a cool courtyard » – ▤. AE ⓢ E VISA JCB EU x
*closed Sunday, Monday-Wednesday lunch, August and 18 to 27 December* – **Meals** (booking essential) 90000 (lunch) 160/180000 (dinner) and a la carte 90/240000
**Spec.** Petto di piccione al lardo di Colonnata con fagiolini e orzo perlato. "Gnudi" toscani (pasta) con fricassea d'astice e creste di gallo. Composizione di coniglio arrosto con sedano brasato e salsa al rosmarino.

XXXX **Sabatini,** via de' Panzani 9/a ✉ 50123 ✆ (055)211559, *Fax (055)210293,* Elegant traditional decor – ▤. AE ⓢ ⓞ E VISA JCB. ✂ Y a
*closed Monday* – **Meals** a la carte 75/125000 (13 %).

XXX **Don Chisciotte,** via Ridolfi 4 r ✉ 50129 ✆ (055)475430, *Fax (055)485305* – ▤. AE ⓢ ⓞ E VISA JCB DT x
*closed Sunday, Monday lunch and August* – **Meals** (booking essential) a la carte 65/105000 (10 %).

XXX **Taverna del Bronzino,** via delle Ruote 25/27 r ✉ 50129 ✆ (055)495220 – ▤. AE ⓢ ⓞ E VISA ET c
*closed Sunday and August* – **Meals** a la carte 65/90000.

XXX **Harry's Bar,** lungarno Vespucci 22 r ✉ 50123 ✆ (055)2396700, *Fax (055)2396700* – ▤. AE ⓢ E VISA DU w
*closed Sunday and 15 December-5 January* – **Meals** (booking essential) a la carte 60/95000 (16 %).

XX **Osteria n. 1,** via del Moro 20 r ✉ 50123 ✆ (055)284897, *Fax (055)294318* – ▤. AE ⓢ ⓞ E VISA JCB Z f
*closed Sunday, Monday lunch and 3 to 26 August* – **Meals** a la carte 70/105000.

XX **Dino,** via Ghibellina 51 r ✉ 50122 ✆ (055)241452, *Fax (055)241378* – ▤. AE ⓢ ⓞ E VISA EU d
*closed Sunday dinner and Monday* – **Meals** a la carte 50/70000.

XX **Le Fonticine,** via Nazionale 79 r ✉ 50123 ✆ (055)282106, « Collection of paintings » – AE ⓢ ⓞ E VISA JCB. ✂ DT b
*closed Monday, 22 July-22 August, Christmas and New Year* – **Meals** a la carte 50/85000.

XX **I 4 Amici,** via degli Orti Oricellari 29 ✉ 50123 ✆ (055)215413, *Fax (055)289767* – ▤. AE ⓢ ⓞ E VISA. ✂ DT e
**Meals** seafood a la carte 50/90000 (12 %).

XX **Cantinetta Antinori,** piazza Antinori 3 ✉ 50123 ✆ (055)292234, Rest. and wine bar – ▤. AE ⓢ ⓞ E VISA JCB. ✂ Y n
*closed Saturday, Sunday, August and Christmas* – **Meals** (booking essential for dinner) Tuscan rest. a la carte 70/85000.

XX **Acquerello,** via Ghibellina 156 r ✉ 50122 ✆ (055)2340554, *Fax (055)2340554* – ▤. AE ⓢ E VISA EU b
*closed Thursday* – **Meals** a la carte 40/60000.

XX **Mamma Gina,** borgo Sant'Jacopo 37 r ✉ 50125 ✆ (055)2396009, *Fax (055)213908* – ▤. AE ⓢ ⓞ E VISA JCB Z s
*closed Sunday and 7 to 21 August* – **Meals** a la carte 50/75000 (12 %).

XX **Ottorino,** via delle Oche 12/16 r ✉ 50122 ✆ (055)215151, *Fax (055)287140* – ▤. AE ⓢ ⓞ E VISA JCB YZ x
*closed Sunday* – **Meals** a la carte 50/85000.

X **Vineria Cibreo-Cibreino,** piazza Ghiberti 35 ✉ 50122 ✆ (055)2341100, *Fax (055)244966* – ▤. AE ⓢ ⓞ E VISA JCB FU f
*closed Sunday, Monday, 26 July-6 September and 31 December-6 January* – **Meals** a la carte 35/75000.

X **La Baraonda,** via Ghibellina 67 r ✉ 50122 ✆ (055)2341171, *Fax (055)2341171* – AE ⓞ EU d
*closed Sunday, Monday lunch and August* – **Meals** a la carte 40/70000 (10 %).

X **Il Cigno,** via Varlungo 3 r ✉ 50136 ✆ (055)691762, *Fax (055)691762,* ☂ – Ⓟ. ⓢ E VISA. ✂ by Lungarno del Tempio FU
*closed Monday and 10 to 20 August* – **Meals** a la carte 45/65000.

X **Il Profeta,** borgo Ognissanti 93 r ✉ 50123 ✆ (055)212265 – ▤. AE ⓢ ⓞ VISA DU c
*closed Sunday and 15 to 31 August* – **Meals** a la carte 40/65000 (12 %).

X **Baldini,** via il Prato 96 r ✉ 50123 ✆ (055)287663, *Fax (055)287663* – ▤. AE ⓢ ⓞ E VISA. ✂ CT h
*closed 1 to 20 August, 24 December-3 January, Saturday and Sunday dinner, June-July also Sunday lunch* – **Meals** a la carte 40/50000.

X **La Martinicca,** via del Sole 27 r ✉ 50123 ✆ (055)218928, *Fax (055)218928* – ▤. AE ⓢ ⓞ E VISA Z y
*closed Sunday and August* – **Meals** a la carte 45/70000.

**Cafaggi,** via Guelfa 35 r ✉ 50129 ℘ (055)294989 – ▤. AE ⓢ E VISA ET e
*closed Sunday and July or August* – **Meals** a la carte 40/90000.

**Trattoria Vittoria,** via della Fonderia 52 r ✉ 50142 ℘ (055)225657 – ▤. AE ⓢ ◐ E VISA JCB CU d
*closed Wednesday and August* – **Meals** seafood a la carte 40/85000.

**Antico Fattore,** via Lambertesca 1/3r ✉ 50122 ℘ (055)288975 – ▤. AE ⓢ ◐ E VISA Z a
*closed 15 July-15 August* – **Meals** a la carte 35/70000 (12 %).

**Angiolino,** via Santo Spirito 36 r ✉ 50125 ℘ (055)2398976, Typical trattoria – ▤. AE ⓢ ◐ E VISA. ✂ DU r
*closed Monday* – **Meals** a la carte 45/65000 (10 %).

**Il Latini,** via dei Palchetti 6 r ✉ 50123 ℘ (055)210916, Typical trattoria – AE ⓢ ◐ E VISA. ✂ Z j
*closed Monday, and 24 December-1 January* – **Meals** a la carte 40/60000.

**Del Fagioli,** corso Tintori 47 r ✉ 50122 ℘ (055)244285, Typical Tuscan trattoria – ✂
*closed Saturday, Sunday and August* – **Meals** a la carte 40/50000. EV k

**on the hills** *S : 3 km :*

**Gd H. Villa Cora** ⛭, viale Machiavelli 18 ✉ 50125 ℘ (055)2298451, *Fax (055)229086*, ⛱, « 19C house in floral park with ⛲ » – |⇕| ▤ TV ☎ P – 🧑‍🏫 150. AE ⓢ ◐ E VISA JCB
**Meals** ***Taverna Machiavelli*** Rest. a la carte 60/90000 – **38 rm** ☕ 440/820000, 10 suites 1320/1900000. DV c

**Torre di Bellosguardo** ⛭ without rest., via Roti Michelozzi 2 ✉ 50124 ℘ (055)2298145, *Fax (055)229008*, ✳ town and hills, « Park and terrace with ⛲ » – |⇕| ☎ P. AE ⓢ E VISA CV a
☕ 30000 – **10 rm** 340/450000, 6 suites 550/650000.

**Villa Belvedere** ⛭ without rest., via Benedetto Castelli 3 ✉ 50124 ℘ (055)222501, *Fax (055)223163*, ≤ town and hills, « Garden-park with ⛲ », ✂ – |⇕| ▤ TV ☎ ♿ P. AE ⓢ ◐ E VISA. ✂ by via Senese CV
*March-November* – **23 rm** ☕ 230/320000, 3 suites.

**Villa Carlotta** ⛭, via Michele di Lando 3 ✉ 50125 ℘ (055)2336134, *Fax (055)2336147*, ⛱ – |⇕| ▤ TV ☎ P. AE ⓢ ◐ E VISA JCB. ✂ rest DV a
**Meals** (residents only) a la carte 50/80000 – **32 rm** ☕ 270/390000.

**Classic** without rest., viale Machiavelli 25 ✉ 50125 ℘ (055)229351, *Fax (055)229353*, ⛱ – |⇕| TV ☎ P. AE ⓢ E VISA DV c
☕ 10000 – **16 rm** 130/190000, 3 suites.

**at Arcetri** *S : 5 km – ✉ 50125 Firenze :*

**Omero,** via Pian de' Giullari 11 r ℘ (055)220053, Country trattoria with ≤, « Summer service dinner on terrace » – AE ⓢ ◐ E VISA. ✂ by viale Machiavelli DV
*closed Tuesday and August* – **Meals** a la carte 45/65000 (13 %).

**at Galluzzo** *S : 6,5 km – ✉ 50124 Firenze :*

**Trattoria Bibe,** via delle Bagnese 15 ℘ (055)2049085, *Fax (055)2047167*, « Outdoor summer service » – P. AE ⓢ VISA AS c
*closed Wednesday, Thursday lunch, 15 to 28 February and 10 to 25 November* – **Meals** a la carte 40/55000.

**at Candeli** *E : 7 km – ✉ 50010 :*

**Villa La Massa** ⛭, via La Massa 24 ℘ (055)6510101, *Fax (055)6510109*, ≤, ⛱, « 17C house and furnishings », ⛲, ⛱, ✂ – |⇕| ▤ TV ☎ ♿ P – 🧑‍🏫 120. AE ⓢ ◐ E VISA. ✂ rest
**Meals** ***Il Verrocchio*** Rest. *(closed Monday)* a la carte 60/80000 – ☕ 37000 – **33 rm** 250/495000, 5 suites.

**at Serpiolle** *N : 8 km – ✉ 50141 Firenze :*

**Lo Strettoio,** via Serpiolle 7 ℘ (055)4250044, ≤, ⛱, « 17C villa among the olive trees » – ▤ P. AE ⓢ E VISA. ✂
*closed Sunday, Monday and August* – **Meals** (booking essential) a la carte 55/80000.

**on the motorway at ring-road A1-A11** *NW : 10 km :*

**Forte Agip,** ✉ 50013 Campi Bisenzio ℘ (055)4205081, *Fax (055)4219015* – |⇕|, ⇆ rm, ▤ TV ☎ ♿ P – 🧑‍🏫 200. AE ⓢ ◐ E VISA JCB. ✂
**Meals** a la carte 55/85000 – **163 rm** ☕ 205/245000.

**close to motorway station A1 Florence South** *SE : 6 km :*

**Sheraton Firenze Hotel,** ✉ 50126 ℘ (055)64901, *Fax (055)680747*, ⛲, ✂ – |⇕|, ⇆ rm, ▤ TV ☎ ♿ 🚗 P – 🧑‍🏫 1500. AE ⓢ ◐ E VISA JCB. ✂
**Meals** a la carte 55/85000 – **311 rm** ☕ 300/360000, 3 suites.

**San Casciano in Val di Pesa** *50026 Firenze* 988 ⑭ ⑮, 429, 430 L 15 *G. Toscana – pop. 16 130 alt. 306.*
*Roma 283 – Firenze 17 – Livorno 84 – Siena 53.*

**a Cerbaia** *NO : 6 km – ✉ 50020 :*

XXX ✿✿ **La Tenda Rossa,** piazza del Monumento 9/14 ✆ (055)826132, *Fax (055)825210* – ▤. AE ⓢ ⓓ E VISA JCB. ✂
*closed Wednesday, Thursday lunch and August* – **Meals** (booking essential) a la carte 90/140000
**Spec.** Fiore di zucchina croccante ripieno di mazzancolle con salsa di zafferano e cuore di carciofo (spring-autumn). Ravioli di crostacei in sfoglia al latte con passato di fagioli bianchi all'alloro. Petto di piccione al fegato grasso in cartoccio di spinaci e salsa al balsamico.

**San Vincenzo** *57027 Livorno* 988 ⑭, 430 M 13 *G. Toscana – pop. 7 042 – High Season : 15 June-15 September.*
ℹ *via Beatrice Alliata 2 ✆ (0565)701533, Fax (0565)701533.*
*Roma 260 – Firenze 146 – Grosseto 73 – Livorno 60 – Piombino 21 – Siena 109.*

XXX ✿✿ **Gambero Rosso,** piazza della Vittoria 13 ✆ (0565)701021, *Fax (0565)704542*, ≤ – AE ⓢ ⓓ E VISA. ✂
*closed Tuesday and 28 October-10 December* – **Meals** (booking essential) 100/120000 (10 %) and a la carte 80/130000 (10 %)
**Spec.** Passatina di ceci con crostacei. Ravioli di cozze con carote alle spezie. Piccione al rosmarino.

---

**MILAN** *20100* Ⓟ 988 ③, 428 F 9 *G. Italy – pop. 1 303 925 alt. 122.*
**See** : *Cathedral★★★ (Duomo)* MZ – *Cathedral Museum★★* MZ **M¹** – *Via and Piazza Mercanti★* MZ **155** – *La Scala Opera House★★* MZ – *Manzoni House★* MZ **M⁷** – *Brera Art Gallery★★★* KV – *Castle of the Sforzas★★★* JV – *Ambrosian Library★★* MZ : *portraits★★★ of Gaffurio and Isabella d'Este, Raphael's cartoons★★★* – *Poldi-Pezzoli Museum★★* KV **M²** : *portrait of a woman★★★ (in profile) by Pollaiolo* – *Palazzo Bagatti Valsecchi★★* KV **L** – *Natural History Museum★* LV **M⁶** – *Leonardo da Vinci Museum of Science and Technology★* HX **M⁴** – *Church of St. Mary of Grace★* HX : *Leonardo da Vinci's Last Supper★★★* – *Basilica of St. Ambrose★★* HJX : *altar front★★* – *Church of St. Eustorgius★* JY : *Portinari Chapel★★* – *General Hospital★* KXY – *Church of St. Satiro★ : dome★* MZ – *Church of St. Maurice★★* JX – *Church of St. Lawrence Major★* JY.
**Envir.** : *Chiaravalle Abbey★ SE : 7 km by corso Lodi* LY.
⛳18, ⛳9 *(closed Monday) at Monza Park ✉ 20052 Monza ✆ (039) 303081, Fax (039)304427, by N : 20 km;*
⛳18 *Molinetto (closed Monday) at Cernusco sul Naviglio ✉ 20063 ✆ (02)92105128, Fax (02)92106635, by NE : 14 km;*
⛳18 *Barlassina (closed Monday) at Birago di Camnago ✉ 20030 ✆ (0362) 560621, Fax (0362)560934, by N : 26 km;*
⛳18 *(closed Monday) at Zoate di Tribiano ✉ 20067 ✆ (02)90632183, Fax (02)90631861, SE : 20 km;*
⛳18 *Le Rovedine (closed Monday) at Noverasco di Opera ✉ 20090 ✆ (02)57606420, Fax (02)57606405, by via Ripamonti* BP.
**Motor-Racing circuit** *at Monza Park by N : 20 km, ✆ (039) 22366.*
✈ *Forlanini of Linate E : 8 km ✆ (02)74852200 and Malpensa by NW : 45 km ✆ (02)74852200 – Alitalia, corso Como 15 ✉ 20154 ✆ (02)62818, Fax (02)62811 and via Albricci 5 ✉ 20122 ✆ (02)62817, Fax (02)8056249.*
🚗 *✆ (02)675001.*
ℹ *via Marconi 1 ✉ 20123 ✆ (02)72524300, Fax (02)72022999 – Central Station ✉ 20124 ✆ (02)6690532.*
**A.C.I.** *corso Venezia 43 ✉ 20121 ✆ (02)77451.*
*Roma 572 – Genève 323 – Genova 142 – Torino 140.*

Plans on following pages

**Historical centre** Duomo, Scala, Sforza Castle, corso Magenta, via Torino, corso Vittorio Emanuele, via Manzoni :

**Four Seasons,** via Gesù 8 ✉ 20121 ✆ (02)77088, *Fax (02)77085000*, ⛹, 🌳 – ⇅ ⊁ ▤ ▭ ☎ ♿ 🚗 – 🏛 280. AE ⓢ ⓓ E VISA JCB. ✂ rest KV a
**Meals** ***Il Teatro*** Rest. *(closed lunch, Sunday and August)* a la carte 80/125000 and ***La Veranda*** Rest. a la carte 75/115000 – ☕ 40000 – **82 rm** 870/1095000, 16 suites.

**Grand Hotel et de Milan,** via Manzoni 29 ✉ 20121 ✆ (02)723141, *Fax (02)86460861* – ⇅ ▤ ▭ ☎ ♿ – 🏛 100. AE ⓢ ⓓ E VISA JCB. ✂ rest KV g
**Meals** ***Caruso*** Rest. *(closed dinner except Sunday)* 65/85000 (lunch) 105/130000 (dinner) and a la carte 85/135000 see also rest ***Don Carlos*** below – ☕ 32000 – **87 rm** 650/770000, 8 suites.

**Jolly Hotel President,** largo Augusto 10 ✉ 20122 ℘ (02)77461, *Fax (02)783449* – |\$|, ⇎ rm, ▤ TV ☎ – 🔹 100. AE ⓢ ⓓ E VISA JCB. ⛔ rest NZ q
Meals a la carte 70/115000 – **206 rm** ☐ 460/540000, 13 suites.

**Brunelleschi** M, via Baracchini 12 ✉ 20123 ℘ (02)8843, *Fax (02)804924* – |\$| ▤ TV ☎ ♿ – 🔹 50. AE ⓢ ⓓ E VISA JCB. ⛔ MZ z
Meals a la carte 60/90000 – **123 rm** ☐ 350/450000, 5 suites.

**Pierre Milano,** via Edmondo De Amicis 32 ✉ 20123 ℘ (02)72000581, *Fax (02)8052157* – |\$| ▤ TV ☎. AE ⓢ ⓓ E VISA JCB JY b
*closed August* – Meals a la carte 60/80000 – **45 rm** ☐ 350/550000, 4 suites.

**Radisson SAS Bonaparte Hotel,** via Cusani 13 ✉ 20121 ℘ (02)8560, *Fax (02)8693601* – |\$| ▤ TV ☎ 🚗 – 🔹 25. AE ⓢ ⓓ E VISA JCB. ⛔ rest JV a
Meals 50/60000 – **55 rm** ☐ 360/460000, 10 suites.

**Carlton Hotel Baglioni,** via Senato 5 ✉ 20121 ℘ (02)77077, *Fax (02)783300* – |\$|, ⇎ rm, ▤ TV ☎ ♿ 🚗. AE ⓢ ⓓ E VISA. ⛔ KV b
Meals a la carte 70/110000 – ☐ 39000 – **61 rm** 475/600000, 2 suites.

**Sir Edward** without rest., via Mazzini 4 ✉ 20123 ℘ (02)877877, *Fax (02)877844*, ≘s – |\$| ▤ TV ☎ ♿. AE ⓢ ⓓ E VISA JCB. ⛔ MZ h
**38 rm** ☐ 305/410000, suite.

**Spadari al Duomo** M without rest., via Spadari 11 ✉ 20123 ℘ (02)72002371, *Fax (02)861184*, « Collection of modern art » – |\$| ▤ TV ☎. AE ⓢ ⓓ E VISA. ⛔ MZ f
**38 rm** ☐ 340/420000.

**Grand Hotel Duomo,** via San Raffaele 1 ✉ 20121 ℘ (02)8833, *Fax (02)86462027*, ≤ Duomo, 🍽 – |\$| ▤ TV ☎ – 🔹 100. AE ⓢ ⓓ E VISA JCB. ⛔ MZ u
Meals 70/90000 – **132 rm** ☐ 450/625000, 16 suites.

**Galileo,** corso Europa 9 ✉ 20122 ℘ (02)7743, *Fax (02)76020584* – |\$| ▤ TV ☎. AE ⓢ ⓓ E VISA JCB. ⛔ NZ x
a la carte 60/90000 – **81 rm** ☐ 330/450000, 8 suites.

**Regina** without rest., via Cesare Correnti 13 ✉ 20123 ℘ (02)58106913, *Fax (02)58107033*, « 18C building » – ▤ TV ☎ ♿ – 🔹 40. AE ⓢ ⓓ E VISA JY a
*closed August and 24 December-2 January* – **43 rm** ☐ 280/360000.

**Dei Cavalieri,** piazza Missori 1 ✉ 20123 ℘ (02)88571, *Fax (02)72021683* – |\$| ▤ TV ☎ – 🔹 60. AE ⓢ ⓓ E VISA JCB. ⛔ rest MZ m
Meals 60000 – **171 rm** ☐ 280/340000, 7 suites.

**Starhotel Rosa,** via Pattari 5 ✉ 20122 ℘ (02)8831, *Fax (02)8057964* – |\$| ▤ TV ☎ – 🔹 120. AE ⓢ ⓓ E VISA JCB. ⛔ NZ v
Meals 65/95000 – **185 rm** ☐ 420/570000.

**De la Ville** M, via Hoepli 6 ✉ 20121 ℘ (02)867651, *Fax (02)866609* – |\$| ▤ TV ☎ – 🔹 60. AE ⓢ ⓓ E VISA JCB. ⛔ rest NZ h
Meals see rest. ***Canova*** below – **99 rm** ☐ 385/510000, 3 suites.

**Ascot** without rest., via Lentasio 3/5 ✉ 20122 ℘ (02)58303300, *Fax (02)58303203* – |\$| ▤ TV ☎ 🚗. AE ⓢ ⓓ E VISA KY c
*closed August and Christmas* – **63 rm** ☐ 230/320000.

**Cavour,** via Fatebenefratelli 21 ✉ 20121 ℘ (02)6572051, *Fax (02)6592263* – |\$| ▤ TV ☎ – 🔹 100. AE ⓢ ⓓ E VISA JCB KV x
*closed 11 to 24 August, Christmas and New Year* – **Meals *Conte Camillo*** Rest. *(closed Sunday)* 30/50000 (lunch) 50/80000 (lunch) and a la carte 50/90000 – ☐ 25000 – **111 rm** 240/300000.

**Carrobbio** without rest., via Medici 3 ✉ 20123 ℘ (02)89010740, *Fax (02)8053334* – |\$| ▤ TV ☎. AE ⓢ ⓓ E VISA JCB JX d
*closed August and 22 December-6 January* – **35 rm** ☐ 220/310000.

**Manzoni** without rest., via Santo Spirito 20 ✉ 20121 ℘ (02)76005700, *Fax (02)784212* – |\$| TV ☎ 🚗. AE ⓢ ⓓ E VISA. ⛔ KV s
☐ 20000 – **49 rm** 180/235000, 3 suites.

**Lloyd** without rest., corso di Porta Romana 48 ✉ 20122 ℘ (02)58303332, *Fax (02)58303365* – |\$| ▤ TV ☎ – 🔹 100. AE ⓢ ⓓ E VISA KY c
**56 rm** ☐ 280/380000.

**Ambrosiano** without rest., via Santa Sofia 9 ✉ 20122 ℘ (02)58306044, *Fax (02)58305067*, 🏋 – |\$| ▤ TV ☎ – 🔹 35. AE ⓢ ⓓ E VISA. ⛔ KY f
*closed 23 December-7 January* – **78 rm** ☐ 175/255000.

**Zurigo** without rest., corso Italia 11/a ✉ 20122 ℘ (02)72022260, *Fax (02)72000013* – |\$| ▤ TV ☎. AE ⓢ ⓓ E VISA JCB. ⛔ KY j
*closed 24 December-7 January* – ☐ 8000 – **41 rm** 185/270000.

**Casa Svizzera** without rest., via San Raffaele 3 ✉ 20121 ℘ (02)8692246, *Fax (02)72004690* – |\$| ▤ TV ☎. AE ⓢ ⓓ E VISA MZ u
*closed 28 July-24 August* – **45 rm** ☐ 220/280000.

# MILANO

| | | |
|---|---|---|
| Aurispa (V.) | JY | 14 |
| Battisti (V. C.) | KLX | 20 |
| Bocchetto (V.) | JX | 30 |
| Borgogna (V.) | KX | 36 |
| Borgonuovo (V.) | KV | 38 |
| Calatafimi (V.) | JY | 45 |
| Caradosso (V.) | HX | 49 |
| Ceresio (V.) | JU | 59 |
| Circo (V.) | JX | 63 |
| Col di Lana (Via) | JY | 65 |
| Col Moschin (V.) | JY | 66 |
| Conça del Naviglio (V.) | JY | 69 |
| Copernico (V.) | LT | 72 |
| Cordusio (Pza) | KX | 73 |
| Cune (Vie P.M.) | HV | 77 |
| Dugnani (V.) | HY | 80 |
| Fatebenefratelli (V.) | KV | 92 |
| Gangliano (V.) | KT | 98 |
| Generale Fara (V.) | KT | 100 |
| Ghislen (V. A.) | HY | 101 |
| Giardini (V. dei) | KV | 102 |

Within the green shaded area, the city is divided into zones wich are signposted all the way round. Once entered, it is not possible to drive from one zone into another.

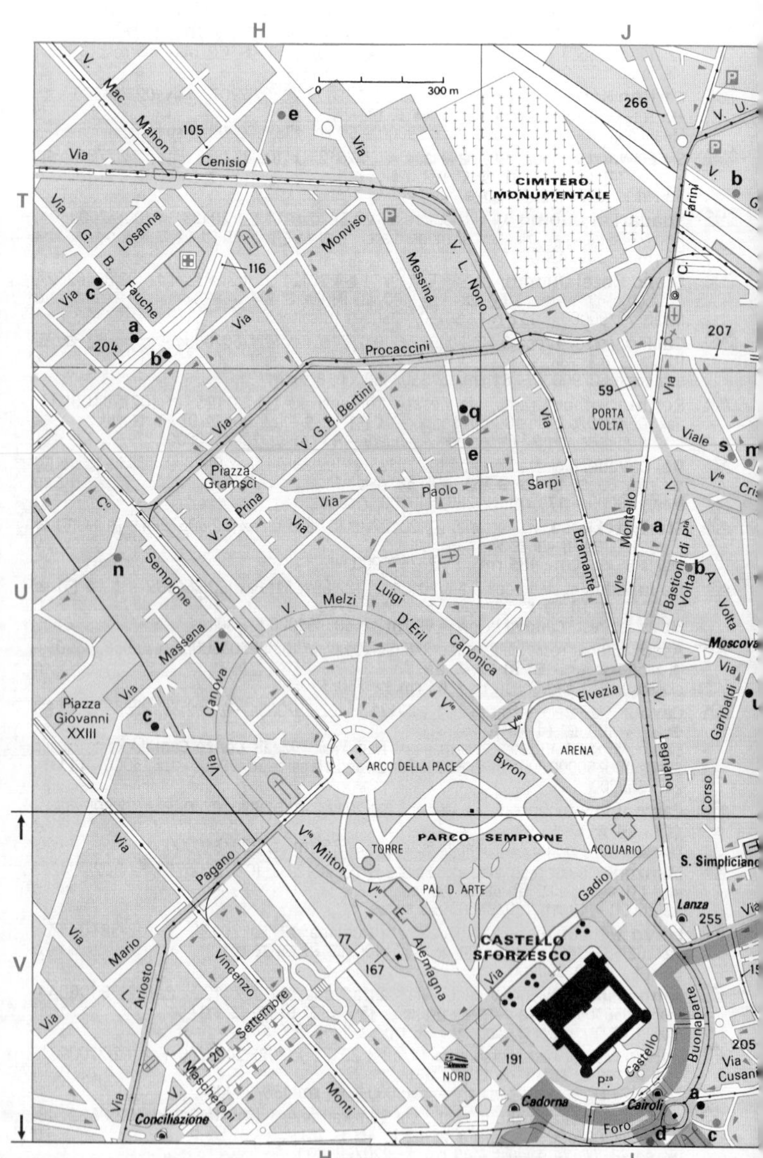

| Street | Grid | No. |
|---|---|---|
| Gran S. Bernardo (V.) | HT | 105 |
| Guastalla (V.) | KX | 110 |
| Induno (V. Fratelli) | HT | 116 |
| Lambertenghi (V.P.) | KT | 122 |
| Lepetit (V.) | LTU | 128 |
| Maffei (V. A.) | LY | 135 |
| Melzö (V.) | LU | 152 |
| Mercato (V.) | JV | 158 |
| Modestino (V.) | HY | 165 |
| Molière (Vie E.) | HV | 167 |
| Muraton (V.L.) | LY | 180 |
| Oggiono (V. M. d') | HJY | 183 |
| Orseolo (V.) | HY | 189 |
| Paleocapa (V.) | JV | 191 |
| Pastrengo (V.) | KT | 195 |
| Perasto (V.) | KT | 198 |
| Poliziano (V.) | HTU | 204 |
| Ponte Vetero (V.) | JY | 205 |
| Quadrio (V.M.) | JT | 207 |
| Restelli (Vie F.) | KT | 214 |
| Ruffini (V. Fratelli) | HX | 225 |
| S. Babila (Pza) | KX | 228 |
| S. Calimero (V.) | KY | 230 |
| Savoia (Vie F. di) | KU | 243 |
| Tivoli (V.) | HV | 255 |
| Torchio (V.) | JX | 257 |
| Tornani (V.N.) | LU | 258 |
| Trau (V.) | KT | 260 |
| Valtellina (V.) | JT | 266 |
| Vercelli (Cso) | HX | 267 |
| Verdi (V.) | KV | 269 |
| Vittono Veneto (Vie) | KLU | 278 |
| Zezon (V.) | LU | 281 |

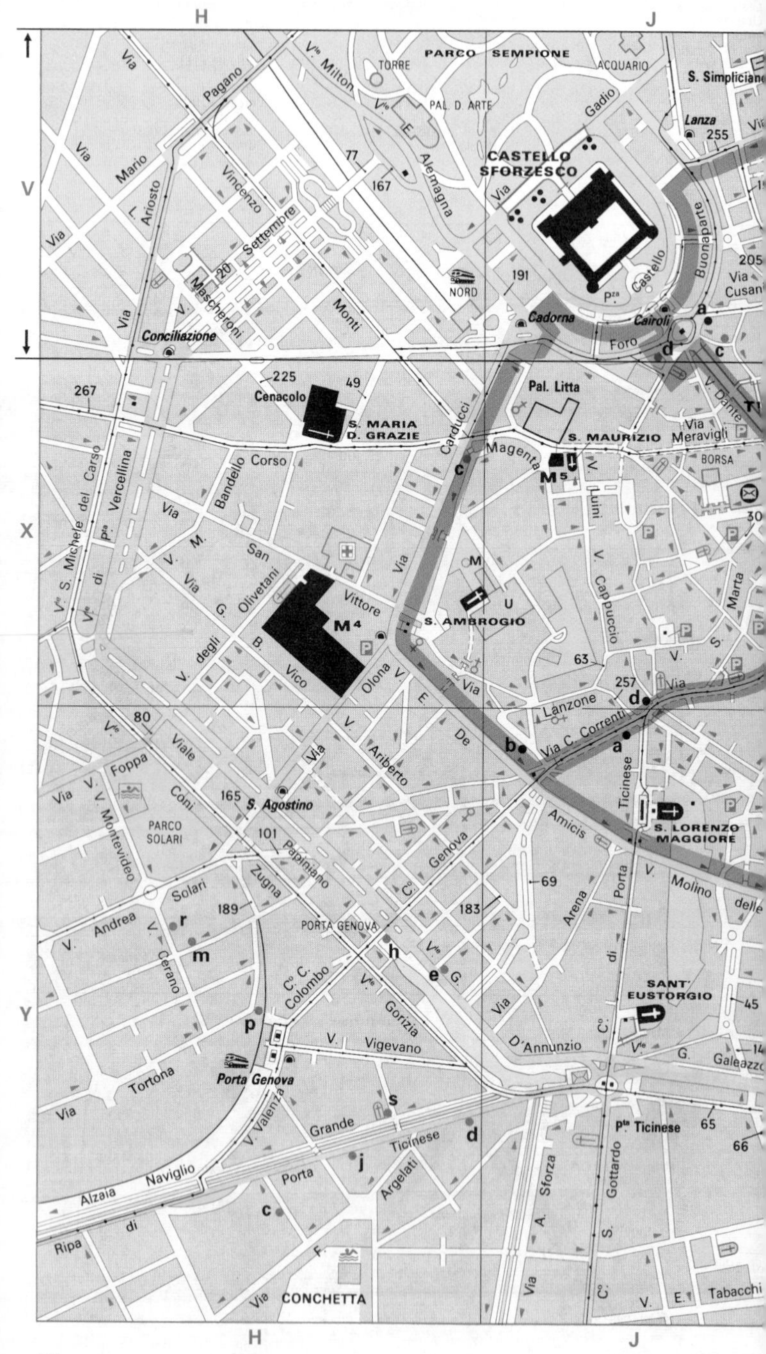
H
J
V
X
Y
PARCO SEMPIONE
TORRE
ACQUARIO
PAL. D. ARTE
CASTELLO SFORZESCO
S. Simpliciano
Lanza
Cadorna
Cairoli
NORD
Conciliazione
Cenacolo
S. MARIA D. GRAZIE
Pal. Litta
S. MAURIZIO
BORSA
S. AMBROGIO
M⁴
M⁵
S. Agostino
PARCO SOLARI
PORTA GENOVA
S. LORENZO MAGGIORE
SANT' EUSTORGIO
Porta Genova
Pᵗᵉ Ticinese
CONCHETTA
Via Vincenzo Monti
Via Carducci
Corso Magenta
Via San Vittore
Via Olona
Via C. Correnti
Corso di Porta Ticinese
Viale Papiniano
Corso Genova
Via D'Annunzio
Alzaia Naviglio Grande
Ripa di Porta Ticinese
Corso S. Gottardo
Via Tortona
Via Solari
Corso C. Colombo
Viale Gorizia
V. Vigevano
Via Foppa
Via Montevideo
Viale di Pᵗᵃ Vercellina
V. Lanzone
Via Arena
V. Molino delle
Tabacchi

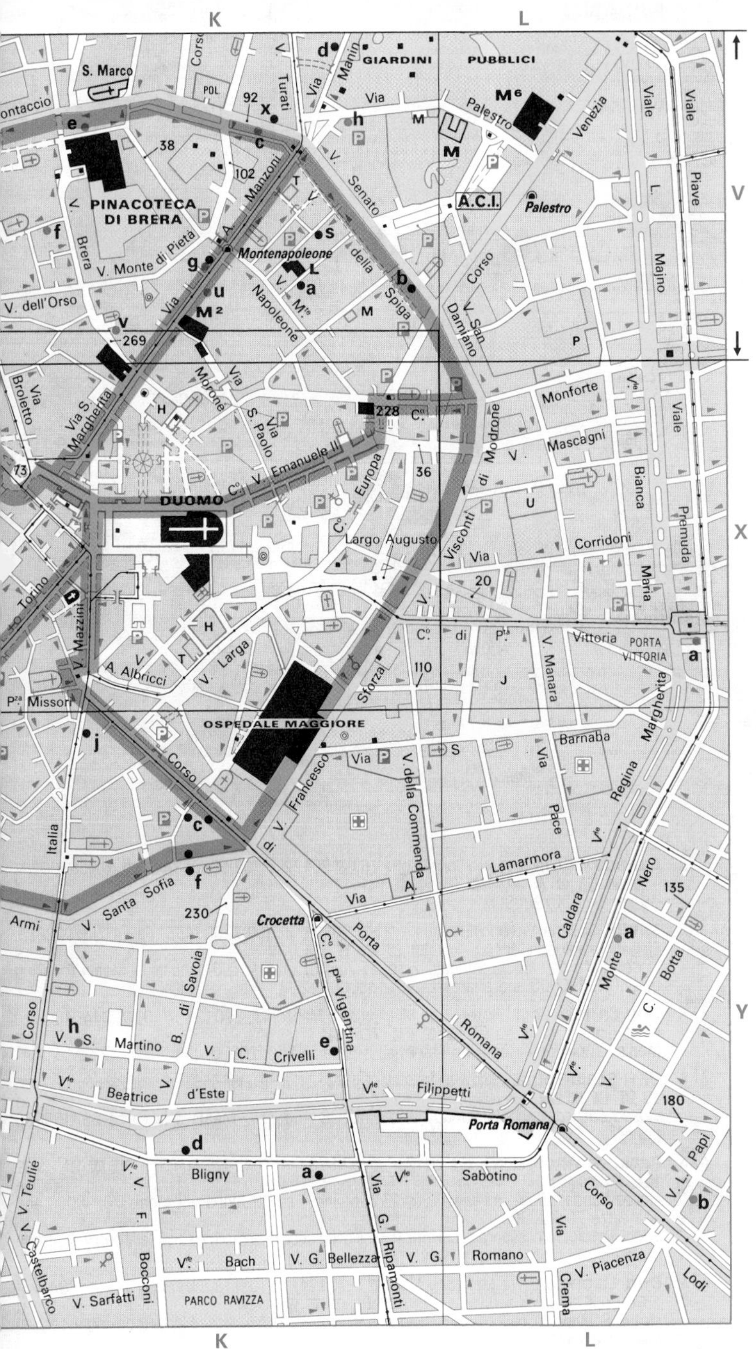

# MILANO

| Street | Grid | No. |
|---|---|---|
| Albricci (V.A.) | MZ | 3 |
| Arcivescovado (V.) | MNZ | 10 |
| Augusto (Largo) | NZ | 12 |
| Baracchini (V.) | MZ | 17 |
| Bergamini (V.) | NZ | 27 |
| Borgogna (V.) | NZ | 36 |
| Cantu (V.C.) | MZ | 48 |
| Cordusio (Pza) | MZ | 73 |
| Edison (Pza) | MZ | 83 |
| Festa del Perdono (V.) | NZ | 93 |
| Gonzaga (V.) | MZ | 104 |
| Laghetto (V.) | NZ | 120 |
| Manzoni (V.A.) | MZ | 140 |
| Marçoni (V.) | MZ | 144 |
| Manno (Pza) | MZ | 147 |
| Mengoni (V.) | MZ | 153 |
| Mercanti (Pza) | MZ | 155 |
| Mercanti (V.) | MZ | 156 |
| Misson (Pza) | MZ | 162 |
| Monforte (Cso) | NZ | 168 |
| Monte Napoleone (V.) | NZ | 171 |
| Morone (V.) | MNZ | 176 |
| Orefici (V.) | MZ | 188 |
| Pattan (V.) | NZ | 197 |
| S. Clemente (NZ) | NZ | 231 |
| S. Radegonda (V.) | MZ | 237 |
| S. Stefano (Pza) | NZ | 240 |
| Sforza (V.F.) | NZ | 248 |
| Unione (V.) | MZ | 264 |
| Verdi (V.) | MZ | 269 |
| Verziere (V.) | NZ | 270 |
| Visconti di Modrone (V.) | NZ | 275 |

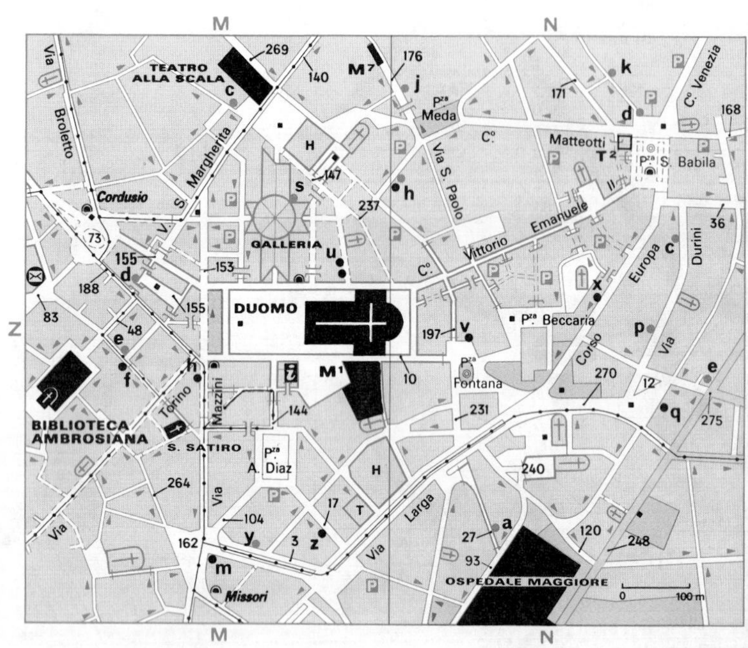


**Canada** without rest., via Santa Sofia 16 ✉ 20122 ℘ (02)58304844, *Fax (02)58300282* – |‡| ≡ TV ☎ ♿ 🚗. AE 🄱 ⊕ E VISA — KY f
35 rm ☕ 190/280000.

**Savini,** galleria Vittorio Emanuele II ✉ 20121 ℘ (02)72003433, *Fax (02)72022888,* Elegant traditional decor – ≡. AE 🄱 ⊕ E VISA JCB — MZ s
*closed Saturday lunch, Sunday, 7 to 21 August and 1 to 6 January* – **Meals** (booking essential) 110000 and a la carte 90/135000 (12 %).

**Don Carlos** - Grand Hotel et de Milan, vicolo Manzoni ✉ 20121 ℘ (02)72314640, Late night dinners – ≡. AE 🄱 ⊕ E VISA JCB. ✻ — KV g
**Meals** (dinner only) (booking essential) a la carte 85/120000.

**Biffi Scala-Toulà,** piazza della Scala ✉ 20121 ℘ (02)866651, *Fax (02)866653* – ≡. AE 🄱 ⊕ E VISA. ✻ — MZ c
*closed Saturday lunch, Sunday and 2 to 28 August* – **Meals** a la carte 65/105000 (13 %).

**Peck,** via Victor Hugo 4 ✉ 20123 ℘ (02)876774, *Fax (02)860408* – ≡. AE 🄱 ⊕ E VISA JCB. ✻ — MZ e
✿ *closed Sunday, Bank Holidays, 2 to 23 July and 1 to 10 January* – **Meals** 70/90000 and a la carte 70/120000
**Spec.** Tavolozza di asparagi (spring). Ravioli di chiocciole di mare e sogliola al curry. Quenelle di salmone e trota al burro bianco.

**Don Lisander,** via Manzoni 12/a ✉ 20121 ℘ (02)76020130, *Fax (02)784573,* « Outdoor summer service » – ≡. AE 🄱 ⊕ E VISA JCB — KV u
*closed Sunday, 12 to 22 August and 24 December-10 January* – **Meals** (booking essential) a la carte 75/100000.

**Canova** - Hotel De la Ville, via Hoepli 6 ✉ 20121 ☎ (02)8051231, *Fax (02)860094* – ▤. AE ⑤ ⊙ E VISA JCB. ✻ NZ h
*closed Sunday* – **Meals** (booking essential) a la carte 55/90000

**Boeucc,** piazza Belgioioso 2 ✉ 20121 ☎ (02)76020224, *Fax (02)796173,* ☂ – ▤. AE. ✻ NZ j
*closed Saturday, Sunday lunch, August and 24 December-2 January* – **Meals** (booking essential) a la carte 70/95000.

**Suntory,** via Verdi 6 ✉ 20121 ☎ (02)8693022, *Fax (02)72023282* – ▤. AE ⑤ ⊙ E VISA. ✻ KV v
*closed Sunday, 9 to 16 August and Christmas* – **Meals** Japanese rest. 30/80000 (lunch) 80/120000 (dinner) and a la carte 100/120000.

**L'Ulmet,** via Disciplini ang. via Olmetto ✉ 20123 ☎ (02)86452718 – ▤. AE ⑤ E VISA JCB JY d
*closed Sunday, Monday, August and 25 December-7 January* – **Meals** (booking essential) a la carte 90/125000.

**Peppino,** via Durini 7 ✉ 20122 ☎ (02)781729, *Fax (02)76002511* – ▤. AE ⑤ ⊙ E VISA JCB NZ p
*closed Friday, Saturday lunch and 10 July-4 August* – **Meals** a la carte 55/90000.

**La Dolce Vita,** via Bergamini 11 ✉ 20122 ☎ (02)58303843 – ▤. AE ⑤ ⊙ E VISA
*closed Saturday lunch, Sunday and August* – **Meals** (booking essential for dinner) 20/30000 (lunch only) and a la carte 50/65000 (dinner only). NZ a

**La Bitta,** via del Carmine 3 ✉ 20121 ☎ (02)72003185, *Fax (02)72003185* – ▤. AE ⑤ ⊙ E VISA KV f
*closed Saturday lunch, Sunday and 6 to 31 January* – **Meals** seafood 30/40000 (lunch) 40/60000 (dinner) and a la carte 35/60000.

**4 Mori,** largo Maria Callas 1 (angolo Largo Cairoli) ✉ 20121 ☎ (02)878483, « Outdoor summer service » – AE ⑤ ⊙ E VISA JV d
*closed Saturday lunch and Sunday* – **Meals** a la carte 60/90000.

**Sogo-Brera,** via Fiori Oscuri 3 ✉ 20121 ☎ (02)86465367 – ▤. AE ⑤ ⊙ E VISA JCB. ✻ KV e
*closed Sunday and 2 to 27 August* – **Meals** Japanese rest. 20/50000 (lunch only) and a la carte 65/75000.

**Akasaka,** via Durini 23 ✉ 20122 ☎ (02)76023679 – ▤. AE ⑤ ⊙ E VISA JCB. ✻ NZ c
*closed Sunday and 10 to 19 August* – **Meals** Japanese rest. 20/65000 (10 %) lunch 80/150000 (10 %) dinner and a la carte 50/100000 (10 %).

**Al Mercante,** piazza Mercanti 17 ✉ 20123 ☎ (02)8052198, *Fax (02)86465250,* « Outdoor summer service » – ▤. AE ⑤ ⊙ E VISA MZ d
*closed Sunday and 3 to 28 August* – **Meals** a la carte 50/75000.

**Moon Fish,** via Bagutta 2 ✉ 20121 ☎ (02)76005780, ☂ – ▤. ⑤ NZ d
*closed Sunday and 7 to 28 August* – **Meals** seafood a la carte 65/115000.

**Albric,** via Albricci 3 ✉ 20122 ☎ (02)86461329, *Fax (02)86461329* – ▤. AE ⑤ ⊙ E VISA JCB. ✻ MZ y
*closed Saturday lunch, Sunday and 1 to 22 August* – **Meals** a la carte 65/90000.

**Rovello,** via Rovello 18 ✉ 20121 ☎ (02)864396 – ▤. AE ⊙ E VISA. ✻ JV c
*closed Saturday lunch, Sunday and also Saturday dinner July-August* – **Meals** a la carte 60/90000.

**Boccondivino,** via Carducci 17 ✉ 20123 ☎ (02)866040 – ▤. ⑤ E VISA HX c
*closed Sunday and August* – **Meals** (dinner only) (booking essential) specialities salami, cheese and regional wines 50/70000.

**Bagutta,** via Bagutta 14 ✉ 20121 ☎ (02)76002767, *Fax (02)799613,* ☂, Meeting place for artists, « Original paintings and caricatures » – AE ⑤ ⊙ E VISA. ✻ NZ k
*closed Sunday and 23 December-5 January* – **Meals** a la carte 70/125000.

**La Tavernetta-da Elio,** via Fatebenefratelli 30 ✉ 20121 ☎ (02)653441 – AE ⑤ E VISA KV c
*closed Saturday lunch, Sunday and August* – **Meals** Tuscan rest. a la carte 50/70000.

**Taverna Visconti,** via Marziale 11 ✉ 20122 ☎ (02)795821, Rest. and wine bar NZ e
*closed Sunday* – **Meals** a la carte 45/85000.

**Directional centre** via della Moscova, via Solferino, via Melchiorre Gioia, viale Zara, via Carlo Farini :

**Executive,** viale Luigi Sturzo 45 ✉ 20154 ☎ (02)62941, *Fax (02)29010238* – ▤ TV ☎ – 🏛 800. AE ⑤ ⊙ E VISA JCB. ✻ KTU e
**Meals** a la carte 55/90000 – **414 rm** ☕ 330/420000, 6 suites.

**Carlyle Brera Hotel** without rest., corso Garibaldi 84 ✉ 20121 ☎ (02)29003888, *Fax (02)29003993* – ▤ TV ☎ ♿ 🚗. AE ⑤ ⊙ E VISA JCB. ✻ JU u
**98 rm** ☕ 395/435000.

**Royal Hotel Mercure,** via Cardano 1 ✉ 20124 ☎ (02)667461, *Fax (02)6703024* – |♦|, ⇋ rm, ▤ TV ☎ ⇔ – 🚶 180. AE ⓢ ⓓ E VISA JCB. ✂ rest KT b
Meals 40/80000 – **205 rm** ☕ 335/450000.

**Sunflower** without rest., piazzale Lugano 10 ✉ 20158 ☎ (02)39314071, *Fax (02)39320377* – |♦| ▤ TV ☎ ♿ ⇔ – 🚶 120. AE ⓢ ⓓ E VISA JCB. ✂
☕ 18000 – **55 rm** 180/250000. by via Mac Mahon HT

**A Riccione,** via Taramelli 70 ✉ 20124 ☎ (02)6686807 – ▤. AE ⓢ ⓓ E VISA JCB
*closed Saturday lunch and August* – **Meals** (booking essential) seafood a la carte 75/100000. by via Melchiorre Gioia KLT

**Gianni e Dorina,** via Pepe 38 ✉ 20159 ☎ (02)606340, *Fax (02)606340* – ▤. AE ⓢ ⓓ E VISA JT b
*closed Saturday lunch, Sunday, 31 July-10 September and Christmas* – **Meals** (booking essential) Pontremolesi rest. a la carte 65/100000

**Serendib,** via Pontida 2 ✉ 20121 ☎ (02)6592139, *Fax (02)6592139* – ▤. ⓢ E VISA. ✂ JU b
*closed Monday and 13 to 25 August* – **Meals** (dinner only) (booking essential) Sri Lankan and Indian Rest. a la carte 35/40000.

**Al Tronco,** via Thaon di Revel 10 ✉ 20159 ☎ (02)606072 – ▤. AE ⓢ ⓓ E VISA. ✂ by via Melchiorre Gioia KLT
*closed Saturday lunch, Sunday and August* – **Meals** a la carte 40/65000.

**Piccolo Teatro-Fuori Porta,** viale Pasubio 8 ✉ 20154 ☎ (02)6572105 – ▤. AE ⓢ ⓓ VISA. ✂ JU m
*closed Friday and 25 December-6 January* – **Meals** (booking essential) a la carte 60/100000.

**Alla Cucina delle Langhe,** corso Como 6 ✉ 20154 ☎ (02)6554279 – ▤. AE ⓢ ⓓ E VISA KU d
*closed Sunday and August* – **Meals** Piedmontese rest. 60000 and a la carte 50/80000.

**Casa Fontana-23 Risotti,** piazza Carbonari 5 ✉ 20125 ☎ (02)6704710 – ▤. AE ⓢ E VISA. ✂ by via M. Gioia LT
*closed 5 to 27 August, Monday, Saturday lunch and Saturday dinner-Sunday in July* – **Meals** (booking essential) a la carte 65/90000.

**Trattoria della Pesa,** viale Pasubio 10 20154 ☎ (02)6555741, *Fax (02)29006859*, Typical old Milanese trattoria – ▤. AE ⓢ ⓓ VISA. ✂ JU s
*closed Sunday and August* – **Meals** Lombardy rest. a la carte 70/95000.

**San Fermo,** via San Fermo 1 ✉ 20121 ☎ (02)29000901 – AE ⓢ ⓓ E VISA JCB KU h
*closed Saturday lunch and Sunday* – **Meals** Spanish rest. a la carte 45/80000.

**Il Verdi,** piazza Mirabello 5 ✉ 20121 ☎ (02)6590797 – ▤ KU k
*closed Sunday (except December) and 11 to 24 August* – **Meals** 25000 b.i. (lunch only) and a la carte 50/85000.

**Fuji,** viale Montello 9 ✉ 20154 ☎ (02)6552517 – AE ⓢ ⓓ E VISA JCB. ✂ JU a
*closed Sunday, Easter, August and Christmas* – **Meals** (dinner only) (booking essential) Japanese rest. a la carte 60/115000.

## Central Station corso Buenos Aires, via Vittor Pisani, piazza della Repubblica :

**Principe di Savoia,** piazza della Repubblica 17 ✉ 20124 ☎ (02)62301 and rest ☎ (02)62302026, *Fax (02)6595838*, 🏋, ♨, 🏊, 🏊 – |♦| ⇋ ▤ TV ☎ ♿ ⇔ – 🚶 700. AE ⓢ ⓓ E VISA JCB. ✂ KU a
Meals 95/120000 and ***Galleria*** Rest. *(closed Saturday)* a la carte 100/155000 – ☕ 60000 – **252 rm** 640/825000, 47 suites.

**Palace,** piazza della Repubblica 20 ✉ 20124 ☎ (02)63361 and rest ☎ (02)29000803, *Fax (02)654485* – |♦|, ⇋ rm, ▤ TV ☎ ♿ ⇔ P – 🚶 250. AE ⓢ ⓓ E VISA JCB. ✂ rest
Meals ***Casanova Grill*** Rest. (booking essential) a la carte 110/165000 – ☕ 55000 – **208 rm** 495/660000, 8 suites. LU b

**Excelsior Gallia,** piazza Duca d'Aosta 9 ✉ 20124 ☎ (02)67851, *Fax (02)66713239*, 🏋, ♨ – |♦|, ⇋ rm, ▤ TV ☎ – 🚶 500. AE ⓢ ⓓ E VISA JCB. ✂ LT a
Meals a la carte 50/135000 – ☕ 26000 – **224 rm** 440/510000, 10 suites.

**Milano Hilton,** via Galvani 12 ✉ 20124 ☎ (02)69831, *Fax (02)66710810* – |♦|, ⇋ rm, ▤ TV ☎ ♿ ⇔ – 🚶 250. AE ⓢ ⓓ E VISA JCB. ✂ rest LT c
Meals a la carte 60/135000 (10 %) – ☕ 35000 – **321 rm** 390/440000, 2 suites.

**Duca di Milano,** piazza della Repubblica 13 ✉ 20124 ☎ (02)62841, *Fax (02)6555966* – |♦| ▤ TV ☎ ♿ – 🚶 90. AE ⓢ ⓓ E VISA JCB. ✂ rest KU c
*closed August* – **Meals** a la carte 95/145000 – ☕ 32000 – 99 suites 695/840000.

**Michelangelo,** via Scarlatti 33 ang. piazza Luigi di Savoia ✉ 20124 ☎ (02)67551, *Fax (02)6694232* – |♦|, ⇋ rm, ▤ TV ☎ ♿ ⇔ – 🚶 500. AE ⓢ ⓓ E VISA JCB LTU s
*closed August* – **Meals** a la carte 85/115000 – **300 rm** ☕ 380/500000, 7 suites.

**Jolly Hotel Touring,** via Tarchetti 2 20121 (02)6335, *Fax (02)6592209* – rm, – 120. rest KU f
Meals ***Amadeus*** Rest. a la carte 65/85000 – **294 rm** 320/340000, 7 suites.

**Starhotel Ritz,** via Spallanzani 40 20129 (02)2055, *Fax (02)29518679* – rm, – 160. rest
Meals (residents only) – **185 rm** 380/510000. by Corso Buenos Aires LU

**Century Tower Hotel,** via Fabio Filzi 25/b 20124 (02)67504, *Fax (02)66980602* – – 60. LT f
Meals *(closed August)* a la carte 50/70000 – 144 suites 300/360000.

**Doria Grand Hotel,** viale Andrea Doria 22 20124 (02)6696696, *Fax (02)6696669* – – 70. by corso Buenos Aires LU
Meals *(closed lunch in August)* 60000 – **108 rm** 370/430000, 2 suites.

**Manin,** via Manin 7 20121 (02)6596511, *Fax (02)6552160,* – – 100. rest KV d
*closed 1 to 23 August* – **Meals** *(closed Saturday)* a la carte 50/85000 – 25000 – **112 rm** 255/335000, 6 suites.

**Bristol** without rest., via Scarlatti 32 20124 (02)6694141, *Fax (02)6702942* – – 50. LT m
*closed August* – **68 rm** 205/300000.

**Atlantic** without rest., via Napo Torriani 24 20124 (02)6691941, *Fax (02)6706533* – – 25. LU h
**62 rm** 220/300000.

**Augustus** without rest., via Napo Torriani 29 20124 (02)66988271, *Fax (02)6703096* – . LU q
*closed 25 July-22 August and 23 to 29 December* – **56 rm** 155/240000.

**Mediolanum** without rest., via Mauro Macchi 1 20124 (02)6705312, *Fax (02)66981921* – . LU n
**52 rm** 260/360000.

**Sanpi** without rest., via Lazzaro Palazzi 18 20124 (02)29513341, *Fax (02)29402451* – – 30. LU e
*closed 2 to 23 August and 24 December-5 January* – **63 rm** 300/400000.

**Berna** without rest., via Napo Torriani 18 20124 (02)6691441, *Fax (02)6693892* – – 30. LU h
**115 rm** 230/305000.

**Auriga** without rest., via Pirelli 7 20124 (02)66985851, *Fax (02)66980698* – – 25. LTU k
*closed August* – **54 rm** 225/340000.

**Madison** without rest., via Gasparotto 8 20124 (02)67074150, *Fax (02)67075059* – – 100. LT j
**92 rm** 230/340000, 8 suites.

**Galles,** piazza Lima ang. corso Buenos Aires 20129 (02)204841, *Fax (02)2048422,* – – 150. rest
**Meals** *(closed Sunday and in lunch August)* a la carte 60/90000 – **111 rm** 260/390000, 2 suites. by corso Buenos Aires LU

Fenice, without rest., corso Buenos Aires 2 20124 (02)29525541, *Fax (02)29523942* – LU x
**42 rm.**

**Albert** without rest., via Tonale 2 ang. Sammartini 20125 (02)66985446, *Fax (02)66985624* – – 40.
**62 rm** 165/255000 by via G.B. Sammartini LT

**Demidoff** without rest., via Plinio 2 20129 (02)29513889, *Fax (02)29405816* – . by via Vitruvio LU
*closed 2 to 26 August and 24 December-2 January* – **36 rm** 150/210000.

**New York** without rest., via Pirelli 5 20124 (02)66985551, *Fax (02)6697267* – – 50. LTU k
*closed 1 to 28 August and 24 December-5 January* – **69 rm** 160/250000.

**City** without rest., corso Buenos Aires 42/5 20124 (02)29523382, *Fax (02)2046957* – . by corso Buenos Aires LU
*closed 9 to 24 August and 23 December-2 January* – **55 rm** 190/280000.

**Mini Hotel Aosta** without rest., piazza Duca d'Aosta 16 20124 (02)6691951, *Fax (02)6696215* – . LT p
**63 rm** 170/240000.

**San Carlo** without rest., via Napo Torriani 28 20124 (02)6693236, *Fax (02)6703116* – – 30. LU u
**75 rm** 160/220000.

**Bolzano** without rest., via Boscovich 21 ✉ 20124 ℘ (02)6691451, *Fax (02)6691455*, – ▤ ☎. AE ⓈⓄ E VISA. LU t
15000 – **35 rm** 150/200000.

**Sempione,** via Finocchiaro Aprile 11 ✉ 20124 ℘ (02)6570323, *Fax (02)6575379* – ▤ ☎. AE Ⓢ E VISA JCB LU r
**39 rm** 180/240000.

**Florida** without rest., via Lepetit 33 ✉ 20124 ℘ (02)6705921, *Fax (02)6692867* – ▤ ☎. AE Ⓢ Ⓞ E VISA LTU s
23000 – **53 rm** 165/225000.

**Club Hotel** without rest., via Copernico 18 ✉ 20125 ℘ (02)67072221, *Fax (02)67072050* – ▤ ☎. AE Ⓢ Ⓞ E VISA LT v
**53 rm** 130/200000.

**La Terrazza di Via Palestro,** via Palestro 2 ✉ 20121 ℘ (02)76002186, *Fax (02)76003328*, « Summer service on terrace » – ▤. AE Ⓢ Ⓞ E VISA JCB KV h
*closed Sunday, Monday lunch, 8 to 24 August and 24 December-12 January* – **Meals** (booking essential) a la carte 60/80000.

**Mediterranea,** piazza Cincinnato 4 ✉ 20124 ℘ (02)29522076, *Fax (02)29522076* – ▤. AE Ⓢ Ⓞ E VISA. LU d
*closed Sunday, 5 to 25 August and 1 to 10 January* – **Meals** seafood a la carte 55/95000.

**Nino Arnaldo,** via Poerio 3 ✉ 20129 ℘ (02)76005981 – ▤.
*closed Saturday lunch and Sunday* – **Meals** (booking essential) a la carte 50/95000. by corso Monforte LX

**Calajunco,** via Stoppani 5 ✉ 20129 ℘ (02)2046003 – ▤. Ⓢ Ⓞ E VISA.
*closed Sunday, 10 to 31 August and 23 December-4 January* – **Meals** (dinner only) (booking essential) a la carte 75/120000. by corso Buenos Aires LU

**Cavallini,** via Mauro Macchi 2 ✉ 20124 ℘ (02)6693771, *Fax (02)6693174*, « Outdoor summer service » – AE Ⓢ Ⓞ E VISA LU y
*closed Saturday, Sunday, 3 to 23 August and 22 to 26 December* – **Meals** a la carte 50/85000.

**Joia,** via Panfilo Castaldi 18 ✉ 20124 ℘ (02)29522124 – ▤. AE Ⓢ Ⓞ E VISA JCB
*closed Saturday lunch, Sunday, Easter, August and 28 December-11 January* – **Meals** (booking essential) vegetarian cuisine 25/55000 (lunch) 55/95000 (dinner) and a la carte 70/100000 LU c
**Spec.** Antipasto "colori gusti e consistenze" con foglia d'oro e tartufo. Riso basmati profumato all'arancia con scampi e zucchine con il loro fiore fritto (spring-summer). Sformato fondente di crescenza e aneto con taccole saltate allo scalogno.

**I Malavoglia,** via Lecco 4 ✉ 20124 ℘ (02)29531387 – ▤. AE Ⓢ Ⓞ E VISA.
*closed August, Monday and lunch (except Sunday and holidays)* – **Meals** (booking essential) Sicilian and seafood rest. a la carte 55/80000. LU g

**13 Giugno,** via Goldoni 44 ang. via Uberti ✉ 20129 ℘ (02)719654, *Fax (02)713875*, – ▤. AE Ⓢ Ⓞ E VISA by via Mascagni LX
*closed Sunday* – **Meals** (booking essential) Sicilian rest. a la carte 60/95000.

**Le 5 Terre,** via Appiani 9 ✉ 20121 ℘ (02)6575177, *Fax (02)653034* – ▤. AE Ⓢ Ⓞ E VISA JCB KU j
*closed Saturday lunch, Sunday and 10 to 20 August* – **Meals** seafood a la carte 55/85000.

**Da Bimbi,** viale Abruzzi 33 ✉ 20131 ℘ (02)29526103, Habitués rest. – ▤. AE Ⓢ Ⓞ E VISA. by corso Buenos Aires LU
*closed Sunday, Monday lunch, August and 25 December-1 January* – **Meals** a la carte 55/90000.

**Giglio Rosso,** piazza Luigi di Savoia 2 ✉ 20124 ℘ (02)6692129, *Fax (02)6694174*, – ▤. AE Ⓢ Ⓞ E VISA LT p
*closed Saturday, Sunday lunch, August and 24 December-6 January* – **Meals** a la carte 40/75000 (12 %).

**Altopascio,** via Gustavo Fara 17 ✉ 20124 ℘ (02)6702458 – ▤. AE Ⓢ Ⓞ E VISA KU n
*closed Saturday, Sunday lunch and August* – **Meals** Tuscan rest. a la carte 45/65000.

Osteria la Risacca 2, viale Regina Giovanna 14 ✉ 20129 ℘ (02)29531801 – ▤
**Meals** seafood. by corso Buenos Aires LU

**Sukrity,** via Panfilo Castaldi 22 ✉ 20124 ℘ (02)201315 – AE Ⓢ Ⓞ E VISA. LU f
*closed Monday* – **Meals** (booking essential for dinner) Indian rest. 20/30000 (lunch) 40/50000 (dinner) and a la carte 40/55000.

**La Tana del Lupo,** viale Vittorio Veneto 30 ✉ 20124 ℘ (02)6599006, Typical taverna – ▤. Ⓢ VISA. KU q
*closed Sunday, August and 1 to 7 January* – **Meals** (booking essential) Venetian and montain specialities 65000 b.i.

**Lon Fon,** via Lazzaro Palazzo 24 ✉ 20124 ✆ (02)29405153 – ▤. AE ⑬ VISA LU w
*closed Wednesday and August* – **Meals** Chinese rest. 20/30000 (lunch) 30/60000 (dinner) and a la carte 30/40000.

**Romana-Vittoria** corso Porta Romana, corso Lodi, corso XXII Marzo, corso Porta Vittoria

**Mistral,** viale Monte Nero 34 ✉ 20135 ✆ (02)55019104 – ▤. AE ⑬ E VISA LY a
*closed Saturday lunch and Sunday* – **Meals** (booking essential) a la carte 50/90000.

**Hosteria del Cenacolo,** via Archimede 12 ✉ 20129 ✆ (02)5455536, « Summer service in garden » – AE ⑬ E VISA. ✻ by corso di Porta Vittoria LX
*closed Saturday lunch, Sunday and August* – **Meals** a la carte 60/80000.

**La Risacca 6,** via Marcona 6 ✉ 20129 ✆ (02)55181658, *Fax (02)55017796,* 🏠 – ▤. AE ⑬ ⓓ E VISA by corso di Porta Vittoria LX
*closed Sunday, Monday lunch, August and Christmas* – **Meals** seafood a la carte 70/100000.

**I Matteoni,** piazzale 5 Giornate 6 angolo Regina Margherita ✉ 20129 ✆ (02)55188293, Habitués rest. – ▤. AE ⑬ ⓓ E VISA LX a
*closed Sunday, 1 to 21 August and 1 to 7 January* – **Meals** a la carte 50/80000.

**Da Giacomo,** via B. Cellini ang. via Sottocrono 6 ✉ 20129 ✆ (02)76023313 – ▤. AE ⑬ ⓓ E VISA. ✻ by corso Monforte LX
*closed Monday, August and 24 December-2 January* – **Meals** (booking essential) a la carte 60/90000.

**Masuelli San Marco,** viale Umbria 80 ✉ 20135 ✆ (02)55184138, *Fax (02)55184138,* Typical trattoria – ▤. AE ⑬ ⓓ E VISA JCB by corso di Porta Vittoria LX
*closed Sunday, Monday lunch, 16 August-10 September and 25 December-6 January* – **Meals** (booking essential for dinner) Lombardy-Piedmontese rest. a la carte 50/75000.

**Merluzzo Felice,** via Lazzaro Papi 6 ✉ 20135 ✆ (02)5454711
AE ⑬ ⓓ E VISA LY b
*closed Sunday* – **Meals** (booking essential) Sicilian rest. a la carte 40/70000.

**Navigli** via Solari, Ripa di Porta Ticinese, viale Bligny, piazza XXIV Maggio :

**D'Este** without rest., viale Bligny 23 ✉ 20136 ✆ (02)58321001, *Fax (02)58321136* – ⎘ ▤ TV ☎ – 🏛 80. AE ⑬ ⓓ E VISA. ✻ KY d
☕ 25000 – **79 rm** 250/340000.

**Crivi's** without rest., corso Porta Vigentina 46 ✉ 20122 ✆ (02)582891, *Fax (02)58318182* – ⎘ ▤ TV ☎ 🚗 – 🏛 120. AE ⑬ ⓓ E VISA JCB KY e
*closed August* – **83 rm** ☕ 235/335000, 3 suites.

**Liberty** without rest., viale Bligny 56 ✉ 20136 ✆ (02)58318562, *Fax (02)58319061* – ⎘ ▤ TV ☎ 🚗. AE ⑬ E VISA. ✻ KY a
*closed 10 to 25 August* – ☕ 20000 – **52 rm** 165/250000.

**Sadler,** via Ettore Troilo 14 angolo via Conchetta ✉ 20136 ✆ (02)58104451, *Fax (02)58112343,* 🏠 – ▤. ⑬ ⓓ E VISA JCB by corso S. Gottardo JY
*closed Sunday, 10 to 31 August and 1 to 15 January* – **Meals** (dinner only) (booking essential) 100/110000 and a la carte 90/130000
**Spec.** Fritto di fiori di zucchina farciti di rombo e tartufo nero (spring). Maccheroni al torchio al ragú d'astice, melanzane e pomodorini (summer). Costata di manzo con fagioli cannellini e patate (winter).

**Al Porto,** piazzale Generale Cantore ✉ 20123 ✆ (02)89407425, *Fax (02)8321481* – ▤. AE ⓓ E VISA HY h
*closed Sunday, Monday lunch, August and 24 December-3 January* – **Meals** (booking essential) seafood a la carte 70/110000.

**Osteria di Porta Cicca,** ripa di Porta Ticinese 51 ✉ 20143 ✆ (02)8372763, *Fax (02)8372763* – ▤. AE ⑬ ⓓ E VISA. ✻ HY j
*closed Saturday lunch and Sunday* – **Meals** (booking essential) a la carte 50/70000.

**Trattoria Aurora,** via Savona 23 ✉ 20144 ✆ (02)8323144, *Fax (02)89404978,* 🏠 – AE ⑬ ⓓ E VISA HY m
*closed Monday, 18 to 31 August and 2 to 12 January* – **Meals** Piedmontese rest. 30000 b.i. (lunch) and 60000 b.i. (dinner).

**Osteria del Binari,** via Tortona 1 ✉ 20144 ✆ (02)89409428, *Fax (02)89407470,* 🏠, Old Milan atmosphere – ▤. AE ⑬ ⓓ E VISA HY p
*closed Sunday* – **Meals** (dinner only) (booking essential) 60000 b.i.

**Il Torchietto,** via Ascanio Sforza 47 ✉ 20136 ✆ (02)8372910, *Fax (02)8372000* – ▤. AE ⑬ ⓓ E VISA. ✻ by via A. Sforza JY
*closed Monday, August and 26 December-3 January* – **Meals** Mantuan rest. a la carte 55/75000.

**Le Buone Cose,** via San Martino 8 ✉ 20122 ☎ (02)58310589 – ▤. AE ⓢ VISA. ✂
*closed Saturday lunch, Sunday and August* – **Meals** (booking essential) seafood a la carte 60/115000. KY h

**Grand Hotel Pub,** via Ascanio Sforza 75 ✉ 20141 ☎ (02)89511586, ☂ – AE ⓢ VISA. ✂ by via A. Sforza JY
*closed Monday* – **Meals** (dinner only) a la carte 50/80000.

**Al Capriccio,** via Washington 106 ✉ 20146 ☎ (02)48950655 – ▤. AE ⓢ E VISA. ✂
*closed Monday and August* – **Meals** seafood a la carte 70/85000. by via Foppa JY

**Shri Ganesh,** via Lombardini 8 ✉ 20143 ☎ (02)58110933 – ▤. AE ⓢ ⓞ E VISA HY c
*closed Tuesday and 14 to 17 August* – **Meals** (dinner only) Indian rest. 35/50000.

**Olivia,** viale D'Annunzio 7/9 ✉ 20123 ☎ (02)89406052 – ▤. AE ⓢ ⓞ E VISA
*closed Saturday lunch and Sunday* – **Meals** a la carte 55/75000. HY e

**Alzaia 26,** alzaia Naviglio Grande 26 ✉ 20144 ☎ (02)8323526, Rest. and bistrot – ▤. AE ⓢ ⓞ VISA HY s
*closed Monday and August* – **Meals** (booking essential) a la carte 55/85000.

**Trattoria all'Antica,** via Montevideo 4 ✉ 20144 ☎ (02)58104860 – ▤. AE ⓢ ⓞ E VISA. ✂ HY r
*closed Saturday lunch, Sunday, August and 26 December-7 January* – **Meals** Lombardy rest. 45000 (dinner only) and a la carte 45/65000.

**Ponte Rosso,** Ripa di Porta Ticinese 23 ✉ 20143 ☎ (02)8373132, Trattoria-bistrot
*closed Sunday* – **Meals** Triestine and Lombardy specialities a la carte 40/70000. HY d

**Fiera-Sempione** corso Sempione, piazzale Carlo Magno, via Monte Rosa, via Washington :

**Hermitage** M, via Messina 10 ✉ 20154 ☎ (02)33107700, *Fax (02)33107399*, ⚒ – ⇕ ▤ TV ☎ ♿ 🚗 – 🏛 200. AE ⓢ ⓞ E VISA. ✂ HJU q
*closed August* – **Meals** (see rest. ***Il Sambuco*** below) – **123 rm** ☕ 320/400000, 7 suites.

**Grand Hotel Ramada** M, via Washington 66 ✉ 20146 ☎ (02)48521, *Fax (02)4818925* – ⇕, ⇎ rm, ▤ TV ☎ ♿ 🚗 – 🏛 1200. AE ⓢ ⓞ E VISA JCB. ✂ rest
Meals 40/60000 and ***La Brasserie*** Rest. a la carte 55/80000 – **322 rm** ☕ 340/400000, suite. by corso Magenta HX

**Radisson SAS Scandinavia Hotel Milano,** via Fauchè, 15 ✉ 20154 ☎ (02)336391, *Fax (02)33104510*, ⚒ – ⇎ rm, ▤ TV ☎ ♿ 🚗 – 🏛 180. AE ⓢ ⓞ E VISA JCB. ✂ rest
Meals a la carte 50/80000 – **148 rm** ☕ 400/425000, suite. HT c

**Regency** without rest., via Arimondi 12 ✉ 20155 ☎ (02)39216021, *Fax (02)39217734*, « In an early 20C mansion » – ⇕ ⇎ ▤ TV ☎ – 🏛 50. AE ⓢ ⓞ E VISA. ✂
*closed August* – **57 rm** ☕ 250/340000, 2 suites. by corso Sempione HU

**Poliziano** without rest., via Poliziano 11 ✉ 20154 ☎ (02)33602494, *Fax (02)33106410* – ⇕ ▤ TV ☎ 🚗 – 🏛 60. AE ⓢ ⓞ E VISA JCB HT a
**98 rm** ☕ 235/325000, 2 suites.

**Capitol** without rest., via Cimarosa 6 ✉ 20144 ☎ (02)48003050, *Fax (02)4694724* – ⇕ ▤ TV ☎ – 🏛 60. AE ⓢ ⓞ E VISA JCB by corso Magenta HX
**95 rm** ☕ 275/350000.

**Domenichino** without rest., via Domenichino 41 ✉ 20149 ☎ (02)48009692, *Fax (02)48003953* – ⇕ ▤ TV ☎ 🚗 Ⓟ – 🏛 50. AE ⓢ ⓞ E VISA. ✂
*closed 1 to 23 August and 20 December-4 January* – **75 rm** ☕ 185/250000, 2 suites. by corso Sempione HU

**Mozart** without rest., piazza Gerusalemme 6 ✉ 20154 ☎ (02)33104215, *Fax (02)33103231* – ⇕ ▤ TV ☎. AE ⓢ ⓞ E VISA. ✂ HT b
**88 rm** ☕ 210/310000, 3 suites.

**Admiral** without rest., via Domodossola 16 ✉ 20145 ☎ (02)3492151, *Fax (02)33106660* – ⇕ ▤ TV ☎ 🚗 Ⓟ – 🏛 65. AE ⓢ ⓞ E VISA
*closed 25 July-1 September* – **60 rm** ☕ 140/180000. by via Procaccini HTU

**Berlino** without rest., via Plana 33 ✉ 20155 ☎ (02)324141, *Fax (02)39210611* – ⇕ ▤ TV ☎. AE ⓢ ⓞ E VISA JCB by corso Sempione HU
*closed 26 July-25 August and 24 December-3 January* – **47 rm** ☕ 170/260000.

**Lancaster** without rest., via Abbondio Sangiorgio 16 ✉ 20145 ☎ (02)344705, *Fax (02)344649* – ⇕ ▤ TV ☎. AE ⓢ E VISA HU c
*closed August* – **30 rm** ☕ 170/270000.

**Metrò** without rest., corso Vercelli 61 ✉ 20144 ☎ (02)468704, *Fax (02)48010295* – ⇕ ▤ TV ☎ – 🏛 35. AE ⓢ ⓞ E VISA JCB by via Ariosto HV
**37 rm** ☕ 180/240000.

**Mini Hotel Portello,** via Guglielmo Silva 12 ✉ 20149 ☎ (02)4814944, *Fax (02)4819243* – ⇕ ▤ TV ☎ Ⓟ – 🏛 100. AE ⓢ ⓞ E VISA JCB
**96 rm** ☕ 170/240000. by Vincenzo Monti HV

**Mini Hotel Tiziano** without rest., via Tiziano 6 ☎ (02)4699035, *Fax (02)4812153*, « Small park » – 🛗 ▤ 📺 ☎ 🅿. AE 🅂 ⓞ E VISA JCB by Vincenzo Monti HV
**54 rm** ☕ 170/240000.

**Il Sambuco** - Hotel Hermitage, via Messina 10 ✉ 20154 ☎ (02)33610333, *Fax (02)3319425* – ▤. AE 🅂 ⓞ E VISA HU q
*closed Saturday lunch, Sunday, 1 to 20 August and 27 December-3 January* – **Meals** seafood a la carte 80/155000
**Spec.** Gallinella di mare con pomodorini, patate e taccole. Sarde ed alici alla napoletana. Zuppa di pesce alla chioggiota.

**Alfredo-Gran San Bernardo,** via Borgese 14 ✉ 20154 ☎ (02)3319000, *Fax (02)29006859* – ▤. AE 🅂 ⓞ E VISA HT e
*closed August, 23 December-9 January, Sunday and Saturday June-July* – **Meals** (booking essential) Milanese rest. a la carte 55/120000
**Spec.** Risotto al salto o all'onda. Stracotto al vino rosso. Foiolo alla milanese.

**Trattoria del Ruzante,** via Massena 1 angolo corso Sempione ✉ 20145 ☎ (02)316102, *Fax (02)316102* – AE 🅂 ⓞ E VISA. ✻ HU v
*closed Saturday lunch, Sunday and August* – **Meals** (booking essential) a la carte 70/125000.

**Taverna della Trisa,** via Francesco Ferruccio 1 ✉ 20145 ☎ (02)341304, ☂ – 🅂 E VISA HU n
*closed Monday and August* – **Meals** Trentine rest. a la carte 50/85000.

**Al Vecchio Porco,** via Messina 8 ✉ 20154 ☎ (02)313862, ☂ – ▤. AE 🅂 ⓞ HU e
*closed Sunday lunch, Monday and August* – **Meals** a la carte 40/60000.

**Trattoria del Previati,** via Gaetano Previati 21 ✉ 20149 ☎ (02)48000064 – ▤. AE 🅂 E VISA by via Vincenzo Monti HV
*closed Thursday, Saturday lunch and August* – **Meals** a la carte 40/80000.

**Al Vöttantott,** corso Sempione 88 ✉ 20154 ☎ (02)33603114 – ▤. AE 🅂 E VISA
*closed Sunday and August* – **Meals** a la carte 45/75000. by corso Sempione HU

## Zone periferiche

**North-Western area** viale Fulvio Testi, Niguarda, viale Fermi, viale Certosa, San Siro, via Novara :

**Grand Hotel Brun** ♨, via Caldera 21 ✉ 20153 ☎ (02)452711, *Fax (02)48204746* – 🛗 ▤ 📺 ☎ ♿ 🚗 🅿 – 🎤 500. AE 🅂 ⓞ E VISA JCB. ✻
*closed 23 December-7 January* – **Meals** 65000 – **306 rm** ☕ 370/480000, 24 suites. by corso Sempione HU

**Rubens** without rest., via Rubens 21 ✉ 20148 ☎ (02)40302, *Fax (02)48193114*, « Rooms with fresco murals » – 🛗 ⇸ ▤ 📺 ☎ 🅿 – 🎤 35. AE 🅂 E VISA
**87 rm** ☕ 230/320000. by corso Magenta HX

**Accademia** without rest., viale Certosa 68 ✉ 20155 ☎ (02)39211122, *Fax (02)33103878*, « Rooms with fresco murals » – 🛗 ▤ 📺 ☎ 🚗. AE 🅂 E VISA
**67 rm** ☕ 270/385000, 2 suites. by corso Sempione HU

**Raffaello** without rest., viale Certosa 108 ✉ 20156 ☎ (02)3270146, *Fax (02)3270440* – 🛗 ▤ 📺 ☎ 🚗 – 🎤 120. AE 🅂 ⓞ E VISA. ✻ by corso Sempione HU
*closed 10 to 24 August and 23 December-2 January* – **140 rm** ☕ 230/370000, 3 suites.

**Blaise e Francisc,** via Butti 9 ✉ 20158 ☎ (02)66802366, *Fax (02)66802909* – 🛗 ⇸ ▤ 📺 ☎ ♿ 🚗 – 🎤 200. AE 🅂 ⓞ E VISA JCB. ✻ rest by via Carlo Farini JT
**Meals** *(closed June-August)* (residents only) (dinner only) 45/70000 – **110 rm** ☕ 280/320000.

**Novotel Milano Nord,** viale Suzzani 13 ✉ 20162 ☎ (02)66101861, *Fax (02)66101961*, 🏊 – 🛗, ⇸ rm, ▤ 📺 ☎ ♿ 🚗 🅿 – 🎤 500. AE 🅂 ⓞ E VISA. ✻ rest
**Meals** a la carte 45/75000 – **172 rm** ☕ 370/390000. by via Valtellina JT

**Ibis,** viale Suzzani 13/15 ✉ 20162 ☎ (02)66103000, *Fax (02)66102797* – 🛗, ⇸ rm, ▤ 📺 ☎ ♿ 🚗 🅿 – 🎤 50. AE 🅂 ⓞ E VISA. ✻ rest by via Valtellina JT
**Meals** 20/35000 – **132 rm** ☕ 145/170000.

**Valganna** without rest., via Varè 32 ✉ 20158 ☎ (02)39310089, *Fax (02)39312566* – ▤ 📺 ☎ 🚗. AE 🅂 ⓞ E VISA JCB by via Carlo Farini JT
**36 rm** ☕ 120/170000.

**Mirage** without rest., via Casella 61 angolo viale Certosa ✉ 20156 ☎ (02)39210471, *Fax (02)39210589* – 🛗 ▤ 📺 ☎ – 🎤 60. AE 🅂 ⓞ E VISA by corso Sempione HU
**50 rm** ☕ 245/340000, 5 suites.

XX **Innocenti Evasioni,** via privata della Bindellina ✉ 20155 ☎ (02)33001882, *Fax (02)33001882*, – AE ⓢ ⓓ E VISA by via Carlo Farini JT
*closed Sunday, Monday, August and Christmas* – **Meals** (dinner only) a la carte 45/65000.

XX **La Pobbia,** via Gallarate 92 ✉ 20151 ☎ (02)38006641, *Fax (02)38006641*, Modern rustic rest., « Outdoor summer service » – 40. AE ⓢ ⓓ E VISA
*closed Sunday and August* – **Meals** a la carte 55/80000 (12 %). by corso Sempione HU

XX **Ribot,** via Cremosano 41 ✉ 20148 ☎ (02)33001646, *Fax (02)39267187*, « Summer service in garden » – P. AE ⓢ ⓓ E VISA by corso Sempione HU
*closed Monday, 10 to 25 August and Christmas* – **Meals** a la carte 60/80000.

XX **Al Bimbo,** via Marcantonio dal Re 38 ang. via Certosa ✉ 20156 ☎ (02)3272290, *Fax (02)39216365* – . AE ⓢ ⓓ E VISA by corso Sempione HU
*closed Sunday and August* – **Meals** 25/50000 (lunch) 40/70000 (dinner) and a la carte 40/70000.

**Northern-Eastern area** viale Monza, via Padova, via Porpora, viale Romagna, viale Argonne, viale Forlanini

**Concorde** without rest., viale Monza 132 ✉ 20125 ☎ (02)26112020, *Fax (02)26147879* – TV – 160. AE ⓢ ⓓ E VISA. by corso Buenos Aires LU
**120 rm** 300/430000.

**Starhotel Tourist,** viale Fulvio Testi 300 ✉ 20126 ☎ (02)6437777, *Fax (02)6472516*, – , rm, TV P – 170. AE ⓢ ⓓ E VISA JCB. rest
Meals 65/95000 – **140 rm** 310/420000. by corso Buenos Aires LU

**Lombardia,** viale Lombardia 74 ✉ 20131 ☎ (02)2824938, *Fax (02)2893430* – , rm, TV – 100. AE ⓢ ⓓ E VISA. by corso Buenos Aires LU
*closed 9 to 24 August* – **Meals** ***La Festa*** *Rest (dinner only) (closed Saturday and Sunday)* a la carte 40/70000 – **81 rm** 180/270000, 6 suites.

XXXX **L'Ami Berton,** via Nullo 14 angolo via Goldoni ✉ 20129 ☎ (02)70123476, Elegant rest. – . AE ⓢ E VISA. by via Mascagni LX
*closed Saturday lunch, Sunday, August and 1 to 10 January* – **Meals** (booking essential for dinner) a la carte 90/150000
**Spec.** Filetti di triglia e canocchie in citronette calda. Lasagnette di mare con pesto e pinoli. Rana pescatrice alla mediterranea.

XX **Osteria Corte Regina,** via Rottole 60 ✉ 20132 ☎ (02)2593377, *Fax (02)2593377*, , Elegant rustic rest. – AE ⓢ E VISA by corso buenos Aires LU
*closed Saturday lunch, Sunday and 10 to 25 August* – **Meals** (booking essential) a la carte 55/80000.

XX **L'Altra Scaletta,** viale Zara 116 ✉ 20125 ☎ (02)6888093, *Fax (02)6888093* – . AE ⓢ ⓓ E VISA. by corso Buenos Aires LU
*closed Saturday lunch, Sunday and August* – **Meals** a la carte 50/65000.

XX **3 Pini,** via Tullo Morgagni 19 ✉ 20125 ☎ (02)66805413, *Fax (02)66801346*, « Summer service under pergola » – AE ⓢ ⓓ E VISA. by corso Buenos Aires LU
*closed Saturday, 5 to 31 August and 25 December-4 January* – **Meals** (booking essential) a la carte 60/85000.

XX **Da Renzo,** piazza Sire Raul 4 ✉ 20131 ☎ (02)2846261, *Fax (02)2896634*, – . AE ⓢ ⓓ E VISA – *closed Monday dinner, Tuesday, August and 26 December-2 January* – **Meals** a la carte 45/70000. by corso Buenos Aires LU

XX **Baia Chia,** via Bazzini 37 ✉ 20131 ☎ (02)2361131, – . ⓢ VISA.
*closed Sunday, Easter, August and 24 December-2 January* – **Meals** (booking essential) seafood a la carte 50/90000. by corso Buenos Aires LU

XX **Piero e Pia,** piazza Aspari 2 angolo via Vanvitelli ✉ 20129 ☎ (02)718541, , Trattoria – . AE ⓢ ⓓ E VISA JCB – *closed Sunday and August* – **Meals** (booking essential for dinner) Piacentine specialities a la carte 55/65000. by viale Tunisia LU

X **Mykonos,** via Tofane 5 ✉ 20125 ☎ (02)2610209 by corso Buenos Aires LU
*closed Tuesday and August* – **Meals** (dinner only) (booking essential) Greek rest. a la carte 30/40000.

**Southern-Eastern area** viale Molise, corso Lodi, via Ripamonti, corso San Gottardo :

**Quark,** via Lampedusa 11/a ✉ 20141 ☎ (02)84431, *Fax (02)8464190*, , – , rm, TV P – 1100. AE ⓢ ⓓ E VISA JCB. rest
*closed 22 July-25 August* – **Meals** a la carte 60/95000 – **285 rm** 275000. by corso Italia KY

**Starhotel Business Palace,** via Gaggia 3 ✉ 20139 ☎ (02)53545, *Fax (02)57307550* – TV – 200. AE ⓢ ⓓ E VISA JCB. rest by corso Italia KY
Meals 65/95000 – **225 rm** 310/420000, 34 suites.

**Novotel Milano Est Aeroporto,** via Mecenate 121 ✉ 20138 ☎ (02)58011085, *Fax (02)58011086*, – , rm, TV P – 350. AE ⓢ ⓓ E VISA. rest
**Meals** a la carte 45/75000 – **206 rm** 325/400000. by corso di Porta Vittoria LX

XX **Antica Trattoria Monluè,** via Monluè 75 ✉ 20138 ☎ (02)7610246, *Fax (02)7610246,* Country trattoria with summer service – ▤ 🅟. AE ⓈⓘE VISA. ✂ by corso di Porta Vittoria LX
*closed Saturday lunch, Sunday and 4 to 20 August* – **Meals** a la carte 50/75000.

XX **La Plancia,** via Cassinis 13 ✉ 20139 ☎ (02)55211269, *Fax (02)5390558* – ▤. AE Ⓢ ⓘ E VISA JCB. ✂ by corso Lodi LY
*closed Sunday and August* – **Meals** Seafood and pizzeria a la carte 40/70000.

X **Taverna Calabiana,** via Calabiana 3 ✉ 20139 ☎ (02)55213075 – ▤. AE Ⓢ ⓘ VISA. ✂
*closed Sunday, Monday, 12 to 20 April, August and 24 December-5 January* – **Meals** Rest. and pizzeria a la carte 50/70000. by corso Lodi LY

**Southern-Western area** viale Famagosta, viale Liguria, via Lorenteggio, viale Forze Armate, via Novara :

**Holiday Inn,** via Lorenteggio 278 ✉ 20152 ☎ (02)410014, *Fax (02)48304729,* – 🛗, rm, ▤ TV ☎ & 🅟 – 70. AE Ⓢ ⓘ E VISA JCB by via Foppa HY
Meals *L'Univers Gourmand* Rest. a la carte 50/70000 – ☕ 30000 – **119 rm** 390/470000.

**Green House** without rest., viale Famagosta 50 ✉ 20142 ☎ (02)8132451, *Fax (02)816624* – 🛗 ▤ TV ☎ &. AE Ⓢ ⓘ E VISA JCB. ✂
☕ 16000 – **45 rm** 140/190000. by Ripa di Porta Ticinese HY

XXX ✿✿ **Aimo e Nadia,** via Montecuccoli 6 ✉ 20147 ☎ (02)416886, *Fax (02)48302005* – ▤. AE Ⓢ ⓘ E VISA. ✂ by via Foppa HY
*closed Saturday lunch, Sunday, August and 1 to 6 January* – **Meals** (booking essential) 60/110000 (lunch) 115000 (dinner) and a la carte 90/145000
**Spec.** Fiocchetti di crescione e semola con ricotta, pomodoro crudo e basilico (spring-autumn). Petto d'anatra al vino cotto e nocciole con porri farciti di fegato d'anatra (autumn-spring). Mousse di cioccolato fondente con noci caramellate e salsa amara al caffè.

**on national road 35-Milanofiori** *by via Francesco Sforza* JY *: 10 km :*

**Royal Garden Hotel** M, via Di Vittorio ✉ 20090 Assago ☎ (02)457811, *Fax (02)45702901* – 🛗 ▤ TV ☎ & 🅟 – 140. AE Ⓢ ⓘ E VISA. ✂
**Meals** a la carte 70/90000 – **111 rm** ☕ 280/380000, 40 suites.

**Jolly Hotel Milanofiori,** Strada 2 ✉ 20090 Assago ☎ (02)82221, *Fax (02)89200946,* – 🛗, rm, ▤ TV ☎ & 🅟 – 120. AE Ⓢ ⓘ E VISA
*closed 22 December-7 January* – **Meals** a la carte 55/110000 – **255 rm** ☕ 255/290000.

**at Forlanini Park (West Wide)** *by corso di Porta Vittoria* LX *: 10 km :*

XX **Osteria i Valtellina,** via Taverna 34 ✉ 20134 Milano ☎ (02)7561139, « Summer service under pergola » – 🅟. AE Ⓢ ⓘ E VISA
*closed Monday and 4 to 24 August* – **Meals** Valtellina rest. a la carte 60/80000.

**on road New Vigevanese-Zingone** *by via Foppa* HY *: 11 km :*

**Eur** without rest., via Leonardo da Vinci 36 A ✉ 20090 Trezzano sul Naviglio ☎ (02)4451951, *Fax (02)4451075* – 🛗 ▤ TV ☎ 🅟 – 70. AE Ⓢ ⓘ E VISA JCB
**39 rm** ☕ 140/180000.

**Blu Visconti**, via Goldoni 49 ✉ 20090 Trezzano sul Naviglio ☎ (02)48402094, *Fax (02)48403095,* – 🛗 ▤ TV ☎ & 🅟 – 100. AE Ⓢ ⓘ E VISA
**Meals** *Alla Cava* Rest. *(closed Monday and 11 to 25 August)* a la carte 40/85000 – **63 rm** ☕ 120/170000, suite

**Tiffany,** via Leonardo da Vinci 207/209 ✉ 20090 Trezzano sul Naviglio ☎ (02)4452859, *Fax (02)4450944,* – 🛗 ▤ TV ☎ 🅟 – 70. AE Ⓢ ⓘ E VISA. ✂
*closed 11 to 21 August* – **Meals** *(closed Saturday dinner, Sunday and 28 July-29 August)* a la carte 50/95000 – **36 rm** ☕ 100/140000.

**on national road West-Assago** *by via Foppa* HY *: 11 km :*

**Forte Agip,** ✉ 20090 Assago ☎ (02)4880441, *Fax (02)48843958,* – 🛗, rm, ▤ TV ☎ & 🅟 – 300. AE Ⓢ ⓘ E VISA JCB. ✂ rest
**Meals** a la carte 50/75000 – **194 rm** ☕ 225/245000.

**Abbiategrasso** *20081 Milano* 988 ③, 428 *F 8 – pop. 27 327 alt. 120.*
*Roma 590 – Alessandria 80 – Milano 24 – Novara 29 – Pavia 33.*

**at Cassinetta di Lugagnano** *N : 3 km – ✉ 20081 :*

XXXX ✿✿ **Antica Osteria del Ponte,** piazza G. Negri 9 ☎ (02)9420034, *Fax (02)9420610,* – ▤ 🅟. AE Ⓢ ⓘ E VISA. ✂
*closed Sunday, Monday, August and 25 December-12 January* – **Meals** (booking essential) 80000 (lunch) 160000 (dinner) and a la carte 100/195000
**Spec.** Insalata di argosta alle pesche e salsa alla vangilia (June-September). Tortelli di ricotta e borragine in salsa di fave, prosciutto e pomodorini canditi (February-May). Oca alla "Royale" disossata e farcita al foie gras (January-March).

**Bergamo** 24100 P 988 ③, 428 E 11 *G. Italy – pop. 117 193 alt. 249.*
*18, 18 and 18 L'Albenza (closed Monday) at Almenno San Bartolomeo ✉ 24030 ☎ (035)640028, Fax (035)643066;*
*18 La Rossera (closed Tuesday) at Chiuduno ✉ 24060 ☎ (035)838600, Fax (035)4427047.*
*✈ Orio al Serio ☎ (035)326323, Fax (035)313432 – Alitalia, via Casalino 5 ☎ (035)224044, Fax (035)235127.*
*ℹ piazzale Marconi 7 ✉ 24122 ☎ (035)42226, Fax (035)242994.*
*A.C.I. via Angelo Maj 16 ✉ 24121 ☎ (035)247621.*
*Roma 601 – Brescia 52 – Milano 47.*

XXX ✿✿ **Da Vittorio,** viale Papa Giovanni XXIII 21 ✉ 24121 ☎ (035)213266, *Fax (035)218060* – ✈ ▤. AE ⓢ ⓓ E VISA
*closed Wednesday and August* – **Meals** (booking essential) 60/95000 (lunch) 95/130000 (dinner) and a la carte 105/140000
**Spec.** Filetto di tonno alla griglia (spring-summer). Ravioli di scampi e bottarga (spring-summer). Filetto di rombo con patate e porcini (autumn-spring).

**Canneto sull'Oglio** *46013 Mantova* 428 429 *G 13 – pop. 4 542 alt. 35.*
*Roma 493 – Brescia 51 – Cremona 32 – Mantova 38 – Milano 123 – Parma 44.*

**towards Carzaghetto** *NW : 3 km :*

XXXX ✿✿✿ **Dal Pescatore,** ✉ 46013 ☎ (0376)723001, *Fax (0376)70304,* « Outdoor dinner summer service » – ▤ Ⓟ. AE ⓢ ⓓ E VISA JCB. ✈
*closed Monday, Tuesday, 5 to 30 August, Christmas and 1 to 18 January* – **Meals** (booking essential) 150000 and a la carte 110/175000
**Spec.** Ravioli verdi di faraona e salvia fritta. Tortelli di pecorino, ricotta e parmigiano. Capretto arrosto, salsa alla diavola (March-September).

**Erbusco** *25030 Brescia* 428 429 *F 11 – pop. 6 624 alt. 251.*
*Roma 578 – Bergamo 35 – Brescia 22 – Milano 69.*

XXXX ✿✿ **Gualtiero Marchesi,** via Vittorio Emanuele 11, località Bellavista N : 1,5 ; km ☎ (030)7760562, *Fax (030)7760379,* ≤ lake and mountains, Elegant installation – ▤ Ⓟ. AE ⓢ ⓓ E VISA JCB. ✈
*closed Sunday dinner, Monday, and 12 January-2 February* – **Meals** (booking essential) 160/180000 and a la carte 120/180000
**Spec.** Stravaganza "Marchesiana". Riso, oro e zafferano. Filetto di vitello alla Rossini.

**Soriso** *28018 Novara* 428 *E 7,* 219 ⑯ *– pop. 749 alt. 452.*
*Roma 654 – Arona 20 – Milano 78 – Novara 40 – Stresa 35 – Torino 114 – Varese 46.*

XXXX ✿✿✿ **Al Sorriso** with rm, via Roma 18 ☎ (0322)983228, *Fax (0322)983328* – ▤ rest, TV ☎. AE ⓢ E VISA. ✈
*closed 3 to 26 August and 7 to 24 January* – **Meals** *(closed Monday and Tuesday lunch)* (booking essential) a la carte 100/165000 – **8 rm** ☐ 180/250000
**Spec.** Purea di zucca con fegato d'oca alle rose (autumn-spring). Ravioloni verdi di formaggio di capra al burro alpino. Piccione rosolato all'aceto balsamico.

**NAPLES** (NAPOLI) 80100 P 988 ㉗, 431 E 24 *G. Italy – pop. 1 045 874 – High Season : April-October.*

**See :** *National Archaeological Museum*★★★ KY – *New Castle*★★ KZ – *Port of Santa Lucia*★★ BU : ≤★★ *of Vesuvius and bay* – ≤★★★ *at night from via Partenope of the Vomero and Posillipo* FX – *San Carlo Theatre*★ KZ T¹ – *Piazza del Plebiscito*★ JKZ – *Royal Palace*★ KZ – *Carthusian Monastery of St. Martin*★★ JZ : ≤★★★ *ofthe Bay of Naples from gallery 25. Spacca-Napoli quarter*★★ KY – *Tomb*★★ *of King Robert the Wise in Church of Santa Chiara*★ KY – *Caryatids*★ *by Tino da Camaino in Church of St. Dominic Major* KY – *Sculptures*★ *in Chapel of St. Severo* KY – *Arch*★, *Tomb*★ *of Catherine of Austria, apse*★ *in Church of St. Lawrence Major* LY – *Capodimonte Palace and National Gallery*★★. *Mergellina*★ : ≤★★ *of the bay* – *Villa Floridiana*★ EVX : ≤★ – *Catacombs of St. Gennaro*★★ – *Church of Santa Maria Donnaregina*★ LY – *Church of. St. Giovanni a Carbonara*★ LY – *Capuan Gate*★ LMY – *Como Palace*★ LY – *Sculptures*★ *in the Church of St. Anne of the Lombards* KYZ – *Posillipo*★ – *Marechiaro*★ – ≤★★ *of the Bay from Virgiliano Park (or Rimembranza Park).*

**Exc. :** *Bay of Naples*★★★ *road to Campi Flegrei*★★, *to Sorrento Penisula Island of Capri*★★★ *Island of Ischia*★★★.

*9 (closed Tuesday) at Arco Felice ✉ 80078 ☎ (081)660772, Fax (081)660566, W : 19 km.*

*✈ Ugo Niutta of Capodichino NE : 6 km (except Saturday and Sunday) ☎ (081)5425333 – Alitalia, via Medina 41 ✉ 80133 ☎ (081)5425222.*

*⛴ to Capri (1 h 15 mn), Ischia (1 h 15 mn) e Procida (1 h), daily – Caremar-Travel and Holidays, molo Beverello ✉ 80133 ☎ (081)5513882 Fax (081)5522011; to Cagliari 19 June-17 September Thursday and Saturday, Thursday October-May (15 h 45 mn) and Palermo daily (11 h) – Tirrenia Navigazione, Stazione Marittima, molo Angioino ✉ 80133 ☎ (081)5891050, Fax (081)7201567 ; to Ischia daily (1 h 15 mn) – Alilauro and Linee Lauro, molo Beverello ✉ 80133 ☎ (081)5522838, F ax (081)5513236 ; to Aeolian Island Wednesday and Friday, 15 June-15 September Monday, Tuesday, Thursday, Friday, Saturday and Sunday (14 h) – Siremar-Genovese Agency, via De Petris 78 ✉ 80133 ☎ (081)5512112, Fax (081)5512114.*

*⛴ to Capri (45 mn), Ischia (45 mn) and Procida (35 mn), daily – Caremar-Travel and Holidays, molo Beverello ✉ 80133 ☎ (081)5513882, Fax (081)5522011; to Ischia (30 mn) and Capri (40 mn), daily – Alilauro, via Caracciolo 11 ✉ 80122 ☎ (081)7611004, Fax (081)76142 50 ; to Capri daily (40 mn) – Navigazione Libera del Golfo, molo Beverello ✉ 80133 ☎ (081)5520763, Fax (081)5525589; to Capri (45 mn), to Aeolian Island June-September (4 h) and Procida-Ischia daily (35 mn) – Aliscafi SNAV, via Caracciolo 10 ✉ 80122 ☎ (081)7612348, Fax (081)7612141.*

*ℹ piazza dei Martiri 58 ✉ 80121 ☎ (081)405311 – piazza del Plebiscito (Royal Palace) ✉ 80132 ☎ (081)418744, Fax (081)418619 – Central Station ✉ 80142 ☎ 268779 - Capodichino Airport ✉ 80133 ☎ (081)7805761 – piazza del Gesì Nuovo 7 ✉ 80135 ☎ (081)5523328 - Passaggio Castel dell'Ovo ✉ 80132 ☎ (081)7645688.*

A.C.I. *piazzale Tecchio 49/d ✉ 80125 ☎ (081)2394511.*

*Roma 219 – Bari 261*

Plans on following pages

**Grande Albergo Vesuvio,** via Partenope 45 ✉ 80121 ☎ (081)7640044, *Fax (081)5890380,* ≤ gulf and Castel dell'Ovo, Fā – |‡|, ⇆ rm, ▤ TV ☎ ⇔ – 🏠 400. AE ⑤ ◑ E VISA JCB. ✂ rest FX n
**Meals** (see rest. ***Caruso*** below) – **149 rm** ⊒ 370/470000, 16 suites.

**Excelsior,** via Partenope 48 ✉ 80121 ☎ (081)7640111, *Fax (081)7649743,* « Roof-garden, solarium with ≤ gulf and Castel dell'Ovo » – |‡|, ⇆ rm, ▤ TV ☎ ⇔. AE ⑤ ◑ E VISA JCB. ✂ rest GX w
**Meals** a la carte 60/100000 – **104 rm** ⊒ 370/470000, 12 suites.

**Gd H. Parker's,** corso Vittorio Emanuele 135 ✉ 80121 ☎ (081)7612474, *Fax (081)663527,* « Roof-garden rest. with ≤ town and gulf » – |‡| ▤ TV ☎ ⇔ – 🏠 250. AE ⑤ ◑ E VISA JCB. ✂ EX r
**Meals** *(closed Sunday dinner)* a la carte 65/115000 – **70 rm** ⊒ 265/370000, 9 suites.

**Santa Lucia,** via Partenope 46 ✉ 80121 ☎ (081)7640666, *Fax (081)7648580,* ≤ gulf and Castel dell'Ovo – |‡| ▤ TV ☎ – 🏠 110. AE ⑤ ◑ E VISA. ✂ GX w
**Meals** *(closed 10 to 20 August)* a la carte 65/110000 see also rest. ***Megaris*** below – **97 rm** ⊒ 320/440000, 5 suites.

**Grand Hotel Terminus** M, piazza Garibaldi 91 ✉ 80142 ☎ (081)7793111, *Fax (081)206689,* Fā, ≘s – |‡| ▤ TV ☎ ⇔ – 🏠 300. AE ⑤ ◑ E VISA. ✂ rest MY a
**Meals** a la carte 50/80000 – **168 rm** ⊒ 190/250000, 12 suites.

# NAPOLI

Giordano (Via L.) . . . . . . . . EV 64
Scarlatti
(Via Alessandro) . . . . . . EV 153

Arena della Sanità (Via) . . . GU 6
Artisti (Piazza degli) . . . . . . EV 9
Bernini (Via G. L.) . . . . . . . . EV 12
Bonito (Via G.) . . . . . . . . . . FV 13
Carducci (Via G.) . . . . . . . . FX 20
Chiatamone (Via) . . . . . . . . . FX 25
Cirillo (Via D.) . . . . . . . . . . . GU 27

Colonna (Via Vittoria) . . . . . FX 29
Crocelle (Via) . . . . . . . . . . . GU 35
D'Auria (Via G.) . . . . . . . . . FV 40
Ferraris (Via Galileo) . . . . . HV 54
Gaetani (Via) . . . . . . . . . . . FX 61
Gen. Pignatelli (Via) . . . . . . HU 63
Martini (Via Simone) . . . . . EV 75

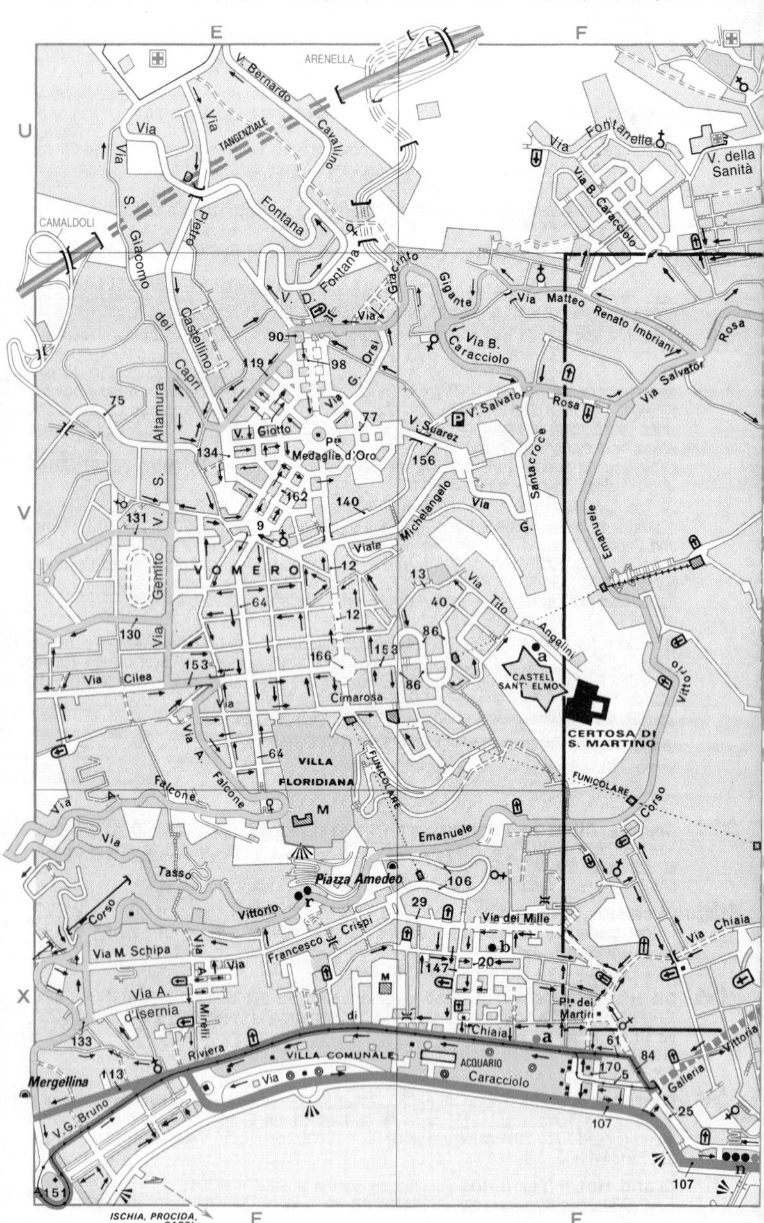

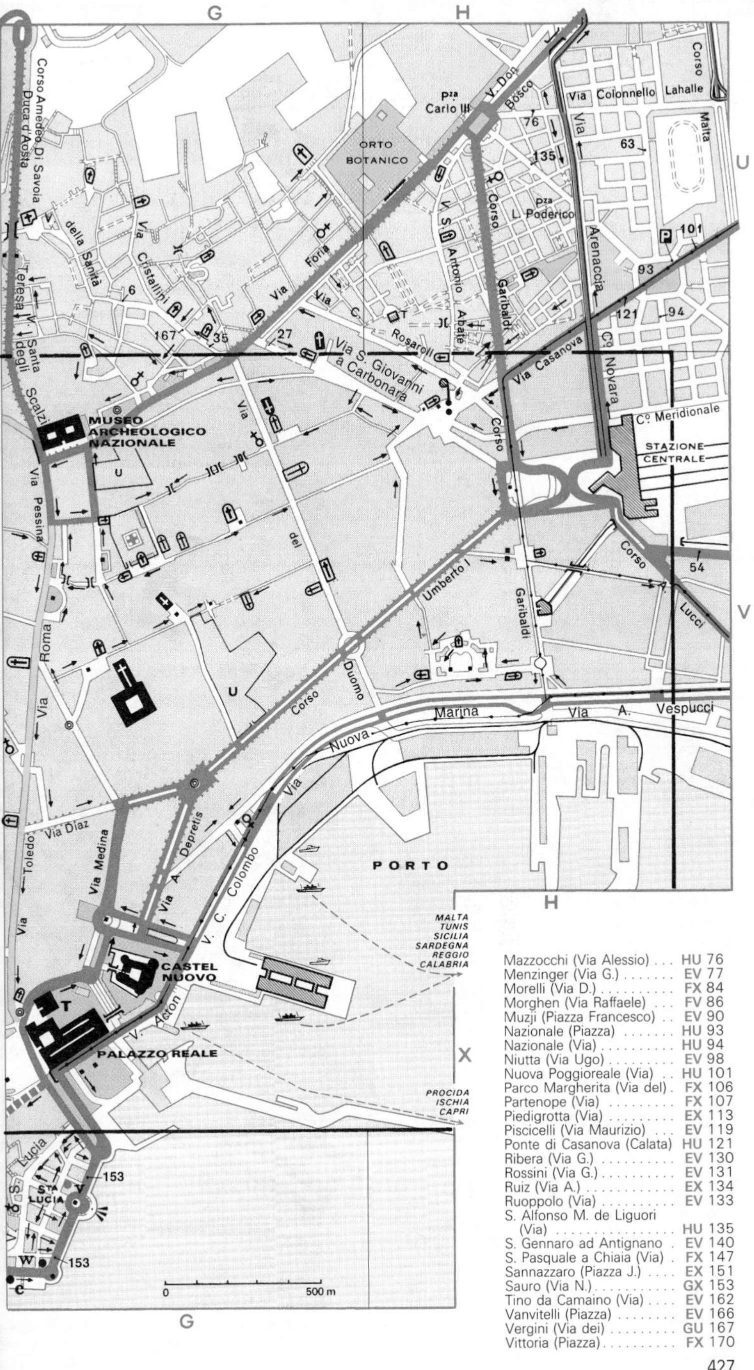
G
H
U
V
X
Corso Amedeo Di Savoia Duca d'Aosta
Pza Carlo III
V. Don Bosco
ORTO BOTANICO
Via Colonnello Lahalle
Corso Malta
Via Arenaccia
Pza L. Poderico
Corso Garibaldi
V. S. Antonio Abate
Via Foria
della Sanità
Via Cristallini
Via Santa Teresa degli Scalzi
Via C. Rosaroll
Via S. Giovanni a Carbonara
Via Casanova
Co Novara
Co Meridionale
STAZIONE CENTRALE
MUSEO ARCHEOLOGICO NAZIONALE
Via Pessina
Via del Duomo
Corso Umberto I
Corso Lucci
Garibaldi
Via Roma
Via Toledo
Via Diaz
Via Medina
Via A. Depretis
V. C. Colombo
Via Nuova Marina
Via A. Vespucci
PORTO
CASTEL NUOVO
PALAZZO REALE
V. Acton
MALTA TUNIS SICILIA SARDEGNA REGGIO CALABRIA
PROCIDA ISCHIA CAPRI
STA LUCIA
S. Lucia
0
500 m

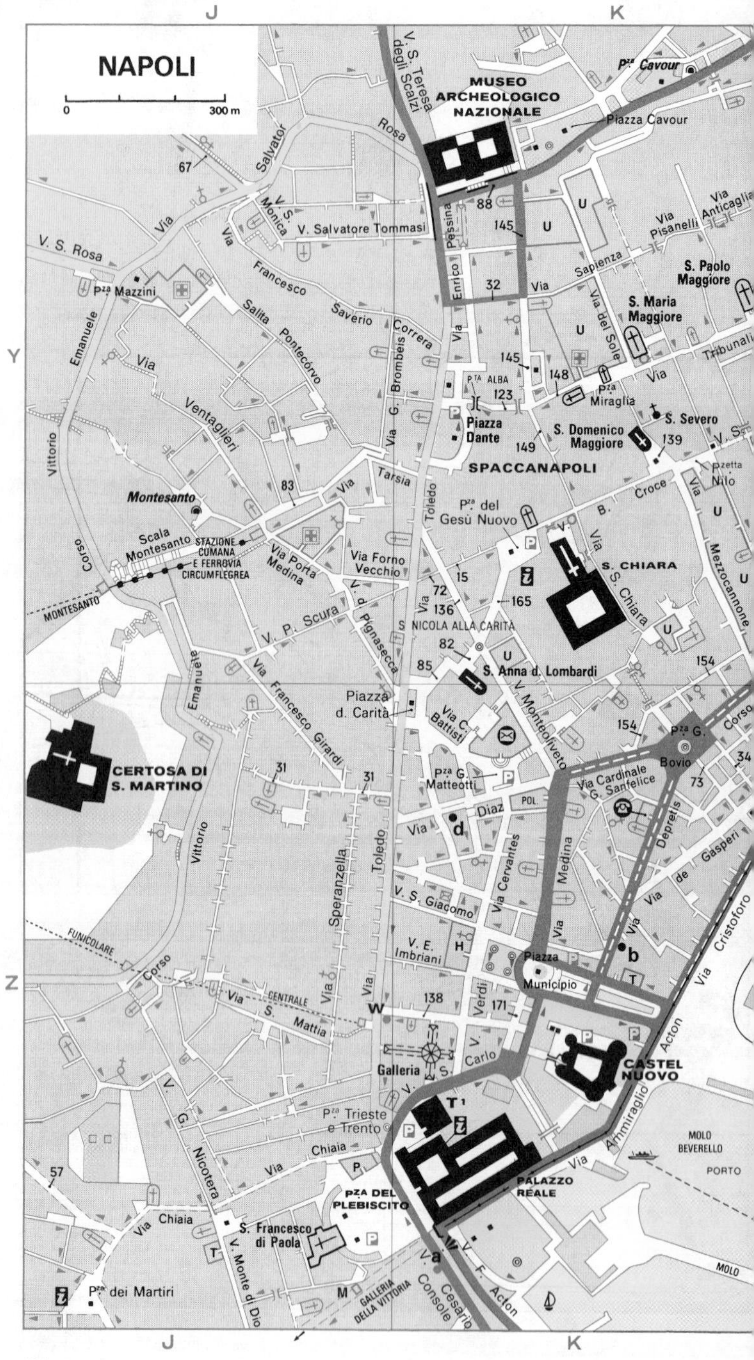
NAPOLI
0
300 m
MUSEO ARCHEOLOGICO NAZIONALE
Piazza Cavour
CERTOSA DI S. MARTINO
SPACCANAPOLI
S. CHIARA
CASTEL NUOVO
PALAZZO REALE
Piazza Dante
Montesanto
Piazza Municipio
Galleria
Pza DEL PLEBISCITO
S. Francesco di Paola
Pza dei Martiri
S. Domenico Maggiore
S. Severo
S. Maria Maggiore
S. Paolo Maggiore
S. Anna d. Lombardi
Piazza d. Carità
Via Toledo
MOLO BEVERELLO
PORTO
FUNICOLARE CENTRALE
STAZIONE CUMANA E FERROVIA CIRCUMFLEGREA

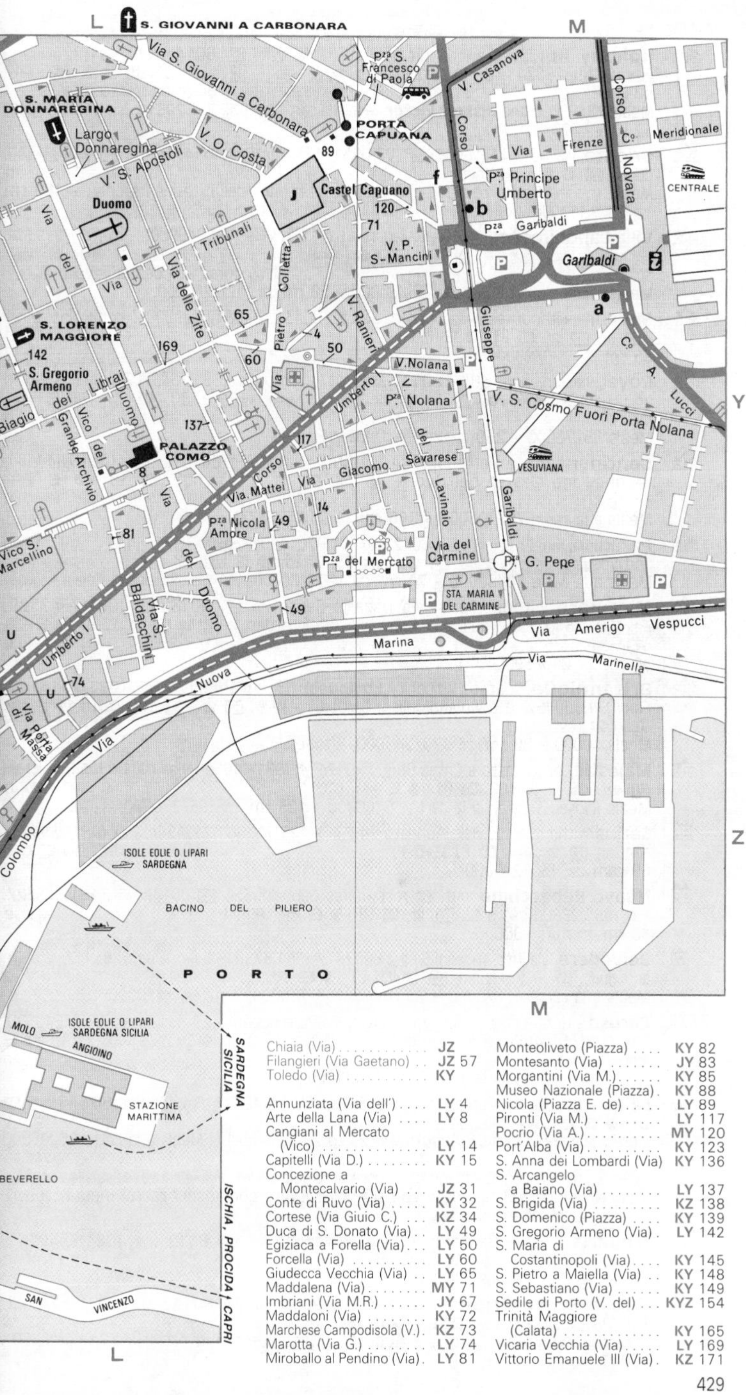


Chiaia (Via) . . . . . . . . . . . JZ
Filangieri (Via Gaetano) . . JZ 57
Toledo (Via) . . . . . . . . . . . KY

Annunziata (Via dell') . . . . LY 4
Arte della Lana (Via) . . . . LY 8
Cangiani al Mercato (Vico) . . . . . . . . . . . . LY 14
Capitelli (Via D.) . . . . . . . . KY 15
Concezione a Montecalvario (Via) . . . JZ 31
Conte di Ruvo (Via) . . . . . KY 32
Cortese (Via Giulio C.) . . . KZ 34
Duca di S. Donato (Via) . . LY 49
Egiziaca a Forella (Via) . . . LY 50
Forcella (Via) . . . . . . . . . . LY 60
Giudecca Vecchia (Via) . . LY 65
Maddalena (Via) . . . . . . . . MY 71
Imbriani (Via M.R.) . . . . . . JY 67
Maddaloni (Via) . . . . . . . . KY 72
Marchese Campodisola (V.) . KZ 73
Marotta (Via G.) . . . . . . . . LY 74
Miroballo al Pendino (Via) . LY 81
Monteoliveto (Piazza) . . . . KY 82
Montesanto (Via) . . . . . . . JY 83
Morgantini (Via M.) . . . . . . KY 85
Museo Nazionale (Piazza) . KY 88
Nicola (Piazza E. de) . . . . . LY 89
Pironti (Via M.) . . . . . . . . . LY 117
Pocrio (Via A.) . . . . . . . . . MY 120
Port'Alba (Via) . . . . . . . . . KY 123
S. Anna dei Lombardi (Via) KY 136
S. Arcangelo a Baiano (Via) . . . . . . . . LY 137
S. Brigida (Via) . . . . . . . . . KZ 138
S. Domenico (Piazza) . . . . KY 139
S. Gregorio Armeno (Via) . LY 142
S. Maria di Costantinopoli (Via) . . . . KY 145
S. Pietro a Maiella (Via) . . KY 148
S. Sebastiano (Via) . . . . . . KY 149
Sedile di Porto (V. del) . . . KYZ 154
Trinità Maggiore (Calata) . . . . . . . . . . . . KY 165
Vicaria Vecchia (Via) . . . . . LY 169
Vittorio Emanuele III (Via) . KZ 171

**Holiday Inn** M, centro direzionale Isola e/6 ✉ 80143 ✆ (081)2250111, *Fax (081)5628074* – |♦|, ⇜ rm, ▤ TV ☎ ♿ 🚗 – 🔑 1200. AE ⑤ ⊙ E VISA JCB. ✗ by corso Meridionale MY
**Meals** 25/55000 and ***Bistrot Victor*** Rest. a la carte 55/85000 – **298 rm** ☕ 310/350000, 32 suites 420/460000.

**Oriente,** via Diaz 44 ✉ 80134 ✆ (081)5512133, *Fax (081)5514915* – ▤ TV ☎ – 🔑 300. AE ⑤ ⊙ E VISA. ✗ rest KZ d
**Meals** *(closed Friday to Sunday and August)* (dinner only) (residents only) – **130 rm** ☕ 250/350000, 2 suites.

**Villa Capodimonte** ⛰, via Moiariello 66 ✉ 80131 ✆ (081)459000, *Fax (081)299344*, ≤, ☂, 🌳, ✗ – |♦| ▤ TV ☎ 🚗 P – 🔑 50. AE ⑤ ⊙ E VISA. ✗ rest by corso Amedeo di Savoia GU
**Meals** (dinner only) a la carte 35/60000 – **58 rm** ☕ 165/265000.

**Mercure** without rest., via Depretis 123 ✉ 80133 ✆ (081)5529500, *Fax (081)5529509* – |♦| ▤ TV ☎. AE ⑤ ⊙ E VISA KZ b
**85 rm** ☕ 220/280000.

**Royal,** via Partenope 38 ✉ 80121 ✆ (081)7644800, *Fax (081)7645707*, ≤ gulf, Posillipo and Castel dell'Ovo, ⛱ – |♦| ▤ TV ☎ 🚗 – 🔑 180. AE ⑤ ⊙ E VISA. ✗ rest FX n
**Meals** 55/70000 – **259** ☕ 210/340000, 16 suites.

**Continental,** via Partenope 44 ✉ 80121 ✆ (081)7644636, *Fax (081)7644661*, ≤ gulf and Castel dell'Ovo – |♦| ▤ TV ☎ – 🔑 600. AE ⑤ ⊙ E VISA. ✗ rest FX n
**Meals** a la carte 70/100000 – **166 rm** ☕ 210/340000.

**Paradiso,** via Catullo 11 ✉ 80122 ✆ (081)7614161, *Fax (081)7613449*, ≤ gulf, town and Vesuvius, ☂ – |♦| ▤ TV ☎ – 🔑 80. AE ⑤ ⊙ E VISA. ✗ rest
**Meals** a la carte 50/80000 – **71 rm** ☕ 190/280000. by Riviera di Chiaia EFX

**Miramare** without rest., via Nazario Sauro 24 ✉ 80132 ✆ (081)7647589, *Fax (081)7640775*, ≤ gulf and Vesuvius, « Roof-garden » – |♦| ▤ TV ☎. AE ⑤ ⊙ E VISA JCB GX e
**30 rm** ☕ 210/390000.

**Britannique,** corso Vittorio Emanuele 133 ✉ 80121 ✆ (081)7614145, *Fax (081)660457*, ≤ town and gulf, « Garden » – |♦| ▤ TV ☎ – 🔑 100. AE ⑤ ⊙ E VISA JCB. ✗ rest EX r
**Meals** 40000 – **80 rm** ☕ 170/245000, 8 suites.

**Majestic,** largo Vasto a Chiaia 68 ✉ 80121 ✆ (081)416500, *Fax (081)410145* – |♦| ▤ TV ☎ 🚗 – 🔑 100. AE ⑤ ⊙ E VISA. ✗ FX b
**Meals** *(closed Sunday)* a la carte 35/60000 – **123 rm** ☕ 195/270000.

**Serius** without rest., viale Augusto 74 ✉ 80125 ✆ (081)2394844, *Fax (081)2399251* – |♦| ▤ TV ☎ 🚗. AE ⑤ E VISA by Riviera di Chiaia EFX
**69 cam** ☕ 130/200000.

**Nuovo Rebecchino** without rest., corso Garibaldi 356 ✉ 80142 ✆ (081)5535327, *Fax (081)268026* – |♦| ▤ TV ☎. AE ⑤ ⊙ E VISA JCB MY b
**58 rm** ☕ 160/200000.

**Belvedere,** via Tito Angelini 51 ✉ 80129 ✆ (081)5788169, *Fax (081)5785417*, ≤ town and gulf, ☂ – |♦|, ▤ rm, TV ☎. AE ⑤ ⊙ E. ✗ FV a
**Meals** a la carte 45/70000 – **25 rm** ☕ 165/230000, 2 suites, ▤30000.

**Caruso** - Hotel Grande Albergo Vesuvio, via Partenope 45 ✉ 80121 ✆ (081)7640520, *Fax (081)7644483*, « Roof-garden with ≤ gulf and Castel dell'Ovo » – 🚗. AE ⑤ ⊙ E VISA JCB. ✗ FX n
*closed Monday* – **Meals** a la carte 80/115000.

**La Cantinella,** via Cuma 42 ✉ 80132 ✆ (081)7648684, *Fax (081)7648769* – ▤. AE ⑤ ⊙ E VISA JCB. ✗ GX v
*closed Sunday, 11 to 18 August and 24 to 26 December* – **Meals** a la carte 55/95000 (12 %)
**Spec.** Fiore di zucchina ripieno di mousse di spigola sul letto di verdure, salsa alle zucchine (April-November). Pappardelle con scampi, zucca e pomodorini acerbi (April-October). Spigola alla mediterranea.

**Megaris** - Hotel Santa Lucia, via Partenope 46 ✉ 80121 ✆ (081)7640511, *Fax (081)7648580* – ▤. AE ⑤ E VISA. ✗ GX c
*closed Sunday* – **Meals** a la carte 55/95000.

**Ciro a Santa Brigida,** via Santa Brigida 73 ✉ 80132 ✆ (081)5524072, *Fax (081)5528992* – ▤. AE ⑤ ⊙ E VISA JZ w
*closed Sunday and 14 to 29 August* – **Meals** Rest. and pizzeria a la carte 50/80000.

XX **Giuseppone a Mare,** via Ferdinando Russo 13-Capo Posillipo ✉ 80123 ☎ (081)5756002, seafood rest. with ≤ - P. AE S O E VISA. by via Caracciolo FX
*closed Monday, 24-25 December and New Year* - **Meals** 25/40000 (lunch) 40/60000 (dinner) and a la carte 60/80000.

XX **Il Posto Accanto-Rosolino,** via Nazario Sauro 2/7 ✉ 80132 ☎ (081)7649873, *Fax (081)7640547* - ▤- 70. AE S O E VISA. GX a
*closed Sunday dinner* - **Meals** Rest. and pizzeria a la carte 40/60000 (15 %).

XX **San Carlo,** via Cesario Console 18/19 ✉ 80132 ☎ (081)7649757 - ▤. AE S O E VISA JCB. KZ a
*closed Sunday and 3 August-3 September* - **Meals** (booking essential) a la carte 45/85000 (10 %).

XX **Don Salvatore,** strada Mergellina 4 A ✉ 80122 ☎ (081)681817, *Fax (081)661241* - ▤. AE S O E VISA by Riviera di Chiaia EFX
*closed Wednesday* - **Meals** Rest. and pizzeria a la carte 50/75000.

XX **A' Fenestella,** calata Ponticello a Marechiaro ✉ 80123 ☎ (081)7690020, *Fax (081)5750686,* « Summer service in terrace on sea » - P. AE S E VISA
*closed 11 to 18 August, Sunday and lunch in August* - **Meals** a la carte 45/70000 (15 %). by via V. G. Bruno EX

XX **Da Mimì alla Ferrovia,** via Alfonso d'Aragona 21 ✉ 80139 ☎ (081)5538525 - ▤. AE S O E VISA MY f
*closed Sunday and 10 to 20 August* - **Meals** a la carte 45/65000 (10 %).

X **Sbrescia,** rampe Sant'Antonio a Posillipo 109 ✉ 80122 ☎ (081)669140, « Typical rest. with ≤ town and gulf » - AE S O VISA. by Riviera di Chiaia EFX
*closed Monday and 15 to 28 August* - **Meals** a la carte 40/65000 (13 %).

## Island of Capri

**Island of Capri** *80073 Napoli* 988 ㉗, 431 F 24 *G. Italy - pop. 12 972 alt. - High Season : Easter and June-September.*
*The limitation of motor-vehicles' access is regulated by legislative rules.*

**Gd H. Quisisana,** via Camerelle 2 ☎ (081)8370788, *Fax (081)8376080,* ≤ sea and Certosa, « Garden with », ₺, ≘s, ▣, ⅋ - ▤ TV ☎ - 550. AE S O E VISA.
*Easter-October* - **Meals** ***La Colombaia*** Rest. *(closed dinner)* a la carte 70/95000 see also rest. ***Quisi*** - **150 rm** ☐ 350/800000, 13 suites.

**Scalinatella** without rest., via Tragara 8 ☎ (081)8370633, *Fax (081)8378291,* ≤ sea and Certosa, heated - ▤ TV ☎. AE S E VISA
*15 March-5 November* - **28 rm** ☐ 550/700000.

**Punta Tragara** , via Tragara 57 ☎ (081)8370844, *Fax (081)8377790,* ≤ Faraglioni and coast, , « Panoramic terrace with heated » - ▤ TV ☎. AE S O E VISA.
*Easter-October* - **Meals** a la carte 55/80000 (15 %) - **10 rm** ☐ 450/530000, 30 suites ☐ 650/800000.

**Casa Morgano** M without rest., via Tragara 6 ☎ (081)8370158, *Fax (081)8370681,* ≤ sea and Certosa, « Floral terraces in pinewood », heated - ▤ TV ☎. AE S O E VISA
*26 March-5 November* - **28 rm** ☐ 320/550000.

**Luna** , viale Matteotti 3 ☎ (081)8370433, *Fax (081)8377459,* ≤ sea, Faraglioni and Certosa, , « Terraces and garden with » - ▤ TV ☎. AE S O E VISA.
*Easter-October* - **Meals** a la carte 65/85000 - **50 rm** ☐ 380/480000, 4 suites.

**La Palma,** via Vittorio Emanuele 39 ☎ (081)8370133, *Fax (081)8376966,* , ≘s - ▤ TV ☎ - 200. AE S O E VISA. rest
**Meals** a la carte 45/70000 - **74 rm** ☐ 255/430000.

**La Pazziella** without rest., via Giuliani 4 ☎ (081)8370044, *Fax (081)8370085,* « Floral garden » - ▤ TV ☎. AE S O VISA.
*15 March-15 October and New Year* - **19 rm** ☐ 240/340000, suite.

**Villa Brunella** , via Tragara 24 ☎ (081)8370122, *Fax (081)8370430,* ≤ sea and coast, , « Floral terraces », heated - ▤ rm, TV ☎. AE S O E VISA.
*19 March-5 November* - **Meals** a la carte 40/80000 (12 %) - **20 rm** ☐ 320/470000.

**Sirene,** via Camerelle 51 ☎ (081)8370102, *Fax (081)8370957,* ≤, , « Lemon-garden with » - ▤ TV ☎. AE S O E VISA JCB.
*April-October* - **Meals** *(closed Tuesday except June to September)* a la carte 50/65000 - **35 rm** ☐ 300/420000.

**Canasta** without rest., via Campo di Teste ☎ (081)8370561, *Fax (081)8376675,* - ▤ TV ☎. AE S O E VISA.
**17 rm** ☐ 160/300000.

XXX **Quisi** - Gd H. Quisisana, via Camerelle 2 ☎ (081)8370788, *Fax (081)8376080* – ▤. AE ⑤ ⓓ E VISA. ✂
*Easter-October ; dinner only* – **Meals** a la carte 75/105000.

XX **La Capannina,** via Le Botteghe 14 ☎ (081)8370732, *Fax (081)8376990* – ▤. AE ⑤ ⓓ E VISA. ✂
*27 December-5 January and 10 March-10 November* – **Meals** (booking essential for dinner) a la carte 55/80000 (15 %).

XX **Villa Verde,** via Sella Orta 6/a ☎ (081)8377024, ☂ – ▤. AE ⑤ ⓓ E VISA. ✂
*closed Tuesday October-February* – **Meals** Rest. and pizzeria a la carte 40/55000 (10 %).

**at Anacapri** *alt. 275* – ✉ *80071* :

**Europa Palace,** via Capodimonte 2 ☎ (081)8373800, *Fax (081)8373191*, ≤, ☂, « Floral terraces with ⛱ », Ꮭ, ≘, ⛱ – |♦| ▤ TV ☎ – 🏛 200. AE ⑤ ⓓ E VISA JCB. ✂
*April-October* – **Meals** a la carte 85/125000 – **90 rm** ☐ 440/530000, suite.

**at Marina Piccola** – ✉ *80073 Capri* :

XXX **Canzone del Mare,** ☎ (081)8370104, *Fax (081)8370541*, ≤ Faraglioni and sea, ☂, « Bathing establishment with ⛱ »
*Easter-October* – **Meals** (lunch only) a la carte 60/100000.

**Sant'Agata sui due Golfi** *80064 Napoli* 431 F 25 *G. Italy* – alt. 391 – High Season : April-September.
*Roma 266 – Castellammare di Stabia 28 – Napoli 55 – Salerno 56 – Sorrento 9.*

XXX ✿✿✿ **Don Alfonso 1890** with rm, ☎ (081)8780026, *Fax (081)5330226*, ☂ – Ⓟ. AE ⑤ ⓓ E VISA. ✂
*closed 6 January-26 February* – **Meals** *(closed Monday June-September and Tuesday October-May)* (booking essential) a la carte 90/140000 – 3 suites ☐ 170/270000
**Spec.** Astice in insalata con fiori di gelsomino, fagiolini e pistacchi (summer). Gattò di patate con fonduta di mozzarella, percorino e basilico. Casseruola di pesce di scoglio con crostacei e frutti di mare.

*For the quickest route use the* ***MICHELIN Country Maps :***

**907** ***Benelux,*** **908** ***Netherlands,*** **909** ***Belgium,*** **923** ***Ireland,***
**924** ***Luxembourg,*** **925** ***Hungary,*** **926** ***Austria,*** **927** ***Switzerland,***
**940** ***Portugal,*** **970** ***Europe,*** **974** ***Poland,***
**976** ***Czech Republic-Slovak Republic,*** **980** ***Greece,*** **984** ***Germany,***
**985** ***Scandinavia-Finland,*** **986** ***Great Britain and Ireland,***
**987** ***Germany-Austria-Benelux,*** **988** ***Italy,*** **989** ***France,***
**990** ***Spain-Portugal*** *and* **991** ***Yugoslavia.***

---

**PALERMO** (Sicily) *90100* Ⓟ 988 ㉟, 432 M 22 *G. Italy – pop. 687 855.*

**See :** *Palace of the Normans★★ : the palatine Chapel★★★, mosaics★★★* AZ – *Regional Gallery of Sicily★★ in Abbatellis Palace★ : Death Triumphant fresco★★★* CY – *Piazza Bellini★* BY : *Martorana Church★★, Church of St. Cataldo★★ – Church of St. John of the Hermits★★* AZ – *Capuchin Catacombs★★ – Piazza Pretoria★* BY : *fountain★★ – Archaeological Museum★ : metopes from the temples at Selinus★★, the Ram★★* BY – *Chiaramonte Palace★ : magnolia fig trees★★ in Garibaldi Gardens* CY – *Quattro Canti★* BY – *Cathedral★* AYZ *Mirto Palace★* CY **B** *Villa Bonanno★* AZ *Zisa Palace★ – Botanical garden★* CDZ – *International Museum of Marionettes★* CY **A** *Sicilian carts★ in Ethnographic Museum* **M.**

**Envir.** : *Monreale★★★* AZ *by Corso Calatafimi : 8 km – Monte Pellegrino★★* BX *by via Crispi : 14 km.*

✈ *Punta Raisi E : 30 km ☎ (091)591690, Fax (091)595030 – Alitalia, via Mazzini 59 ✉ 90139 ☎ (091)6019111.*

⛴ *to Genova daily (20 h) and to Livorno Tuesday, Thursday and Saturday (17 h) – Grandi Navi Veloci, calata Marinai d'italia ✉ 90133 ☎ (091)587404, Fax (091)6110088; to Napoli daily (11 h), to Genova Monday, Wednesday and Friday and Sunday 18 June-31 December (24 h) and Cagliari Saturady (14 h 30 mn) – Tirrenia Navigazione, calata Marinai d'Italia ✉ 90133 ☎ (091)333300, Fax (091)6021221.*

⛴ *to Aeolian Island June-September daily (1 h 50 mn) – SNAV Barbaro Agency, piazza Principe di Belmonte 51/55 ✉ 90139 ☎ (091)586533, Fax (091)584830.*

ℹ *piazza Castelnuovo 34 ✉ 90141 ☎ (091)583847, Fax (091)331854 – Punta Raisi Airport at Cinisi ☎ (091)591698.*

**A.C.I.** *via delle Alpi 6 ✉ 90144 ☎ (091)300468.*
*Messina 235.*

**Villa Igiea Gd H.**, salita Belmonte 43 ✉ 90142 ☎ (091)543744, *Fax (091)547654*, ≤, 🍴, « 19C mansion with seafront terrace », sea wather, ✂, – ☰ TV ☎ ♿ P – 🏛 400. AE ⓢ ◐ E VISA. ✂ rest by via Crispi BX
**Meals** a la carte 80/120000 – **109 rm** ☕ 245/370000, 6 suites.

**Astoria Palace,** via Monte Pellegrino 62 ✉ 90142 ☎ (091)6371820, *Fax (091)6372178* – ☰ TV ☎ P – 🏛 800. AE ⓢ ◐ E VISA. ✂ by via Crispi BX
**Meals** 55/90000 and ***Il Cedro*** Rest. a la carte 55/90000 – **310 rm** ☕ 220/285000, 8 suites.

**Centrale Palace Hotel** M, corso Vittorio Emanuele 327 ✉ 90134 ☎ (091)336666, *Fax (091)334881*, « In a 17C building » – ☰ TV ☎ ♿. AE ⓢ ◐ E VISA. ✂ BY b
**Meals** (residents only) 50000 – ☕ 20000 – **61 rm** 200/295000, 3 suites.

**San Paolo Palace,** via Messina Marine 91 ✉ 90123 ☎ (091)6211112, *Fax (091)6215300*, ≤, « Roof-garden rest. », Fø, ≘s, ✂, – ☰ TV ☎ ♿ P – 🏛 1500. AE ⓢ ◐ E VISA. ✂ by via Ponte di Mare DZ
**Meals** 50000 – **285 rm** ☕ 170/210000, 10 suites.

**Jolly,** Foro Italico 22 ✉ 90133 ☎ (091)6165090, *Fax (091)6161441*, 🍴, ✂, – ☰ TV ☎ P – 🏛 300. AE ⓢ ◐ E VISA. ✂ rest DY s
**Meals** a la carte 55/85000 – **234 rm** ☕ 185/250000.

Politeama Palace, piazza Ruggero Settimo 15 ✉ 90139 ☎ (091)322777, *Fax (091)6111589* – ☰ TV ☎ – 🏛 130 AX s
**102 rm.**

**Forte Agip** M, viale della Regione Siciliana 2620 ✉ 90145 ☎ (091)552033, *Fax (091)408198* – ☰ TV ☎ P – 🏛 90. AE ⓢ ◐ E VISA JCB. ✂
**Meals** a la carte 50/60000 – **105 rm** ☕ 180/225000. by via della Libertà AX

**Villa d'Amato,** via Messina Marine 180 ✉ 90123 ☎ (091)6212767, *Fax (091)6212767* – ☰ TV ☎ P – 🏛 100. AE ⓢ ◐ E VISA. ✂ rest by via Ponte di Mare DZ
**Meals** *(closed Sunday)* a la carte 50/70000 – **25 rm** ☕ 130/170000, 12 suites.

XXX **La Scuderia,** viale del Fante 9 ✉ 90146 ☎ (091)520323, *Fax (091)520467* – ☰ P. AE ⓢ ◐ E VISA. ✂ by via C.A. Dalla Chiesa AX
*closed Sunday* – **Meals** a la carte 55/95000.

XX **Gourmand's,** via della Libertà 37/e ✉ 90139 ☎ (091)323431, *Fax (091)322507* – ☰. AE ⓢ ◐ E VISA. ✂ AX e
*closed Sunday and August* – **Meals** a la carte 45/75000.

XX **Friend's Bar,** via Brunelleschi 138 ✉ 90145 ☎ (091)201401, *Fax (091)201066*, 🍴 – ☰. AE ⓢ ◐ E VISA. ✂ by via della Libertà AX
*closed Monday and 16 to 31 August* – **Meals** (booking essential) a la carte 50/70000.

XX **Lo Scudiero,** via Turati 7 ✉ 90139 ☎ (091)581628 – ☰. AE ⓢ ◐ E VISA JCB. ✂ AX c
*closed Sunday dinner, Monday lunch and 10 to 20 August* – **Meals** a la carte 50/80000.

XX **Il Ristorantino,** piazza De Gasperi 19 ✉ 90146 ☎ (091)512861, *Fax (091)6702999*, 🍴 – ☰. AE ⓢ ◐ E VISA. ✂ by via C.A. Dalla Chiesa AX
*closed Monday and 1 to 20 August* – **Meals** a la carte 50/80000.

XX **Regine,** via Trapani 4/a ✉ 90141 ☎ (091)586566 – ☰. AE ⓢ ◐ E VISA JCB. ✂
*closed Sunday and August* – **Meals** a la carte 60/70000. AX d

X **Trattoria Biondo,** via Carducci 15 ✉ 90141 ☎ (091)583662 – ☰. AE ⓢ E VISA. ✂ AX a
*closed Wednesday and 15 July-15 September* – **Meals** a la carte 35/50000 (15 %).

X **Il Vespro,** via B. D'Acquisto 9 ✉ 90141 ☎ (091)589932 – ☰. AE ⓢ ◐ E VISA. ✂
**Meals** Rest. and pizzeria a la carte 35/55000. AX b

**at Sferracavallo** *NO : 12 Km – ✉ 90148 Palermo :*

X **Il Delfino,** via Torretta 80 ☎ (091)530282
☰. AE ⓢ ◐ VISA. ✂
*closed Monday* – **Meals** seafood 40000.

## Villafrati *90030 Palermo 988 ㊱, 432 N 22 – pop. 3 437 alt. 450.*

*Palermo 36 – Agrigento 87 – Caltanissetta 100.*

XX **Mulinazzo,** strada statale 121, località Bolognetta N : 9 ; Km ☎ (091)8724870, *Fax (091)8724870* – ☰ P. AE ⓢ ◐ E VISA
✿ *closed Sunday dinner, Monday, 6 to 26 July and 5 to 18 January* – **Meals** a la carte 45/60000
**Spec.** Couscous di verdure e pesce. Spaghetti con pesce spada e gamberi. Petto d'anatra al Calvados.

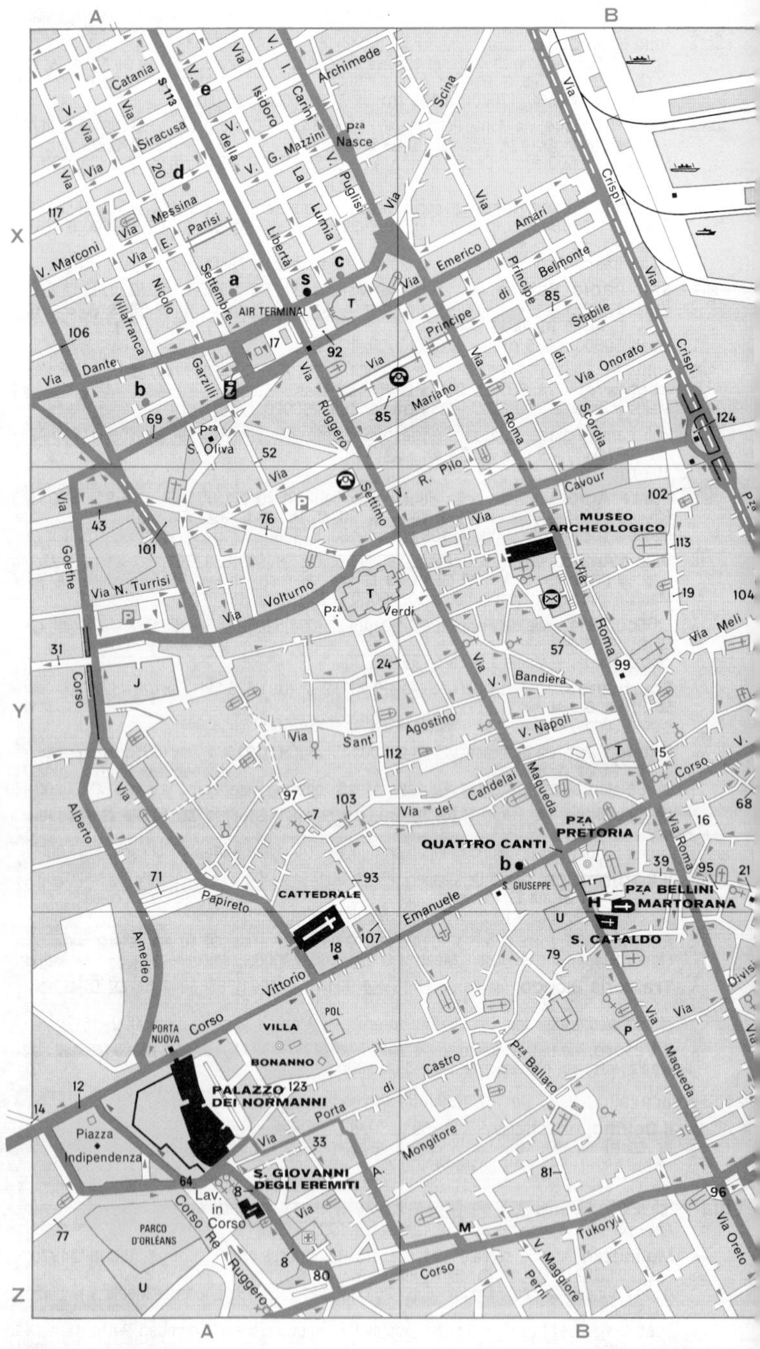
A
B
X
Y
Z
Via Catania
Via Siracusa
Via Messina
V. Marconi
Via E. Parisi
Via Nicolo Garzilli
Via Villafranca
Via Dante
Via Isidoro La Lumia
Via della Libertà
V. G. Mazzini
V. I. Carini
Archimede
Pza Nasce
V. Puglisi
Via Scina
Via Emerico Amari
Via Principe di Belmonte
Via Principe di Stabile
Via Onorato
Via Mariano
Via Scordia
Via Crispi
Via Ruggero Settimo
V. R. Pilo
Via Cavour
MUSEO ARCHEOLOGICO
Via Roma
Via Goethe
Via N. Turrisi
Via Volturno
Pza Verdi
Via Sant' Agostino
V. Napoli
Via V. Bandiera
Via Meli
Corso Alberto Amedeo
Via Papireto
Via dei Candelai
Via Maqueda
QUATTRO CANTI
Pza PRETORIA
Pza BELLINI
MARTORANA
S. CATALDO
S. GIUSEPPE
CATTEDRALE
Corso Vittorio Emanuele
PORTA NUOVA
VILLA BONANNO
POL.
PALAZZO DEI NORMANNI
Piazza Indipendenza
Via Porta di Castro
Pza Ballaro
Via Mongitore
S. GIOVANNI DEGLI EREMITI
Lav. in Corso
Corso Re Ruggero
PARCO D'ORLÉANS
Corso Tukory
V. Maggiore Perni
Via Oreto
Divisi
AIR TERMINAL
S 113

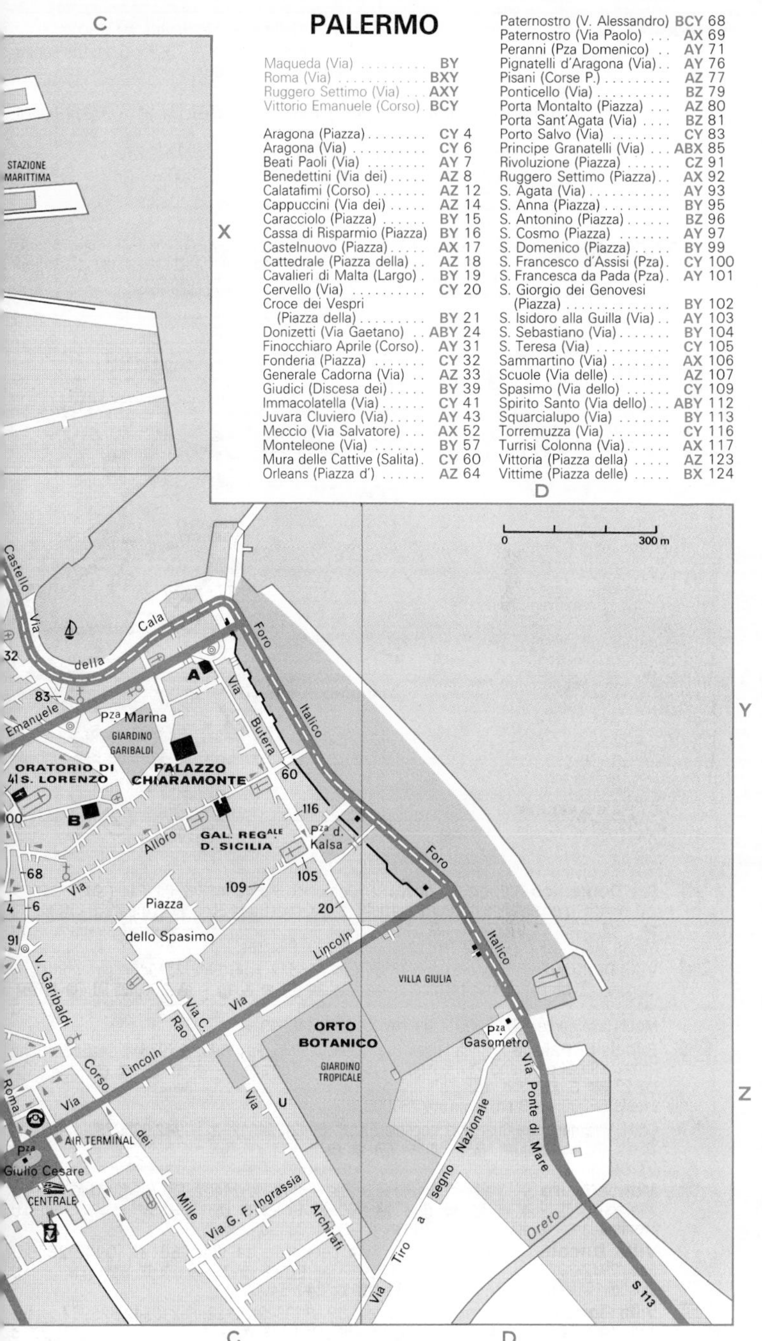
PALERMO
Maqueda (Via) ......... BY
Roma (Via) ........... BXY
Ruggero Settimo (Via) ... AXY
Vittorio Emanuele (Corso). BCY
Aragona (Piazza)........ CY 4
Aragona (Via) .......... CY 6
Beati Paoli (Via) ........ AY 7
Benedettini (Via dei)..... AZ 8
Calatafimi (Corso) ....... AZ 12
Cappuccini (Via dei) ..... AZ 14
Caracciolo (Piazza) ...... BY 15
Cassa di Risparmio (Piazza) BY 16
Castelnuovo (Piazza)..... AX 17
Cattedrale (Piazza della) .. AZ 18
Cavalieri di Malta (Largo) . BY 19
Cervello (Via) .......... CY 20
Croce dei Vespri (Piazza della).......... BY 21
Donizetti (Via Gaetano) .. ABY 24
Finocchiaro Aprile (Corso). AY 31
Fonderia (Piazza) ....... CY 32
Generale Cadorna (Via) .. AZ 33
Giudici (Discesa dei)..... BY 39
Immacolatella (Via)...... CY 41
Juvara Cluviero (Via)..... AY 43
Meccio (Via Salvatore) ... AX 52
Monteleone (Via) ....... BY 57
Mura delle Cattive (Salita). CY 60
Orleans (Piazza d') ...... AZ 64
Paternostro (V. Alessandro) BCY 68
Paternostro (Via Paolo) ... AX 69
Peranni (Pza Domenico) .. AY 71
Pignatelli d'Aragona (Via).. AY 76
Pisani (Corse P.) ......... AZ 77
Ponticello (Via) ......... BZ 79
Porta Montalto (Piazza) ... AZ 80
Porta Sant'Agata (Via) .... BZ 81
Porto Salvo (Via) ........ CY 83
Principe Granatelli (Via) ... ABX 85
Rivoluzione (Piazza) ...... CZ 91
Ruggero Settimo (Piazza).. AX 92
S. Agata (Via)........... AY 93
S. Anna (Piazza) ......... BY 95
S. Antonino (Piazza)...... BZ 96
S. Cosmo (Piazza) ....... AY 97
S. Domenico (Piazza) ..... BY 99
S. Francesco d'Assisi (Pza). CY 100
S. Francesca da Pada (Pza). AY 101
S. Giorgio dei Genovesi (Piazza) ............. BY 102
S. Isidoro alla Guilla (Via).. AY 103
S. Sebastiano (Via)....... BY 104
S. Teresa (Via) .......... CY 105
Sammartino (Via)........ AX 106
Scuole (Via delle)........ AZ 107
Spasimo (Via dello) ...... CY 109
Spirito Santo (Via dello)... ABY 112
Squarcialupo (Via) ....... BY 113
Torremuzza (Via) ........ CY 116
Turrisi Colonna (Via)...... AX 117
Vittoria (Piazza della) ..... AZ 123
Vittime (Piazza delle) ..... BX 124
C
D
X
Y
Z
0
300 m
STAZIONE MARITTIMA
Castello
Via
Cala
della
Foro
Italico
Emanuele
Pza Marina
GIARDINO GARIBALDI
ORATORIO DI S. LORENZO
PALAZZO CHIARAMONTE
Via Butera
GAL. REGALE D. SICILIA
Pza d. Kalsa
Alloro
Via
Piazza dello Spasimo
Lincoln
Via
VILLA GIULIA
V. Garibaldi
Via C. Rao
ORTO BOTANICO
GIARDINO TROPICALE
Pza Gasometro
Via Ponte di Mare
Corso Lincoln
Via
Roma
AIR TERMINAL
Pza Giulio Cesare
CENTRALE
Corso dei Mille
Via G. F. Ingrassia
Archirafi
Via Tiro a segno Nazionale
Oreto
S 113
A
B
U
32
83
41
100
68
4
6
91
60
116
105
109
20

**TAORMINA** (Sicily) *98039 Messina* 988 ㊲, 432 N 27 *G. Italy – pop. 10 465 alt. 250.*

**See** : *Site★★★ – Greek Theatre★★ : ≤★★★* B *– Public garden★★* B *– ✱★★ from the Square 9 Aprile* A **13** *– Corso Umberto★* A *– Belvedere★* B *– Castle★ : ≤★* A.

**Exc.** : *Etna★★★, SW : for Linguaglossa.*

*18 Picciolo, contrada Rovitello ✉ 95012 Castiglione di Sicilia ☎ (0942)986171, Fax (0942)986252, O : 25 km.*

*ℹ piazza Santa Caterina (Corvaja palace) ☎ (0942)23243, Fax (0942)24941.*

*Catania 52 ② – Enna 135 ② – Messina 52 ① – Palermo 255 ② – Siracusa 111 ② – Trapani 359 ②.*

## TAORMINA

| | | | | | |
|---|---|---|---|---|---|
| Umberto (Corso) | A | Cappuccini (Via) | A 2 | S. Antonio (Piazza) | A 9 |
| | | Crocifisso (Via) | A 3 | Vinci (V. Leonardo da) | A 10 |
| | | Dionisio Primo (Via) | A 5 | Vittorio Emanuele II (Pza) | B 12 |
| | | Duomo (Piazza) | A 6 | 9 Aprile (Piazza) | A 13 |

Traffic restricted in the town centre from June to September

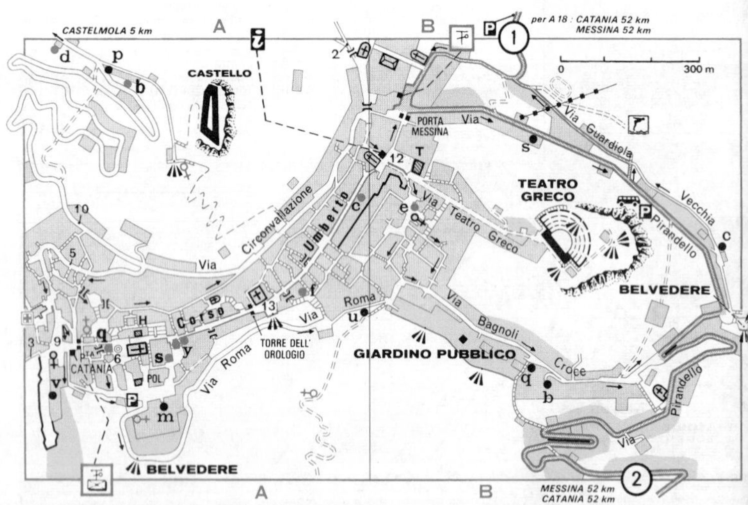


**San Domenico Palace** 🐦, piazza San Domenico 5 ☎ (0942)23701, *Fax (0942)625506*, « 15C monastery with floral garden, ≤ sea, coast and Etna », heated – AE VISA. A m
**Meals** 100/110000 – **102 rm** 400/685000, 9 suites.

**Villa Diodoro,** via Bagnolo Croci 75 ☎ (0942)23312, *Fax (0942)23391*, ≤ sea, coast and Etna, « on panoramic terrace », – – 300. AE VISA. B q
**Meals** a la carte 55/85000 – **99 rm** 240/340000.

**Excelsior Palace** 🐦, via Toselli 8 ☎ (0942)23975, *Fax (0942)23978*, ≤ sea, coast and Etna, « Small park and heated on panoramic terrace » – – 100. AE VISA. rest A v
**Meals** 65000 – **88 rm** 190/280000.

Gd H. Miramare, via Guardiola Vecchia 27 ☎ (0942)23401, *Fax (0942)626223*, ≤ sea and coast, heated, – B c
**67 rm.**

**Monte Tauro** 🐦, via Madonna delle Grazie 3 ☎ (0942)24402, *Fax (0942)24403*, ≤ sea and coast, – – 100. AE VISA JCB. AB u
**Meals** a la carte 40/60000 – **70 rm** 210/300000.

**Villa Ducale** 🐦 without rest., via Leonardo da Vinci 60 ☎ (0942)28153, *Fax (0942)28710*, ≤ sea, coast and Etna – AE VISA JCB A p
*closed 15 January-15 February* – **12 rm** 240/340000.

**Villa Fiorita** without rest., via Pirandello 39 ☎ (0942)24122, *Fax (0942)625967*, ≤ sea and coast, – AE VISA B s
**24 rm** 160/170000.

**Villa Belvedere** without rest., via Bagnoli Croci 79 (0942)23791, *Fax (0942)625830*, gardens, sea and Etna, « Garden with » – rm, . B b
*closed November-20 December and 10 January-15 March* – **47 rm** 155/245000.

**Villa Sirina,** contrada Sirina (0942)51776, *Fax (0942)51671*, – . AE VISA. 2 km by via Crocifisso A
*closed 10 January-20 March* – **Meals** (residents only) (dinner only) – **15 rm** 170/200000.

**La Giara,** vico La Floresta 1 (0942)23360, *Fax (0942)23233*, Rest. and piano bar – . AE VISA. A f
*closed October, November (except Friday-Saturday) and Monday (except July-September)* – **Meals** *(dinner only)* (booking essential) a la carte 60/85000.

**Maffei's,** via San Domenico de Guzman 1 (0942)24055, *Fax (0942)24055*, – AE VISA A y
*closed 10 January to 20 February and Tuesday (except Easter and October)* – **Meals** (booking essential) a la carte 65/95000.

**La Griglia,** corso Umberto 54 (0942)23980 – . AE VISA. A c
*closed Tuesday and 20 November-20 December* – **Meals** a la carte 40/60000.

**Al Duomo,** vico Ebrei 11 (0942)625656, « Summer service on terrace » – . AE VISA A q
**Meals** (booking essential) Sicilian rest. a la carte 50/70000.

**Al Castello,** via Madonna della Rocca 11 (0942)28158, « Summer service on panoramic terrace with sea and coast » – AE VISA. A b
*closed Wednesday except dinner June-September and 15 January-20 February* – **Meals** a la carte 50/90000.

**La Piazzetta,** via Paladini 5 (0942)626317 – . AE VISA A s
*closed Monday, 15 to 30 November and 15 to 30 January* – **Meals** a la carte 45/70000.

**Il Baccanale,** piazzetta Filea 1 (0942)625390, – . VISA. B e
*closed Thursday except April-September* – **Meals** a la carte 35/60000.

**La Chioccia d'Oro,** via Leonardo da Vinci (0942)28066, A d
*closed Thursday and November* – **Meals** a la carte 35/50000.

**at Mazzarò** *by ② : 5,5 km – 98030 :*

**Mazzarò Sea Palace,** via Nazionale 147 (0942)24004, *Fax (0942)626237*, small bay, , « Solarium-terrace with », – – 90. AE VISA.
*April-October* – **Meals** a la carte 55/100000 – **83 rm** 240/470000, 4 suites.

**at Capo Taormina** *by ② : 7 Km – 98030 Mazzarò :*

**Grande Albergo Capotaormina,** via Nazionale 105 (0942)24000, *Fax (0942)625467*, sea and coast, « Garden-terrace on cliffs, lifts to beach », sea water, – , rm, – 450. AE VISA.
*April-October* – **Meals** a la carte 50/90000 and ***La Scogliera*** Rest. *(closed until May, October and dinner Monday and Tuesday)* (booking essential) a la carte 65/100000 – **203 rm** 260/350000.

**at Lido di Spisone** *by ① : 7 km – 98030 Mazzarò :*

**Lido Caparena,** via Nazionale 189 (0942)652033, *Fax (0942)36913*, , « Extensive flower garden with outdoor rest. summer service », , – – 200. AE VISA.
**Meals** a la carte 50/80000 – **88 rm** 250/340000.

**Lido Mediterranée,** (0942)24422, *Fax (0942)24774*, , , – – 100. AE VISA. rest
*28 March-October* – **Meals** a la carte 65/90000 – **72 rm** 300/350000.

**Bay Palace,** via Nazionale (0942)626200, *Fax (0942)626199*, « Solarium-terrace with panoramic » – . AE VISA. rest
**Meals** (dinner only) 30/65000 – **47 rm** 160/220000.

*Don't confuse :*
Comfort of hotels : ...
Comfort of restaurants : XXXXX ... X
Quality of the cuisine : , , , Meals

**TURIN** (TORINO) *10100* P 988 ⑫, 428 G 5 *G. Italy – pop. 919612 alt. 239.*

**See** : *Piazza San Carlo★★* CXY – *Egyptian Museum★★, Sabauda Gallery★★ in Academy of Science* CX **M**¹ – *Cathedral★* VX : *relic of the Holy Shroud★★★ – Mole Antonelliana★ : ※★★* DX – *Madama Palace★ : museum of Ancient Art★* CX **A** – *Royal Palace★ : Royal Armoury★* CDVX – *Risorgimento Museum★ in Carignano Palace* CX **M**² – *Carlo Biscaretti di Ruffia Motor Museum★ – Model medieval village★ in the Valentino Park* CDZ.

**Envir.** : *Basilica of Superga★ : ≤★★★, royal tombs★ – Tour to the pass, Colle della Maddalena★ : ≤★★ of the city from the route Superga-Pino Torinese, ≤★ of the city from the route Colle Colle della Maddalena-Cavoretto.*

*18, 9 I Roveri (March-November ; closed Monday) at La Mandria ✉ 10070 Fiano Torinese (011)9235719, Fax (011)9235669, N : 18 km;*

*18, 18 (closed Monday, January and February), at Fiano Torinese ✉ 10070 ✆ (011)9235440, Fax (011)9235886, N : 20 km;*

*18 Le Fronde (closed Tuesday, January and February) at Avigliana ✉ 10051 ✆ (011)9328053, Fax (011)9320928, W : 24 km;*

*9 Stupinigi (closed Monday), ✆ (011)3472640, Fax (011)3978038;*

*9 (closed Monday and 21 December-9 January) at Vinovo ✉ 10048 ✆ (011)9653880, Fax (011)9623748.*

*Turin Airport of Caselle N : 15 km ✆ (011)5676361, Fax (011) 5676420 – Alitalia, via Lagrange 35 ✉ 10123 ✆ (011)57697, Fax (011)57691.*

*✆ (011)6651111-int. 2611.*

*via Roma 226 (piazza C.L.N.) ✉ 10121 ✆ (011)535901, Fax (011)530070 – Porta Nuova Railway Station ✉ 10125 ✆ (011)531327.*

A.C.I. *via Giovanni Giolitti 15 ✉ 10123 ✆ (011)57791.*

*Roma 669 – Briançon 108 – Chambéry 209 – Genève 252 – Genova 170 – Grenoble 224 – Milano 140 – Nice 220.*

Plans on following pages

**Turin Palace Hotel,** via Sacchi 8 ✉ 10128 ✆ (011)5625511, *Fax (011)5612187* – AE VISA. rest CY u
Meals *(closed August)* a la carte 65/100000 – **121 rm** 310/390000, 2 suites.

**Jolly Principi di Piemonte,** via Gobetti 15 ✉ 10123 ✆ (011)5629693, *Fax (011)5620270* – – 300. AE VISA JCB. rest CY z
Meals a la carte 70/115000 – **99 rm** 420/450000, 8 suites.

**Le Meridien Lingotto,** via Nizza 262 ✉ 10126 ✆ (011)6642000, *Fax (011)6642001* – rm, – 35. AE VISA. rest by via Nizza CZ
*closed Monday and August* – **Meals** a la carte 80/110000 – **244 rm** 350/420000.

**Gd H. Sitea,** via Carlo Alberto 35 ✉ 10123 ✆ (011)5170171, *Fax (011)548090* – – 100. AE VISA. rest CY t
Meals a la carte 70/100000 – **117 rm** 295/395000.

**Jolly Ambasciatori,** corso Vittorio Emanuele II 104 ✉ 10121 ✆ (011)5752, *Fax (011)544978* – rm, – 400. AE VISA. rest
Meals 55/65000 – **195 rm** 300/360000, 4 suites. BX a

**Diplomatic,** via Cernaia 42 ✉ 10122 ✆ (011)5612444, *Fax (011)540472* – – 200. AE VISA JCB.
Meals (residents only) – **123 rm** 340/450000, 3 suites.

**Jolly Hotel Ligure,** piazza Carlo Felice 85 ✉ 10123 ✆ (011)55641, *Fax (011)535438* – – 200. AE VISA. rest CY b
Meals a la carte 55/100000 – **167 rm** 320/380000, 2 suites.

**Starhotel Majestic** without rest., corso Vittorio Emanuele II 54 ✉ 10123 ✆ (011)539153, *Fax (011)534963* – AE VISA JCB. CY e
**148 rm** 340/440000.

**City** without rest., via Juvarra 25 ✉ 10122 ✆ (011)540546, *Fax (011)548188* – – 60. AE VISA JCB. BV e
**50 rm** 250/360000, 10 suites.

**Victoria** without rest., via Nino Costa 4 ✉ 10123 ✆ (011)5611909, *Fax (011)5611806*, « Elegant and personal ambience » – AE VISA. CY v
**90 rm** 185/265000.

**Relais Villa Sassi**, strada al Traforo del Pino 47 ✉ 10132 ✆ (011)8980556, *Fax (011)8980095*, « 18C country house in extensive parkland » – P – 200. AE VISA. rest by corso Casale DY
*closed August* – **Meals** ***El Toulà*** Rest. *(closed Sunday)* a la carte 80/120000 – **16 rm** 270/400000.

**Holiday Inn Turin City Centre**, via Assietta 3 ✉ 10128 ☎ (011)5167111, *Fax (011)5167699* – rm, – 40. rest
**Meals** (dinner only) 30/60000 – 24000 – **57 rm** 260/360000. CY a

**Boston** without rest., via Massena 70 ✉ 10128 ☎ (011)500359, *Fax (011)599358*, – . BZ c
**51 rm** 170/240000, 2 suites.

**Genio** without rest., corso Vittorio Emanuele II 47 ✉ 10125 ☎ (011)6505771, *Fax (011)6508264* – – 25. CYZ w
**90 rm** 170/220000.

**Concord,** via Lagrange 47 ✉ 10123 ☎ (011)5176756, *Fax (011)5176305* – – 180. rest CY s
**Meals** 40/60000 – **135 rm** 290/350000, 4 suites.

**Royal,** corso Regina Margherita 249 ✉ 10144 ☎ (011)4376777, *Fax (011)4376393* – – 600. BV u
*closed 1 to 28 August* – **Meals** a la carte 40/70000 – **70 rm** 190/240000.

**Genova e Stazione** without rest., via Sacchi 14/b ✉ 10128 ☎ (011)5629400, *Fax (011)5629896* – – 60. CZ b
*closed 1 to 18 August* – **58 rm** 170/220000, suite.

**President** without rest., via Cecchi 67 ✉ 10152 ☎ (011)859555, *Fax (011)2480465* – . CV s
**72 rm** 150/190000.

**Alexandra** without rest., lungo Dora Napoli 14 ✉ 10152 ☎ (011)858327, *Fax (011)2483805* – . CV c
**56 rm** 170/220000.

**Crimea** without rest., via Mentana 3 ✉ 10133 ☎ (011)6604700, *Fax (011)6604912* – . . DZ e
**48 rm** 170/220000, suite.

**Gran Mogol** without rest., via Guarini 2 ✉ 10123 ☎ (011)5612120, *Fax (011)5623160* – . CY r
*closed August and 23 December-3 January* – **45 rm** 170/220000.

**Piemontese** without rest., via Berthollet 21 ✉ 10125 ☎ (011)6698101, *Fax (011)6690571* – . . CZ x
**35 rm** 160/220000.

**Lancaster** without rest., corso Filippo Turati 8 ✉ 10128 ☎ (011)5681982, *Fax (011)5683019* – . BZ r
*closed 5 to 31 August* – **77 rm** 165/210000.

Venezia without rest., via 20 Settembre 70 ✉ 10122 ☎ (011)5623384, *Fax (011)5623726* – – 60 CX r
**75 rm.**

**Due Mondi** without rest., via Saluzzo 3 ✉ 10125 ☎ (011)6698981, *Fax (011)6699383* – . CZ k
*closed 10 to 20 August* – 15000 – **36 rm** 150/180000.

**Del Cambio,** piazza Carignano 2 ✉ 10123 ☎ (011)543760, *Fax (011)535282*, Historic traditional restaurant, « 19C decor » – . . CX a
*closed Sunday, August and 1 to 6 January* – **Meals** (booking essential) 70/100000 (lunch) 90/110000 (dinner) and a la carte 70/125000 (15 %).

**Balbo,** via Andrea Doria 11 ✉ 10123 ☎ (011)8395775, *Fax (011)8151042* – . . CY n
*closed Monday and 25 July-20 August* – **Meals** (booking essential) a la carte 95/140000
**Spec.** Rotolo d'anguilla in carpione di Moscato (spring-summer). Agnolotti d'asparagi alla crema di rosso d'uovo (spring). Piccioncino disossato con lenticchie di Castelluccio e salsa di fegato d'oca (autumn-winter).

**Rendez Vous,** corso Vittorio Emanuele II 38 ✉ 10123 ☎ (011)887666, *Fax (011)889362* – . . CZ g
*closed Saturday lunch and Sunday* – **Meals** (booking essential for dinner) 35/80000 (lunch) and a la carte 55/90000.

**Villa Somis,** strada Val Pattonera 138 ✉ 10133 ☎ (011)6613086, *Fax (011)6614626*, ≤, « 18C house with park ; summer service under a pergola » – . HU e
*closed 4 to 25 August, 26 December to 7 January, Monday and lunch October-May (except weekends)* – **Meals** (booking essential) a la carte 40/65000.

**Tiffany,** piazza Solferino 16/h ✉ 10121 ☎ (011)535948 – . CX x
*closed Saturday lunch, Sunday and August* – **Meals** a la carte 50/85000.

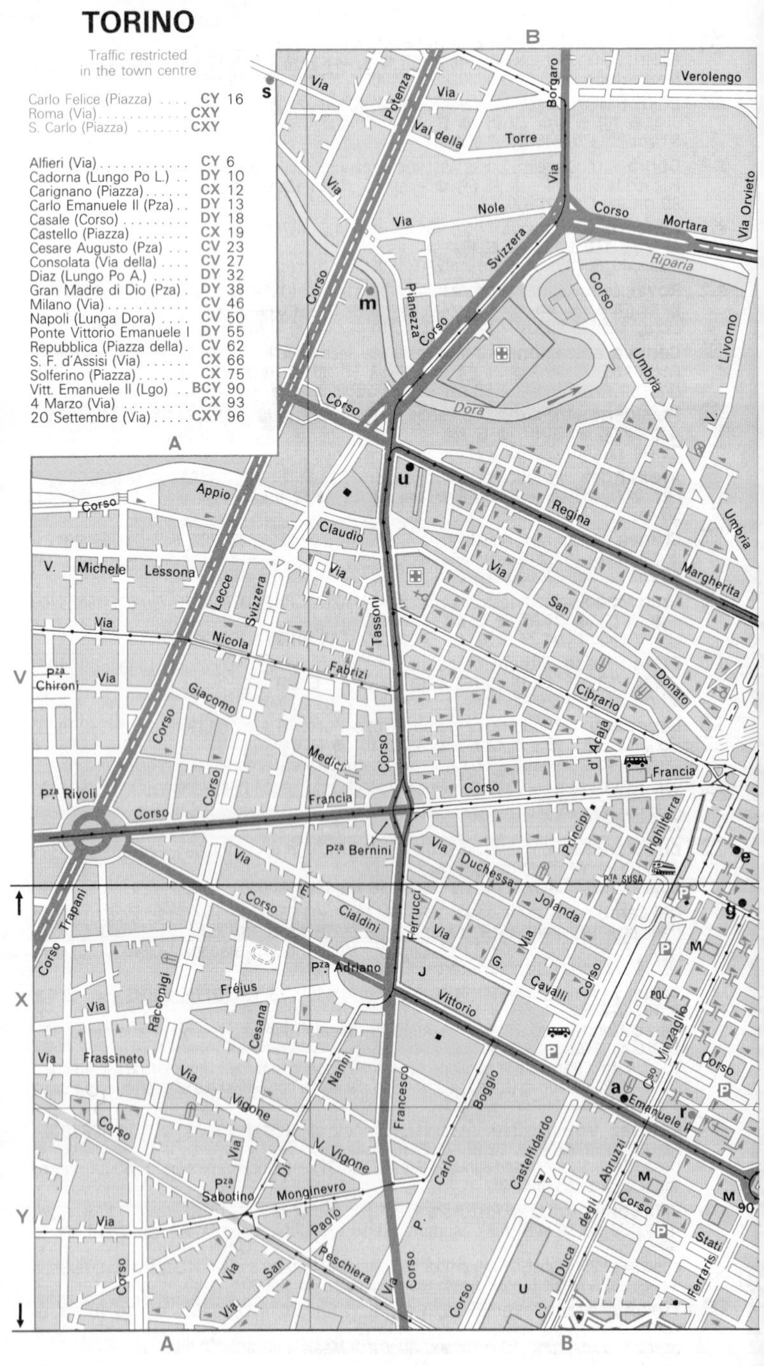
TORINO
Traffic restricted in the town centre
Carlo Felice (Piazza) .... CY 16
Roma (Via) .......... CXY
S. Carlo (Piazza) ....... CXY
Alfieri (Via) .......... CY 6
Cadorna (Lungo Po L.) .. DY 10
Carignano (Piazza) ..... CX 12
Carlo Emanuele II (Pza) .. DY 13
Casale (Corso) ......... DY 18
Castello (Piazza) ....... CX 19
Cesare Augusto (Pza) ... CV 23
Consolata (Via della) .... CV 27
Diaz (Lungo Po A.) ..... DY 32
Gran Madre di Dio (Pza) . DY 38
Milano (Via) .......... CV 46
Napoli (Lunga Dora) .... CV 50
Ponte Vittorio Emanuele I DY 55
Repubblica (Piazza della). CV 62
S. F. d'Assisi (Via) ...... CX 66
Solferino (Piazza) ....... CX 75
Vitt. Emanuele II (Lgo) .. BCY 90
4 Marzo (Via) .......... CX 93
20 Settembre (Via) ..... CXY 96
A
B
V
X
Y
Via Verolengo
Via Borgaro
Via Potenza
Via Val della Torre
Via Nole
Corso Mortara
Via Orvieto
Riparia
Corso Svizzera
Corso Pianezza
Dora
Corso Umbria
Corso Livorno
Corso Regina Margherita
Corso Appio Claudio
V. Michele Lessona
Via Lecce
Via Svizzera
Via Tassoni
Via Nicola Fabrizi
Via San Donato
Via Cibrario
P^za Chironi
Via Giacomo Medici
Corso Francia
Via d' Acaja
Via Principi
Via Inghilterra
P^za Rivoli
P^za Bernini
Via Duchessa Jolanda
P^TA SUSA
Corso Trapani
Via E. Cialdini
Corso Ferrucci
Via G. Cavalli
P^za Adriano
Corso Vittorio Emanuele II
Via Fréjus
Via Racconigi
Via Cesana
Via Frassineto
Via Vigone
Via Nanni
Corso Francesco
Via Boggio
Corso Vinzaglio
Via Castelfidardo
Corso Duca degli Abruzzi
Corso Stati
Ferraris
P^za Sabotino
Via Monginevro
V. Vigone
Via Di Paolo
Via San Paolo
Via Peschiera
Corso Carlo
Corso P.
POL
90

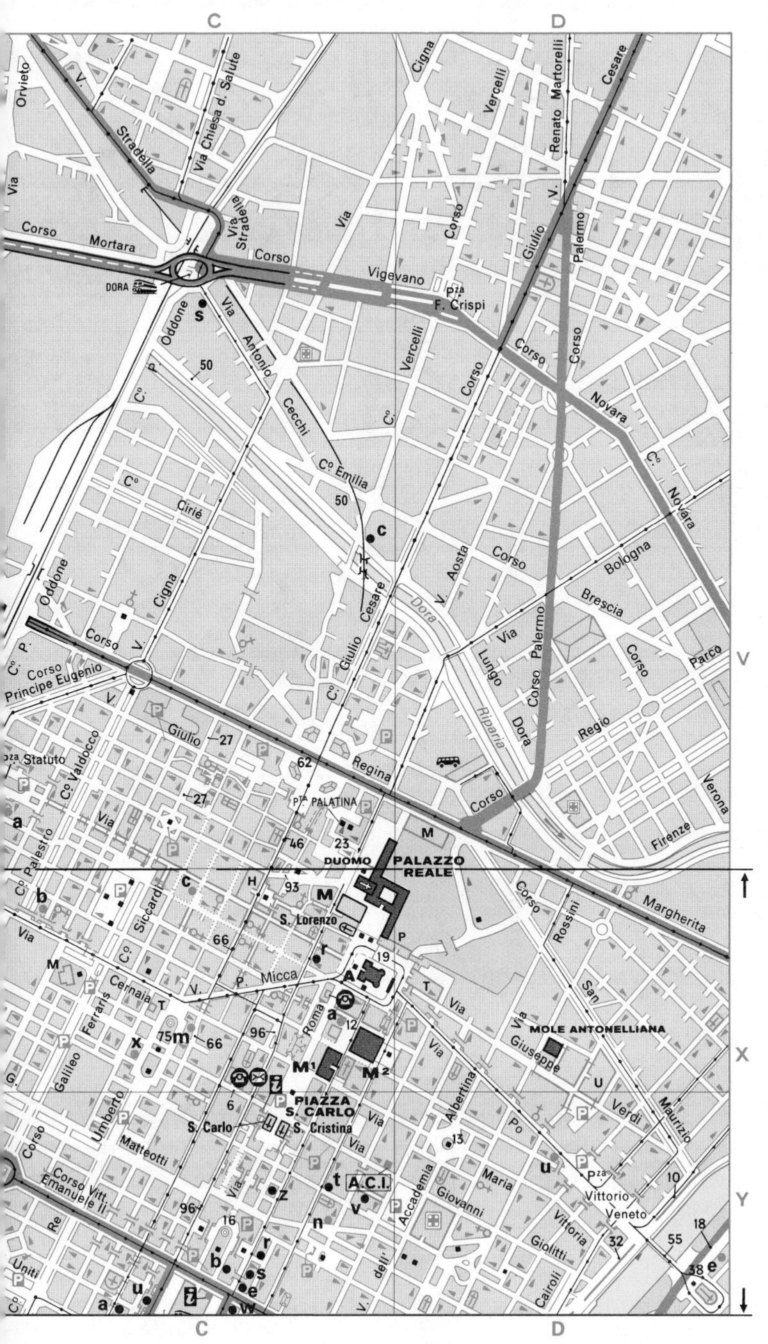
C
D
PALAZZO REALE
DUOMO
MOLE ANTONELLIANA
PIAZZA S. CARLO
A.C.I.
Pza F. Crispi
Pza Statuto
PTA PALATINA
Pza Vittorio Veneto
Corso Vigevano
Corso Regina Margherita
Corso Novara
Corso Principe Eugenio
Via Po
V
X
Y

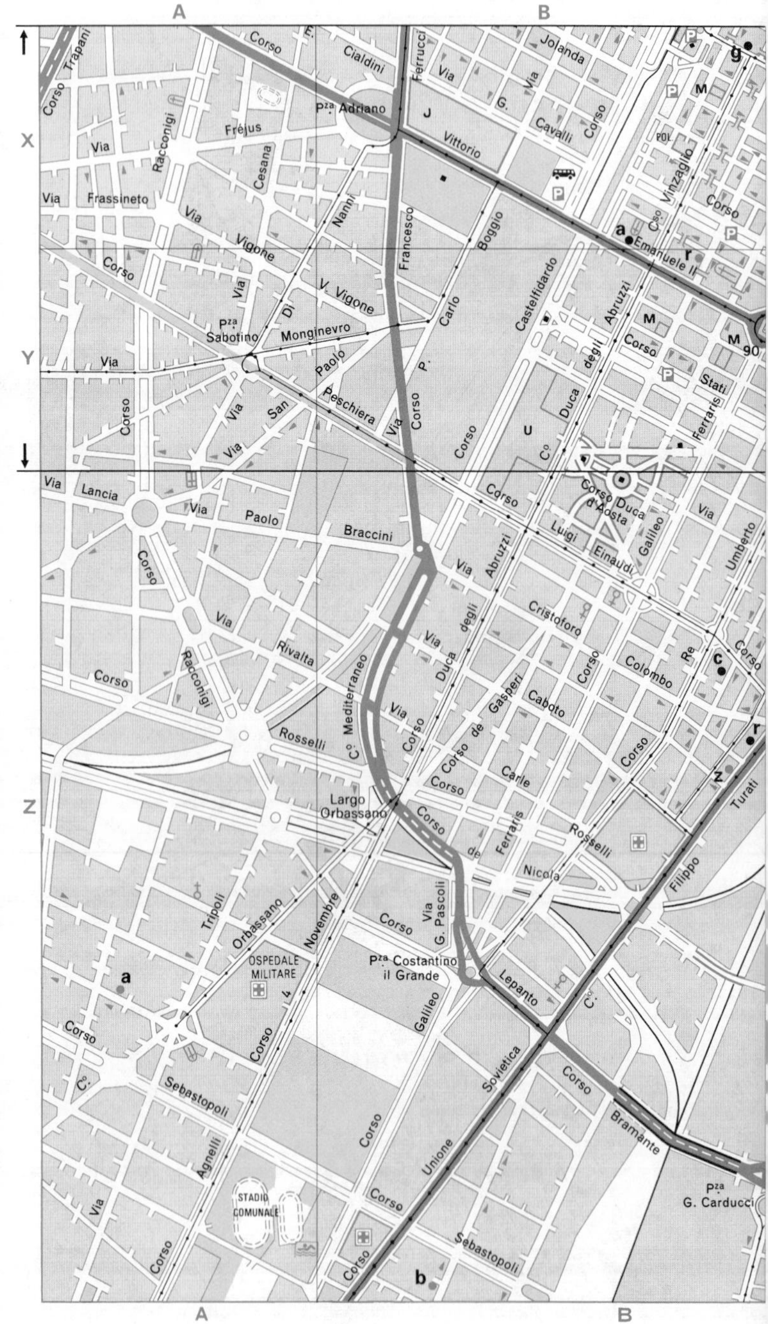

A
B
X
Y
Z
Corso Trapani
Corso Cialdini
Pza. Adriano
Via Ferrucci
Via Jolanda
Via G. Cavalli
Corso Vittorio Emanuele II
Via Fréjus
Via Racconigi
Via Cesana
Via Frassineto
Via Vigone
Via Nanni
Corso Francesco
Corso Boggio
Corso Vinzaglio
Corso Castelfidardo
Corso Di V. Vigone
Pza. Sabotino
Via Monginevro
Corso P. Carlo
Via San Paolo
Via Peschiera
Corso Duca degli Abruzzi
Corso Stati
Ferraris
Corso Duca d'Aosta
Corso Luigi Einaudi
Galileo
Via Umberto
Via Lancia
Via Paolo Braccini
Corso Racconigi
Via Rivalta
Via Duca degli Abruzzi
Cristoforo Colombo
Re
Corso
Corso de Gasperi
Caboto
C° Mediterraneo
Via Rosselli
Carle
Corso Rosselli
Corso Turati
Largo Orbassano
Corso de Nicola
Ferraris
Filippo
Via G. Pascoli
Corso Tripoli
Orbassano
Corso 4 Novembre
OSPEDALE MILITARE
Pza. Costantino il Grande
Lepanto
Corso Galileo
Corso Sebastopoli
Sovietica
Corso Bramante
Unione
Corso Agnelli
Via
STADIO COMUNALE
Pza. G. Carducci
Corso Sebastopoli
POL.
J
U
M
P
a
b
c
g
r
90

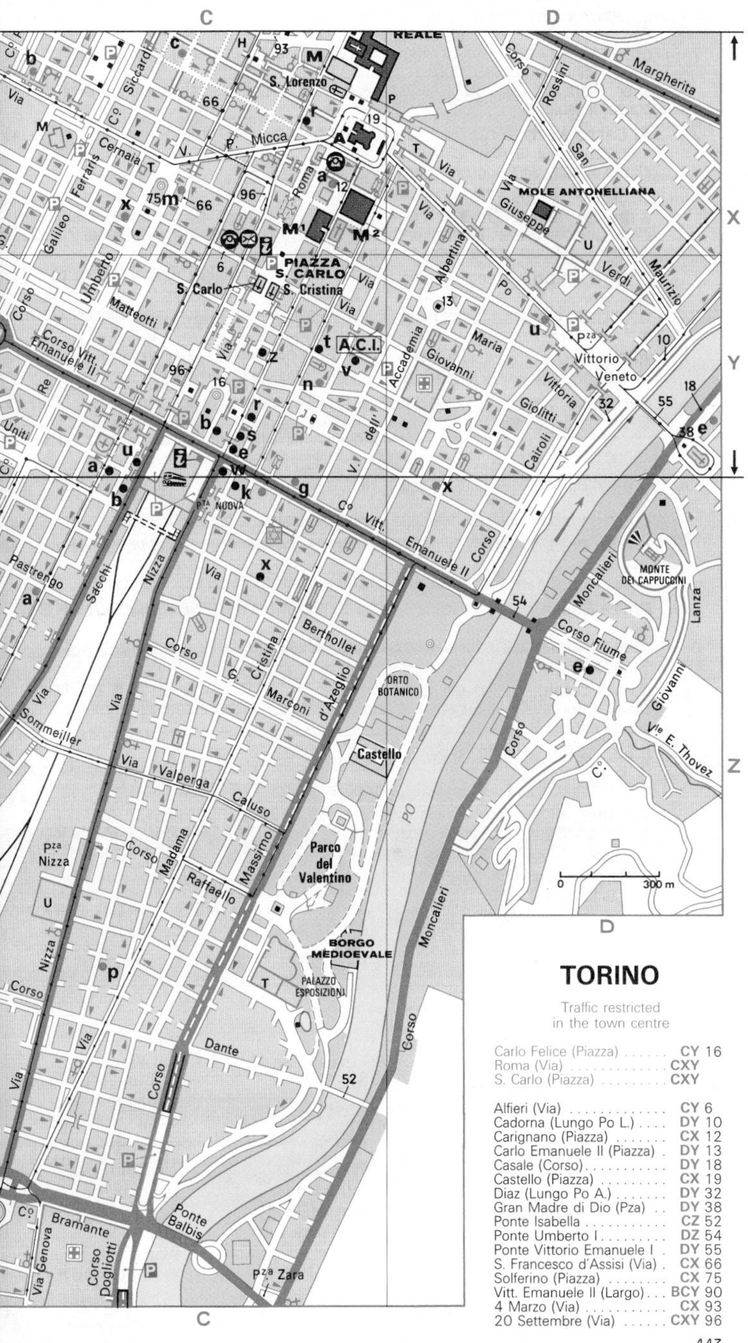


# TORINO

Traffic restricted in the town centre

XXX **La Prima Smarrita,** corso Unione Sovietica 244 ✉ 10134 ✆ (011)3179657, *Fax (011)3179191* – ▤. AE ⓢ ⓓ E VISA. ✻ GTU c
*closed Monday and 3 to 27 August* – **Meals** (booking essential) Mediterranean cuisine 50000 (lunch) and 60/90000
**Spec.** Filetti di triglia con mosaico di verdure. Tortelli di pescatrice. Filetto di rombo con punte di asparagi.

XXX **Al Gatto Nero,** corso Filippo Turati 14 ✉ 10128 ✆ (011)590414, *Fax (011)502245* – ▤. AE ⓢ ⓓ E VISA. ✻ BZ z
*closed Sunday and August* – **Meals** a la carte 70/90000.

XXX **La Cloche,** strada al Traforo del Pino 106 ✉ 10132 ✆ (011)8994213, *Fax (011)8981522* – Ⓟ – 100. AE ⓢ ⓓ E VISA by corso Moncalieri CDZ
*closed Sunday dinner, Monday and 10 to 24 August* – **Meals** (surprise menu) 25/50000 (lunch) 35/60000 (dinner) and a la carte 50/110000.

XX **Trait d'Union,** via degli Stampatori 4 ✉ 10122 ✆ (011)5612506, – AE ⓢ ⓓ E VISA. ✻ CX c
*closed Saturday lunch, Sunday and August* – **Meals** (booking essential for dinner) a la carte 50/70000.

XX **Al Bue Rosso,** corso Casale 10 ✉ 10131 ✆ (011)8191393 – ▤. AE ⓢ ⓓ E VISA DY e
*closed Saturday lunch, Monday and August* – **Meals** a la carte 60/85000 (10 %).

XX **Perbacco,** via Mazzini 31 ✉ 10123 ✆ (011)882110, Late night dinners – ▤. AE ⓢ ⓓ E VISA DZ x
*closed Sunday and August* – **Meals** (dinner only) (booking essential) a la carte 30/45000.

XX **Galante,** corso Palestro 15 ✉ 10122 ✆ (011)537757 – ▤. AE ⓢ ⓓ E VISA JCB CX b
*closed Saturday lunch, Sunday and August* – **Meals** a la carte 50/80000.

XX **Marco Polo,** via Marco Polo 38 ✉ 10129 ✆ (011)599900, *Fax (011)500096* – ▤. AE VISA BZ f
*closed Monday and lunch (except Sunday)* – **Meals** (booking essential) seafood 80000.

XX **Porta Rossa,** via Passalacqua 3/b ✉ 10122 ✆ (011)530816 – ▤. AE ⓢ ⓓ E VISA. ✻ CV a
*closed Saturday lunch, Sunday and August* – **Meals** 25/30000 (lunch only) and a la carte 45/90000.

XX **Il Porticciolo,** via Barletta 58 ✉ 10136 ✆ (011)321601 – ▤. AE ⓢ E VISA. ✻ AZ a
*closed Saturday lunch, Sunday and August* – **Meals** (booking essential) seafood a la carte 50/80000.

XX **Il 58,** via San Secondo 58 ✉ 10128 ✆ (011)505566 – ▤. ⓢ E VISA CZ a
*closed Monday and July* – **Meals** seafood a la carte 40/60000.

X **Trômlin,** a Cavoretto, via alla Parrocchia 7 ✉ 10133 ✆ (011)6613050
*closed lunch (except Bank Holidays), Monday and 10 to 25 August* – **Meals** (booking essential) (surprise piemontese menu) 50000 b.i. by corso Moncalieri DZ

X **'l Birichin,** via Monti 16 ✉ 10126 ✆ (011)657457
▤. AE ⓢ E VISA JCB CZ p
*closed Sunday, 5 to 25 August and 1 to 7 January* – **Meals** a la carte 35/60000.

**VENICE** (VENEZIA) *30100* **P** 988 ⑤, 429 F 19 *G. Venice – pop. 296 422.*

See : *St. Marks Square*★★★ FKZ : *Basilica*★★★ LZ – *Doges Palace*★★★ LZ – *Campanile*★★ : ✻★★ KLZ **Q** – *Correr Museum*★★ FZ **M**¹ – *Bridge of Sighs*★★ LZ.
*Grand Canal*★★★ : *Rialto Bridge*★★ **KY** – *Ca' d'Oro*★★★ JX – *Academy of Fine Arts*★★★ BV – *Cà Dario*★ BV – *Cà Rezzonico*★★ BV – *Grassi Palace*★ BV – *Peggy Guggenheim Collection*★ *in Palace Venier dei Leoni* DV **M**² – *Vendramin-Calergi Palace*★ CT – *Cà Pesaro*★ JX.
*Churches : Santa Maria della Salute*★★ DV – *St. Giorgio Maggiore*★ : ✻★★★ *from campanile* FV – *St. Zanipolo*★★ LX – *Santa Maria Gloriosa dei Frari*★★★ BTU – *St. Zaccaria*★★ LZ – *Interior decoration*★★ *by Veronese in the Church of St. Sebastiano* BV – *Ceiling*★ *of the Church of St. Pantaleone* BU – *Santa Maria dei Miracoli*★ KLX – *St. Francesco della Vigna*★ FT – *Redentore*★ *(Giudecca Island)* BV – *Ghetto*★★ BT.
*Scuola di St. Rocco*★★★ BU – *Scuola di St. Giorgio degli Schiavoni*★★★ FU – *Scuola dei Carmini*★ BV – *Scuola di St. Marco*★ LX – *Palazzo Labia*★★ BT.
*The Lido*★★ – *Murano*★★ : *Glass Museum*★, *Church of Santi Maria e Donato*★★ – *Burano*★★ - *Torcello*★★ : *mosaics*★★ *in the Cathedral of Santa Maria Assunta.*

18 *(closed Monday) at Lido Alberoni* ✉ *30011* ☎ *(041)731333, Fax (041)731339 15 mn by boat and 9 km;*

18, 9 *Cà della Nave (closed Tuesday and January) at Martellago* ✉ *30030* ☎ *(041)5401555, Fax (041)5401926, NW : 12 km;*

18, 9 *Villa Condulmer (closed Monday), at Zerman* ✉ *31020* ☎ *(041)457062, Fax (041)457202, N : 17 km.*

✈ *Marco Polo of Tessera, NE : 13 km* ☎ *(041)2609260 – Alitalia, via Sansovino 7 Mestre-Venezia* ✉ *30173* ☎ *(041)2581222.*

⛴ *to Lido-San Nicolò from piazzale Roma (Tronchetto) daily (35 mn); to island of Pellestrina-Santa Maria del Mare from Lido Alberoni daily (15 mn).*

⛴ *to Punta Sabbioni from Riva degli Schiavoni daily (40 mn) ; to islands of Burano (30 mn), Torcello (40 mn), Murano (1 h 10 mn) from Punta Sabbioni daily ; to islands of Murano (10 mn), Burano (50 mn), Torcello (50 mn) from Fondamenta Nuove daily; to Treporti-Cavallino from Fondamenta Nuove daily (1 h 10 mn); to Venezia-Fondamenta Nuove from Treporti-Cavallino (1 h 10 mn), to islands of Murano (1 h), Burano (20 mn), Torcello (25 mn) daily – Information : ACTV-Venetian Trasport Union, piazzale Roma* ✉ *30135* ☎ *(041)5287886, Fax (041)5207135.*

**i** *Palazzetto Selva-Molo di San Marco 71/c* ✉ *30124* ☎ *(041)5226356, Fax (041)5298730 – Santa Lucia Railway station* ✉ *30121* ☎ *(041)5298727, Fax (041)719078.*

*Roma 528* ① *– Bologna 152* ① *– Milano 267* ① *– Trieste 158* ①

Plans on following pages

**Cipriani**, isola della Giudecca 10 ✉ 30133 ☎ (041)5207744, *Fax (041)5203930*, ≤, « Floral garden with heated pool », – 80. AE VISA. CV h
*closed 9 November-3 April* – **Meals** a la carte 130/180000 – **59 rm** 950/1400000, 12 suites (**Palazzo Vendramin** 7 apartments closed 7 November-20 February).

**Danieli,** riva degli Schiavoni 4196 ✉ 30122 ☎ (041)5226480, *Fax (041)5200208*, ≤ San Marco Canal, « Hall in a small Venetian style courtyard and summer rest. service on terrace with panoramic view » – 150. AE VISA JCB. rest GZ a
**Meals** a la carte 120/185000 – 38000 – **221 rm** 525/935000, 9 suites.

**Gritti Palace,** campo Santa Maria del Giglio 2467 ✉ 30124 ☎ (041)794611, *Fax (041)5200942*, ≤ Grand Canal, « Outdoor rest. summer service on the Grand Canal » – rm, – 100. AE VISA JCB. EZ a
**Meals** a la carte 115/195000 – 36000 – **87 rm** 935/1100000, 6 suites.

**Bauer Grünwald,** campo San Moisè 1459 ✉ 30124 ☎ (041)5207022, *Fax (041)5207557*, « Summer service in terrace with ≤ Grand Canal » – rm, – 150. AE VISA. rest FZ h
**Meals** a la carte 100/150000 – **210 rm** 490/780000, 3 suites.

**Londra Palace,** riva degli Schiavoni 4171 ✉ 30122 ☎ (041)5200533, *Fax (041)5225032*, ≤ San Marco Canal, private pier – AE VISA JCB GZ t
**Meals** ***Do Leoni*** Rest (Elegant rest., booking essential) a la carte 80/165000 – **53 rm** 700/800000.

**Luna Hotel Baglioni,** calle larga dell'Ascensione 1243 ✉ 30124 ☎ (041)5289840, *Fax (041)5287160* – rm, – 150. AE VISA. rest FZ p
**Meals** 100/120000 and ***Canova*** Rest. a la carte 85/130000 – **111 rm** 370/660000, 7 suites.

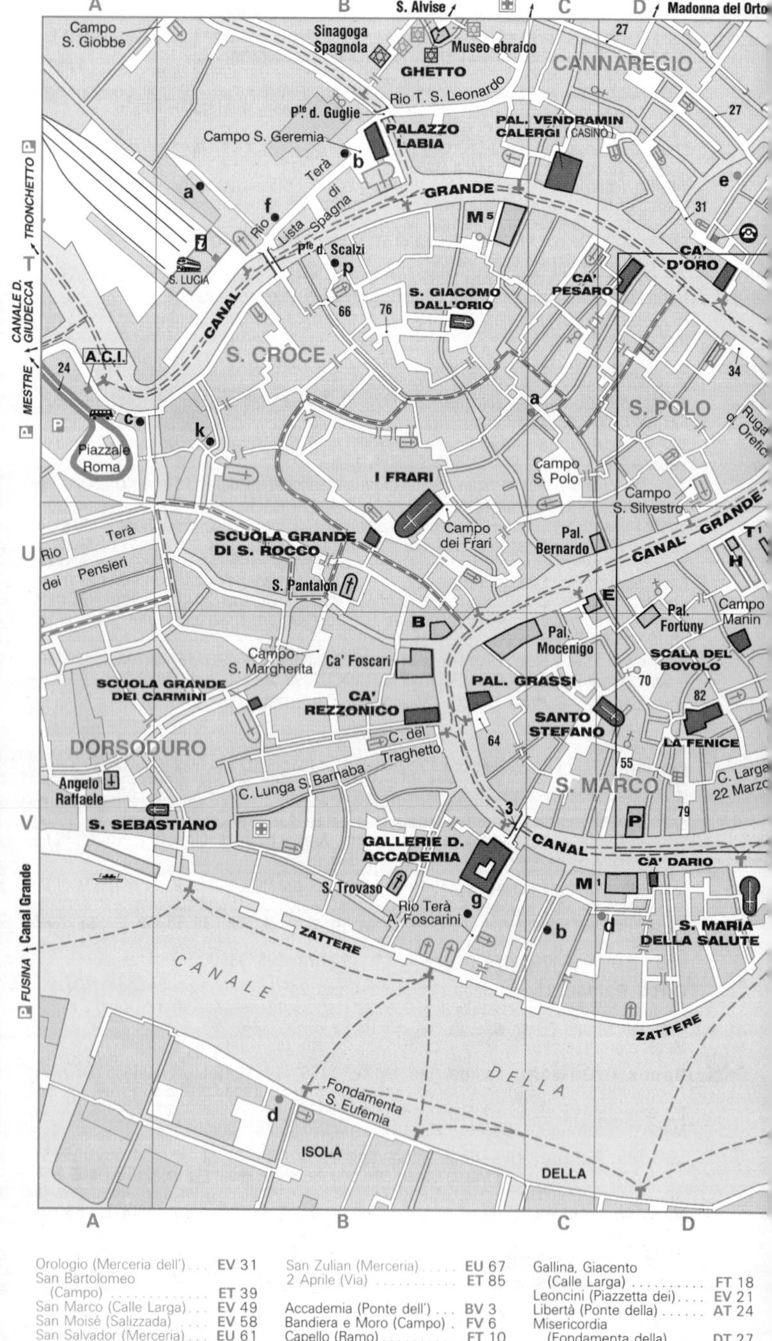


| | | | | | | | |
|---|---|---|---|---|---|---|---|
| Orologio (Merceria dell') | EV 31 | San Zulian (Merceria) | EU 67 | Gallina, Giacento (Calle Larga) | FT 18 |
| San Bartolomeo (Campo) | ET 39 | 2 Aprile (Via) | ET 85 | Leoncini (Piazzetta dei) | EV 21 |
| San Marco (Calle Larga) | EV 49 | Accademia (Ponte dell') | BV 3 | Libertà (Ponte della) | AT 24 |
| San Moisé (Salizzada) | EV 58 | Bandiera e Moro (Campo) | FV 6 | Misericordia (Fondamenta della) | DT 27 |
| San Salvador (Merceria) | EU 61 | Capello (Ramo) | FT 10 | | |

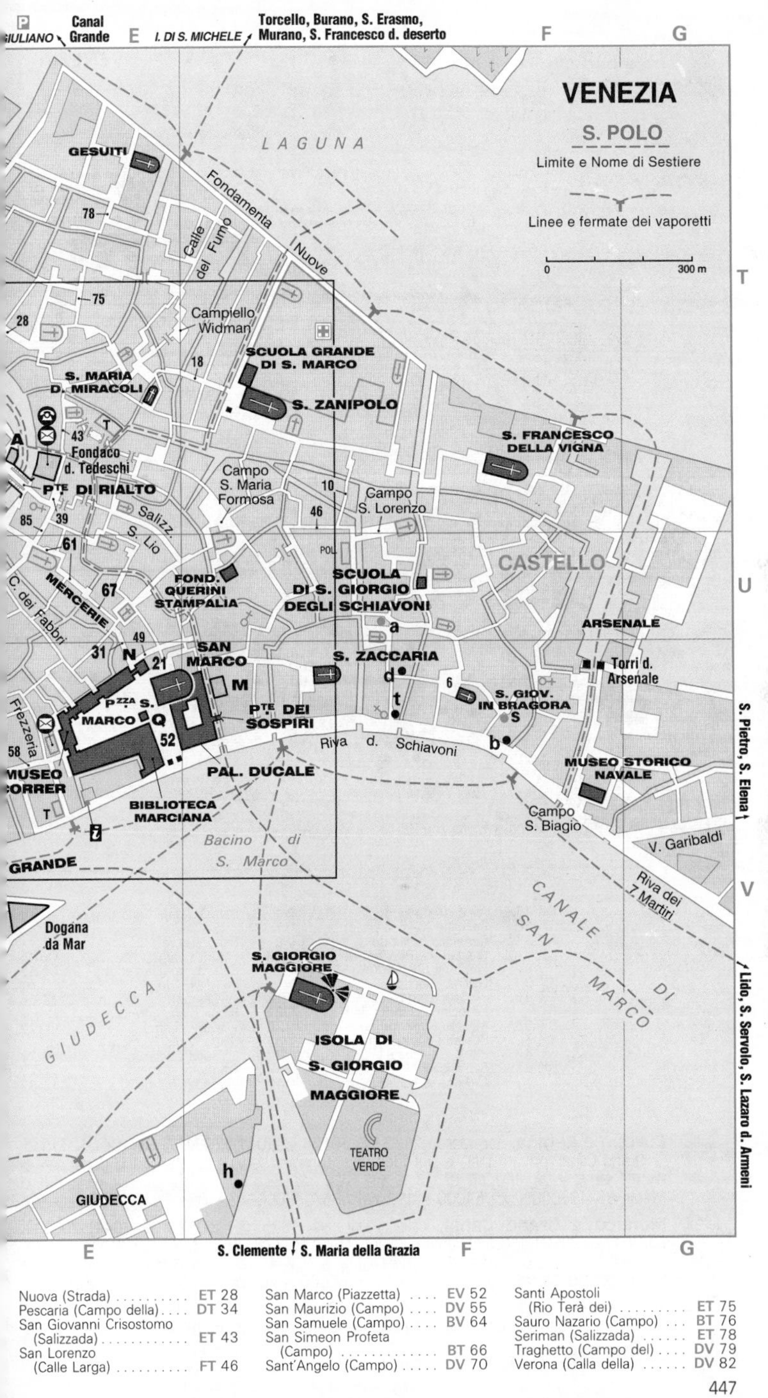


Nuova (Strada) .......... ET 28
Pescaria (Campo della) .... DT 34
San Giovanni Crisostomo (Salizzada) ............ ET 43
San Lorenzo (Calle Larga) .......... FT 46
San Marco (Piazzetta) .... EV 52
San Maurizio (Campo) .... DV 55
San Samuele (Campo) .... BV 64
San Simeon Profeta (Campo) ............ BT 66
Sant'Angelo (Campo) ..... DV 70
Santi Apostoli (Rio Terà dei) .......... ET 75
Sauro Nazario (Campo) ... BT 76
Seriman (Salizzada) ...... ET 78
Traghetto (Campo del) .... DV 79
Verona (Calla della) ...... DV 82

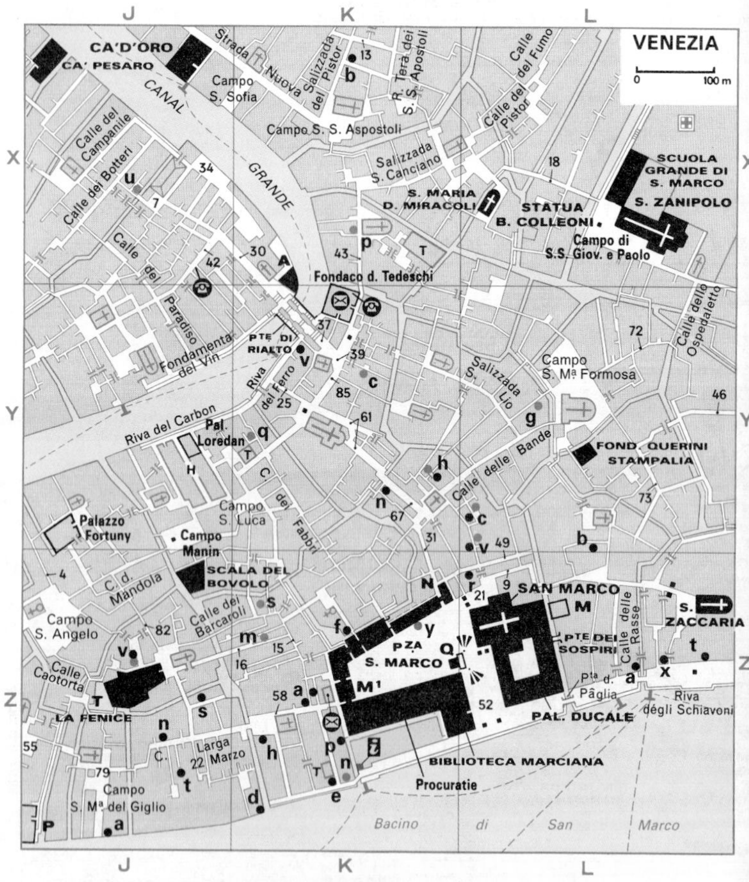


Frezzeria . . . . . . . . . . . . . KZ 15
Orefici (Ruga degli) . . . . . . . . KX 30
Orologio (Merceria dell') . . . KY 31
Rialto (Ponte di) . . . . . . . . . . KY
San Bartolomeo
(Campo) . . . . . . . . . . . . KY 39
San Marco (Calle Larga) . . . LYZ 49
San Marco (Piazza) . . . . . . . KZ
San Moisé (Salizzada) . . . . KZ 58
San Salvador (Merceria) . . . KY 61
San Zulian (Merceria) . . . . . KY 67
2 Aprile (Via) . . . . . . . . . . . KY 85
22 Marzo (Calle Larga) . . . . JZ

Avvocati (Calle degli) . . . . . JZ 4
Beccarie (Campo delle) . . . JX 7
Canonica (Calle di) . . . . . . . LZ 9
Franceschi (Rio Terà dei) . . KX 13
Frezzeria (Piscina di) . . . . . . KZ 16
Gallina, Giacento
(Calle Larga) . . . . . . . . . . LX 18
Leoncini (Piazzetta dei) . . . . LZ 21
Mazzini (Calle Larga) . . . . . KY 25
Pescaria (Campo della) . . . . JX 34
Pio X (Salizzada) . . . . . . . . . KY 37
San Giovanni
(Ruga Vecchia) . . . . . . . . JX 42

San Giovanni Crisostomo
(Salizzada) . . . . . . . . . . . . KX 43
San Lorenzo
(Calle Larga) . . . . . . . . . . LY 46
San Marco (Piazzetta) . . . . LZ 52
San Maurizio
(Campo) . . . . . . . . . . . . . JZ 55
Santa Maria Formosa
(Calle Lunga) . . . . . . . . . . LY 72
Santa Maria Formosa
(Ruga Giuffa) . . . . . . . . . . LY 73
Traghetto (Campo del) . . . . JZ 79
Verona (Calle della) . . . . . . JZ 82

**Europa e Regina,** San Marco 2159 ✉ 30124 ✆ (041)5200477, *Fax (041)5231533,* ≤ Grand Canal, private pier, « Outdoor rest. summer service on the Grand Canal » – |♦| ▤ TV ☎ ♿ – 🏛 140. AE Ⓢ ⓞ E VISA JCB. ✂ rest FZ d
**Meals** 85/105000 – ☕ 51000 – **192 rm** 465/935000, 13 suites.

**Monaco e Grand Canal,** calle Vallaresso 1325 ✉ 30124 ✆ (041)5200211, *Fax (041)5200501,* ≤ Grand Canal and Santa Maria della Salute Church, « Outdoor rest. summer service on the Grand Canal » – |♦| ▤ TV ☎ ♿ – 🏛 40. AE Ⓢ ⓞ E VISA JCB. ✂ FZ e
**Meals** ***Grand Canal*** Rest. a la carte 110/160000 – **70 rm** ☕ 450/680000, 2 suites.

**Metropole,** riva degli Schiavoni 4149 ✉ 30122 ✆ (041)5205044, *Fax (041)5223679,* ≤ San Marco Canal, « Collection of period bric-a-brac » – |♦| ▤ TV ☎ – 🏛 40. AE Ⓢ ⓞ E VISA JCB GZ t
**Meals** ***Buffet*** Rest. 60000 – **74 rm** ☕ 520/620000.

**Sofitel** M, giardini Papadopoli Santa Croce 245 ✉ 30135 ☏ (041)710400, *Fax (041)710394*, private pier, « service rest. in pleasant winter garden » – |♦|, ⇔ rm, ▤ TV ☎ – 🏃 60. AE ⓢ ⓞ E VISA. ✱ rest AT k
**Meals** a la carte 80/120000 – **92 rm** ☐ 490/590000, 5 suites.

**Starhotel Splendid-Suisse,** San Marco-Mercerie 760 ✉ 30124 ☏ (041)5200755, *Fax (041)5286498* – |♦|, ⇔ rm, ▤ TV ☎ – 🏃 50. AE ⓢ ⓞ E VISA JCB. ✱ rest FY n
**Meals** (residents only) – **166 rm** ☐ 460/690000.

**Saturnia e International,** calle larga 22 Marzo 2398 ✉ 30124 ☏ (041)5208377, *Fax (041)5207131*, ⛱, « 14C nobleman's town house » – |♦| ▤ TV ☎ – 🏃 60. AE ⓢ E VISA JCB. ✱ rest EZ n
**Meals** (see rest. **La Caravella** below) – **95 rm** ☐ 380/585000.

**Rialto,** riva del Ferro 5149 ✉ 30124 ☏ (041)5209166, *Fax (041)5238958*, ≤ Rialto bridge – ▤ TV ☎. AE ⓢ ⓞ E VISA JCB. ✱ EZ v
**Meals** *(closed Thursday and November-April)* a la carte 55/85000 (12 %) – **71 rm** ☐ 250/360000.

**Gabrielli Sandwirth,** riva degli Schiavoni 4109 ✉ 30122 ☏ (041)5231580, *Fax (041)5209455*, ⛱, private pier, « Small courtyard and garden with ≤ San Marco Canal » – |♦| ▤ TV ☎. AE ⓢ ⓞ E VISA JCB. ✱ rest DU b
*closed 29 November-5 February* – **Meals** 50/75000 – **95 rm** ☐ 370/590000.

**Cavalletto** without rest., calle del Cavalletto 1107 ✉ 30124 ☏ (041)5200955, *Fax (041)5238184*, ≤ – |♦| ▤ TV ☎. AE ⓢ ⓞ E VISA JCB FZ f
**96 rm** ☐ 370/500000.

**Amadeus,** Lista di Spagna 227 ✉ 30121 ☏ (041)715300, *Fax (041)5240841*, « Garden » – |♦| ▤ TV ☎ – 🏃 120. AE ⓢ ⓞ E VISA JCB AT b
**Meals** ***Il Papageno*** Rest. *(closed Wednesday except May-September)* a la carte 60/80000 (12 %) – **63 rm** ☐ 380/420000.

**Bellini** without rest., Cannaregio 116-Lista di Spagna ✉ 30121 ☏ (041)5242488, *Fax (041)715193* – |♦| ▤ TV ☎. AE ⓢ ⓞ E VISA JCB. ✱ rest AT f
**Meals** (residents only) 55/70000 – **64 rm** ☐ 340/470000, 3 suites.

**Concordia** without rest., calle larga San Marco 367 ✉ 30124 ☏ (041)5206866, *Fax (041)5206775* – |♦| ▤ TV ☎. AE ⓢ ⓞ E VISA GZ r
**57 rm** ☐ 450/590000.

**Giorgione** without rest., SS. Apostoli 4587 ✉ 30131 ☏ (041)5225810, *Fax (041)5239092*, « Floral courtyard » – |♦| ▤ TV ☎. AE ⓢ ⓞ E VISA. ✱ FX b
**58 rm** ☐ 230/350000, 10 suites.

**Montecarlo** without rest., calle dei Specchieri 463 ✉ 30124 ☏ (041)5207144, *Fax (041)5207789* – |♦| ▤ ☎. AE ⓢ ⓞ E VISA JCB LY c
**48 rm** ☐ 300/400000.

**Flora** ⚲ without rest., calle larga 22 Marzo 2283/a ✉ 30124 ☏ (041)5205844, *Fax (041)5228217*, « Small flower garden » – |♦| ▤ TV ☎. AE ⓢ ⓞ E VISA JCB
**44 rm** ☐ 240/325000. EZ t

**La Fenice et des Artistes** without rest., campiello de la Fenice 1936 ✉ 30124 ☏ (041)5232333, *Fax (041)5203721* – |♦| ▤ TV ☎. AE ⓢ ⓞ E VISA EZ v
**65 rm** ☐ 190/310000, 3 suites.

**Savoia e Jolanda,** riva degli Schiavoni 4187 ✉ 30122 ☏ (041)5206644, *Fax (041)5207494*, ≤ San Marco Canal, ⛱ – |♦| ▤ ☎. AE ⓢ ⓞ E VISA. ✱ rest
**Meals** *(closed Tuesday)* 50000 (12 %) – **79 rm** ☐ 230/330000. GZ x

**Ai Due Fanali** ⚲ without rest., Santa Croce 946 ✉ 30135 ☏ (041)718490, *Fax (041)718344*, « Solarium-terrace » – |♦| ▤ TV ☎. AE ⓢ ⓞ E VISA. ✱ AT p
*closed January* – **16 rm** ☐ 250/320000.

**Firenze** without rest., San Marco 1490 ✉ 30124 ☏ (041)5222858, *Fax (041)5202668* – |♦| ▤ TV ☎. AE ⓢ E VISA JCB FZ a
**25 rm** ☐ 210/310000.

**Panada** without rest., San Marco-calle dei Specchieri 646 ✉ 30124 ☏ (041)5209088, *Fax (041)5209619* – |♦| ▤ TV ☎. AE ⓢ ⓞ E VISA JCB GY v
**48 rm** ☐ 280/380000.

**Kette** without rest., San Marco-piscina Saan Moisè ✉ 30124 ☏ (041)5207766, *Fax (041)5228964* – |♦| ▤ TV ☎. AE ⓢ ⓞ E VISA. ✱ JZ s
**60 rm** ☐ 230/330000.

**Abbazia** without rest., calle Priuli 68 ✉ 30121 ☏ (041)717333, *Fax (041)717949*, « In an old monastery », ⛱ – ▤ TV ☎. AE ⓢ ⓞ E VISA. ✱ BT a
**39 rm** ☐ 280/300000

**Belle Arti** without rest., Dorsoduro 912 ✉ 30123 ☏ (041)5226230, *Fax (041)5280043*, ✂ – |♦| ▤ TV ☎ ♿. ⓢ E VISA. ✱ BV g
**66 rm** ☐ 180/300000.

**Bisanzio** without rest., calle della Pietà 3651 ✉ 30122 ☎ (041)5203100, *Fax (041)5204114* – AE E VISA JCB DU d
**40 rm** 310/340000, 2 suites.

**American** without rest., San Vio 268 ✉ 30123 ☎ (041)5204733, *Fax (041)5204048* – AE E VISA.
**29 rm** 210/320000.

**Castello** without rest., Castello-calle Figher 4365 ✉ 30122 ☎ (041)5230217, *Fax (041)5211023* – AE E VISA LY b
**26 rm** 320/370000.

**Santa Chiara** without rest., Santa Croce 548 ✉ 30125 ☎ (041)5206955, *Fax (041)5228799* – AE E VISA. AT c
**28 rm** 210/340000.

**Caffè Quadri,** piazza San Marco 120 ✉ 30124 ☎ (041)5289299, *Fax (041)5208041* – AE E VISA JCB. FZ y
*closed Monday* – **Meals** (booking essential) a la carte 100/170000.

**Harry's Bar,** calle Vallaresso 1323 ✉ 30124 ☎ (041)5285777, *Fax (041)5208822*, American bar rest. – AE E VISA FZ n
**Meals** (booking essential) a la carte 145/200000 (10 %)
**Spec.** Tagiolini gratinati : Scampi alla Thermidor. Carpaccio alla "Cipriani".

**La Caravella** - Hotel Saturnia e International, calle Larga 22 Marzo 2397 ✉ 30124 ☎ (041)5208901, Typical rest. – AE E VISA JCB. JZ m
*closed Wednesday except June-September* – **Meals** (booking essential) a la carte 90/150000.

**La Colomba,** piscina di Frezzeria 1665 ✉ 30124 ☎ (041)5221175, *Fax (041)5221468*, « Collection of contemporary art » – 60. AE E VISA JCB. FZ m
*closed Wednesday except May-June and September-November* – **Meals** a la carte 100/180000 (15 %).

**Taverna la Fenice,** campiello de la Fenice ✉ 30124 ☎ (041)5223856, *Fax (041)5236866*, « Outdoor summer service » – AE E VISA JCB. EZ v
*closed Sunday, Monday lunch and 10 to 31 January* – **Meals** 40/60000 (15 %) lunch 60/90000 (15 %) dinner and a la carte 55/105000 (15 %).

**Do Forni,** calle dei Specchieri 457/468 ✉ 30124 ☎ (041)5237729, *Fax (041)5288132* – AE E VISA JCB GY c
**Meals** (booking essential) a la carte 65/95000 (12 %).

**Osteria da Fiore,** San Polo-calle del Scaleter 2202/A ✉ 30125 ☎ (041)721308, *Fax (041)721343* – AE E VISA BT a
*closed Sunday, Monday, August and 24 December-12 January* – **Meals** (booking essential) seafood a la carte 85/135000
**Spec.** Cappesante al timo. Ravioli di pesce. Filetto di branzino all'aceto balsamico.

**Harry's Dolci,** Giudecca 773 ✉ 30133 ☎ (041)5224844, *Fax (041)5222322*, « Outdoor summer service on the Giudecca canal » – AE E VISA AV a
*April-10 November ; closed Tuesday* – **Meals** 75/80000 (12 %) and a la carte 85/105000 (12 %).

**Al Covo,** campiello della Pescaria 3968 ✉ 30122 ☎ (041)5223812 – FV s
*closed Wednesday, Thursday, 10 to 20 August, and January* – **Meals** 45000 (lunch only) and a la carte 80/105000.

**Fiaschetteria Toscana,** San Giovanni Crisostomo 5719 ✉ 30121 ☎ (041)5285281, *Fax (041)5285521*, – AE E VISA FX p
*closed Tuesday and 6 July-2 August* – **Meals** a la carte 55/90000.

**Ai Mercanti,** Calle dei Fuseri-Corte Coppo 4346/A ✉ 30125 ☎ (041)5238269, *Fax (041)5238269* – AE E VISA. EX u
*closed Sunday and Monday lunch* – **Meals** a la carte 70/105000 (12 %).

**Antico Pignolo,** calle dei Specchieri 451 ✉ 30124 ☎ (041)5228123, *Fax (041)5209007*, – AE E VISA JCB GY v
*closed Tuesday except May-June and September-October* – **Meals** a la carte 75/120000 (12 %).

**Da Remigio,** Salizzata dei Greci 3416 ✉ 30122 ☎ (041)5230089, *Fax (041)5230089* – AE E VISA FU a
*closed Monday dinner and Tuesday* – **Meals** (booking essential) seafood a la carte 40/65000 (12 %).

**Ai Gondolieri,** Dorsoduro-San Vio 366 ✉ 30123 ☎ (041)5286396 – AE E VISA. BV d
*closed Tuesday* – **Meals** beef dishes only a la carte 70/120000 (10 %).

XX **Da Ivo,** San Marco-calle dei Fuseri 1809 ✉ 30124 ☎ (041)5285004, *Fax (041)5205889* – ▤. AE ⓢ ◑ E VISA. ✻ KZ s
*closed January and Sunday (except September-October)* – **Meals** (booking essential) a la carte 75/130000 (14 %).

XX **Da Mario-alla Fava,** San Bartolomeo-calle Stagneri 5242 e Galiazzo 5265 ✉ 30124 ☎ (041)5285147 – AE ⓢ ◑ E VISA KY c
*closed Wednesday and 7 to 20 January* – **Meals** 30000 and a la carte 60/85000 (12 %).

XX **Vini da Gigio,** Cannaregio 3628/a-Fondamenta San Felice ✉ 30131 ☎ (041)5285140, Inn serving food – AE ⓢ ◑ E VISA BT e
*closed Monday, 15 to 31 August and 15 to 31 January* – **Meals** (booking essential) a la carte 50/80000.

X **Alle Testiere,** calle del Mondo Novo Castello 5801 ✉ 30122 ☎ (041)5227220, *Fax (041)5227220*, Inn serving food – ▤. ⓢ E VISA LY g
*closed Sunday and August* – **Meals** (booking essential) a la carte 55/75000.

X **Antica Carbonera,** calle Bembo 4648 ✉ 30124 ☎ (041)5225479, Venetian trattoria – ▤. AE ⓢ ◑ E VISA JCB FY q
*closed July, Sunday in August and Thursday September-June* – **Meals** a la carte 60/85000 (12 %).

X **Al Conte Pescaor,** piscina San Zulian 544 ✉ 30124 ☎ (041)5221483, *Fax (041)5221483*, ☂, Rustic rest. – ▤. AE ⓢ ◑ E VISA JCB. ✻ FY h
*closed Sunday and 7 January-7 February* – **Meals** a la carte 50/80000.

**in Lido** : *15 mn by boat from San Marco* KZ – ✉ *30126 Venezia Lido.*
ℹ *Gran Viale S. M. Elisabetta 6* ☎ *(041)5265721* :

**Excelsior,** lungomare Marconi 41 ☎ (041)5260201, *Fax (041)5267276*, ←, ☂, ⛱, ⛵, 18 – 🛗 ▤ TV ☎ ♿ 🚗 P – 🏛 600. AE ⓢ ◑ E VISA. ✻ rest
*15 March-15 November* – **Meals** 135000 – ☕ 64000 – **182 rm** 640/740000.

**Des Bains,** lungomare Marconi 17 ☎ (041)5265921, *Fax (041)5260113*, ←, ☂, « Floral park with heated ⛱ and ✂ », ⛵, ⛵ – 🛗 ▤ TV ☎ P – 🏛 380. AE ⓢ ◑ E VISA. ✻ rest
*15 March-15 November* – **Meals** a la carte 105/175000 – ☕ 35000 – **190 rm** 600/670000, suite.

**Villa Mabapa,** riviera San Nicolò 16 ☎ (041)5260590, *Fax (041)5269441*, « Summer service rest. in garden » – 🛗 ▤ TV ☎ – 🏛 85. AE ⓢ ◑ E VISA JCB. ✻ rest
**Meals** a la carte 60/85000 – **60 rm** ☕ 270/400000.

**Quattro Fontane** 🐦, via 4 Fontane 16 ☎ (041)5260227, *Fax (041)5260726*, « Summer service rest. in garden », ✂ – ▤ TV ☎ P – 🏛 40. AE ⓢ ◑ E VISA. ✻ rest
*April-3 November* – **Meals** a la carte 105/160000 – **58 rm** ☕ 420/460000.

**Le Boulevard** without rest., Gran Viale S. M. Elisabetta 41 ☎ (041)5261990, *Fax (041)5261917* – 🛗 ▤ TV ☎ P. AE ⓢ ◑ E VISA JCB. ✻
**45 rm** ☕ 330/450000.

X **Trattoria Favorita,** via Francesco Duodo 33 ☎ (041)5261626, *Fax (041)5261626*, « Outdoor summer service » – AE ⓢ ◑ E VISA JCB
*closed Monday and 15 January-1 March* – **Meals** a la carte 65/85000.

**in Murano** *10 mn by boat from Fondamenta Nuove* EFT *and 1 h 10 mn by boat from Punta Sabbioni* – ✉ *30121* :

X **Ai Frati,** ☎ (041)736694, ☂, « Outdoor terrace summer service on the canal »
*closed Thursday and February* – **Meals** seafood a la carte 45/65000 (12 %).

**in Burano** *50 mn by boat from Fondamenta Nuove* EFT *and 32 mn by boat from Punta Sabbioni* – ✉ *30012* :

X **Al Gatto Nero-da Ruggero,** ☎ (041)730120, *Fax (041)735570*, ☂, Typical trattoria – AE ⓢ ◑ E VISA
*closed Monday, 15 to 30 November and 15 to 31 January* – **Meals** a la carte 40/75000.

**in Torcello** *45 mn by boat from Fondamenta Nuove* EFT *and 37 mn by boat from Punta Sabbioni* – ✉ *30012 Burano* :

XX **Locanda Cipriani,** ☎ (041)730150, *Fax (041)735433*, « Summer service in garden » – ▤. AE ⓢ ◑ E VISA
*closed Tuesday and January-18 February* – **Meals** a la carte 95/135000.

**in Pellestrina** *1 h and 10 mn by boat from Riva degli Schiavoni* GZ *o 45 mn by bus from Lido* – ✉ *30010* :

X **Da Celeste,** via Nelli 625 ☎ (041)967355, *Fax (041)967355*, « Summer service in terrace on sea » – ▤
*closed Wednesday dinner* – **Meals** a la carte 55/85000.

**Padova** *35100* 🅿 988 ⑤, 429 F 17 *G. Italy – pop. 212 542 alt. 12.*

*18 and 9 Montecchia (closed Monday) at Selvazzano Dentro ✉ 35030 ☎ (049)8055550, Fax (049)8055737, W : 8 km;*

*18 Frassanelle (closed Tuesday except April, May, September and October) ✉ 35030 Frassanelle di Rovolon ☎ (049)9910722, Fax (049)9910691, SW : 20 km;*

*18 (closed Monday and January) at Valsanzibio di Galzignano ✉ 35030 ☎ (049)9130078, Fax (049)9131193, E : 21 km.*

*Central Station ✉ 35131 ☎ (049)8752077 - Museo Eremitani ☎ (049)8750655.*

A.C.I. *via Enrico degli Scrovegni 19 ✉ 35131 ☎ 654935.*

*Roma 491 – Milano 234 – Venezia 42 – Verona 81.*

**at Rubano** *W : 8 km – ✉ 35030 :*

XXX ✿✿ **Le Calandre,** strada statale 11, località Sarmeola ☎ (049)630303, *Fax (049)633000* – ▤ P. AE ⓢ ⓓ E VISA. ✂
*closed 14-15 August, 1 to 4 January, Sunday except lunch October-May and Monday* – **Meals** (booking essential) a la carte 75/130000
**Spec.** Involtini di scampi fritti su salsa di lattuga. Quaglia arrostita al Verduzzo con krapfen di patate ai fegatini. "Trionfo" di desserts.

**Verona** *37100* 🅿 988 ④, 428, 429 F 14 *G. Italy – pop. 254 520 alt. 59.*

*18 (closed Tuesday) at Sommacampagna ✉ 37066 ☎ (045)510060, Fax (045)510242, W : 13 km.*

*✈ of Villafranca SE : 14 km ☎ (045)8095666 – Alitalia, corso Porta Nuova 61 ✉ 37122 ☎ (045)8035700.*

*🚗 ☎ (045)590688.*

*via Leoncino 61 (Barbieri Palace) ✉ 37121 ☎ (045)592828, Fax (045)8003638 – piazza delle Erbe 42 ✉ 37121 ☎ (045)8000065 - Stazione Porta Nuova ☎ (045)8000861.*

A.C.I. *via della Valverde 34 ✉ 37122 ☎ (045)595333.*

*Roma 503 – Milano 157 – Venezia 114.*

XXX ✿✿ **Il Desco,** via Dietro San Sebastiano 7 ✉ 37121 ☎ (045)595358, *Fax (045)590236* – ▤. AE ⓢ ⓓ E VISA. ✂
*closed Sunday, Easter, 17 to 30 June, 25-26 December and January* – **Meals** (booking essential) a la carte 85/140000 (15 %)
**Spec.** Scaloppa di fegato grasso al Recioto e pere. Ravioli di patate e rosmarino al lardo croccante. Petto d'anatra al miele con purea di zucca e di melanzane.

# *Norway*

## *Norge*

OSLO

# PRACTICAL INFORMATION

## LOCAL CURRENCY

**Norwegian Kroner:** *100 NOK = 13,61 USD ($) (Jan. 98)*

## TOURIST INFORMATION

*The telephone number and address of the Tourist Information office is given in the text under* ℹ.

**National Holiday in Norway:** *17 May.*

## FOREIGN EXCHANGE

*In the Oslo area banks are usually open between 8.15am and 3.30pm but in summertime, 15/5 - 31/8, they close at 3pm. Thursdays they are open till 5pm. Saturdays and Sundays closed.*

*Most large hotels, main airports and railway stations have exchange facilities. At Fornebu Airport the bank is open from 6.30am to 8pm (weekdays), 6.30am to 6pm (Saturday), 7am to 8pm (Sunday), all year round.*

## MEALS

*At lunchtime, follow the custom of the country and try the typical buffets of Scandinavian specialities.*

*At dinner, the a la carte and set menus will offer you more conventional cooking.*

## SHOPPING IN OSLO

*Knitware and silverware*

*Your hotel porter should be able to help you with information.*

## CAR HIRE

*The international car hire companies have branches in each major city. Your hotel porter should be able to give details and help you with your arrangements.*

## TIPPING IN NORWAY

*A service charge is included in hotel and restaurant bills and it is up to the customer to give something in addition if he wants to.*

*The cloakroom is sometimes included in the bill, sometimes an extra charge is made.*

*Taxi drivers and baggage porters don't expect to be tipped. It is up to you if you want to give a gratuity.*

## SPEED LIMITS

*The maximum permitted speed within built-up areas is 50 km/h - 31mph. Outside these areas it is 80 km/h - 50mph. Where there are other speed limits (lower or higher) they are signposted.*

## SEAT BELTS

*The wearing of seat belts in Norway is compulsory for drivers and all passengers.*

# OSLO

*Norge* 985 M 7 – *pop. 458 364.*

*Hamburg 888 – København 583 – Stockholm 522.*

*Norwegian Information Centre Vestbaneplassen 1 ☎ 22 83 00 50, Fax 22 83 81 50 – KNA (Kongelig Norsk Automobilklub) Royal Norwegian Automobile Club, Drammensveien 20C ☎ 22 56 19 00 – NAF (Norges Automobil Forbund), Storg. 2 ☎ 22 34 14 00.*

18 *Oslo Golfklubb ☎ 22 50 44 02.*

*Oslo NE: 5 km (opening October 1998) – Fornebu SW: 8 km ☎ 67 59 67 16 SAS Head Office: Oslo City, Stenersg. 1 a ☎ 22 17 41 60 – Air Terminal: Havnegata, main railway station, seaside.*

*Copenhagen, Frederikshavn, Kiel, Hirtshals : contact tourist information centre (see above).*

**See:** *Bygdøy* ABZ *Viking Ship Museum★★★ (Vikingskipshuset) ; Folk Museum★★★ (Norsk Folkemuseum) ; Fram Museum★★ (Frammuseet) ; Kon-Tiki Museum★★ (Kon-Tiki Museet) ; Maritime Museum★★ (Norsk Sjøfartsmuseum) – Munch Museum★★ (Munch-Museet)* DY *– National Gallery★★ (Nasjonalgalleriet)* CY **M¹** *– Vigelandsanlegget★ (Vigeland sculptures and museum)* AX *– Akershus Castle★ (Akershus Festning : Resistance Museum★ )* CZ **M²** *– Oslo Cathedral (Domkirke: views★★ from steeple)* CY.

**Outskirts:** *Holmenkollen★ (NW: 10 km): view from ski-jump tower and ski museum* BX *– Sonie Henie-Onstad Art Centre★★ (Sonie Henie-Onstad Kunstsenter) (W: 12 km)* AY

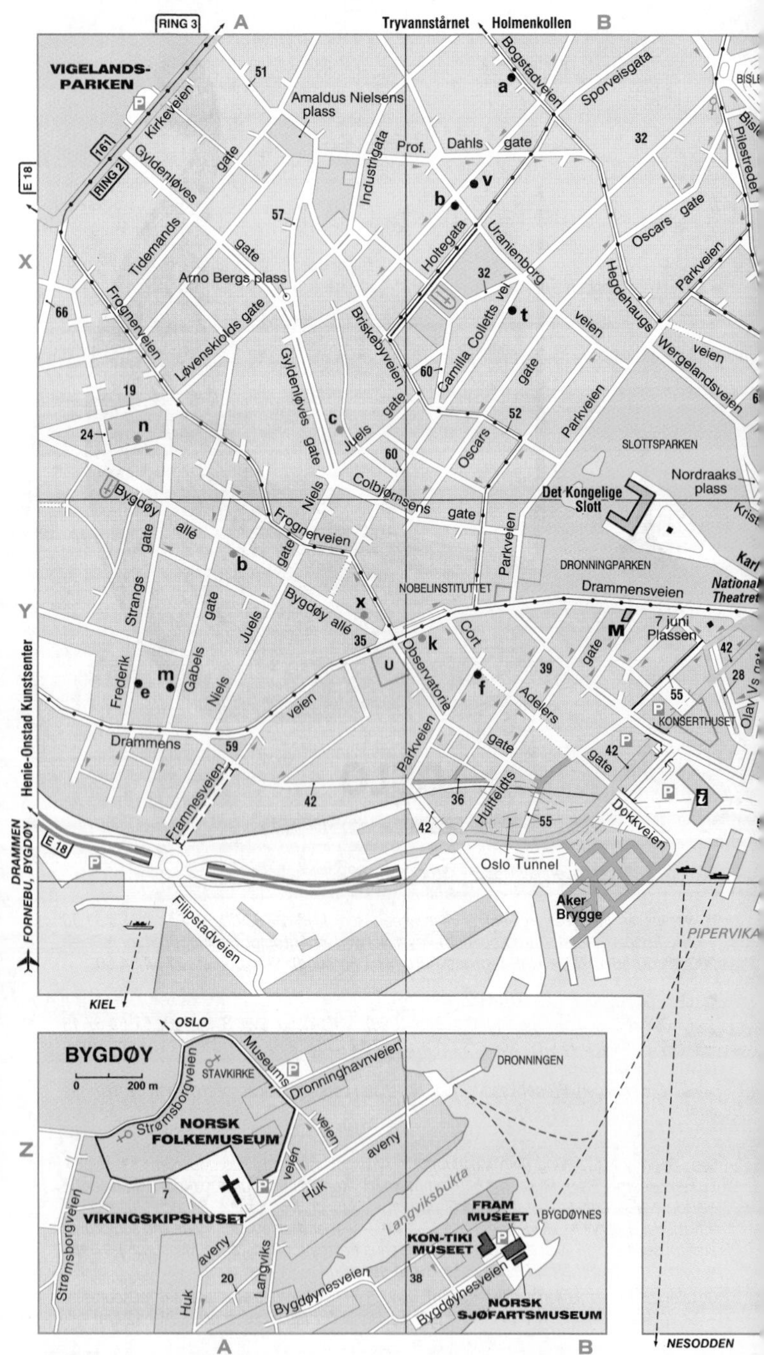
VIGELANDS-PARKEN
RING 3
RING 2
Tryvannstårnet
Holmenkollen
Bogstadveien
Sporveisgata
Amaldus Nielsens plass
Kirkeveien
Gyldenløves gate
Prof. Dahls gate
Industrigata
Holtegata
Uranienborg
Oscars gate
Parkveien
Hegdehaugsveien
Tidemands gate
Arno Bergs plass
Frognerveien
Løvenskiolds gate
Briskebyveien
Camilla Colletts vei
Wergelandsveien
Gyldenløves gate
Juels gate
Oscars gate
Colbjørnsens gate
SLOTTSPARKEN
Nordraaks plass
Det Kongelige Slott
Bygdøy allé
Strangs gate
Frognerveien
Niels Juels gate
Parkveien
DRONNINGPARKEN
NOBELINSTITUTTET
Drammensveien
Nationaltheatret
7 juni Plassen
Frederik Stangs gate
Gabels gate
Observatorieveien
Cort Adelers gate
KONSERTHUSET
Drammensveien
Framnesveien
Huitfeldts gate
Dokkveien
Oslo Tunnel
Aker Brygge
PIPERVIKA
Filipstadveien
Henie-Onstad Kunstsenter
DRAMMEN
FORNEBU, BYGDØY
E 18
KIEL
OSLO
BYGDØY
0 200 m
STAVKIRKE
Museumsveien
Dronninghavnveien
Strømsborgveien
NORSK FOLKEMUSEUM
DRONNINGEN
Huk aveny
VIKINGSKIPSHUSET
Langviksbukta
FRAM MUSEET
BYGDØYNES
KON-TIKI MUSEET
Langviksveien
Bygdøynesveien
NORSK SJØFARTSMUSEUM
NESODDEN
A
B
X
Y
Z

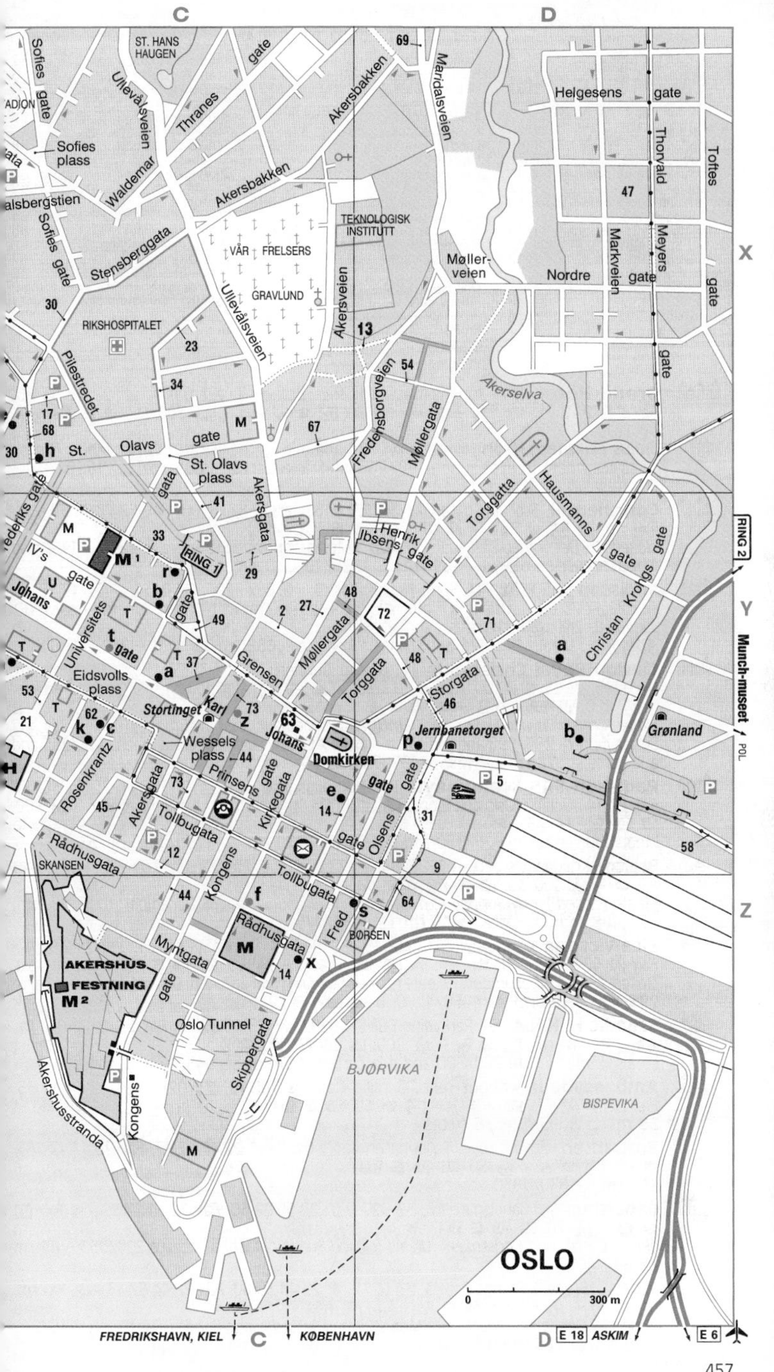
C
D
X
Y
Z
ST. HANS HAUGEN
Sofies gate
Sofies plass
Ullevålsveien
Thranes gate
Akersbakken
Maridalsveien
Helgesens gate
Thorvald Meyers gate
Toftes gate
Waldemar Thranes gate
TEKNOLOGISK INSTITUTT
VÅR FRELSERS GRAVLUND
Akersveien
Møller-veien
Nordre gate
Markveien
Stensberggata
RIKSHOSPITALET
Pilestredet
Fredensborgveien
Møllergata
Akerselva
St. Olavs gate
St. Olavs plass
Akersgata
Henrik Ibsens gate
Torggata
Hausmanns gate
Christian Krohgs gate
RING 1
RING 2
Munch-museet
Universitets gate
Eidsvolls plass
Stortinget
Karl Johans gate
Grensen
Wessels plass
Prinsens gate
Kirkegata
Domkirken
Storgata
Jernbanetorget
Grønland
Rosenkrantz gate
Tollbugata
Rådhusgata
SKANSEN
Kongens gate
Olsens gate
Fred Olsens gate
BØRSEN
Myntgata
AKERSHUS FESTNING
Oslo Tunnel
Skippergata
BJØRVIKA
BISPEVIKA
Akershusstranda
OSLO
0
300 m
FREDRIKSHAVN, KIEL
KØBENHAVN
E 18 ASKIM
E 6

**STREET INDEX TO OSLO TOWN PLAN**

Karl Johans gate . . . . . . . BCDY
Grensen . . . . . . . . . . . . . . CY
Lille Grensen . . . . . . . . . . . CY 37
Torggata . . . . . . . . . . . . . . CDY

Apotekergata . . . . . . . . . . . CY 2
Biskop Gunnerus' gate . . . . DY 5
Bygdøy kappellvei . . . . . . . AZ 7
Christian Frederiks plass . . . DY 9
Christiania torv . . . . . . . . . . CY 12
Damstredet . . . . . . . . . . . .CDX 13
Dronningens gate . . . . . . . CYZ 14
Dronning Mauds gate . . . . BY 16
Edvard Storms gate . . . . . . CX 17
Elisenbergveien . . . . . . . . . AX 19
Fredriksborgveien . . . . . . . . AZ 20
Fridtjof Nansens plass . . . . CY 21
Frimanns gate . . . . . . . . . . CX 23
Gimleveien . . . . . . . . . . . . . AX 24
Grubbegata . . . . . . . . . . . . CY 27
Haakon VII's gate . . . . . . . . BY 28
Hammersborgtunnelen . . . . CY 29
Holbergs gate . . . . . . . . . . CX 30
Jernbanetorget . . . . . . . . . DY 31
Josefines gate . . . . . . . . . . ABX 32
Kristian Augusts gate . . . . BCY 33
Langés gate . . . . . . . . . . . CX 34
Lapsetorvet . . . . . . . . . . . . AY 35
Lassons gate . . . . . . . . . . . BY 36
Løchenveien . . . . . . . . . . . ABZ 38
Løkkeveien . . . . . . . . . . . . BY 39
Munchs gate . . . . . . . . . . .CXY 41
Munkedamsveien . . . . . . . ABY 42
Nedre Slottsgate . . . . . . . .CYZ 44
Nedre Vollgate . . . . . . . . . . CY 45
Nygata . . . . . . . . . . . . . . . DY 46
Olaf Ryes plass . . . . . . . . . DX 47
Pløens gate . . . . . . . . . . . . DY 48
Professor Aschehougs pl. . . CY 49
Professor Dahls gate . . . . . AX 51
Riddervolds gate . . . . . . . . . BX 52
Roald Amundsens gate . . . CY 53
Rosteds gate . . . . . . . . . . . . DX 54
Ruseløkkveien . . . . . . . . . .ABY 55
Rådhusplassen . . . . . . . . . .BCY 56
Schives gate . . . . . . . . . . . . AX 57
Schweigaards gate . . . . . . . DY 58
Skillebekk . . . . . . . . . . . . . . AY 59
Skovveien . . . . . . . . . . . . . ABX 60
Stortingsgata . . . . . . . . . . . CY 62
Stortorvet . . . . . . . . . . . . . . CY 63
Strandgata . . . . . . . . . . . . . DZ 64
Sven Bruns gate . . . . . . . . . BX 65
Thomas Heftyes gate . . . . . AX 66
Thor Olsens gate . . . . . . . . CX 67
Tullins gate . . . . . . . . . . . . CX 68
Uelands gate . . . . . . . . . . . DX 69
Vaterlandtunnelen . . . . . . . DY 71
Youngstorget . . . . . . . . . . . DY 72
Øvre Slottsgate . . . . . . . . . . CY 73

**Grand Hotel,** Karl Johans Gate 31, P.O. Box 346, ✉ 0101, ☎ 22 42 93 90, *Fax 22 42 12 25,* – rm, – 300. AE E VISA JCB. rest — CY a
***Julius Fritzner*** : **Meals** (dinner only) 395 and a la carte – ***Grand Café*** : **Meals** *(closed 25 December)* (buffet lunch) 90/265 and a la carte – **281 rm** 1590/3300, 6 suites.

**Continental,** Stortingsgaten 24-26, ✉ 0161, ☎ 22 82 40 00, *Fax 22 42 96 89* – rm, – 200. AE E VISA. — CY n
*closed 23 December-2 January* – ***Lipp*** : **Meals** approx. 350 and a la carte – (see also ***Theatercaféen*** below) – **151 rm** 1625/1990, 8 suites.

**Radisson SAS Plaza** M, Sonja Henies Plass 3, P.O. Box 9206, ✉ 0134, ☎ 22 17 10 00, *Fax 22 17 73 00,* ≤ Oslo and Fjord, – rm, – 1000. AE E VISA JCB. rest — DY b
***Abelone*** : **Meals** 195/375 and dinner a la carte – **659 rm** 1730/1930, 14 suites.

**Clarion Royal Christiania** M, Biskop Gunnerus' Gate 3, P.O. Box 768 Sentrum, ✉ 0106, ☎ 23 10 80 00, *Fax 23 10 80 80,* – rm, – 400. AE E VISA JCB. — DY p
*closed Christmas and New Year* – ***Lindgrens*** : **Meals** *(closed in summer)* (dinner only and Sunday lunch) 295/695 and a la carte – ***Café Atrium*** : **Meals** (buffet lunch) 215/255 and a la carte – **378 rm** 1295/1495, 73 suites.

**Radisson SAS Scandinavia** M, Holbergsgate 30, ✉ 0166, ☎ 22 11 30 00, *Fax 22 11 30 17,* ≤ Oslo and Fjord, – rm, – 800. AE E VISA JCB. — CX e
**Meals** (buffet lunch) 225/350 and a la carte – **479 rm** 1730/1930, 9 suites.

**Bristol,** Kristian IV's Gate 7, ✉ 0164, ☎ 22 82 60 00, *Fax 22 82 60 01* – rm, – 100. AE E VISA JCB. — CY b
**Meals** *(closed lunch Sunday and Bank Holidays and 24 to 26 December)* (buffet lunch) 190/465 and a la carte – **138 rm** 1195/1750, 3 suites.

**Rica Victoria** M, Rosenkrantzgate 13, P.O. Box 1718, Vika, ✉ 0121, ☎ 22 42 99 40, *Fax 22 42 99 43* – rm, – 50. AE E VISA JCB. rest
*closed 23 to 29 December* – **Meals** *(closed Sunday)* (buffet lunch) 90 and dinner a la carte 295/400 – **194 rm** 1050/1280, 5 suites. — CY k

**Scandic H. K.N.A.** M, Parkveien 68, ✉ 0202, ☎ 23 15 57 63, *Fax 22 44 26 01,* – rm, – 100. AE E VISA. — BY f
**Meals** (buffet lunch) 200/360 and a la carte – **187 rm** 945/1645, 2 suites.

**Ambassadeur** without rest., Camilla Colletts Vei 15, ✉ 0258, ☎ 22 44 18 35, *Fax 22 44 47 91,* – . AE E VISA — BX t
**33 rm** 1095/1245, 8 suites.

**Bosparken** without rest., Tollbugaten 4, ✉ 0152, ☎ 22 47 17 17, *Fax 22 47 17 18* – – 50. AE E VISA — CDZ s
**198 rm** 830/1030.

**Gabelshus** , Gabelsgate 16, ✉ 0272, ☎ 22 55 22 60, *Fax 22 44 27 39* – – 70. AE E VISA. — AY m
*closed Easter and Christmas* – **Meals** *(closed Sunday lunch)* a la carte 290/355 – **43 rm** 880/1080.

**Ritz** , Frederik Stangs Gate 3, ✉ 0272, ☎ 22 44 39 60, *Fax 22 44 67 13* – rm, – 60. AE E VISA JCB. rest — AY e
*closed 22 December-2 January* – **Meals** *(closed Saturday and Sunday)* (lunch only) 175/250 – **48 rm** 860/1060.

**Bastion** without rest., Skippergaten 7, ✉ 0152, ☎ 22 47 77 00, *Fax 22 33 11 80*, – . CZ x
*closed 2 weeks Christmas-New Year* – **61 rm** 995/1645.

**Europa** M, St. Olavsgate 31, ✉ 0166, ☎ 22 20 99 90, *Fax 22 11 27 27*, – rm, . CX h
*closed 8 to 14 April and 23 December-3 January* – **Meals** *(closed Sunday dinner)* 135/245 and a la carte – **162 rm** 825/925, 4 suites.

**Spectrum** M without rest., Brugate 7, ✉ 0186, ☎ 22 17 60 30, *Fax 22 17 60 80* – . DY a
*closed 8 to 14 April and 22 December-2 January* – **119 rm** 610/810.

**Stefan** M, Rosenkrantzgate 1, ✉ 0159, ☎ 22 42 92 50, *Fax 22 33 70 22* – rm, – 50. CY r
*closed 8 to 14 April and 22 December-2 January* – **Meals** (buffet lunch) 185/215 and a la carte – **138 rm** 825/975.

**Cecil** M without rest., Stortingsgaten 8, ✉ 0161, *(entrance in Rosenkrantzgate)* ☎ 22 42 70 00, *Fax 22 42 26 70* – . CY c
*closed Easter and Christmas* – **112 rm** 825/995.

**Gyldenløve** M without rest., Bogstadveien 20, ✉ 0355, ☎ 22 60 10 90, *Fax 22 60 33 90* – . BX a
*closed 8 to 14 April and 22 December-2 January* – **168 rm** 610/810.

**Norlandia Saga** without rest., Eilert Sundtsgt. 39, ✉ 0259, ☎ 22 43 04 85, *Fax 22 44 08 63* – – 25. BX b
*closed Christmas* – **37 rm** 795/1000.

**Vika Atrium** M, Munkedamsveien 45, ✉ 0250, ☎ 22 83 33 00, *Fax 22 83 09 57*, – rm, – 240. rest BY d
**Meals** *(closed Friday dinner, Saturday, Sunday, Easter and Christmas)* (buffet lunch) 125/295 and dinner a la carte – **91 rm** 790/1095.

**Astoria** M without rest., Dronningensgt. 21, ✉ 0154, ☎ 22 42 00 10, *Fax 22 42 57 65* – . CY e
**132 rm** 610/810.

**Westside** without rest., Eilert Sundtsgt. 43, ✉ 0355, ☎ 22 56 87 70, *Fax 22 56 63 20*, – rm, rm . BX v
**31 rm** 720/850.

**Bagatelle** (Hellstrøm), Bygdøy Allé 3, ✉ 0257, ☎ 22 44 63 97, *Fax 22 43 64 20* – AY x
*closed Sunday, 1 week Easter, 3 weeks late July-early August and 1 week Christmas* – **Meals** (booking essential) (dinner only) 450/850 and a la carte 510/740
**Spec.** Rosette de St. Jacques et tarte friande à la tomate, sauce acidulée. Salade de homard "César". Perdrix de neige, sauce au foie gras.

**Le Canard,** President Harbitz Gate 4, ✉ 0259, ☎ 22 54 34 00, *Fax 22 54 34 10*, « Tastefully decorated 1900 villa » – AX c
*closed Sunday, Easter and Christmas* – **Meals** (dinner only) 500/545 and a la carte 445/695
**Spec.** Médaillons de St. Jacques au magret fumé, jus à l'huile de noix. Composition de canard, sauce Cognac. Homard poêlé aux parfums de gingembre et cumin, vinaigrette tiède á l'encre.

**Statholdergaarden** (Stiansen), Rådhusgate 11, (entrance by Kirkegate) 1st floor, ✉ 0151, ☎ 22 41 88 00, *Fax 22 41 22 24* – . CZ f
*closed Sunday, 13 July-3 August and 23 December-3 January* – **Meals** (booking essential) (dinner only) 420/550 and a la carte 420/550
**Spec.** Lasagne of scallops and trout. Noisettes of lamb with morel sauce. Rhubarb symphony.

**D'Artagnan,** Øvre Slottsgate 16 (1st floor), ✉ 0157, ☎ 22 41 74 04, *Fax 23 10 01 61* – . CY z
*closed Sunday, July and 22 December-6 January* – **Meals** (dinner only) 350/625 and a la carte.

**Spisestedet Feinschmecker,** Balchensgate 5, ✉ 0265, ☎ 22 44 17 77, *Fax 22 56 11 39*, « Tasteful decor » – . AX n
*closed Sunday, 1 week Easter, 3 weeks in summer and 1 week Christmas* – **Meals** (booking essential) (dinner only) 410/545 and a la carte 385/545
**Spec.** Sautéed crayfish tails. Fillet of reindeer with glazed turnips. Crème brûlée with Tahiti vanilla.

**Det Blå Kjøkken,** Drammensveien 30, ✉ 0203, ☎ 22 44 26 50, *Fax 22 55 71 56* – . BY k
*closed Easter, Christmas and Bank Holidays* – **Meals** (dinner only) 400/700 and a la carte.

**Blom,** Paléet, Karl Johansgate 41b, ✉ 0162, ☎ 22 42 73 00, *Fax 22 42 04 28*, « Collection of heraldic shields and paintings » – CY t
*closed Sunday and Bank Holidays* – **Meals** (buffet lunch) 185/595 and a la carte.

XX **Babette's Gjestehus,** 1 Rådhuspassagen, Fridtjof Nansens Pl. 2, ✉ 0160, ✆ 22 41 64 64, « Attractive decor » – ▤. AE ⓓ E VISA BY f
*closed Sunday, Easter and 23 to 26 december* – **Meals** (booking essential) (dinner only) 500/700 and a la carte.

XX **Kastanjen,** Bygdøy Allé 18, ✉ 0262, ✆ 22 43 44 67, *Fax 22 55 48 72* – AE ⓓ E VISA JCB AY b
*closed Saturday lunch, Sunday and 3 weeks in summer* – **Meals** 145/355 and a la carte.

XX **Theatercaféen** (at Continental H.), Stortingsgaten 24-26, ✉ 0161, ✆ 22 82 40 50, *Fax 22 41 20 94* – ⊁. AE ⓓ E VISA. ⊁ CY n
*closed 25 December* – **Meals** (booking essential) a la carte 305/485.

**at Fornebu Airport** *SW : 8 km by E 18 – AY – and Snarøyveien :*

**Radisson SAS Park,** Fornebuparken, P.O. Box 185, ✉ 1324 Lysaker, ✆ 67 12 02 20, *Fax 67 12 00 11,* « Private beach and park », Fő, ≘s, ⚘ – |♦|, ⊁ rm, ▤ TV ☎ ✆ ♿ – 🏠 150. AE ⓓ E VISA JCB. ⊁
**Meals** (buffet lunch) 185/325 and a la carte – **254 rm** ☕ 1375/1750.

**at Sandvika** *SW : 14 km by E 18 – AY – exit E 68 :*

**Oslofjord** M, Sandviksveien 184, ✉ 1300 *Sandvika,* ✆ 67 54 57 00, *Fax 67 54 27 33,* Fő, ≘s – |♦|, ⊁ rm, ▤ TV ☎ ♿ 🚗 Ⓟ – 🏠 350. AE ⓓ E VISA. ⊁
***Fontaine :*** **Meals** (buffet lunch) 210 and a la carte 295/405 – ***Orchidee :*** **Meals** *(closed Sunday and Monday)* (dinner only) 335 and a la carte – **227 rm** ☕ 1175/1400, 15 suites.

**at Holmenkollen** *NW : 10 km by Bogstadveien – BX – Sørkedalsveien and Holmenkollveien :*

**Holmenkollen Park** M 🐎, Kongeveien 26, ✉ 0390, ✆ 22 92 20 00, *Fax 22 14 61 92,* ≤ Oslo and Fjord, ≘s, 🏊 – |♦|, ⊁ rm, ▤ TV ☎ ✆ ♿ 🚗 Ⓟ – 🏠 350. AE ⓓ E VISA JCB. ⊁ rest
*closed Christmas* – ***De Fem Stuer :*** **Meals** *(closed Sunday lunch)* (buffet lunch) 295/445 and dinner a la carte – ***Galleriet :*** **Meals** *(closed Christmas)* (buffet lunch) 225/350 and dinner a la carte – **221 rm** ☕ 1395/1495, 11 suites.

# Poland

## Polska

Warsaw

# PRACTICAL INFORMATION

## LOCAL CURRENCY

**Zloty** : *100 ZT = 28,58 US $ (Jan. 98)*

**National Holiday in Poland:** *3 May.*

## PRICES

*Prices may change if goods and service costs in Poland are revised and it is therefore always advisable to confirm rates with the hotelier when making a reservation.*

## FOREIGN EXCHANGE

*It is strongly advised against changing money other than in banks, exchange offices or authorised offices such as large hotels and Kantor. Banks are usually open on weekdays from 8am to 6pm.*

## HOTEL RESERVATIONS

*In case of difficulties in finding a room through our hotel selection, it is always possible to apply to the Tourist Office, ✆ 94 31, Fax (022) 27 11 23, open on weekdays from 8am to 7pm.*

## POSTAL SERVICES

*Post offices are open from 8am to 8pm on weekdays.*

*The* **General Post Office** *is open 7 days a week and 24 hours a day : Poczta Główna, Świetokrzyska 31/33.*

## SHOPPING IN WARSAW

*In the index of street names, those printed in red are where the principal shops are found. They are generally open from 10am to 7pm on weekdays and Saturday.*

## THEATRE BOOKING

*Your hotel porter will be able to make your arrangements or direct you to a theatre booking office: Kasy Teatralne, al Jerozolimskie 29 ✆ (022) 621 93 83, open from 11am to 2pm and 3pm to 6pm on weekdays and 11am to 2pm on Saturday.*

## TIPPING

*Hotel, restaurant and café bills include service in the total charge but it is usual to leave the staff a gratuity which will vary depending upon the service given.*

## CAR HIRE

*The international car hire companies have branches in Warsaw. Your hotel porter should be able to give details and help you with your arrangements.*

## BREAKDOWN SERVICE

*A 24 hour breakdown service is operated calling ✆ 981.*

## SPEED LIMIT

*On motorways, the maximum permitted speed is 110 km/h – 68 mph, 90 km/h – 56 mph on other roads and 60 km/h – 37 mph in built up areas.*

## SEAT BELTS

*In Poland, the wearing of seat belts is compulsory for drivers and all passengers.*

# WARSAW

(Warsawa) *Polska* 970 NO 4 – *Pop. 1 700 000.*

*Berlin 591 – Budapest 670 – Gdansk 345 – Kiev 795 – Moscow 1253 – Zagreb 993.*

*Warsaw Tourist Information Centre, Rynek Starego Miasta 28, ☎ 94 31, Fax (022) 31 04 64.*

*18 First Warsaw Golf Club and Country Club, 05110 Jabłonna ☎ (022) 774 06 55.*
*Okęcie (Warsaw Airport) SW 10 km, by Żwirki i Wigury ☎ 952 or 953.*
*Bus to airport: from major hotels in the town centre (ask the reception).*
*Polish Airlines (Lot) al Jerozolmiskie 67, Warsaw ☎ 952 or 953.*

## Sights

### OLD TOWN★★★ (STARE MIASTO) BX

*Castle Square★ (Plac Zamkowy)* BX **33** – *Royal Palace★★ (Zamek Królewski)* BX – *Beer Street (Ulica Piwna)* BX – *Ulica Świętojańska* BX **57** – *St John's Cathedral★ (Katedra Św. Jana)* BX – *Old Town Marketplace★★★ (Rynek Starego Miasta)* BX **54** – *Warsaw History Museum★ (Muzeum Historyczne Warsawy)* BX **M¹** – *Barbakan* BX **A**.

### NEW TOWN★ (NOWE MIASTO) ABX

*New Town Marketplace (Rynek Nowego Miasta)* ABX **36** – *Memorial to the Warsaw Uprising (Pomnik Powstania Warzszawskiego)* AX **D**.

### ROYAL WAY★ (TRAKT KRÓLEWSKI)

*St Anne's Church (Kościół Św. Anny)* BX – *Krakow's District Street (Krakowskie Przedmieście)* BXY – *New World Street (Nowy Świat)* BYZ – *Holy Cross Church (Św. Krzyża)* BY – *National Museum★★ (Muzeum Narodowe)* CZ.

### LAZIENKI PARK★★★ (PARK ŁAZIENKOWSKI) FUV

*Chopin Memorial (Pomnik Chopina) – Palace-on-the-Water★★ (Pałac na Wodzie) – Belvedere Palace (Belweder).*

### WILANÓW★★★ GV

### ADDITIONAL SIGHTS

*John Paul II Collection★★ (Muzeum Kolekcji im. Jana Pawła II)* AY – *Palace of Culture and Science (Pałac Kultury i Nauki): view★★ from panoramic gallery* AZ.

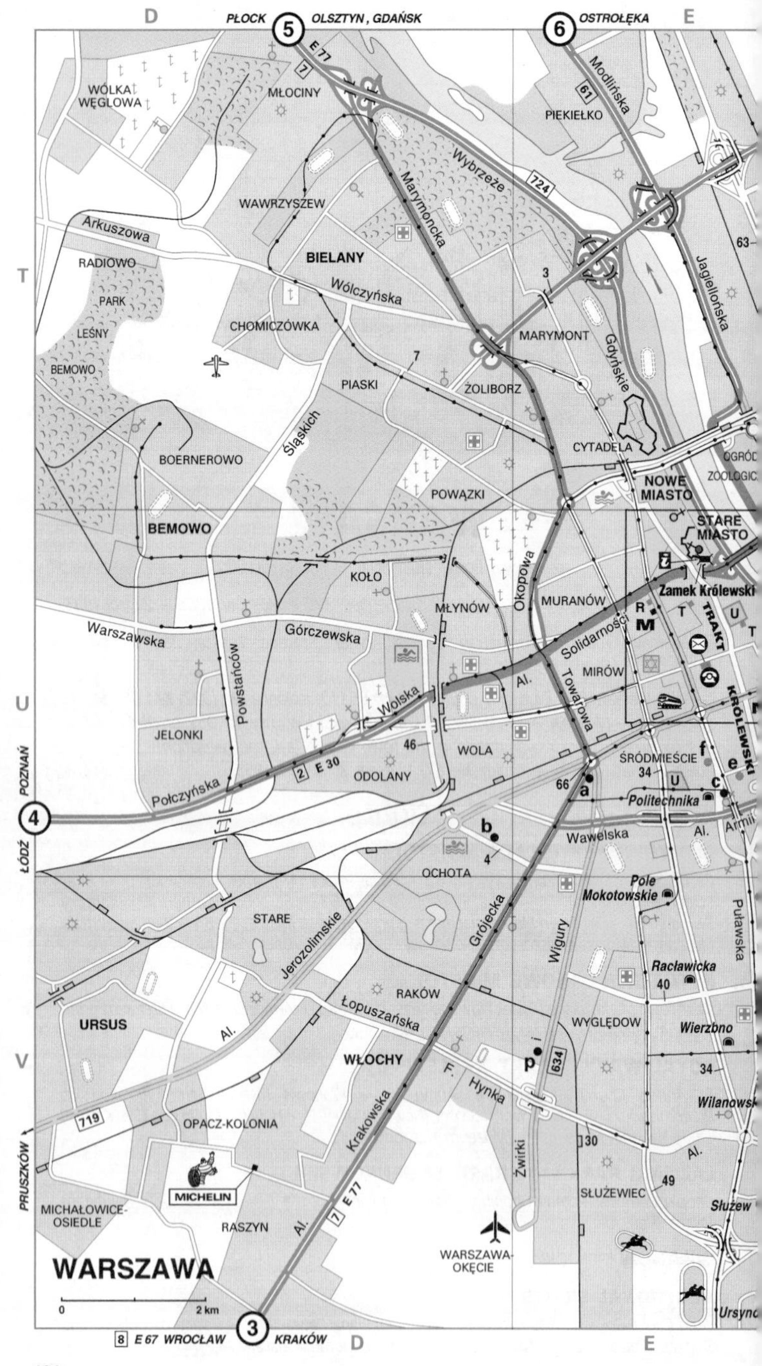

PŁOCK
OLSZTYN, GDAŃSK
OSTROŁĘKA
WÓLKA WĘGLOWA
MŁOCINY
PIEKIEŁKO
Modlińska
Wybrzeże
Marymoncka
WAWRZYSZEW
Arkuszowa
RADIOWO
BIELANY
Wólczyńska
PARK LEŚNY BEMOWO
CHOMICZÓWKA
MARYMONT
Gdyńskie
Jagiellońska
PIASKI
ŻOLIBORZ
BOERNEROWO
Śląskich
CYTADELA
POWĄZKI
NOWE MIASTO
STARE MIASTO
OGRÓD ZOOLOGICZNY
BEMOWO
KOŁO
Zamek Królewski
MŁYNÓW
Okopowa
MURANÓW
Warszawska
Górczewska
Solidarności
TRAKT KRÓLEWSKI
Powstańców
Al.
MIRÓW
Towarowa
Wolska
JELONKI
WOLA
ŚRÓDMIEŚCIE
E 30
ODOLANY
Połczyńska
Politechnika
POZNAŃ
ŁÓDŹ
Wawelska
Al. Armii
OCHOTA
Pole Mokotowskie
STARE
Grójecka
Jerozolimskie
Wigury
Puławska
Racławicka
URSUS
RAKÓW
Łopuszańska
WYGLĘDOW
Wierzbno
Al.
WŁOCHY
F. Hynka
Wilanowska
OPACZ-KOLONIA
Żwirki
Krakowska
Al.
SŁUŻEWIEC
PRUSZKÓW
MICHELIN
Służew
MICHAŁOWICE-OSIEDLE
RASZYN
Al.
E 77
WARSZAWA-OKĘCIE
WARSZAWA
0
2 km
Ursynów
E 67 WROCŁAW
KRAKÓW

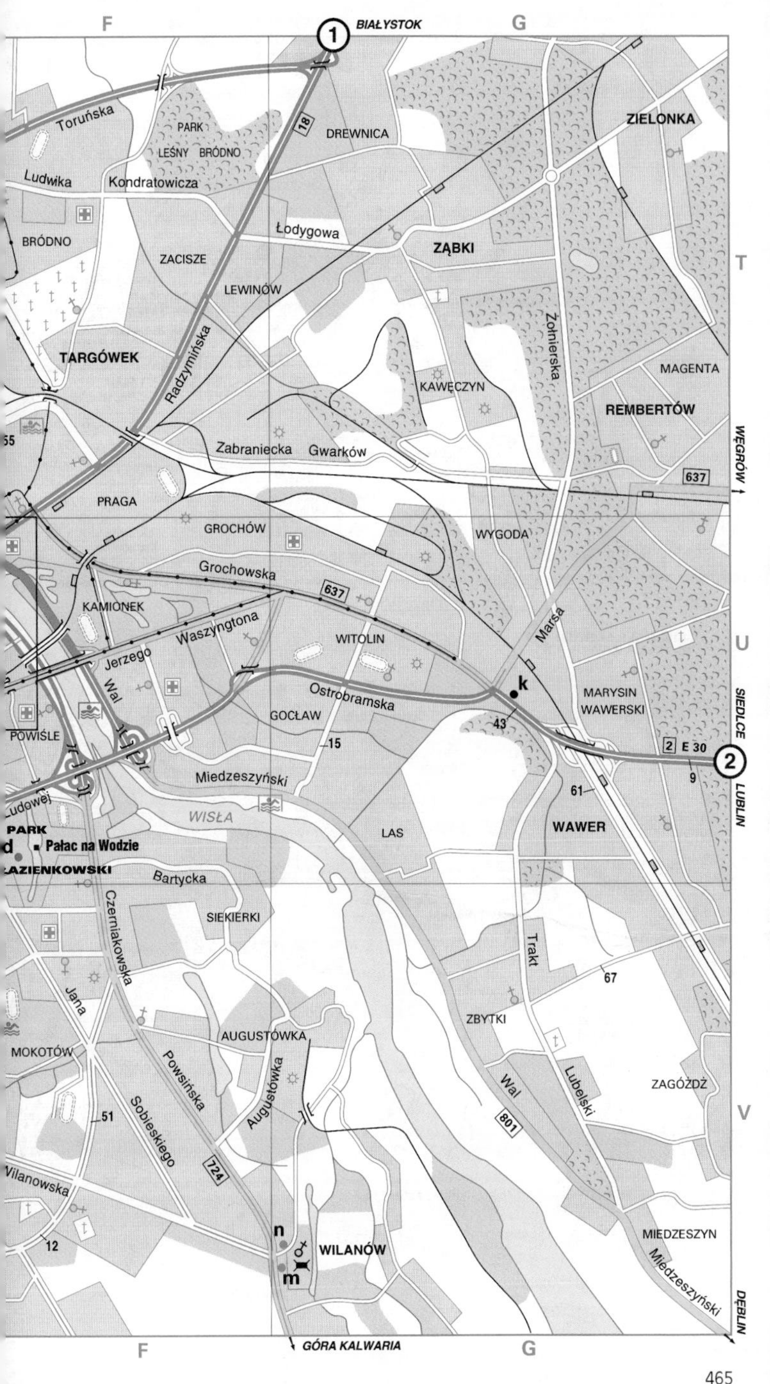
F
G
BIAŁYSTOK
1
18
Toruńska
PARK
LEŚNY BRÓDNO
DREWNICA
ZIELONKA
Ludwika
Kondratowicza
BRÓDNO
Łodygowa
ZĄBKI
ZACISZE
LEWINÓW
T
TARGÓWEK
Radzymińska
Żołnierska
MAGENTA
KAWĘCZYN
REMBERTÓW
WĘGRÓW
Zabraniecka
Gwarków
637
PRAGA
GROCHÓW
WYGODA
Grochowska
637
KAMIONEK
Waszyngtona
Jerzego
Wal
WITOLIN
Marsa
U
k
Ostrobramska
MARYSIN
WAWERSKI
SIEDLCE
POWIŚLE
GOCŁAW
43
15
2
E 30
9
Miedzeszyński
Ludowej
LUBLIN
61
WISŁA
LAS
WAWER
PARK
d
Pałac na Wodzie
ŁAZIENKOWSKI
Bartycka
SIEKIERKI
Czerniakowska
Trakt
67
Jana
ZBYTKI
AUGUSTÓWKA
MOKOTÓW
Powsińska
Lubelski
Augustówka
Wal
ZAGÓŹDŹ
V
Sobieskiego
801
51
724
Wilanowska
n
WILANÓW
MIEDZESZYN
12
m
Miedzeszyński
DĘBLIN
GÓRA KALWARIA
F
G

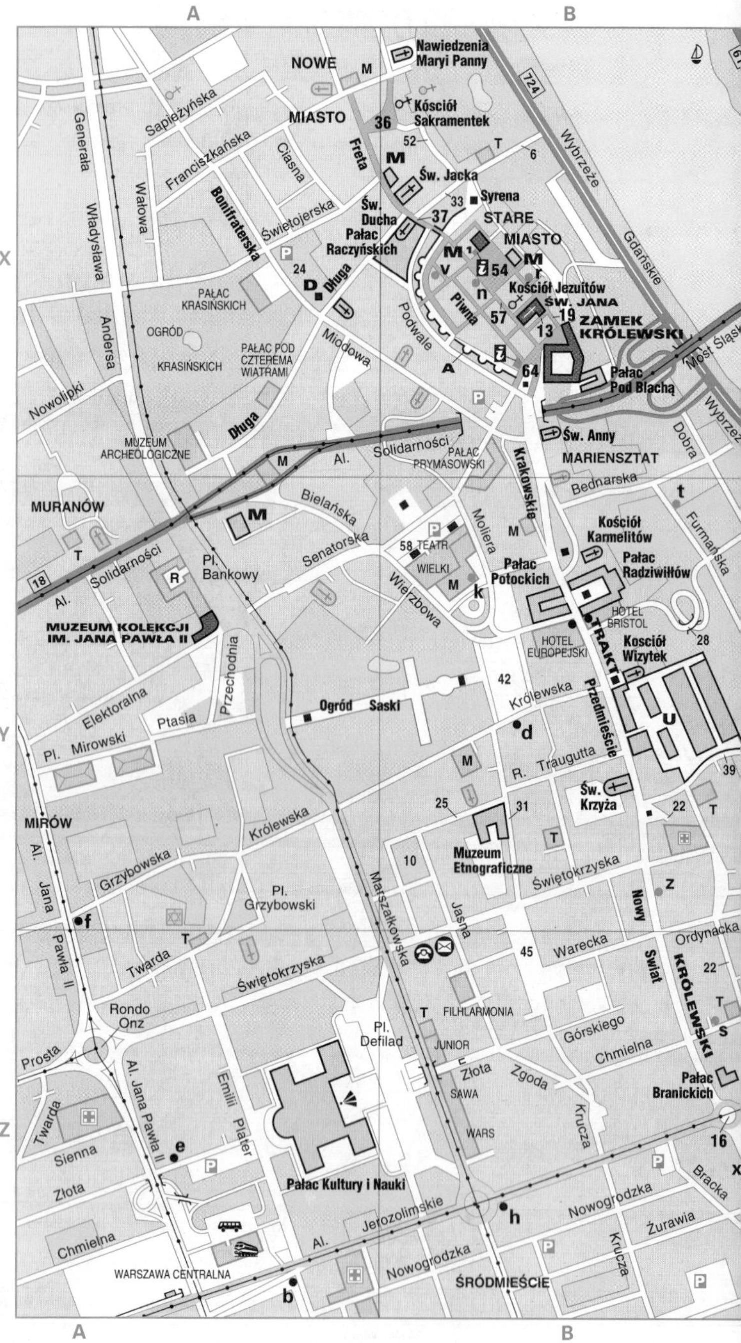
A
B
NOWE
MIASTO
Nawiedzenia Maryi Panny
Kościół Sakramentek
Freta
Sapieżyńska
Franciszkańska
Ciasna
Świętojerska
Bonifraterska
Generała Władysława Andersa
Wałowa
Św. Jacka
Syrena
Św. Ducha
Pałac Raczyńskich
STARE MIASTO
Kościół Jezuitów
ŚW. JANA
ZAMEK KRÓLEWSKI
Piwna
Podwale
Długa
Miodowa
PAŁAC KRASIŃSKICH
OGRÓD KRASIŃSKICH
PAŁAC POD CZTEREMA WIATRAMI
Nowolipki
MUZEUM ARCHEOLOGICZNE
Al. Solidarności
PAŁAC PRYMASOWSKI
Krakowskie
Św. Anny
MARIENSZTAT
Bednarska
Pałac Pod Blachą
Wybrzeże Gdańskie
Most Śląsk
Dobra
MURANÓW
Bielańska
Senatorska
TEATR WIELKI
Moliera
Kościół Karmelitów
Pałac Radziwiłłów
Furmańska
Pałac Potockich
Pl. Bankowy
MUZEUM KOLEKCJI IM. JANA PAWŁA II
Wierzbowa
HOTEL BRISTOL
HOTEL EUROPEJSKI
TRAKT
Kosciół Wizytek
Przechodnia
Elektoralna
Ptasia
Ogród Saski
Królewska
Przedmieście
Pl. Mirowski
R. Traugutta
Św. Krzyża
MIRÓW
Muzeum Etnograficzne
Grzybowska
Pl. Grzybowski
Świętokrzyska
Al. Jana Pawła II
Twarda
Marszałkowska
Jasna
Warecka
Ordynacka
Nowy Świat
KRÓLEWSKI
Rondo Onz
Prosta
FILHARMONIA
Pl. Defilad
JUNIOR
Górskiego
Chmielna
Złota
Zgoda
SAWA
WARS
Emilii Plater
Pałac Branickich
Sienna
Pałac Kultury i Nauki
Krucza
Bracka
Jerozolimskie
Nowogrodzka
Żurawia
WARSZAWA CENTRALNA
ŚRÓDMIEŚCIE
X
Y
Z

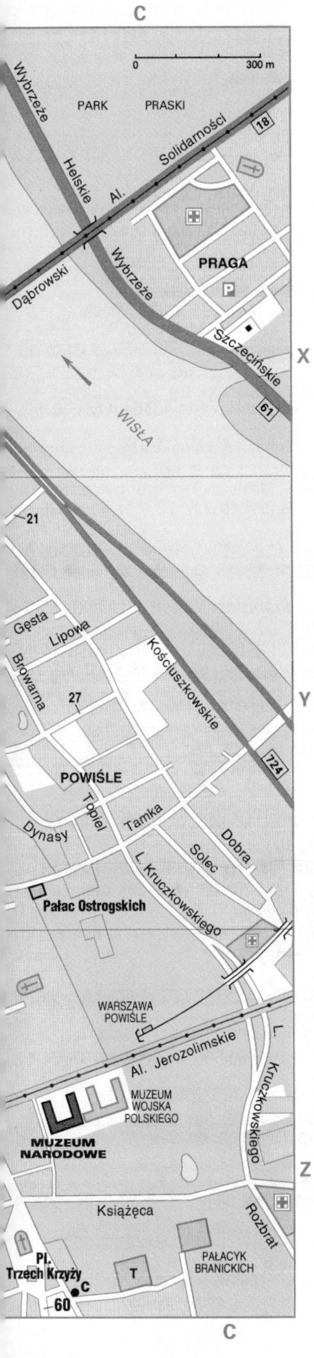

## STREET INDEX TO WARSZAWA TOWN PLANS

Chmielna (ul.) . . . . . . ABZ
Krakowskie
  Przedmieście (ul.) . BXY
Nowy Świat (ul.) . . . . BYZ
Piwna (ul.) . . . . . . . . . BX
Świętojańska (ul.) . . . BX 57

Andersa (ul. Gen. Wł.). AX
Arkuszowa (ul.) . . . . . DT
Armii Krajowej (al.) . . DET 3
Armii Ludowej (al.) . . EFU
Augustówka (ul.) . . . . FGV
Bankowy (pl.) . . . . . . AY
Bartycka (ul.) . . . . . . . FU
Bednarska (ul.) . . . . . BXY
Bielańska (ul.) . . . . . . AY
Bitwy Warszawskiej
  (ul.) . . . . . . . . . . . . . DU 4
Boleść (ul.) . . . . . . . . BX 6
Bonifraterska (ul.) . . . . AX
Bracka (ul.) . . . . . . . . . BZ
Broniewskiego (ul.) . . DET 7
Browarna (ul.) . . . . . . CY
Ciasna (ul.) . . . . . . . . . AX
Czecha (ul. Br.) . . . . . GU 9
Czerniakowska (ul.) . . FV
Dąbrowskiego
  (pl. J.H.) . . . . . . . . . BY 10
Defilad (pl.) . . . . . . . . ABZ
Długa (ul.) . . . . . . . . . ABX
Dobra (ul.) . . . . . . . . . BX
Dolina Służewiecka
  (ul.) . . . . . . . . . . . . . EFV 12
Dynasy (ul.) . . . . . . . . CY
Dziekania (ul.) . . . . . . BX 13
Elektoralna (ul.) . . . . . AY
Emilii Plater (ul.) . . . . AZ
Fieldorfa
  (ul. Gen. Emila) . . . GU 15
Franciszkańska (ul.) . . AX
Freta (ul.) . . . . . . . . . . AX
Furmańska (ul.) . . . . . BY
Gaulla (Rondo
  Gen. Ch. de) . . . . . BZ 16
Gęsta (ul.) . . . . . . . . . CY
Górczewska (ul.) . . . . DU
Górskiego (ul.) . . . . . . BZ
Grochowska (ul.) . . . . FGU
Grójecka (ul.) . . . . . . . DEV
Grzybowska (ul.) . . . . AY
Grzybowski (pl.) . . . . . AY
Hynka Franciszka
  (ul.) . . . . . . . . . . . . . DV
Jagiellońska (ul.) . . . . ET
Jana Pawxa II (al.) . . . AYZ
Jasna (ul.) . . . . . . . . . BYZ
Jerozolimskie (al.) . . ABCZ
Kanonia (ul.) . . . . . . . BX 19
Karowa (ul.) . . . . . . . . CY 21
Kondratowicza (ul. L.) . FT
Kopernika (ul. M.) . . . BYZ 22
Krakowska (al.) . . . . . DV
Krasińskich (pl.) . . . . AX 24
Kredytowa (ul.) . . . . . BY 25
Królewska (ul.) . . . . . . ABY
Krucza (ul.) . . . . . . . . . BZ
Kruczkowskiego
  (ul. L.) . . . . . . . . . . . CYZ
Książęca (ul.) . . . . . . . CZ
Leszczyńska (ul.) . . . . CY 27
Lipowa (ul.) . . . . . . . . CY
Łodygowa (ul.) . . . . . . FGT
Łopuszańska (ul.) . . . . DV
Markiewicza
  (wiadukt) . . . . . . . . BY 28
Marsa (ul.) . . . . . . . . . GU
Marszałkowska (ul.) . ABYZ
Marynarska (ul.) . . . . . EV 30
Mazowiecka (ul.) . . . . BY 31
Miodowa (ul.) . . . . . . ABX
Mirowski (pl.) . . . . . . . AY
Modlińska (ul.) . . . . . . ET
Moliera (ul.) . . . . . . . . BY
Mostowa (ul.) . . . . . . . BX 33
Niepodległości (al.) . . EUV 34
Nowego Miasta
  (rynek) . . . . . . . . . . ABX 36
Nowogrodzka (ul.) . . . BZ
Nowolipki (ul.) . . . . . . AX
Nowomiejska (ul.) . . . . BX 37
Oboźna (ul.) . . . . . . . . BCY 39
Odyńca Antoniego
  (ul.) . . . . . . . . . . . . . EV 40
ONZ (rondo) . . . . . . . AZ
Ordynacka (ul.) . . . . . BY
Ostrobramska (ul.) . . . GU
Piłsudskiego (pl. J.) . . BY 42
Płowiecka (ul.) . . . . . . GU 43
Podwale (ul.) . . . . . . . BX
Połczyńska (ul.) . . . . . DU
Powsińska (ul.) . . . . . . FV
Powstańców
  Slaskich (ul.) . . . . . DTU
Powstańców
  Warszawy (pl.) . . . . BYZ 45
Prosta (ul.) . . . . . . . . . AZ
Prymasa
  Tysiąclecia (al.) . . . DU 46
Przechodnia (ul.) . . . . AY
Ptasia (ul.) . . . . . . . . . AY
Puławska (ul.) . . . . . . EUV
Radzymińska (ul.) . . . . FT
Rozbrat (ul.) . . . . . . . . CZ
Rzymowskiego
  (ul. W.) . . . . . . . . . . EV 49
Sapieżyńska (ul.) . . . . AX
Senatorska (ul.) . . . . . ABY
Sienna (ul.) . . . . . . . . AZ
Sikorskiego
  (al. Gen. W.) . . . . . . FV 51
Sobieskiego Jana
  (ul.) . . . . . . . . . . . . . FV
Solec (ul.) . . . . . . . . . CY
Solidarności (al.) . . . ACXY
Stara (ul.) . . . . . . . . . BX 52
Starego Miasta
  (rynek) . . . . . . . . . . BX 54
Starzyńskiego
  (ul. Stefana) . . . . . . EFT 55
Śląsko-Dąbrowski
  (most) . . . . . . . . . . BCX
Świętojerska (ul.) . . . . AX
Świętokrzyska (ul.) . . ABYZ
Tamka (ul.) . . . . . . . . . CY
Teatralny (pl.) . . . . . . BY 58
Topiel (ul.) . . . . . . . . . CY
Toruńska (ul.) . . . . . . . EFT
Trakt Lubelski (ul.) . . . GUV
Traugutta (ul. R.) . . . . BY
Twarda (ul.) . . . . . . . . AYZ
Ujazdovskie (al.) . . . . . CZ 60
Wał Miedzeszyński
  (ul.) . . . . . . . . . . . . FGUV
Wałowa (ul.) . . . . . . . . AX
Warecka (ul.) . . . . . . . BYZ
Warszawska (ul.) . . . . DU
Waszyngtona
  Uerzego (ul.) . . . . . FU
Wawelska (ul.) . . . . . . EU
Widoczna (ul.) . . . . . . GU 61
Wierzbowa (ul.) . . . . . BY
Wilanowska (al.) . . . . EFV
Wolska (ul.) . . . . . . . . DU
Wólczyńska (ul.) . . . . . DT
Wybrzeże Gdańskie
  (ul.) . . . . . . . . . . . . . BX
Wybrzeże Gdyńskie
  (ul.) . . . . . . . . . . . . . DET
Wybrzeże Helskie (ul.) . CX
Wybrzeże
  Kosciuszkowskie
  (ul.) . . . . . . . . . . . . . BX
Wybrzeże
  Szczecińskie (ul.) . . CX
Wysockiego (ul. P.) . . ET 63
Zamkowy (pl.) . . . . . . BX 64
Zawiszy (pl.) . . . . . . . EU 66
Zgoda (ul.) . . . . . . . . . BZ
Złota (ul.) . . . . . . . . . . ABZ
Zwoleńska (ul.) . . . . . GV 67
Zołnierska (ul.) . . . . . . GT
Zurawia (ul.) . . . . . . . . BZ
Zwirki i Wigury
  (ul.) . . . . . . . . . . . . . EUV

*For maximum information from town plans : consult the conventional signs key.*

**Bristol,** Krakowskie Przedmieście 42-44, ✉ 00 325, ℘ (022) 625 25 25, *Fax (022) 625 25 77,* « Late 19C facade, partly decorated in Art Nouveau style », Fá, ≘s, ◻ – |‡|, ⇔ rm, ▤ TV ☎ – 🏆 100. AE ⓓ E VISA JCB. ⛔ rest BY a
***Marconi* : Meals** - Italian - 60/105 and a la carte (see also ***Malinowa*** below) – **120 rm** ⊒ 920/1060, 42 suites.

**Marriott** M, Al. Jerozolimskie 65-79, ✉ 00 697, ℘ (022) 630 63 06, *Fax (022) 830 00 41,* ⩽ Warsaw, Fá, ≘s, ◻ – |‡| ⇔ ▤ TV ☎ ♿ ⇔ – 🏆 700. AE ⓓ E VISA JCB. ⛔ AZ b
***Chicago Grill* : Meals** *(closed Easter and 24 to 31 December)* (dinner only) 180/250 and a la carte – ***Parmizzano's* : Meals** - Italian - *(closed 25, 26 and 31 December)* 150/250 and a la carte – ***Lila Weneda* : Meals** (buffet lunch) 65/120 and a la carte – **488 rm** ⊒ 860/1010, 34 suites.

**Sheraton** M, Ul. B. Prusa 2, ✉ 00 493, ℘ (022) 657 61 00, *Fax (022) 657 62 00,* Fá, ≘s – |‡|, ⇔ rm, ▤ TV ☎ ♿ ⇔ – 🏆 550. AE ⓓ E VISA JCB. ⛔ rest CZ c
***The Oriental* : Meals** - Oriental - approx. 110 and a la carte – ***Lalka* : Meals** - Central European - (buffet lunch) 85/175 and a la carte – ⊒ 35 – **331 rm** 880/995, 19 suites.

**Victoria** M, Ul. Królewska 11, ✉ 00 065, ℘ (022) 657 80 11, *Fax (022) 657 80 57,* Fá, ≘s, ◻ – |‡|, ⇔ rm, ▤ TV ☎ ♿ ⇔ – 🏆 450. AE ⓓ E VISA JCB. ⛔ rest BY d
***Canaletto* : Meals** 90/250 and a la carte – ***Opera* : Meals** *(closed Sunday)* (dinner only) 80/120 and a la carte – ***Hetmańska* : Meals** 75/200 and a la carte – **330 rm** ⊒ 670/960, 30 suites.

**Holiday Inn** M, Ul. Złota 48-54, ✉ 00 120, ℘ (022) 697 39 99, *Fax (022) 697 38 99,* Fá, ≘s – |‡|, ⇔ rm, ▤ TV ☎ ♿ ⇔ Ⓟ – 🏆 190. AE ⓓ E VISA JCB. ⛔ rest AZ e
***Symfonia* : Meals** a la carte 80/125 – ***Rotisserie* : Meals** *(closed Saturday and Sunday)* (dinner only) a la carte 65/95 – ***Brasserie* : Meals** (buffet only) 70 – ⊒ 45 – **326 rm** 650/845, 10 suites.

**Mercure Fryderyk Chopin** M, Al. Jana Pawła II 22, ✉ 00 133, ℘ (022) 620 02 01, *Fax (022) 620 87 79,* Fá, ≘s – |‡|, ⇔ rm, ▤ TV ☎ ♿ ⇔ Ⓟ – 🏆 250. AE ⓓ E VISA JCB. ⛔ rest AY f
***Balzac* : Meals** - French - 120/190 and a la carte – ***Stanislas* : Meals** (buffet lunch) 55/95 and a la carte – **242 rm** ⊒ 630/700, 8 suites.

**Jan III Sobieski** M, Plac Artura Zawiszy 1, ✉ 02 025, ℘ (022) 658 44 44, *Fax (022) 659 88 28,* 🍽 – |‡|, ⇔ rm, ▤ rm, TV ☎ ♿ ⇔ – 🏆 180. AE ⓓ E VISA JCB. ⛔ EU a
**Meals** a la carte 150/300 – **374 rm** ⊒ 490/650, 33 suites.

**Forum,** Ul. Nowogrodzka 24-26, ✉ 00 511, ℘ (022) 621 02 71, *Fax (022) 625 04 76* – |‡|, ⇔ rm, ▤ TV ☎ ♿ – 🏆 450. AE ⓓ E VISA JCB. ⛔ rest BZ h
***Soplica* : Meals** a la carte 40/55 – ***Maryla* : Meals** (buffet lunch only) a la carte approx. 40 – **723 rm** ⊒ 530/575, 10 suites.

**Europejski,** Ul. Krakowskie Przedmieście 13, ✉ 00 065, ℘ (022) 26 50 51, *Fax (022) 26 11 11,* 🍽 – |‡| TV ☎ – 🏆 450. AE ⓓ E VISA. ⛔ rest BY
**Meals** 50/150 and a la carte – **139 rm** ⊒ 270/460, 11 suites.

**Vera,** Ul. Bitwy Warszawskiej 1920 roku 16, ✉ 02 366, ℘ (022) 822 74 21, *Fax (022) 823 62 56* – |‡|, ▤ rest TV ☎ ♿ Ⓟ – 🏆 150. AE ⓓ E VISA JCB. ⛔ rest
**Meals** a la carte 50/90 – **134 rm** ⊒ 355/420, 6 suites. DU b

**M.D.M.** without rest., Pl. Konstytucji 1, ✉ 00 647, ℘ (022) 621 62 11, *Fax (022) 621 41 73* – |‡| TV ☎. AE ⓓ E VISA JCB. ⛔ EU c
**115 rm** ⊒ 245/490.

XXX **Malinowa** (at Bristol H.), Krakowskie Przedmieście 42-44, ✉ 00 325, ℘ (022) 625 25 25, *Fax (022) 625 25 77* – ⇔ ▤. AE ⓓ E VISA JCB BY a
*closed Sunday and August* – **Meals** - French - (dinner only) 140 and a la carte.

XXX **La Gioconda,** Plac Piłsudskiego 9, ✉ 00 078, ℘ (022) 827 94 42, *Fax (022) 826 36 13,* 🍽 – ▤. AE ⓓ E VISA JCB BY k
*closed 24 to 26 December* – **Meals** - Italian - a la carte 100/250.

XX **Belvedere,** Ul. Agrykoli 1A, ✉ 00 460, ℘ (022) 41 48 06, *Fax (022) 41 71 35,* ⩽, 🍽, « Late 19C orangery in Łazienkowski park » – Ⓟ. AE ⓓ E VISA JCB FU d
*closed 25 December-15 January* – **Meals** a la carte 80/230.

XX **Casa Valdemar,** Ul. Piękna 7-9, ✉ 00 539, ℘ (022) 628 81 40, *Fax (022) 622 88 96,* « Elegant Spanish style installation » – ▤. AE ⓓ E VISA JCB EU e
**Meals** - Spanish - a la carte 80/170.

XX **Fukier,** Rynek Starego Miasta 27, ✉ 00 272, ℘ (022) 831 10 13, *Fax (022) 831 10 13,* « Traditional Polish decor » – ⇔. AE ⓓ E VISA JCB BX n
*closed Easter Sunday and 24, 25 and 31 December* – **Meals** a la carte 75/250.

XX **Kahlenberg,** Ul. Koszykowa 54, ✉ 00 675, ℘ (022) 630 88 50, *Fax (022) 630 88 50* – ▤. AE ⓓ E VISA JCB EU f
**Meals** 60/100 and a la carte.

**Montmartre,** Nowy Swiat 7, ✉ 00 496, ☎ (022) 628 63 15 – AE BZ x
*closed 15 to 31 August* – **Meals** - French - a la carte 60/200.

**Swiętoszek,** Ul. Jezuicka 6-8, ✉ 00 281, ☎ (022) 831 56 34, *Fax (022) 635 59 47,* « Vaulted cellar » – AE ⓓ E VISA JCB BX r
*closed Easter Sunday, Christmas and New Year* – **Meals** 45 (lunch) and a la carte 50/80.

**Flik,** Ul. Puławska 43, ✉ 02 508, ☎ (022) 49 44 34, *Fax (022) 49 44 34,* – . AE ⓓ E VISA JCB EV h
*closed Easter Sunday and 25 December* – **Meals** (buffet lunch) 40/80 and dinner a la carte 55/85 – ***Petit Flik* : Meals** 20/50.

**Tsubame,** Ul. Foksal 16, ✉ 00 372, ☎ (022) 826 51 27, *Fax (022) 826 48 51,* Japanese decor – . AE ⓓ E VISA JCB BZ s
*closed 24-25 December and 1 January* – **Meals** - Japanese - 30/60 and a la carte.

**Pod Retmanem,** Ul. Bednarska 9, ✉ 00 310, ☎ (022) 826 87 58, *Fax (022) 826 87 58,* « Fresco depicting the old port of Gdansk » – AE ⓓ E VISA JCB BY t
**Meals** (music Thursday to Saturday evenings) a la carte 50/200.

**Rycerska,** Ul. Szeroki Dunaj 11, ✉ 00 254, ☎ (022) 831 36 68, *Fax (022) 831 47 33,* , « Medieval theme » – AE ⓓ E VISA BX v
**Meals** a la carte 70/150.

**Kuchcik,** Ul. Nowy Świat 64, ✉ 00 357, ☎ (022) 826 93 53, *Fax (022) 827 39 00* – . AE ⓓ E VISA JCB BY z
**Meals** a la carte 40/80 – ***Pod Kuchcikiem*** (wine bar in cellar) **: Meals** (dinner only) a la carte 20/40.

**to the E :**

**in Wawer District** *E : 10 km on Lublin road :*

**Zajazd Napoleoński,** Ul. Płowiecka 83, ✉ 04 501, ☎ (022) 15 30 68, *Fax (022) 15 22 16* – rest, TV P. AE ⓓ E VISA JCB. GU k
*closed 24 December-2 January* – **Meals** a la carte 70/110 – **21 rm** 250/330, 3 suites.

**to the S :**

**at Wilanów** *S : 9 km at Pałac Wilanowski entrance :*

**Wilanów,** Ul. Wiertnicza 27, ✉ 02 952, ☎ (022) 42 18 52, *Fax (022) 42 18 52,* « Hunting atmosphere » – AE ⓓ E VISA JCB GV m
**Meals** a la carte 40/70.

**Kuźnia Królewska,** Ul. Wiertnicza 24, ✉ 02 958, ☎ (022) 42 31 71, – AE ⓓ E VISA JCB GV n
**Meals** a la carte 30/85.

**to the SW :**

**Novotel,** Ul. Sierpnia 1, ✉ 02 134, 6 km on airport rd ☎ (022) 846 40 51, *Fax (022) 846 36 86,* , , – , rm, rest, TV ☎ & P – 200. AE ⓓ E VISA JCB. rest EV p
**Meals** 65 and a la carte – **146 rm** 345/415.

# *Portugal*

LISBON

# PRACTICAL INFORMATION

## LOCAL CURRENCY

**Escudo:** *100 PTE = 0,55 USD ($) (Jan. 98).*
**National Holiday in Portugal:** *10 June.*

## FOREIGN EXCHANGE

*Hotels, restaurants and shops do not always accept foreign currencies and the tourist is therefore advised to change cheques and currency at banks, saving banks and exchange offices. The general opening times are as follows: banks 8.30am to 3pm (closed on Saturdays, Sundays, and Bank Holidays), money changers 9.30am to 6pm (usually closed on Sundays and Bank Holidays).*

## TRANSPORT

*Taxis may be hailed when showing the green light or "Livre" sign on the windscreen.*
*Metro (subway) network. In each station complete information and plans will be found.*

## SHOPPING IN LISBON

*Shops and boutiques are generally open from 9am to 1pm and 3 to 7pm. In Lisbon, the main shopping streets are: Rua Augusta, Rua do Carmo, Rua Garrett (Chiado), Rua do Ouro, Rua da Prata, Av. de Roma, Av. da Liberdade, Shopping Center Amoreiras.*

## TIPPING

*A service charge is added to all bills in hotels, restaurants and cafés; it is usual, however, to give an additional tip for personal service; 10 % of the fare or ticket price is also the usual amount given to taxi drivers and cinema and theatre usherettes.*

## SPEED LIMITS

*The speed limit on motorways is 120 km/h - 74 mph, on other roads 90 km/h - 56 mph and in built up areas 50 km/h - 37 mph.*

## SEAT BELTS

*The wearing of seat belts is compulsory for drivers and all passengers.*

## THE FADO

*The Lisbon Fado (songs) can be heard in restaurants in old parts of the town such as the Alfama, the Bairro Alto and the Mouraria. A selection of fado cabarets will be found at the end of the Lisbon restaurant list.*

# LISBON

(LISBOA) *1100* P 440 P 2 - *Pop. 662 782 - alt. 111.*

*Paris 1820 - Madrid 658 - Bilbao/Bilbo 907 - Porto 314 - Sevilla 417.*

*Palácio Foz, Praça dos Restaudores ✉ 1200 ☎ (01) 346 63 07, Fax (01) 346 87 72 and airport ☎ (01) 849 36 89 - A.C.P. Rua Rosa Araújo 24, ✉ 1200, ☎ (01) 356 39 31, Fax (01) 57 47 32.*

*9, 18 Estoril Golf Club W : 25 km ☎ (01) 468 01 76 - 18 Lisbon Sports Club NW : 20 km ☎ (01) 431 00 77 - 18 Club de Campo da Aroeira S : 15 km ☎ (01) 297 13 14 Aroeira, Monte da Caparica*

*Lisbon Airport N : 8 km from city centre ☎ (01) 841 35 00 - T.A.P., Praça Marquês de Pombal 3, ✉ 1200, ☎ (01) 386 40 80 and airport ☎ (01) 841 50 00.*

*Santa Apolónia ☎ (01) 888 40 25* MX.

*to Madeira : E.N.M., Rua de São Julião 5-1°, ✉ 1100, ☎ (01) 887 01 21.*

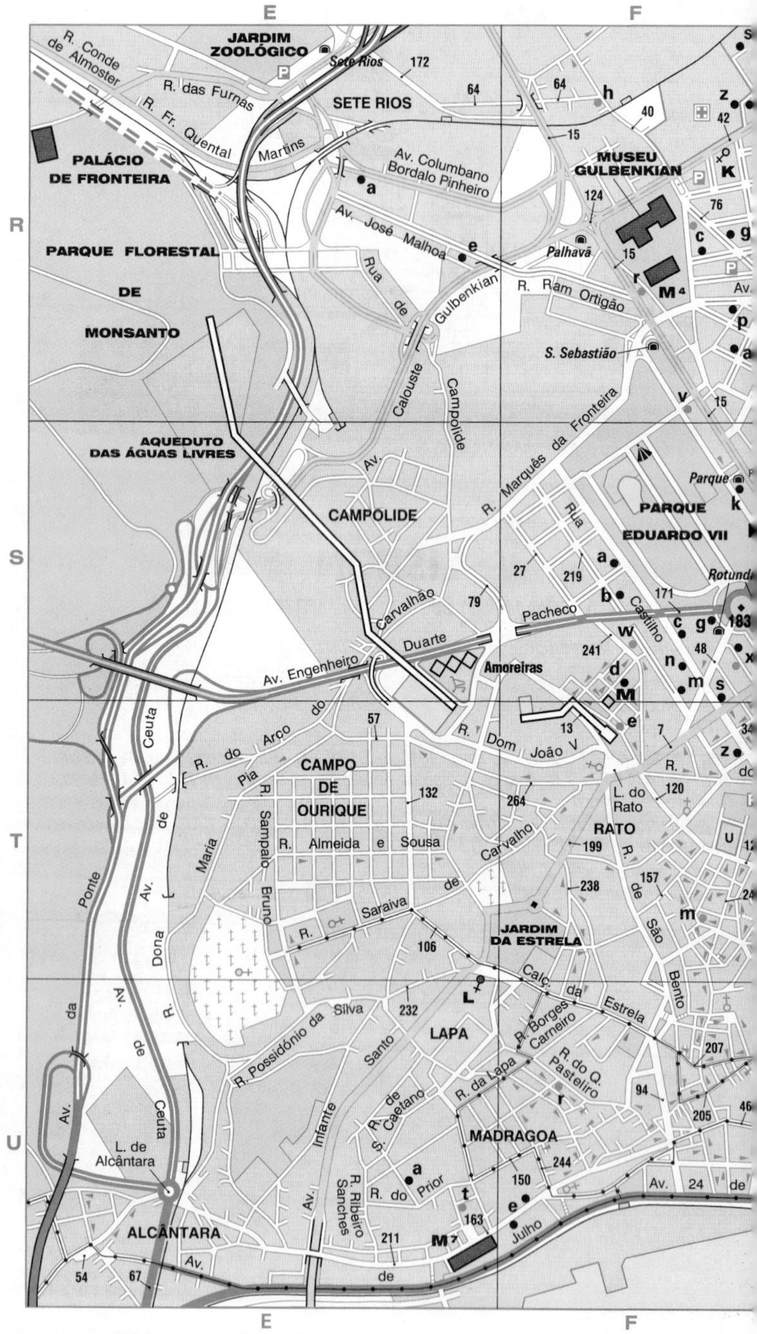

JARDIM ZOOLÓGICO
SETE RIOS
PALÁCIO DE FRONTEIRA
PARQUE FLORESTAL DE MONSANTO
MUSEU GULBENKIAN
AQUEDUTO DAS ÁGUAS LIVRES
CAMPOLIDE
PARQUE EDUARDO VII
Amoreiras
CAMPO DE OURIQUE
RATO
JARDIM DA ESTRELA
LAPA
MADRAGOA
ALCÂNTARA

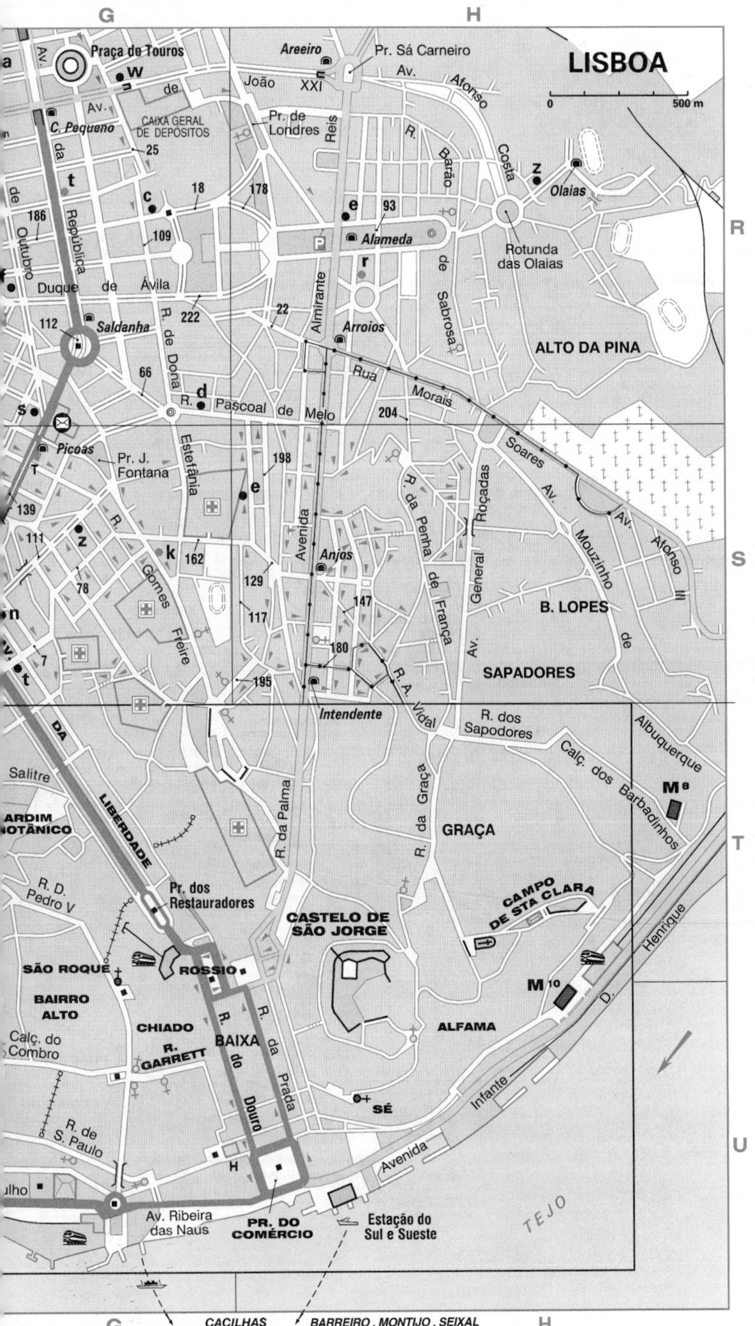
LISBOA
G
H
R
S
T
U
0
500 m
Praça de Touros
Areeiro
Pr. Sá Carneiro
C. Pequeno
CAIXA GERAL DE DEPÓSITOS
Pr. de Londres
Olaias
Rotunda das Olaias
Alameda
Saldanha
Arroios
ALTO DA PINA
Picoas
Pr. J. Fontana
Anjos
B. LOPES
SAPADORES
Intendente
R. dos Sapadores
Calç. dos Barbadinhos
GRAÇA
JARDIM BOTÂNICO
LIBERDADE
Pr. dos Restauradores
CASTELO DE SÃO JORGE
CAMPO DE STA CLARA
SÃO ROQUE
ROSSIO
BAIRRO ALTO
CHIADO
R. GARRETT
BAIXA
ALFAMA
SÉ
Av. Ribeira das Naus
PR. DO COMÉRCIO
Estação do Sul e Sueste
TEJO
CACILHAS
BARREIRO, MONTIJO, SEIXAL

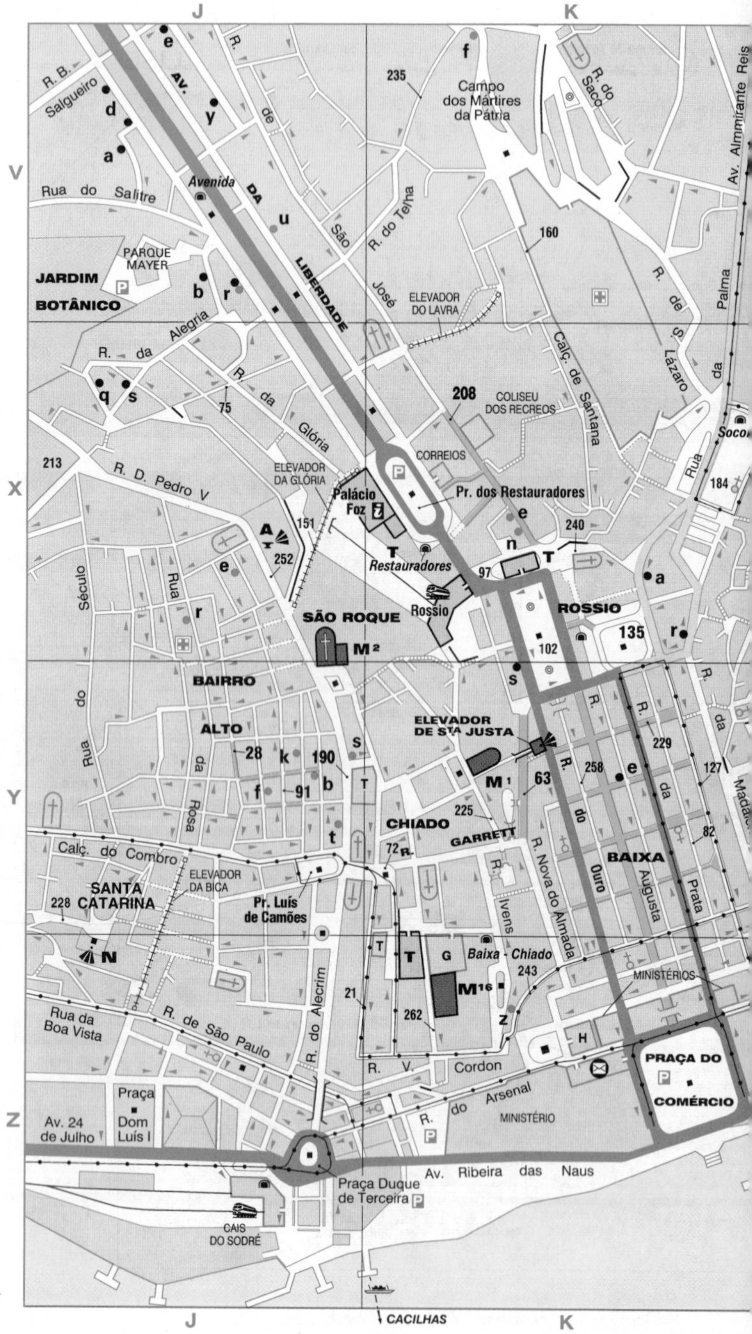
J
K
V
X
Y
Z
R. B. Salgueiro
Rua do Salitre
Avenida DA LIBERDADE
R. de São José
R. do Telha
Campo dos Mártires da Pátria
R. do Saco
Av. Almirante Reis
R. de S. Lázaro
Calç. de Santana
Rua da Palma
PARQUE MAYER
JARDIM BOTÂNICO
ELEVADOR DO LAVRA
R. da Alegria
R. da Glória
COLISEU DOS RECREOS
CORREIOS
R. D. Pedro V
ELEVADOR DA GLÓRIA
Palácio Foz
Pr. dos Restauradores
Restauradores
Rossio
ROSSIO
SÃO ROQUE
Rua do Século
Rua da Rosa
BAIRRO ALTO
ELEVADOR DE S^TA JUSTA
CHIADO
GARRETT
R. Ivens
R. Nova do Almada
R. do Ouro
R. Augusta
R. da Prata
BAIXA
R. da Madalena
Calç. do Combro
ELEVADOR DA BICA
SANTA CATARINA
Pr. Luís de Camões
R. do Alecrim
Baixa - Chiado
MINISTÉRIOS
Rua da Boa Vista
R. de São Paulo
R. V. Cordon
R. do Arsenal
MINISTÉRIO
PRAÇA DO COMÉRCIO
Praça Dom Luís I
Av. 24 de Julho
Praça Duque de Terceira
Av. Ribeira das Naus
CAIS DO SODRÉ
CACILHAS
J
K

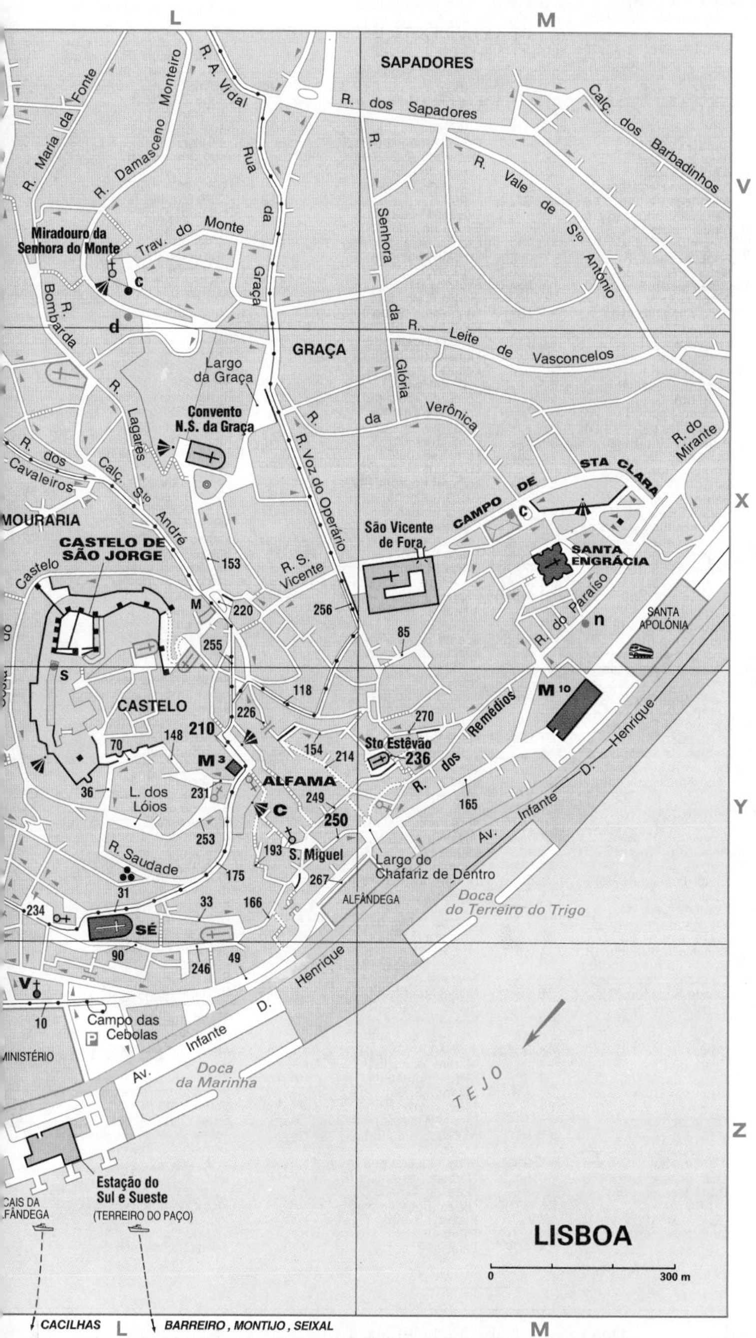
L
M
SAPADORES
R. dos Sapadores
Calç. dos Barbadinhos
R. Vale de Sto António
R. Senhora da Glória
R. A. Vidal
Rua da Graça
R. Damasceno Monteiro
R. Maria da Fonte
Miradouro da Senhora do Monte
Trav. do Monte
R. Bombarda
GRAÇA
R. Leite de Vasconcelos
Largo da Graça
Convento N.S. da Graça
R. Lagares
R. dos Cavaleiros
Calç. Sto André
R. da Verônica
R. Voz do Operário
R. do Mirante
CAMPO DE STA CLARA
MOURARIA
CASTELO DE SÃO JORGE
Castelo
R. S. Vicente
São Vicente de Fora
SANTA ENGRÁCIA
R. do Paraíso
SANTA APOLÓNIA
CASTELO
ALFAMA
Sto Estêvão
R. dos Remédios
L. dos Lóios
R. Saudade
S. Miguel
Largo do Chafariz de Dentro
ALFÂNDEGA
Doca do Terreiro do Trigo
Av. Infante D. Henrique
SÉ
Campo das Cebolas
MINISTÉRIO
Doca da Marinha
TEJO
Estação do Sul e Sueste
(TERREIRO DO PAÇO)
CAIS DA ALFÂNDEGA
CACILHAS
BARREIRO, MONTIJO, SEIXAL
LISBOA
0
300 m
V
X
Y
Z

## STREET INDEX TO LISBOA TOWN PLANS

Augusta (R.) KY
Carmo (R. do) KY 63
Garrett (R.) (Chiado) KY
Ouro (R. do) KY
Prata (R. da) KY

Afonso Costa (Av.) HR
Alecrim (R. do) JZ
Alegria (R. da) JX
Alexandre Herculano (R.) FT 7
Alfândega (R. da) LZ 10
Almeida e Sousa (R.) ET
Almirante Reis (Av.) HR
Amoreiras (R. das) FT 13
Angelina Vidal (R.) LV
António Augusto de Aguiar (Av.) FR 15
António José de Almeida (Av.) GR 18
António Maria Cardoso (R.) JZ 21
António Pereira Carrilho (R.) HR 22
Arco do Carvalhão (R. do) ET
Arco do Cego (R.) GR 25
Arsenal (R. do) KZ
Artilharia Um (R. da) FS 27
Atalaia (R. da) JY 28
Augusto Rosa (R.) LY 31
Barão (R.) LY 33
Barão de Sabrosa (R.) HR
Barata Salgueiro (R.) FT 34
Barbadinhos (Calç. dos) MV
Bartolomeu de Gusmão (R.) LY 36
Beneficência (R. da) FR 40
Berna (Av. de) FR 42
Boa Vista (R. da) FU 46
Bombarda (R.) LV
Borges Carneiro (R.) FU
Braancamp (R.) FS 48
Cais de Santarém (R.) LZ 49
Calouste Gulbenkian (Av.) ER
Calvário (L. do) EU 54
Campo das Cebolas LZ
Campo de Ourique (R. do) ET 57
Campo de Santa Clara MX
Campo dos Mártires da Pátria KV
Casal Ribeiro (Av.) GR 66
Cascais (R.) EU 67
Castilho (R.) FS
Cavaleiros (R. dos) LX
Chafariz de Dentro (L. do) MY
Chão da Feira (R. do) LY 70
Chiado (L. do) KY 72
Combro (Calç. do) JY
Comércio (Pr. do) (Terreiro do Paço) KZ
Conceição da Gloriá (R.) JX 75
Conde de Almoster (R.) ER
Conde de Valbom (Av.) FR 76
Conde Redondo (R.) GS 78
Conselheiro F. de Sousa (Av.) ES 79
Correeiros (R. dos) KY 82
Corvos (R. dos) MX 85
Costa do Castelo LX
Cruzes da Sé (R.) LZ 90
Damasceno Monteiro (R.) LV
Diário de Notícias (R. do) JY 91
Dom Afonso Henriques (Alameda) HR 93
Dom Carlos I (Av.) FU 94
Dom João da Câmara (Pr.) KX 97
Dom Luis I (Pr.) JZ
Dom Pedro IV (Pr.) (Rossio) KX 102

Dom Pedro V (R.) JX
Domingos Sequeira (R.) ET 106
Dona Estefânia (R. de) GS
Dona Filipa de Vilhena (Av.) GR 109
Dona Maria Pia (R.) ET
Duque de Ávila (Av.) GR
Duque de Loulé (Av.) GS 111
Duque de Saldanha (Pr.) GR 112
Duque de Terceira (Pr.) JZ
Escola do Exército (R.) HS 117
Escolas Gerais (R. das) LY 118
Escola Politécnica (R. da) FT 120
Espanha (Pr. de) FR 124
Estrela (Calç. da) FU
Fanqueiros (R. dos) KY 127
Febo Moniz (R.) HS 129
Ferreira Borges (R.) ET 132
Figueira (Pr. da) KX 135
Fontes Pereira de Melo (Av.) GS 139
Forno do Tijolo (R.) HS 147
Francisco Quental Martins (R.) ER
Funil (Trav. do) LY 148
Furnas (R. das) ER
Garcia da Horta (R.) FU 150
General Roçadas (Av.) HS
Glória (Calç. da) JX 151
Glória (R. da) JX
Gomes Freire (R.) GS
Graça (Calç. da) LX 153
Graça (L. da) LX
Graça (R. da) LV
Guilherme Braga (R.) LY 154
Imprensa Nacional (R.) FT 157
Infante D. Henrique (Av.) MY
Infante Santo (Av.) EU
Instituto Bacteriológico (R.) KV 160
Ivens (R.) KY
Jacinta Marto (R.) GS 162
Janelas Verdes (R. das) EU 163
Jardim do Tabaco (R. do) MY 165
João da Praça (R. de) LY 166
João XXI (Av. de) HR
Joaquim António de Aguiar (R.) FS 171
José Fontana (Pr.) GS
José Malhoa (Av.) ER
Lagares (R.) LX
Lapa (R. da) EU
Laranjeiras (Estr. das) ER 172
Leite de Vasconcelos (R.) MX
Liberdade (Av. da) JV
Limoeiro (L. do) LY 175
Lóios (L. dos) LY
Luís de Camões (Pr.) JY
Madalena (R. da) KY
Manuel da Maia (Av.) HR 178
Maria Andrade (R.) HS 180
Maria da Fonte (R.) LV
Marquês de Pombal (Pr.) FS 183
Martim Moniz (L.) KX 184
Miguel Bombarda (Av.) GR 186
Mirante (R. do) MX
Misericórdia (R. da) JY 190
Monte (Trav. do) LV
Morais Soares (R.) HR
Mouzinho de Albuquerque (Av.) HS
Norberto de Araújo (R.) LY 193
Nova de Almada (R.) KY
Olaias (Rotunda das) HR
Paço da Rainha HS 195
Palma (R. da) KV
Paraíso (R. do) MX

Passos Manuel (R.) HS 198
Pedro Álvares Cabral (Av.) FT 199
Penha de França (R. da) HS
Poço dos Mouros (Calç. do) HR 204
Poço dos Negros (R. do) FU 205
Poiais de S. Bento (R.) FU 207
Ponte (Av. da) ET
Portas de Santo Antão (R.) KX 208
Portas do Sol (L. das) LY 210
Possidónio da Silva (R.) EU
Presidente Arriaga (R.) EU 211
Príncipe Real (Pr. do) JX 213
Prior (R. do) EU
Quelhas Pasteleiro (R. do) FU
Ramalho Ortigão (R.) FR
Rato (L. do) FT
Regueira (R. da) LY 214
Remédios (R. dos) MY
Restauradores (Pr. dos) KX
Ribeira das Naus (Av.) KZ
Ribeiro Sanches (R.) EU
Rodrigo da Fonseca (R.) FS 219
Rodrigues de Freitas (L.) LX 220
Rosa (R. da) JY
Rovisco Pais (Av.) GR 222
Sá Carneiro (Pr.) HR
Saco (R. do) KV
Sacramento (Calç. do) KY 225
Salitre (R. do) JV
Salvador (R. do) LY 226
Sampaio Bruno (R.) ET
Santa Catarina (R. de) JY 228
Santa Justa (R. de) KY 229
Santa Luzia (Trav. de) LY 231
Santana (Calç. de) KX
Santo André (Calç. de) LX
Santo António (R. de) EU 232
Santo António da Sé (L.) LY 234
Santo António dos Capuchos (R.) KV 235
Santo Estêvão (Escadinhas de) MZ 236
S. Bernardo (R. de) FT 238
S. Caetano (R. de) EU
S. Domingos (L. de) KX 240
S. Filipe de Nery (R.) FS 241
S. Francisco (Calç. de) KZ 243
S. João da Mata (R.) FU 244
S. João da Praça (R.) LZ 246
S. José (R. de) JV
S. Lázaro (R. de) KX
S. Marçal (R. de) FT 247
S. Miguel (R. de) LY 249
S. Paulo (R. de) JZ
S. Pedro (R. de) LY 250
S. Pedro de Alcântara (R. de) JX 252
S. Tiago (R. de) LY 253
S. Tomé (R. de) LX 255
S. Vicente (Calç. de) LX 256
S. Vicente (R.) LX
Sapadores (R. dos) MV
Sapateiros (R. dos) KY 258
Saudade (R.) LY
Século (R. do) JX
Senhora da Glória (R.) MV
Serpa Pinto (R.) KZ 262
Sol ao Rato (R. do) FT 264
Telhal (R. do) KV
Terreiro do Trigo (R. do) LY 267
Vale de Sto António (R.) MV
Verónica (R. da) MX
Victor Cordon (R.) KZ
Vigário (R. do) MY 270
Voz do Operário (R.) LX
24 de Julho (Av.) FU

# Sights

## VIEWS OVER LISBON

*★★ from the Suspension Bridge (Ponte 25 de Abril★) S: by Av. da Ponte* EU *– ☼★★ from Christ in Majesty (Cristo Rei) S: by Av. da Ponte* EU *– St. Georges Castle★★ (Castelo de São Jorge: ⩽★★★)* LX *– Santa Luzia Belvedere★ (Miradouro de Santa Luzia): ⩽★★* LY **C** *– Santa Justa Lift★ (Elevador de Santa Justa): ⩽★* KY *– São Pedro de Alcântara Belvedere★ (Miradouro de São Pedro de Alcâtara): ⩽* JX **A** *– Alto de Santa Catarina Belvedere★* JZ **N** *– Senhora do Monte Belvedere (Miradouro da Senhora do Monte): ☼★★★* LV *– Largo das Portas do Sol★: ⩽* LY *– Nossa Senhora da Graça Belvedere (Miradouro): ⩽★* LX

## MUSEUMS

*Museum of Ancient Art★★★ (Museum Nacional de Arte Antiga; polyptych da Adoração de São Vicente★★★, Tentação de Santo Antão★★★, Japanese folding screens★★, Twelve' Apostles★, Anunciação★, Chapel★)* EU **M7** *– Gulbenkian Foundation (Calouste Gulbenkian Museum★★★* FR*, Modern Art Centre★* FR **M4***) – Maritime Museum★★ (Museu de Marinha: model boats★★★)* **W***: by Av. 24 de Julho* EU *– Coach Museum★★ (Museu Nacional dos Coches)* **W***: by Av. 24 de Julho* EU *– Azulejo Museum★★(Madre de Deus Convent: Church★★, chapter house★)* **NE***: by Av. Infante D. Henrique* MX *– Water Museum EPAL★ (Museu da Água da EPAL)* HT **M8** *– Costume Museum★ (Museu Nacional do Traje)* **N***: by Av. da República* GR *– Theatre Museum★ (Museu Nacional do Teatro)* **N***: by Av. da República* GR *– Military Museum (Museu Militar; cellings★)* MY **M10** *– Museum of Decorative Arts★★ (Museu de Artes Decorativas: Fundação Ricardo do Espírito Santo Silva)* LY **M3** *– Archaeological Museum – Carmelite Church (Igreja do Carmo★)* KY M1 *– São Roque Arte Sacra Museum★ (vestments★)* JKX M2 *– Chiado Museum★ (Museu Nacional do Chiado)* KZ **M16** *– Music Museum★ (Museu da Música)* **N***: by Av. da República* GR *– Rafael Bordalo Pinheiro Museum (ceramics★)* **N***: by av. da Republica* GR

## CHURCHES AND MONASTERIES

*Cathedral★★ (See: gothic tombs★, grille★, tresor★)* LY *– Hieronymite Monastery★★★ (Monasteiro dos Jerónimos): Santa Maria Church★★★ (vaulting★★, cloister★★★; Archaeological Museum: treasury★)* **W***: by Av. 24 de Julho* EU *– São Roque Church★ (São João Baptista Chapel★★, interior★)* JX *– São Vicente de Fora Church (azulejos★)* MX *– Our Lady of Fátima Church (Igraja de Nossa Senhora de Fátima: windows★)* FR **K** *– Estrela Basilica★ (garden★)* EU **L** *– Old Conception Church (Igreja da Conceição Velha: south front★)* LZ **V** *– Santa Engrácia Church★* MX

## HISTORIC QUARTERS

*Belém★★ (Culture Centre★)* **W***: by Av. 24 de Julho* EU *– The Baixa★★* JKXYZ *– Alfama★★* LY *– Chiado and Bairro Alto★* JKY

## PLACES OF INTEREST

*Praça do Comércio★★ (or Terreiro do Paço)* KZ *– Belém Tower★★★ (Torre de Belém)* **W***: by Av. 24 de Julho* EU *– Marquis Fronteira Palace★★ (Palácio dos Marqueses de Fronteira: azulejos★★)* ER *– Rossio★ (station: neo-manuelina façade★)* KX *– Do Carmo st. and Garrett st. (Rua do Carmo and Rua Garrett)* KY *– Liberdade Ave★ (Avenida da Liberdade)* JV *– Edward VII Park★ (Parque Eduardo VII: ⩽★, greenhouse★)* FS *– Zoological Garden★★ (Jardin Zoológico)* ER *– Águas Livres Aqueduct★ (Aqueduto das Águas Livres)* ES *– Botanic Garden★ (Jardim Botánico)* JV *– Monsanto Park★ (Parque Florestal de Monsanto): Belvedere (Miradouro): ☼★)* ER *– Campo de Santa Clara★* MX *– Santo Estêvão stiarway and terrace★ (⩽★)* MY *– Ajuda Palace★ (Palacio da Ajuda)* **M***: by Av. 24 de Julho* EU *– Arpad Szenes-Vieira da Silva Foundation★* EFS *– Boat trip on the river Tagus★ (⩽★★)*

**Centre** : Av. da Liberdade, Rua Augusta, Rua do Ouro, Praça do Comércio, Praça Dom Pedro IV (Rossio), Praça dos Restauradores

**Tivoli Lisboa,** Av. da Liberdade 185, ✉ 1250, ☎ (01) 353 01 81, *Fax (01) 357 94 61*, « Terrace with ≤ town », heated – 40/200. AE VISA JCB. JV d
***Grill Terraço :*** **Meals** a la carte 5650/8450 - ***Zodíaco :*** **Meals** a la carte 5100/5300 – **298 rm** 38000/42000, 29 suites.

**Sofitel Lisboa,** Av. da Liberdade 125, ✉ 1250, ☎ (01) 342 92 02, *Telex 42557*, *Fax (01) 342 92 22* – 25/300. AE VISA JCB. rest JV r
**Meals** (see rest. ***Cais da Avenida*** below) – 2500 – **166 rm** 30000/35000, 4 suites.

**Lisboa Plaza,** Travessa do Salitre 7, ✉ 1250, ☎ (01) 346 39 22, *Fax (01) 347 16 30* – 25/140. AE VISA JCB. JV b
**Meals** a la carte 4400/5500 – **94 rm** 24500/26950, 12 suites.

**Tivoli Jardim,** Rua Julio Cesar Machado 7, ✉ 1250, ☎ (01) 353 99 71, *Fax (01) 355 65 66*, heated – AE VISA JCB. JV a
**Meals** a la carte approx. 5000 – **119 rm** 23000/27000.

**Mundial,** Rua D. Duarte 4, ✉ 1100, ☎ (01) 886 31 01, *Telex 12308*, *Fax (01) 887 91 29*, ≤ – 25/120. AE VISA JCB. KX a
**Meals** a la carte 5700/8700 – **141 rm** 16380/19760, 6 suites.

**Lisboa** coffee shop only, Rua Barata Salgueiro 5, ✉ 1150, ☎ (01) 355 41 31, *Telex 60228*, *Fax (01) 355 41 39* – AE VISA. JV e
**55 rm** 25000/30000, 6 suites.

**Veneza** without rest, Av. da Liberdade 189, ✉ 1250, ☎ (01) 352 26 18, *Fax (01) 352 66 78*, « Old palace » – AE VISA JCB. JV d
**36 rm** 20000/22000.

**Príncipe Real,** Rua da Alegria 53, ✉ 1250, ☎ (01) 346 01 16, *Fax (01) 342 21 04* – AE VISA JCB. JX q
**Meals** 3000 – **24 rm** 16300/19500.

**Britânia** without rest, Rua Rodrigues Sampaio 17, ✉ 1150, ☎ (01) 315 50 16, *Fax (01) 315 50 21* – AE VISA JCB. JV y
**30 rm** 21200/22300.

**Metropole** without rest, Praça do Rossio 30, ✉ 1100, ☎ (01) 346 91 64, *Fax (01) 346 91 66* – AE VISA JCB KY s
**36 rm** 22000/25000.

**Botánico** without rest, Rua Mãe de Água 16, ✉ 1250, ☎ (01) 342 03 92, *Fax (01) 342 01 25* – AE VISA JCB. JX s
**30 rm** 13000/16000.

**Albergaria Senhora do Monte** without rest, Calçada do Monte 39, ✉ 1170, ☎ (01) 886 60 02, *Fax (01) 887 77 83*, ≤ São Jorge castle, town and river Tejo – AE VISA. LV c
**28 rm** 15000/18500.

**Lisboa Tejo** without rest, Poço do Borratém 4, ✉ 1100, ☎ (01) 886 61 82, *Fax (01) 886 51 63* – AE VISA. KX r
**58 rm** 12500/15500.

**Insulana** without rest, Rua da Assunção 52, ✉ 1100, ☎ (01) 342 76 25 – AE VISA. KY e
**32 rm** 8000/10500.

**Tágide,** Largo da Académia Nacional de Belas Artes 18, ✉ 1200, ☎ (01) 342 07 20, *Fax (01) 347 18 80*, ≤ – AE VISA. KZ z
*closed Saturday lunch and Sunday* – **Meals** a la carte 6100/7600.

**Clara,** Campo dos Mártires da Pátria 49, ✉ 1150, ☎ (01) 885 30 53, *Fax (01) 885 20 82*, « Garden terrace » – AE VISA. KV f
*closed Saturday lunch, Sunday and 1 to 15 August* – **Meals** a la carte approx. 6100.

**Tavares,** Rua da Misericórdia 37, ✉ 1200, ☎ (01) 342 11 12, *Fax (01) 347 81 25*, « Late 19C decor » – AE VISA. JY t
*closed Saturday and Sunday lunch* – **Meals** a la carte 6200/9500.

**Bachus,** Largo da Trindade 9, ✉ 1200, ☎ (01) 342 28 28, *Fax (01) 342 12 60* – AE VISA JCB. JY s
*closed Saturday lunch and Sunday* – **Meals** a la carte 4500/5300.

**Gambrinus,** Rua das Portas de Santo Antão 25, ✉ 1150, ☎ (01) 342 14 66, *Fax (01) 346 50 32* – AE VISA. KX n
**Meals** a la carte 11000/14000.

**Escorial,** Rua das Portas de Santo Antão 47, ✉ 1100, ☎ (01) 346 44 29, *Fax (01) 346 37 58* – AE VISA JCB. KX e
**Meals** a la carte 4400/6820.

XXX **Cais da Avenida,** Av. da Liberdade 123, ✉ 1250, ☎ (01) 342 92 24, *Fax (01) 342 92 22* – ▤ ⇔. AE ⓓ E VISA JCB. ✗ JV r
**Meals** a la carte 4300/5100.

XXX **Jardim Tropical,** Av. da Liberdade 144, ✉ 1250, ☎ (01) 346 88 39, *Fax (01) 342 31 24,* « Tropical conservatory » – ▤ ⇔. AE ⓓ E VISA JCB JV u
**Meals** a la carte 4450/6700.

XXX **Casa do Leão,** Castelo de São Jorge, ✉ 1100, ☎ (01) 887 59 62, *Fax (01) 887 63 29,* ≤ – ▤. AE ⓓ E VISA. ✗ LXY s
**Meals** a la carte 4500/6950.

XX **Via Graça,** Rua Damasceno Monteiro 9-B, ✉ 1170, ☎ (01) 887 08 30, *Fax (01) 887 03 05,* ≤ São Jorge castle, town and river Tejo – ▤. AE ⓓ E VISA JCB. ✗ LV d
*closed Saturday lunch and Sunday* – **Meals** a la carte 3200/4900.

XX **O Faz Figura,** Rua do Paraíso 15-B, ✉ 1100, ☎ (01) 886 89 81, ≤, 🏠 – ▤. AE ⓓ E VISA. ✗ MX n
*closed Sunday and Bank Holidays* – **Meals** a la carte 3600/5550.

X **Porta Branca,** Rua do Teixeira 35, ✉ 1250, ☎ (01) 342 10 24, *Fax (01) 347 92 57* – ▤. AE ⓓ E VISA JCB. ✗ JX e
*closed Saturday lunch and Sunday* – **Meals** a la carte 3840/5740.

X **Mercado de Santa Clara,** Campo de Santa Clara (at market), ✉ 1170, ☎ (01) 887 39 86, *Fax (01) 887 39 86,* ≤ – ▤. AE ⓓ E VISA. ✗ MX c
*closed Sunday dinner, Monday and August* – **Meals** a la carte 2950/4150.

**East** : Av. da Liberdade, Av. Almirante Reis, Av. Estados Unidos de América, Av. de Roma, Av. João XXI, Av. da República, Praça Marquês de Pombal

**Radisson SAS,** Av. Marechal Craveiro Lopes 390, ✉ 1700, ☎ (01) 759 96 39, *Telex 61170, Fax (01) 758 66 05,* Ⅰ6 – |‡| ▤ TV ☎ ♿ ⇔ – 🏛 25/200. AE ⓓ E VISA JCB. ✗ N : by Av. da República GR
**Meals** 4200 – ☕ 1600 – **205 rm** 31000/33000, 16 suites.

**Holiday Inn Lisboa,** Av. António José de Almeida 28-A, ✉ 1000, ☎ (01) 793 52 22, *Telex 60330, Fax (01) 793 66 72,* Ⅰ6 – |‡| ▤ TV ☎ ♿ ⇔ – 🏛 25/250. AE ⓓ E VISA JCB. ✗ GR c
**Meals** 3400 – ☕ 1600 – **161 rm** 24000/28000, 8 suites.

**Altis Park H.,** Av. Engenheiro Arantes e Oliveira 9, ✉ 1900, ☎ (01) 846 08 66, *Fax (01) 846 08 38* – |‡| ▤ TV ☎ ♿ ⇔ – 🏛 25/400. AE ⓓ E VISA. ✗ rest HR z
**Meals** 3200 – **285 rm** ☕ 23000/26000, 15 suites.

**Lutécia,** Av. Frei Miguel Contreiras 52, ✉ 1700, ☎ (01) 840 31 21, *Telex 12457, Fax (01) 840 78 18,* ≤ – |‡| ▤ TV ☎ – 🏛 25/100. AE ⓓ E VISA JCB. ✗
**Meals** a la carte 3700/5450 – **142 rm** ☕ 18000/21000, 8 suites. N : by Av. Almirante Reis HR

**Alif** without rest, Campo Pequeno 51, ✉ 1000, ☎ (01) 795 24 64, *Telex 64460, Fax (01) 795 41 16* – |‡| ▤ TV ☎ ♿ ⇔ – 🏛 25/40. AE ⓓ E VISA. ✗ GR w
**107 rm** ☕ 14500/16500, 8 suites.

**Meliá Confort Lisboa,** Av. Duque de Loulé 45, ✉ 1050, ☎ (01) 353 21 08, *Fax (01) 353 18 65,* 🏊 – |‡| ▤ TV ☎ ♿ ⇔. AE ⓓ E VISA JCB. ✗ GS z
**Meals** *(closed Sunday)* a la carte 4100/4800 – **80 rm** ☕ 33000/35000, 4 suites.

**A.S. Lisboa** without rest, Av. Almirante Reis 188, ✉ 1000, ☎ (01) 847 30 25, *Fax (01) 847 30 34* – |‡| ▤ TV ☎ – 🏛 25/80. AE ⓓ E VISA. ✗ HR e
**75 rm** ☕ 14000/16000.

**Presidente** coffee shop only, Rua Alexandre Herculano 13, ✉ 1150, ☎ (01) 353 95 07, *Fax (01) 352 02 72* – |‡| ▤ TV ☎ – 🏛 25/40. AE ⓓ E VISA. ✗ GS t
**59 rm** ☕ 15600/18000.

**Dom Carlos** without rest, Av. Duque de Loulé 121, ✉ 1050, ☎ (01) 353 90 71, *Fax (01) 352 07 28* – |‡| ▤ TV ☎ – 🏛 25/40. AE ⓓ E VISA JCB. ✗ GS n
**76 rm** ☕ 17500/20800.

**Roma,** Av. de Roma 33, ✉ 1700, ☎ (01) 796 77 61, *Telex 16586, Fax (01) 793 29 81,* ≤, 🏊 – |‡| ▤ TV ☎ – 🏛 25/230. AE ⓓ E VISA JCB. ✗
**Meals** 2950 – **263 rm** ☕ 15000/17500. N : by Av. Almirante Reis HR

**Dom João** without rest, Rua José Estêvão 43, ✉ 1100, ☎ (01) 314 41 71, *Fax (01) 352 45 69* – |‡| ▤ TV ☎. AE ⓓ E VISA. ✗ HS e
**18 rm** ☕ 7000/8000.

XXXX **Antonio Clara-Clube de Empresários,** Av. da República 38, ✉ 1050, ☎ (01) 796 63 80, *Fax (01) 797 41 44,* « Former old palace » – ▤ Ⓟ. AE ⓓ E VISA JCB. ✗ GR t
*closed Sunday and 15 to 30 August* – **Meals** a la carte approx. 5500.

**Chez Armand,** Rua Carlos Mardel 38, ✉ 1900, ☎ (01) 847 57 70, *Fax (01) 887 19 19* – ▤. AE ⓓ E VISA. ✂ HR r
*closed Saturday lunch, Sunday and August* – **Meals** - French rest - a la carte 4180/5050.

**Celta,** Rua Gomes Freire 148, ✉ 1150, ☎ (01) 357 30 69 – ▤. AE E VISA. ✂ GS k
*closed Sunday* – **Meals** a la carte 3020/4440.

**West** : Av. da Liberdade, Av. 24 de Julho, Av. da India, Av. Infante Santo, Av. de Berna, Av. António Augusto de Aguiar, Largo de Alcântara, Praça Marquês de Pombal, Praça de Espanha

**Ritz Four Seasons,** Rua Rodrigo da Fonseca 88, ✉ 1093, ☎ (01) 383 20 20, *Telex 12589, Fax (01) 383 17 83*, ≤, 🏞 – |♦| ▤ TV ☎ ♿ 🚗 P – 🏛 25/600. AE ⓓ E VISA JCB. ✂ rest FS b
***Varanda*** : **Meals** a la carte 5050/8400 – ☕ 2500 – **264 rm** 42000/46000, 20 suites.

**Sheraton Lisboa H.,** Rua Latino Coelho 1, ✉ 1097, ☎ (01) 357 57 57, *Telex 12774, Fax (01) 354 71 64*, ≤, Fб, ⛱ heated – |♦| ▤ TV ☎ ♿ 🚗 – 🏛 25/550. AE ⓓ E VISA JCB. ✂ GR s
***Alfama Grill*** *(closed Saturday, Sunday and August)* **Meals** a la carte approx. 7700 - ***Caravela*** : **Meals** a la carte approx. 6000 – ☕ 2500 – **377 rm** 35000/38000, 7 suites.

**Da Lapa** ⛺, Rua do Pau de Bandeira 4, ✉ 1200, ☎ (01) 395 00 05, *Fax (01) 395 06 65*, ≤, 🏞, « Park with waterfall and ⛱ » – |♦| ▤ TV ☎ ♿ 🚗 P – 🏛 25/225. AE ⓓ E VISA. ✂ EU a
**Meals** a la carte 5100/7000 – ☕ 2350 – **78 rm** 45000/47500, 8 suites.

**Le Meridien Park Atlantic Lisboa,** Rua Castilho 149, ✉ 1070, ☎ (01) 381 87 00, *Fax (01) 383 32 31*, ≤ – |♦| ▤ TV ☎ 🚗 – 🏛 25/550. AE ⓓ E VISA JCB FS a
**Meals** 4100 - ***Brasserie des Amis*** : **Meals** a la carte 5000/6000 – ☕ 2400 – **313 rm** 25000, 17 suites.

**Alfa Lisboa,** Av. Columbano Bordalo Pinheiro, ✉ 1070, ☎ (01) 726 21 21, *Telex 18477, Fax (01) 726 30 31*, ≤, Fб, ⛱ – |♦| ▤ TV ☎ 🚗 – 🏛 25/600. AE ⓓ E VISA JCB. ✂
***A Aldeia*** : **Meals** a la carte 4650/5000 - ***Grill Pombalino*** : ***Meals*** a la carte approx. 5300 – **440 rm** ☕ 37000/39000. ER a

**Altis,** Rua Castilho 11, ✉ 1250, ☎ (01) 357 92 62, *Telex 13314, Fax (01) 354 86 96*, Fб, ⛱ – |♦| ▤ TV ☎ 🚗 – 🏛 25/700. AE ⓓ E VISA JCB. ✂ FT z
**Meals** 4750 - ***Girassol*** *(lunch only except Sunday)* **Meals** a la carte 4200/5250 - ***Grill Dom Fernando*** *(closed Sunday)* **Meals** a la carte 4700/5700 – **290 rm** ☕ 32000/35000, 13 suites.

**Novotel Lisboa,** Av. José Malhoa 1642, ✉ 1000, ☎ (01) 726 60 22, *Telex 40114, Fax (01) 726 64 96*, ≤, ⛱ – |♦| ▤ TV ☎ ♿ 🚗 – 🏛 25/300. AE ⓓ E VISA. ✂ rest
**Meals** 3200 – ☕ 1200 – **246 rm** 12300/13600. ER e

**Holiday Inn Lisboa-Continental,** Rua Laura Alves 9, ✉ 1050, ☎ (01) 793 50 05, *Telex 65632, Fax (01) 797 36 69* – |♦| ▤ TV ☎ 🚗 – 🏛 25/180. AE ⓓ E VISA JCB. ✂
***D. Miguel*** *(closed Saturday and Sunday)* **Meals** a la carte 4350/5800 - ***Coffee Shop Continental*** : **Meals** a la carte 3700/4350 – ☕ 1600 – **210 rm** 29000/34000, 10 suites. FR q

**Real Parque,** Av. Luís Bívar 67, ✉ 1050, ☎ (01) 357 01 01, *Fax (01) 357 07 50* – |♦| ▤ TV ☎ ♿ 🚗 – 🏛 25/100. AE ⓓ E VISA JCB. ✂ FR a
**Meals** 4500 - ***Cozinha do Real*** : **Meals** a la carte 4900/6300 – **147 rm** ☕ 28000/31000, 6 suites.

**Lisboa Penta,** Av. dos Combatentes, ✉ 1600, ☎ (01) 726 40 54, *Telex 18437, Fax (01) 726 42 81*, ≤, Fб, ⛱ – |♦| ▤ TV ☎ 🚗 P – 🏛 25/600. AE ⓓ E VISA JCB. ✂ rest NW : by Av. A. Augusto de Aguiar FR
**Meals** 3300 - ***Grill Passarola*** : **Meals** a la carte 4100/6600 - ***Verde Pino*** : **Meals** a la carte 2050/3750 – **584 rm** ☕ 20000/24000, 4 suites.

**Fénix,** Praça Marquês de Pombal 8, ✉ 1250, ☎ (01) 386 21 21, *Telex 12170, Fax (01) 386 01 31* – |♦| ▤ TV ☎ ♿ – 🏛 25/100. AE ⓓ E VISA. ✂ rest FS g
***Bodegón*** : **Meals** a la carte approx. 5700 – **119 rm** ☕ 22000/25000, 4 suites.

**Zurique,** Rua Ivone Silva 18, ✉ 1050, ☎ (01) 793 71 11, *Telex 65349, Fax (01) 793 72 90*, ⛱ – |♦| ▤ TV ☎ 🚗 – 🏛 25/150. AE ⓓ E VISA. ✂ FR s
**Meals** 3250 – **248 rm** ☕ 14000/17000, 4 suites.

**Diplomático,** Rua Castilho 74, ✉ 1200, ☎ (01) 386 20 41, *Telex 13713, Fax (01) 386 21 55* – |♦| ▤ TV ☎ – 🏛 25/60. AE ⓓ E VISA JCB. ✂ rm FS c
**Meals** 3000 – **73 rm** ☕ 15000/17300, 17 suites.

**Flórida** without rest, Rua Duque de Palmela 32, ✉ 1250, ☎ (01) 357 61 45, *Fax (01) 354 35 84* – |♦| ▤ TV ☎ – 🏛 25/100. AE ⓓ E VISA JCB. ✂ FS x
**108 rm** ☕ 16000/19800.

**Barcelona** without rest, Rua Laura Alves 10, ✉ 1050, ☎ (01) 795 42 73, *Fax (01) 795 42 81*, Fб – |♦| ▤ TV ☎ ♿ 🚗 – 🏛 25/230. AE ⓓ E VISA. ✂ FR z
**120 rm** ☕ 17000/20000, 5 suites.

**Quality H.**, Campo Grande 7, ✉ 1700, ℘ (01) 795 75 55, *Fax (01) 795 75 00*, – ▤ TV ☎ ♿ – 25/50. AE ⓓ E VISA JCB. rest
Meals 3250 – **80 rm** ☕ 16000/17000, 2 suites. N : by Av. da República GR

**Executive Inn** without rest, Av. Conde Valbom 56, ✉ 1050, ℘ (01) 795 11 57, *Telex 65618, Fax (01) 795 11 66* – ▤ TV ☎. AE ⓓ E VISA FR g
**72 rm** ☕ 18000/20000.

**Metropolitan Lisboa H.**, Rua Soeiro Gomes-parcela 2, ✉ 1600, ℘ (01) 798 25 00, *Fax (01) 795 08 64* – ▤ TV ☎ ♿ – 25/250. AE ⓓ E VISA JCB.
Meals 3500 – **315 rm** ☕ 19000/23000. N : by Av. da República GR

**Amazónia Lisboa** coffee shop only, Travessa Fábrica dos Pentes 12, ✉ 1250, ℘ (01) 387 70 06, *Telex 66361, Fax (01) 387 90 90*, heated – ▤ TV ☎ – 25/200. AE ⓓ E VISA. FS d
**192 rm** ☕ 14250/16100.

**Dom Manuel I** without rest, Av. Duque de Ávila 189, ✉ 1050, ℘ (01) 357 61 60, *Telex 43558, Fax (01) 357 69 85*, « Tasteful decor » – ▤ TV ☎. AE ⓓ E VISA.
**64 rm** ☕ 13000/15000. FR p

**Dom Rodrigo Suite H.** coffee shop only, Rua Rodrigo da Fonseca 44, ✉ 1250, ℘ (01) 386 38 00, *Fax (01) 386 30 00*, – ▤ TV ☎. AE ⓓ E VISA FS m
☕ 900 – **57 suites** 20000/26000.

**Nacional** without rest, Rua Castilho 34, ✉ 1250, ℘ (01) 355 44 33, *Fax (01) 356 11 22* – ▤ TV ☎. AE ⓓ E VISA. FST s
**59 rm** ☕ 13800/16200, 2 suites.

**York House**, Rua das Janelas Verdes 32, ✉ 1200, ℘ (01) 396 25 44, *Fax (01) 397 27 93*, « Former 16C convent. Portuguese decor » – TV ☎. AE ⓓ E VISA JCB. FU e
Meals a la carte approx. 4800 – **31 rm** ☕ 27500/32500, 3 suites.

**Miraparque**, Av. Sidónio Pais 12, ✉ 1050, ℘ (01) 352 42 86, *Telex 16745, Fax (01) 357 89 20* – ▤ TV ☎. AE ⓓ E VISA. FS k
Meals 3200 – **101 rm** ☕ 15000/16000.

**Eduardo VII**, Av. Fontes Pereira de Melo 5, ✉ 1050, ℘ (01) 353 01 41, *Fax (01) 353 38 79*, ≤ – ▤ TV ☎ – 25/60. AE ⓓ E VISA. FS p
***Varanda*** : Meals a la carte approx. 4500 – **127 rm** ☕ 12500/14700, 2 suites.

**Marquês de Sá**, Av. Miguel Bombarda 130, ✉ 1050, ℘ (01) 791 10 14, *Fax (01) 793 69 86* – ▤ TV ☎ – 25/150. AE ⓓ E VISA. FR c
Meals 3500 – **97 rm** ☕ 18000/20000.

**Amazónia Jamor**, Av. Tomás Ribeiro 129 Queijas, ✉ 2795 Linda-A-Pastora, ℘ (01) 417 56 38, *Fax (01) 417 56 30*, ≤, – ▤ TV ☎ ♿ P – 25/200. AE ⓓ E VISA. W : 10 km by Av. Engenheiro Duarte Pacheco ES
Meals 4000 – **93 rm** ☕ 13500/15300, 4 suites.

**As Janelas Verdes** without rest, Rua das Janelas Verdes 47, ✉ 1200, ℘ (01) 396 81 43, *Fax (01) 396 81 44*, « Late 18C house with attractive courtyard » – ▤ TV ☎. AE ⓓ E VISA JCB. FU e
**17 rm** ☕ 26000/28800.

**Da Torre**, Rua dos Jerónimos 8, ✉ 1400, ℘ (01) 363 62 62, *Fax (01) 364 59 95* – ▤ TV ☎ – 25/50. AE ⓓ E VISA JCB. W : by Av. 24 de Julho EU
Meals (see rest. ***São Jerónimo*** below) – **50 rm** ☕ 12650/15200.

**Flamingo**, Rua Castilho 41, ✉ 1250, ℘ (01) 386 21 91, *Fax (01) 386 12 16* – ▤ TV ☎. AE ⓓ E VISA. FS n
Meals 2500 – **39 rm** ☕ 14000/17000.

**Berna** without rest, Av. António Serpa 13, ✉ 1050, ℘ (01) 793 67 67, *Telex 62516, Fax (01) 793 62 78* – ▤ TV ☎ – 25/140. AE ⓓ E VISA. GR a
**240 rm** ☕ 12000/15000.

**Imperador** without rest, Av. 5 de Outubro 55, ✉ 1050, ℘ (01) 352 48 84, *Fax (01) 352 65 37* – ▤ TV ☎. AE ⓓ E VISA JCB. GR f
**43 rm** ☕ 8000/10000.

**Casa da Comida**, Travessa das Amoreiras 1, ✉ 1250, ℘ (01) 388 53 76, *Fax (01) 387 51 32*, « Patio with plants » – ▤. AE ⓓ E VISA. FT e
*closed Saturday lunch and Sunday* – **Meals** a la carte 5900/9000.

**Pabe**, Rua Duque de Palmela 27-A, ✉ 1250, ℘ (01) 353 74 84, *Fax (01) 353 64 37*, « English pub style » – ▤. AE ⓓ E VISA. FS x
Meals a la carte 5100/7000.

**Conventual**, Praça das Flores 45, ✉ 1200, ℘ (01) 390 91 96, *Fax (01) 390 91 96* – ▤. AE ⓓ E VISA FT m
*closed Saturday lunch, Bank Holidays lunch and Sunday* – **Meals** a la carte approx. 6300
**Spec.** Creme de coentros. Bacalhau coentrada. Ensopado de borrego.

XXX **São Jerónimo,** Rua dos Jerónimos 12, ✉ 1400, ☎ (01) 364 87 97, *Fax (01) 363 26 92*, « Modern decor » – ▤. AE ⓓ E VISA JCB. ✻ W : by Av. 24 de Julho EU
**Meals** a la carte 4530/6780.

XXX **Chester,** Rua Rodrigo da Fonseca 87-D, ✉ 1250, ☎ (01) 385 73 47, *Fax (01) 388 78 11* – ▤. AE ⓓ E VISA JCB. ✻ FS w
*closed Saturday lunch and Sunday* – **Meals** - Meat specialities - a la carte 3810/5900.

XX **Saraiva's,** Rua Engenheiro Canto Resende 3, ✉ 1050, ☎ (01) 354 06 09, *Fax (01) 353 19 87*, « Modern decor » – ▤. AE ⓓ E VISA JCB. ✻ FR v
*closed Saturday and Bank Holidays* – **Meals** a la carte 3250/5350.

XX **Espelho d'Água,** Av. de Brasilia, ✉ 1400, ☎ (01) 301 73 73, *Fax (01) 363 26 92*, ≤, terrace, « Lakeside setting. Modern decor » – ▤. AE ⓓ E VISA JCB. ✻
*closed Saturday lunch and Sunday* – **Meals** a la carte 4780/6380.
W : by Av. 24 de Julho EU

XX **Adega Tía Matilde,** Rua da Beneficéncia 77, ✉ 1600, ☎ (01) 797 21 72, *Fax (01) 793 90 00* – ▤. AE ⓓ E VISA. ✻ FR h
*closed Saturday dinner and Sunday* – **Meals** a la carte 3850/5940.

XX **O Nobre,** Rua das Mercês 71, ✉ 1300, ☎ (01) 363 38 27, *Fax (01) 362 21 06* – ▤. AE E VISA W : by Av. 24 de Julho EU
*closed Saturday lunch and Sunday* – **Meals** a la carte 4840/6310.

XX **O Mercado do Peixe,** Estrada do Casal Pedro Teixeira-Caramão da Ajuda, ✉ 1400, ☎ (01) 362 31 40, *Fax (01) 362 30 23* – ▤. AE ⓓ E VISA. ✻
*closed Sunday dinner and Monday* – **Meals** - Seafood - a la carte approx. 8900.
W : by Av. 24 de Julho EU

XX **O Polícia,** Rua Marquês Sá da Bandeira 112, ✉ 1050, ☎ (01) 796 35 05, *Fax (01) 796 02 19* – ▤. AE VISA. ✻ FR c
*closed Saturday dinner and Sunday* – **Meals** a la carte 3800/4550.

X **Sua Excelência,** Rua do Conde 34, ✉ 1200, ☎ (01) 390 36 14, *Fax (01) 396 75 85* – ▤. AE ⓓ E VISA JCB EU t
*closed Saturday lunch, Sunday lunch, Wednesday and September* – **Meals** a la carte 3100/6250.

Typical atmosphere :

XX **O Faia,** Rua da Barroca 56, ✉ 1200, ☎ (01) 342 67 42, *Fax (01) 342 19 23*, Fado cabaret – ▤. AE ⓓ E VISA JCB. ✻ JY f
*closed Sunday* – **Meals** - dinner only - a la carte 6900/8550.

XX **Sr. Vinho,** Rua do Meio-à-Lapa 18, ✉ 1200, ☎ (01) 397 74 56, *Fax (01) 395 20 72*, Fado cabaret – ▤. AE ⓓ E VISA. ✻ FU r
*closed Sunday* – **Meals** - dinner only - a la carte 5160/7500.

XX **A Severa,** Rua das Gáveas 51, ✉ 1200, ☎ (01) 342 83 14, *Fax (01) 346 40 06*, Fados at dinner – ▤. AE ⓓ E VISA JCB. ✻ JY b
*closed Thursday* – **Meals** a la carte 5900/8800.

X **Adega Machado,** Rua do Norte 91, ✉ 1200, ☎ (01) 342 87 13, *Fax (01) 346 75 07*, Fado cabaret – ▤. AE ⓓ E VISA JCB JY k
*closed Monday* – **Meals** - dinner only - a la carte 7500/9000.

X **D'Avis,** Rua do Grilo 98, ✉ 1900, ☎ (01) 868 13 54, *Fax (01) 868 13 54*, « Typical decor » – ▤. VISA E : Av. Infante D. Henrique MX
*closed Sunday and August* – **Meals** - Alentejo rest - a la carte 2500/3150.

# Spain

## España

MADRID – BARCELONA – BILBAO
MÁLAGA – SEVILLA – VALENCIA

# PRACTICAL INFORMATION

## LOCAL CURRENCY

**Peseta:** *100 ESP = 0,66 USD ($) (Jan. 98)*

**National Holiday in Spain:** *12 October*

## TOURIST INFORMATION

*The telephone number and address of the Tourist Information offices is given in the text of the towns under* **ℹ**.

## FOREIGN EXCHANGE

*Banks are usually open fron 8.30am to 2pm (closed on Saturdays and Sundays in summer).*

*Exchange offices in Sevilla and Valencia airports open from 9am to 2pm, in Barcelona airport from 9am to 2pm and 7 to 11pm. In Madrid and Málaga airports, offices operate a 24-hour service.*

## TRANSPORT

*Taxis may be hailed when showing the green light or "Libre" sign on the windscreen. Madrid, Barcelona, Bilbao and Valencia have a Metro (subway) network. In each station complete information and plans will be found.*

## SHOPPING

*In the index of street names, those printed in red are where the principal shops are found.*

*The big stores are easy to find in town centres; they are open from 10am to 9.30pm. Exclusive shops and boutiques are open from 10am to 2pm and 5 to 8pm. In Madrid they will be found in Serrano, Princesa and the Centre; in Barcelona, Passeig de Gràcia, Diagonal and the Rambla de Catalunya.*

*Second-hand goods and antiques: El Rastro (Flea Market), Las Cortes, Serrano in Madrid; in Barcelona, Les Encantes (Flea Market), Barrio Gótico.*

## TIPPING

*Hotel, restaurant and café bills always include service in the total charge. Nevertheless it is usual to leave the staff a small gratuity which may vary depending upon the district and the service given. Doormen, porters and taxi-drivers are used to being tipped.*

## SPEED LIMITS

*The maximum permitted speed on motorways is 120 km/h - 74 mph, and 90 km/h - 56 mph on other roads.*

## SEAT BELTS

*The wearing of seat belts is compulsory for drivers and all passengers.*

## "TAPAS"

*Bars serving "tapas" (typical Spanish food to be eaten with a glass of wine or an aperitif) will usually be found in central, busy or old quarters of towns. In Madrid, search out the Calle de Cuchilleros (Plaza Mayor). In Sevilla, search out the Barrio de Santa Cruz, El Arenal and Triana.*

# MADRID

*Madrid 28000* **P** 444 K 19 - *Pop. 3 084 673 - alt. 646.*

*Paris (by Irún) 1310 - Barcelona 627 - Bilbao/Bilbo 397 - La Coruña/A Coruña 603 - Lisboa 653 - Málaga 548 - Porto 599 - Sevilla 550 - Valencia 351 - Zaragoza 322.*

*Duque de Medinaceli 2, ✉ 28014, ✆ (91) 429 49 51, Pl. Mayor 3, ✆ 28012, ✆ (91) 366 54 77, Puerta de Toledo Market, ✉ 28005, ✆ (91) 364 18 76, Chamartín Station, ✉ 28036, ✆ (91) 315 99 76 and Madrid-Barajas airport ✆ (91) 305 86 56 - R.A.C.E. José Abascal 10, ✉ 28003, ✆ (91) 447 32 00, Fax (91) 593 20 64.*

*Racecourse of the Zarzuela ✆ (91) 307 01 40 NW : by Av. Puerta de Hierro* DV *- 18, 18 Puerta de Hierro ✆ (91) 316 17 45 NW : by Av. Puerta de Hierro* DV *- 9, 18 Club de Campo ✆ (91) 357 21 32 NW : by Av. Puerta de Hierro* DV *- 18 La Moraleja N : 11 km ✆ (91) 650 07 00 - 9 Club Barberán SW : 10 km ✆ (91) 509 11 40 - 18 Las Lomas - El Bosque SW : 18 km ✆ (91) 616 75 00 - 18 Real Automóvil Club de España N : 28 km ✆ (91) 657 00 11 - 18 Nuevo Club de Madrid, Las Matas W : 26 km ✆ (91) 630 08 20 - 9 Somosaguas W : 10 km by Casa de Campo ✆ (91) 352 16 47 - 9 Club Olivar de la Hinojosa NE by M 30 ✆ (91) 721 18 89.*

*Madrid-Barajas E : 13 km ✆ (91) 393 60 00 - Iberia : Velázquez 130, ✉ 28006, ✆ (91) 587 87 87* HV *at airport, ✉ 28042, ✆ (91) 329 57 67, and Aviaco, Maudes 51, ✉ 28003, ✉ 534 42 00* FV.

*Chamartín ✆ (91) 733 11 22* HR.

## Sights

### VIEW OVER MADRID

*Moncloa Beacon (Faro de Moncloa):* ✻★★ DV

### MUSEUMS

*Prado-Museum*★★★ NY – *Thyssen Bornemisza Museum*★★★ MY **M⁶** – *Royal Palace*★★ *(Palacio Real)* KX *(Palace*★*; Throne Room*★*; Royal Armoury*★★*; Royal Carriage Museum*★ DY **M¹**) – *National Archaeological Museum*★★ *(Dama de Elche*★★★*)* NV – *Lázaro Galdiano Museum*★★ *(collection of enamels and ivories*★★★*)* HV **M⁴** – *Casón del Buen Retiro*★ *(annexe to the Prado)* NY – *Reina Sofia Art Museum*★ *(Picasso's Guernica*★★★*)* MZ – *Army Museum*★ *(Museo del Ejército)* NY – *Museum of the Americas*★ *(Museo de América; Treasure of Los Quimbayas*★*, Cortesano Manuscript*★★★*)*, DV – *San Fernando Royal Fine Arts Academy*★ *(Real Academia de Bellas Artes de San Fernando)* LX **M²** – *Cerralbo Museum*★ KV – *Sorolla Museum*★ GV **M⁵** – *City Museum (Museo de la Ciudad Models*★*)* HU – *Waxworks Museum* ★ *(Museo de Cera)* NV – *Naval Museum (ship models*★*, map of Juan de la Cosa*★★*)* MXY **M³**

### CHURCHES AND MONASTERIES

*Descalzas Reales Monastery*★★ KLX – *San Francisco el Grande Church (stall*★ *in chancel and sacristy)* KZ – *Royal Convent of the Incarnation*★ *(Real Monasterio de la Encarnatión)* KX – *San Antonio de la Florida Chapel (frescoes*★★*)* DX

### THE OLD TOWN

*Eastern Quarter*★★ *(Barrio de Oriente)* KVXY – *Bourbon Madrid*★★ MNXYZ – *Old Madrid*★ KYZ

### PLACES OF INTEREST

*Plaza Mayor*★★ KY – *Buen Retiro Park*★★ NYZ – *Zoo*★★ *W; by Casa de Campo Park*★ DX – *Plaza de la Villa*★ KY – *Vistillas Gardens* (✻) KYZ – *Campo del Moro Winter Garden*★ DY – *University City*★ *(Ciudad Universitaria)* DV – *Plaza de la Cibeles*★ MNX – *Paseo del Prado*★ MNXYZ – *Alcalá Arch*★ *(Puerta de Alcalá)* NX **B** – *Bullring*★ *(Plaza Monumental de las Ventas)* JV **B** – *West Park*★ *(Parque del Oeste)* DV

# MADRID

| Street | Grid | No. |
|---|---|---|
| Caídos de la División Azul | HS | 21 |
| Capitán Haya | GS | 25 |
| Comandante Zorita | FT | 45 |
| Costa Rica | HS | 55 |
| Cuatro Caminos (Glorieta de) | FU | 56 |
| Doctor Arce (Av. del) | HU | 62 |
| Doctor Fléming | GT | 63 |
| Enrique Larreta | HS | 76 |
| Estébanez Calderón | GS | 80 |
| Fray Bernardino Sahagún | HS | 90 |
| Gen. López Pozas | HS | 92 |
| Gen. Moscardó | FT | 95 |
| Jerez | HS | 107 |
| Pedro Teixeira | GT | 145 |
| Pinos Alta | FS | 146 |
| Pintor Juan Gris | FS | 148 |
| Presidente Carmona | FT | 157 |
| Raimundo Fernández Villaverde | FU | 162 |
| Reina Mercedes | FT | 168 |
| República Dominicana (Pl.) | HS | 172 |
| Rosa de Silva | FS | 177 |
| Rosario Pino | GS | 179 |
| San Amaro (Pl.) | FT | 183 |
| Segre | HT | 206 |
| Sinesio Delgado | GR | 209 |
| Sor Ángela de la Cruz | GS | |
| Teruel | FT | 210 |
| Víctor Andrés Belaunde | HT | 229 |
| Víctor de la Serna | HT | 231 |

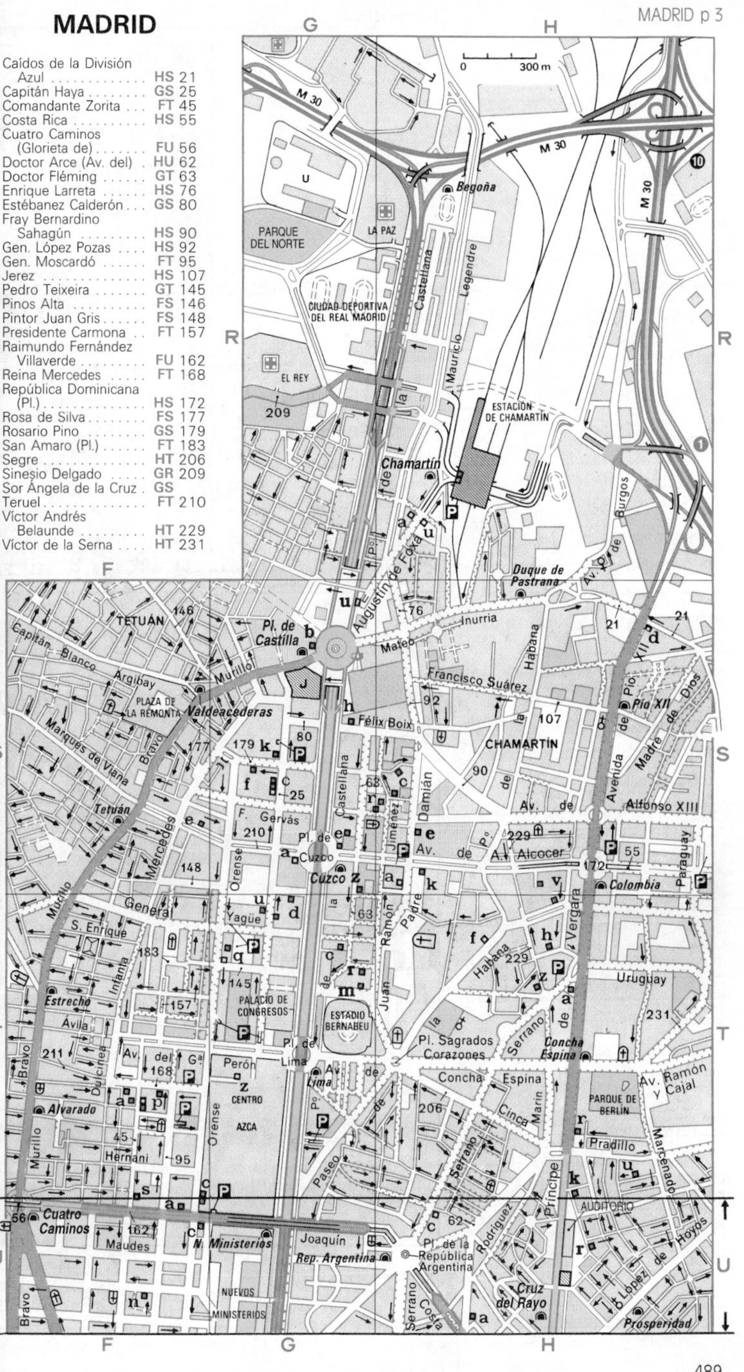

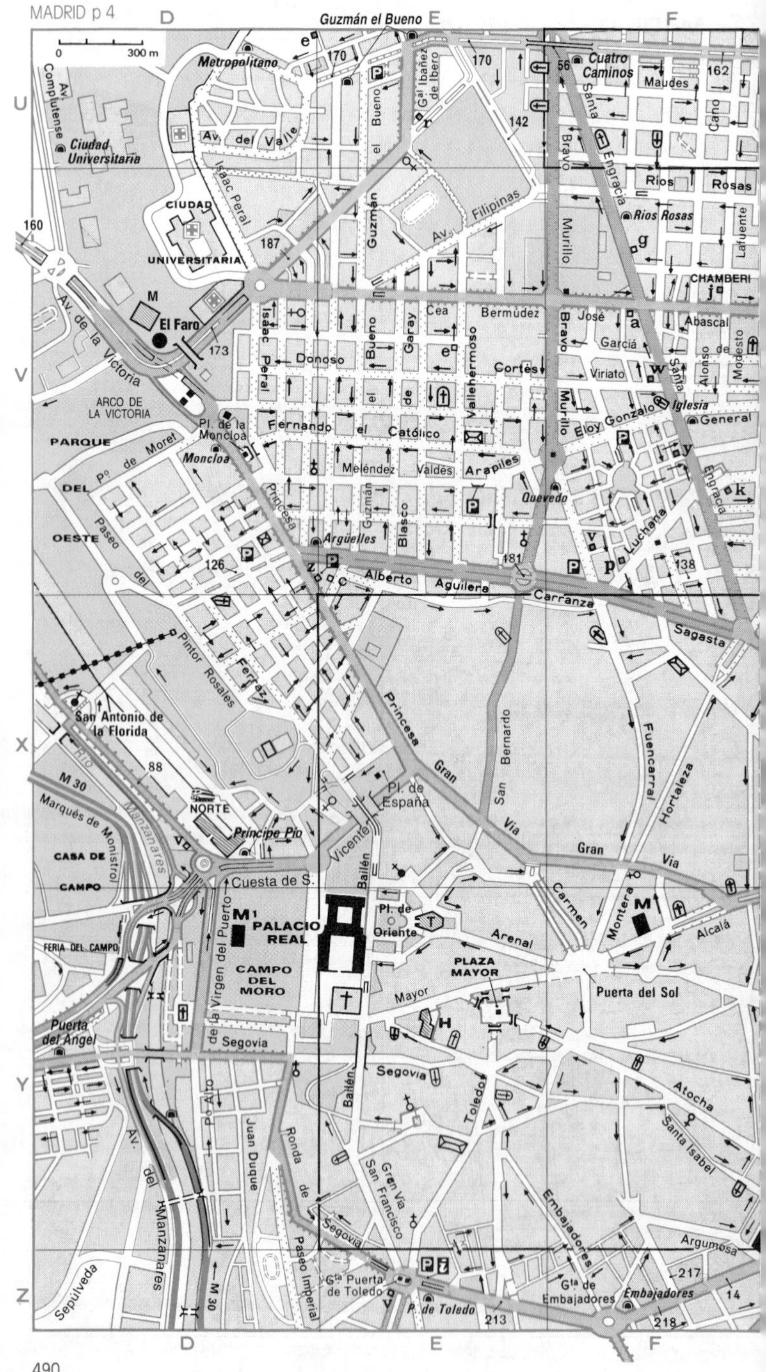

0 300 m
Guzmán el Bueno
Metropolitano
Cuatro Caminos
Ciudad Universitaria
CIUDAD UNIVERSITARIA
Av. Complutense
Av. del Valle
Isaac Peral
Av. Filipinas
Gal Ibañez de Ibero
Santa Engracia
Bravo Murillo
Maudes
Cano
Ríos Rosas
Lafuente
CHAMBERI
El Faro
Av. de la Victoria
ARCO DE LA VICTORIA
PARQUE DEL OESTE
Pl. de la Moncloa
Moncloa
Pº de Moret
Paseo del Pintor Rosales
Princesa
Donoso
Fernando el Católico
Meléndez Valdés
Arapiles
Argüelles
Blasco
Garay
Cea Bermúdez
José Abascal
García
Vallehermoso
Cortés
Viriato
Eloy Gonzalo
Iglesia
General
Alonso de Modesto
Quevedo
Luchana
Alberto Aguilera
Carranza
Sagasta
Ferraz
San Antonio de la Florida
Río Manzanares
M 30
Marqués de Monistrol
CASA DE CAMPO
NORTE
Príncipe Pío
Pl. de España
Gran Vía
San Bernardo
Fuencarral
Hortaleza
Cuesta de S. Vicente
Bailén
PALACIO REAL
CAMPO DEL MORO
Pl. de Oriente
Arenal
Carmen
Montera
Alcalá
PLAZA MAYOR
Puerta del Sol
Mayor
FERIA DEL CAMPO
Virgen del Puerto
Puerta del Angel
Segovia
Toledo
Atocha
Santa Isabel
Pº Alto
Juan Duque
Ronda de Segovia
Gran Vía San Francisco
Embajadores
Argumosa
Av. del Manzanares
Sepúlveda
Paseo Imperial
Gta Puerta de Toledo
P. de Toledo
Gta de Embajadores

MADRID
Atocha (Ronda de) . . FZ 14
Florida
(Paseo de la) . . . . . DX 88
Lagasca . . . . . . . . . . HVX 116
Marqués de
Salamanca (Pl.) . . . HV 125
Marqués de Urquijo . DV 126
Miguel Ángel . . . . . . GV 136
Puerta de Hierro (Av.) . DV 160
Reina Cristina
(Paseo) . . . . . . . . . HZ 166
Reina Victoria (Av.) . . EU 170
Reyes Católicos (Av.) . DV 173
Ruiz Jiménez
(Glorieta) . . . . . . . . EV 181
San Francisco
de Sales (Pas.) . . . DV 187
Toledo
(Ronda de) . . . . . . EZ 213
Valencia . . . . . . . . . . FZ 217
Valencia
(Ronda de) . . . . . . FZ 218
G
H
J
U
V
X
Y
Z
N. Ministerios
Joaquín
Rep. Argentina
Pl. de la República Argentina
AUDITORIO
Cruz del Rayo
Prosperidad
Costa Rica
Castellana
Pl. de S. Juan de la Cruz
Serrano
Velázquez
Gta López de Hoyos
Hoyos
Cartagena
Av. de América
María de Molina
Francisco Silvela
Paredes
Zurbano
Pl. Emilio Castelar
Diego de León
Martínez Campos
Eduardo Dato
R. Darío
N. Balboa
Juan Bravo
Príncipe de Vergara
Peñalver
Av. de los Toreros
PLAZA DE TOROS
Ventas
J. Ortega y Gasset
Lista
Almagro
Don Ramón de la Cruz
Ayala
SALAMANCA
M. Becerra
Pl. de M. Becerra
P.º del Marqués de Zafra
Génova
Pl. de Colón
Conde
Alcalá
Goya
Serrano
Velázquez
PALACIO DE LOS DEPORTES
Juan
Pl. S. Dalí
P. de Vergara
Recoletos
Retiro
O'Donnell
TORRE TV
Narváez
Pl. de la Independencia
Ibiza
Esquerdo
PL. DE CIBELES
PASEO DEL PRADO
Alfonso XII
ESTANQUE
PARQUE DEL BUEN RETIRO
Menéndez Pelayo
Alcalde Sainz de Baranda
Sainz de Baranda
MUSEO DEL PRADO
PALACIO DE CRISTAL
LA CHOPERA
MICHELIN
Doctor
Atocha
Pl. de Mariano de Cavia
Av. M. y Pelayo
Avenida del Mediterráneo
Conde de Casal
Pl. Conde de Casal
166
PANTEÓN
ATOCHA
REAL FÁBRICA DE TAPICES
M 30

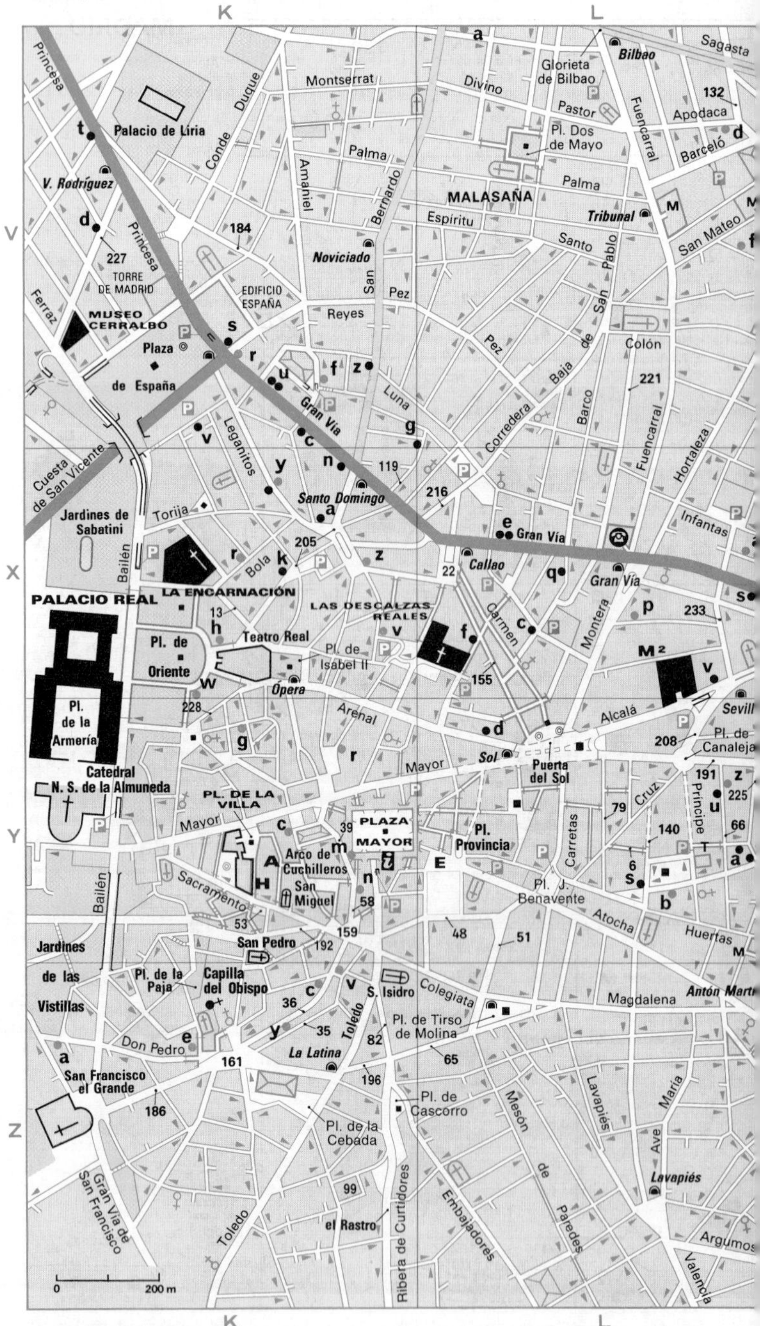
K
L
V
X
Y
Z
Princesa
Palacio de Liria
V. Rodríguez
Conde Duque
Montserrat
Divino
Glorieta de Bilbao
Bilbao
Sagasta
Pastor
Pl. Dos de Mayo
Fuencarral
Apodaca
Barceló
Palma
Amaniel
San Bernardo
MALASAÑA
Espíritu
Tribunal
Santo
San Mateo
TORRE DE MADRID
EDIFICIO ESPAÑA
Noviciado
Pez
Reyes
Ferraz
MUSEO CERRALBO
Plaza de España
Colón
Baja de San Pablo
Luna
Gran Vía
Corredera
Barco
Leganitos
Hortaleza
Cuesta de San Vicente
Santo Domingo
Infantas
Jardines de Sabatini
Torija
Bailén
Bola
LA ENCARNACIÓN
Callao
Gran Vía
PALACIO REAL
LAS DESCALZAS REALES
Carmen
Montera
Teatro Real
Pl. de Oriente
Pl. de Isabel II
Ópera
M²
Pl. de la Armería
Arenal
Alcalá
Sevill
Pl. de Canaleja
Catedral N. S. de la Almuneda
Mayor
Sol
Puerta del Sol
PL. DE LA VILLA
PLAZA MAYOR
Cruz
Príncipe
Arco de Cuchilleros
Pl. Provincia
Carretas
Sacramento
San Miguel
Pl. J. Benavente
Atocha
Huertas
Jardines de las Vistillas
San Pedro
Pl. de la Paja
Capilla del Obispo
S. Isidro
Colegiata
Magdalena
Antón Mart
Toledo
Pl. de Tirso de Molina
Don Pedro
La Latina
San Francisco el Grande
Pl. de Cascorro
Lavapiés
Mesón de Paredes
Ave María
Pl. de la Cebada
Gran Vía de San Francisco
Ribera de Curtidores
Embajadores
el Rastro
Argumos
Valencia
0
200 m

# MADRID

| Street | Grid | No. |
|---|---|---|
| Alcalá | LMXY | |
| Arenal | KY | |
| Carmen | LX | |
| Fuencarral | LV | |
| Gran Vía | KLX | |
| Hortaleza | LVX | |
| Mayor | KLY | |
| Mayor (Plaza) | KY | |
| Montera | LX | |
| Preciados | LX | 155 |
| Puerta del Sol (Pl.) | LY | |
| San Jerónimo (Carrera de) | LMY | 191 |
| Álvarez Gato | LY | 6 |
| Arrieta | KX | 13 |
| Ayala | NV | 18 |
| Bárbara de Braganza | NV | 19 |
| Callao (Pl. del) | LX | 22 |
| Cava Alta | KZ | 35 |
| Cava Baja | KZ | 36 |
| Cava de San Miguel | KY | 39 |
| Ciudad de Barcelona | NZ | 41 |
| Colón (Pl. de) | NV | 44 |
| Concepción Jerónima | LY | 48 |
| Conde de Romanones | LY | 51 |
| Cortes (Pl. de las) | MY | 53 |
| Cuchilleros | KY | 58 |
| Duque de Alba | LZ | 65 |
| Echegaray | LY | 66 |
| Espoz y Mina | LY | 79 |
| Estudios | KZ | 82 |
| Fernando el Santo | NV | 85 |
| Gen. Vara del Rey (Pl.) | KZ | 99 |
| Goya | NV | 100 |
| Independencia (Pl. de la) | NX | 103 |
| Infanta Isabel (Pas.) | NZ | 105 |
| Libreros | KX | 119 |
| Madrazo (Los) | MY | 121 |
| Mejía Lequerica | LMV | 132 |
| Núñez de Arce | LY | 140 |
| Puerta Cerrada (Pl.) | KY | 159 |
| Puerta de Moros (Pl.) | KZ | 161 |
| Recoletos | NX | 163 |
| San Bernardino | KV | 184 |
| San Francisco (Carrera de) | KZ | 186 |
| San Justo | KY | 192 |
| San Millán | KZ | 196 |
| Santa Engracia | MV | 203 |
| Santo Domingo (Cuesta, Pl. de) | KX | 205 |
| Sevilla | LY | 208 |
| Tudescos | LX | 216 |
| Valverde | LV | 221 |
| Ventura de la Vega | LY | 225 |
| Ventura Rodríguez | KV | 227 |
| Vergara | KY | 228 |
| Villa de París (Pl.) | NV | 232 |
| Virgen de los Peligros | LX | 233 |

*The names of main shopping streets are indicated in red at the beginning of the list of streets.*

**Centre** : Paseo del Prado, Puerta del Sol, Gran Vía, Alcalá, Paseo de Recoletos, Plaza Mayor

**Palace,** pl. de las Cortes 7, ✉ 28014, ℘ (91) 360 80 00, *Telex 22272, Fax (91) 360 81 00* – 25/600. AE VISA JCB. rest MY e
**Meals** - buffet - 5100 - ***La Cupola*** *(Italian rest. closed Sunday, Monday and August)* **Meals** a la carte approx. 6500 – 3100 – **440 rm** 52000/59000, 40 suites.

**Husa Princesa,** Princesa 40, ✉ 28008, ℘ (91) 542 21 00, *Fax (91) 542 73 28,* – 25/825. AE VISA JCB. DEV z
**Meals** 2700 – 2075 – **263 rm** 26200/32100, 12 suites.

**Villa Real,** pl. de las Cortes 10, ✉ 28014, ℘ (91) 420 37 67, *Fax (91) 420 25 47,* « Tasteful decor » – 35/100. AE VISA MY c
**Meals** a la carte 4200/5200 – 1900 – **96 rm** 26400/33000, 19 suites.

**Holiday Inn Crowne Plaza,** pl. de España, ✉ 28013, ℘ (91) 547 12 00, *Telex 27383, Fax (91) 548 23 89,* – 25/350. AE VISA JCB. KV s
**Meals** 4200 – 1800 – **295 rm** 19800/22800, 11 suites.

**Tryp Ambassador,** Cuesta de Santo Domingo 5, ✉ 28013, ℘ (91) 541 67 00, *Telex 49538, Fax (91) 559 10 40* – 25/280. AE VISA JCB. KX k
**Meals** a la carte 3260/4850 – 1500 – **163 rm** 18350/23000, 18 suites.

**NH Nacional,** paseo del Prado 48, ✉ 28014, ℘ (91) 429 66 29, *Fax (91) 369 15 64* – 25/200. AE VISA. NZ r
1700 – **214 rm** 14800/16800, 1 suite.

**Liabeny,** Salud 3, ✉ 28013, ℘ (91) 531 90 00, *Fax (91) 532 74 21* – 25/125. AE VISA. LX c
**Meals** 2900 – 1500 – **222 rm** 10500/18000.

**Moncloa Garden** without rest, Serrano Jover 1, ✉ 28015, ℘ (91) 542 45 82, *Fax (91) 542 71 69* – AE VISA JCB. EV c
995 – **103 rm** 14000/16560, 20 suites.

**Emperador** without rest, Gran Vía 53, ✉ 28013, ℘ (91) 547 28 00, *Telex 46261, Fax (91) 547 28 17,* – 25/150. AE VISA KX n
1735 – **232 rm** 16320/20400.

**Arosa** coffee shop only, Salud 21, ✉ 28013, ℘ (91) 532 16 00, *Telex 43618, Fax (91) 531 31 27* – 25/60. AE VISA JCB LX q
1300 – **139 rm** 12730/19680.

**G.H. Reina Victoria,** pl. de Santa Ana 14, ✉ 28012, ℘ (91) 531 45 00, *Fax (91) 522 03 07* – 25/350. AE VISA. LY s
**Meals** 3645 – 1650 – **195 rm** 20000/25000, 6 suites.

**Santo Domingo,** pl. de Santo Domingo 13, ✉ 28013, ℘ (91) 547 98 00, *Fax (91) 547 59 95* – 25/60. AE VISA JCB. KX a
**Meals** 3650 – 1400 – **120 rm** 14450/22125.

**Mayorazgo,** Flor Baja 3, ✉ 28013, ℘ (91) 547 26 00, *Telex 45647, Fax (91) 541 24 85* – 25/250. AE VISA JCB. KV c
**Meals** 2240 – 1200 – **200 rm** 13000/17000.

**El Coloso,** Leganitos 13, ✉ 28013, ℘ (91) 559 76 00, *Telex 47017, Fax (91) 547 49 68* – 25/200. AE VISA JCB. KX y
**Meals** 1825 – 1400 – **84 rm** 17445/21770.

**Suecia,** Marqués de Casa Riera 4, ✉ 28014, ℘ (91) 531 69 00, *Telex 22313, Fax (91) 521 71 41* – 25/150. AE VISA JCB. MX r
**Meals** 3500 - ***Bellman*** *(Scandinavian rest)* **Meals** a la carte 3005/3875 – 1500 – **119 rm** 18900/23700, 9 suites.

**Gaudí,** Gran Vía 9, ✉ 28013, ℘ (91) 531 22 22, *Fax (91) 531 54 69,* – 25/120. AE VISA JCB. LX s
**Meals** 2500 – 1650 – **88 rm** 18850/22600.

**Tryp Menfis,** Gran Vía 74, ✉ 28013, ℘ (91) 547 09 00, *Telex 48773, Fax (91) 547 51 99* – AE VISA. KV u
**Meals** 2000 – 700 – **115 rm** 15525/20175.

**Regina** without rest, Alcalá 19, ✉ 28014, ℘ (91) 521 47 25, *Telex 27500, Fax (91) 521 47 25* – AE VISA. LX v
750 – **142 rm** 9200/12400.

**Casón del Tormes** without rest, Río 7, ✉ 28013, ℘ (91) 541 97 46, *Fax (91) 541 18 52* – VISA. KV v
700 – **63 rm** 9000/13000.

**El Prado,** Prado 11, ✉ 28014, ℘ (91) 369 02 34, *Fax (91) 429 28 29* – 25/50. AE VISA JCB LY a
**Meals** *(closed Sunday and August)* 1500 – 500 – **47 rm** 11760/14700.

**Mercator** coffee shop only, Atocha 123, ✉ 28012, ☎ (91) 429 05 00, *Fax (91) 369 12 52* – AE VISA NZ b
850 – **89 rm** 8900/12400.

**Carlos V** without rest, Maestro Vitoria 5, ✉ 28013, ☎ (91) 531 41 00, *Telex 48547, Fax (91) 531 37 61* – AE VISA JCB. LX f
**67 rm** 11020/13870.

**Atlántico** without rest, Gran Vía 38-3º, ✉ 28013, ☎ (91) 522 64 80, *Telex 43142, Fax (91) 531 02 10* – AE VISA JCB. LX e
**80 rm** 11455/15650.

**Tryp Washington,** Gran Vía 72, ✉ 28013, ☎ (91) 541 72 27, *Telex 48773, Fax (91) 547 51 99* – AE VISA. KV u
Meals (at Hotel ***Tryp Menfis***) – 700 – **120 rm** 13350/17450.

**Los Condes** without rest, Los Libreros 7, ✉ 28004, ☎ (91) 521 54 55, *Telex 42730, Fax (91) 521 78 82* – AE VISA JCB. KLV g
600 – **68 rm** 7500/10490.

**California** without rest, Gran Vía 38, ✉ 28013, ☎ (91) 522 47 03, *Fax (91) 531 61 01* – AE VISA. LX e
350 – **26 rm** 6700/8900.

**Alexandra** without rest, San Bernardo 29, ✉ 28015, ☎ (91) 542 04 00, *Fax (91) 559 28 25* – AE VISA JCB. KV z
800 – **78 rm** 8130/10165.

**Paradis Madrid,** Marqués de Cubas 14, ✉ 28014, ☎ (91) 429 73 03, *Fax (91) 429 32 95* – AE VISA MY v
*closed Saturday lunch, Sunday, Holy Week and August* – **Meals** a la carte 4400/5300.

**El Landó,** pl. Gabriel Miró 8, ✉ 28005, ☎ (91) 366 76 81, *Fax (91) 366 76 81,* « Tasteful decor » – AE VISA. KZ a
*closed Sunday, Bank Holidays and August* – **Meals** a la carte 3600/6200.

**Moaña,** Hileras 4, ✉ 28013, ☎ (91) 548 29 14, *Fax (91) 541 65 98* – AE VISA JCB. KY r
*closed Sunday dinner* – **Meals** - Galician rest - a la carte 4140/5600.

**Bajamar,** Gran Vía 78, ✉ 28013, ☎ (91) 548 48 18, *Fax (91) 559 13 26* – AE VISA JCB. KV r
**Meals** - Seafood - a la carte 4800/6950.

**El Espejo,** paseo de Recoletos 31, ✉ 28004, ☎ (91) 308 23 47, *Fax (91) 593 22 23,* « Old Parisian style café » – AE VISA. NV a
*closed Saturday lunch* – **Meals** a la carte approx. 2850.

**Errota-Zar,** Jovellanos 3-1º, ✉ 28014, ☎ (91) 531 25 64, *Fax (91) 531 25 64* – AE VISA MY s
*closed Sunday, Holy Week and 10 to 17 August* – **Meals** a la carte 3400/4850.

**Ainhoa,** Bárbara de Braganza 12, ✉ 28004, ☎ (91) 308 27 26 – AE VISA. NV s
*closed Sunday and August* – **Meals** - Basque rest - a la carte 3600/5000.

**Horno de Santa Teresa,** Santa Teresa 12, ✉ 28004, ☎ (91) 308 66 98 – VISA JCB. MV t
**Meals** a la carte 3725/4250.

**Café de Oriente,** pl. de Oriente 2, ✉ 28013, ☎ (91) 541 39 74, *Fax (91) 547 77 07,* « In a cellar » – AE VISA. KXY w
**Meals** a la carte 4550/5650.

**La Gastroteca de Stéphane y Arturo,** pl. de Chueca 8, ✉ 28004, ☎ (91) 532 25 64 – AE VISA MV e
*closed Saturday lunch, Sunday and August* – **Meals** - French rest - a la carte 4460/5600.

**Platerías,** pl. de Santa Ana 11, ✉ 28012, ☎ (91) 429 70 48, « Early 20C style café » – AE VISA. LY b
*closed Saturday lunch, Sunday, Holy Week and August* – **Meals** a la carte approx. 5500.

**El Asador de Aranda,** Preciados 44, ✉ 28013, ☎ (91) 547 21 56, *Fax (91) 556 62 02,* « Castilian decor » – AE VISA. KX z
*closed Monday dinner and 21 July-12 August* – **Meals** - Roast lamb - a la carte approx. 3950.

**Arce,** Augusto Figueroa 32, ✉ 28004, ☎ (91) 522 04 40, *Fax (91) 522 59 13* – AE VISA JCB. MV c
*closed Saturday lunch, Sunday and 15 to 31 August* – **Meals** a la carte 5365/6115.

**El Mentidero de la Villa,** Santo Tomé 6, ✉ 28004, ☎ (91) 308 12 85, *Fax (91) 319 87 92,* « Original decor » – AE VISA. MV b
*closed Saturday lunch and 15 to 31 August* – **Meals** a la carte approx. 4500.

**Julián de Tolosa,** Cava Baja 18, ✉ 28005, ☎ (91) 365 82 10, « Neorustic decor » – AE VISA JCB KZ c
*closed Sunday* – **Meals** - Braised meat specialities - a la carte approx. 4600.

XX **Casa Gallega,** pl. de San Miguel 8, ✉ 28005, ☎ (91) 547 30 55 – ▤. AE ⓓ E VISA JCB. ✂ KY c
**Meals** - Galician rest - a la carte 3100/4900.

XX **La Ópera de Madrid,** Amnistía 5, ✉ 28013, ☎ (91) 559 50 92, *Fax (91) 559 50 92* – ▤. AE ⓓ E VISA JCB. ✂ KY g
*closed Sunday and August* – **Meals** a la carte 3275/4400.

XX **Casa Parrondo,** Trujillos 4, ✉ 28013, ☎ (91) 522 62 34 – ▤. AE ⓓ E VISA. ✂ KX v
**Meals** - Asturian rest - a la carte 4600/7500.

XX **El Rincón de Esteban,** Santa Catalina 3, ✉ 28014, ☎ (91) 429 92 89, *Fax (91) 365 87 70* – ▤. AE ⓓ E VISA. ✂ MY a
*closed Sunday dinner and 15 to 31 August* – **Meals** a la carte 3700/5200.

X **La Barraca,** Reina 29, ✉ 28004, ☎ (91) 532 71 54, *Fax (91) 521 58 96* – ▤. AE ⓓ E VISA JCB. ✂ LX a
**Meals** - Rice dishes - a la carte 3600/5350

X **Robata,** Reina 31, ✉ 28004, ☎ (91) 521 85 28, *Fax (91) 531 30 63* – ▤. AE ⓓ VISA JCB. ✂ LX a
*closed Tuesday* – **Meals** - Japanese rest - a la carte 4100/5100.

X **La Vaca Verónica,** Moratín 38, ✉ 28014, ☎ (91) 429 78 27 – ▤. AE ⓓ E VISA. ✂
*closed Saturday lunch, Sunday and 3 to 25 August* – **Meals** a la carte approx. 4300. MZ e

X **Casa Vallejo,** San Lorenzo 9 ☎ (91) 308 61 58 – ▤. VISA JCB. ✂ LV f
*closed Sunday, Monday dinner, Bank Holidays and August* – **Meals** a la carte 2550/3550.

X **Ciao Madrid,** Argensola 7, ✉ 28004, ☎ (91) 308 25 19 – ▤. AE ⓓ E VISA JCB MV t
*closed Saturday lunch, Sunday and August* – **Meals** - Italian rest - a la carte 2900/3750.

X **La Bola,** Bola 5, ✉ 28013, ☎ (91) 547 69 30, *Fax (91) 547 04 63* – ▤. ✂ KX r
*closed Saturday dinner (July-August) and Sunday* – **Meals** - Madrid style stew - a la carte 3550/4225.

X **Taberna Carmencita,** Libertad 16, ✉ 28004, ☎ (91) 531 66 12, « Typical taverna » – ▤. AE ⓓ E VISA. ✂ MX u
*closed Saturday lunch and Sunday* – **Meals** a la carte 2100/3900.

X **Donzoko,** Echegaray 3, ✉ 28014, ☎ (91) 429 57 20, *Fax (91) 429 57 20* – ▤. AE ⓓ E VISA JCB. ✂ LY z
*closed Sunday* – **Meals** - Japanese rest - a la carte 3150/6700.

X **La Esquina del Real,** Amnistía 2, ✉ 28013, ☎ (91) 559 43 09 – ▤. AE E VISA. ✂
*closed Saturday lunch, Sunday and August* – **Meals** a la carte 3770/4625. KY e

X **Ciao Madrid,** Apodaca 20, ✉ 28004, ☎ (91) 447 00 36 – ▤. AE ⓓ E VISA JCB LV d
*closed Saturday lunch, Sunday, first week in April and September* – **Meals** - Italian rest - a la carte 3200/4200.

X **El Ingenio,** Leganitos 10, ✉ 28013, ☎ (91) 541 91 33, *Fax (91) 547 35 34* – ▤. AE ⓓ E VISA JCB. ✂ KX y
*closed Sunday, Bank Holidays and August* – **Meals** a la carte 2200/3300.

Typical atmosphere :

XX **Posada de la Villa,** Cava Baja 9, ✉ 28005, ☎ (91) 366 18 80, *Fax (91) 366 18 80,* « Castilian decor » – ▤. ⓓ E VISA. ✂ KZ v
*closed Sunday dinner and August* – **Meals** a la carte 3600/5825.

XX **Botín,** Cuchilleros 17, ✉ 28005, ☎ (91) 366 42 17, *Fax (91) 366 84 94,* « Old Madrid decor. Typical cellar » – ▤. AE ⓓ E VISA JCB. ✂ KY n
**Meals** a la carte 3350/5855.

X **Casa Lucio,** Cava Baja 35, ✉ 28005, ☎ (91) 365 32 52, *Fax (91) 366 48 66,* « Castilian decor » – ▤. AE ⓓ E VISA. ✂ KZ y
*closed Saturday lunch and August* – **Meals** a la carte approx. 5500.

X **Las Cuevas de Luis Candelas,** Cuchilleros 1, ✉ 28005, ☎ (91) 366 54 28, *Fax (91) 366 49 37,* « Old Madrid decor. Staff in bandit costumes » – ▤. ⓓ E VISA. ✂
**Meals** a la carte 3275/5125. KY m

X **Taberna del Alabardero,** Felipe V-6, ✉ 28013, ☎ (91) 547 25 77, *Fax (91) 547 77 07,* « Typical taverna » – ▤. AE ⓓ E VISA JCB KX h
**Meals** - Basque rest - a la carte 3800/5350.

**Retiro, Salamanca, Ciudad Lineal :** Paseo de la Castellana, Velázquez, Serrano, Goya, Príncipe de Vergara, Narváez, Don Ramón de la Cruz

**Ritz,** pl. de la Lealtad 5, ✉ 28014, ☎ (91) 521 28 57, *Fax (91) 532 87 76,* ⌂, Fø – |‡| ▤ TV ☎ – 🏛 25/280. AE ⓓ E VISA JCB. ✂ rest NY k
**Meals** a la carte 7500/9300 – ☕ 2950 – **127 rm** 44000/51000, 29 suites.

**Villa Magna,** paseo de la Castellana 22, ✉ 28046, ☎ (91) 587 12 34, *Fax (91) 575 31 58*, – 25/250. AE ⓓ E VISA JCB. rest
Meals 5500 - ***Berceo*** : Meals a la carte 5600/8450 - ***Tsé Yang*** *(Chinese rest)* Meals a la carte 4000/5600 – ☐ 2950 – **164 rm** 50000/55000, 18 suites. GV y

**Wellington,** Velázquez 8, ✉ 28001, ☎ (91) 575 44 00, *Telex 22700, Fax (91) 576 41 64*, – 25/300. AE ⓓ E VISA. HX t
Meals (see rest. ***El Fogón*** below) – ☐ 2200 – **198 rm** 27000/34250, 25 suites.

**Meliá Confort Los Galgos,** Claudio Coello 139, ✉ 28006, ☎ (91) 562 66 00, *Telex 43957, Fax (91) 561 76 62* – – 25/300. AE ⓓ E VISA JCB. HV a
***Diábolo*** : Meals a la carte 3225/4975 – ☐ 1450 – **358 rm** 16750/28400.

**Tryp Fénix,** Hermosilla 2, ✉ 28001, ☎ (91) 431 67 00, *Fax (91) 576 06 61* – – 25/100. AE ⓓ E VISA JCB. NV c
Meals 2625 – ☐ 1650 – **213 rm** 24100/30190, 13 suites.

**Meliá Avenida América,** Juan Ignacio Luca de Tena 36, ✉ 28027, ☎ (91) 320 30 30, *Fax (91) 320 14 40*, – 25/1200. AE ⓓ E VISA. NE : by Av. de América HV
Meals a la carte approx. 5500 – ☐ 1800 – **210 rm** 22700/28000, 18 suites.

**Sofitel Madrid-Aeropuerto,** Campo de las Naciones, ✉ 28042, ☎ (91) 721 00 70, *Telex 45008, Fax (91) 721 05 15*, – 50/120. AE ⓓ E VISA NE : by Av. de América HV
Meals a la carte 4625/6045 – ☐ 2035 – **175 rm** 26535/31030, 3 suites.

**NH Príncipe de Vergara,** Príncipe de Vergara 92, ✉ 28006, ☎ (91) 563 26 95, *Fax (91) 563 72 53* – – 25/300. AE ⓓ E VISA JCB. HV c
Meals a la carte 4850/5350 – ☐ 1900 – **167 rm** 17500/19000, 3 suites.

**Emperatriz,** López de Hoyos 4, ✉ 28006, ☎ (91) 563 80 88, *Fax (91) 563 98 04* – – 25/150. AE ⓓ E VISA JCB. GV z
Meals 3500 – ☐ 1800 – **155 rm** 19200/24000, 3 suites.

**NH Sanvy,** Goya 3, ✉ 28001, ☎ (91) 576 08 00, *Fax (91) 575 24 43* – – 25/150. AE ⓓ E VISA JCB. NV r
Meals (see rest. ***Sorolla*** below) – ☐ 1900 – **144 rm** 19500, 15 suites.

**Agumar** coffee shop only, paseo Reina Cristina 7, ✉ 28014, ☎ (91) 552 69 00, *Telex 22814, Fax (91) 433 60 95* – – 25/150. AE ⓓ E VISA JCB. – ☐ 1400 – **245 rm** 14750/18500. HZ a

**Novotel Madrid,** Albacete 1, ✉ 28027, ☎ (91) 405 46 00, *Fax (91) 404 11 05*, – 25/250. AE ⓓ E VISA E : by M 30 JY
Meals 1950 – ☐ 1500 – **236 rm** 17700/19375.

**Pintor,** Goya 79, ✉ 28001, ☎ (91) 435 75 45, *Telex 23281, Fax (91) 576 81 57* – – 25/350. AE ⓓ E VISA. HX c
Meals 1900 – ☐ 1700 – **174 rm** 16540/20675, 2 suites.

**Conde de Orgaz,** av. Moscatelar 24, ✉ 28043, ☎ (91) 388 40 99, *Fax (91) 388 00 09* – – 25/100. AE ⓓ E VISA. rest NE : by López de Hoyos HU
Meals 1500 – ☐ 1250 – **89 rm** 11800/18000.

**NH Parque Avenidas,** Biarritz 2, ✉ 28028, ☎ (91) 361 02 88, *Fax (91) 361 21 38*, – 25/400. AE ⓓ VISA JCB. rest JV a
Meals 4750 – ☐ 1700 – **198 rm** 17300, 1 suite.

**NH Lagasca,** Lagasca 64, ✉ 28001, ☎ (91) 575 46 06, *Fax (91) 575 16 94* – – 25/60. AE ⓓ VISA JCB. rest HX k
Meals *(closed Saturday, Sunday and August)* 1650 – ☐ 1700 – **100 rm** 17500.

**NH Alcalá,** Alcalá 66, ✉ 28009, ☎ (91) 435 10 60, *Fax (91) 435 11 05* – – 25/100. AE ⓓ E VISA. HX w
Meals 2500 – ☐ 1800 – **146 rm** 17500/18600.

**El Madroño,** General Díaz Porlier 101, ✉ 28006, ☎ (91) 562 52 92, *Fax (91) 563 06 97* – – 25/250. AE ⓓ E VISA JCB. HV z
Meals 1300 – ☐ 950 – **66 rm** 13800/17000.

**G.H. Colón,** Pez Volador 11, ✉ 28007, ☎ (91) 573 59 00, *Fax (91) 573 08 09*, – – 25/250. AE ⓓ E VISA JCB. JY x
Meals 1900 – ☐ 1100 – **380 rm** 9500/14400.

**Novotel Madrid-Campo de las Naciones,** Campo de las Naciones, ✉ 28042, ☎ (91) 721 18 18, *Fax (91) 721 11 22*, – – 25/400. AE ⓓ E VISA JCB. rest NE : by Av. de América HV
Meals 2400 – ☐ 1500 – **240 rm** 17475/18560, 6 suites.

**Convención** coffee shop only, O'Donnell 53, ✉ 28009, ☎ (91) 574 84 00, *Telex 23944, Fax (91) 574 56 01* – – 25/800. AE ⓓ E VISA JCB. JX a
☐ 1390 – **739 rm** 11770/14710, 51 suites.

**Serrano** without rest, Marqués de Villamejor 8, ✉ 28006, ✆ (91) 435 52 00, *Fax (91) 435 48 49* – AE VISA JCB. GHV k
1000 – **30 rm** 13750/17100, 4 suites.

**NH Balboa,** Núñez de Balboa 112, ✉ 28006, ✆ (91) 563 03 24, *Fax (91) 562 69 80* – 25/30. AE E VISA JCB. HV n
Meals 2500 – 1700 – **122 rm** 15600/17700.

**NH Sur** without rest, paseo Infanta Isabel 9, ✉ 28014, ✆ (91) 539 94 00, *Fax (91) 467 09 96* – 25/30. AE E VISA. NZ a
1500 – **68 rm** 12500/13900.

**Abeba** without rest, Alcántara 63, ✉ 28006, ✆ (91) 401 16 50, *Fax (91) 402 75 91* – AE E VISA JCB. HV r
600 – **90 rm** 8000/10500.

**Club 31,** Alcalá 58, ✉ 28014, ✆ (91) 531 00 92 – AE E VISA JCB. NX e
*closed August* – **Meals** a la carte 5850/8700.

**El Amparo,** Puigcerdá 8, ✉ 28001, ✆ (91) 431 64 56, *Fax (91) 575 54 91,* « Original decor » – AE E VISA JCB HX h
*closed Saturday lunch, Sunday, Holy Week and 10 to 16 August* – **Meals** a la carte 7100/8675
**Spec.** Milhojas de manzana ácida, con pescado ahumado y foie-gras. Rabo de buey guisado al vino tinto con su puré de patata especial. Soufflé caliente de chocolate con crema helada.

**El Fogón,** Villanueva 34, ✉ 28001, ✆ (91) 575 44 00, *Telex 22700, Fax (91) 576 41 64* – AE E VISA. HX t
*closed August* – **Meals** a la carte 6100/7400.

**Sorolla,** Hermosilla 4, ✉ 28001, ✆ (91) 431 27 15, *Telex 44994, Fax (91) 575 24 43* – AE E VISA. NV r
*closed Sunday and August* – **Meals** a la carte approx. 4800.

**Suntory,** paseo de la Castellana 36, ✉ 28046, ✆ (91) 577 37 34, *Fax (91) 577 44 55* – AE E VISA JCB GV d
*closed Sunday and Bank Holidays* – **Meals** - Japanese rest - a la carte 5250/7300.

**Villa y Corte de Madrid,** Serrano 110, ✉ 28006, ✆ (91) 563 52 74, *Fax (91) 564 50 19,* « Tasteful decor » – AE E VISA JCB. HV a
*closed Sunday and August* – **Meals** a la carte approx. 5100.

**Balzac,** Moreto 7, ✉ 28014, ✆ (91) 420 01 77, *Fax (91) 429 83 70* – AE E VISA. NY a
*closed Sunday and August* – **Meals** a la carte 5000/5900.

**Pedro Larumbe,** Serrano 61-top floor, ✉ 28006, ✆ (91) 575 11 12, *Fax (91) 562 16 09* – AE E VISA. HV d
*closed Saturday lunch, Sunday and 15 days in August* – **Meals** a la carte 5600/6400.

**Paradis Casa América,** paseo de Recoletos 2, ✉ 28001, ✆ (91) 575 45 40, *Fax (91) 576 02 15,* « Within the Palacio de Linares » – AE E VISA. NX n
*closed Saturday lunch and Sunday* – **Meals** a la carte approx. 5500.

**Ponteareas,** Claudio Coello 96, ✉ 28006, ✆ (91) 575 58 73, *Fax (91) 541 65 98* – AE E VISA JCB. HV w
*closed Sunday, Bank Holidays and August* – **Meals** - Galician rest - a la carte 4140/5795.

**Castelló 9,** Castelló 9, ✉ 28001, ✆ (91) 435 00 67, *Fax (91) 435 91 34* – AE E VISA. HX e
*closed Sunday and Bank Holidays* – **Meals** a la carte 5000/5875.

**La Paloma,** Jorge Juan 39, ✉ 28001, ✆ (91) 576 86 92 – AE E VISA. HX g
*closed Sunday, Bank Holidays, Holy Week and August* – **Meals** 7500 and a la carte 4150/5350
**Spec.** Ensalada templada de paloma torcaz (season). Medallones de rape sobre lasagna de verduras y colas de gambas al jugo de mariscos. Merengue con crema de castañas y helado de ciruelas pasas al ron.

**Viridiana,** Juan de Mena 14, ✉ 28014, ✆ (91) 523 44 78, *Fax (91) 532 42 74* – AE VISA NY r
*closed Sunday and August* – **Meals** a la carte 5200/7500
**Spec.** Langostinos de la marisma con garbanzos fritos a la manzanilla de Sanlúcar. Escalopines de ternera rellenos de flores de calabacín y torta del Casar. Flan de chocolate amargo en salsa de cacao blanco.

**Al Mounia,** Recoletos 5, ✉ 28001, ✆ (91) 435 08 28, « Oriental atmosphere » – AE E VISA. NV u
*closed Sunday, Monday and August* – **Meals** - North African rest - a la carte 4300/4750.

**El Chiscón de Castelló,** Castelló 3, ✉ 28001, ✆ (91) 575 56 62, « Welcoming atmosphere » – ▤. AE E VISA. HX e
*closed Sunday, Bank Holidays and August* – **Meals** a la carte 3050/4275.

**Rafa,** Narváez 68, ✉ 28009, ✆ (91) 573 10 87, – ▤. AE ① E VISA JCB. HY a
**Meals** a la carte 4450/6550.

**El Asador de Aranda,** Diego de León 9, ✉ 28006, ✆ (91) 563 02 46, *Fax (91) 556 62 02* – ▤. AE ① E VISA. HV s
*closed Sunday dinner and August* – **Meals** - Roast lamb - a la carte approx. 3950.

**Guisando,** Núñez de Balboa 75, ✉ 28006, ✆ (91) 575 10 10 – ▤. AE ① E VISA.
*closed Saturday lunch, Sunday, Holy Week and August* – **Meals** a la carte 2700/3800. HV f

**St. James,** Juan Bravo 26, ✉ 28006, ✆ (91) 575 00 69, – ▤. AE VISA. HV t
*closed Sunday* – **Meals** - Rice dishes - a la carte 4500/6300.

**Nicolás,** Villalar 4, ✉ 28001, ✆ (91) 431 77 37, *Fax (91) 431 77 37* – ▤. AE ① E VISA JCB. NX t
*closed Sunday, Monday, Holy Week and August* – **Meals** a la carte 3600/4400.

**Casa d'a Troya,** Emiliano Barral 14, ✉ 28043, ✆ (91) 416 44 55 – ▤. E VISA.
*closed Sunday, Bank Holidays and 15 July-1 September* – **Meals** - Galician rest, seafood, booking essential - a la carte approx. 4950 E : by M 30 JY
**Spec.** Pulpo a la gallega. Merluza a la gallega. Lacón con grelos (October-May).

**La Giralda IV,** Claudio Coello 24, ✉ 28001, ✆ (91) 576 40 69 – ▤. AE ① E VISA.
*closed Sunday dinner in winter, Sunday in summer and 15 to 31 August* – **Meals** - Andalusian rest - a la carte approx. 5500. HX h

**Asador Velate,** Jorge Juan 91, ✉ 28009, ✆ (91) 435 10 24, *Fax (91) 574 38 54* – ▤. AE ① E VISA. HJX x
*closed Sunday and August* – **Meals** - Basque rest - a la carte 4350/ 5900.

**Pelotari,** Recoletos 3, ✉ 28001, ✆ (91) 578 24 97, *Fax (91) 431 60 04* – ▤. AE ① E VISA. NV u
*closed Sunday and 15 days in August* – **Meals** a la carte approx. 5225.

**La Trainera,** Lagasca 60, ✉ 28001, ✆ (91) 576 05 75, *Fax (91) 575 06 31* – ▤. AE ① E VISA JCB. HX k
*closed Sunday and August* – **Meals** - Seafood - a la carte 4700/5950
**Spec.** Salpicón de marisco. Rodaballo. Bogavante plancha.

**El Pescador,** José Ortega y Gasset 75, ✉ 28006, ✆ (91) 402 12 90, *Fax (91) 401 30 26* – ▤. E VISA. JV t
*closed Sunday, Holy Week and August* – **Meals** - Seafood - a la carte 4550/5450
**Spec.** Lenguado Evaristo. Mero al horno. Almejas a la marinera.

**Arganzuela, Carabanchel, Villaverde :** Antonio López, Paseo de Las Delicias, Paseo Santa María de la Cabeza

**Rafael Pirámides,** paseo de las Acacias 40, ✉ 28005, ✆ (91) 517 18 28, *Fax (91) 517 00 90* – ▤ TV ☎ ♿. AE ① E VISA. rest
**Meals** *(closed Saturday, Sunday and August)* 1200 – ☕ 1175 – **84 rm** 11500/14200, 9 suites. S : by Gta. Puerta de Toledo EZ

**Carlton,** paseo de las Delicias 26, ✉ 28045, ✆ (91) 539 71 00, *Telex 44571, Fax (91) 527 85 10* – ▤ TV ☎. AE ① E VISA. GZ n
**Meals** 3300 – ☕ 1450 – **112 rm** 17500/22600.

**Praga** coffee shop only, Antonio López 65, ✉ 28019, ✆ (91) 469 06 00, *Telex 22823, Fax (91) 469 83 25* – ▤ TV ☎ – 25/350. AE ① E VISA JCB.
☕ 850 – **428 rm** 10100/12800. S : by Gta. Puerta de Toledo EZ

**Aramo,** paseo Santa María de la Cabeza 73, ✉ 28045, ✆ (91) 473 91 11, *Telex 45885, Fax (91) 473 92 14* – ▤ TV ☎. AE ① E VISA. rest
**Meals** 1500 – ☕ 1000 – **105 rm** 9600/12000. S : by pl. Emperador Carlos V NZ

**Puerta de Toledo,** glorieta Puerta de Toledo 4, ✉ 28005, ✆ (91) 474 71 00, *Telex 22291, Fax (91) 474 07 47* – ▤ TV ☎ – 25/30. AE ① E VISA JCB. EZ v
**Meals** (see rest. ***Puerta de Toledo*** below) – ☕ 900 – **152 rm** 7600/11600.

**Hontoria,** pl. del General Maroto 2, ✉ 28045, ✆ (91) 473 04 25 – ▤. AE E VISA. S : by Gta. de Embajadores FZ
*closed Sunday, Bank Holidays, Holy Week and August* – **Meals** a la carte 3450/4700.

**Puerta de Toledo,** glorieta Puerta de Toledo 4, ✉ 28005, ✆ (91) 474 76 75, *Fax (91) 474 30 35* – ▤. ① E VISA. EZ v
**Meals** a la carte 3300/3700.

**Moncloa** : Princesa, Paseo del Pintor Rosales, Paseo de la Florida, Casa de Campo

**Meliá Madrid,** Princesa 27, ✉ 28008, ☎ (91) 541 82 00, *Telex 22537, Fax (91) 541 19 88*, – |‡| ▤ TV ☎ – 25/200. AE ⓓ E VISA JCB. ✗ KV t
**Meals** a la carte 3100/5700 – ☕ 2000 – **253 rm** 28300/32500, 23 suites.

**Tryp Monte Real** ⊗, Arroyofresno 17, ✉ 28035, ☎ (91) 316 21 40, *Fax (91) 316 39 34*, « Garden », – |‡| ▤ TV ☎ ⇔ P – 25/250. AE ⓓ E VISA. ✗ NW : 8 km by Av. Puerta de Hierro DV
**Meals** a la carte approx. 4450 – ☕ 1500 – **76 rm** 18350/23000, 4 suites.

**Florida Norte,** paseo de la Florida 5, ✉ 28008, ☎ (91) 542 83 00, *Telex 23675, Fax (91) 547 78 33* – |‡| ▤ TV ☎ ⇔. AE ⓓ E VISA JCB. ✗ DX v
**Meals** 2600 – ☕ 900 – **399 rm** 12000/17000.

**Sofitel-Plaza de España** without rest, Tutor 1, ✉ 28008, ☎ (91) 541 98 80, *Fax (91) 542 57 36* – |‡| ▤ TV ☎. AE ⓓ E VISA JCB KV d
☕ 2000 – **97 rm** 29000/33000.

**Sal Gorda,** Beatriz de Bobadilla 9, ✉ 28040, ☎ (91) 553 95 06 – ▤. AE ⓓ E VISA. ✗
*closed Sunday and August* – **Meals** a la carte 3540/4000. DEU e

**Currito,** Casa de Campo-Pabellón de Vizcaya, ✉ 28011, ☎ (91) 464 57 04, *Fax (91) 479 72 54*, – ▤ P. AE ⓓ VISA. ✗ W : by Feria del Campo DY
*closed Sunday dinner* – **Meals** - Basque rest - a la carte 5000/6300.

**Chamberí** : San Bernardo, Fuencarral, Alberto Aguilera, Santa Engracia

**Santo Mauro,** Zurbano 36, ✉ 28010, ☎ (91) 319 69 00, *Fax (91) 308 54 77*, « Elegant palace with garden », – |‡| ▤ TV ☎ ⇔ – 25/70. AE ⓓ E VISA JCB GV e
*Belagua* : **Meals** a la carte 6500/7500 – ☕ 2500 – **33 rm** 32000/35000, 4 suites.

**Miguel Ángel,** Miguel Ángel 31, ✉ 28010, ☎ (91) 442 00 22, *Telex 44235, Fax (91) 442 53 20*, – |‡| ▤ TV ☎ ⇔ – 25/300. AE ⓓ E VISA JCB. ✗
**Meals** a la carte 3500/6000 – ☕ 2000 – **251 rm** 25200/35700, 20 suites. GV c

**Castellana Inter-Continental,** paseo de la Castellana 49, ✉ 28046, ☎ (91) 310 02 00, *Telex 27686, Fax (91) 319 58 53*, « Garden », – |‡| ▤ TV ☎ ⇔ – 25/550. AE ⓓ E VISA JCB. ✗ GV a
**Meals** a la carte 3695/6930 – ☕ 2500 – **278 rm** 34600/41800, 27 suites.

**Mindanao,** San Francisco de Sales 15, ✉ 28003, ☎ (91) 549 55 00, *Telex 22631, Fax (91) 544 55 96*, – |‡| ▤ TV ☎ ⇔ – 25/200. AE ⓓ E VISA JCB. ✗ DV a
**Meals** *(closed August)* 3750 – ☕ 1600 – **272 rm** 14250/17850, 9 suites.

**Gran Versalles** without rest, Covarrubias 4, ✉ 28010, ☎ (91) 447 57 00, *Telex 49150, Fax (91) 446 39 87* – |‡| ▤ TV ☎ – 25/120. AE ⓓ E VISA. ✗ MV a
☕ 1250 – **143 rm** 15200, 2 suites.

**NH Zurbano,** Zurbano 79, ✉ 28003, ☎ (91) 441 45 00, *Telex 27578, Fax (91) 441 32 24* – |‡| ▤ TV ☎ ⇔ – 25/100. AE ⓓ E VISA JCB. ✗ GV x
**Meals** a la carte 3500/4500 – ☕ 1700 – **266 rm** 16800, 1 suite.

**NH Embajada,** Santa Engracia 5, ✉ 28010, ☎ (91) 594 02 13, *Fax (91) 447 33 12*, « Spanish style building » – |‡| ▤ TV ☎ – 25/45. AE ⓓ E VISA. ✗ MV r
**Meals** 2500 – ☕ 1600 – **101 rm** 16000/17800.

**NH Prisma,** Santa Engracia 120, ✉ 28003, ☎ (91) 441 93 77, *Fax (91) 442 58 51* – |‡| ▤ TV ☎ – 25/70. AE ⓓ E VISA JCB. ✗ FV g
**Meals** a la carte approx. 3750 – ☕ 1700 – **103 suites** 16800.

**NH Argüelles** coffee shop only, Vallehermoso 65, ✉ 28015, ☎ (91) 593 97 77, *Fax (91) 594 27 39* – ▤ TV ☎ ⇔. AE ⓓ E VISA JCB. ✗ EV e
☕ 1500 – **75 rm** 13900/15400.

**Escultor,** Miguel Ángel 3, ✉ 28010, ☎ (91) 310 42 03, *Fax (91) 319 25 84* – |‡| ▤ TV ☎ – 25/150. AE ⓓ E VISA. ✗ GV s
**Meals** a la carte approx. 3800 – ☕ 1300 – **79 rm** 19950/24675, 3 suites.

**Sol Inn Alondras** coffee shop only, José Abascal 8, ✉ 28003, ☎ (91) 447 40 00, *Telex 49454, Fax (91) 593 88 00* – |‡| ▤ TV ☎. AE ⓓ VISA. ✗ FV a
☕ 975 – **72 rm** 17220/20790.

**Jockey,** Amador de los Ríos 6, ✉ 28010, ☎ (91) 319 24 35, *Fax (91) 319 24 35* – ▤. AE ⓓ E VISA JCB. ✗ NV k
*closed Saturday lunch, Sunday, Bank Holidays and August* – **Meals** a la carte 6500/10050
**Spec.** Huevos escalfados a la muselina de trufas. Lomos de lubina en papillote. Pichón de sangre a la parrilla con patatas paja.

**Las Cuatro Estaciones,** General Ibáñez de Íbero 5, ✉ 28003, ☎ (91) 553 63 05, *Fax (91) 553 32 98*, « Modern decor » – ▤. AE ⓓ E VISA JCB. ✗ EU r
*closed Saturday lunch, Sunday and August* – **Meals** 4500 and a la carte 4580/5880
**Spec.** Espárragos verdes a la plancha con langostinos (season). Arroz negro con chipirones. Foie a las uvas.

**Lur Maitea,** Fernando el Santo 4, ✉ 28010, ☎ (91) 308 03 50, *Fax (91) 308 03 93* – ▤. AE ⓓ E VISA. ✗ MV u
*closed Saturday lunch, Sunday, Bank Holidays and August* – **Meals** - Basque rest - a la carte 4900/5950.

**Annapurna,** Zurbano 5, ✉ 28010, ☎ (91) 308 32 49, *Fax (91) 308 32 49* – ▤. AE ⓓ E VISA. ✗ MV w
*closed Saturday lunch, Sunday and Bank Holidays* – **Meals** - Indian rest - a la carte approx. 3990.

**Solchaga,** pl. Alonso Martínez 2, ✉ 28004, ☎ (91) 447 14 96, *Fax (91) 593 22 23* – ▤. AE E VISA. ✗ MV x
*closed Saturday lunch, Sunday and August* – **Meals** a la carte 4100/5500.

**Kulixka,** Fuencarral 124, ✉ 28010, ☎ (91) 447 25 38 – ▤. AE ⓓ E VISA JCB. ✗ FV v
*closed Sunday and August* – **Meals** - Seafood - a la carte 3800/5500.

**Polizón,** Viriato 39, ✉ 28010, ☎ (91) 593 39 19 – ▤. AE ⓓ E VISA JCB. ✗ FV w
*closed Sunday in summer, Sunday dinner the rest of the year and August* – **Meals** - Seafood - a la carte 3425/4350.

**La Plaza de Chamberí,** pl. de Chamberí 10, ✉ 28010, ☎ (91) 446 06 97 – ▤. AE ⓓ E VISA JCB FV k
*closed Sunday* – **Meals** a la carte 3650/4300.

**La Fuente Quince,** Modesto Lafuente 15, ✉ 28003, ☎ (91) 399 14 75, *Fax (91) 441 90 24* – ▤. AE ⓓ E VISA. ✗ FV j
*closed Saturday lunch, Sunday and August* – **Meals** a la carte 3150/4150.

**Doña,** Zurbano 59, ✉ 28010, ☎ (91) 319 25 51, *Fax (91) 441 90 20* – ▤. AE E VISA. ✗
*closed Sunday dinner and 15 to 31 August* – **Meals** a la carte 2800/3500. GV h

**Pinocchio,** Orfila 2, ✉ 28010, ☎ (91) 308 16 47, *Fax (91) 766 98 04* – ▤. AE ⓓ E VISA. ✗ NV d
*closed Saturday lunch, Sunday, Bank Holidays and August* – **Meals** - Italian rest - a la carte 3030/3835.

**Balear,** Sagunto 18, ✉ 28010, ☎ (91) 447 91 15 – ▤. AE E VISA. ✗ FV y
*closed Sunday dinner and Monday dinner* – **Meals** - Rice dishes - a la carte 3450/4500.

**La Despensa,** Cardenal Cisneros 6, ✉ 28010, ☎ (91) 446 17 94 – ▤. AE ⓓ E VISA. ✗ FV p
*closed Sunday and Monday dinner in summer, Sunday dinner and Monday the rest of the year and September* – **Meals** a la carte 2450/3200.

**Chamartín, Tetuán :** Paseo de la Castellana, Capitán Haya, Orense, Alberto Alcocer, Paseo de la Habana

**Meliá Castilla,** Capitán Haya 43, ✉ 28020, ☎ (91) 567 50 00, *Telex 23142, Fax (91) 567 50 51,* – ▤ – 25/800. AE ⓓ E VISA JCB. ✗ GS c
**Meals** (see rest – ***L'Albufera*** and rest – ***La Fragata*** below) – 2400 – **896 rm** 28200/32400, 14 suites.

**Holiday Inn Madrid,** pl. Carlos Trías Beltrán 4 (entrance by Orense 22-24), ✉ 28020, ☎ (91) 456 80 00, *Fax (91) 456 80 01,* – ▤ – 25/400. AE ⓓ E VISA JCB. ✗ rest GT z
***La Terraza :*** **Meals** a la carte 3850/5250 - ***Big Blue :*** **Meals** a la carte 4035/4585 – 2150 – **282 rm** 26695/29795, 31 suites.

**NH Eurobuilding,** Padre Damián 23, ✉ 28036, ☎ (91) 345 45 00, *Telex 22548, Fax (91) 345 45 76,* « Garden and terrace with », – ▤ – 25/900. AE ⓓ E VISA JCB. ✗ HS a
***La Taberna :*** **Meals** a la carte 4700/5700 - ***Le Relais :*** **Meals** a la carte 3200/4500 – 2000 – **416 rm** 25250/30850, 84 suites.

**Cuzco** coffee shop only, paseo de la Castellana 133, ✉ 28046, ☎ (91) 556 06 00, *Telex 22464, Fax (91) 556 03 72,* – ▤ – 25/450. AE ⓓ E VISA. ✗ GS a
1190 – **320 rm** 18900/23625, 8 suites.

**Augusta,** López de Hoyos 143, ✉ 28002, ☎ (91) 519 91 91, *Fax (91) 519 67 73* – ▤ – 25/80. AE E VISA. ✗ NE : by López de Hoyos HU
**Meals** 1980 – 1025 – **120 suites** 14850/17600.

**Chamartín,** Chamartín railway station, ✉ 28036, ☎ (91) 334 49 00, *Telex 49201, Fax (91) 733 02 14* – ▤ – 25/500. AE ⓓ VISA JCB. ✗ HR
**Meals** (see rest. ***Cota 13*** below) – 1400 – **360 rm** 16500/19100, 18 suites.

**NH La Habana,** paseo de la Habana 73, ✉ 28036, ☎ (91) 345 82 84, *Fax (91) 457 75 79* – ▤ – 25/250. AE ⓓ E VISA JCB. ✗ rest HT f
**Meals** a la carte 3600/5050 – 1800 – **157 rm** 16000/17800.

**Orense,** Pedro Teixeira 5, ✉ 28020, ✆ (91) 597 15 68, *Fax (91) 597 12 95* – AE ⓓ E VISA. GT q
Meals 1300 – ☕ 1150 – **140 rm** 20175/24335.

**Foxá 32,** Agustín de Foxá 32, ✉ 28036, ✆ (91) 733 10 60, *Fax (91) 314 11 65* – 25/250. AE ⓓ E VISA. HR u
Meals 3700 – ☕ 1200 – **63 rm** 19000, 98 suites.

**Foxá 25,** Agustín de Foxá 25, ✉ 28036, ✆ (91) 323 11 19, *Fax (91) 314 53 11* – AE ⓓ E VISA. HR a
Meals 3700 – ☕ 1200 – **121 suites** 19000.

**Castilla Plaza,** paseo de la Castellana 220, ✉ 28046, ✆ (91) 323 11 86, *Fax (91) 315 54 06* – 25/150. AE ⓓ E VISA. GS n
Meals 2500 – ☕ 1450 – **147 rm** 23600/25400.

**El Gran Atlanta** without rest, Comandante Zorita 34, ✉ 28020, ✆ (91) 553 59 00, *Fax (91) 533 08 58,* – 25/120. AE ⓓ E VISA. FT p
☕ 1200 – **180 rm** 18800/23500.

**El Jardín** without rest, carret. N I-km 5'7 (entrance by M 40-service road), ✉ 28050, ✆ (91) 302 83 36, *Fax (91) 766 86 91,* AE ⓓ E VISA
**41 suites** ☕ 11000/12500. N : by M 30 HR

**Aristos,** av. Pío XII-34, ✉ 28016, ✆ (91) 345 04 50, *Fax (91) 345 10 23* – AE ⓓ E VISA JCB. HS d
Meals (see rest. ***El Chaflán*** below) – ☕ 900 – **24 rm** 15200/19000, 1 suite.

**La Residencia de El Viso** without rest, Nervión 8, ✉ 28002, ✆ (91) 564 03 70, *Fax (91) 564 19 65* – AE ⓓ E VISA. HU c
Meals 1700 – ☕ 750 – **12 rm** 9000/16000.

**Zalacaín,** Álvarez de Baena 4, ✉ 28006, ✆ (91) 561 48 40, *Fax (91) 561 47 32,* – AE ⓓ E VISA JCB. GV b
*closed Saturday lunch, Sunday, Bank Holidays, Holy Week and August* – **Meals** 6950 and a la carte 6050/8800
**Spec.** Lasagna de hongos y foie. Suprema de lubina al Noilly Prat. Gratinado de frutas de temporada.

**Príncipe y Serrano,** Serrano 240, ✉ 28016, ✆ (91) 458 62 31, *Fax (91) 458 62 31* – AE ⓓ E VISA. HT a
*closed Saturday lunch, Sunday and August* – **Meals** a la carte 5200/7300.

**La Máquina,** Sor Ángela de la Cruz 22, ✉ 28020, ✆ (91) 572 33 18, *Fax (91) 570 13 04* – AE ⓓ VISA. FS e
*closed Sunday* – **Meals** a la carte 4450/5200.

**El Bodegón,** Pinar 15, ✉ 28006, ✆ (91) 562 88 44 – AE ⓓ E VISA. GV q
*closed Saturday lunch, Sunday and August* – **Meals** a la carte 6200/7650.

**Príncipe de Viana,** Manuel de Falla 5, ✉ 28036, ✆ (91) 457 15 49, *Fax (91) 457 52 83,* – AE ⓓ E VISA JCB. GT c
*closed Saturday lunch, Sunday, Bank Holidays, Holy Week and August* – **Meals** - Basque rest - a la carte 5200/5775
**Spec.** Ensalada de salmonetes con aceite de calabacín. Bacalao con patatas y puerro. Costillar de cordero a la diabla.

**Nicolasa,** Velázquez 150, ✉ 28002, ✆ (91) 563 17 35, *Fax (91) 564 32 75* – AE ⓓ E VISA. HU a
**Meals** a la carte approx. 6100.

**O'Pazo,** Reina Mercedes 20, ✉ 28020, ✆ (91) 553 23 33, *Fax (91) 554 90 72* – E VISA. FT p
*closed Sunday and August* – **Meals** - Seafood - a la carte 4500/5650
**Spec.** Cocochas en salsa verde. Rapito al horno. Filloas.

**L'Albufera,** Capitán Haya 43, ✉ 28020, ✆ (91) 567 51 97, *Fax (91) 567 50 51* – AE ⓓ E VISA JCB. GS c
**Meals** - Rice dishes - a la carte 4550/6100.

**La Fragata,** Capitán Haya 43, ✉ 28020, ✆ (91) 567 51 96 – AE ⓓ E VISA JCB.
*closed Bank Holidays and August* – **Meals** a la carte approx. 5950. GS c

**José Luis,** Rafael Salgado 11, ✉ 28036, ✆ (91) 457 50 36, *Fax (91) 344 18 37* – AE ⓓ E VISA. GT m
*closed Sunday and August* – **Meals** a la carte approx. 5500.

**La Misión,** Comandante Zorita 6, ✉ 28020, ✆ (91) 533 27 57, *Fax (91) 534 50 90* – AE ⓓ VISA. FTU s
*closed Saturday lunch, Sunday and 9 to 24 August* – **Meals** a la carte 3650/4625.

**Bogavante,** Capitán Haya 20, ✉ 28020, ✆ (91) 556 21 14, *Fax (91) 597 00 79* – AE ⓓ E VISA JCB. GT d
*closed Sunday dinner* – **Meals** - Seafood - a la carte 4300/6650.

XXX **Vandelvira,** Suero de Quiñones 42, ✉ 28002, ☎ (91) 411 01 18, *Fax (91) 411 01 17* – ▤. AE ⓓ E VISA HTU k
*closed Saturday lunch, Sunday and August* – **Meals** a la carte 4000/4250.

XXX **Señorío de Alcocer,** av. de Alberto Alcocer 1, ✉ 28036, ☎ (91) 345 16 96, *Fax (91) 345 16 96* – ▤. AE ⓓ E VISA. ✻ GS e
*closed Saturday lunch, Sunday, Bank Holidays and 15 days in August* – **Meals** a la carte 4400/6100.

XXX ✿ **El Olivo,** General Gallegos 1, ✉ 28036, ☎ (91) 359 15 35, *Fax (91) 345 91 83* – ▤. AE ⓓ E VISA JCB HS c
*closed Sunday, Monday and 15 to 31 August* – **Meals** 5600 and a la carte 4800/5900
**Spec.** Pastel de verduritas con langosta y su vinagreta de aceitunas negras. Lamprea a la bordelesa (February-March). Foie gras caliente con salsa de Pedro Ximénez.

XXX ✿ **Goizeko Kabi,** Comandante Zorita 37, ✉ 28020, ☎ (91) 533 01 85, *Fax (91) 533 02 14* – ▤. AE ⓓ E VISA. ✻ FT a
*closed Saturday lunch (20 June-20 August) and Sunday* – **Meals** - Basque rest - a la carte 5800/7780
**Spec.** Terrina de foie gras. Txipirones encebollados. Bacalao al estilo de la casa.

XXX **Cabo Mayor,** Juan Ramón Jiménez 37, ✉ 28036, ☎ (91) 350 87 76, *Fax (91) 359 16 21* – ▤. AE ⓓ E VISA. ✻ GHS r
*closed Saturday lunch, Sunday, Holy Week and 7 days in August* – **Meals** a la carte 5200/7100.

XXX **Blanca de Navarra,** av. de Brasil 13, ✉ 28020, ☎ (91) 555 10 29 – ▤. AE ⓓ E VISA
*closed Sunday, Holy Week and August* – **Meals** a la carte approx. 5400. GT q

XXX **Lutecia,** Corazón de María 78, ✉ 28002, ☎ (91) 519 34 15 – ▤. AE ⓓ E VISA. ✻ NE : by López de Hoyos HU
*closed Saturday lunch, Sunday, Bank Holidays and August* – **Meals** a la carte 3100/3650.

XXX **Aldaba,** av. de Alberto Alcocer 5, ✉ 28036, ☎ (91) 345 21 93 – ▤. AE ⓓ E VISA GS e
*closed Saturday lunch, Sunday and August* – **Meals** a la carte 4775/6000.

XXX **El Foque,** Suero de Quiñones 22, ✉ 28002, ☎ (91) 519 25 72, *Fax (91) 519 52 61* – ▤. AE ⓓ E VISA. ✻ HU r
*closed Sunday* – **Meals** - Cod dishes - a la carte 4300/4750.

XX **Combarro,** Reina Mercedes 12, ✉ 28020, ☎ (91) 554 77 84, *Fax (91) 534 25 01* – ▤. AE ⓓ E VISA JCB. ✻ FT a
*closed Sunday dinner and August* – **Meals** - Seafood - a la carte 4600/7800.

XX **La Tahona,** Capitán Haya 21 (side), ✉ 28020, ☎ (91) 555 04 41, *Fax (91) 556 62 02,* « Castilian medieval decor » – ▤. AE ⓓ E VISA. ✻ GT u
*closed Sunday dinner and August* – **Meals** - Roast lamb - a la carte 3400/3975.

XX **De Funy,** Serrano 213, ✉ 28016, ☎ (91) 457 95 22, *Fax (91) 458 85 84,* 🏠 – ▤. AE ⓓ E VISA. ✻ HT z
**Meals** - Lebanese rest - a la carte 3700/5050.

XX **Gaztelupe,** Comandante Zorita 32, ✉ 28020, ☎ (91) 534 90 28 – ▤. AE ⓓ E VISA. ✻
*closed Sunday (20 June-15 August) and Sunday dinner the rest of the year* – **Meals** - Basque rest - a la carte 5100/5600. FT p

XX **Asador Frontón II,** Pedro Muguruza 8, ✉ 28036, ☎ (91) 345 36 96, *Fax (91) 350 95 33* – ▤. AE ⓓ E VISA. ✻ HS c
*closed Sunday dinner* – **Meals** a la carte 4200/6050.

XX **Carta Marina,** Padre Damián 40, ✉ 28036, ☎ (91) 458 68 26, *Fax (91) 350 78 83* – ▤. AE ⓓ E VISA JCB. ✻ HS k
*closed Sunday and August* – **Meals** a la carte 4450/5650.

XX **El Telégrafo,** Padre Damián 44, ✉ 28036, ☎ (91) 350 61 19, *Fax (91) 401 34 43,* « Designed to look like the inside of a boat » – ▤. AE ⓓ E VISA. ✻ HS e
**Meals** - Seafood - a la carte 3750/5100.

XX **Serramar,** Rosario Pino 12, ✉ 28020, ☎ (91) 570 07 90, *Fax (91) 570 48 09* – ▤. AE ⓓ E VISA. ✻ GS k
*closed Sunday* – **Meals** - Seafood - a la carte 4100/4500.

XX **Sacha,** Juan Hurtado de Mendoza 11 (back), ✉ 28036, ☎ (91) 345 59 52, 🏠 – ▤. AE ⓓ VISA. ✻ GHS r
*closed Sunday, Holy Week and 10 to 31 August* – **Meals** a la carte 3850/6550.

XX **Rianxo,** Oruro 11, ✉ 28016, ☎ (91) 457 10 06, *Fax (91) 457 22 04* – ▤. AE ⓓ E VISA. ✻
*closed Sunday in August* – **Meals** - Galician rest - a la carte 3900/6350. HT h

XX **El Chaflán,** av. Pío XII-34, ✉ 28016, ☎ (91) 350 61 93, *Fax (91) 345 10 23,* 🏠 – ▤. AE ⓓ E VISA JCB. ✻ HS d
*closed Sunday dinner and Holy Week* – **Meals** a la carte 4100/5000.

XX **La Broche,** Dr. Fleming 36, ✉ 28036, ☎ (91) 457 99 60 – ▤. AE ⓓ E VISA GS z
*closed Saturday lunch, Sunday, Holy Week and August* – **Meals** a la carte 3900/4950.

**Asador de Roa,** Pintor Juan Gris 5, ✉ 28020, ☎ (91) 555 39 28, *Fax (91) 555 86 29* - AE VISA. GT d
Meals a la carte 3500/4400.

**House of Ming,** paseo de la Castellana 74, ✉ 28046, ☎ (91) 561 10 13, *Fax (91) 561 98 27* - AE E VISA. GV f
Meals - Chinese rest - a la carte 2805/3565.

**La Ancha,** Príncipe de Vergara 204, ✉ 28002, ☎ (91) 563 89 77, - AE E VISA JCB. HT r
*closed Sunday, Bank Holidays, Holy Week and Christmas* – **Meals** a la carte 3400/4900.

**El Asador de Aranda,** pl. de Castilla 3, ✉ 28046, ☎ (91) 733 87 02, *Fax (91) 556 62 02,* « Castilian decor » – AE E VISA. GS b
*closed Sunday dinner and 17 August-13 September* – Meals - Roast lamb - a la carte approx. 3950.

**Zacarías de Santander,** Rosario Pino 17, ✉ 28020, ☎ (91) 571 28 86, *Fax (91) 548 30 70,* – AE E VISA. GS f
Meals a la carte 4450/7400.

**Casa Benigna,** Benigno Soto 9, ✉ 28002, ☎ (91) 413 33 56, *Fax (91) 416 93 57* – AE E VISA HT u
Meals a la carte 4000/5300.

**El Cenachero,** Manuel de Falla 8, ✉ 28036, ☎ (91) 457 59 04 – AE E VISA. GT r
*closed Saturday lunch, Sunday, Holy Week and August* – Meals a la carte 3025/4275.

## Environs

**on the road to the airport** *E : 12,5 km* – ✉ *28042 Madrid :*

**Tryp Diana,** Galeón 27 (Alameda de Osuna) ☎ (91) 747 13 55, *Telex 45688, Fax (91) 747 97 97,* – 25/220. AE E VISA JCB. rest
Meals 2000 - ***Asador Duque de Osuna*** *(closed Sunday, Bank Holidays and August)* **Meals** a la carte 3100/4500 – 1500 – **220 rm** 13450/16800, 40 suites.

**by motorway N VI** – ✉ *28023 Madrid :*

**Concordy** coffee shop only, at the junction of the N VI and M 40 - El Plantío - NW : 11,7 km ☎ (91) 307 65 54, *Fax (91) 372 81 95* – E VISA.
300 – **22 rm** 6000/9000.

**Gaztelubide,** Sopelana 13 - La Florida - NW : 12,8 km ☎ (91) 372 85 44, *Fax (91) 372 84 19,* – AE E VISA.
*closed Sunday dinner* – **Meals** - Basque rest - a la carte approx. 5500.

**Los Remos,** La Florida - NW : 13 km ☎ (91) 307 72 30, *Fax (91) 372 84 35* – AE E VISA.
Meals - Seafood - a la carte 4500/5400.

**Hacienda Santa Fé,** av. de la Victoria 46 - El Plantío - NW : 13,7 km ☎ (91) 307 66 03, *Fax (91) 372 91 95,* – AE E VISA.
*closed Sunday dinner and Monday in winter, Sunday and Monday lunch the rest of the year* – **Meals** a la carte 3050/4200.

**by motorway N I** *N : 13 km* – ✉ *28100 Alcobendas :*

**La Moraleja** without rest, av. de Europa 17 - parque empresarial La Moraleja ☎ (91) 661 80 55, *Fax (91) 661 21 88,* – AE E VISA.
1350 – **37 suites** 25600.

**at Barajas** *E : 14 km* – ✉ *28042 Madrid :*

**Barajas,** av. de Logroño 305 ☎ (91) 747 77 00, *Telex 22255, Fax (91) 747 87 17,* – 25/675. AE E VISA JCB. rest
Meals 4350 – **218 rm** 16950/20850, 12 suites.

**Alameda,** av. de Logroño 100 ☎ (91) 747 48 00, *Telex 43809, Fax (91) 747 89 28,* – 25/280. AE E VISA JCB. rest
Meals a la carte approx. 4400 – 1300 – **136 rm** 18750/23500, 9 suites.

**Moralzarzal** *28411 Madrid* 444 J 18 – *pop. 2 248 alt. 979.*
*Madrid 42.*

**El Cenador de Salvador,** av. de España 30 ☎ (91) 857 77 22, *Fax (91) 857 77 80,* « Garden terrace » – AE VISA.
*closed Sunday dinner, Monday and 1 to 15 October* – **Meals** 6000 and a la carte 5775/7725
**Spec.** Ensalada de bacalao con salsa de toronja y mango. Infusión especiada de percebes y vieiras. Lubina en celosía de arroz con emulsión de acelgas.

**BARCELONA** *08000* P 443 H36 – *pop. 1681132.*

**See** : *Gothic Quarter★★ (Barri Gòtic : Cathedral★* MX, *No 10 Carrer del Paradis (Roman columns★)* MX **135**, *Plaça del Rei★★* MX **149**, *Museum of the City's History★ (The Roman City★★)* MX **M**[1], *Santa Ágata Chapel★ (Altarpiece of the Constable★★)* MX **F**, *Rei Martí Belvedere ≤★★* MX **K**, *Frederic Marès Museum★* MX **M**[2] – *La Rambla★★ : Barcelona Contemporary Art Museum★★ (MACBA)* HX **M**[10], *Barcelona Contemporary Culture Centre (CCCB) : patio★* HX **R**, *(Former) Hospital of Santa Creu (Gothic patio★)* LY, *Santa Maria del Pi Church★* LX, *Güell Palace★★* LY, *Plaça Reial★★* MY – *The Sea Front★ : Shipyards (Drassanes) and Maritime Museum★★* MY, *Old Harbour★ (Port Vell)* NY, *Mercè Basilica★* NY, *La Llotja★ (Gothic Hall★★)* NX, *França Station★* NVX, *Ciutadella Park★* NV, KX *(Three Dragons Pavilion★★* NV **M**[7], *Zoology Museum★* NV **M**[7], *Zoo★* KX*)* – *La Barceloneta★* KXY, *Vila Olímpica★ (marina★★, twin towers ✻★★★) E : by Av. D'Icària* KX, *Carrer de Montcada★★ : Picasso Museum★* NV, *Santa Maria del Mar Church★★ (rose window★)* NX – *Montjüic★ (≤★ from castle terraces) S : by Av. de la Reina María Cristina* GY *: Mies van der Rohe Pavilion★★, National Museum of Catalonian Art★★★, Spanish Village★ (Poble Espanyol), Anella Olímpica★ (Olympic Stadium★, Sant Jordi Sports Centre★★)* – *Joan Miró Foundation★★★, Greek Theatre★, Archaeological Museum★* – *Eixample District★★ : La Sagrada Familia Church★★★ (East or Nativity Façade★★, ≤★★ from east spire)* JU, *Hospital Sant Pau★ N : by Padilla* JU, *Passeig de Gràcia★★* HV *(Lleó Morera House★* HV **Y**, *Amatller House★* HV **Y**, *Batlló House★★* HV **Y**, *La Pedrera or Milà House★★★* HV **P***)* – *Terrades or les Punxes House★* HV **Q**, *Güell Park★★ (rolling bench★★) N : by Padilla* JU – *Catalonian Concert Hall★★ (Palau de la Misica Catalana : façade★, inverted cupola★★)* MV - *Antoni Tàpies Foundation★★* HV **S**.

**Additional sights** : *Santa Maria de Pedralbes Monastery★★ (Church★, Cloisters★, Sant Miquel Chapel frescoes★★★, Thyssen Bornemisza Collection★) W : by Av. de Pedralbes* EV, *Pedralbes Palace (Ceramics Museum★)* EX – *Güell Stables★ (Pabellones)* EX, *Sant Pau del Camp Church (Cloister★)* LY.

18, 18 *Prat SW : 16 km ☎ (93) 379 02 78* – 18 *Sant Cugat NW : 20 km ☎ (93) 674 39 08, Fax (93) 675 51 52.*

✈ *Barcelona SW : 12 km ☎ (93) 298 38 38* – *Iberia : Passeig de Gràcia 30,* ✉ *08007, ☎ (93) 412 56 67* HV – *and Aviaco : Airport ☎ (93) 478 24 11.*

🚗 *Sants ☎ (93) 490 75 91.*

⛴ *to the Balearic Islands : Cía. Trasmediterránea, Moll de Barcelona - Estació Marítima,* ✉ *08039, ☎ (93) 443 25 32, Fax (93) 443 27 81.*

ℹ *pl. de Catalunya 17-S* ✉ *08002 ☎ (93) 304 31 34 Fax (93) 304 31 55 Sants Estació, ☎ (93) 491 44 31 and at Airport ☎ (93) 478 05 75* – R.A.C.C. *Santaló 8,* ✉ *08021, ☎ (93) 200 33 11, Fax (93) 414 31 63.*

*Madrid 627 – Bilbao/Bilbo 607 – Lérida/Lleida 169 – Perpignan 187 – Tarragona 109 – Toulouse 388 – Valencia 361 – Zaragoza 307.*

Plans on following pages

**Old Town and the Gothic Quarter** : Ramblas, Pl. de Catalunya, Via Laietana, Pl. St. Jaume, Passeig de Colom, Passeig de Joan Borbó Comte de Barcelona

**Le Meridien Barcelona,** La Rambla 111, ✉ 08002, ☎ (93) 318 62 00, *Telex 54634, Fax (93) 301 77 76* – |♦| ▤ TV ☎ ♿ 🚗 – 🏛 25/200. AE ⓓ E VISA JCB LX b
**Meals** a la carte 3850/6350 – ☕ 2350 – **198 rm** 24000/30000, 7 suites.

**Colón,** av. de la Catedral 7, ✉ 08002, ☎ (93) 301 14 04, *Telex 52654, Fax (93) 317 29 15* – |♦| ▤ TV ☎ ♿ – 🏛 25/120. AE ⓓ E VISA JCB. ⚡ rest MV e
**Meals** 3500 – ☕ 1700 – **138 rm** 15500/23000, 9 suites.

**Rivoli Rambla,** La Rambla 128, ✉ 08002, ☎ (93) 302 66 43, *Telex 99222, Fax (93) 317 20 38,* Lδ – |♦| ▤ TV ☎ ♿ – 🏛 25/180. AE ⓓ E VISA. ⚡ LX r
**Meals** 3500 – ☕ 1900 – **81 rm** 19000/24000, 9 suites.

**Royal** coffee shop only, La Rambla 117, ✉ 08002, ☎ (93) 301 94 00, *Telex 97565, Fax (93) 317 31 79* – |♦| ▤ TV ☎ 🚗 – 🏛 25/100. AE ⓓ E VISA JCB. ⚡ LX e
☕ 1500 – **108 rm** 20000/23000.

**Meliá Confort Apolo** without rest, av. del Paral.lel 57, ✉ 08004, ☎ (93) 443 11 22, *Fax (93) 443 00 59* – |♦| ▤ TV ☎ ♿ P – 🏛 25/500. AE ⓓ E VISA JCB. ⚡ LY e
☕ 1000 – **314 rm** 16000/20000.

**Ambassador,** Pintor Fortuny 13, ✉ 08001, ☎ (93) 412 05 30, *Telex 99222, Fax (93) 317 20 38,* Lδ, 🏊 – |♦| ▤ TV ☎ ♿ 🚗 – 🏛 25/200. AE ⓓ E VISA. ⚡ LX v
**Meals** 3000 – ☕ 1600 – **96 rm** 17000/21000, 9 suites.

**Duques de Bergara,** Bergara 11, ✉ 08002, ☎ (93) 301 51 51, *Fax (93) 317 34 42* – |♦| ▤ TV ☎ – 🏛 25/80. AE ⓓ E VISA JCB. ⚡ LV f
**Meals** 1900 – ☕ 1200 – **51 rm** 16800/20200.

**G.H. Barcino** without rest, Jaume I-6, ✉ 08002, ☎ (93) 302 20 12, *Fax (93) 301 42 42* – |♦| ▤ TV ☎ ♿. AE ⓓ E VISA JCB MX r
☕ 1760 – **53 rm** 19360/24200.

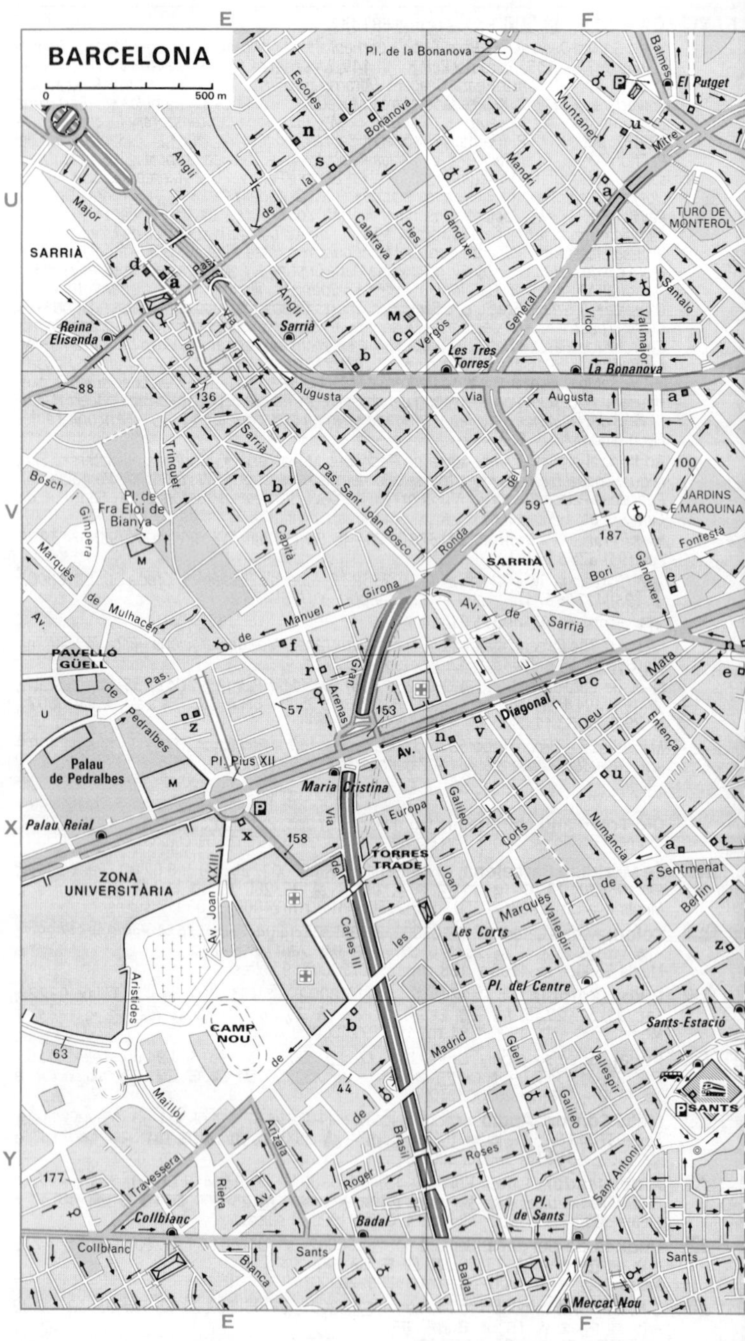
BARCELONA
0
500 m
E
F
U
V
X
Y
Pl. de la Bonanova
El Putget
Balmes
Muntaner
Mitre
Mandri
Escoles
Bonanova
Angli
Major
SARRIÀ
de
la
Calatrava
Pies
Ganduxer
TURÓ DE MONTEROL
Santaló
Vico
Vallmajor
General
Vergós
Les Tres Torres
La Bonanova
Reina Elisenda
Sarrià
Pas.
Via
Augusta
88
136
Trinquet
Pas. Sant Joan Bosco
Ronda
del
Via
Augusta
100
JARDINS E.MARQUINA
59
187
Fontestà
Bosch
Gimpera
Pl. de Fra Eloi de Bianya
Marquès
de
Mulhacén
Capità
Girona
SARRIÀ
Bori
Ganduxer
Av.
de
Sarrià
Manuel
de
PAVELLÓ GÜELL
Pas.
de
Pedralbes
Gran
Arenas
57
153
Diagonal
Av.
Deu
Mata
Entença
Palau de Pedralbes
Pl. Pius XII
Maria Cristina
Via
Europa
Galileo
Corts
Numància
Palau Reial
158
TORRES TRADE
del
ZONA UNIVERSITÀRIA
Av. Joan XXIII
Carles III
Joan
les
Sentmenat
de
Berlín
Marquès
Vallespir
Les Corts
Aristides
Pl. del Centre
Sants-Estació
CAMP NOU
de
Madrid
Güell
Vallespir
63
44
de
Maillol
Arizala
Brasil
Galileo
SANTS
Travessera
Roses
Sant Antoni
177
Riera
Av.
Roger
Pl. de Sants
Collblanc
Badal
Collblanc
Blanca
Sants
Badal
Sants
Mercat Nou

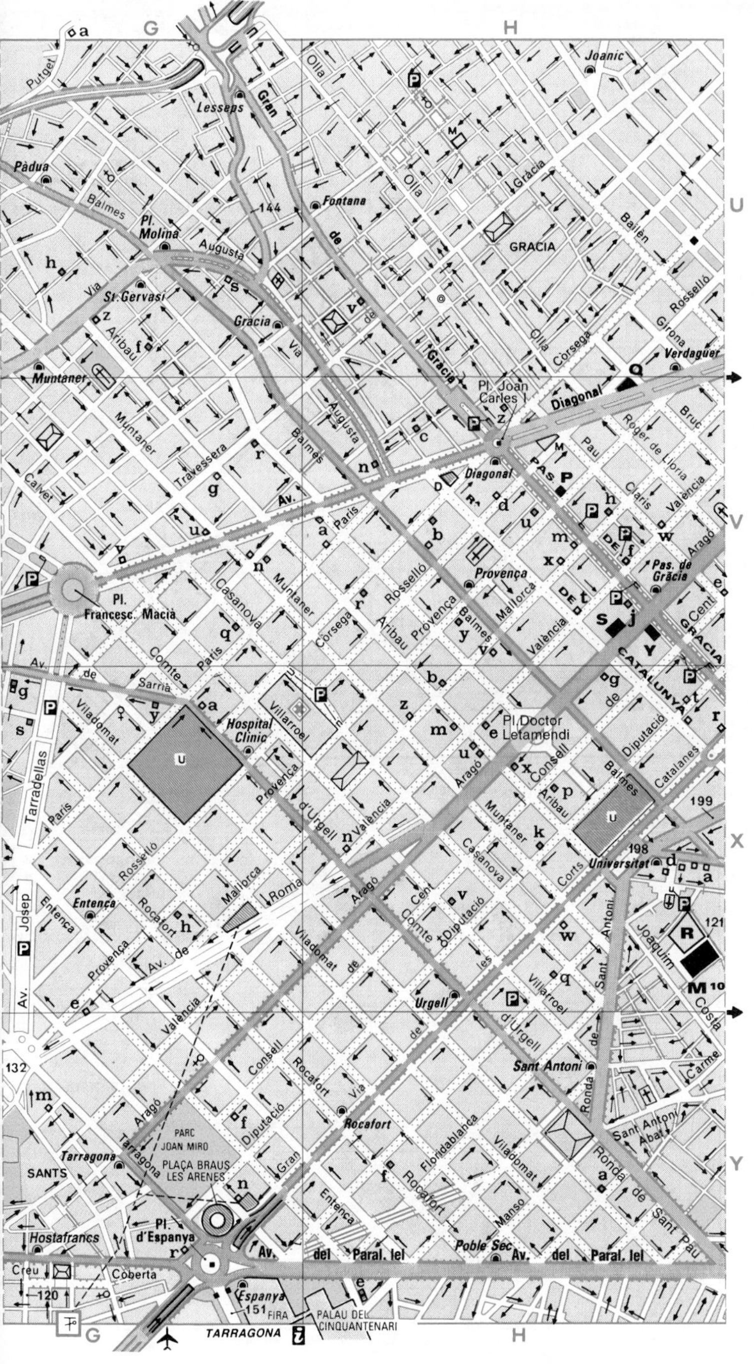
G
H
U
V
X
Y
Joanic
Lesseps
Gran
de
Gràcia
Olla
Pàdua
Balmes
Pl. Molina
Augusta
Fontana
GRACIA
Bailèn
Rosselló
Girona
Verdaguer
Via
St. Gervasi
Gracia
Aribau
Muntaner
Còrsega
Pl. Joan Carles I
Diagonal
Bruc
Roger de Llúria
Pau
Claris
València
Travessera
Calvet
Av.
Paris
Pl. Francesc. Macià
Casanova
Provença
Mallorca
Pas. de Gràcia
Cent
CATALUNYA
Comte
Sarrià
Viladomat
Tarradellas
Hospital Clinic
Villarroel
Pl. Doctor Letamendi
Consell
Diputació
Catalanes
Aragó
d'Urgell
Universitat
Corts
Sant Antoni
Joaquim
Costa
Roma
Entença
Rocafort
Josep
Urgell
Sant Antoni
Ronda de
Carme
Sant Antoni Abat
Floridablanca
Manso
Ronda de Sant Pau
Poble Sec
Av. del Paral. lel
Tarragona
SANTS
PARC JOAN MIRÓ
PLAÇA BRAUS LES ARENES
Pl. d'Espanya
Hostafrancs
Creu
Coberta
Espanya
FIRA
PALAU DEL CINQUANTENARI
TARRAGONA
144
199
198
121
132
120
151

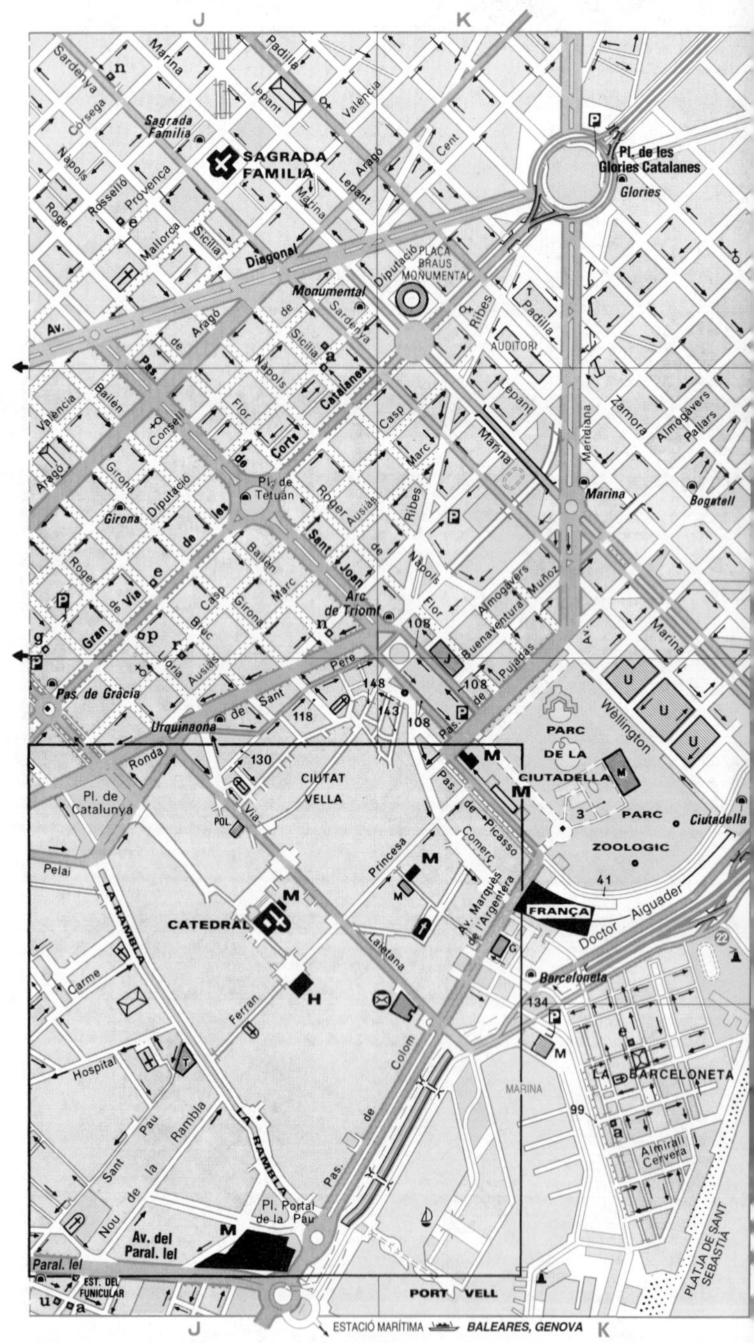
J
K
SAGRADA FAMILIA
Sagrada Familia
Pl. de les Glories Catalanes
Glories
Diagonal
PLAÇA BRAUS MONUMENTAL
Monumental
AUDITORI
Pl. de Tetuan
Girona
Marina
Bogatell
Arc de Triomf
Pas. de Gràcia
Urquinaona
PARC DE LA CIUTADELLA
PARC ZOOLOGIC
Ciutadella
CIUTAT VELLA
Pl. de Catalunya
CATEDRAL
LA RAMBLA
FRANÇA
Barceloneta
LA BARCELONETA
MARINA
Pl. Portal de la Pau
Av. del Paral. lel
Paral. lel
EST. DEL FUNICULAR
PORT VELL
PLATJA DE SANT SEBASTIÀ
ESTACIÓ MARÍTIMA
BALEARES, GENOVA

## STREET INDEX TO BARCELONA TOWN PLAN

# BARCELONA

| Street | Grid | No. |
|---|---|---|
| Caputxins (Rambla dels) | MY | 35 |
| Catalunya (Pl. de) | LV | |
| Estudis (Rambla dels) | LX | |
| Sant Josep (Rambla de) | LX | 168 |
| Santa Mònica (Rambla de) | MY | |
| Universitat (Ronda de la) | LV | 199 |
| Bacardí (Pas.) | MY | 4 |
| Banys Nous | MX | 7 |
| Bergara | LV | 10 |
| Bisbe Irurita | MX | 15 |
| Bòria | MV | 18 |
| Born (Pas. del) | NX | 20 |
| Boters | MX | 23 |
| Canaletes (Rambla de) | LV | 27 |
| Canonge Colom (Pl.) | LY | 28 |
| Canvis Vells | NX | 32 |
| Cardenal Casañas | LX | 36 |
| Catedral (Av.) | MV | 40 |
| Ciutat | MX | 43 |
| Comercial (Pl.) | NV | 45 |
| Cucurella | LX | 55 |
| Doctor Joaquim Pou | MV | 61 |
| Escudellers | MY | |
| Francesc Cambó (Av.) | MV | 79 |
| Garriga i Bach | MX | 81 |
| Isabel II (Pas. d') | NX | 98 |
| Montcada | NX | 122 |
| Montjuïc del Bisbe | MX | 123 |
| Nou de Sant Francesc | MY | 126 |
| Nova (Pl.) | MX | 128 |
| Paradís | MX | 133 |
| Pi (Pl. del) | LX | 137 |
| Pintor Fortuny | LX | 140 |
| Portal de Santa Madrona | MY | 142 |
| Ramon Berenguer el Gran (Pl.) | MX | 147 |
| Rei (Plaça del) | MX | 149 |
| Sant Felip Neri (Pl.) | MX | 163 |
| Sant Miquel (Pl. de) | MX | 173 |
| Sant Sever | MX | 181 |
| Santa Anna | LV | 182 |
| Santa Maria (Pl.) | NX | 189 |

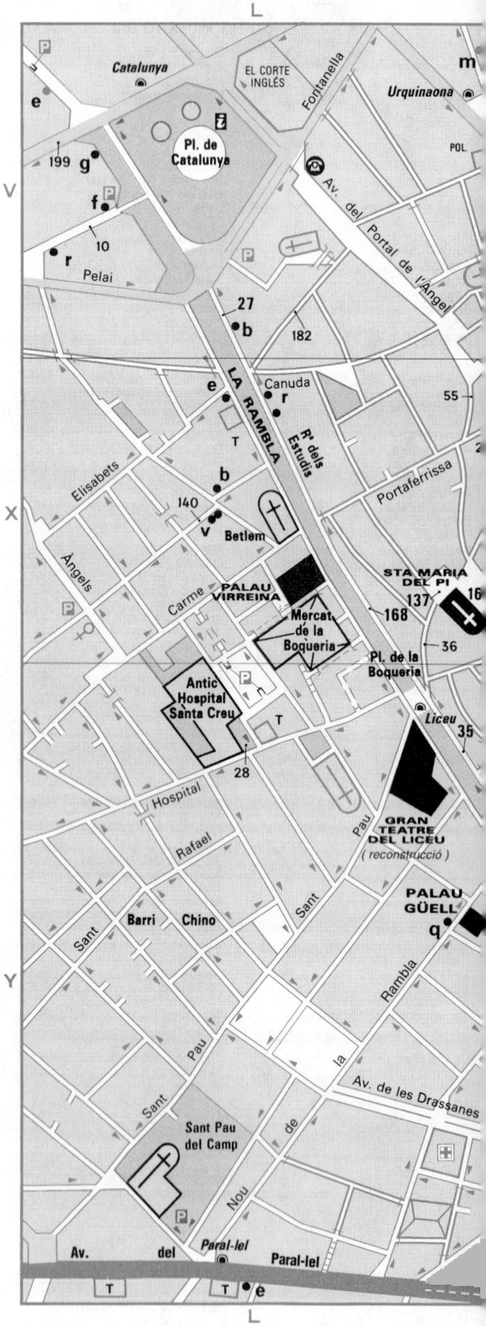

*We suggest:*

*For a successful tour, that you prepare it in advance.* ***Michelin maps*** *and* ***guides*** *will give you much useful information on route planning, places of interest, accommodation, prices, etc.*

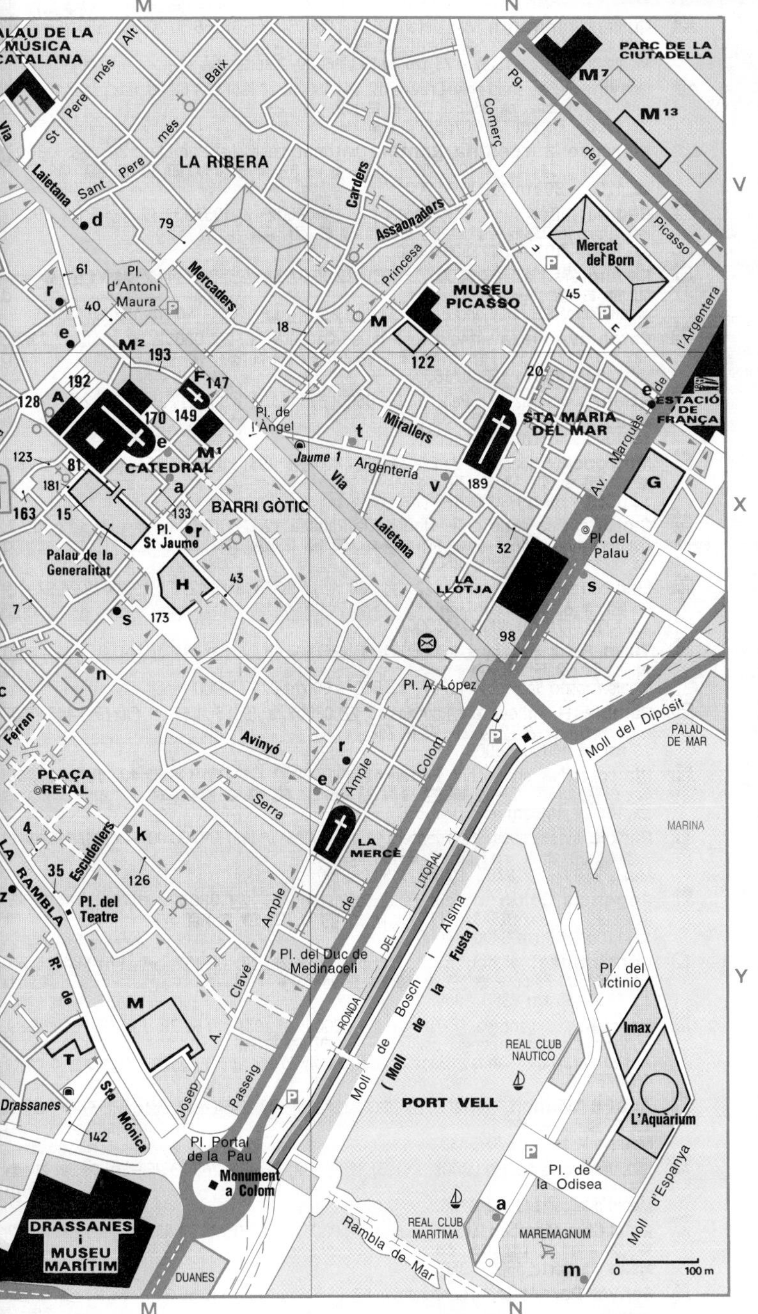
M
N
V
X
Y
PALAU DE LA MÚSICA CATALANA
PARC DE LA CIUTADELLA
LA RIBERA
MUSEU PICASSO
Mercat del Born
STA MARIA DEL MAR
ESTACIÓ DE FRANÇA
CATEDRAL
BARRI GÒTIC
Palau de la Generalitat
Pl. St Jaume
Pl. d'Antoni Maura
Pl. de l'Àngel
Jaume 1
LA LLOTJA
Pl. del Palau
Pl. A. López
Moll del Dipósit
PALAU DE MAR
MARINA
PLAÇA REIAL
LA MERCÈ
LA RAMBLA
Pl. del Teatre
Pl. del Duc de Medinaceli
RONDA DEL LITORAL
Moll de Bosch i Alsina (Moll de la Fusta)
PORT VELL
REAL CLUB NAUTICO
Pl. del Ictinio
Imax
L'Aquàrium
Moll d'Espanya
Pl. de la Odisea
MAREMAGNUM
REAL CLUB MARITIMA
Rambla de Mar
Pl. Portal de la Pau
Monument a Colom
DRASSANES i MUSEU MARÍTIM
Drassanes
DUANES
Sta Mònica
Passeig Josep A. Clavé
Via Laietana
Argenteria
Miralles
Princesa
Assaonadors
Carders
Mercaders
Sant Pere més Alt
Sant Pere més Baix
Pg. Comerç
de Picasso
Av. Marquès de l'Argentera
Avinyó
Ample
Serra
Colom
Escudellers
Ferran
0 100 m

**Guitart Almirante,** Via Laietana 42, ✉ 08003, ☏ (93) 268 30 20, *Fax (93) 268 31 92* – |♦| ▤ TV ☎ 🚗 – 🏛 25/40. AE ◑ E VISA JCB. ✻ MV d
Meals 3000 – ☕ 1300 – **73 rm** 12150/16200, 3 suites.

**Gravina** coffee shop only, Gravina 12, ✉ 08001, ☏ (93) 301 68 68, *Fax (93) 317 28 38* – |♦| ▤ TV ☎ – 🏛 25/50. AE ◑ E VISA. ✻ HX d
☕ 1200 – **81 rm** 10900/15900, 4 suites.

**Mercure Barcelona Rambla** without rest, La Rambla 124, ✉ 08002, ☏ (93) 412 04 04, *Fax (93) 318 73 23* – |♦| ▤ TV ☎ ♿ 🚗. AE ◑ E VISA. ✻ LX r
☕ 1200 – **80 rm** 10000/16000.

**Regina** coffee shop only, Bergara 2, ✉ 08002, ☏ (93) 301 32 32, *Telex 59380, Fax (93) 318 23 26* – |♦| ▤ TV ☎. AE ◑ E VISA JCB. ✻ LV r
☕ 1050 – **102 rm** 11350/16850.

**Reding,** Gravina 5, ✉ 08001, ☏ (93) 412 10 97, *Fax (93) 268 34 82* – |♦| ▤ TV ☎ 🚗. AE ◑ E VISA JCB. ✻ HX d
Meals *(closed Sunday and Bank Holidays)* 2350 – ☕ 1200 – **44 rm** 15200/19100.

**Catalunya Plaza** without rest, pl. de Catalunya 7, ✉ 08002, ☏ (93) 317 71 71, *Fax (93) 317 78 55* – |♦| ▤ TV ☎ – 🏛 25. AE ◑ E VISA. ✻ LV g
☕ 1400 – **46 rm** 16000/18000.

**Atlantis** without rest, Pelai 20, ✉ 08001, ☏ (93) 318 90 12, *Fax (93) 412 09 14* – |♦| ▤ TV ☎. AE ◑ E VISA JCB. ✻ HX a
☕ 1000 – **42 rm** 7500/10000.

**Metropol** without rest, Ample 31, ✉ 08002, ☏ (93) 310 51 00, *Fax (93) 319 12 76* – |♦| ▤ TV ☎. AE ◑ E VISA. ✻ NY r
☕ 1050 – **68 rm** 9000/12900.

**Gaudí** coffee shop only, Nou de la Rambla 12, ✉ 08001, ☏ (93) 317 90 32, *Fax (93) 412 26 36* – |♦| ▤ TV ☎ 🚗. AE ◑ E VISA JCB LY q
☕ 750 – **73 rm** 9250/12500.

**Lleó** coffee shop only, Pelai 22, ✉ 08001, ☏ (93) 318 13 12, *Fax (93) 412 26 57* – |♦| ▤ TV ☎ ♿. AE E VISA JCB HX a
☕ 1025 – **75 rm** 10000/13500.

**Turín,** Pintor Fortuny 9, ✉ 08001, ☏ (93) 302 48 12, *Fax (93) 302 10 05* – |♦| ▤ TV ☎ ♿. AE ◑ E VISA. ✻ LX v
Meals *(closed Saturday)* 1000 – ☕ 900 – **60 rm** 8250/9900.

**Ramblas H.** without rest, Rambles 33, ✉ 08002, ☏ (93) 301 57 00, *Fax (93) 412 25 07* – |♦| ▤ TV ☎ ♿ – 🏛 25. AE E VISA MY z
**70 rm** ☕ 14000/18000.

**Rialto** coffee shop only, Ferran 42, ✉ 08002, ☏ (93) 318 52 12, *Telex 97206, Fax (93) 318 53 12* – |♦| ▤ TV ☎ – 🏛 25/50. AE ◑ E VISA JCB MX s
☕ 1430 – **149 rm** 11700/14630.

**Park H.,** av. Marquès de l'Argentera 11, ✉ 08003, ☏ (93) 319 60 00, *Fax (93) 319 45 19* – |♦| ▤ TV ☎ ♿ 🚗. AE ◑ E VISA JCB. ✻ NX e
Meals 2500 – ☕ 975 – **87 rm** 9350/12650.

**Regencia Colón** without rest, Sagristans 13, ✉ 08002, ☏ (93) 318 98 58, *Telex 98175, Fax (93) 317 28 22* – |♦| ▤ TV ☎. AE ◑ E VISA JCB MV r
☕ 1100 – **55 rm** 8400/14000.

**Continental** without rest, Rambles 138-2°, ✉ 08002, ☏ (93) 301 25 70, *Fax (93) 302 73 60* – |♦| TV ☎. AE ◑ E VISA JCB LV b
☕ 350 – **35 rm** 6950/9900.

**Hofmann,** Argenteria 74-78 (1°), ✉ 08003, ☏ (93) 319 58 89, *Fax (93) 319 58 89*, « Pleasant setting amongst plants » – ▤. AE ◑ E VISA. ✻ NX v
*closed Saturday, Sunday, Bank Holidays, Holy Week and August* – **Meals** a la carte 4690/6000.

**Agut d'Avignon,** Trinitat 3, ✉ 08002, ☏ (93) 302 60 34, *Fax (93) 302 53 18* – ▤. AE ◑ E VISA JCB. ✻ MY n
**Meals** a la carte 3870/5430.

**Flo,** Jonqueres 10, ✉ 08003, ☏ (93) 319 31 02, *Fax (93) 268 23 95* – ▤. AE ◑ E VISA JCB LV m
**Meals** a la carte 3110/5740.

**Reial Club Marítim,** Moll d'Espanya, ✉ 08039, ☏ (93) 221 71 43, *Fax (93) 221 44 12*, ≤, 🏖 – ▤. E VISA JCB. ✻ NY a
**Meals** a la carte 3650/4950.

**Senyor Parellada,** Argenteria 37, ✉ 08003, ☏ (93) 310 50 94 – ▤. AE ◑ E VISA JCB. ✻ NX t
*closed Sunday and Bank Holidays* – **Meals** a la carte 2800/3560.

**7 Portes,** passeig d'Isabel II-14, 08003, (93) 319 30 33, *Fax (93) 319 30 46* – . NX s
Meals a la carte 3250/5390.

**Tikal,** Rambla de Catalunya 5, 08007, (93) 302 22 21 – . LV e
*closed Saturday lunch and Sunday dinner* – **Meals** a la carte 2680/3590.

**Can Ramonet,** Maquinista 17, 08003, (93) 319 30 64, *Fax (93) 319 70 14* – . KY e
**Meals** - Seafood - a la carte 2975/4350.

**Pitarra,** Avinyó 56, 08002, (93) 301 16 47, *Fax (93) 301 85 62*, « Period decor with memorabilia of the poet Pitarra » – . NY e
*closed Sunday, Bank Holidays dinner and August* – **Meals** a la carte 2300/3450.

**L'Elx al Moll,** Moll d'Espanya-Maremagnun, Local 9, 08039, (93) 225 81 17, *Fax (93) 225 81 20*, – . NY m
**Meals** - Rice dishes - a la carte 2810/4780.

**Can Solé,** Sant Carles 4, 08003, (93) 221 50 12, *Fax (93) 221 58 15* – . KY a
*close Sunday dinner, Monday and 15 days in August* – **Meals** a la carte approx. 4500.

**South of Av. Diagonal** : Gran Via de les Corts Catalanes, Passeig de Gràcia, Balmes, Muntaner, Aragó

**Rey Juan Carlos I**, av. Diagonal 661, 08028, (93) 448 08 08, *Fax (93) 448 06 07*, city, « Modern facilities. Park with lake and », – – 25/1000. W : by Av. Diagonal EX
***Chez Vous*** *(closed Saturday lunch and Sunday)* **Meals** a la carte 4700/6850 - ***Café Polo :*** Meals a la carte 3850/5250 – 2300 – **375 rm** 28000/38000, 37 suites.

**Arts**, Marina 19, 08005, (93) 221 10 00, *Fax (93) 221 10 70*, – – 25/900. E : by Av. d'Icària KX
***Newport Room*** *(closed Sunday lunch and August)* **Meals** a la carte 4950/7100 – 2700 – **397 rm** 27000, 58 suites.

**Palace,** Gran Via de les Corts Catalanes 668, 08010, (93) 318 52 00, *Telex 52739, Fax (93) 318 01 48*, – – 25/350. rest JV p
Meals a la carte 5700/7650 – 2300 – **148 rm** 28000/35000, 13 suites.

**Claris**, Pau Claris 150, 08009, (93) 487 62 62, *Fax (93) 215 79 70*, « Modern facilities with antiques. Archaelogical museum », – – 25/60. rest HV w
**Meals** 6000 - ***Beluga :*** **Meals** a la carte approx. 8000 – 2500 – **106 rm** 30000/37500, 18 suites.

**Barcelona Hilton,** av. Diagonal 589, 08014, (93) 419 22 33, *Fax (93) 405 25 73*, – – 25/800. FX v
**Meals** 3500 – 2300 – **285 rm** 28000/34000, 2 suites.

**Meliá Barcelona,** av. de Sarrià 50, 08029, (93) 410 60 60, *Telex 51638, Fax (93) 321 51 79*, – – 25/500. FV n
**Meals** a la carte approx. 6750 – 1875 – **308 rm** 23500/30500, 4 suites.

**Princesa Sofía Inter-Continental,** pl. Pius XII-4, 08028, (93) 330 71 11, *Telex 51032, Fax (93) 330 76 21*, – – 25/1200. EX x
**Meals** 3550 - ***L'Empordà*** *(closed Saturday, Sunday, July and August)* **Meals** a la carte 4650/5900 – 1800 – **467 rm** 19000/22000, 20 suites.

**G.H. Havana,** Gran Via de les Corts Catalanes 647, 08010, (93) 412 11 15, *Fax (93) 412 26 11* – – 25/200. JV e
**Meals** 2950 – 1350 – **141 rm** 18500/20500, 4 suites.

**Fira Palace,** av. Rius i Taulet 1, 08004, (93) 426 22 23, *Telex 97588, Fax (93) 424 86 79*, – – 25/1300.
**Meals** 3250 - ***El Mall :*** **Meals** a la carte 3250/4200 – 1500 – **258 rm** 19200/24000, 18 suites. S : by Lleida HY

**Barcelona Plaza H.,** pl. d'Espanya 6, 08014, (93) 426 26 00, *Fax (93) 426 04 00*, – – 25/600. GY r
**Meals** 3100 - ***Gourmet Plaza :*** **Meals** a la carte 3400/4800 – 1500 – **338 rm** 29000/35000, 9 suites.

**Majestic,** passeig de Gràcia 70, 08008, (93) 488 17 17, *Telex 52211, Fax (93) 488 18 80*, – – 25/600. HV f
**Meals** 2500 – 1900 – **328 rm** 19000/22000, 1 suite.

**Diplomatic,** Pau Claris 122, 08009, (93) 488 02 00, *Telex 54701, Fax (93) 488 12 22*, – – 25/250. HV e
***La Salsa :*** **Meals** a la carte 3400/4550 – 1600 – **210 rm** 17500/22000, 7 suites.

**NH Calderón,** Rambla de Catalunya 26, ✉ 08007, ✆ (93) 301 00 00, *Fax (93) 317 31 57,* – 25/200. AE ① E VISA JCB. rest — HX t
Meals a la carte approx. 4600 – ☐ 2200 – **245 rm** 19000, 17 suites.

**Barceló Sants,** pl. dels Països Catalans (Barcelona Sants railway station), ✉ 08014, ✆ (93) 490 95 95, *Telex 97568, Fax (93) 490 60 45,* – 25/1500. AE ① E VISA JCB. — FY
Meals 3550 – ☐ 1650 – **364 rm** 20000/22000, 13 suites.

**G.H. Catalonia,** Balmes 142, ✉ 08008, ✆ (93) 415 90 90, *Telex 98718, Fax (93) 415 22 09* – 50/260. AE ① E VISA JCB. — HV b
Meals 2700 – ☐ 1500 – **82 rm** 18850/22600, 2 suites.

**Condes de Barcelona** *(Monument and Centre)*, passeig de Gràcia 75, ✉ 08008, ✆ (93) 488 11 52, *Telex 51531, Fax (93) 487 14 42,* – 25/300. AE ① E VISA JCB. — HV m
Meals a la carte approx. 5500 – ☐ 1700 – **180 rm** 25000/27000, 2 suites.

**L'Illa** without rest, av. Diagonal 555, ✉ 08029, ✆ (93) 410 33 00, *Fax (93) 410 88 92* – 25/100. AE ① E VISA. — FX c
☐ 1400 – **103 rm** 21800/26950, 10 suites.

**Avenida Palace,** Gran Via de les Corts Catalanes 605, ✉ 08007, ✆ (93) 301 96 00, *Fax (93) 318 12 34* – 25/350. AE ① E VISA JCB. rest — HX r
Meals *(closed Saturday, Sunday and Bank Holidays)* 3500 – ☐ 1700 – **146 rm** 19000/24000, 14 suites.

**Gallery H.,** Rosselló 249, ✉ 08008, ✆ (93) 415 99 11, *Telex 97518, Fax (93) 415 91 84,* – 25/200. AE ① E VISA. — HV d
Meals 3075 – ☐ 1800 – **110 rm** 17500/20000, 5 suites.

**St. Moritz,** Diputació 262, ✉ 08007, ✆ (93) 412 15 00, *Telex 97340, Fax (93) 412 12 36* – 25/140. AE ① E VISA JCB. rest — JV g
Meals 2450 – ☐ 1950 – **92 rm** 20400/25500.

**Gran Derby** without rest, Loreto 28, ✉ 08029, ✆ (93) 322 20 62, *Telex 97429, Fax (93) 419 68 20* – 25/100. AE ① E VISA JCB — GX g
☐ 1700 – **31 rm** 18700/20900, 12 suites.

**Balmes,** Mallorca 216, ✉ 08008, ✆ (93) 451 19 14, *Fax (93) 451 00 49,* « Terrace with » – 25/70. AE ① E VISA JCB. rest — HV v
Meals 2000 – ☐ 1500 – **92 rm** 17050/19100, 8 suites.

**City Park H.,** Nicaragua 47, ✉ 08029, ✆ (93) 419 95 00, *Fax (93) 419 71 63* – 25/40. AE ① E VISA JCB. rest — FX z
Meals 2800 – ☐ 1400 – **80 rm** 14500/20900.

**NH Podium,** Bailén 4, ✉ 08010, ✆ (93) 265 02 02, *Fax (93) 265 05 06,* – 25/240. AE ① E VISA JCB. — JV n
Meals 2700 – ☐ 1800 – **140 rm** 15500, 5 suites.

**Derby** coffee shop only, Loreto 21, ✉ 08029, ✆ (93) 322 32 15, *Telex 97429, Fax (93) 410 08 62* – 25/100. AE ① E VISA JCB — FX e
☐ 1700 – **107 rm** 17050/19085, 4 suites.

**Alexandra,** Mallorca 251, ✉ 08008, ✆ (93) 467 71 66, *Telex 81107, Fax (93) 488 02 58* – 25/100. AE ① E VISA JCB. — HV x
Meals 2500 – ☐ 1900 – **73 rm** 16500/18000, 2 suites.

**Astoria** without rest, París 203, ✉ 08036, ✆ (93) 209 83 11, *Telex 81129, Fax (93) 202 30 08* – 25/30. AE ① E VISA JCB — HV a
☐ 1300 – **114 rm** 15700/17900, 3 suites.

**NH Master,** València 105, ✉ 08011, ✆ (93) 323 62 15, *Telex 81258, Fax (93) 323 43 89* – 25/170. AE ① E VISA JCB. rest — HX n
Meals 2500 – ☐ 1400 – **80 rm** 14000, 1 suite.

**Cristal,** Diputació 257, ✉ 08007, ✆ (93) 487 87 78, *Telex 54560, Fax (93) 487 90 30* – 25/70. AE ① E VISA JCB — HX t
Meals 1400 – **148 rm** ☐ 10250/15150.

**NH Numància,** Numància 74, ✉ 08029, ✆ (93) 322 44 51, *Fax (93) 410 76 42* – 25/70. AE ① E VISA JCB. — FX f
Meals a la carte approx. 3700 – ☐ 1400 – **140 rm** 14000.

**NH Sant Angelo** coffe shop dinner only, Consell de Cent 74, ✉ 08015, ✆ (93) 423 46 47, *Fax (93) 423 88 40* – 25. AE ① E VISA JCB. — GY f
☐ 1400 – **50 rm** 14000.

**Guitart Grand Passage,** Muntaner 212, ✉ 08036, ✆ (93) 201 03 06, *Fax (93) 201 00 04* – 25/80. AE ① E VISA. rest — GV n
Meals *(closed Sunday dinner and 10 to 25 August)* – ☐ 1200 – **40 suites** 16000/20000.

**Núñez Urgel** without rest, Comte d'Urgell 232, ✉ 08036, ℘ (93) 322 41 53, *Fax (93) 419 01 06* – 25/100. GX a
1450 – **106 rm** 10000/14500, 2 suites.

**Expo H.,** Mallorca 1, ✉ 08014, ℘ (93) 325 12 12, *Telex 54147, Fax (93) 325 11 44,* – 25/900. GY m
Meals 1900 – 1200 – **435 rm** 15000/18000.

**Dante** coffee shop dinner only, Mallorca 181, ✉ 08036, ℘ (93) 323 22 54, *Fax (93) 323 74 72* – 25/70. HX z
1350 – **81 rm** 11500/17800.

**Regente** without rest, Rambla de Catalunya 76, ✉ 08008, ℘ (93) 487 59 89, *Telex 51939, Fax (93) 487 32 27,* – 25/120. HV t
1800 – **79 rm** 14900/17500.

**Caledonian** without rest, Gran Via de les Corts Catalanes 574, ✉ 08011, ℘ (93) 453 02 00, *Fax (93) 451 77 03* – HX w
900 – **44 rm** 9300/14800.

**Abbot** without rest, av. de Roma 23, ✉ 08029, ℘ (93) 430 04 05, *Fax (93) 419 57 41* – 25/100. GXY e
1100 – **39 rm** 10500/13500.

**NH Forum,** Ecuador 20, ✉ 08029, ℘ (93) 419 36 36, *Fax (93) 419 89 10* – 25/50. rest FX t
Meals 2500 – 1300 – **47 rm** 11900, 1 suite.

**NH Rallye,** Travessera de les Corts 150, ✉ 08028, ℘ (93) 339 90 50, *Fax (93) 411 07 90,* – 25/200. rest EY b
Meals 2000 – 1400 – **106 rm** 14000.

**NH Les Corts,** Travessera de les Corts 292, ✉ 08029, ℘ (93) 322 08 11, *Fax (93) 322 09 08* – 25/80. FX u
Meals *(closed Saturday, Sunday and August)* 2500 – 1400 – **80 rm** 14000, 1 suite.

**Onix** without rest, Llançà 30, ✉ 08015, ℘ (93) 426 00 87, *Fax (93) 426 19 81,* – 25/150. GY n
1050 – **80 rm** 11500/13500.

**Antibes** without rest, Diputació 394, ✉ 08013, ℘ (93) 232 62 11, *Fax (93) 265 74 48* – JVU a
550 – **71 rm** 5800/7500.

**Beltxenea,** Mallorca 275, ✉ 08008, ℘ (93) 215 30 24, *Fax (93) 487 00 81,* « Garden terrace » – HV h
*closed Saturday lunch, Sunday, Christmas and August* – **Meals** a la carte approx. 6400.

**La Dama,** av. Diagonal 423, ✉ 08036, ℘ (93) 202 06 86, *Fax (93) 200 72 99,* « Housed in a Modernist style building » – HV a
**Meals** a la carte 5275/6975
**Spec.** Pequeñas coles rellenas de centollo con salsa de caviar. Gratinado de bogavante sobre lecho de espinacas. Carro de pastelería.

**Casa Calvet,** Casp 48, ✉ 08010, ℘ (93) 412 40 12, *Fax (93) 412 43 36* – JVX r
*closed Sunday, Bank Holidays and 15 days in August* – **Meals** a la carte 4600/6125.

**Jaume de Provença,** Provença 88, ✉ 08029, ℘ (93) 430 00 29, *Fax (93) 439 29 50* – GX h
*closed Sunday dinner, Monday, Holy Week, August and Christmas* – **Meals** 7250 and a la carte 4850/6600
**Spec.** Ensalada de raya con escalivada al pesto. Tian de fideuá con mariscos y esencia de bullabesa. Crujiente de manitas de cerdo relleno de foie y trufas.

**Windsor,** Còrsega 286, ✉ 08008, ℘ (93) 415 84 83, *Fax (93) 217 42 65* – HV s
*closed Sunday and August* – **Meals** a la carte 4000/5300.

**Oliver y Hardy,** av. Diagonal 593, ✉ 08014, ℘ (93) 419 31 81, *Fax (93) 419 18 99,* – FX n
*closed Saturday lunch, Sunday and Holy Week* – **Meals** a la carte 3800/5900.

**Talaia Mar,** Marina 16, ✉ 08005, ℘ (93) 221 90 90, *Fax (93) 221 89 89,* ← – E : by Av. d'Icària KX
*closed 6 to 29 August* – **Meals** a la carte 5050/6250.

**El Tragaluz,** passatge de la Concepció 5-1º, ✉ 08008, ℘ (93) 487 01 96, *Fax (93) 217 01 19,* « Original decor with glass roof » – HV u
**Meals** a la carte approx. 4500.

**Els Pescadors,** pl. Prim 1, ✉ 08005, ℘ (93) 225 20 18, *Fax (93) 225 20 18,* – E : by Av. d'Icària KX
*closed Holy Week* – **Meals** a la carte 3510/5075.

XX **El Asador de Aranda,** Londres 94, ✉ 08036, ℘ (93) 414 67 90, *Fax (93) 414 67 90* – ▤. AE ⓓ E VISA. ✂ GV n
*cosed Sunday dinner and 15 to 31 August* – **Meals** - Roast lamb - a la carte approx. 3900.

XX **Rías de Galicia,** Lleida 7, ✉ 08004, ℘ (93) 424 81 52, *Fax (93) 426 13 07* – ▤. AE ⓓ E VISA JCB. ✂ HY e
**Meals** - Seafood - a la carte 4100/6400.

XX **La Provença,** Provença 242, ✉ 08008, ℘ (93) 323 23 67, *Fax (93) 451 23 89* – ▤. AE ⓓ E VISA HV y
**Meals** a la carte 2570/3430.

XX **Boix de la Cerdanya,** passeig de Gràcia 51, ✉ 08007, ℘ (93) 487 38 20 – ▤. AE VISA. ✂ HV j
*closed Sunday and Bank Holidays* – **Meals** a la carte 3250/3800.

XX **Vinya Rosa-Magí,** av. de Sarrià 17, ✉ 08029, ℘ (93) 430 00 03, *Fax (93) 430 00 41* – ▤. AE ⓓ E VISA GX y
*closed Saturday lunch and Sunday* – **Meals** a la carte 3865/5670.

XX **Gorría,** Diputació 421, ✉ 08013, ℘ (93) 245 11 64, *Fax (93) 232 78 57* – ▤. AE ⓓ E VISA JCB. ✂ JU a
*closed Sunday, Bank Holidays dinner, Holy Week and August* – **Meals** - Basque rest - a la carte 4800/5500.

XX **Sibarit,** Aribau 65, ✉ 08011, ℘ (93) 453 93 03 – ▤. AE ⓓ E VISA. ✂ HX u
*closed Saturday lunch, Sunday, Bank Holidays, Holy Week and 15 to 31 August* – **Meals** a la carte approx. 5200.

XX **La Llotja,** Aribau 55, ✉ 08011, ℘ (93) 453 89 58, *Fax (93) 453 89 58* – ▤. AE ⓓ E VISA. ✂ HX u
*closed Sunday and August* – **Meals** - Meat, braised fish and cod specialities - a la carte 2925/3900.

XX **Casa Darío,** Consell de Cent 256, ✉ 08011, ℘ (93) 453 31 35, *Fax (93) 451 33 95* – ▤. AE ⓓ E VISA JCB. ✂ HX p
*closed Sunday and August* – **Meals** a la carte 3850/6900.

XX **El Túnel del Port,** Moll de Gregal 12 (Port Olímpic), ✉ 08005, ℘ (93) 221 03 21, *Fax (93) 221 35 86*, ≤, 🏖 – ▤. AE ⓓ E VISA E : by Av. d'Icària KX
*closed Sunday dinner and Monday* – **Meals** a la carte 3500/4900.

X **El Celler de Casa Jordi,** Rita Bonnat 3, ✉ 08029, ℘ (93) 430 10 45 – ▤. AE ⓓ E VISA JCB. ✂ GX s
*closed Sunday* – **Meals** a la carte 2200/4100.

X **Nervión,** Còrsega 232, ✉ 08036, ℘ (93) 218 06 27 – ▤. AE E VISA JCB. ✂ HV r
*closed Sunday, Bank Holidays dinner and August* – **Meals** - Basque rest - a la carte 3200/4950.

X **Rosamar,** Sepúlveda 159, ✉ 08011, ℘ (93) 453 31 92 – ▤. AE ⓓ E VISA HX q
*closed Sunday dinner, Monday, Holy Week and August* – **Meals** a la carte 2100/2950.

X **Chicoa,** Aribau 73, ✉ 08036, ℘ (93) 453 11 23, « Rustic decor » – ▤. AE E VISA HX m
*closed Sunday, Bank Holidays and August* – **Meals** a la carte approx. 4200.

X **Els Perols de l'Empordà,** Villarroel 88, ✉ 08011, ℘ (93) 323 10 33 – ▤. AE ⓓ E VISA. ✂ HX v
*closed Sunday and August* – **Meals** a la carte 2700/4250.

X **Elche,** Vila i Vilà 71, ✉ 08004, ℘ (93) 441 30 89, *Fax (93) 329 40 12* – ▤. AE ⓓ E VISA. ✂ JY a
*closed Sunday dinner* – **Meals** - Rice dishes - a la carte 2800/3400.

X **Cañota,** Lleida 7, ✉ 08004, ℘ (93) 325 91 71, *Fax (93) 426 13 07* – ▤. VISA. ✂ HY e
**Meals** - Braised meat specialities - a la carte 2450/3900.

X **Azpiolea,** Casanova 167, ✉ 08036, ℘ (93) 430 90 30 – ▤. AE ⓓ E VISA. ✂ GV q
*closed Sunday and August* – **Meals** - Basque rest - a la carte 3500/4500.

**North of Av. Diagonal :** Via Augusta, Capità Arenas, Ronda General Mitre, Passeig de la Bonanova, Av. de Pedralbes

**Tryp Presidente,** av. Diagonal 570, ✉ 08021, ℘ (93) 200 21 11, *Fax (93) 209 51 06* – |‡| ▤ TV ☎ – 🏛 25/420. AE ⓓ E VISA. ✂ GV u
**Meals** a la carte approx. 5500 – ☕ 1200 – **155 rm** 16000/20500.

**Alimara,** Berruguete 126, ✉ 08035, ℘ (93) 427 00 00, *Fax (93) 427 92 92* – |‡| ▤ TV ☎ ♿ 🚗 – 🏛 25/470. AE ⓓ E VISA. ✂ rest N : by Padilla JU
**Meals** 2950 – ☕ 1300 – **156 rm** 14900/17200.

**Hesperia** coffee shop only, Vergós 20, ✉ 08017, ℘ (93) 204 55 51, *Telex 98403, Fax (93) 204 43 92* – 🛗 ▤ 📺 ☎ 🚗 – 🏛 25/150. AE ⓓ E VISA. ✂ EU c
☕ 1300 – **139 rm** 17450/21000.

**Suite H.,** Muntaner 505, ✉ 08022, ℘ (93) 212 80 12, *Telex 99077, Fax (93) 211 23 17* – 🛗 ▤ 📺 ☎ 🚗 – 🏛 25/90. AE ⓓ E VISA JCB. ✂ FU a
Meals 1500 – ☕ 1200 – **77 suites** 13800/17800.

**Balmoral** without rest, Via Augusta 5, ✉ 08006, ℘ (93) 217 87 00, *Fax (93) 415 14 21* – 🛗 ▤ 📺 ☎ 🚗 – 🏛 25/250. AE ⓓ E VISA JCB. ✂ HV n
☕ 1250 – **106 rm** 9200/14800.

**Turó de Vilana** without rest, Vilana 7, ✉ 08017, ℘ (93) 434 03 63, *Fax (93) 418 89 03* – 🛗 ▤ 📺 ☎ 🚗. AE ⓓ E VISA. ✂ EU r
☕ 1500 – **20 rm** 14800/18500.

**NH Cóndor,** Via Augusta 127, ✉ 08006, ℘ (93) 209 45 11, *Fax (93) 202 27 13* – 🛗 ▤ 📺 ☎ – 🏛 25/50. AE ⓓ E VISA. ✂ rest GU z
Meals *(closed Sunday)* 2800 – ☕ 1200 – **78 rm** 13900/15000, 12 suites.

**Arenas** coffee shop only, Capità Arenas 20, ✉ 08034, ℘ (93) 280 03 03, *Fax (93) 280 33 92* – 🛗 ▤ 📺 ☎ – 🏛 25/50. AE ⓓ E VISA EX r
☕ 1300 – **58 rm** 14500/18000, 1 suite.

**Victoria,** av. de Pedralbes 16 bis, ✉ 08034, ℘ (93) 280 15 15, *Fax (93) 280 52 67*, 🏋, 🏊 – 🛗 ▤ 📺 ☎ 🚗. AE ⓓ E VISA. ✂ rest EX z
Meals *(closed weekends, Bank Holidays and August)* 1575 – ☕ 1350 – **74 suites** 14800/18600.

**Park Putxet,** Putxet 68, ✉ 08023, ℘ (93) 212 51 58, *Telex 98718, Fax (93) 418 58 17* – 🛗 ▤ 📺 ☎ 🚗 – 🏛 25/200. AE ⓓ E VISA JCB. ✂ GU a
Meals 1800 – ☕ 950 – **141 rm** 10200/13000.

**NH Belagua,** Via Augusta 89, ✉ 08006, ℘ (93) 237 39 40, *Fax (93) 415 30 62* – 🛗 ▤ 📺 ☎ – 🏛 25/90. AE ⓓ E VISA JCB. ✂ rest GU s
Meals *(dinner only, closed Saturday and 2 to 24 August)* 2500 – ☕ 1400 – **72 rm** 14000.

**Mitre** without rest, Bertràn 9, ✉ 08023, ℘ (93) 212 11 04, *Fax (93) 418 94 81* – 🛗 ▤ 📺 ☎. AE ⓓ E VISA JCB FU t
☕ 800 – **57 rm** 11500/14700.

**Condado** without rest, Aribau 201, ✉ 08021, ℘ (93) 200 23 11, *Fax (93) 200 25 86* – 🛗 ▤ 📺 ☎. AE ⓓ E VISA GV g
☕ 1200 – **88 rm** 11110/12335.

**NH Pedralbes** coffee shop dinner only, Fontcuberta 4, ✉ 08034, ℘ (93) 203 71 12, *Fax (93) 205 70 65* – 🛗 ▤ 📺 ☎ – 🏛 25. AE ⓓ E VISA JCB EV b
☕ 1300 – **30 rm** 12500.

**Covadonga** without rest, av. Diagonal 596, ✉ 08021, ℘ (93) 209 55 11, *Fax (93) 209 58 33* – 🛗 ▤ 📺 ☎. AE ⓓ E VISA JCB. ✂ GV v
☕ 1000 – **85 rm** 9100/15400.

**Albéniz** without rest, Aragó 591, ✉ 08026, ℘ (93) 265 26 26, *Fax (93) 265 40 07* – 🛗 ▤ 📺 ☎ – 🏛 25/50. AE ⓓ E VISA JCB. ✂
☕ 950 – **47 rm** 10700/13000. NE : by Gran Via de les Corts Catalanes HX

XXXX ✿ **Via Veneto,** Ganduxer 10, ✉ 08021, ℘ (93) 200 72 44, *Fax (93) 201 60 95*, « Early 20C style » – ▤. AE ⓓ E VISA JCB. ✂ FV e
*closed Saturday lunch, Sunday and 1 to 20 August* – **Meals** 7000 and a la carte 5720/8270
**Spec.** Centolla en su propia salsa con espárragos trigueros. Pintada deshuesada y dorada al horno con vino rancio, ciruelas y lentejas. Tartaleta de chocolate a la crema de vainilla Bourbon.

XXXX **Reno,** Tuset 27, ✉ 08006, ℘ (93) 200 91 29, *Fax (93) 414 41 14* – ▤. AE ⓓ E VISA JCB. ✂ GV r
*closed Saturday lunch* – **Meals** a la carte approx. 6650.

XXXX ✿✿ **Neichel,** Beltran i Rózpide 16 bis, ✉ 08034, ℘ (93) 203 84 08, *Fax (93) 205 63 69* – ▤. AE ⓓ E VISA EX z
*closed Saturday lunch, Sunday, Holy Week and August* – **Meals** 7700 and a la carte 6050/7300
**Spec.** Carpaccio de pato y alcachofas con vinagreta de trufas y forum. San Pedro y espardenyes en emulsión de erizos de mar. Crujientes de especias y helado de mató a la miel de lavanda.

XXX ✿ **Jean Luc Figueras,** Santa Teresa 10, ✉ 08012, ℘ (93) 415 28 77, *Fax (93) 218 92 62*, « Tasteful decor » – ▤. AE ⓓ E VISA. ✂ HV z
*closed Saturday lunch, Sunday and 15 days in August* – **Meals** a la carte 5600/7300
**Spec.** Ensalada de gambas de Palamós, vinagreta de pomelo. Pescado de playa con tomate confitado al aceite de Jabugo. Pichón de Bresse con papillote de butifarra negra y salsa de soja.

XXX **Gaig,** passeig de Maragall 402, ✉ 08031, ☎ (93) 429 10 17, *Fax (93) 429 70 02,* – ▤. AE ⓓ E VISA N : by Travessera de Gràcia HU
*closed Monday, Bank Holidays dinner, Holy Week and August* – **Meals** a la carte 5100/7700
**Spec.** Templado de patatas buffet y caviar ocietra. Salteado de pulpitos y lomo de conejo ahumado. Semi caliente de manzana ácida con sabayon de Calvados.

XXX **Botafumeiro,** Gran de Gràcia 81, ✉ 08012, ☎ (93) 218 42 30, *Fax (93) 415 58 48* – ▤. AE ⓓ E VISA JCB. HU v
*closed August* – **Meals** - Seafood - a la carte 4890/6290.

XXX **Roncesvalles,** Via Augusta 201, ✉ 08021, ☎ (93) 209 01 25, *Fax (93) 209 12 95* – ▤. AE ⓓ E VISA. FV a
*closed Saturday lunch, Sunday and Holy Week* – **Meals** a la carte 3650/5400.

XX **El Trapío,** Esperanza 25, ✉ 08017, ☎ (93) 211 58 17, *Fax (93) 417 10 37,* « Terrace » – ▤. AE ⓓ VISA. EU t
*closed Sunday dinner* – **Meals** a la carte 3200/4250.

XX **La Petite Marmite,** Madrazo 68, ✉ 08006, ☎ (93) 201 48 79, *Fax (93) 202 23 43* – ▤. AE ⓓ E VISA. GU f
*closed Sunday, Bank Holidays, Holy Week and August* – **Meals** a la carte 2925/4350.

XX **Can Cortada,** av. de l'Estatut de Catalunya, ✉ 08035, ☎ (93) 427 23 15, *Fax (93) 427 02 94,* « 16C farm » – ▤ P. AE ⓓ E VISA JCB. N : by Padilla JU
**Meals** a la carte 3150/4100.

XX **El Asador de Aranda,** av. del Tibidabo 31, ✉ 08022, ☎ (93) 417 01 15, *Fax (93) 212 24 82,* « Former palace » – AE ⓓ E VISA. NW : by Balmes FU
*closed Sunday dinner* – **Meals** - Roast lamb - a la carte approx. 3950.

XX **El Racó d'en Freixa,** Sant Elíes 22, ✉ 08006, ☎ (93) 209 75 59, *Fax (93) 209 79 18* – ▤. AE ⓓ E VISA. GU h
*closed Monday, Bank Holidays dinner, Holy Week and August* – **Meals** a la carte 5225/6600
**Spec.** Tomate con tomate, betas de sepia y buñuelo de flor de calabacín (summer). Escórpora asada con ceps y caracoles (autumn). Liebre a la Royal trufada (winter).

XX **Roig Robí,** Sèneca 20, ✉ 08006, ☎ (93) 218 92 22, *Fax (93) 415 78 42,* « Garden terrace » – ▤. AE ⓓ E VISA HV c
*closed Saturday lunch, Sunday and two weeks in August* – **Meals** a la carte 4500/6300.

XX **Tram-Tram,** Major de Sarrià 121, ✉ 08017, ☎ (93) 204 85 18, – ▤. AE E VISA. EU d
*closed Saturday lunch, Sunday, Holy Week, 15 days in August and 23 to 30 December* – **Meals** a la carte 4550/6100.

XX **St. Rémy,** Iradier 12, ✉ 08017, ☎ (93) 418 75 04, *Fax (93) 434 04 34* – ▤. AE ⓓ E VISA EU n
**Meals** a la carte approx. 3170.

X **Vivanda,** Major de Sarrià 134, ✉ 08017, ☎ (93) 205 47 17, *Fax (93) 203 19 18,* – ▤. VISA EU a
*closed Sunday and Monday lunch* – **Meals** a la carte approx. 3600.

X **La Venta,** pl. Dr. Andreu, ✉ 08035, ☎ (93) 212 64 55, *Fax (93) 212 51 44,* « Former cafe » – AE ⓓ E VISA NW : by Balmes FU
*closed Sunday* – **Meals** a la carte approx. 5000.

X **Sal i Pebre,** Alfambra 14, ✉ 08034, ☎ (93) 205 36 58, *Fax (93) 205 56 72* – ▤. AE ⓓ E VISA. W : by Pas. de Manuel Girona EX
**Meals** a la carte 2150/3175.

X **La Taula,** Sant Màrius 8-12, ✉ 08022, ☎ (93) 417 28 48 – ▤. AE ⓓ E VISA JCB. FU u
*closed Saturday lunch, Sunday, Bank Holidays and August* – **Meals** a la carte 2750/3550.

X **La Yaya Amelia,** Sardenya 364, ✉ 08025, ☎ (93) 456 45 73 – ▤. AE E VISA JCB. JU n
*closed Sunday, Holy Week and three weeks in August* – **Meals** a la carte 2675/3975.

Typical atmosphere :

X **La Cuineta,** Paradís 4, ✉ 08002, ☎ (93) 315 01 11, *Fax (93) 315 07 98,* « In a 17C cellar. Typical rest. » – ▤. AE ⓓ E VISA JCB. MX e
**Meals** a la carte 3750/6050.

X **Can Culleretes,** Quintana 5, ✉ 08002, ☎ (93) 317 64 85, *Fax (93) 317 64 85,* « Typical rest » – ▤. AE ⓓ E VISA JCB. MY c
*closed Sunday dinner, Monday and 6 to 29 July* – **Meals** a la carte 2200/3100.

X **Los Caracoles,** Escudellers 14, ✉ 08002, ☎ (93) 302 31 85, *Fax (93) 302 07 43,* « Typical rest. Rustic regional decor » – ▤. AE ⓓ E VISA JCB. MY k
**Meals** a la carte 2900/5375.

X **Pá i Trago,** Parlament 41, ✉ 08015, ☎ (93) 441 13 20, *Fax (93) 441 13 20,* « Typical rest » – ▤. ⓓ E VISA HY a
*closed Monday except Bank Holidays and 22 June-10 July* – **Meals** a la carte 2400/4200.

X **A la Menta,** passeig Manuel Girona 50, ✉ 08034, ☎ (93) 204 15 49, « Typical taverna » – ▤. AE ⓓ E VISA. ⚡ EV f
*closed Sunday in summer and Sunday dinner the rest of the year* – **Meals** a la carte 3200/4650.

## Environs

**at Esplugues de Llobregat** *W : 5 km – ✉ 08950 Esplugues de Llobregat :*

XXX **La Masía,** av. Països Catalans 58 ☎ (93) 371 00 09, *Fax (93) 372 84 00,* 🍽, « Terrace under pine trees » – ▤ Ⓟ. AE ⓓ E VISA JCB. ⚡
*closed Sunday dinner* – **Meals** a la carte 3450/5150.

X **Quirze,** Laureà Miró 202 ☎ (93) 371 10 84, *Fax (93) 371 65 12,* 🍽 – ▤ Ⓟ. AE E VISA. ⚡
*closed Saturday dinner, Sunday and August* – **Meals** a la carte 3400/5100.

**at Sant Just Desvern** *W : 6 km – ✉ 08960 Sant Just Desvern :*

**Sant Just,** Frederic Mompou 1 ☎ (93) 473 25 17, *Fax (93) 473 24 50,* Fø – |‡| ▤ TV ☎ 🚗 – 🏃 25/450. AE ⓓ E VISA. ⚡
**Meals** 3000 - ***Alambí :*** **Meals** a la carte 2700/4850 – ☕ 1300 – **138 rm** 13900/14900, 12 suites.

**at Sant Cugat del Vallés** *NW : 18 km – ✉ 08190 Sant Cugat del Vallés :*

**Novotel Barcelona-Sant Cugat** ⛰, pl. Xavier Cugat, ✉ apartado 122, ☎ (93) 589 41 41, *Fax (93) 589 30 31,* ≤, 🍽, 🏊 – |‡| ▤ TV ☎ ♿ 🚗 Ⓟ – 🏃 25/300. AE ⓓ E VISA
**Meals** a la carte approx. 4400 – ☕ 1500 – **146 rm** 12850/16000, 4 suites.

**Rosas** o **Roses** *17480 Gerona* 443 F 39 – *pop. 10 303 – Seaside resort.*
See : *Ciudadela★.*
ℹ *Av. de Rhode 101 ☎ (972) 25 73 31 Fax (972) 15 11 50.*
*Madrid 763 – Barcelona 153 – Gerona/Girona 56.*

**at Cala Montjoi** *SE : 7 km – ✉ 17480 Rosas :*

XXX ✿✿✿ **El Bulli,** ✉ apartado 30, ☎ (972) 15 04 57, *Fax (972) 15 07 17,* 🍽, « Pleasant rustic villa overlooking a creek » – ▤ Ⓟ. AE ⓓ E VISA
*15 March-15 October* – **Meals** *(closed Monday and Tuesday except July-September)* 13500 and a la carte 8800/11200
**Spec.** Moluscada en gelatina. Gazpacho de buey de mar. Fardo de espardenyes en agridulce.

**San Celoni** o **Sant Celoni** *08470 Barcelona* 443 G 37 – *pop. 11 937 alt. 152.*
**Envir.** : *NO : Sierra de Montseny★ : itinerary★★ from San Celoni to Santa Fé del Montseny – Road★ from San Celoni to Tona by Montseny.*
*Madrid 662 – Barcelona 49 – Gerona/Girona 57.*

XXX ✿✿✿ **El Racó de Can Fabes,** Sant Joan 6 ☎ (93) 867 28 51, *Fax (93) 867 38 61,* « Rustic decor » – ▤ 🚗. AE ⓓ E VISA JCB
*closed Sunday dinner, Monday, 2 to 16 February and 22 June-6 July* – **Meals** 12500 and a la carte 9000/11000
**Spec.** Ancas de rana con sofrito de cebolla y tomate. Langosta del Mediterráneo con verduras (summer). Plátanos con crujientes y salsa de chocolate.

**San Pol de Mar** o **Sant Pol de Mar** *08395 Barcelona* 443 H 37 – *pop. 2 383 – Seaside resort.*
*Madrid 679 – Barcelona 44 – Gerona/Girona 53.*

XXX ✿✿ **Sant Pau,** Nou 10 ☎ (93) 760 06 62, *Fax (93) 760 09 50* – ▤ Ⓟ. AE E VISA. ⚡
*closed Sunday dinner, Monday, 13 to 29 April and 2 to 18 November* – **Meals** 8900 and a la carte 6700/8400
**Spec.** Pagel al horno con cebollas, ajos tiernos y salsa de garnatxa. Hamburguesa de pie de cerdo con cebolla confitada y patatas finas. Tatin de berenjena y manzana con biscuit de vainilla.

**BILBAO** o **BILBO** *48000* 🅿 *Vizcaya* 442 C 20 – *pop. 372 054.*

**See** : *Museo de Bellas Artes★ (Fine Arts Museum : Ancien Art Collections★★)* CY **M** – *Guggenheim Museum★★* CY.

*Laukariz, carret de Munguía NE by BI 631* (A) *(94) 674 04 62.*

*de Bilbao, Sondica NE : 11 km by railway BI 631 (94) 486 93 01 – Iberia : Ercilla 20 ✉ 48009 (94) 471 12 10* CZ.

*Abando (94) 423 06 17.*

*. Cía Trasmediterránea, Colón de Larreategui 30 ✉ 48009 (94) 423 43 00 Fax (94) 424 74 59* DZ.

*pl. Arriaga 1 ✉ 48005 (94) 416 00 22 Fax (94) 416 81 68* – R.A.C.V.N. *(R.A.C. Vasco Navarro) Rodriguez Arias 59 bis ✉ 48013 (94) 442 58 08 Fax (94) 441 27 12.*

*Madrid 397 ② – Barcelona 607 ② – La Coruña/A Coruña 622 ③ – Lisboa 907 ② – San Sebastián/Donostia 100 ① – Santander 116 ③ – Toulouse 449 ① – Valencia 606 ② – Zaragoza 305 ②*

Plans on following pages

**López de Haro,** Obispo Orueta 2, ✉ 48009, (94) 423 55 00, *Telex 34787, Fax (94) 423 45 00* – – 25/40. VISA. rest CY r
**Meals** 3500 - ***Náutico*** : **Meals** a la carte 4300/5050 – 1475 – **49 rm** 16200/21800, 4 suites.

**Carlton,** pl. de Federico Moyúa 2, ✉ 48009, (94) 416 22 00, *Fax (94) 416 46 28* – – 25/200. VISA JCB. CZ x
**Meals** 3000 – 1200 – **141 rm** 19000/24000, 7 suites.

**Indautxu,** pl. Bombero Etxaniz 2, ✉ 48010, (94) 421 11 98, *Fax (94) 422 13 31* – – 25/400. VISA CZ b
**Meals** (see rest. ***Etxaniz*** below) – 1450 – **181 rm** 17500/20500, 3 suites.

## BILBO/BILBAO

| Street | Grid | No. |
|---|---|---|
| Bidebarreta | DZ | 5 |
| Correo | DZ | |
| Gran Vía de López de Haro | BCYZ | |
| Amézola (Plaza) | CZ | 2 |
| Arenal (Puente del) | DZ | 3 |
| Ayuntamiento (Puente del) | DYZ | 4 |
| Bilbao la Vieja | DZ | 5 |
| Bombero Echániz (Pl.) | CZ | 6 |
| Buenos Aires | DZ | 7 |
| Circular (Plaza) | DZ | 8 |
| Cruz | DZ | 9 |
| Deusto (Puente de) | BCY | 10 |
| Emilio Campuzano (Plaza) | CZ | 12 |
| Enécuri (Av. de) | AZ | 13 |
| Ernesto Erkoreka (Plaza) | DY | 15 |
| Federico Moyúa (Plaza de) | CZ | 19 |
| Gardoqui | CZ | 20 |
| Huertas de la Villa | DY | 24 |
| Iparraguirre | CYZ | 25 |
| Juan de Garay | CZ | 27 |
| Lehendakari Aguirre (Av.) | BY | 28 |
| Luís Luciano Bonaparte | AZ | 29 |
| Montevideo (Avenida de) | AZ | 30 |
| Múgica y Butrón | DY | 31 |
| Navarra | DZ | 32 |
| Pintor Losada | AZ | 33 |
| Pío Baroja (Pl. de) | DY | 35 |
| Rodríguez Arias | BCYZ | 36 |
| San Antón (Puente de) | DZ | 37 |
| San José (Plaza) | CY | 38 |
| San Mamés (Alameda de) | CZ | 39 |
| Santuchu | AZ | 40 |
| Viuda de Epalza | DZ | 42 |
| Zabalbide | AZ | 43 |
| Zabálburu (Plaza de) | CZ | 45 |
| Zumalacárregui (Avenida) | DY | 46 |

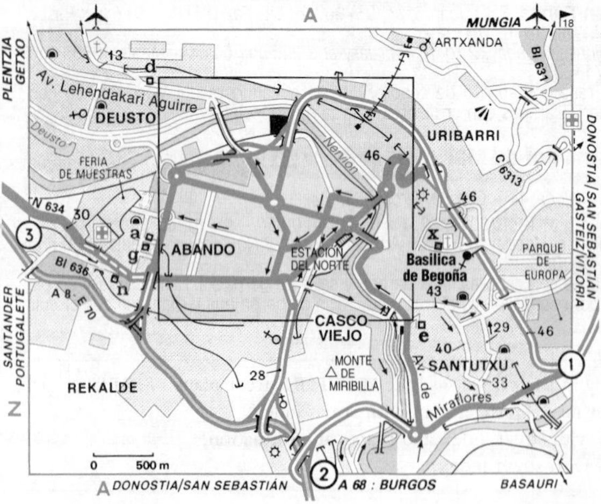

**G.H. Ercilla,** Ercilla 37, ✉ 48011, ℘ (94) 470 57 00, *Fax (94) 443 93 35* – 25/400. AE DC E VISA JCB. rest CZ a
Meals (see rest. ***Bermeo*** below) – 1475 – **338 rm** 17685/22915, 8 suites.

**Abando,** Colón de Larreategui 9, ✉ 48001, ℘ (94) 423 62 00, *Fax (94) 424 55 25* – 25/150. AE DC E VISA JCB. DZ b
Meals *(closed Sunday and Bank Holidays)* 2500 – 1200 – **142 rm** 10500/17000, 3 suites.

**NH Villa de Bilbao,** Gran Vía de Don Diego López de Haro 87, ✉ 48011, ℘ (94) 441 60 00, *Fax (94) 441 65 29* – 25/250. AE DC E VISA JCB. BY n
Meals 2700 - ***La Pérgola*** **: Meals** a la carte 4050/4650 – 1400 – **139 rm** 15000/17000, 3 suites.

**Nervión,** paseo Campo de Volantín 11, ✉ 48007, ℘ (94) 445 47 00, *Fax (94) 445 56 08* – rest, 25/250. AE DC E VISA. DY a
Meals *(closed Sunday)* 1800 – 1150 – **324 rm** 9400/14400, 24 suites.

**NH de Deusto** without rest, Francisco Maciá 9, ✉ 48014, ℘ (94) 476 00 06, *Fax (94) 476 21 99* – 25/90. AE DC E VISA. BY f
1300 – **70 rm** 14800/19800.

**Conde Duque,** paseo Campo de Volantín 22, ✉ 48007, ℘ (94) 445 60 00, *Fax (94) 445 60 66* – 25/120. AE DC E VISA. DY m
**Meals** *(closed Saturday, Sunday and Bank Holidays)* 1600 – 1100 – **65 rm** 11000/17000, 2 suites.

**Estadio** without rest, Juan Antonio Zunzunegui 10 bis, ✉ 48013, ℘ (94) 442 42 41, *Fax (94) 442 50 11* – VISA. AZ a
270 – **18 rm** 8000/12000.

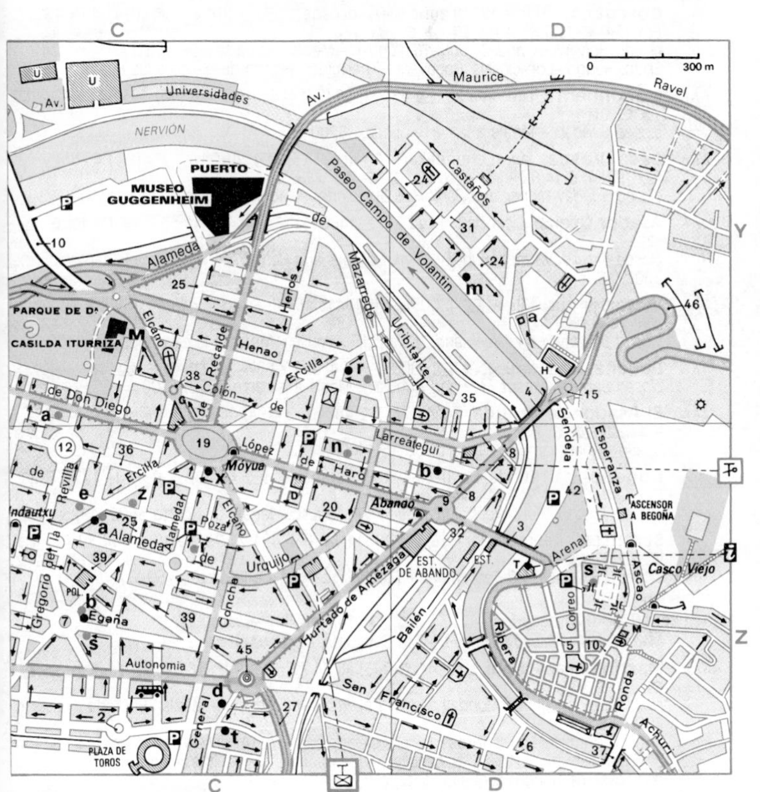

**Vista Alegre** without rest, Pablo Picasso 13, ✉ 48012, ☎ (94) 443 14 50, *Fax (94) 443 14 54* – TV ☎ . VISA. CZ t
☕ 350 – **35 rm** 5600/7300.

**Zabálburu** without rest, Pedro Martínez Artola 8, ✉ 48012, ☎ (94) 443 71 00, *Fax (94) 410 00 73* – TV ☎ . E VISA. CZ d
☕ 450 – **38 rm** 6100/8500.

XXXXX ✿ **Zortziko,** Alameda de Mazarredo 17, ✉ 48001, ☎ (94) 423 97 43, *Fax (94) 423 56 87* – ▤. AE ⓓ E VISA. CY r
*closed Sunday and 24 August-15 September* – **Meals** a la carte 6500/7500
**Spec.** Foie en copa con gelée de tempranillo. Mero al señorío de Otxaran. Suprema de pintada al jugo de trufas.

XXXX **Guria,** Gran Vía de Don Diego López de Haro 66, ✉ 48011, ☎ (94) 441 05 43, *Fax (94) 471 02 80* – ▤. AE ⓓ E VISA JCB. BY s
*closed Sunday, Holy Week and 23 August-6 September* – **Meals** a la carte 6100/8400.

XXXX **Bermeo,** Ercilla 37, ✉ 48011, ☎ (94) 470 57 00, *Fax (94) 443 93 35* – ▤. AE ⓓ E VISA JCB. CZ a
*closed Saturday lunch and Sunday dinner* – **Meals** a la carte approx. 5525.

XXX **Etxaniz,** Gordoniz 15, ✉ 48010, ☎ (94) 421 11 98, *Fax (94) 422 13 31* – ▤. AE ⓓ E VISA. CZ b
*closed Sunday, Bank Holidays, Holy Week and 1 to 15 August* – **Meals** a la carte approx. 6500.

XXX ✿ **Goizeko Kabi,** Particular de Estraunza 4, ✉ 48011, ☎ (94) 441 50 04, *Fax (94) 442 11 29* – ▤. AE ⓓ E VISA. CY a
*closed Sunday and 1 to 15 August* – **Meals** a la carte 4050/6150
**Spec.** Canelón de pichón y canela gratinado con Idiazábal. Láminas de bacalao en ensalada con pimientos asados naturales. Vieiras a la brasa con foie en su jugo.

XXX ✿ **Gorrotxa,** Alameda Urquijo 30 (arcade), ✉ 48008, ☎ (94) 443 49 37, *Fax (94) 422 05 35* – ▤. AE ⓓ E VISA JCB. CZ r
*closed Holy Week and 26 July-16 August* – **Meals** a la carte 5300/7300
**Spec.** Hongos con cigalas. Bogavante Thermidor. Hígado de ganso a las uvas.

XXX **Matxinbenta,** Ledesma 26, ✉ 48001, ☎ (94) 424 84 95, *Fax (94) 423 84 03* – ▤. AE ⓓ E VISA CZ n
*closed Sunday* – **Meals** a la carte approx. 5200.

XXX **Casa Vasca,** av. Lehendakari Aguirre 13, ✉ 48014, ☎ (94) 475 47 78, *Fax (94) 476 14 87* – ▤ . AE ⓓ E VISA JCB. BY d
*closed Sunday dinner and Bank Holidays dinner* – **Meals** a la carte 3425/4350.

XX **Asador Oteiza,** Licenciado Poza 27, ✉ 48011, ☎ (94) 441 41 33 – ▤. AE ⓓ E VISA. CZ e
*closed Saturday lunch, Sunday, Bank Holidays and Holy Week* – **Meals** a la carte approx. 5200.

XX **Víctor,** pl. Nueva 2-1º, ✉ 48005, ☎ (94) 415 16 78, *Fax (94) 415 06 16* – ▤. AE ⓓ E VISA JCB. DZ s
*closed Sunday, Holy Week and 15 July-15 August* – **Meals** a la carte approx. 6100.

XX **Begoña,** Virgen de Begoña, ✉ 48006, ☎ (94) 412 72 57 – ▤. AE ⓓ E VISA. AZ x
*closed Sunday except May and August* – **Meals** a la carte 3600/5500.

XX **El Asador de Aranda,** Egaña 27, ✉ 48010, ☎ (94) 443 06 64, *Fax (94) 443 06 64* – ▤. AE ⓓ E VISA. CZ s
Meals - Roast lamb - a la carte 3050/3400.

X **Rogelio,** carret. de Basurto a Castrejana 7, ✉ 48002, ☎ (94) 427 30 21, *Fax (94) 427 17 78* – ▤. AZ n
*closed Sunday, Holy Week and 25 July-24 August* – **Meals** a la carte 3625/4925.

X **Serantes,** Licenciado Poza 16, ✉ 48011, ☎ (94) 421 21 29, *Fax (94) 444 59 79* – ▤. AE ⓓ E VISA. CZ z
*closed 28 August-20 September* – **Meals** - Seafood - a la carte 4750/6100.

## Lasarte *20160 Guipúzcoa* 442 C 23 – *pop. 18 165 alt. 42 – Racecourse.*

*Madrid 491 – Bilbao/Bilbo 98 – San Sebastián/Donostia 9.*

XXXX ✿✿ **Martín Berasategui,** Loidi 4 ☎ (943) 36 64 71, *Fax (943) 36 61 07,* ←, – ▤ Ⓟ. AE ⓓ E VISA.
*closed Sunday dinner, Monday and 14 December-14 January* – **Meals** 7500 and a la carte 4900/5800
**Spec.** Lágrimas de guisantitos fríos en gelée de percebes (April-May). Milhojas caramelizado de anguila ahumada, foie gras, cebolleta y manzana verde. Manitas de cerdo ibérico rellenas con tosta de hongos y queso Idiazábal.

**Oyarzun** u **Oiartzun** *20180 Guipúzcoa* 442 C 24 – *pop. 8 393 alt. 81.*
*Madrid 481 – Bilbao/Bilbo 113 – San Sebastián/Donostia 13.*

XXX ✿✿ **Zuberoa,** barrio Iturriotz 8 ☎ (943) 49 12 28, *Fax (943) 49 26 79,* «Stylish traditional restaurant in a 15C manor house with pleasant terrace and ≤ » – ▤ Ⓟ. AE ⓞ E VISA
*closed Sunday dinner, Monday, 1 to 15 January, 14 to 24 April and 15 to 31 October* – **Meals** 9000 and a la carte 6250/8450
**Spec.** Gazpacho de tomate, gelée de bogavante y crema de limón (June-15 October). Milhojas de ternera en salsa de vino tinto. Copa de arroz con leche, infusión de limón y gelatina de canela.

**San Sebastián** o **Donostia** *20000* Ⓟ *Guipúzcoa* 442 C 24 – *pop. 176 019 – Seaside resort.*
See : *Location and bay*★★★ – *Monte Igueldo* ≤★★★ – *Monte Urgull* ≤★★.
**Envir.** : *Monte Ulía* ≤★ *NE : 7 km by N I.*
*Racecourse of Lasarte SW : 9 km* ☎ *(943) 37 32 39.*
18 *of San Sebastián Jaizkíbel E : 14 km by N I* ☎ *(943) 61 68 45.*
✈ *of San Sebastián, Fuenterrabía NE : 20 km* ☎ *(943) 66 85 00 – Iberia : Bengoetxea 3* ✉ *20004* ☎ *(943) 42 35 86 and Aviaco airport* ✉ *20280* ☎ *(943) 64 12 67.*
ℹ *Reina Regente* ✉ *20003* ☎ *(943) 48 11 66 Fax (943) 48 11 72 and Fueros 1* ✉ *20005* ☎ *(943) 42 62 82 Fax (943) 43 17 46* – **R.A.C.V.N.** *(R.A.C. Vasco Navarro) Echalde 12* ✉ *20005* ☎ *(943) 43 08 00 Fax (943) 42 91 50.*
*Madrid 488 – Bayonne 54 – Bilbao/Bilbo 100 – Pamplona/Iruñea 94 – Vitoria/Gasteiz 115.*

**María Cristina,** Okendo, ✉ 20004, ☎ (943) 42 49 00, *Fax (943) 42 39 14,* ≤ – |‡| ▤ TV ☎ – 🅰 25/300. AE ⓞ E VISA. ✂
**Meals** 4500 - ***Easo*** : **Meals** a la carte 5250/6900 – ☕ 2300 – **108 rm** 30000/44000, 28 suites.

XXXX ✿✿✿ **Arzak,** alto de Miracruz 21, ✉ 20015, ☎ (943) 27 84 65, *Fax (943) 27 27 53* – ▤ Ⓟ. AE ⓞ E VISA JCB. ✂
*closed Sunday dinner, Monday, 14 June-1 July and 2 to 25 November* – **Meals** 8900 and a la carte 8650/9900
**Spec.** Contraste de patata con marisco y cecina crujiente. Ocho verduras con pescado del día a la marinera. Canutillos de membrillo y queso con helado de naranja y nuez.

XXXX ✿✿ **Akelare,** paseo del Padre Orcolaga 56 - barrio de Igueldo W : 7,5 km, ✉ 20008, ☎ (943) 21 20 52, *Fax (943) 21 92 68,* ≤ *mar* – ▤ Ⓟ. AE ⓞ E VISA. ✂
*closed Sunday dinner, Monday except Bank Holiday weekends, February and 1 to 15 October* – **Meals** 8000 and a la carte 6100/7500
**Spec.** Xangurro frío con gelatina de setas, levístico y salsa de calabacín. Filetes de chicharro con puré de garbanzos y aceite de pimienta verde. Torre de chocolate con nuez moscada, salsa de jengibre y helado de plátano.

---

**MÁLAGA** *29000* 446 V 16 – *pop. 534 683 – Seaside resort.*
See : *Gibralfaro* : ≤★★ DY – *Alcazaba*★ *(Archaeological Museum*★*)* DY – *Cathedral*★ CZ – *El Sagrario Church (marienista altarpiece*★*)* CY.
**Envir.** : *Finca de la Concepción*★ *N : 7 km.*
18 *Málaga SW : 9 km* ☎ *(95) 237 66 77, Fax (95) 237 66 12* – 9 *El Candado E : 5 km* ☎ *(95) 229 93 40 Fax (95) 229 08 45.*
✈ *Málaga SW : 9 km* ☎ *(95) 204 84 84 – Iberia : Molina Larios 13,* ✉ *29015,* ☎ *(95) 213 61 48* CY *and Airport* ☎ *(95) 204 84 84.*
🚗 ☎ *(95) 212 82 25.*
⛴ *to Melilla : Cía Trasmediterránea, Estación Marítima, Local E-1* ✉ *29016* CZ, ☎ *(95) 222 43 91, Fax (95) 222 48 83.*
ℹ *Pasaje de Chinitas 4* ✉ *29015* ☎ *(95) 221 34 45 Fax (95) 222 94 21* – **R.A.C.E.** *Calderería (galerías Goya 5º-1)* ✉ *29008,* ☎ *(95) 221 42 60, Fax (95) 221 20 32.*
*Madrid 548 – Algeciras 133 – Córdoba 175 – Sevilla 217 – Valencia 651.*

Plan on next page

**Parador de Málaga-Gibralfaro** ⛰, Castillo de Gibralfaro, ✉ 29016, ☎ (95) 222 19 02, *Fax (95) 222 19 04,* « Magnificent setting with ≤ Málaga and sea », 🏊 – |‡| ▤ TV ☎ ♿ Ⓟ – 🅰 25/60. AE ⓞ E VISA JCB. ✂ DY
**Meals** 3700 – ☕ 1300 – **38 rm** 15200/19000.

**Larios,** Marqués de Larios 2, ✉ 29005, ☎ (95) 222 22 00, *Fax (95) 222 24 07* – |‡| ▤ TV ☎ – 🅰 25/150. AE ⓞ E VISA. ✂ CY s
**Meals** *(closed Sunday)* a la carte approx. 3300 – ☕ 1250 – **40 rm** 13000/15500.

# MÁLAGA

Constitución . . . . . . . . . . . . CY 40
Granada . . . . . . . . . . . . . . CDY
Marqués de Larios . . . . . . CYZ 84
Nueva . . . . . . . . . . . . . . . . CYZ
Santa Lucía . . . . . . . . . . . CY 123

Aduana (Pl. de la) . . . . . . DY 2
Arriola (Pl. de la) . . . . . . . CZ 5
Atocha (Pasillo) . . . . . . . . CZ 8
Calderería . . . . . . . . . . . . . . CY 13
Cánovas del Castillo (Pas.) . DZ 18
Cárcer . . . . . . . . . . . . . . . . . CY 27
Casapalma . . . . . . . . . . . . . CY 30
Colón (Alameda de) . . . . . . CZ 32
Comandante Benítez
(Av. del) . . . . . . . . . . . . . CZ 35
Compañía . . . . . . . . . . . . . . CY 37
Cortina del Muelle . . . . . . . CZ 42
Especerías . . . . . . . . . . . . . . CY 56
Frailes . . . . . . . . . . . . . . . . CDY 61
Huerto del Conde . . . . . . . . DY 67
Mariblanca . . . . . . . . . . . . . CY 77
Martínez . . . . . . . . . . . . . . . CZ 86
Molina Larios . . . . . . . . . . CYZ 95
Postigo de los Abades . . CDZ 106
Reding (Paseo de) . . . . . . DY 110
Santa Isabel (Pasillo de) . CYZ 120
Santa María . . . . . . . . . . . . CY 125
Sebastián Souvirón . . . . . CZ 130
Strachan . . . . . . . . . . . . . . CZ 133
Teatro (Pl. del) . . . . . . . . . CY 135
Tejón y Rodríguez . . . . . . CY 138
Tetuán (Puente de) . . . . . CZ 140

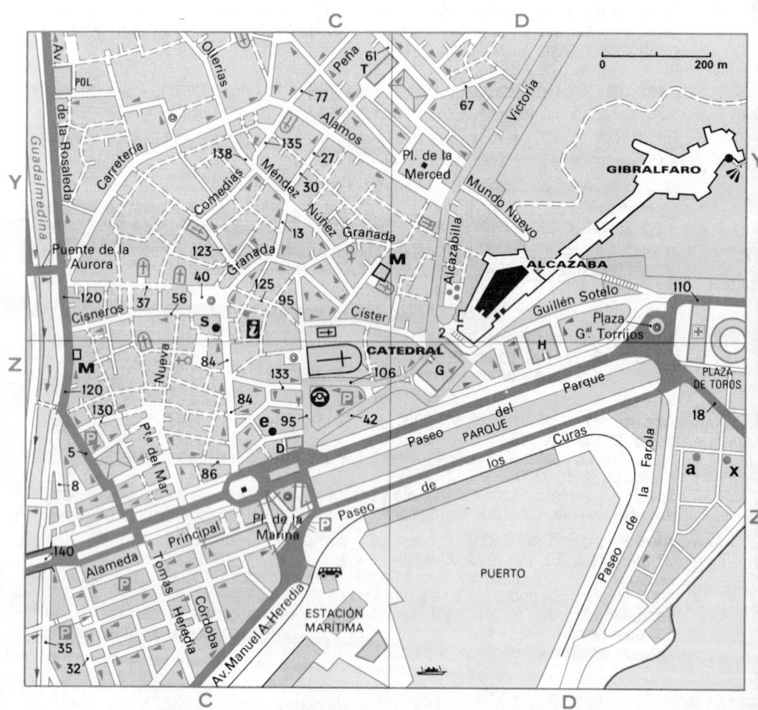


**Don Curro** coffee shop only, Sancha de Lara 7, 29015, (95) 222 72 00, *Fax (95) 221 59 46* – 25/60. AE E VISA JCB CZ e
650 – **118 rm** 8500/12000.

**Los Naranjos** without rest, paseo de Sancha 35, 29016, (95) 222 43 19, *Fax (95) 222 59 75* – AE E VISA.
900 – **40 rm** 10800/14900, 1 suite. E : by Pas. Cánovas del Castillo DZ

**Don Paco** without rest, Salitre 53, 29002, (95) 231 90 08, *Fax (95) 231 90 62* – AE E VISA. SW : by Alameda Principal CZ
375 – **25 rm** 6300/8000.

**Café de París,** Vélez Málaga 8, 29016, (95) 222 50 43, *Fax (95) 260 38 64* – P. AE E VISA JCB. E : by Pas. Cánovas del Castillo DZ
*closed Sunday and 15 to 31 July* – **Meals** a la carte approx. 3900.

**Adolfo,** paseo Marítimo Pablo Ruiz Picasso 12, 29016, (95) 260 19 14 – AE E VISA. E : by Pas. Cánovas del Castillo DZ
*closed Sunday* – **Meals** a la carte 2200/3900.

**Doña Pepa,** Vélez Málaga 6, 29016, (95) 260 34 89 – AE E VISA. DZ a
*closed Sunday and September* – **Meals** a la carte 2450/3850.

**El Refectorium,** Cervantes 8, 29016, (95) 221 89 90 – AE E VISA. E : by Pas. Cánovas del Castillo DZ
*closed Sunday and 1 to 15 June* – **Meals** a la carte 3100/4300.

**at Club de Campo** *SW : 9 km – ✉ 29000 Málaga :*

**Parador de Málaga del Golf,** at the golf course, ✉ 29080 apartado 324 Málaga, ☎ (95) 238 12 55, *Fax (95) 238 89 63,* ≤, « Overlooking the golf course », 18 – ▤ TV ☎ P – 25/70. AE ⓓ E VISA.
Meals 3500 – ☕ 1300 – **56 rm** 14000/17500, 4 suites.

**at Urbanización Mijas Golf** *by N 340 - SW : 30 km – ✉ 29640 Fuengirola :*

**Byblos Andaluz**, ☎ (95) 247 30 50, *Fax (95) 247 67 83,* ≤ *golf course and mountains,* , Thalassotherapy facilities, « Tasteful Andalusian style situated between two golf courses », 18 18 – ▤ TV ☎ P – 20/170. AE ⓓ E VISA.
**Meals** 5800 - ***Le Nailhac*** *(dinner only, closed Wednesday)* **Meals** a la carte 5600/7200 - ***El Andaluz :*** **Meals** a la carte 3900/5300 – ☕ 2250 – **108 rm** 31500/44000, 36 suites.

**Marbella** *29600 Málaga* 446 W 15 – *pop. 84410 – Seaside resort.*
See : *The Old town★.*
Envir. : *Puerto Banús (Pleasure harbour★) by ② : 8 km.*
*18 Río Real by ① : 5 km ☎ (95) 277 95 09 Fax (95) 277 21 40 – 18 Los Naranjos by ② : 7 km ☎ (95) 281 24 28 – 18 Aloha, urb. Aloha by ② : 8 km ☎ (95) 281 23 88 – 18 Las Brisas, Nueva Andalucía by ② : 11 km, ☎ (95) 281 08 75.*
*Glorieta de la Fontanilla ☎ (95) 277 14 42 Fax (95) 277 94 57 and Pl. de los Naranjos ☎ (95) 282 35 50 Fax (95) 277 36 21.*
*Madrid 602 ① – Algeciras 77 ② – Cádiz 201 ② – Málaga 56 ①*

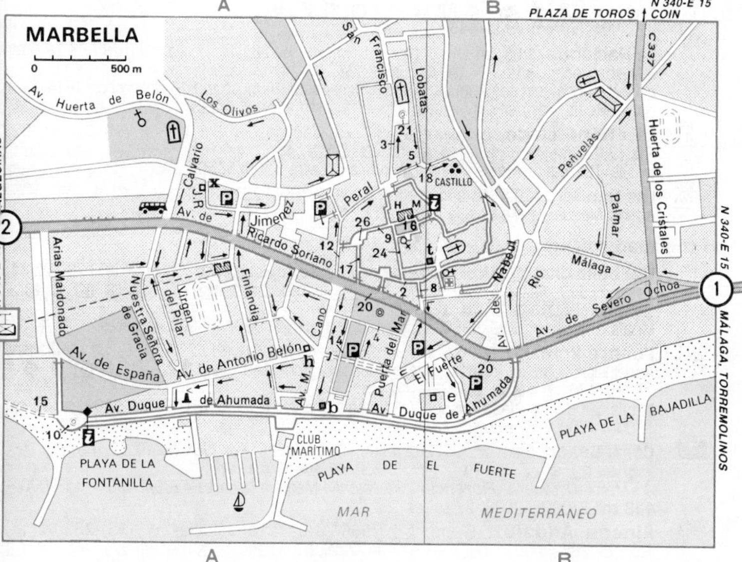


| | | | | | | | |
|---|---|---|---|---|---|---|---|
| Alameda | A 2 | Ancha | A 3 | Mar (Av. del) | A 14 |
| Huerta Chica | A 12 | Carlos Mackintosch | A 4 | Marítimo (Pas.) | A 15 |
| Naranjos (Pl. de los) | A 16 | Chorrón | A 5 | Portada | B 18 |
| Pedraza | A 17 | Enrique del Castillo | AB 8 | Ramón y Cajal (Av.) | AB 20 |
| Victoria (Pl.) | A 26 | Estación | A 9 | Santo Cristo (Pl.) | A 21 |
| | | Fontanilla (Glorieta) | A 10 | Valdés | A 24 |

**Gran Meliá Don Pepe**, José Meliá ☎ (95) 277 03 00, *Fax (95) 277 99 54,* ≤ sea and mountains, , « Subtropical plants », – ▤ TV ☎ P – 25/300. AE ⓓ E VISA. by ②
**Meals** 5950 - ***Grill La Farola*** *(dinner only)* **Meals** a la carte 5600/8750 – ☕ 2400 – **198 rm** 34500/37900, 6 suites.

**El Fuerte,** av. del Fuerte (95) 286 15 00, *Telex 77523, Fax (95) 282 44 11,* <, « Terraces with garden and palm trees », heated, , - rest AB e
**Meals** (dinner only except July-August) a la carte 4350/5600 - 1500 - **244 rm** 11000/19900, 19 suites.

**Marbella Inn** coffee shop only, Jacinto Benavente - bloque 6 (95) 282 54 87, *Fax (95) 282 54 87,* heated - A x
700 - **24 rm** 8700/11600, 32 suites.

**Lima** without rest, av. Antonio Belón 2 (95) 277 05 00, *Fax (95) 286 30 91* - A h
495 - **64 rm** 8360/10450.

**Santiago,** av. Duque de Ahumada 5 (95) 277 43 39, *Fax (95) 282 45 03,* - A b
*closed November* - **Meals** - Seafood - a la carte 3950/5700.

**Triana,** Gloria 11 (95) 277 99 62 - B t
*closed Monday and 10 January-5 March* - **Meals** - Rice dishes - a la carte 2750/5300.

**Cenicienta,** av. Cánovas del Castillo 52 (by pass) (95) 277 43 18, - by ②
*closed 15 January-15 February* - **Meals** - dinner only - a la carte 3350/4500.

**on the road to Málaga** *by ① - 29600 Marbella :*

**Don Carlos**, 10 km (95) 283 11 40, *Fax (95) 283 34 29,* <, « Extensive gardens », heated, - 25/1200.
***Los Naranjos*** *(dinner only)* **Meals** a la carte 4895/8300 - 1500 - **223 rm** 28000/33000, 15 suites.

**Artola** without rest, 12,5 km (95) 283 13 90, *Fax (95) 283 04 50,* <, « On a golf course », 9 -
900 - **29 rm** 7500/11500, 2 suites.

**La Hacienda,** 11,5 km and detour 1,5 km (95) 283 12 67, *Fax (95) 283 33 28,* « Rustic decor. Patio » -
*closed Monday except August, Tuesday except July-August and 16 November-18 December* - **Meals** - dinner only in August - a la carte approx. 6450.

**Le Chêne Liège,** La Mairena - 10 km and detour 5,5 km (95) 283 60 92, *Fax (95) 283 62 23,* -
*closed Tuesday* - **Meals** - dinner only - a la carte 3300/5350.

**Las Banderas,** 9,5 km and detour 0,5 km (95) 283 18 19, -
*closed Monday* - **Meals** a la carte 2700/4700.

**on the road to Cádiz** *by ② - 29600 Marbella :*

**Marbella Club**, Boulevard Príncipe Alfonso de Hohenlohe : 3 km (95) 282 22 11, *Telex 77319, Fax (95) 282 98 84,* heated, - 25/180.
**Meals** a la carte 7250/9150 - 2400 - **83 rm** 34000/46500, 46 suites.

**Puente Romano**, 3,5 km (95) 282 09 00, *Fax (95) 277 57 66,* « Elegant Andalusian complex in attractive gardens », heated, - 25/170. rest
**Meals** 5900 - ***La Plaza*** *(dinner only)* **Meals** a la carte 5500/6200 - 2500 - **142 rm** 33000/45000, 77 suites.

**Coral Beach,** 5 km (95) 282 45 00, *Telex 79816, Fax (95) 282 62 57,* - - 25/200.
*15 March-October* - ***Florencia*** *(dinner only)* **Meals** a la carte 4200/6400 - 2000 - **148 rm** 27000/32000, 22 suites.

**Rincón Andaluz,** 8 km, 29660 Nueva Andalucía, (95) 281 15 17, *Fax (95) 281 41 80,* « In the style of an Andalusian village », heated, - - 25/100.
**Meals** 3500 - 1400 - **224 rm** 18900/28000.

**Tryp Marbella Dinamar,** 6 km, 29660 Nueva Andalucía, (95) 281 05 00, *Fax (95) 281 23 46,* <, « Garden with », - - 25/150.
**Meals** 3200 - **116 rm** 19200/25000.

**La Meridiana,** camino de la Cruz : 3,5 km (95) 277 61 90, *Fax (95) 282 60 24,* <, « Garden terrace » -
*closed Monday, Tuesday lunch and 7 January-20 February* - **Meals** - dinner only in summer - a la carte 5300/7500.

**Villa Tiberio,** 2,5 km (95) 277 17 99, *Fax (95) 282 47 72,* « Garden terrace » -
*closed Sunday* - **Meals** a la carte 4050/6650.

XX **Trascorrales,** 8 km, ✉ 29660 Nueva Andalucía, ☎ (95) 281 45 17, « Villa with pleasant terrace and garden » – E VISA.
*closed Sunday and February* – **Meals** a la carte 3300/4900.

XX **El Portalón,** 3 km ☎ (95) 282 78 80, *Fax (95) 277 71 04* – ▤ P. AE ① E VISA.
**Meals** - Braised meat specialities - a la carte 4900/5800.

**at Puerto Banús** *W : 8 km – ✉ 29660 Nueva Andalucía :*

XXX **Cipriano,** av. Playas del Duque - edificio Sevilla ☎ (95) 281 10 77, *Fax (95) 281 10 77,* – ▤ P. AE ① E VISA
**Meals** a la carte 4550/6250.

XXX **Taberna del Alabardero,** muelle Benabola ☎ (95) 281 27 94, *Fax (95) 281 86 30,* – ▤. AE ① E VISA JCB
**Meals** a la carte approx. 4300.

---

**SEVILLA** *41000* P 446 T 11 y 12 – *pop. 704 857 alt. 12.*

**See :** *La Giralda★★★ (※★★)* BX – *Cathedral★★★ (Capilla Mayor altarpiece★★★, Capilla Real★★)* BX – *Reales Alcázares★★★* BXY *(Admiral Apartment : Virgin of the Mareantes altarpiece★ ; Pedro el Cruel Palace★★★ : Ambassadors room vault★★ ; – Carlos V Palace : tapestries★★, gardens★) – Santa Cruz Quarter★★* BCX *(Venerables Hospital★) – Fine Arts Museum★★ (room V★★★, room X★★)* AV – *Pilate's House★★ (Azulejos★★, staircase★ : cupule★)* CX – *María Luisa Park★★ (España Square★, – Archaelogical Museum : Carambolo tresor★) S : by Paseo de las Delicias* BY.

**Other curiosities :** *Charity hospital★* BY - *Santa Paula Convent★* CV *(front★ church) – Salvador Church★* BX *(baroque altarpieces★) – Sant Josep Chappel★* BX – *Town Hall (Ayuntamiento) : east front★* BX.

18 *Pineda SE : 3 km ☎ (95) 461 14 00 – ✈ Sevilla - San Pablo NE : 14 km ☎ (95) 444 90 00 – Iberia : Almirante Lobo 2, ✉ 41001, ☎ (95) 422 89 01* BX – *Santa Justa ☎ (95) 453 86 86.*

*Av. de la Constitución 21 B ✉ 41004 ☎ (95) 422 14 04 Fax (95) 422 97 53 and Paseo de las Delicias 9 ✉ 41012 ☎ (95) 423 44 65* – R.A.C.E. *Av. Eduardo Dato 22, ✉ 41018 ☎ (95) 463 13 50, Fax (95) 465 96 04.*

*Madrid 550 – La Coruña/A Coruña 950 – Lisboa 417 – Málaga 217 – Valencia 682.*

Plans on following pages

**Alfonso XIII,** San Fernando 2, ✉ 41004, ☎ (95) 422 28 50, *Telex 72725, Fax (95) 421 60 33,* « Magnificent Andalusian building », – ▤ TV ☎ P – 25/500. AE ① E VISA JCB. BY c
**Meals** a la carte approx. 5500 – 2500 – **127 rm** 49500/61600, 19 suites.

**Príncipe de Asturias**, Isla de La Cartuja, ✉ 41092, ☎ (95) 446 22 22, *Fax (95) 446 04 28,* – ▤ TV ☎ – 25/900. AE ① E VISA.
**Meals** 4000 – **288 rm** 24000/30000, 7 suites. N : by Torneo AV

**Tryp Colón,** Canalejas 1, ✉ 41001, ☎ (95) 422 29 00, *Telex 72726, Fax (95) 422 09 38,* – ▤ TV ☎ – 25/240. AE ① E VISA. AX s
**Meals** (see rest. ***El Burladero*** below) – 1700 – **204 rm** 33600/42000, 14 suites.

**Occidental Porta Coeli,** av. Eduardo Dato 49, ✉ 41018, ☎ (95) 453 35 00, *Telex 72913, Fax (95) 453 23 42,* – ▤ TV ☎ P – 25/600. AE ① E VISA JCB. E : by Demetrio de los Ríos CXY
**Meals** (see rest. ***Florencia*** below) – 1500 – **241 rm** 15000/20000, 3 suites.

**Meliá Lebreros,** Luis Morales 2, ✉ 41005, ☎ (95) 457 94 00, *Fax (95) 458 27 26,* – ▤ TV ☎ – 25/600. AE ① E VISA.
**Meals** (see rest. ***La Dehesa*** below) – 1500 – **431 rm** 15800/19200, 6 suites.
E : by Luis Montoto CX

**Meliá Sevilla,** Doctor Pedro de Castro 1, ✉ 41004, ☎ (95) 442 15 11, *Fax (95) 442 16 08,* – ▤ TV ☎ – 25/1000. AE ① E VISA JCB.
*closed July and August* – **Meals** 3500 – 1500 – **361 rm** 25200/28300, 5 suites.
SE : by Av. de Portugal CY

**Meliá Confort Macarena,** San Juan de Ribera 2, ✉ 41009, ☎ (95) 437 58 00, *Fax (95) 438 18 03,* – ▤ TV ☎ – 25/700. AE ① E VISA JCB.
**Meals** a la carte 2650/4300 – 1500 – **317 rm** 12700/15700, 10 suites.
N : by María Auxiliadora CV

**Occidental Sevilla** coffee shop only, av. Kansas City, ✉ 41018, ☎ (95) 458 20 00, *Fax (95) 458 46 15,* – ▤ TV ☎ – 25/320. AE ① E VISA JCB.
1500 – **228 rm** 23000/29000, 14 suites. E : by Luis Montoto CX

**Inglaterra,** pl. Nueva 7, ✉ 41001, ☎ (95) 422 49 70, *Fax (95) 456 13 36* – ▤ TV ☎ – 25/200. AE ① E VISA JCB. rest AX r
**Meals** 3000 – 1200 – **109 rm** 13600/17000, 4 suites.

# SEVILLA

Francos .............. BX
Sierpes .............. BVX
Tetuán ............... BX

Alemanes ............ BX 12
Alfaro (Pl.) ........... CXY 15
Almirante Apodaca .... CV 20
Almirante Lobo ....... BY 22
Álvarez Quintero ...... BX 23
Amparo ............ BV 25
Aposentadores ........ BV 28
Argote de Molina ...... BX 30
Armas (Pl. de) ........ AX 31
Banderas (Patio de) ... BXY 35
Capitán Vigueras ...... CY 42
Cardenal Spínola ...... AV 47
Castelar ............. AX 55
Chapina (Puente) ...... AX 59
Cruces .............. CX 75
Doña Elvira ........... BX 95
Doña Guiomar ........ AX 97
Escuelas Pías ......... CV 114
Farmaceútico E.
Murillo Herrera ...... AY 115
Feria ............... BV 123
Francisco Carrión
Mejías ............. CV 126
Fray Ceferino
González ........... BX 127
García de Vinuesa ..... BX 130
General Polavieja ...... BX 135
Jesús de la Vera Cruz .. AV 147
José María Martínez
Sánchez Arjona ..... AY 150
Julio César .......... AX 152
Luis Montoto ......... CX 160
Marcelino Champagnat . AY 172
Martín Villa .......... BV 190
Mateos Gago ......... BX 192
Murillo ............. AV 202
Museo (Pl.) .......... AV 205
Navarros ............ CVX 207
O'Donnell ........... BV 210
Pascual de Gayangos ... AV 220
Pastor y Landero ...... AX 222
Pedro del Toro ........ AV 227
Ponce de León (Pl.) .... CV 234
Puente y Pellón ....... BV 239
Puerta de Jerez ....... BY 242
República Argentina
(Av.) ............... AY 255
Reyes Católicos ....... AX 260
San Gregorio ......... BY 272
San Juan
de la Palma ........ BV 277
San Pedro (Pl.) ....... BV 286
San Sebastián (Pl.) ..... CY 287
Santa María
la Blanca ........... CX 297
Santander ........... BY 300
Saturno ............. CV 302
Triunfo (Pl.) .......... BX 307
Velázquez ........... BV 310
Venerables (Pl.) ....... BX 312
Viriato ............. BV 329

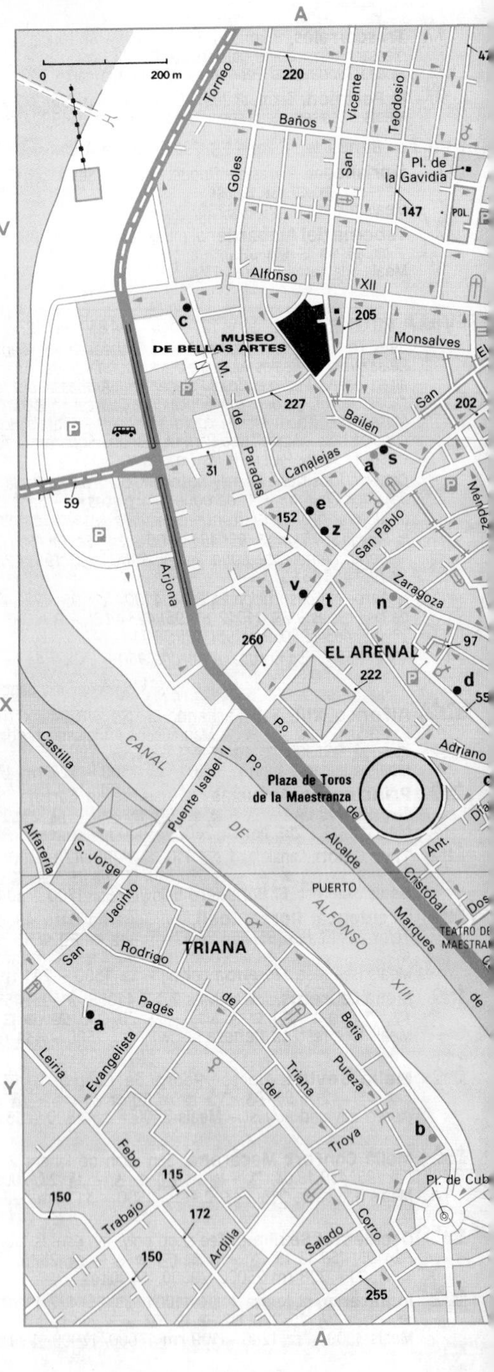


*Inclusion in the Michelin Guide cannot be achieved by pulling strings or by offering favours.*

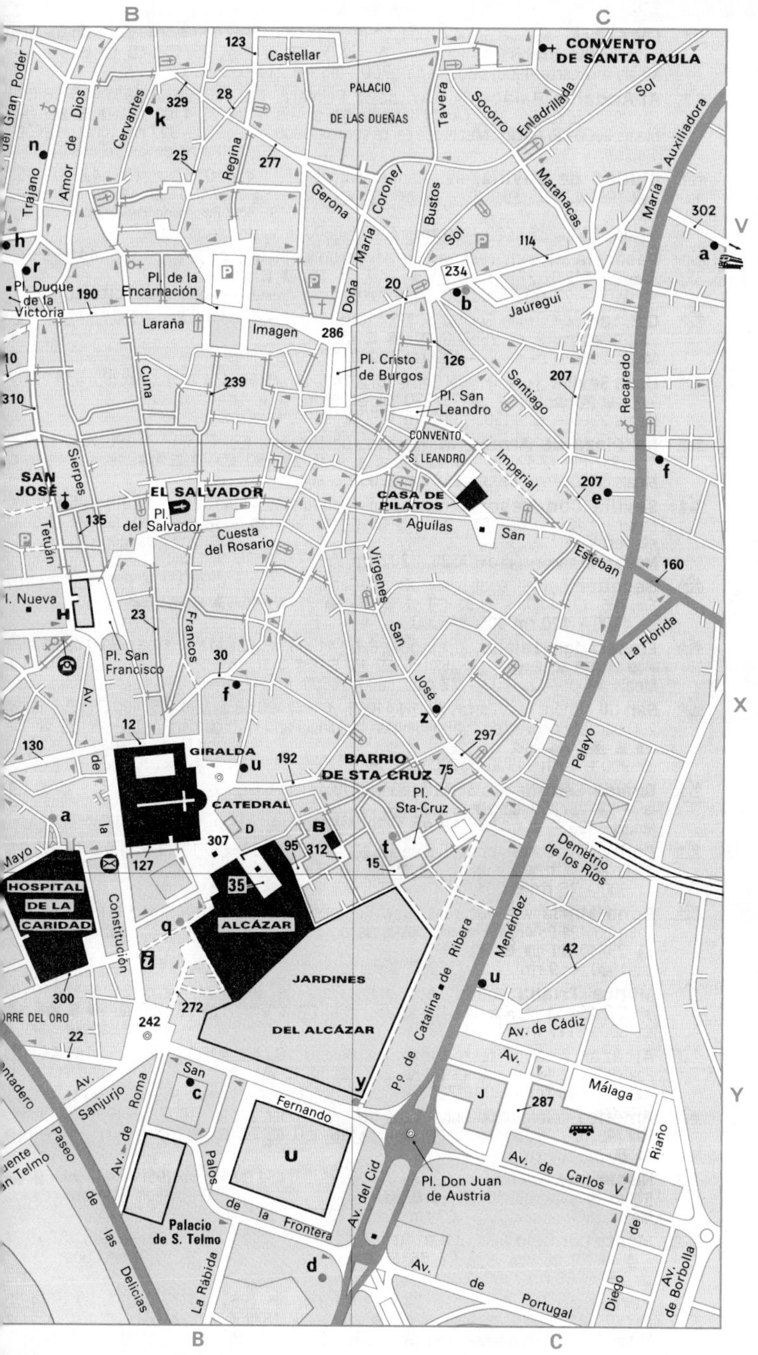
B
C
CONVENTO
DE SANTA PAULA
123
Castellar
PALACIO
DE LAS DUEÑAS
329
28
k
Cervantes
Amor de Dios
Trajano
n
25
Regina
277
Gerona
Doña María Coronel
Bustos
Tavera
Socorro
Enladrillada
Sol
Matahacas
María Auxiliadora
302
V
a
h
r
Pl. Duque de la Victoria
190
Pl. de la Encarnación
Laraña
Imagen
286
20
234
b
Jaúregui
114
Sol
Pl. Cristo de Burgos
126
Santiago
207
Recaredo
Pl. San Leandro
CONVENTO S. LEANDRO
Imperial
Cuna
239
10
310
Sierpes
SAN JOSÉ
EL SALVADOR
Pl. del Salvador
CASA DE PILATOS
Aguílas
San Esteban
207
e
f
160
Tetuán
135
Cuesta del Rosario
Vírgenes
San José
La Florida
Pl. Nueva
H
23
Pl. San Francisco
Francos
30
f
z
X
Av. de la Constitución
12
130
GIRALDA
u
192
BARRIO DE STA CRUZ
75
297
Pelayo
CATEDRAL
a
D
B
Pl. Sta-Cruz
t
Demetrio de los Ríos
Mayo
HOSPITAL DE LA CARIDAD
127
307
95
312
15
35
ALCÁZAR
q
Menéndez
42
JARDINES DEL ALCÁZAR
Po de Catalina de Ribera
u
300
TORRE DEL ORO
272
242
22
Av. de Cádiz
Av. Málaga
Y
J
287
San Fernando
y
c
Av. Sanjurjo
Roma
Av. de Roma
Paseo de las Delicias
Puente San Telmo
U
Palos de la Frontera
Av. del Cid
Pl. Don Juan de Austria
Av. de Carlos V
Riaño
Palacio de S. Telmo
La Rábida
d
Av. de Portugal
Diego de Riaño
Av. de Borbolla
B
C

**Los Seises,** Segovias 6, ✉ 41004, ☎ (95) 422 94 95, *Fax (95) 422 43 34*, « On the 3rd patio of the Archbishop's Palace », – ▤ – 25/100. AE ⦿ E VISA. ✻ Meals a la carte 4900/6600 – 1700 – **43 rm** 21000/25000. BX f

**Al-Andalus Palace**, av. de la Palmera, ✉ 41012, ☎ (95) 423 06 00, *Fax (95) 423 02 00*, – ▤ – 25/1100. AE ⦿ E VISA. ✻ Meals 2000 - ***El Patio*:** **Meals** a la carte approx. 3900 – 1500 – **327 rm** 14800/18500, 1 suite. SE : by Paseo de las Delicias BY

**Ciudad de Sevilla,** av. Manuel Siurot 25, ✉ 41013, ☎ (95) 423 05 05, *Fax (95) 423 85 39*, – ▤ – 25/300. AE ⦿ E VISA JCB. ✻ SE : by Paseo de las Delicias BY Meals 2800 – 1500 – **90 rm** 13200/18800, 3 suites.

**Pasarela** without rest, av. de la Borbolla 11, ✉ 41004, ☎ (95) 441 55 11, *Fax (95) 442 07 27* – ▤ – 25. AE ⦿ E VISA. ✻ 1100 – **77 rm** 12000/20000, 5 suites. SE : by Av. de Portugal CY

**G.H. Lar,** pl. Carmen Benítez 3, ✉ 41003, ☎ (95) 441 03 61, *Fax (95) 441 04 52* – ▤ – 25/300. AE ⦿ E VISA. ✻ CX f Meals 2600 – 1000 – **129 rm** 12000/17000, 8 suites.

**Husa Sevilla**, Pagés del Corro 90, ✉ 41010, ☎ (95) 434 24 12, *Fax (95) 434 27 07* – ▤ – 25/220. AE ⦿ E VISA JCB. ✻ AY a Meals 2000 – 1150 – **114 rm** 15600/19500, 14 suites.

**NH Plaza de Armas,** av. Marqués de Paradas, ✉ 41001, ☎ (95) 490 19 92, *Fax (95) 490 12 32*, – ▤ – 25/250. AE ⦿ E VISA. ✻ AV c Meals 3500 – 1400 – **260 rm** 27000, 2 suites.

**Sevilla Congresos,** Alcalde Luis Uruñuela, ✉ 41020, ☎ (95) 425 90 00, *Fax (95) 425 95 00*, – ▤ – 25/270. AE ⦿ E VISA. ✻ rest NE : by Luis Montoto CX Meals a la carte approx. 4325 – **202 rm** 10000/12500, 1 suite.

**Bécquer** coffee shop only, Reyes Católicos 4, ✉ 41001, ☎ (95) 422 89 00, *Fax (95) 421 44 00* – ▤ – 25/45. AE ⦿ E VISA. ✻ AX v 1100 – **120 rm** 9000/13000.

**Emperador Trajano,** José Laguillo 8, ✉ 41003, ☎ (95) 441 11 11, *Fax (95) 453 57 02* – ▤ – 25/150. AE ⦿ E VISA JCB. ✻ CV a Meals 1900 – 1000 – **77 rm** 13000/16600.

**San Gil** without rest, Parras 28, ✉ 41002, ☎ (95) 490 68 11, *Fax (95) 490 69 39*, « Early 20C partially converted typical Sevilian building. Patio with garden », – ▤. AE ⦿ E VISA JCB. ✻ N : by María Auxiliadora CV 900 – **4 rm** 11300/13200, 35 suites.

**Giralda,** Sierra Nevada 3, ✉ 41003, ☎ (95) 441 66 61, *Fax (95) 441 93 52* – ▤ – 25/250. AE ⦿ E VISA JCB. ✻ CX e Meals 1800 – 1000 – **98 rm** 12700/15900.

**Derby** without rest, pl. del Duque 13, ✉ 41002, ☎ (95) 456 10 88, *Fax (95) 421 33 91*, « Terrace with ≤ » – ▤. AE ⦿ E VISA. ✻ BV r 800 – **75 rm** 9000/10000.

**Doña María** without rest, Don Remondo 19, ✉ 41004, ☎ (95) 422 49 90, *Fax (95) 421 95 46*, « Elegant classic decor. Terrace with and ≤ » – ▤ – 25/40. AE ⦿ E VISA. ✻ BX u 1500 – **59 rm** 17000/26000, 2 suites.

**Monte Triana** coffee shop only, Clara de Jesús Montero 24, ✉ 41010, ☎ (95) 434 31 11, *Fax (95) 434 33 28* – ▤ – 25/100. AE ⦿ E VISA. ✻ 800 – **117 rm** 10500/13000. W : by Puente Isabel II AX

**Alcázar** without rest, Menéndez Pelayo 10, ✉ 41004, ☎ (95) 441 20 11, *Fax (95) 442 16 59* – ▤. AE ⦿ E VISA. ✻ CY u 750 – **93 rm** 13500/17000.

**América** coffee shop only, Jesús del Gran Poder 2, ✉ 41002, ☎ (95) 422 09 51, *Fax (95) 421 06 26* – ▤ – 25/150. AE ⦿ E VISA. ✻ BV h 800 – **100 rm** 9000/10000.

**Hispalis,** av. de Andalucía 52, ✉ 41006, ☎ (95) 452 94 33, *Fax (95) 467 53 13* – ▤ – 25/50. AE ⦿ E VISA. ✻ E : by Luis Montoto CX Meals 2500 – 1000 – **67 rm** 10700/12600, 1 suite.

**Monte Carmelo** without rest, Turia 7, ✉ 41011, ☎ (95) 427 90 00, *Fax (95) 427 10 04* – ▤ – 25/35. AE E VISA S : by Pl. de Cuba AY 750 – **68 rm** 7700/12000.

**Fernando III,** San José 21, ✉ 41004, ☎ (95) 421 77 08, *Telex 72491*, *Fax (95) 422 02 46*, – ▤ – 25/250. AE ⦿ VISA. ✻ rest CX z Meals 2300 – 1100 – **156 rm** 10000/12500, 1 suite.

**Regina** coffee shop only, San Vicente 97, ✉ 41002, ☎ (95) 490 75 75, *Fax (95) 490 75 62* – ⇕ ▤ TV ☎ 🚗. AE ⓓ E VISA. ✗ N : by San Vicente AV
☕ 950 – **68 rm** 11770/19260, 4 suites.

**Cervantes** without rest, Cervantes 10, ✉ 41003, ☎ (95) 490 05 52, *Fax (95) 490 05 36* – ⇕ ▤ TV ☎ 🚗. AE ⓓ E VISA. ✗ BV k
☕ 600 – **46 rm** 8000/11000.

**Puerta de Triana** without rest, Reyes Católicos 5, ✉ 41001, ☎ (95) 421 54 04, *Fax (95) 421 54 01* – ⇕ ▤ TV ☎. AE ⓓ E VISA JCB. ✗ AX t
**65 rm** ☕ 8000/12000.

**La Rábida,** Castelar 24, ✉ 41001, ☎ (95) 422 09 60, *Telex 73062, Fax (95) 422 43 75* – ⇕, ▤ rm, TV ☎. AE ⓓ E VISA. ✗ rest AX d
Meals 1950 – ☕ 400 – **100 rm** 5700/8750.

**Baco** no ☕, pl. Ponce de León 15, ✉ 41003, ☎ (95) 456 50 50, *Fax (95) 456 36 54* – ⇕ ▤ TV ☎. AE ⓓ E VISA JCB CV b
Meals (see rest. ***El Bacalao*** below) – **25 rm** 6000/8000.

**Montecarlo** (annexe 🏨), Gravina 51, ✉ 41001, ☎ (95) 421 75 03, *Fax (95) 421 68 25* – ⇕ ▤ TV ☎. AE ⓓ E VISA. ✗ AX e
Meals *(closed Sunday and 15 January-15 February)* 1900 – ☕ 600 – **47 rm** 7000/10000, 4 suites.

**Reyes Católicos** without rest, no ☕, Gravina 57, ✉ 41001, ☎ (95) 421 12 00, *Fax (95) 421 63 12* – ⇕ ▤ TV ☎. AE ⓓ E VISA. ✗ AX z
**27 rm** 7000/10000.

**Egaña Oriza,** San Fernando 41, ✉ 41004, ☎ (95) 422 72 54, *Fax (95) 421 04 29*, « Winter garden » – ▤. AE ⓓ E VISA JCB. ✗ CY y
*closed Saturday lunch, Sunday and August* – **Meals** a la carte 5200/6650
**Spec.** Pulpo en ensalada con láminas de patata al pimentón. Lomo de merluza con almejas en salsa verde. Redondillas de venado estofado con verduras (November-February).

**Florencia,** av. Eduardo Dato 49, ✉ 41018, ☎ (95) 453 35 00, *Telex 72913, Fax (95) 453 23 42*, « Tasteful decor » – ▤ P. AE ⓓ E VISA JCB. ✗
*closed August* – **Meals** a la carte 4600/6100. E : by Demetrio de los Ríos CXY

**Taberna del Alabardero** with rm, Zaragoza 20, ✉ 41001, ☎ (95) 456 06 37, *Fax (95) 456 36 66*, « Former palace » – ⇕ ▤ TV ☎ 🚗. AE ⓓ E VISA JCB. ✗ AX n
*closed August* – **Meals** a la carte 4400/6100 – **7 rm** ☕ 19000/23000
**Spec.** Pimientos de piquillo con cola de toro. Urta sobre compota de tomate aromatizada al cilantro. Delicias de solomillo ibérico con foie a la pimienta verde.

**El Burladero,** Canalejas 1, ✉ 41001, ☎ (95) 422 29 00, *Telex 72726, Fax (95) 422 09 38*, « Bullfighting theme » – ▤. AE ⓓ E VISA. ✗ AX a
*closed August* – **Meals** a la carte 4500/5700.

**La Dehesa,** Luis Morales 2, ✉ 41005, ☎ (95) 457 94 00, *Fax (95) 458 23 09*, 🏖, « Typical Andalusian decor » – ▤. AE ⓓ E VISA. ✗ E : by Luis Montoto CX
Meals - Braised meat specialities - a la carte approx. 3900.

**Marea Grande,** Diego Angulo Íñiguez, ✉ 41018, ☎ (95) 453 80 00, *Fax (95) 453 80 00* – ▤. AE ⓓ E VISA. ✗ E : by Demetrio de los Ríos CXY
*closed Sunday and August* – **Meals** - Seafood - a la carte 3775/5075.

**Al-Mutamid,** Alfonso XI-1, ✉ 41005, ☎ (95) 492 55 04, *Fax (95) 492 25 02*, 🏖 – ▤. AE ⓓ E VISA JCB. ✗ E : by Demetrio de los Ríos CXY
*closed August* – **Meals** a la carte 3650/4850.

**La Albahaca,** pl. Santa Cruz 12, ✉ 41004, ☎ (95) 422 07 14, *Fax (95) 456 12 04*, 🏖, « Former manor house » – ▤. AE ⓓ E VISA JCB. ✗ CX t
*closed Sunday* – **Meals** a la carte 4100/5300.

**Rincón de Curro,** Virgen de Luján 45, ✉ 41011, ☎ (95) 445 02 38, *Fax (95) 445 02 38* – ▤. AE ⓓ E VISA. ✗ S : by Pl. de Cuba AY
*closed Sunday dinner and August* – **Meals** a la carte 2600/4500.

**Rincón de Casana,** Santo Domingo de la Calzada 13, ✉ 41018, ☎ (95) 453 17 10, *Fax (95) 453 78 37*, « Regional decor » – ▤. AE ⓓ E VISA. ✗
*closed Sunday in August* – **Meals** a la carte 3400/5000.
E : by Demetrio de los Ríos CXY

**La Isla,** Arfe 25, ✉ 41001, ☎ (95) 421 26 31, *Fax (95) 456 22 19* – ▤. AE ⓓ E VISA. ✗
*closed Monday and August* – **Meals** a la carte 4800/5900. BX a

**Ox's,** Betis 61, ✉ 41010, ☎ (95) 427 95 85, *Fax (95) 427 84 65* – ▤. AE ⓓ E VISA JCB. ✗ AY b
*closed Sunday dinner and Monday* – **Meals** - Basque rest - a la carte 4200/5100.

**Horacio,** Antonia Díaz 9, ✉ 41001, ☎ (95) 422 53 85, *Fax (95) 421 79 27* – ▤. AE ⓓ E VISA JCB. ✗ AX c
*closed Sunday in August* – **Meals** a la carte 2975/4400.

**El Bacalao,** pl. Ponce de León 15, ✉ 41003, ☎ (95) 421 66 70, *Fax (95) 422 49 12* – ▤. AE ⓓ VISA. ⛌ CV b
**Meals** - Cod specialities - a la carte 3100/4300.

**Los Alcázares,** Miguel de Mañara 10, ✉ 41004, ☎ (95) 421 31 03, *Fax (95) 456 18 29*, ☂, « Regional decor » – ▤. E VISA. ⛌ BY q
*closed Sunday* – **Meals** a la carte approx. 3500.

**at San Juan de Aznalfarache** *W : 4 km – ✉ 41920 San Juan de Aznalfarache :*

**Alcora** ⛰ coffee shop only, carret. de Tomares ☎ (95) 476 94 00, *Fax (95) 476 94 98*, ←, « Patio with plants », Ƒő, ⛱ – |‡| ▤ TV ☎ ♿ 🚗 P – 🏛 25/1200. AE ⓓ E VISA. ⛌
☕ 1500 – **331 rm** 20000/25000, 70 suites.

**at Castilleja de la Cuesta** *W : 5 km – ✉ 41950 Castilleja de la Cuesta :*

**Hacienda San Ygnacio,** Real 194 ☎ (95) 416 04 30, *Fax (95) 416 14 37*, ☂, « In an old rustic inn », ⛱, 🌳 – ▤ TV ☎ P – 🏛 25/200. AE ⓓ E VISA JCB. ⛌ rest
***Almazara*** *(closed Monday in August)* **Meals** a la carte approx. 4800 – ☕ 1000 – **16 rm** 14000/19000.

**at Benacazón** *W : 23 km – ✉ 41805 Benacazón :*

**Andalusi Park H.,** motorway A 49 - exit 6 ☎ (95) 570 56 00, *Fax (95) 570 50 79*, « Arabian style building. Garden », Ƒő, ⛱ – |‡| ▤ TV ☎ ♿ P – 🏛 25/500. AE ⓓ E VISA. ⛌
**Meals** a la carte approx. 5100 – ☕ 1500 – **189 rm** 12800/16000, 11 suites.

**at Sanlúcar la Mayor** *W : 27 km – ✉ 41800 Sanlúcar la Mayor :*

**Hacienda Benazuza** ⛰, Virgen de las Nieves ☎ (95) 570 33 44, *Fax (95) 570 34 10*, ←, « In a 10C Arabian farmhouse », ⛱, 🌳, 🎾 – |‡| ▤ TV ☎ P – 🏛 25/400. AE ⓓ E VISA. ⛌ rest
*closed 15 July-August* – **Meals** 6500 - ***La Alquería*** : **Meals** a la carte 4700/8900 – ☕ 1500 – **26 rm** 34000/42000, 18 suites.

---

## VALENCIA *46000* P 445 N 28 y 29 – *pop. 777 427 alt. 13.*

See : *The Old town★ : Cathedral★ (El Miguelete★)* EX – *Palacio de la Generalidad★ (golden room : ceiling★)* EX **D** – *Lonja★ (silkhall★★, Maritime consulate hall : ceiling★)* DY.

**Other curiosities :** *Ceramic Museum★★ (Palacio del Marqués de Dos Aguas★)* EY **M**[1] - *San Pío V Museum★ (valencian primitifs★★)* FX – *Patriarch College or of the Corpus Christi★ (Passion triptych★)* EY **N** – *Serranos Towers★* EX.

*⛳9 Manises E : 12 km, ☎ (96) 152 38 04 – ⛳18 Club Escorpión NW : 19 km by road to Liria ☎ (96) 160 12 11 – ⛳18 El Saler-Parador Luis Vives SE : 15 km ☎ (96) 161 11 86.*

*✈ Valencia - Manises Airport E : 9,5 km ☎ (96) 370 95 00 – Iberia : Paz 14, ✉ 46003, ☎ (96) 352 75 52* EFY.

*⛴. To the Balearic Islands : Estación Marítima ✉ 46024 ☎ (96) 367 65 12 Fax (96) 367 06 44 by Av. Regne de València* FZ.

*ℹ Pl. del Ayuntamiento 1, ✉ 46002 ☎ (96) 351 04 17, Av. Cataluña 5, ✉ 46010 ☎ (96) 369 79 32, Paz 48 ✉ 46003 ☎ (96) 394 22 22 and Xàtiva 24 (North Station) ✉ 46007 ☎ (96) 352 85 73* – R.A.C.E. *(R.A.C. de València) Av. Regne de València 64, ✉ 46005, ☎ (96) 374 94 05 Fax (96) 373 71 06.*

*Madrid 351 – Albacete 183 – Alicante/Alacant (by coast) 174 – Barcelona 361 – Bilbao/Bilbo 606 – Castellón de la Plana/Castelló de la Plana 75 – Málaga 651 – Sevilla 682 – Zaragoza 330.*

Plans on following pages

**Meliá Valencia Palace** ⛰, paseo de la Alameda 32, ✉ 46023, ☎ (96) 337 50 37, *Fax (96) 337 55 32*, ←, Ƒő, ⛱ – |‡| ▤ TV ☎ ♿ 🚗 – 🏛 25/800. AE ⓓ E VISA JCB. ⛌ E : by Puente de Aragón FZ
**Meals** a la carte 3500/4500 – ☕ 1500 – **183 rm** 25145/32960, 16 suites.

**Meliá Rey Don Jaime,** av. Baleares 2, ✉ 46023, ☎ (96) 337 50 30, *Fax (96) 337 15 72*, ⛱ – |‡| ▤ TV ☎ P – 🏛 25/250. AE ⓓ E VISA. ⛌ E : by Puente de Aragón FZ
**Meals** 4000 – ☕ 1425 – **312 rm** 17430/21900, 2 suites.

**Astoria Palace,** pl. Rodrigo Botet 5, ✉ 46002, ☎ (96) 352 67 37, *Telex 62733*, *Fax (96) 352 80 78* – |‡| ▤ TV ☎ ♿ – 🏛 25/500. AE ⓓ E VISA JCB. ⛌ EY p
***Vinatea*** : **Meals** a la carte 4250/5750 – ☕ 1500 – **196 rm** 20500/25700, 7 suites.

**Turia,** Profesor Beltrán Baguena 2, ✉ 46009, ☎ (96) 347 00 00, *Fax (96) 347 32 44* – 25/300. VISA.
**Meals** 3000 – 600 – **160 rm** 10000/14500, 10 suites.
NW : by Gran Vía Fernando el Católico DY

**Acteón Plaza,** Islas Canarias 102, ✉ 46023, ☎ (96) 331 07 07, *Fax (96) 330 22 30*, – 25/400. AE VISA. E : by Av. Regne de València FZ
**Meals** 2250 – 1400 – **182 rm** 18400/23000, 5 suites.

**Mercure Conqueridor,** Cervantes 9, ✉ 46007, ☎ (96) 352 29 10, *Fax (96) 352 28 83* – 25/80. AE VISA. DZ b
**Meals** 2700 – 1400 – **55 rm** 13900/21800, 4 suites.

**Dimar** coffee shop only, Gran Vía Marqués del Turia 80, ✉ 46005, ☎ (96) 395 10 30, *Fax (96) 395 19 26* – 25/50. AE VISA JCB FZ q
1300 – **103 rm** 13200/21800, 1 suite.

**Reina Victoria,** Barcas 4, ✉ 46002, ☎ (96) 352 04 87, *Telex 64755, Fax (96) 352 04 87* – 25/75. AE VISA. EY s
**Meals** 3000 – 1200 – **94 rm** 12500/20000, 3 suites.

**NH Center,** Ricardo Micó 1, ✉ 46009, ☎ (96) 347 50 00, *Fax (96) 347 62 52*, heated – 25/400. AE VISA JCB.
**Meals** 2500 – 1200 – **193 rm** 12000/14000, 3 suites.
N : by Gran Vía Fernando el Católico DY

**NH Ciudad de Valencia,** av. del Puerto 214, ✉ 46023, ☎ (96) 330 75 00, *Fax (96) 330 98 64* – 30/80. AE VISA JCB.
**Meals** 2800 – 1000 – **147 rm** 11500/13000, 2 suites.
E : by Puente de Aragón FZ

**NH Abashiri,** av. Ausias March 59, ✉ 46013, ☎ (96) 373 28 52, *Fax (96) 373 49 66* – 30/250. AE VISA JCB.
**Meals** 3800 – 1000 – **105 rm** 9500/11500. S : by Av. Regne de València FZ

**NH Villacarlos** without rest, av. del Puerto 60, ✉ 46023, ☎ (96) 337 50 25, *Fax (96) 337 50 74* – AE VISA JCB.
1000 – **51 rm** 11500. E : by Puente de Aragón FZ

**Cónsul del Mar,** av. del Puerto 39, ✉ 46021, ☎ (96) 362 54 32, *Fax (96) 362 16 25*, « Old stately home » – AE VISA E : by Puente de Aragón FZ
**Meals** 1250 – 800 – **45 rm** 16000.

**Ad-Hoc,** Boix 4, ✉ 46003, ☎ (96) 391 91 40, *Fax (96) 391 36 67*, « Attractive 19C building » – AE VISA FX a
**Meals** (see rest. ***Chust Godoy*** below) – 815 – **28 rm** 11650/16400.

**Renasa** coffee shop only, av. de Cataluña 5, ✉ 46010, ☎ (96) 369 24 50, *Fax (96) 393 18 24* – 25/75. AE VISA
**69 rm** 7000/11500, 4 suites. E : by Puente del Real FX

**Llar** without rest, Colón 46, ✉ 46004, ☎ (96) 352 84 60, *Fax (96) 351 90 00* – 25/30. AE VISA FZ u
900 – **50 rm** 10000/12500.

**Sorolla** without rest, no, Convento de Santa Clara 5, ✉ 46002, ☎ (96) 352 33 92, *Fax (96) 352 14 65* – AE VISA EZ z
**50 rm** 6500/11300.

**Chambelán,** Chile 4, ✉ 46021, ☎ (96) 393 37 74, *Fax (96) 393 37 72* – AE VISA. E : by Puente de Aragón FZ
*closed Sunday, Holy Week and August* – **Meals** a la carte 3550/5100.

**Eladio,** Chiva 40, ✉ 46018, ☎ (96) 384 22 44, *Fax (96) 384 22 44* – AE VISA. W : by Ángel Guimerá DY
*closed Sunday and August* – **Meals** a la carte 2950/4650.

**Óscar Torrijos,** Dr. Sumsi 4, ✉ 46005, ☎ (96) 373 29 49 – AE VISA.
*closed Sunday except Bank Holiday weekends and 15 August-15 September* – **Meals** 4500 and a la carte 4600/5900 FZ h
**Spec.** Ravioli de rabo de buey y foie con crujiente de manchego y salsa de trufas (October-April). Ensalada templada de vieiras y setas (October-April). Crêpes rellenas de arroz con leche caramelizadas y fruta confitada.

**Rías Gallegas,** Cirilo Amorós 4, ✉ 46004, ☎ (96) 352 51 11, *Fax (96) 351 99 10* – AE VISA EZ r
*closed Sunday and the 2nd and 3rd weeks in August* – **Meals** 4650 and a la carte 4350/6400
**Spec.** Lamprea estilo Arbo (January-March). Lacón con grelos (November-April). Pulpo a la gallega.

**Albacar,** Sorní 35, ✉ 46004, ☎ (96) 395 10 05 – AE VISA. FY s
*closed Saturday lunch, Sunday, Holy Week and August* – **Meals** a la carte approx. 5000.

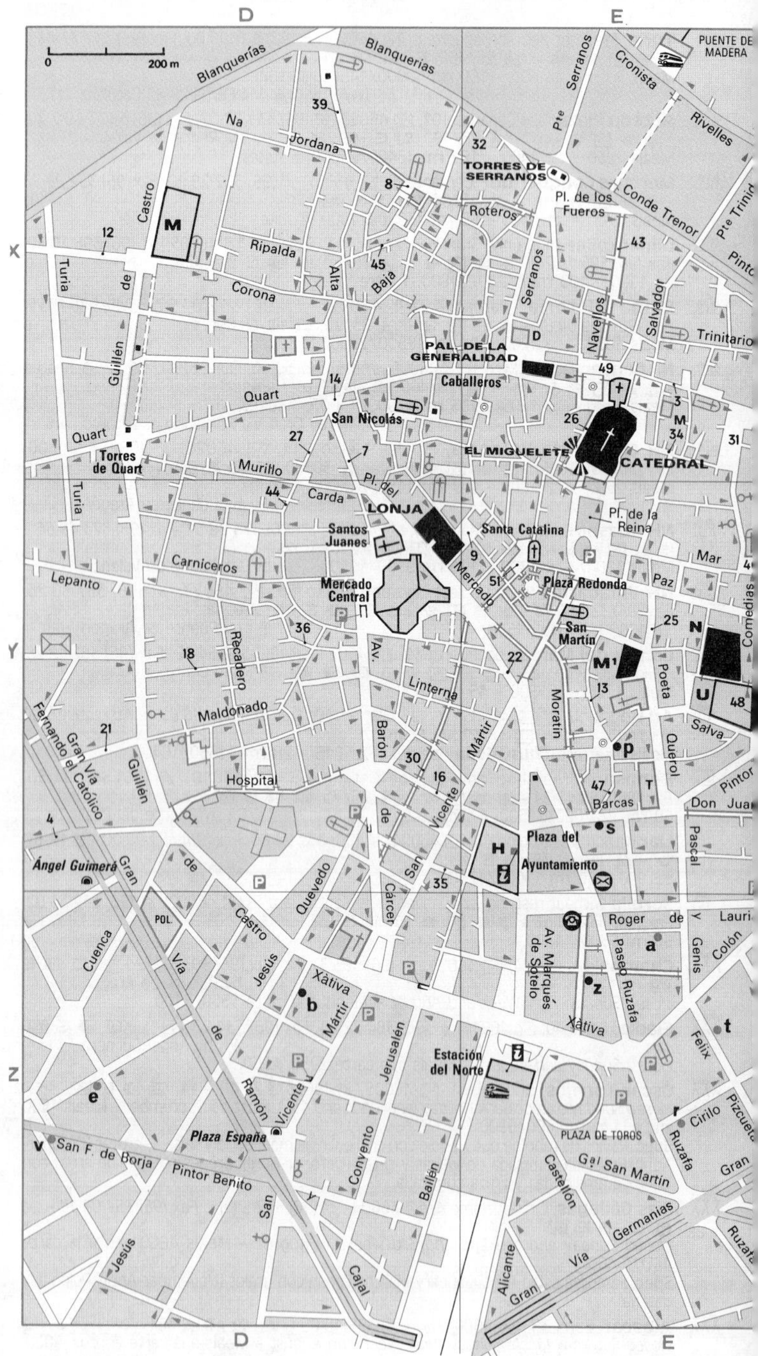
D
E
0
200 m
PUENTE DE MADERA
Blanquerías
Na
Jordana
Castro
M
12
Turia
de
Guillén
Ripalda
Corona
Alta
Baja
45
39
32
8
TORRES DE SERRANOS
Roteros
Pte Serranos
Cronista
Rivelles
Conde Trenor
Pte Trinidad
Pinto
Pl. de los Fueros
43
Serranos
Navellos
Salvador
Trinitarios
D
PAL. DE LA GENERALIDAD
Caballeros
49
3
M
34
31
26
EL MIGUELETE
CATEDRAL
Quart
Torres de Quart
14
San Nicolás
27
7
Murillo
44
Carda
Pl. del
LONJA
Santos Juanes
Santa Catalina
Pl. de la Reina
9
Mercado
Mar
Carniceros
Lepanto
Mercado Central
Plaza Redonda
Paz
San Martín
25
N
Comedias
M1
U
48
Poeta
13
22
Moratín
Recadero
18
36
Av.
Linterna
Maldonado
21
Gran Vía
Fernando el Católico
Hospital
Barón
30
16
Mártir
Vicente
p
Salva
Querol
47
Barcas
T
Pintor
Don Juan
Pascal
4
Ángel Guimerá
Gran
de
Castro
Quevedo
de
San
Cárcer
35
H
Plaza del Ayuntamiento
s
POL.
Vía
Jesús
Cuenca
Xàtiva
b
Mártir
Roger
de
Lauria
a
Av. Marqués de Sotelo
Paseo Ruzafa
y
Genís
Colón
z
Xàtiva
Félix
t
Estación del Norte
Jerusalén
de
Ramón
Vicente
Z
X
Y
e
Plaza España
v
San F. de Borja
Pintor Benito
Convento
Bailén
PLAZA DE TOROS
Gral San Martín
Castellón
r
Cirilo
Pizcueta
Ruzafa
Gran
Germanías
Vía
Gran
Alicante
San
y
Cajal
Jesús
Ruzafa

# VALENCIA

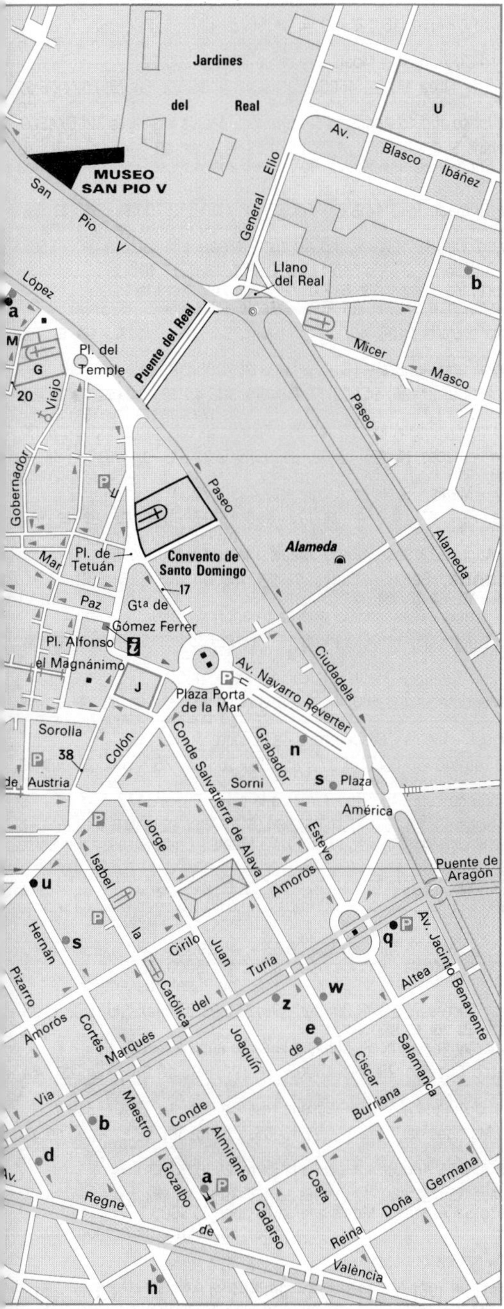

| Street | Grid |
|---|---|
| Ayuntamiento (Pl. del) | EY |
| Marqués de Sotelo (Av.) | EZ |
| Pascual y Genís | EYZ |
| Paz | EFY |
| San Vicente Mártir | DY |
| Almirante | EX 2 |
| Almudin | EX 3 |
| Ángel Guimerá | DY 4 |
| Bolsería | DX 7 |
| Carmen (Pl. del) | DX 8 |
| Dr. Collado (Pl.) | EY 9 |
| Dr. Sanchís Bergón | DX 12 |
| Embajador Vich | EY 13 |
| Esparto (Pl. del) | DX 14 |
| Garrigues | DY 16 |
| General Palanca | FY 17 |
| Guillém Sorolla | DY 18 |
| Maestres | FX 20 |
| Maestro Palau | DY 21 |
| María Cristina (Av.) | EY 22 |
| Marqués de Dos Aguas | EY 25 |
| Micalet | EX 26 |
| Moro Zeit | DX 27 |
| Músico Peydro | DY 30 |
| Nápoles y Sicilia (Pl.) | EX 31 |
| Padre Huérfanos | EX 32 |
| Palau | EX 34 |
| Periodista Azzati | DY 35 |
| Pie de la Cruz | DY 36 |
| Poeta Quintana | FY 38 |
| Salvador Giner | DX 39 |
| San Vicente Ferrer (Pl.) | EY 40 |
| Santa Ana (Muro) | EX 43 |
| Santa Teresa | DY 44 |
| Santo Tomás | DX 45 |
| Transits | EY 47 |
| Universidad | EY 48 |
| Virgen (Pl. de la) | EX 49 |
| Virgen de la Paz (Pl.) | EY 51 |

*We suggest:*
*For a successful tour, that you prepare it in advance.*
***Michelin maps** and **guides** will give you much useful information on route planning, places of interest, accommodation, prices, etc.*

XX **La Sucursal,** av. Navarro Reverter 16, ✉ 46004, ℘ (96) 374 66 65, *Fax (96) 374 66 65* – ▤. AE ⓓ E VISA. ✂ FY n
*closed Sunday and 15 to 30 August* – **Meals** a la carte 3300/4200.

XX **El Ángel Azul,** Conde de Altea 33, ✉ 46005, ℘ (96) 374 56 56, *Fax (96) 374 56 56* – ▤. ⓓ E VISA. ✂ FZ e
*closed Sunday, Monday lunch and 15 August-8 September* – **Meals** a la carte 3250/4500.

XX **Kailuze,** Gregorio Mayáns 5, ✉ 46005, ℘ (96) 374 39 99 – ▤. AE VISA. ✂ FZ d
*closed Saturday lunch, Sunday, Bank Holidays, Holy Week and August* – **Meals** - Basque rest - a la carte 3700/4850.

XX **El Gastrónomo,** av. Primado Reig 149, ✉ 46020, ℘ (96) 369 70 36 – ▤. E VISA. ✂ NE : by Puente del Real FX
*closed Sunday, Monday dinner, Holy Week and August* – **Meals** a la carte 3450/4850.

XX **Joaquín Schmidt,** Visitación 7 ℘ (96) 340 17 10, *Fax (96) 340 17 10*, 🏠, « Set in an historic house with courtyard » – ▤. ⓓ E VISA. ✂ N : by Cronista Rivelles EX
*closed Sunday, Monday lunch and 12 to 23 April* – **Meals** a la carte 3775/5850.

XX **El Gourmet,** Taquígrafo Martí 3, ✉ 46005, ℘ (96) 395 25 09 – ▤. AE ⓓ E VISA. ✂ FZ b
*closed Sunday, Holy Week and August* – **Meals** a la carte 2800/3900.

XX **Civera,** Lérida 11, ✉ 46009, ℘ (96) 347 59 17, *Fax (96) 348 46 38* – ▤. AE ⓓ E VISA. ✂ N : by Cronista Rivelles EX
*closed Sunday dinner, Monday and August* – **Meals** - Seafood - a la carte approx. 6100.

XX **Rio Sil Civera,** Mosén Femades 10, ✉ 46002, ℘ (96) 352 97 64, *Fax (96) 351 38 31*, 🏠 – ▤. AE ⓓ E VISA. ✂ EZ a
*closed 15 June-15 July* – **Meals** - Seafood - a la carte 4950/7200.

XX **El Cabanyal,** Reina 128, ✉ 46011, ℘ (96) 356 15 03 – ▤. AE ⓓ E VISA. ✂ E : by Puente de Aragón FZ
*closed Sunday and 15 August-15 September* – **Meals** a la carte 4000/4750.

XX **El Asador de Aranda,** Félix Pizcueta 9, ✉ 46004, ℘ (96) 352 97 91, *Fax (96) 352 97 91* – ▤. AE ⓓ E VISA. ✂ EZ t
*closed Sunday dinner* – **Meals** - Roast lamb - a la carte approx. 3950.

XX **Chust Godoy,** Boix 6, ✉ 46003, ℘ (96) 391 38 15, *Fax (96) 391 36 67* – ▤. AE E VISA. ✂ FX a
*closed Saturday lunch and Sunday* – **Meals** a la carte approx. 4800.

XX **José Mari,** Estación Marítima 1º, ✉ 46024, ℘ (96) 367 20 15, ← – ▤. AE ⓓ E VISA. ✂ SE : by Puente de Aragón FZ
*closed Sunday and August* – **Meals** - Basque rest - a la carte 3000/4500.

X **Montes,** pl. Obispo Amigó 5, ✉ 46007, ℘ (96) 385 50 25 – ▤. AE ⓓ E VISA DZ v
*closed Sunday dinner, Monday and August* – **Meals** a la carte 2850/3475.

X **Mey Mey,** Historiador Diago 19, ✉ 46007, ℘ (96) 384 07 47 – ▤. AE E VISA. ✂ DZ e
*closed Holy Week and the last three weeks in August* – **Meals** - Chinese rest - a la carte 2280/2870.

X **El Plat,** Císcar 3, ✉ 46005, ℘ (96) 374 12 54 – ▤. AE E VISA JCB FZ w
*closed Sunday dinner and Monday (except Bank Holidays) and Holy Week* – **Meals** a la carte 3150/4250.

X **Eguzki,** av. Baleares 1, ✉ 46023, ℘ (96) 337 50 33 – ▤. E VISA. ✂
*closed Sunday and August* – **Meals** - Basque rest - a la carte 3000/4500. E : by Puente de Aragón FZ

X **Palace Fesol,** Hernán Cortés 7, ✉ 46004, ℘ (96) 352 93 23, *Fax (96) 352 93 23*, « Regional decor » – ▤. AE ⓓ E VISA. ✂ FZ s
*closed Saturday and Sunday in summer* – **Meals** a la carte approx. 3700.

X **Bazterretxe,** Maestro Gozalbo 25, ✉ 46005, ℘ (96) 395 18 94 – ▤. AE VISA. ✂ FZ a
*closed Sunday dinner and August* – **Meals** - Basque rest - a la carte 2200/3350.

X **El Romeral,** Gran Vía Marqués del Turia 62, ✉ 46005, ℘ (96) 395 15 17 – ▤. AE ⓓ E VISA. ✂ FZ z
*closed Monday and 25 July-25 August* – **Meals** a la carte 2950/3950.

X **Olabarrieta,** La Barraca 35, ✉ 46011, ℘ (96) 367 07 79 – ▤. VISA. ✂
*closed Sunday and 15 to 31 August* – **Meals** a la carte approx. 3500. E : by Puente de Aragón FZ

**by road C 234** *NW : 8,5 km – ✉ 46035 Valencia :*

**Feria,** av. de las Ferias 2 ℘ (96) 364 44 11, *Fax (96) 364 54 83* – |≑| ▤ TV ☎ 🚗 – 🏛 25/200. AE ⓓ E VISA. ✂ rest by Gran Vía Fernando el Católico DY
**Meals** 2800 – **136 suites** ☕ 16000/27500.

**at Almàssera** *NE : 9 km – ✉ 46132 Almàssera :*

XX **Lluna de València,** Camí del Mar 56 ☎ (96) 185 10 86, *Fax (96) 185 10 06,* « Old farmhouse » – ▤ Ⓟ. AE ⓓ E VISA. ✻ by Puente del Real FX
*closed Saturday lunch, Sunday and Holy Week* – **Meals** a la carte 3000/3250.

**at El Saler** *S : 8 km – ✉ 46012 Valencia :*

**Sidi Saler** ⑤, beach - 3 km ☎ (96) 161 04 11, *Fax (96) 161 08 38,* ≤, ⛱, Fь, ⛱, ⛱, ⛱, ✂ – |⇕| ▤ TV ☎ Ⓟ – 🏛 25/300. AE ⓓ E VISA JCB
**Meals** 3550 - ***Grill Bendinat*** : **Meals** a la carte 3600/5100 – ☕ 1500 – **260 rm** 17000/21000, 17 suites.

**Parador de El Saler** ⑤, 7 km ☎ (96) 161 11 86, *Fax (96) 162 70 16,* ≤, « In the middle of the golf course », ⛱, ✂, ⛳18 – |⇕| ▤ TV ☎ Ⓟ – 🏛 25/60. AE ⓓ E VISA. ✻
**Meals** 3700 – ☕ 1300 – **58 rm** 15600/19500.

**at Manises** *on the airport road - E : 9,5 km – ✉ 46940 Manises :*

**Meliá Confort Azafata,** autopista del aeropuerto 15 ☎ (96) 154 61 00, *Fax (96) 153 20 19* – |⇕| ▤ TV ☎ 🚗 Ⓟ – 🏛 25/300. AE ⓓ E VISA. ✻ rest
**Meals** 2900 – ☕ 1150 – **124 rm** 12800/19000, 4 suites.

**at Puçol** *N : 25 km by motorway A 7 – ✉ 46760 Puçol :*

**Monte Picayo** ⑤, urb. Monte Picayo ☎ (96) 142 01 00, *Telex 62087, Fax (96) 142 21 68,* ⛱, « On a hillside with ≤ », ⛱, ⛱, ✂ – |⇕| ▤ TV ☎ Ⓟ – 🏛 25/800. AE ⓓ E VISA. ✻
**Meals** 3750 – ☕ 1400 – **79 rm** 19150/23950, 4 suites.

# Sweden

## Sverige

STOCKHOLM – GOTHENBURG

# PRACTICAL INFORMATION

## LOCAL CURRENCY

**Swedish Kronor:** *100 SEK = 12,65 US $ (Jan. 98).*

## TOURIST INFORMATION

*In Stockholm, the Tourist Centre is situated in Sweden House, entrance from Kungsträdgården at Hamngatan. Open Mon-Fri 9am-6pm. Sat. and Sun. 9am-3pm. Telephone weekdays (08) 789 24 00, weekends to Excursion Shop and Tourist Centre. For Gothenburg, see information in the text of the town under* ℹ.

**National Holiday in Sweden:** *6 June.*

## FOREIGN EXCHANGE

*Banks are open between 9.30am and 3pm on weekdays only. Some banks in the centre of the city are usually open weekdays 9am to 6pm. Most large hotels and the Tourist Centre have exchange facilities. Arlanda airport has banking facilities between 7am to 10pm seven days a week.*

## MEALS

*At lunchtime, follow the custom of the country and try the typical buffets of Scandinavian specialities (Smörgåsbord).*
*At dinner, the a la carte and set menus will offer you more conventional cooking.*

## SHOPPING

*In the index of street names, those printed in red are where the principal shops are found.*
*The main shopping streets in the centre of Stockholm are: Hamngatan, Biblioteksgatan, Drottninggatan.*
*In the Old Town mainly Västerlånggatan.*

## THEATRE BOOKINGS

*Your hotel porter will be able to make your arrangements or direct you to Theatre Booking Agents.*

## CAR HIRE

*The international car hire companies have branches in Stockholm, Gothenburg, Arlanda and Landvetter airports. Your hotel porter should be able to give details and help you with your arrangements.*

## TIPPING

*Hotels and restaurants normally include a service charge of 15 per cent. Doormen, baggage porters etc. are generally given a gratuity.*
*Taxis include 10 % tip in the amount shown on the meter.*

## SPEED LIMITS - SEAT BELTS

*The maximum permitted speed on motorways and dual carriageways is 110 km/h - 68 mph and 90 km/h - 56 mph on other roads except where a lower speed limit is indicated.*
*The wearing of seat belts is compulsory for drivers and all passengers.*
*In Sweden, drivers must not drink alcoholic beverages at all.*

## BREAKDOWN SERVICE

*A 24 hour breakdown service is operated ☎ 112.*

# STOCKHOLM

*Sverige* 985 *M 15 – pop. 674 459 Greater Stockholm 1 491 726.*

*Hamburg 935 – Copenhagen 630 – Oslo 522.*

*Stockholm Information Service, Tourist Centre, Sverigehuset, Hamngatan 27 ☎ (08) 789 24 00 – Motormännens Riksförbund ☎ (08) 690 38 00 – Kungliga. Automobilklubben (Royal Automobile Club) Gyllenstiernsgatan 4 ☎ (08) 660 00 55.*

*18 Svenska Golfförbundet (Swedish Golf Federation) ☎ (08) 622 15 00.*

*Stockholm-Arlanda NW : 40 km ☎ (08) 797 61 00 – SAS : Flygcity, Stureplan 8 ☎ (08) 797 41 75, Reservations (020) 727 727 – Air-Terminal : opposite main railway station.*

*Motorail for Southern Europe : Ticket Travel-Agency, Kungsgatan 60 ☎ (08) 24 00 90.*

*To Finland : contact Silja Line ☎ (08) 22 21 40 or Viking Line ☎ (08) 714 57 70 – Excursions by boat : contact Stockholm Information Service (see below).*

**See:** *Old Town★★★ (Gamla Stan)* AZ – *Vasa Museum★★★ (Vasamuseet)* DY – *Skansen Open-Air Museum★★★* DY.
*Royal Palace★★ (Kungliga Slottet)* AZ ; *Royal Apartments★★ ; Royal Armoury★ ; Royal Treasury★★ – Stockholm Cathedral★★ (Storkyrkan)* AZ – *City Hall★★ (Stadhuset) : Blue Hall★★★, Golden Hall★★★ ;* ☼★★★ BY **H** – *Prins Eugens Waldemarsudde★★ (house and gallery)* DY – *Thiel Gallery★★ (Thielska Galleriet)* DZ.
*House of the Nobility★ (Riddarhuset)* AZ **R** – *Riddarholmen Church★ (Riddarholmskyrkan)* AZ **K¹** – *Österlånggatan★* AZ.
*Kaknäs TV Tower (Kaknästornet)* ☼★★★ DY – *Stigberget : Fjällgatan* ☼★ DZ – *Skinnerviksberget :* ☼★ BZ.

**Museums:** *National Art Gallery★★ (Nationalmuseum)* DY **M⁵** – *Nordic Museum★★ (Nordiska Museet)* DY – *Museum of National Antiquities★★ (Historiska Museet)* DY – *Museum of Medieval Stockholm★★ (Stockholms Medeltidsmuseet)* CY **M¹** – *Museum of Far Eastern Antiquities★ (Östasiatiska Museet)* DY **M⁶** – *Hallwyl Collection★ (Hallwylska Museet)* CY **M³** – *Museum of Modern Art (Moderna Museet)* DY **M⁴** – *Strindberg Museum★ (Strindbergsmuseet)* BX **M²**.

**Outskirts** : *Drottningholm Palace★★★ (Drottningholm Slott) W : 12 km* BY – *Stockholm Archipelago★★★ – Millesgården★★ (house and gallery) E : 4 km* BX – *Skogskyrkogården (UNESCO World Heritage Site).*

**Excursions** : *Gripsholms Slott★★ – Skokloster★★ – Ulriksdal★ – Birka★ – Strängnas★ – Sigtuna★ – Uppsala★★.*

# STOCKHOLM

Biblioteksgatan CY 2
Drottninggatan BX, CY 10
Gallerian CY 14
Grev Turegatan CY 18
Hamngatan CY
Kungsgatan BCY
Sergelgatan CY 53
Västerlånggatan AZ
Österlånggatan AZ

Birger Jarlsgatan CXY 3
Brunkebergstorg CY 5
Brunnsgränd AZ 6
Bryggargatan BY 7
Brända Tomten AZ 8
Djurgårdsbron DY 9
Evert Taubes Terrass AZ 13
Gustav Adolfs Torg CY 16
Herkulesgatan CY 19
Hötorget CY 20
Järntorget AZ 21
Järntorgsgatan AZ 23
Kindstugatan AZ 24
Klarabergsgatan CY 25
Klarabergsviadukten BY 27
Kornhamnstorg AZ 28
Kungsträdgårdsgatan CY 32
Köpmangatan AZ 35
Lilla Nygatan AZ 36
Mosebacke Torg CZ 39
Munkbrogatan AZ 40
Myntgatan AZ 41
Mäster Mikaels Gata DZ 42
Norrbro CY 43
Norrlandsgatan CY 44
Nybroplan CY 45
Olof Palmes Gata BY 47
Prästgatan AZ 48
Riddarhusgränd AZ 49
Riddarhustorget AZ 50
Rådhusgränd AZ 52
Sergels Torg CY 54
Sista Styverns Trappor DZ 55
Slottskajen AZ 56
Slussplan AZ 57
Stallgatan CY 59
Stigbergsgatan DZ 60
Storkyrkobrinken AZ 61
Strömbron CY 62
Strömgatan CY 63
Södermalmstorg CZ 64
Södra Blasieholmshamnen CY 66
Tegelbacken CY 67
Tegnérlunden BX 69
Triewaldsgränd AZ 70
Tyska Brinken AZ 73
Urvädersgränd CZ 74
Östermalmstorg DY 76
Östra Järnvägsgatan BY 78

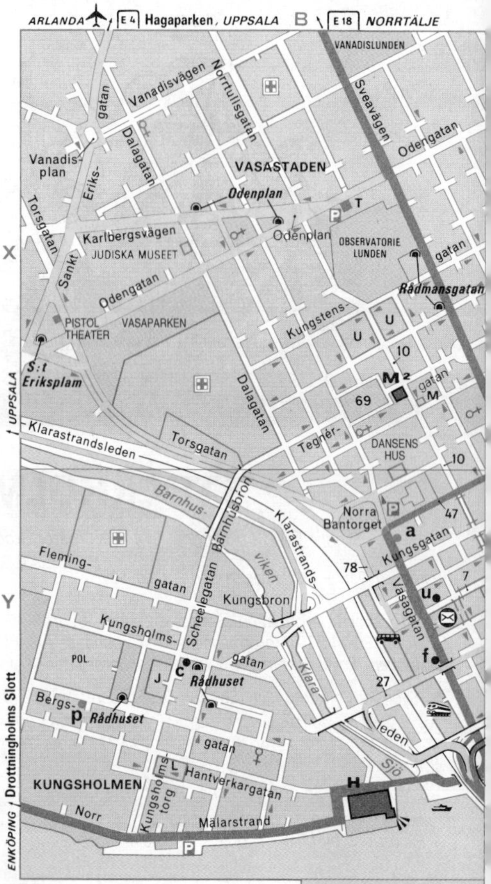

ARLANDA E 4 Hagaparken, UPPSALA B E 18 NORRTÄLJE
VANADISLUNDEN
Vanadisvägen
Norrtullsgatan
Sveavägen
Odengatan
Vanadisplan
Dalagatan
Eriksgatan
VASASTADEN
Odenplan
Torsgatan
Karlbergsvägen
JUDISKA MUSEET
OBSERVATORIE LUNDEN
Sankt
Odengatan
Rådmansgatan
PISTOL THEATER
VASAPARKEN
Kungstensgatan
S:t Eriksplam
X
UPPSALA
Klarastrandsleden
Torsgatan
Tegnérgatan
DANSENS HUS
Barnhusviken
Barnhusbron
Norra Bantorget
Kungsgatan
Fleminggatan
Klarastrandsleden
Scheelegatan
Kungsbron
Vasagatan
Y
Kungsholmsgatan
POL
Rådhuset
Bergsgatan
Rådhuset
Klara
Sjö
Drottningholms Slott
KUNGSHOLMEN
Hantverkargatan
Kungsholms torg
Norr Mälarstrand
ENKÖPING
A

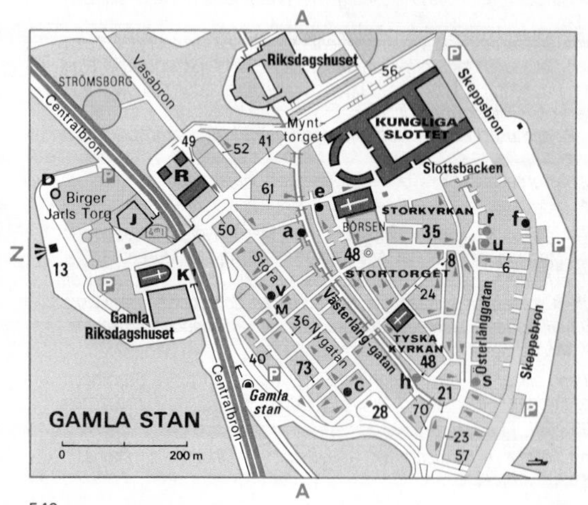

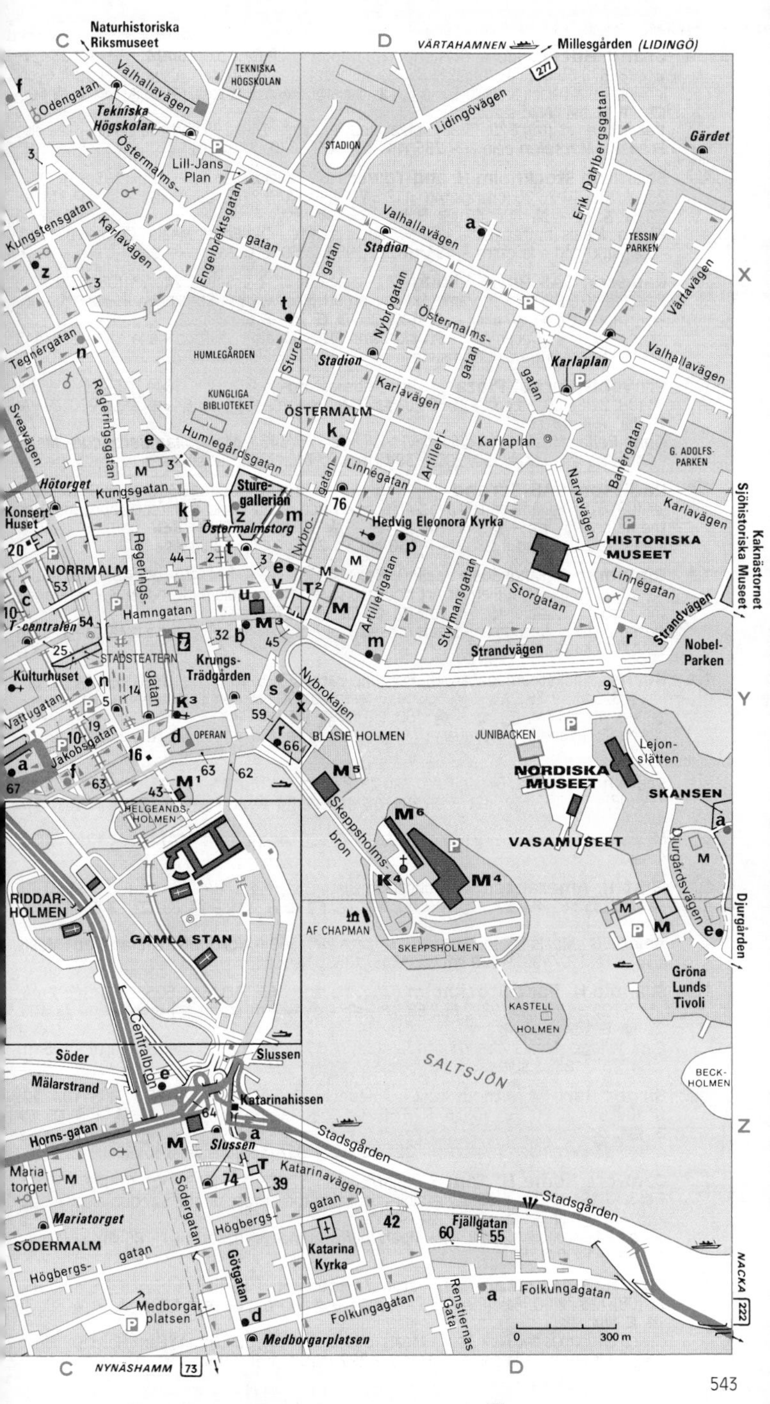

C
Naturhistoriska Riksmuseet
D
VÄRTAHAMNEN
Millesgården (LIDINGÖ)
277
TEKNISKA HÖGSKOLAN
Valhallavägen
Odengatan
Tekniska Högskolan
Östermalms-
Lill-Jans Plan
STADION
Lidingövägen
Erik Dahlbergsgatan
Gärdet
Kungstensgatan
Karlavägen
Engelbrektsgatan
gatan
Valhallavägen
Stadion
TESSIN PARKEN
X
Värtavägen
Östermalms-
Nybrogatan
Sture-
gatan
Tegnérgatan
HUMLEGÅRDEN
Stadion
Karlaplan
Valhallavägen
Regeringsgatan
KUNGLIGA BIBLIOTEKET
Karlavägen
ÖSTERMALM
Sveavägen
Humlegårdsgatan
Karlaplan
Artilleri-
Banérgatan
G. ADOLFS-PARKEN
Hötorget
Kungsgatan
Sture-gallerian
Linnégatan
Narvavägen
Karlavägen
Kaknästornet
Sjöhistoriska Museet
Konsert-Huset
Östermalmstorg
76
Hedvig Eleonora Kyrka
NORRMALM
Regerings-
HISTORISKA MUSEET
Linnégatan
Storgatan
Strandvägen
T-centralen
Hamngatan
Artillerigatan
Styrmansgatan
STADSTEATERN
Krungs-Trädgården
Strandvägen
Nobel-Parken
Kulturhuset
Nybrokajen
Y
Vattugatan
Jakobsgatan
OPERAN
BLASIE HOLMEN
JUNIBACKEN
Lejon-slätten
NORDISKA MUSEET
SKANSEN
HELGEANDS-HOLMEN
Skeppsholmsbron
VASAMUSEET
Djurgårdsvägen
RIDDAR-HOLMEN
GAMLA STAN
AF CHAPMAN
SKEPPSHOLMEN
Djurgården
Gröna Lunds Tivoli
Centralbron
KASTELL HOLMEN
Söder Mälarstrand
Slussen
SALTSJÖN
BECK-HOLMEN
Katarinahissen
Z
Horns-gatan
Slussen
Stadsgården
Maria-torget
Katarinavägen
Stadsgården
Mariatorget
Södergatan
Högbergs-gatan
Fjällgatan
SÖDERMALM
Högbergs-gatan
Katarina Kyrka
Götgatan
NACKA
222
Medborgarplatsen
Folkungagatan
Renstiernas Gata
Folkungagatan
0
300 m
Medborgarplatsen
C
NYNÄSHAMN
73
D

**Grand Hotel,** Södra Blasieholmshamnen 8, P.O. Box 16424, ✉ S-103 27, ☎ (08) 679 35 00, *Fax (08) 611 86 86,* « Elegant late 19C hotel on the waterfront overlooking Royal Palace and Old Town », – rm, rest, – 600. AE VISA JCB. CY r
***Verandan*** *(☎ (08) 679 35 86)* **: Meals** (buffet lunch) 240/295 and a la carte – (see also ***Franska Matsalen*** below) – **285 rm** 1905/3670, 21 suites.

**Sheraton Stockholm H. and Towers** M, Tegelbacken 6, P.O. Box 195, ✉ S-101 23, ☎ (08) 14 26 00 (changing to 412 34 00), *Fax (08) 21 70 26,* ≤, – rm, – 400. AE VISA JCB. rest CY a
***Bistro*** **: Meals** (buffet lunch) 195/345 and a la carte – ***Die Ecke*** **: Meals** - German Bierstub - 220/400 and a la carte – **453 rm** 1950/2650, 6 suites.

**Radisson SAS Royal Viking** M, Vasagatan 1, ✉ S-101 24, ☎ (08) 14 10 00, *Fax (08) 10 81 80,* « Panoramic Sky Bar on 9th floor with ≤ Stockholm », – rm, – 140. AE VISA JCB. rest BY f
*closed 23 to 25 December* – ***Stockholms Fisk*** **: Meals** - Seafood - a la carte 270/445 – **315 rm** 2000/2500, 4 suites.

**Provobis Sergel Plaza** M, Brunkebergstorg 9, P.O. Box 16411, ✉ S-103 27, ☎ (08) 22 66 00, *Fax (08) 21 50 70,* – rm, – 200. AE VISA JCB. rest CY n
***Anna Rella*** **: Meals** *(closed Sunday)* a la carte 225/345 – ***Mongolian Barbecue*** **: Meals** - Chinese - a la carte 150/200 – **394 rm** 1745/2290, 12 suites.

**Radisson SAS Strand** M, Nybrokajen 9, P.O. Box 16396, ✉ S-103 27, ☎ (08) 678 78 00, *Fax (08) 611 24 36,* « Attractive old world architecture, overlooking the harbour », – rm, – 90. AE VISA JCB. CDY x
**Meals** 185/265 and a la carte – **130 rm** 2140/2440, 18 suites.

**Diplomat,** Strandvägen 7c, P.O. Box 14059, ✉ S-104 40, ☎ (08) 663 58 00, *Fax (08) 783 66 34,* « Elegant Art Nouveau style former diplomatic lodgings, overlooking the harbour », – rm, . AE VISA. DY m
*closed 22 to 27 December* – **Meals** *(closed Bank Holidays)* 175/305 and a la carte – **126 rm** 1495/3495, 2 suites.

**Berns,** Näckströmsgatan 8, Berzelii Park, ✉ S-111 47, ☎ (08) 614 07 00, *Fax (08) 611 51 75,* , « Meticulously restored 19C ballroom restaurant and salons » – , rm, rm, – 180. AE VISA JCB. CY b
*closed 23 December-6 January* – **Meals** a la carte 290/415 – **62 rm** 2140/2440, 3 suites.

**Stockholm Plaza,** Birger Jarlsgatan 29, P.O. Box 7707, ✉ S-103 95, ☎ (08) 14 51 20, *Fax (08) 10 34 92,* , – rm, rest, – 45. AE VISA JCB. CX e
**Meals** *(closed lunch Saturday and Sunday)* 175/300 and a la carte – **147 rm** 1295/1850, 4 suites.

**First H. Amaranten** M, Kungsholmsgatan 31, ✉ S-104 20, ☎ (08) 654 10 60, *Fax (08) 652 62 48,* – rm, rest, – 85. AE VISA JCB. BY c
***Amaryllis*** **: Meals** *(closed Sunday)* a la carte 280/360 – ***Nordquist & Ciao-Ciao*** **: Meals** a la carte 350/490 – **422 rm** 1345/1855, 1 suite.

**Scandic H. Park Stockholm** M, Karlavägen 43, P.O. Box 5255, ✉ S-102 46, ☎ (08) 22 96 20, *Fax (08) 21 62 68,* , – rm, rm, – 100. AE VISA JCB. CX t
***Park Village*** **: Meals** *(closed lunch Saturday and Sunday)* 200/350 and a la carte – **195 rm** 1795/2185, 3 suites.

**Birger Jarl** M without rest., Tulegatan 8, P.O. Box 19016, ✉ S-104 32, ☎ (08) 674 10 00, *Fax (08) 673 73 66,* – – 150. AE VISA. CX z
*closed 23 December-3 January* – **221 rm** 1095/1360, 4 suites.

**Comfort Home H. Tapto,** Jungfrugatan 57, ✉ S-115 31, ☎ (08) 664 50 00, *Fax (08) 664 07 00,* « Military exhibits depicting the history of the Swedish army », – . AE VISA. rest DX a
*closed 23 December-2 January* – **Meals** (buffet dinner residents only) – **86 rm** (dinner included) 1400/1750.

**City H. Slöjdgatan,** Slöjdgatan 7, Hötorget, P.O. Box 1132, ✉ S-111 81, ☎ (08) 723 72 00, *Fax (08) 723 72 09,* – rm, rest, – 90. AE VISA. CY c
*closed Christmas and New Year* – **Meals** *(closed Saturday, Sunday and Bank Holidays)* (lunch only) (unlicensed) a la carte 135/200 – **292 rm** 1090/1680.

**Mornington,** Nybrogatan 53, P.O. Box 5197, ✉ S-114 40, ✆ (08) 663 12 40, *Fax (08) 662 21 79*, – rm, . . DX k
*closed 23 to 27 December* – **Meals** *(closed lunch Saturday and Sunday)* 200 (dinner) and a la carte 160/300 – **141 rm** 1295/1595.

**Wellington** without rest., Storgatan 6, ✉ S-114 51, ✆ (08) 667 09 10, *Fax (08) 667 12 54*, – rm, . . DY p
*closed 10 days Christmas-New Year* – **59 rm** 1065/1365, 1 suite.

**Castle** without rest., Riddargatan 14, ✉ S-114 35, ✆ (08) 679 57 00, *Fax (08) 611 20 22* – rest, – 30. . CY e
**48 rm** 1075/1500, 2 suites.

**Freys,** Bryggargatan 12, P.O. Box 594, ✉ S-101 31, ✆ (08) 50 62 13 00, *Fax (08) 50 62 13 13* – rm, . rest BY u
*closed Christmas* – **Meals** (light lunch) 190/380 and dinner a la carte – **112 rm** 1190/1650.

**Operakällaren,** Operahuset, Karl XII's Torg, P.O. Box 1616, ✉ S-111 86, ✆ (08) 676 58 00, *Fax (08) 20 95 92*, ≤, « Historic late 19C restaurant situated in the Opera House, baroque decor » – . CY d
*closed July* – **Meals** (dinner only) 430/510 and a la carte 450/550
**Spec.** Scandinavian delicacies. Baked monkfish with risotto and watercress sauce. Cloudberry parfait on hazelnut pastry with cloudberry liqueur sauce.

**Franska Matsalen** (at Grand Hotel), Södra Blasieholmshamnen 8, P.O. Box 16424, ✉ S-103 27, ✆ (08) 679 35 84, *Fax (08) 611 86 86*, « Elegant Jacobean style dining room, ≤ Royal Palace and Old Town » – . CY r
*closed Saturday, Sunday and July* – **Meals** (dinner only) 685/925 and a la carte.

**Paul and Norbert** (Lang), Strandvägen 9, ✉ S-114 56, ✆ (08) 663 81 83, *Fax (08) 661 72 36* – DY m
*closed Saturday, Sunday, July, Christmas-7 January and Bank Holidays* – **Meals** (booking essential) (dinner only) 440 and a la carte 515/630
**Spec.** Puff pastry baked reindeer broth with sherry. Sautéed pheasant breast with cumin. Warm apricots in Champagne with vanilla ice cream.

**Videgård,** Regeringsgatan 111, ✉ S-111 39, ✆ (08) 411 61 53, *Fax (08) 10 76 35*, « Modern interior design » – . CX n
*closed Saturday lunch, Sunday, 24 June-4 September, 22 December-12 January and Bank Holidays* – **Meals** a la carte 300/435.

**Riche,** Birger Jarlsgatan 4, ✉ S-114 34, ✆ (08) 611 70 22, *Fax (08) 611 32 06* – – **Meals** 225/540 and a la carte – ***Veranda* : Meals** a la carte approx. 255. CY v

**Fredsgatan 12** (Andersson), Fredsgatan 12, ✉ S-111 52, ✆ (08) 24 80 52, *Fax (08) 411 73 48*, « Modern decor » – CY f
*closed Saturday, Sunday and Christmas* – **Meals** (booking essential) (light lunch)/dinner 550 and a la carte 330/460
**Spec.** Rabbit sausage with crayfish risotto. Lamb with pumpkin lasagne and goat's cheese. Cloudberry gazpacho with almond panna cotta.

**Bon Lloc** (Dahlgren), Bergsgatan 33, ✉ S-112 28, ✆ (08) 650 50 82, *Fax (08) 650 50 83* – BY p
*closed Saturday lunch, Sunday, 29 June-2 August and Bank Holidays* – **Meals** - Catalonian influences - (booking essential) (light lunch) a la carte 315/420
**Spec.** Duck liver terrine with truffles and apple purée. Breast of duck with orange sauce and straw potatoes. Crema de chocolate.

**KB,** Smålandsgatan 7, ✉ S-111 46, ✆ (08) 679 60 32, *Fax (08) 611 82 83*, « 19C building, modern art display » – CY u
*closed Saturday lunch, Sunday, 20 June-5 August and Bank Holidays* – **Meals** a la carte 265/595.

**Wedholms Fisk** (Wedholm), Nybrokajen 17, ✉ S-111 48, ✆ (08) 611 78 74, *Fax (08) 678 60 11* – . CY s
*closed Saturday lunch, Sunday, July, Christmas and Bank Holidays* – **Meals** - Seafood - (light lunch) a la carte 330/575
**Spec.** Fricassee of sole, turbot, lobster and scallops with Champagne sauce. Grilled turbot with Dijon hollandaise. Scallops provencale.

**Clas På Hörnet** with rm, Surbrunnsgatan 20, P.O. Box 19156, ✉ S-113 48, ✆ (08) 16 51 30, *Fax (08) 612 53 15*, , « Characterful 18C inn, antique furnishings » – . . CX f
**Meals** *(closed July)* a la carte 275/440 – **10 rm** 990/1290.

**Eriks Bakficka,** Frederikshovsgatan 4, ✉ S-115 24, ✆ (08) 660 15 99, *Fax (08) 663 25 67*, – . DY r
*closed lunch Saturday and Sunday, Easter, last 3 weeks July and 23 December-2 January* – **Meals** - Bistro - 155/375 and a la carte.

**Norrlands Bar & Grill,** Norrlandsgatan 24, ✉ S-111 43, ☎ (08) 611 88 10, *Fax (08) 611 88 30,* – AE ⓓ E VISA CY k
*closed Saturday lunch, Sunday and Bank Holidays* – **Meals** a la carte 310/380.

**Greitz,** Vasagatan 50, ✉ S-111 20, ☎ (08) 23 48 20, *Fax (08) 24 20 93,* « Late 19C bistro » – AE ⓓ E VISA JCB BY a
*closed Saturday lunch, Sunday and July* – **Meals** a la carte 205/375 – ***Pressklubben* :** **Meals** a la carte approx. 200.

## BRASSERIES

**Prinsen,** Mäster Samuelsgatan 4, ✉ S-111 44, ☎ (08) 611 13 31, *Fax (08) 611 70 79* – AE ⓓ E VISA JCB CY t
*closed Sunday lunch, 24, 25 and 31 December and 1 January* – **Meals** (lunch booking essential) a la carte 290/365.

**Sturehof,** Stureplan 2, ✉ S-114 46, ☎ (08) 679 87 50, *Fax (08) 678 11 01,* – AE ⓓ E VISA CY z
**Meals** a la carte 225/405.

**Grodan,** Grev Turegatan 16, ✉ S-114 46, ☎ (08) 679 61 00, *Fax (08) 679 61 10* – AE ⓓ E VISA JCB CY m
*closed Sunday, 2 days midsummer and 24 to 26 December* – **Meals** a la carte 255/310.

## at Gamla Stan (Old Stockholm) :

**First H. Reisen,** Skeppsbron 12-14, ✉ S-111 30, ☎ (08) 22 32 60, *Fax (08) 20 15 59,* ←, « 18C hotel on waterfront with original maritime decor », – |‡|, rm, TV ☎ ♿ – 60. AE ⓓ E VISA. rest AZ f
**Meals** *(closed Sunday and Bank Holidays)* (dinner only) 595 and a la carte – **111 rm** 1360/2025, 3 suites.

**Victory,** Lilla Nygatan 5, ✉ S-111 28, ☎ (08) 14 30 90, *Fax (08) 20 21 77,* « 17C hotel with Swedish rural furnishings and maritime antiques », – |‡|, rm, TV ☎ – 80. AE ⓓ E VISA JCB. AZ v
*closed 20 to 29 December* – **Meals** – (see ***Leijontornet*** below) – **45 rm** 1790/2390, 3 suites.

**Lady Hamilton** without rest., Storkyrkobrinken 5, ✉ S-111 28, ☎ (08) 23 46 80, *Fax (08) 411 11 48,* « 15C house, Swedish rural antiques », – |‡| TV ☎ – 30. AE ⓓ E VISA JCB. AZ e
**34 rm** 1690/2290.

**City H. Gamla Stan** without rest., Lilla Nygatan 25, ✉ S-111 28, ☎ (08) 723 72 50, *Fax (08) 723 72 59,* « 17C house » – |‡| TV ☎ – 30. AE ⓓ E VISA. AZ c
**50 rm** 1150/1690, 1 suite.

**Lord Nelson** without rest., Västerlånggatan 22, ✉ S-111 29, ☎ (08) 23 23 90, *Fax (08) 10 10 89,* « Late 17C house with ship style installation and maritime antiques », – |‡| TV ☎. AE ⓓ E VISA JCB. AZ a
*closed 18 December-5 January* – **31 rm** 1350/1890.

**Eriks,** Österlånggatan 17, ✉ S-111 31, ☎ (08) 23 85 00, *Fax (08) 796 60 69,* « 15C house » – AE ⓓ E VISA AZ u
*closed Sunday, Easter, July, Christmas and Bank Holidays* – **Meals** - mainly Seafood - (booking essential) 425/875 and a la carte 505/720.

**Leijontornet** (at Victory H.), Lilla Nygatan 5, ✉ S-111 28, ☎ (08) 14 23 55, *Fax (08) 406 08 14,* « Remains of a 14C fortification tower in the dining room » – AE ⓓ E VISA JCB AZ v
*closed Sunday, July, 23 December-7 January and Bank Holidays* – **Meals** (booking essential) (dinner only) 375/540 and a la carte – ***Loherummet* : Meals** - Bistro - a la carte approx. 330.

**Fem Små Hus,** Nygränd 10, ✉ S-111 30, ☎ (08) 10 87 75, *Fax (08) 14 96 95,* « 17C cellars, antiques » – AE ⓓ E VISA JCB AZ r
**Meals** (dinner only) 325/370 and a la carte.

**Den Gyldene Freden,** Österlånggatan 51, P.O. Box 2269, ✉ S-103 17, ☎ (08) 24 97 60, *Fax (08) 21 38 70,* « Early 18C inn with vaulted cellars » – AE ⓓ E VISA
*closed Sunday, July and Bank Holidays* – **Meals** (dinner only and Saturday lunch)/dinner 395 and a la carte 250/465. AZ s

**Mårten Trotzig,** Västerlånggatan 79, P.O. Box 2214, ✉ S-103 15, ☎ (08) 24 02 31, *Fax (08) 24 02 51,* , « Contemporary decor in 17C house » – AE ⓓ E VISA AZ h
*closed lunch Saturday and Sunday, Easter, 23 December-7 January and some Bank Holidays* – **Meals** a la carte 320/575.

at Djurgården :

**Arctia H. Hasselbacken** M, Hazeliusbacken 20, P.O. Box 10274, ✉ S-100 55, ☎ (08) 670 50 00, *Fax (08) 663 84 10*, « Historic summer restaurant in former royal park », – |‡|, ⇹ rm, ▤ TV ☎ ♿ – P – 🏊 100. AE ⓓ E VISA. ✂ DZ e
Meals (booking essential) 225/325 and a la carte – **109 rm** ⊒ 1290/1690, 2 suites.

**Ulla Winbladh,** Rosendalsvägen 8, ✉ S-115 21, ☎ (08) 663 05 71, *Fax (08) 663 05 73*, « Late 19C pavilion in former royal hunting ground » – AE ⓓ E VISA DY a
Meals (booking essential) a la carte 270/445.

at Södermalm :

**Scandic H. Slussen** M, Guldgränd 8, P.O. Box 15270, ✉ S-104 65, ☎ (08) 702 25 00, *Fax (08) 642 83 58*, ≤, ⛱, Ⅎ6, ≘s, ☒ – |‡|, ⇹ rm, ▤ TV ☎ ♿ – 🏊 300. AE ⓓ E VISA JCB. ✂ CZ e
***Eken* :** Meals 345/400 and a la carte – **253 rm** ⊒ 1725/2285, 11 suites.

**Scandic H. Malmen** M, Götgatan 49-51, P.O. Box 4274, ✉ S-102 66, ☎ (08) 22 60 80, *Fax (08) 641 11 48*, ≘s – |‡|, ⇹ rm, TV ☎ ♿ – 🏊 90. AE ⓓ E VISA. ✂ CZ d
Meals (dinner only) a la carte 150/275 – **283 rm** ⊒ 1245/1865.

**Gondolen,** Stadsgården 6 (11th floor), P.O. Box 15155, ✉ S-104 56, ☎ (08) 641 70 90, *Fax (08) 641 11 40*, « Glass enclosed passageway with nautical decor, ✲ Stockholm and water » – ▤. AE ⓓ E VISA CZ a
*closed July lunch, Sunday, 24 to 26 December and 1 January* – **Meals** 195/495 and dinner a la carte.

**Nils Emil,** Folkungagatan 122, ✉ S-116 30, ☎ (08) 640 72 09, *Fax (08) 640 37 25* – AE ⓓ E VISA DZ a
*closed lunch Saturday and Sunday, midsummer, July, Christmas and Bank Holidays* – **Meals** 160/415 and a la carte.

**Gässlingen,** Brännkyrkagatan 93, ✉ S-117 26, ☎ (08) 669 54 95, *Fax (08) 84 89 90* – AE ⓓ E VISA BZ
*closed Sunday, Monday, midsummer-1 September and 22 December-10 January* – **Meals** (booking essential) (dinner only) 395/495 and a la carte.

## to the N :

**Stallmästaregården,** Norrtull, ✉ S-113 47, *N : 2 km by Sveavägen (at beginning of E 4)* ☎ (08) 610 13 00, *Fax (08) 32 27 40*, ≤, « 17C inn, waterside setting », ⛱ – P. AE ⓓ E VISA
*closed Sunday and January-April* – **Meals** (buffet lunch except Saturday) 325 and a la carte.

## to the NE :

at the Silja terminal in Värtahamnen *NE : 3 km by Värtavägen* – DX – *and Tegeluddsvägen :*

**Silja H. Ariadne** M, Sodra Kajen 37, ✉ S-115 74, ☎ (08) 665 78 00, *Fax (08) 662 76 70*, ≤, ⛱, ≘s – |‡|, ⇹ rm, ▤ TV ☎ ♿ P – 🏊 250. AE ⓓ E VISA. ✂
Meals (buffet lunch) a la carte 290/380 – **283 rm** ⊒ 1280/1960.

## to the E :

at Ladugårdsgärdet :

**Källhagens Wärdshus** ⛵, Djurgårdsbrunnsvägen 10, ✉ S-115 27, *E : 3 km by Strandvägen* ☎ (08) 665 03 00, *Fax (08) 665 03 99*, ≤, ⛱, « Waterside setting, stylish modern bedrooms », ≘s, ⛱ – |‡|, ⇹ rm, TV ☎ P – 🏊 60. AE ⓓ E VISA. ✂
*closed Christmas* – **Meals** 215/335 and a la carte – **18 rm** ⊒ 1420/1630, 2 suites.

at Fjäderholmarna Island *25 mn by boat, departure every hour from Nybroplan* – CY :

**Fjäderholmarnas Krog,** Stora Fjäderholmen, P.O. Box 14046, ✉ S-100 05, ☎ (08) 718 33 55, *Fax (08) 716 39 89*, ⛱, « Waterside setting on archipelago island with ≤ neighbouring islands and sea » – AE ⓓ E VISA JCB
*closed 23 December-30 April and 1 October-4 December* – **Meals** a la carte 335/460.

## to the S :

at Johanneshov :

**Stockholm Globe** M, Arenaslingan 7, P.O. Box 10004, ✉ S-121 26, *S : 1 ½ km by Rd 73* ☎ (08) 725 90 00, *Fax (08) 649 08 80*, ⛱, ≘s – |‡|, ⇹ rm, ▤ TV ☎ ♿ – 🏊 220. AE ⓓ E VISA JCB. ✂
*closed 21 to 28 December* – ***Arena* :** Meals *(closed Saturday and Sunday)* (lunch only) a la carte 280/450 – ***Tabac* :** Meals a la carte approx. 170 – **279 rm** ⊒ 1095/1950, 8 suites.

to the W :

**at Bromma** *W : 5 ½ km by Norr Mälarstrand – BY – and Drottningholmsvägen :*

**Sjöpaviljongen,** Tranebergs Strand 4, Alvik, ✉ 167 40, *E : 1 ½ km* ☎ (08) 704 04 24, *Fax (08) 704 82 40*, ≤, « Attractive modern pavilion, waterside setting » –, ⚓ P. AE ⓓ E VISA JCB
*closed Saturday lunch, Sunday, 23 December-3 January and Bank Holidays* – Meals 300 and a la carte 350/440 – ***Bistro*** : **Meals** 70 (lunch) and dinner a la carte approx. 200.

to the NW :

**Radisson SAS Royal Park** M 🐎, Frösundaviks Allé 15, ✉ S-171 03, *NW : 5 km by Sveavägan and E 4, Exit Frösunda and Frösundavik rd* ☎ (08) 624 55 00, *Fax (08) 85 85 66*, ≤, « Situated in Royal Park on shores of Brunnsvik Bay », Lб, ≘s, ⊡, park – |≑|, ⚓, ⇎ rm, TV ☎ ♿ 🚗 P – 🏛 280. AE ⓓ E VISA. ⚘ rest
*closed 27 December-5 January* – **Meals** a la carte 200/500 – **184 rm** ☐ 1500/1900, 9 suites.

**Ulriksdals Wärdshus,** , ✉ 170 79, *NW : 8 km by Sveavägen and E 4, taking E 18 towards Norrtälje, following signs for Ulriksdals Slott* ☎ (08) 85 08 15, *Fax (08) 85 08 58*, ≤, « 17C former inn in Royal Park », – P. AE ⓓ E VISA
*closed dinner Sunday and Bank Holidays and 24 to 26 December* – **Meals** (buffet lunch) 225/375 and a la carte 405/610.

**at Sollentuna** *NW : 15 km by Sveavägen – BX – and E 4 (exit Sollentuna c) :*

**Edsbacka Krog** (Lingström), Sollentunavägen 220, ✉ 191 35, ☎ (08) 96 33 00, *Fax (08) 96 40 19*, « 17C inn » – P. AE ⓓ E VISA JCB
*closed Saturday lunch, Monday dinner, Sunday, Easter, Whitsun, midsummer and 4 weeks mid July-mid August* – **Meals** 355/745 and a la carte 295/645
**Spec.** Poached crayfish served in a truffle flavoured bouillon. Lightly smoked halibut on sour-sweet fennel with a butter sauce flavoured with horseradish. Cloudberry soufflé flavoured with rosemary.

**at Arlanda Airport** *NW : 40 km by Sveavägen – BX – and E 4 – ✉ Arlanda :*

**Radisson SAS Sky City** M, P.O. Box 82, ✉ 190 45 *Stockholm-Arlanda, Sky City* ☎ (08) 590 773 00, *Fax (08) 593 781 00*, Lб, ≘s – |≑|, ⇎ rm, ≡ TV ☎ ♿. AE ⓓ E VISA JCB. ⚘
**Meals** a la carte 180/375 – **230 rm** ☐ 1595/1895.

**Radisson SAS Arlandia,** Benstocksvägen 1, P.O. Box 103, ✉ 190 45 *Stockholm-Arlanda, SE : 1 km* ☎ (08) 593 618 00, *Fax (08) 593 619 70*, ≘s, ⊡ – |≑|, ⇎ rm, TV ☎ ♿ P – 🏛 245. AE ⓓ E VISA JCB. ⚘
**Meals** a la carte 225/385 – **334 rm** ☐ 1295/1495, 2 suites.

---

## GOTHENBURG *(Göteborg) Sverige* 985 O 8 – *pop. 437 313.*

See : *Art Gallery★★ (Göteborgs Konstmuseet)* CX **M¹** – *Castle Park★★ (Slottsskogen)* AX – *Botanical Gardens★★ (Botaniska Trädgården)* AX – *East India House★★ (Ostindiska Huset : Göteborgs stadmuseum)* BU **M²** – *Museum of Arts and Crafts★★ (Röhsska Konstlojdmuseet)* BV **M³** – *Liseberg Amusement Park★★ (Liseberg Nöjespark)* DX – *Horticultural Gardens★★ (Trädgårdsföreningen)* CU – *Natural History Museum★ (Naturhistoriska museet)* AX – *Maritime Museum★ (Sjöfartsmuseet)* AV – *Kungsportsavenyn★* BCVX **22** – *Götaplatsen (Carl Milles Poseidon★★)* CX – *Seaman's Tower (Sjömanstornet) (✻★★)* AV *Göteborgs-Utkiken (✻★★)* BT – *Masthugg Church (Masthuggskyrkan) (interior★)* AV.

**Envir.** : *Öckerö Archipelago★ by boat or by car : N : 17 km by E 6 and road 155 – New Älvsborg Fortress★ (Nya Älvsborgs Fästning)* AU – *Bohuslan★★ (The Golden Coast) N : Halland coast to the south : Äskhult Open-Air Museum★ ; Tjolöholms Slott★* AX.

*18 Albatross, Lillhagsvägen Hisings Backa ☎ (031) 55 19 01 – 18 Delsjö, Kallebäck ☎ (031) 40 69 59 – 18 Göteborgs, Golfbanevägen, Hovås ☎ (031) 28 24 44.*

*✈ Scandinavian Airlines System : Svenska Mässan (vid Korsvägen) ☎ (031) 94 20 00 Landvetter Airport : ☎ (031) 94 10 00.*

*⛴ To Denmark : contact Stena Line A/B ☎ (031) 775 00 00, Fax (031) 85 85 95 - Color SeaCat ☎ (031) 775 08 00 – To Continent : contact Scandinavian Seaways ☎ (031) 65 06 50, Fax (031) 53 23 09.*

*ℹ Kungsportplatsen 2 ☎ (031) 10 07 40, Fax (031) 13 21 84.*

*Copenhagen 279 – Oslo 322 – Stockholm 500.*

Plans on following pages

**Sheraton Göteborg H. and Towers,** Södra Hamngatan 59-65, P.O. Box 288, S-401 24, (031) 80 60 00, *Fax (031) 15 98 88,* « Atrium courtyard », – rm, – 450. AE E VISA. BU b
*closed 23 December-2 January* – ***Frascati*** **: Meals** *(closed lunch Saturday and Sunday)* (buffet lunch) 225/390 and a la carte – **333 rm** 1980/2180, 12 suites.

**Radisson SAS Park Avenue,** Kungsportsavenyn 36-38, P.O. Box 53233, S-400 16, (031) 17 65 20, *Fax (031) 16 95 68,* – rm, rest, – 550. AE E VISA JCB. CX f
***Parkbaren*** **: Meals** (buffet lunch) 235 and a la carte – **301 rm** 1545/1795, 17 suites.

**Hotel 11,** Maskingatan 11, Eriksberg, S-417 64, W : 6 km by Götaälvbron follow signs for Torslanda and turn left at Shell garage, or boat from Lilla Bommens Hamn (031) 779 11 11, *Fax (031) 779 11 10,* « Former shipbuilding warehouse, modern interior design », – rm, – 200. AE E VISA JCB. rest
***Bar 67*** **: Meals** (dinner only) a la carte 245/340 – (see also ***Westra Piren*** below) – **132 rm** 1180/1350.

**Scandic H. Crown,** Polhemsplatsen 3, S-411 11, (031) 80 09 00, *Fax (031) 15 45 88,* – rm, – 300. AE E VISA. CU d
**Meals** a la carte 220/320 – **315 rm** 1230/1750, 5 suites.

**Scandic H. Opalen,** Engelbrektsgatan 73, P.O. Box 5106, S-402 23, (031) 81 03 00, *Fax (031) 18 76 22,* – rm, rest, – 180. AE E VISA. rest DV u
**Meals** *(closed Sunday lunch)* (dancing Thursday to Saturday evenings except in summer) (light lunch) 195/295 and a la carte – **237 rm** 1120/1965, 4 suites.

**Gothia,** Mässans Gata 24, P.O. Box 5184, S-402 26, (031) 40 93 00, *Fax (031) 18 98 04,* « Panoramic restaurant on 18th floor », – rm, – 1500. AE E VISA. DX k
***18 : E Våningen*** **: Meals** (buffet lunch) a la carte approx. 260 – **288 rm** 1350/1750, 2 suites.

**Riverton,** Stora Badhusgatan 26, S-411 21, (031) 10 12 00, *Fax (031) 13 08 66,* « 12th floor restaurant with Göta Älv river and docks », – rm, rest, – 300. AE E VISA. AV c
**Meals** *(closed Christmas)* (dinner only) a la carte 290/395 – **187 rm** 1095/1395, 4 suites.

**Europa,** Köpmansgatan 38, P.O. Box 11444, S-404 29, (031) 80 12 80, *Fax (031) 15 47 55,* – rm, – 60. AE E VISA. rest
**Meals** a la carte 300/400 – **453 rm** 1290/1590, 7 suites. BU a

**Scandic H. Rubinen,** Kungsportsavenyn 24, P.O. Box 53097, S-400 14, (031) 81 08 00, *Fax (031) 16 75 86* – rm, – 60. AE E VISA.
**Meals** *(closed Sunday, July-August and Christmas)* (dinner only) a la carte 260/360 – **189 rm** 1295/1965, 1 suite. CV c

**Panorama,** Eklandagatan 51-53, P.O. Box 24037, S-400 22, (031) 767 70 00, *Fax (031) 767 70 70,* – rm, – 120. AE E VISA. rest DX
*closed 23 December-7 January* – **Meals** *(closed Saturday lunch, Sunday and Bank Holidays)* (light lunch) 185/275 and a la carte – **339 rm** 1040/1290.

**Mornington,** Kungsportsavenyn 6, S-411 36, (031) 17 65 40, *Fax (031) 711 34 39,* – rm, – 50. AE E VISA JCB. BV e
*closed 19 December-5 January* – ***Brasserie Lipp*** **: Meals** *(closed Sunday)* a la carte 255/390 – **91 rm** 1295/1595.

**Novotel Göteborg,** Klippan 1, S-414 51, SW : 3 ½ km by Andréeg or boat from Lilla Bommens Hamn (031) 14 90 00, *Fax (031) 42 22 32,* « Converted brewery on waterfront », – rm, – 120. AE E VISA. rest
***Carnegie Kaj*** **: Meals** (buffet lunch) 145 and dinner a la carte 250/380 – **144 rm** 995/1140, 4 suites.

**Victors,** Skeppsbroplatsen 1, S-411 18, (031) 17 41 80, *Fax (031) 13 96 10,* Göta Älv river and harbour, – rm, – 40. AE E VISA JCB. AU b
**Meals** *(closed Friday to Sunday)* (dinner only) a la carte 185/405 – **35 rm** 1050/1250, 9 suites.

**Tidbloms,** Olskroksgatan 23, S-416 66, *NE : 2 ½ km by E 20* (031) 19 20 70, *Fax (031) 19 78 35,* – rm, – 70. AE E VISA.
*closed 23 December-6 January* – **Meals** *(closed Saturday lunch)* 195/225 and a la carte – **42 rm** 990/1250.

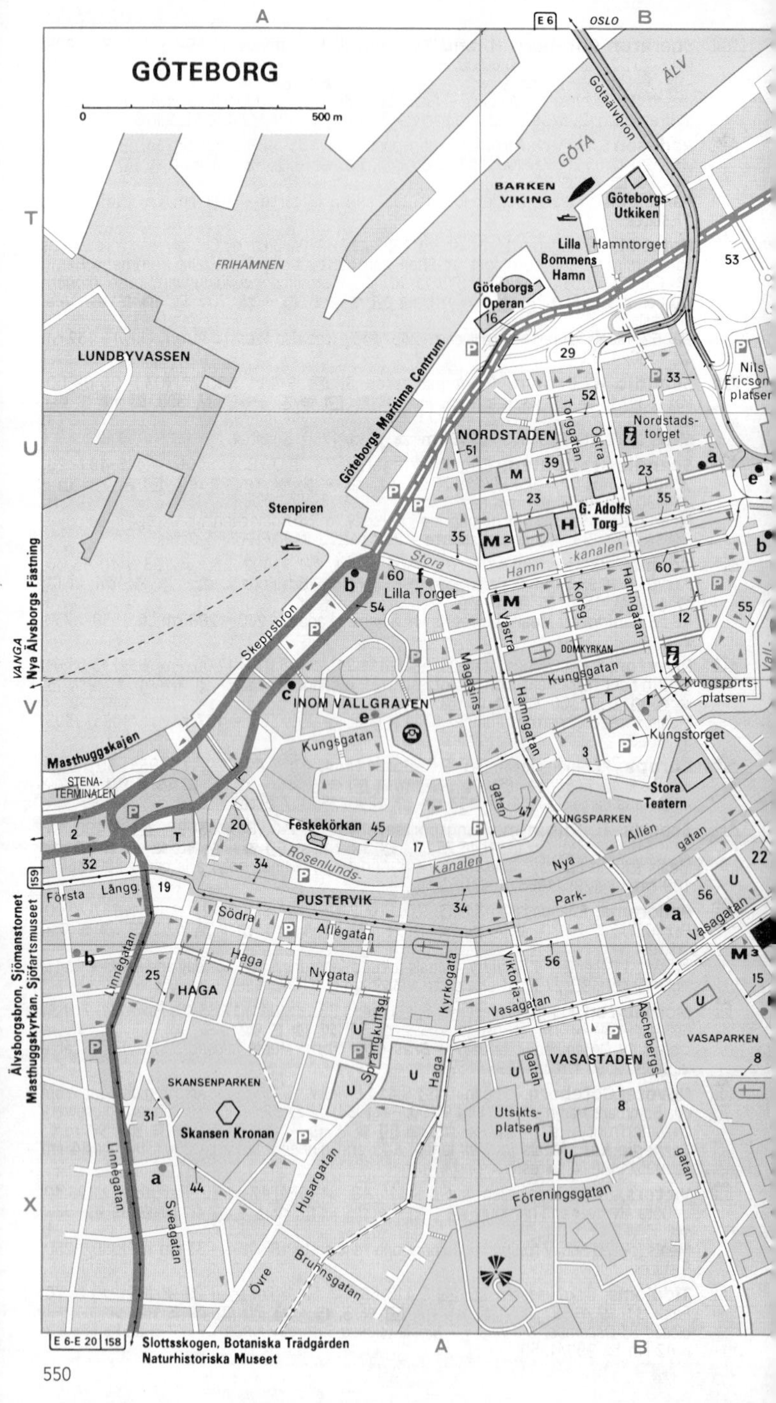
GÖTEBORG
0
500 m
A
B
E 6
OSLO
T
U
V
X
GÖTA
ÄLV
Götaälvbron
BARKEN VIKING
Göteborgs-Utkiken
Lilla Bommens Hamn
Hamntorget
FRIHAMNEN
Göteborgs Operan
LUNDBYVASSEN
Göteborgs Maritima Centrum
Nils Ericson platsen
NORDSTADEN
Nordstads-torget
Torggatan
Östra
G. Adolfs Torg
Stenpiren
Stora
Hamn
-kanalen
Lilla Torget
Korsg.
Hamngatan
Västra
DOMKYRKAN
Kungsgatan
Kungsports-platsen
Skeppsbron
VANGA
Nya Älvsborgs Fästning
INOM VALLGRAVEN
Kungstorget
Magasins-
Hamngatan
Masthuggskajen
STENA-TERMINALEN
Stora Teatern
KUNGSPARKEN
Feskekörkan
Rosenlunds-
kanalen
Allén
Nya
gatan
Första Långg.
PUSTERVIK
Park-
Södra
Allégatan
Vasagatan
Haga
Nygata
Linnégatan
HAGA
Viktoria-
Vasagatan
Kyrkogata
Sprängkullsg.
Aschebergs-
VASAPARKEN
Älvsborgsbron, Sjömanstornet
Masthuggskyrkan, Sjöfartsmuseet
SKANSENPARKEN
Haga
VASASTADEN
Skansen Kronan
Utsikts-platsen
Linnégatan
Sveagatan
Husargatan
Föreningsgatan
Brunnsgatan
Övre
E 6-E 20
158
159
Slottsskogen, Botaniska Trädgården
Naturhistoriska Museet

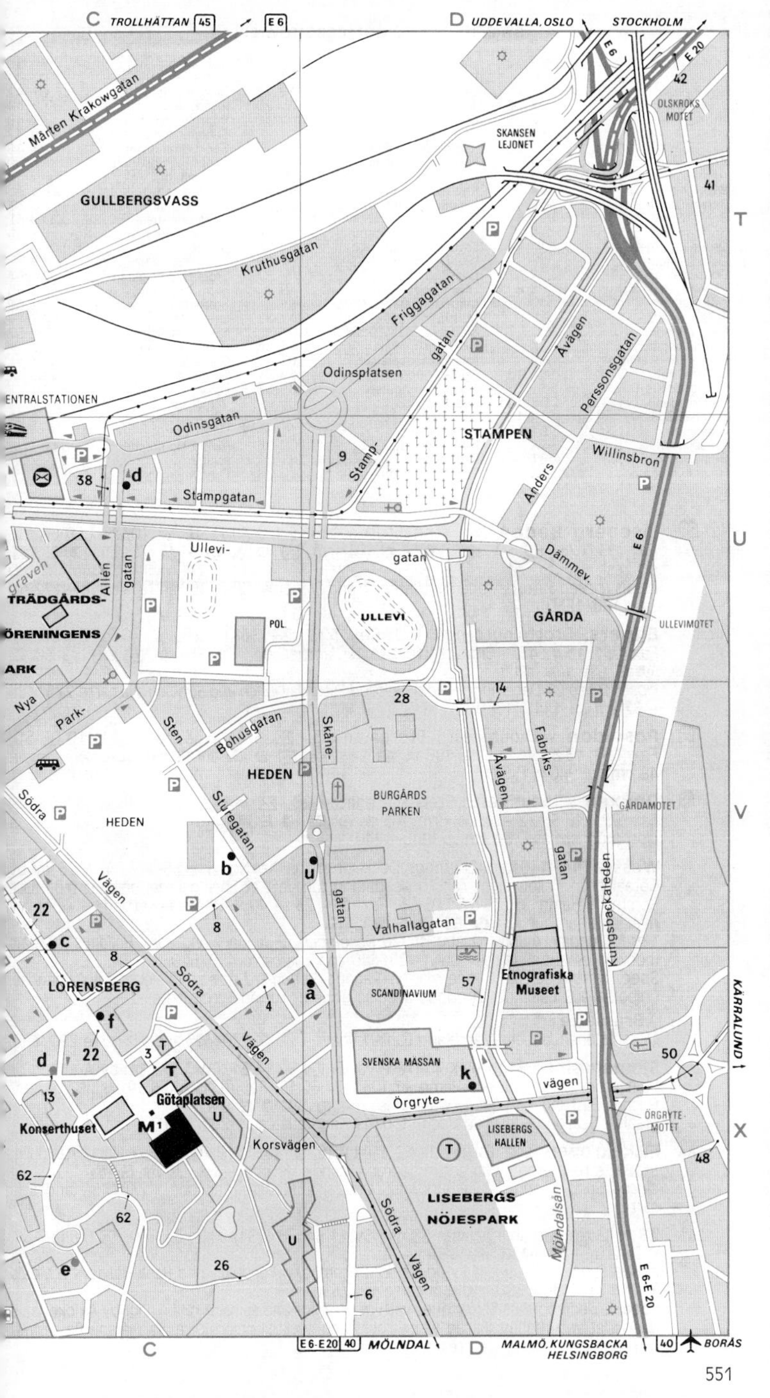
C
TROLLHÄTTAN 45
E 6
D
UDDEVALLA, OSLO
STOCKHOLM
E 6
E 20
42
OLSKROKS MOTET
Mårten Krakowgatan
SKANSEN LEJONET
41
GULLBERGSVASS
T
Kruthusgatan
Friggagatan
Åvägen
Perssonsgatan
Odinsplatsen
gatan
ENTRALSTATIONEN
Odinsgatan
STAMPEN
Willinsbron
9
Stamp-
38
d
Stampgatan
Anders
U
Ullevi-
Dämmev.
E 6
gatan
graven
Allén
gatan
TRÄDGÅRDS-
ÖRENINGENS
ARK
POL.
ULLEVI
GÅRDA
ULLEVIMOTET
14
28
Nya
Park-
Sten
Bohusgatan
Skåne-
Fabriks-
HEDEN
Åvägen
BURGÅRDS PARKEN
GÅRDAMOTET
Södra
HEDEN
Sturegatan
V
b
u
gatan
Vägen
22
8
gatan
Kungsbackaleden
Valhallagatan
c
8
Södra
Etnografiska Museet
LORENSBERG
57
KÄRRALUND
SCANDINAVIUM
4
a
f
Vägen
22
SVENSKA MÄSSAN
50
d
3
T
k
13
T
vägen
Götaplatsen
Örgryte-
ÖRGRYTEMOTET
Konserthuset
M 1
U
LISEBERGS HALLEN
X
Korsvägen
T
48
62
LISEBERGS NÖJESPARK
Södra
62
Mölndalsån
U
Vägen
e
26
E 6-E 20
6
C
E 6-E 20 40
MÖLNDAL
D
MALMÖ, KUNGSBACKA HELSINGBORG
40
BORÅS

**STREET INDEX TO GÖTEBORG TOWN PLAN**



**Liseberg Heden**, Sten Sturegatan, ✉ S-411 38, ℘ (031) 750 69 10, *Fax (031) 750 69 30*, – rm, – 70. AE VISA. rest CV b
**Meals** *(closed Saturday and Sunday lunch and Christmas)* 250/450 and a la carte – **172 rm** 1180/1550.

**Eggers,** Drottningtorget, P.O. Box 323, ✉ S-401 25, ℘ (031) 80 60 70, *Fax (031) 15 42 43*, « Characterful late 19C ambience » – rm, – 30. AE VISA JCB. BU e
*closed 23 to 27 December* – **Meals** *(closed Saturday lunch and Sunday)* a la carte 275/330 – **67 rm** 1115/1660.

**Poseidon** without rest., Storgatan 33, ✉ S-411 33, ℘ (031) 10 05 50, *Fax (031) 13 83 91*, « Late 19C », – . AE VISA JCB. BV a
**48 rm** 940/1150.

**Onyxen** without rest., Sten Sturegatan 23, ✉ S-412 52, ℘ (031) 81 08 45, *Fax (031) 16 56 72* – rm, . AE VISA JCB DX a
*closed Christmas* – **34 rm** 940/1240.

**Westra Piren** (Öster), Eriksberg, Dockepiren, (on Pier No. 4), ✉ S-417 64, W : 6 km by Götaälvbron, follow signs for Torslanda and turn left at Shell garage, or boat from Lilla Bommens Hamn ℘ (031) 51 95 55, *Fax (031) 23 99 40*, « Dockside setting, ≤ Göta Älv river and harbour » – . AE VISA JCB
*closed Sunday, 4 July-10 August, 20 December-12 January and Bank Holidays* – **Meals** (booking essential) (dinner only) 425/640 and a la carte 450/620
**Spec.** Terrine de raie fumée maison. Ragoût de homard noir son velouté à L'Armagnac. Chiboust aux baies de l'Arctique avec sa glace et roulade croquante.

**Brasserie,**
*closed dinner January-March and Bank Holidays* – **Meals** 170/425 and a la carte 290/380.

**Sjömagasinet,** Klippans Kulturreservat 5, ✉ S-414 51, SW : 3 ½ km by Andréeg or boat from Lilla Bommens Hamn ℘ (031) 24 65 10, *Fax (031) 24 55 39*, ≤, , « 18C former East India company warehouse » – . AE VISA
**Meals** - Seafood - (buffet lunch) 150/495 and a la carte 260/600.

**Fiskekrogen,** Lilla Torget 1, ✉ S-411 18, ℘ (031) 10 10 05, *Fax (031) 10 10 06*, « 1920's restaurant with contemporary Scandic decor » – . AE VISA AU f
*closed Sunday and 23 December-7 January* – **Meals** - Seafood - 230/450 and a la carte.

**28 +** (Lyxell), Götabergsgatan 28, ✉ S-411 34, ℘ (031) 20 21 61, *Fax (031) 81 97 57*, « Cellar » – AE VISA JCB BX n
*closed Sunday, 27 June-11 August, 22 December-11 January and Bank Holidays* – **Meals** (dinner only) 305/590 and a la carte 370/590
**Spec.** Grilled coquilles St. Jacques with quails eggs and spinach ravioli. Lightly smoked roe deer fillet with honey glaced white roots and cocktail onion juice. Vanilla soufflé served with arctic raspberry ice cream.

XX **Thörnströms Kök,** Teknologgatan 3, ✉ 411 32, ☎ (031) 16 20 66, *Fax (031) 16 40 17* – ▤. AE ⓞ E VISA CX e
*closed Saturday lunch, Monday dinner, Sunday and July* – **Meals** (booking essential) (light lunch) 140/325 and a la carte.

XX **Mannerström,** Arkivgatan 7, ✉ S-411 34, ☎ (031) 16 03 33, *Fax (031) 16 78 54*, – AE ⓞ E VISA JCB CX d
*closed Saturday lunch, Sunday and 1 July-1 August* – **Meals** 185/245 and a la carte.

XX **Kungstorget,** Kungstorget 14, ✉ S-411 10, ☎ (031) 711 00 22, *Fax (031) 711 00 44* – AE ⓞ E VISA BV r
Meals *(closed Sunday)* 175/625 and a la carte 285/405 – ***Johannes Duk :*** **Meals** - Bistro - *(closed Sunday and Monday)* (dinner only) a la carte 190/340.

XX **Le Village,** Tredje Långgatan 13, ✉ S-413 03, ☎ (031) 24 20 03, *Fax (031) 24 20 69*, « Antique shop » – AE ⓞ E VISA AX b
*closed Sunday lunch* – **Meals** 245/275 and a la carte.

X **Bröderna Dahlbom,** Kungsgatan 12, ✉ S-411 19, (moving in summer 1998 to rest. Trädgatan in Park Gatan) ☎ (031) 701 77 84, *Fax (031) 701 77 85* – AE ⓞ E VISA JCB
*closed Saturday lunch, Sunday and July* – **Meals** 150/455 and a la carte. AV e

X **Hos Pelle,** Djupedalsgatan 2, ✉ S-413 07, ☎ (031) 12 10 31, *Fax (031) 775 38 32* – AE ⓞ E VISA JCB AX a
*closed Sunday and 20 June-10 August* – **Meals** (dinner only) 275/450 and a la carte.

**at Landvetter Airport** *E : 30 km by Rd 40* – DX – ✉ *S-438 02 Landvetter :*

**Landvetter Airport H.,** P.O. Box 2103, ✉ S-438 13, ☎ (031) 97 75 50, *Fax (031) 94 64 70*, – rm, – 25. AE ⓞ E VISA.
*closed 24 to 26 and 31 December* – **Meals** *(closed lunch Saturday and Sunday)* a la carte 255/310 – **41 rm** 1095, 3 suites.

# Switzerland

## Suisse
## Schweiz
## Svizzera

BERNE – BASLE – GENEVA – ZÜRICH

# PRACTICAL INFORMATION

## LOCAL CURRENCY – PRICES

**Swiss Franc:** *100 CHF = 68,78 USD ($) (Jan. 98).*

**National Holiday in Switzerland:** *1st August.*

## LANGUAGES SPOKEN

*German, French and Italian are usually spoken in all administrative departments, shops, hotels and restaurants.*

## AIRLINES

**SWISSAIR:** *P.O. Box 316, 1215 Genève 15, ✆ (022) 799 59 99, Fax (022) 799 31 38. Hirschengraben 84, 8058 Zürich, ✆ (0848) 80 07 00, Fax (01) 258 34 40.*

**AIR FRANCE:** *IBC, 24 Pré-Bois, 1201 Genève, ✆ (022) 798 05 05, Fax (022) 788 50 40.*
*Talstr. 70, 8001 Zürich, ✆ (01) 211 13 77, Fax (01) 212 01 35.*

**ALITALIA:** *rue Lausanne 36, 1201 Genève, ✆ (022) 731 66 50, Fax (022) 732 40 29. Thurgauerstr. 39, 8050 Zürich, ✆ (01) 306 91 11, Fax (01) 306 91 44.*

**AMERICAN AIRLINES:** *Lintheschergasse 15, 8001 Zürich, ✆ (01) 225 16 16, Fax (01) 212 04 21.*

**BRITISH AIRWAYS:** *Chantepoulet 13, 1201 Genève, ✆ (0800) 55 69 69, Talacker 42, 8023 Zürich, ✆ (01) 215 66 66.*

**LUFTHANSA:** *Chantepoulet 1-3, 1201 Genève, ✆ (022) 908 01 80, Fax (022) 908 01 88.*
*Gutenbergstr. 10, 8027 Zürich, ✆ (01) 286 70 00, Fax (01) 286 72 07.*

## POSTAL SERVICES

*In large towns, post offices are open from 7.30am to noon and 1.45pm to 6pm, and Saturdays until 11am. The telephone system is fully automatic.*
*Many public phones are equipped with phone card facilities. Prepaid phone cards are available from post offices, railway stations and tobacconist's shops.*

## SHOPPING

*Department stores are generally open from 8.30am to 6pm, except on Saturdays when they close at 4 or 5pm. They are closed on Monday mornings.*
*In the index of street names, those printed in red are where the principal shops are found.*

## TIPPING

*In hotels, restaurants and cafés the service charge is generally included in the prices.*

## SPEED LIMITS – MOTORWAYS

*The speed limit on motorways is 120 km/h - 74 mph, on other roads 80 km/h - 50 mph, and in built up areas 50 km/h - 31 mph.*
*Driving on Swiss motorways is subject to the purchase of a single rate annual road tax (vignette) obtainable from border posts, tourist offices and post offices.*

## SEAT BELTS

*The wearing of seat belts is compulsory in all Swiss cantons for drivers and all passengers.*

# BERNE

3000 Bern 427 ⑬, 217 ⑥ – *pop. 130 069 – alt. 548.*

*Basle 100 – Lyons 315 – Munich 435 – Paris 556 – Strasbourg 235 – Turin 311.*

*Tourist Office, Railway Station ☎ (031) 311 66 11, Fax (031) 312 12 33 – T.C.S., Thunstr. 63, ☎ (031) 352 22 22, Fax (031) 352 22 29 – A.C.S., Theaterplatz 13, ☎ (031) 311 38 13, Fax (031) 311 26 37.*

*18 Blumisberg, ✉ 3184 Wünnewil (mid-March-mid-November), ☎ (026) 496 34 38, Fax (026) 496 35 23, SW : 18 km.*

*✈ Bern-Belp, ☎ (031) 960 21 11, Fax (031) 960 21 12.*

See: *Old Berne★★ : Marktgasse★* DZ ; *Clock Tower★* EZ **C** ; *Kramgasse★* EZ ; *views★ from the Nydegg Bridge* FY ; *Bear Pit★* FZ ; *Cathedral of St Vincent★* EZ : *tympanum★★, panorama★★ from the tower* EZ – *Rosengarden* FY : *view★ of the Old Berne – Botanical Garden★* DY – *Dählhölzli Zoo★ – Church of St Nicholas★.*

Museums: *Fine Arts Museum★★* DY – *Natural History Museum★★* EZ – *Bernese Historical Museum★★* EZ – *Alpine Museum★★* EZ – *Swiss Postal Museum★* EZ.

Excursions: *The Gurten★★.*

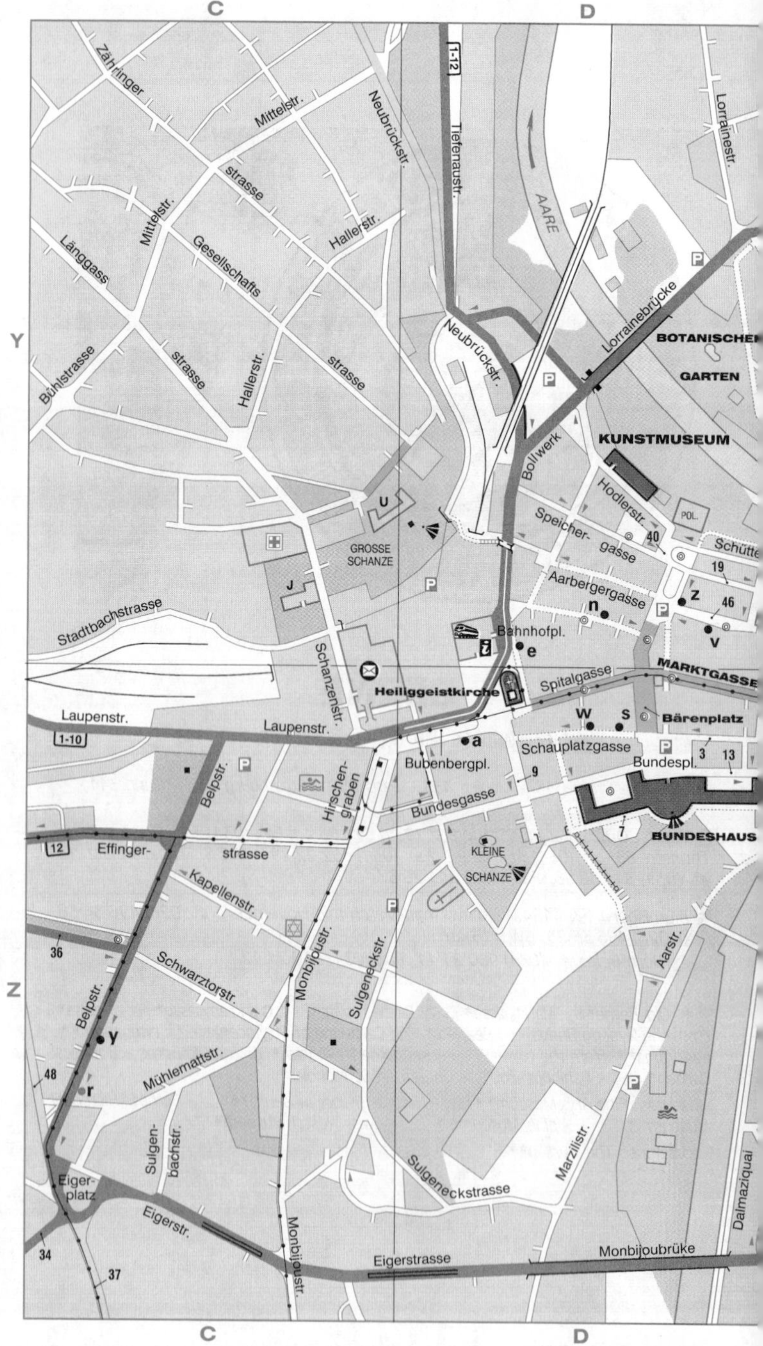
C
D
Y
Z
Zähringer
Mittelstr.
Neubrückstr.
Tiefenaustr.
1-12
AARE
Lorrainestr.
strasse
Hallerstr.
Mittelstr.
Länggass
Gesellschafts
Lorrainebrücke
BOTANISCHE
GARTEN
Bühlstrasse
strasse
Hallerstr.
strasse
Neubrückstr.
KUNSTMUSEUM
Bollwerk
Hodlerstr.
U
Speicher-
gasse
POL.
40
Schütte
GROSSE
SCHANZE
19
J
Aarbergergasse
n
Z
46
Stadtbachstrasse
Bahnhofpl.
e
V
Schanzenstr.
MARKTGASSE
Spitalgasse
Heiliggeistkirche
W
S
Bärenplatz
Laupenstr.
Laupenstr.
1-10
a
Schauplatzgasse
Bubenbergpl.
Bundespl.
3
13
Hirschen-
graben
Belpstr.
9
Bundesgasse
12
Effinger-
strasse
7
BUNDESHAUS
KLEINE
SCHANZE
Kapellenstr.
36
Monbijoustr.
Schwarztorstr.
Sulgeneckstr.
Aarstr.
Belpstr.
y
48
r
Mühlematstr.
Sulgen-
bachstr.
Marzilistr.
Dalmaziquai
Eiger-
platz
Sulgeneckstrasse
Eigerstr.
34
Monbijoustr.
Eigerstrasse
Monbijoubrüke
37
C
D

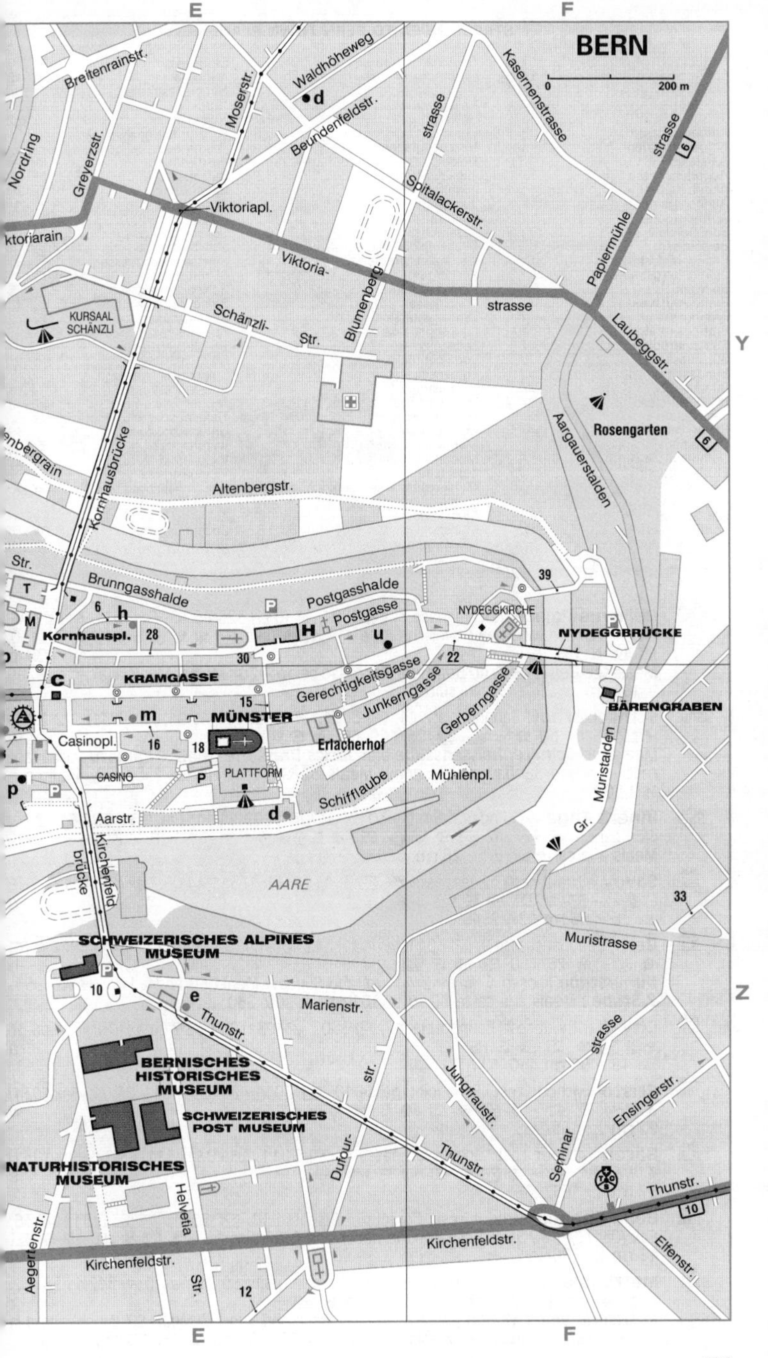

BERN
0
200 m
E
F
Y
Z
Breitenrainstr.
Waldhöheweg
Kasernenstrasse
Moserstr.
Beundenfeldstr.
strasse
Nordring
Greyerzstr.
Viktoriapl.
Spitalackerstr.
Papiermühle
ktoriarain
Viktoria-
Blumenberg-
strasse
KURSAAL SCHÄNZLI
Schänzli-
Str.
Laubeggstr.
Rosengarten
Aargauerstalden
Kornhausbrücke
Altenbergstr.
Brunngasshalde
Postgasshalde
Postgasse
NYDEGGKIRCHE
NYDEGGBRÜCKE
Kornhauspl.
KRAMGASSE
Gerechtigkeitsgasse
Junkerngasse
Gerberngasse
BÄRENGRABEN
MÜNSTER
Casinopl.
Erlacherhof
CASINO
PLATTFORM
Schifflaube
Mühlenpl.
Muristalden
Aarstr.
Kirchenfeld-
brücke
AARE
Gr.
Muristrasse
SCHWEIZERISCHES ALPINES MUSEUM
Marienstr.
Thunstr.
BERNISCHES HISTORISCHES MUSEUM
SCHWEIZERISCHES POST MUSEUM
NATURHISTORISCHES MUSEUM
Jungfraustr.
Dufour-
str.
strasse
Ensingerstr.
Seminar
Thunstr.
Aegertenstr.
Helvetia
Str.
Kirchenfeldstr.
Elfenstr.

## STREET INDEX TO BERN TOWN PLAN

Bärenplatz DZ
Kramgasse EZ
Marktgasse DEZ
Spitalgasse DZ

Aarbergergasse DY
Aargauerstalden FY
Aarstrasse DEZ
Aegertenstrasse EZ
Altenbergrain DEY
Altenbergstrasse EFY
Amthausgasse DEZ 3
Bahnhofplatz DY
Belpstrasse CZ
Beundenfeldstrasse EFY
Blumenbergstrasse EFY
Bollwerk DY
Breitenrainstrasse EY
Brunngasse EY 6
Brunngasshalde EY
Bubenbergplatz DZ
Bühlstrasse CY
Bundesgasse DZ
Bundesplatz DZ
Bundesterrasse DZ 7
Casinoplatz EZ
Christoffelgasse DZ 9
Dalmaziquai DZ
Dufourstrasse EZ
Effingerstrasse CZ
Eigerplatz CZ
Eigerstrasse CDZ
Elfenstrasse FZ
Ensingerstrasse FZ
Gerberngasse FZ
Gerechtigkeitsgasse EYZ
Gesellschaftsstrasse CY
Greyerstrasse EY
Hallerstrasse CY
Helvetiaplatz EZ 10
Helvetiastrasse EZ
Hirschengraben CZ
Holderstrasse DY
Jubiläumsstrasse EZ 12
Jungfraustrasse FZ
Junkerngasse EFZ
Kapellenstrasse CZ
Kasernenstrasse FY
Kirchenfeldbrücke EZ
Kirchenfeldstrasse EFZ
Kochergasse DEZ 13
Kornhausbrücke EY
Kreuzgasse EZ 15
Langassstrasse CY
Laubeggstrasse FY
Laupenstrasse CZ
Lorrainebrücke DY
Lorrainestrasse DY
Luisenstrasse EZ
Marienstrasse EZ
Marzilistrasse DZ
Mittelstrasse CY
Monbijoubrücke DZ
Monbijoustrasse CZ
Moserstrasse EY
Mühlemattstrasse CZ
Mühlenplatz FZ
Münstergasse EZ 16
Münsterplatz EZ 18
Muristalden FZ
Muristrasse FZ
Nägeligasse DY 19
Neubrückstrasse CDY
Nordring EY
Nydeggasse FY 22
Papiermühlestrasse FY
Postgasse EY
Postgasshalde EY
Rathausgasse EY 28
Rathausplatz EY 30
Schanzenstrasse CYZ
Schänzlistrasse EY
Schauplatzgasse DZ
Schifflaube EY
Schosshaldenstrasse FZ 33
Schüttestrasse DEY
Schwarztorstrasse CZ 36
Seftigenstrasse CZ 37
Seminarstrasse FZ
Speichergasse DY
Spitalackerstrasse EFY
Stadtbachstrasse CY
Sulgenbachstrasse CZ
Sulgeneckstrasse CDZ
Thunstrasse EFZ
Tiefenaustrasse DY
Untertorbrücke FY 39
Viktoriaplatz EY
Viktoriarain EY
Viktoriastrasse EFY
Waisenhausplatz DY 40
Waldhöheweg EY
Zähringerstrasse CY
Zeughausgasse DY 46
Zieglerstrasse CZ 48

**Bellevue Palace,** Kochergasse 3, ✉ 3001, (031) 320 45 45, *Fax (031) 311 47 43,* « Terrace with views over the Aare » – rest, – 25/150. AE E VISA JCB. rest EZ p
Meals see ***Bellevue-Grill/Bellevue Terrasse*** below – ***Zur Münz*** **:** **Meals** a la carte 53/96 – **131 rm** 290/430, 14 suites.

**Schweizerhof,** Bahnhofplatz 11, ✉ 3001, (031) 311 45 01, *Fax (031) 312 21 79* – rm, – 25/140. AE E VISA. rest DY e
Meals see ***Schultenheissenstube*** and ***Jack's Brasserie*** below – ***Yamato*** - Japanese rest. - *(closed Sunday and Monday)* **Meals** 52/92 – **81 rm** 290/450, 4 suites – ½ P 50.

**Innere Enge**, Engestr. 54, ✉ 3012, (031) 309 61 11, *Fax (031) 309 61 12,* , park – rm, . AE E VISA by Tiefenaustrasse DY
**Meals** a la carte 37/80 – **26 rm** 180/270.

**Savoy** without rest, Neuengasse 26, ✉ 3011, (031) 311 44 05, *Fax (031) 312 19 78* – . AE E VISA JCB DY n
18 – **56 rm** 127/254.

**Bern,** Zeughausgasse 9, ✉ 3011, (031) 312 10 21, *Fax (031) 312 11 47,* – – 25/200. AE E VISA JCB EY b
***Kurierstube*** *(closed 5 July - 2 August and Sunday)* **Meals** 60 and a la carte 49/95 – ***7 Stube*** **:** **Meals** a la carte 30/76 – **101 rm** 200/260.

**City** M without rest, Bahnhofplatz 7, ✉ 3007, (031) 311 53 77, *Fax (031) 311 06 36* – . AE E VISA DZ a
16 – **58 rm** 110/180.

**Bristol** without rest, Schauplatzgasse 10, ✉ 3011, (031) 311 01 01, *Fax (031) 311 94 79,* – . AE E VISA JCB DZ w
**92 rm** 165/265.

**Bären** without rest, Schauplatzgasse 4, ✉ 3011, (031) 311 33 67, *Fax (031) 311 69 83,* – . AE E VISA JCB DZ s
**57 rm** 165/265.

**Belle Epoque** without rest, Gerechtigkeitsgasse 18, ✉ 3011, (031) 311 43 36, *Fax (031) 311 39 36,* « Belle Epoque decor and furnishings » – . AE E VISA EY u
**16 rm** 200/285.

**Metropole,** Zeughausgasse 28, ✉ 3011, (031) 311 50 21, *Fax (031) 312 11 53,* – rm, – 25/100. AE E VISA DY z
***Rôtisserie Vieux Moulin*** *(closed Saturday lunch and Sunday)* **Meals** 27 (lunch) and a la carte 44/83 – ***Brasserie*** **:** **Meals** a la carte 34/65 – **58 rm** 150/220 – ½ P 25.

**Kreuz,** Zeughausgasse 41, (031) 311 11 62, *Fax (031) 311 37 47* – 25/120. AE E VISA DY v
Meals *(closed Saturday and Sunday)* a la carte 33/73 – **103 rm** 136/200.

**Pergola** without rest, Belpstr. 43, 3007, (031) 381 91 46, *Fax (031) 381 50 54* – AE E VISA CZ y
*closed 22 December - 4 January* – **55 rm** 135/180.

**Waldhorn** without rest, Waldhöheweg 2, 3013, (031) 332 23 43, *Fax (031) 332 18 69* – AE E VISA EY d
**46 rm** 120/175.

**Bellevue Grill / Bellevue Terrasse** - Hotel Bellevue Palace, Kochergasse 3, 3001, (031) 320 45 45, *Fax (031) 311 47 43*, « Terrace with views over the Aare » – AE E VISA JCB. EZ p
*Grill : closed June - September and lunch ; Terrasse : closed dinner in winter* – **Meals** 66/114 and a la carte 77/140.

**Schultheissenstube** - Hotel Schweizerhof, Bahnhofplatz 11 (1st floor), 3001, (031) 311 45 01, *Fax (031) 312 21 79* – AE E VISA. DY e
*closed 20 July - 17 August, Saturday and Sunday* – **Meals** 75 and a la carte 64/118.

**Jack's Brasserie** - Hotel Schweizerhof, Bahnhofplatz 11, 3001, (031) 311 45 01, *Fax (031) 312 21 79*, – AE E VISA. DY e
**Meals** 74 and a la carte 49/110.

**Kirchenfeld,** Thunstr. 5, 3005, (031) 351 02 78, *Fax (031) 351 84 16*, – AE E VISA – *closed 12 to 27 July, Sunday and Monday* – **Meals** 35 (lunch)/55 and a la carte 40/85. EZ e

**Ermitage,** Amtshausgasse 10, 3011, (031) 311 35 41, *Fax (031) 311 35 42* – AE E VISA – *closed 12 July - 10 August, Saturday dinner and Sunday* – **Meals** (booking essential) 45 (lunch)/79 and a la carte 44/97. EZ g

**Frohegg,** Belpstr. 51, 3007, (031) 382 25 24, *Fax (031) 382 25 24*, – AE E VISA
*closed Sunday* – **Meals** (booking essential) 49 (lunch) and a la carte 38/89. CZ r

**Zimmermania,** Brunngasse 19, 3011, (031) 311 15 42, *Fax (031) 312 28 22*, Old Bernese bistro – AE E VISA
*closed 5 July - 3 August, Sunday and Monday* – **Meals** (booking essential) 37 (lunch) and a la carte 41/93. EY h

**Frohsinn,** Münstergasse 54, 3011, (031) 311 37 68, *Fax (031) 311 37 68*, – AE E VISA EZ m
*closed 12 July - 2 August, Sunday and Monday* – **Meals** a la carte 40/90.

**Zum Zähringer,** Badgasse 1, 3011, (031) 311 32 70, – AE E VISA
*closed Sunday* – **Meals** a la carte 44/84. EZ d

**at Muri** *SE : 3,5 km by Thunstrasse – 3074 Muri bei Bern :*

**Sternen,** Thunstr. 80, (031) 950 71 11, *Fax (031) 950 71 00*, – – 25/120. AE E VISA
***Läubli*** **: Meals** 39 (lunch)/60 and a la carte 48/77 – ***Da Pietro*** - Italian rest. - *(closed 6 July - 9 August, Saturday dinner, Sunday dinner and Bank Holidays)* **Meals** a la carte 37/73 – **44 rm** 170/245.

**at Liebefeld** *SW : 3 km direction Schwarzenburg – 3097 Liebefeld :*

**Landhaus,** Schwarzenburgstr. 134, (031) 971 07 58, *Fax (031) 972 02 49*, – AE E VISA
*closed Sunday and Bank Holidays* – ***Rôtisserie :*** **Meals** 54 (lunch)/120 and a la carte 67/110 – ***Taverne Alsacienne :*** **Meals** a la carte 46/75.

**BASLE (BASEL)** *4000 Basel-Stadt 427 ④, 216 ④, 66 ⑩ – 175 510 – alt. 273 – Basle and environs ; from France 0041-61 from Switzerland 061.*

See : *Old town★ : Cathedral★★ (Münster) : ←★* CY *– Fish Market Fountain★ (Fischmarktbrunnen)* BY *– Old Streets★* BY *– Zoological Garden★★★* AZ *– The Port (Hafen) ★, "From Basle to the High Seas"★ Exhibition.*

Museums : *Fine Arts★★★ (Kunstmuseum)* CY *– Historical★ (Historisches Museum)* BY *– Ethnographic★ (Museum für Völkerkunde)* BY **M¹** *– Antiquities★ (Antikenmuseum)* CY *– Paper Museum★ (Basler Papiermühle)* DY **M⁶** *– Haus zum Kirschgarten★* BZ *– Jean Tinguely Museum★.*

Envir : *★ from Bruderholz Water Tower S : 3,5 km – Chapel of St.-Chrischona★ NE : 8 km – Augst Roman Ruins★★ SE : 11 km.*

*18 at Hagenthal-le-Bas, F-68220 (March - November), SW : 10 km, (0033) 389 68 50 91, Fax (0033) 389 68 55 66.*

*Euro-Airport, (061) 325 31 11, Basle (Switzerland) by Flughafenstrasse 8 km and – at Saint-Louis (France), (0033) 389 90 31 11.*

*Tourist Office, Schifflände 5, (061) 268 68 68, Fax (061) 268 68 70 – T.C.S., Steinentorstr. 13, (061) 205 99 99, Fax (061) 205 99 70 – A.C.S., Birsigstr. 4, (061) 272 39 33, Fax (061) 281 36 57.*

*Berne 100 – Freiburg im Breisgau 72 – Lyons 401 – Mulhouse 35 – Paris 554 – Strasbourg 145.*

Plans on following pages

**Drei Könige,** Blumenrain 8, 4001, (061) 261 52 52, *Fax (061) 261 21 53,* – rm, rm, – 25/80. AE E VISA JCB BY a
***Rôtisserie des Rois :*** **Meals** 52 (lunch)/105 and a la carte 67/122 – ***Königsbrasserie :*** **Meals** a la carte 41/81, children 12 – 29 – **82 rm** 255/590, 6 suites.

**Plaza** M, Messeplatz 25, 4021, (061) 690 33 33, *Fax (061) 690 39 70,* – rm, – 35. AE E VISA JCB DX r
***Le Monet*** *(closed early July - mid August)* **Meals** 46 (lunch)/63 and a la carte 56/94 – ***Le Provence :*** **Meals** 23 and a la carte 41/89 – 25 – **238 rm** 359/498.

**Hilton** M, Aeschengraben 31, 4002, (061) 275 66 00, *Fax (061) 275 66 50,* – rm, video – 25/300. AE E VISA JCB. rest CZ d
***Le Wettstein :*** **Meals** 52 and a la carte 49/103 – ***Café Marine Suisse*** *(closed July, Saturday and Sunday)* **Meals** a la carte 30/80 – 25 – **204 rm** 265/495, 10 suites.

**International,** Steinentorstr. 25, 4001, (061) 227 27 27, *Fax (061) 227 28 28,* – rm, – 25/150. AE E VISA JCB BZ b
***Steinenpick*** (Brasserie) **Meals** a la carte 40/88, children 14 – **200 rm** 285/495, 5 suites.

**Europe** M, Clarastr. 43, 4005, (061) 690 80 80, *Fax (061) 690 88 80* – video – 25/180. AE E VISA JCB CX k
**Meals** see ***Les Quatre Saisons*** below – ***Bajazzo*** (Brasserie) **Meals** a la carte 40/73 – **166 rm** 295/395.

**Basel** M, Münzgasse 12, 4001, (061) 264 68 00, *Fax (061) 264 68 11* – – 25. AE E VISA JCB BY x
***Basler Keller*** *(closed 4 July - 3 August, Saturday lunch and Sunday)* **Meals** 39 (lunch) and a la carte 52/116 – ***Brasserie Steiger :*** **Meals** a la carte 40/68 – **72 rm** 260/350.

**Merian** M, Rheingasse 2, 4005, (061) 681 00 00, *Fax (061) 681 11 01,* – – 25/100. AE E VISA JCB BY b
***Café Spitz*** - Fish specialities - **Meals** 49/75 and a la carte 45/91 – **65 rm** 165/261.

**Schweizerhof,** Centralbahnplatz 1, 4002, (061) 271 28 33, *Fax (061) 271 29 19,* – rm, – 25/80. AE E VISA. rest BZ n
**Meals** 38/67 and a la carte 44/106 – **75 rm** 150/300.

**Victoria,** Centralbahnplatz 3, 4002, (061) 271 55 66, *Fax (061) 271 55 01* – rest, – 25/80. AE E VISA JCB BZ d
**Meals** a la carte 39/90, children 15 – **95 rm** 230/310.

**St. Gotthard** M without rest, Centralbahnstr. 13, 4002, (061) 271 52 50, *Fax (061) 271 52 14* – . AE E VISA JCB. BZ f
**62 rm** 180/320.

**Admiral,** Rosentalstr. 5 (on Messeplatz), 4021, (061) 691 77 77, *Fax (061) 691 77 89,* – rm, – 25. AE E VISA JCB. rest DX m
*closed 20 December - 2 January* – **Meals** a la carte 30/78 – **140 rm** 150/350.

**Wettstein** without rest., Grenzacherstr. 8, ✉ 4058, ☎ (061) 690 69 69, *Fax (061) 691 05 45* – AE E VISA DY q
*closed 20 December - 5 January* – **42 rm** 145/210.

**Steinenschanze** without rest, Steinengraben 69, ✉ 4051, ☎ (061) 272 53 53, *Fax (061) 272 45 73* – AE E VISA BY s
**53 rm** 180/250.

**Les Quatre Saisons** - Hotel Europe, Clarastr. 43 (1st floor), ✉ 4005, ☎ (061) 690 87 20, *Fax (061) 690 88 80* – AE E VISA JCB. CX k
*closed 13 July - 12 August and Sunday* – **Meals** 55 (lunch)/165 and a la carte 82/148
**Spec.** Strudel à la truffe noire. Queue de homard à l'infusion d'herbe citronnée. Petit gâteau de pêche chaud et sauce au Moscato.

**Der Teufelhof** with rm, Leonhardsgraben 47, ✉ 4051, ☎ (061) 261 10 10, *Fax (061) 261 10 04*, – AE E VISA BY g
***Bel Etage*** *closed 1 to 5 January, 1 to 15 October, Sunday and Monday (except fairs)* **Meals** 118/180 and a la carte 79/156 – ***Weinstube :*** **Meals** 70 and a la carte 58/110 – **29 rm** 260/290, 4 suites
**Spec.** Sommerbockschinken mit Tannenwipfelvinaigrette und Pfifferlingssalat (summer). Gratiniertes Zackenbarschfilet mit Krustentieren in Estragonsauce. Limonen - Tiramisu mit marinierten Beeren und Spinetta - Eis.

**Chez Donati,** St. Johanns-Vorstadt 48, ✉ 4056, ☎ (061) 322 09 19, *Fax (061) 322 09 81*, , Typical bistro installation from the turn of the century BX p
*closed mid July - mid August, Monday and Tuesday* – **Meals** - Italian rest. - a la carte 58/114.

**Schlüsselzunft,** Freie Strasse 25, ✉ 4001, ☎ (061) 261 20 46, *Fax (061) 261 20 56*, « 15C house » – AE E VISA BY r
*closed Sunday* – **Meals** 48 (lunch) and a la carte 54/106 – ***Höfli :*** **Meals** a la carte 32/60, children 9.

**St. Alban-Eck,** St. Alban-Vorstadt 60, ✉ 4052, ☎ (061) 271 03 20 – AE E VISA. CDY t
*closed 11 July - 9 August, Saturday except dinner from late September - June, Sunday and Bank Holidays* – **Meals** 39 (lunch)/76 and a la carte 65/104.

**Charon,** Schützengraben 62, ✉ 4051, ☎ (061) 261 99 80, *Fax (061) 261 99 09*, Bistro atmosphere – AE E VISA JCB AY s
*closed Easter, July, Christmas, Sunday - Monday from November - April and Saturday - Sunday from May - October* – **Meals** 90 (dinner) and a la carte 70/107.

**Sakura,** Centralbahnstr. 14, ✉ 4051, ☎ (061) 272 05 05, *Fax (061) 295 39 88*, Japanese rest. – E VISA JCB BZ k
*closed 13 July - 9 August, Saturday lunch, Sunday and Bank Holidays* – ***Teppanyaki :*** **Meals** 48/99 and a la carte 41/105, children 30 – ***Yakitori*** (Grill) **Meals** a la carte 41/84.

**St. Alban-Stübli,** St. Ablan-Vorstadt 74, ✉ 4052, ☎ (061) 272 54 15, – AE E VISA DY a
*closed 24 December - 13 January, Saturday lunch and Sunday* – **Meals** 45 and a la carte 44/83.

**at Binningen** *S : 2 km by Oberwilerstrasse* AZ – ✉ *4102 Binningen :*

**Schlüssel,** Schlüsselgasse 1, ☎ (061) 421 25 66, *Fax (061) 421 66 62*, – AE E VISA
**Meals** *(closed Sunday dinner and Saturday)* a la carte 38/80, children 15 – **29 rm** 120/230.

**Schloss Binningen,** Schlossgasse 5, ☎ (061) 421 20 55, *Fax (061) 421 06 35*, , « Old mansion, antique furniture, park » – AE VISA JCB
*closed 9 to 22 February, Sunday and Monday* – **Meals** 45 (lunch)/95 and a la carte 57/119.

**Gasthof Neubad** with rm, Neubadrain 4, ☎ (061) 302 07 05, *Fax (061) 302 81 16*, , – AE E VISA
*closed 20 February - 11 March and Wednesday* – **Meals** 45 (lunch)/54 and a la carte 40/110 – **6 rm** 90/170.

**at Euro-Airport** *NW : 8 km by Kannenfeldstrasse* AX :

**Euroairport,** 5th floor of the airport, ✉ 4030 Basel, ☎ (061) 325 32 32, *Fax (061) 325 32 65*, ← – AE E VISA
***Grill :*** **Meals** 38 and a la carte 38/70 – ***Brasserie :*** **Meals** a la carte 28/50, children 10.

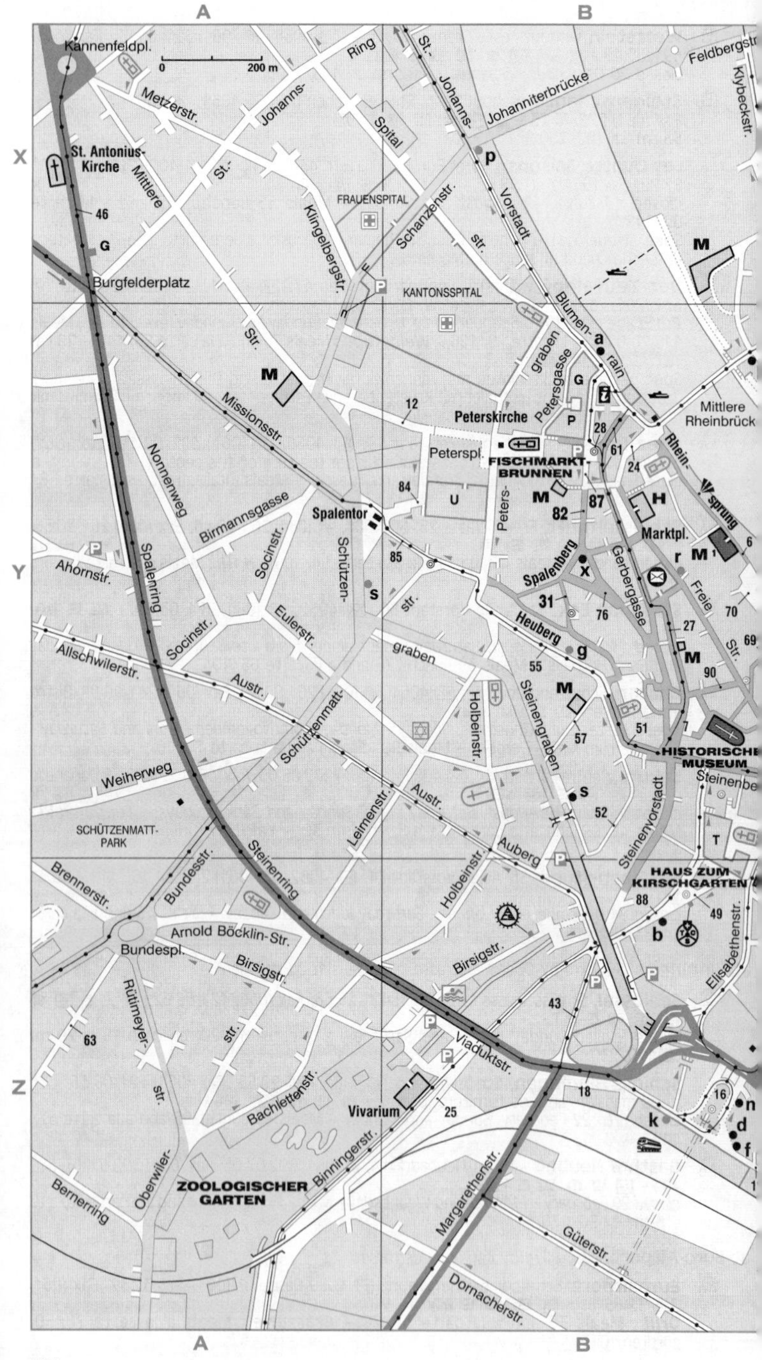
A
B
X
Y
Z
Kannenfeldpl.
0
200 m
Ring
St.-
Johanns-
Feldbergstr.
Klybeckstr.
Metzerstr.
Johanns-
Spital
Johanniterbrücke
St. Antonius-
Kirche
Mittlere
St.-
FRAUENSPITAL
Klingelbergstr.
Schanzenstr.
Vorstadt
str.
46
G
M
Burgfelderplatz
KANTONSSPITAL
Blumen-
rain
Str.
graben
Petersgasse
M
Missionsstr.
12
Peterskirche
Mittlere
Rheinbrück
Rhein-
sprung
Nonnenweg
Peterspl.
FISCHMARKT-
BRUNNEN
28
61
24
Birmannsgasse
84
U
87
82
H
Spalentor
Peters-
Marktpl.
Ahornstr.
Spalenring
Socinstr.
Schützen-
85
Spalenberg
Gerbergasse
Freie
Socinstr.
Eulerstr.
str.
31
76
70
Allschwilerstr.
graben
Heuberg
27
Str.
69
Austr.
55
90
Schützenmatt-
Holbeinstr.
Steinengraben
51
57
Weiherweg
Austr.
Leimenstr.
HISTORISCHE
MUSEUM
Steinenbe
SCHÜTZENMATT-
PARK
52
Auberg
Steinenvorstadt
Brennerstr.
Bundesstr.
Steinenring
Holbeinstr.
HAUS ZUM
KIRSCHGARTEN
88
49
Arnold Böcklin-Str.
Elisabethenstr.
Bundespl.
Birsigstr.
Birsigstr.
Rütimeyer-
43
63
str.
Viaduktstr.
18
Bachlettenstr.
Vivarium
25
str.
16
Oberwiler-
Binningerstr.
Margarethenstr.
ZOOLOGISCHER
GARTEN
Bernerring
Güterstr.
Dornacherstr.
A
B

# BASEL

| Street | Grid | No. |
|---|---|---|
| Aeschenvorstadt | CYZ | |
| Barfüsserplatz | BY | 7 |
| Centralbahnplatz | BZ | 16 |
| Claraplatz | CX | |
| Eisengasse | BY | 24 |
| Falknerstrasse | BY | 27 |
| Freie Strasse | BY | |
| Gerbergasse | BY | |
| Greifengasse | BCY | 33 |
| Marktplatz | BY | |
| Steinenvorstadt | BYZ | |
| Alemannengasse | DY | 3 |
| Andreas Heusler-Strasse | DZ | 4 |
| Augustinergasse | BY | 6 |
| Bäumleingasse | CY | 9 |
| Bernoullistrasse | ABY | 12 |
| Brunngässlein | CYZ | 15 |
| Centralbahnstrasse | BZ | 18 |
| Drahtzugstrasse | CX | 19 |
| Dufourstrasse | CY | 22 |
| Erdbeergraben | BZ | 25 |
| Fischmarkt | BY | 28 |
| Gemsberg | BY | 31 |
| Innere Margarethenstrasse | BZ | 43 |
| Isteinerstrasse | DX | 45 |
| Kannenfeldstrasse | AX | 46 |
| Klingentalstrasse | CX | 48 |
| Klosterberg | BZ | 49 |
| Kohlenberg | BY | 51 |
| Kohlenberggasse | BY | 52 |
| Leonhardsgraben | BY | 55 |
| Leonhardsstrasse | BY | 57 |
| Lindenhofstrasse | CZ | 58 |
| Luftgässlein | CY | 60 |
| Marktgasse | BY | 61 |
| Marschalkenstrasse | AZ | 63 |
| Messeplatz | DX | 64 |
| Mühlenberg | CDY | 66 |
| Münsterberg | BY | 69 |
| Münsterplatz | BY | 70 |
| Peter Merian-Strasse | CZ | 73 |
| Riehentorstrasse | CY | 75 |
| Rümelingsplatz | BY | 76 |
| St.Alban-Graben | CY | 78 |
| Schaffhauserrheinweg | DY | 81 |
| Schneidergasse | BY | 82 |
| Spalengraben | BY | 84 |
| Spalenvorstadt | BY | 85 |
| Stadthausgasse | BY | 87 |
| Steinentorstrasse | BZ | 88 |
| Streitgasse | BY | 90 |
| Wettsteinstrasse | CY | 94 |

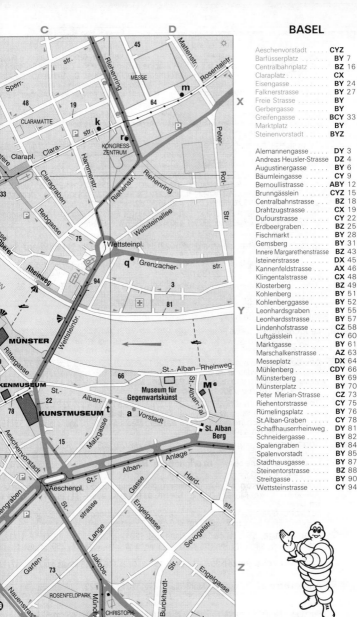

*The names of main shopping streets are printed in red at the beginning of the list of streets.*

**GENEVA** *1200 Genève* 427 ⑪, 217 ⑪, 74 ⑥ *– 170 189 – alt. 375 –* *Geneva, environs : from France 0041-22, from Switzerland 022.*

**See** : *The Shores of the lake★★ : ≤★★★* FGY *– Parks★★ : Mon Repos* GX*, La Perle du Lac and Villa Barton★★ – Botanical Garden★ : alpine rock-garden★★ – Cathedral St-Pierre★ : north Tower ※★★* FZ *– Old Town★ : Reformation Monument★* FZ **D** *; Archaeological Site★ – Palais des Nations★★ – Parc de la Grange★ – Parc des Eaux-Vives★ – Nave★ of Church of Christ the King – Woodwork★ in the Historical Museum of the Swiss Abroad – Baur Collection★ (in 19C mansion)* GZ *– Maison Tavel★* FZ.

**Museums** : *Ariana★★ – Art and History★★* GZ *– Natural History★★* GZ *– International Automobile Museum★ – Petit Palais : Modern Art★★* GZ *– International Red Cross and Red Crescent Museum★.*

**Excursions** : *by boat on the lake, Information : Cie Gén. de Nav., Jardin Anglais ☎ (022) 311 25 21- Mouettes genevoises, 8 quai du Mont-Blanc, ☎ (022) 732 29 44 - Swiss Boat, 4 quai du Mont-Blanc, ☎ (022) 732 47 47.*

*18 at Cologny ✉ 1223 (March - December), ☎ (022) 735 75 40, Fax (022) 735 71 05 ; 18 at Bossey ✉ F-74160 (March - December), ☎ (0033) 450 43 95 50, Fax (0033) 450 95 32 57 by road to Troinex ; 18 at Esery ✉ F-74930 Reignier (March - December), ☎ (0033) 450 36 58 70, Fax (0033) 450 36 57 62.*

*SE : 15 km ; 18 Maison Blanche at Echenevex-Gex ✉ F-01170 (March - mid December), ☎ (0033) 450 42 44 42, Fax (0033) 450 42 44 43, NW : 17 km.*

*✈ Genève-Cointrin, ☎ 717 71 11.*

*ℹ Tourist Office, Place du Molard, ☎ (022) 311 98 27, Fax (022) 311 80 52 and 3 r. du Mont Blanc, ☎ (022) 909 70 00, Fax (022) 909 70 11 – T.C.S., 9 r. Pierre-Fatio, ☎ (022) 737 12 01, Fax (022) 737 13 10 – A.C.S., 21 r. de la Fontenette ✉ 1227 Carouge, ☎ (022) 342 22 33, Fax (022) 301 37 11.*

*Berne 164 – Bourg-en-B. 101 – Lausanne 60 – Lyons 151 – Paris 538 – Turin 252.*

Plans on following pages

**Right Bank (Cornavin Railway Station - Les Quais) :**

**Le Richemond,** Jardin Brunswick, ✉ 1201, ☎ (022) 731 14 00, *Fax (022) 731 67 09,* ≤, 🏖, 𝐹𝑑 – |♦|, ▤ TV video ☎ 🚗 – 🏛 25/230. AE ⓓ E VISA JCB FY u
***Le Jardin* :** **Meals** 44 and a la carte 62/109 – ☕ 37 – **67 rm** 390/720, 31 suites.

**Des Bergues,** 33 quai des Bergues, ✉ 1201, ☎ (022) 731 50 50, *Fax (022) 732 19 89* – |♦|, ▤ rm, TV video ☎ 📞 ♿ – 🏛 25/350. AE ⓓ E VISA FY k
**Meals** see ***Amphitryon*** below – ***Le Pavillon* :** **Meals** 45 (lunch) and a la carte 43/86 – ☕ 32 – **108 rm** 360/730, 10 suites.

**Rhône,** 1 quai Turrettini, ✉ 1211, ☎ (022) 731 98 31, *Fax (022) 732 45 58,* ≤, 🏖 – |♦|, ⇔ rm, ▤ TV video ☎ 🚗 – 🏛 25/150. AE ⓓ E VISA JCB. ✂ rest FY r
**Meals** see ***Le Neptune*** below – ***Café Rafael* :** **Meals** 44 (lunch) and a la carte 53/100 – ☕ 30 – **192 rm** 410/690, 20 suites.

**Noga Hilton,** 19 quai du Mont-Blanc, ✉ 1201, ☎ (022) 908 90 81, *Fax (022) 908 90 90,* ≤, 🏖, 𝐹𝑑, ≘s, 🏊 – |♦|, ⇔ rm, ▤ TV video ☎ ♿ – 🏛 25/850. AE ⓓ E VISA JCB
**Meals** see ***Le Cygne*** below – ***La Grignotière* :** **Meals** a la carte 45/79 – ☕ 31 – **374 rm** 435/655, 36 suites. GY y

**Président Wilson** Ⓜ, 47 quai Wilson, ✉ 1211, ☎ (022) 906 66 66, *Fax (022) 906 66 67,* ≤ lake, 𝐹𝑑, ≘s, 🏊 – |♦|, ⇔ rm, ▤ TV ☎ 📞 🚗 – 🏛 25/1100. AE ⓓ E VISA JCB. ✂ rest GX d
***Le Cirque* :** **Meals** 45 (lunch) and a la carte 50/108 – ***L'Arabesque*** - Libanese rest. - **Meals** a la carte 44/82 – ☕ 32 – **222 rm** 480/800, 13 suites.

**Beau-Rivage,** 13 quai du Mont-Blanc, ✉ 1201, ☎ (022) 716 66 66, *Fax (022) 716 60 60,* ≤, 🏖 – |♦|, ⇔ rm, ▤ rm, TV video ☎ 🚗 – 🏛 25/250. AE ⓓ E VISA JCB. ✂ FY d
**Meals** see ***Le Chat Botté*** below – ***Le Quai 13,*** ☎ (022) 716 69 25 **Meals** a la carte 37/86 – ☕ 34 – **89 rm** 375/570, 8 suites.

**Angleterre** Ⓜ, 17 quai du Mont-Blanc, ✉ 1201, ☎ (022) 906 55 55, *Fax (022) 906 55 56,* ≤, « Tasteful installation », 𝐹𝑑, ≘s – |♦| ▤ TV ☎ 🚗 – 🏛 35. AE ⓓ E VISA JCB FGY n
***Bertie's* :** **Meals** 35 (lunch)/65 and a la carte 51/103 – ☕ 30 – **45 rm** 375/700.

**Ramada Genève,** 19 r. de Zurich, ✉ 1201, ☎ (022) 909 90 00, *Fax (022) 909 90 01* – |♦|, ⇔ rm, ▤ TV video ☎ 📞 🚗 – 🏛 25/110. AE ⓓ E VISA JCB FX s
***The Taj*** - Indian and International rest. - *(closed Sunday lunch)* **Meals** 50 and a la carte 39/86 – ***Le Refuge*** - "fondues" speciality - **Meals** 42/56 and a la carte 39/71 – ☕ 27 – **194 rm** 285/440, 11 suites.

**Bristol,** 10 r. du Mont-Blanc, ✉ 1201, ☎ (022) 732 38 00, *Fax (022) 738 90 39,* 𝐹𝑑, ≘s – |♦| ▤ TV ☎ – 🏛 25/90. AE ⓓ E VISA JCB. ✂ rest FY w
**Meals** 41 and a la carte 41/87 – ☕ 27 – **93 rm** 275/450, 5 suites.

**Warwick,** 14 r. de Lausanne, ✉ 1201, ✆ (022) 731 62 50, *Fax (022) 738 99 35* – rm, – 25/300. AE ⓓ E VISA JCB. rest FY c
***Les 4 Saisons*** *(closed 20 July - 11 August, Saturday lunch and Sunday)* **Meals** 40 (lunch)/55 and a la carte 58/103 – ***La Bonne Brasserie* : Meals** 26 and a la carte 36/70, children 15 – 19 – **169 rm** 280/460.

**Sofitel,** 18 r. du Cendrier, ✉ 1201, ✆ (022) 731 52 00, *Fax (022) 731 91 69,* – rm, rest, . AE ⓓ E VISA JCB FY t
**Meals** *(closed 22 December - 4 January)* 43 and a la carte 42/99 – 31 – **85 rm** 350/390, 10 suites.

**Cornavin** without rest, 23 bd James-Fazy, ✉ 1201, ✆ (022) 732 21 00, *Fax (022) 732 88 43* – . AE ⓓ E VISA FY a
16 – **118 rm** 165/265, 3 suites.

**Grand Pré** without rest, 35 r. du Grand-Pré, ✉ 1202, ✆ (022) 918 11 11, *Fax (022) 734 76 91* – – 25. AE ⓓ E VISA by rue du Fort-Barreau FX
**89 rm** 215/310.

**Eden,** 135 r. de Lausanne, ✉ 1202, ✆ (022) 732 65 40, *Fax (022) 731 52 60* – , rm, . AE ⓓ E VISA JCB
**Meals** *(closed Saturday and Sunday)* 29 and a la carte 30/57 – **54 rm** 180/240.

**Carlton,** 22 r. Amat, ✉ 1202, ✆ (022) 908 68 50, *Fax (022) 908 68 68* – . AE ⓓ E VISA FX a
**Meals** *(closed Sunday lunch and Saturday)* a la carte 29/51 – 20 – **123 rm** 220/260.

**Strasbourg - Univers** without rest, 10 r. Pradier, ✉ 1201, ✆ (022) 906 58 00, *Fax (022) 738 42 08* – . AE ⓓ E VISA. FY q
**51 rm** 130/210.

**Du Midi,** 4 pl. Chevelu, ✉ 1201, ✆ (022) 731 78 00, *Fax (022) 731 00 20* – . AE ⓓ E VISA FY v
**Meals** *(closed Saturday and Sunday)* 30 (lunch) and a la carte 42/62 – 12 – **89 rm** 180/250.

**Le Cygne** - Hotel Noga Hilton, 19 quai du Mont-Blanc, ✉ 1201, ✆ (022) 908 90 85, *Fax (022) 908 90 90,* ≤ – . AE ⓓ E VISA JCB. GY y
*closed 10 to 19 April, 29 June - 20 July and 1 to 7 January* – **Meals** 59 (lunch)/145 and a la carte 85/133
**Spec.** Fricandeau de thon clouté d'anchois, pommes charlotte confites (summer). Bar cuit à la fumée de bois et vinaigrette aux truffes. Pigeonneau rôti à la sauge et olives, galette de pommes de terre et tomates façon pissaladière (spring).

**Le Chat Botté** - Hotel Beau-Rivage, 13 quai du Mont-Blanc, ✉ 1201, ✆ (022) 716 66 66, *Fax (022) 716 60 60,* – AE ⓓ E VISA JCB. FY d
*closed Easter, Christmas - New Year, Saturday, Sunday and Bank Holidays* – **Meals** 60 (lunch)/135 and a la carte 79/129
**Spec.** Filets de perche du Lac de Genève en vinaigrette aux appétits (summer). Etuvée de homard aux chanterelles et jus de volaille. Eventail de truffes glacées en coffret de nougatine.

**Le Neptune** - Hotel du Rhône, quai Turrettini, ✉ 1211, ✆ (022) 738 74 89, *Fax (022) 732 45 58* – . AE ⓓ E VISA JCB. FY r
*closed 20 July - 9 August, Saturday, Sunday and Bank Holidays* – **Meals** 65/125 and a la carte 89/137
**Spec.** Doucette de Saint-Jacques aux racines d'hiver et émulsion d'oursins (winter). Poissons du lac Léman (May - October). Rouget de roche raidi en meunière d'épices et feuille de coriandre.

**Amphitryon** - Hotel Des Bergues, 33 quai des Bergues, ✉ 1201, ✆ (022) 731 50 50, *Fax (022) 732 19 89* – AE ⓓ E VISA FY k
*closed July - August, Saturday, Sunday and Bank Holidays* – **Meals** 65 (lunch)/105 and a la carte 59/116.

**Tsé Yang,** 19 quai du Mont-Blanc, ✉ 1201, ✆ (022) 732 50 81, *Fax (022) 731 05 82,* ≤, « Elegant installation » – . AE ⓓ E VISA JCB GY e
**Meals** - Chinese rest. - 38 (lunch)/125 and a la carte 59/141.

**La Fenice,** 78 av. de Châtelaine, ✉ 1219, ✆ (022) 797 03 70, *Fax (022) 797 01 79,* – AE ⓓ E VISA
*closed 2 to 10 August, 24 December - 2 January, Sunday and Monday* – **Meals** - Italian rest. - a la carte 55/98.

**Bœuf Rouge,** 17 r. Alfred-Vincent, ✉ 1201, ✆ (022) 732 75 37, *Fax (022) 731 46 84* – AE ⓓ E VISA FY z
*closed Saturday and Sunday* – **Meals** - Specialities of Lyons - 33 (lunch)/45 and a la carte 48/88.

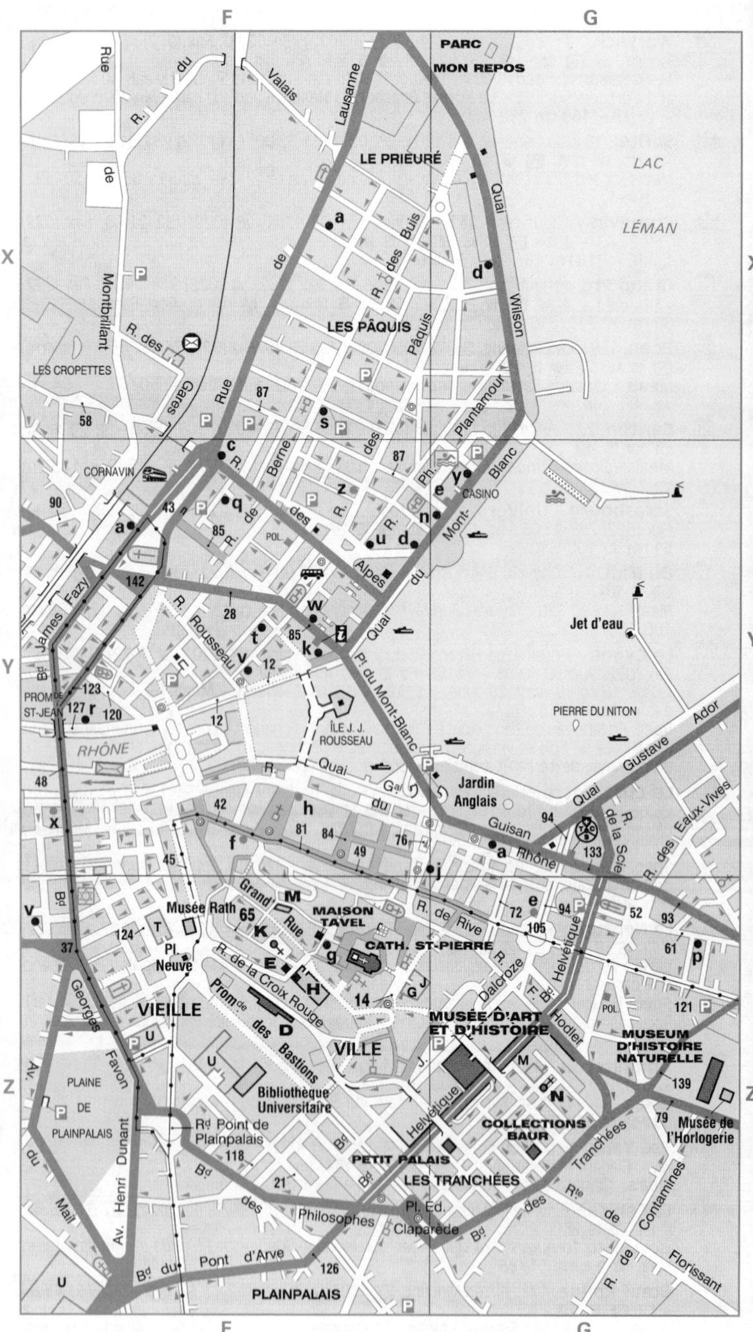

PARC
MON REPOS
LE PRIEURÉ
LAC
LÉMAN
Quai Wilson
LES PÂQUIS
R. des Pâquis
Rue de Lausanne
R. de Berne
R. des Alpes
Quai du Mont-Blanc
CASINO
CORNAVIN
LES CROPETTES
Rue de Montbrillant
R. des Gares
R. du Valais
Bd James Fazy
R. Rousseau
PROM DE ST-JEAN
RHÔNE
ÎLE J. J. ROUSSEAU
Pt. du Mont-Blanc
Jet d'eau
PIERRE DU NITON
Quai Gustave Ador
Jardin Anglais
Quai du Général Guisan
R. du Rhône
R. de Rive
R. de la Scie
R. des Eaux-Vives
Grand Rue
MAISON TAVEL
CATH. ST-PIERRE
Musée Rath
Pl. Neuve
VIEILLE VILLE
R. de la Croix Rouge
Prom de des Bastions
Bibliothèque Universitaire
MUSÉE D'ART ET D'HISTOIRE
MUSEUM D'HISTOIRE NATURELLE
Musée de l'Horlogerie
COLLECTIONS BAUR
PETIT PALAIS
LES TRANCHÉES
Bd Helvétique
R. Dalcroze
Bd des Philosophes
Pl. Ed. Claparède
Rte de Florissant
R. de Contamines
PLAINE DE PLAINPALAIS
Rd Point de Plainpalais
Av. Henri Dunant
Av. du Mail
Bd Georges Favon
Bd du Pont d'Arve
PLAINPALAIS

## STREET INDEX TO GENEVE TOWN PLAN



## Left Bank (Commercial Centre) :

**Métropole,** 34 quai Général-Guisan, ✉ 1211, ℘ (022) 318 32 00, *Fax (022) 318 33 00*, – video – 25/200. AE ⓓ E VISA. rest GY a
Meals see ***L'Arlequin*** below – ***Le Grand Quai :*** Meals a la carte 46/98 – 20 – **121 rm** 299/470, 6 suites.

**La Cigogne,** 17 pl. Longemalle, ✉ 1204, ℘ (022) 818 40 40, *Fax (022) 818 40 50*, « Tastefully decorated and furnished » – video . AE ⓓ E VISA. rest
**Meals** 59 (lunch)/90 and a la carte 73/107 – **45 rm** 315/405, 7 suites. FGY j

**Les Armures**, 1 r. du Puits-Saint-Pierre, ✉ 1204, ℘ (022) 310 91 72, *Fax (022) 310 98 46*, « Attractive rustic furnishings in a 17C house » – , rm, video – 25. AE ⓓ E VISA JCB FZ g
**Meals** *(closed 11 to 13 April, Christmas and New Year)* 45 and a la carte 43/80, children 17 – **28 rm** 280/430.

**Century** without rest, 24 av. de Frontenex, ✉ 1207, ℘ (022) 736 80 95, *Fax (022) 786 52 74* – – 35. AE ⓓ E VISA JCB GZ p
**118 rm** 165/360, 14 suites.

**Tiffany** M, 18 r. de l'Arquebuse, ✉ 1204, ℘ (022) 329 33 11, *Fax (022) 320 89 91* – , rm, video . AE ⓓ E VISA JCB FZ v
**Meals** *(closed Christmas and New Year)* 42 (dinner) and a la carte 36/75 – **28 rm** 205/350.

**Parc des Eaux-Vives,** 82 quai G.-Ador, ✉ 1211, ℘ (022) 735 41 40, *Fax (022) 786 87 65*, <, , « Pleasant setting in extensive park » – . AE E VISA JCB
*closed 27 March - 5 April, 25 October - 2 November, 26 December - 8 January, Sunday except lunch May - September and Monday* – **Meals** 72/118 and a la carte 60/150.
by quai G. Ador GY

**L'Arlequin** - Hotel Métropole, 34 quai Général-Guisan, ✉ 1211, ℘ (022) 318 32 00, *Fax (022) 318 33 00* – . AE ⓓ E. GY a
*closed 15 July - 15 August, Saturday, Sunday and Bank Holidays* – **Meals** 58 (lunch)/100 and a la carte 62/142.

**Le Béarn** (Goddard), 4 quai de la Poste, ✉ 1204, ℘ (022) 321 00 28, *Fax (022) 781 31 15* – . AE ⓓ E VISA FY x
*closed 18 July - 16 August, 23 February - 1 March, Saturday except dinner October - May and Sunday* – **Meals** 50 (lunch)/155 and a la carte 85/167
**Spec.** Les trois gourmandises de l'été : homard, cappuccino et rillettes de tourteau. Sauté gourmand de turbot aux cèpes et herbes de Vandouvan (autumn and winter). Saint-Pierre rôti à la feuille de laurier, pomme verte et céleri (spring).

**Baron de la Mouette (Mövenpick Fusterie),** 40 r. du Rhône, ✉ 1204, ℘ (022) 311 88 55, *Fax (022) 310 93 22* – AE ⓓ E VISA JCB FY h
*closed Saturday - Sunday and dinner* – **Meals** 55 a la carte 50/109.

**Roberto,** 10 r. Pierre-Fatio, ✉ 1204, ℘ (022) 311 80 33, *Fax (022) 311 84 66* – . AE E VISA GZ e
*closed Saturday dinner and Sunday* – **Meals** - Italian rest. - a la carte 54/102.

**Brasserie Lipp,** 8 r. de la Confédération (2nd floor), ✉ 1204, ℘ (022) 311 10 11, *Fax (022) 312 01 04*, – . AE ⓓ E VISA FY f
**Meals** a la carte 37/88.

## Environs

### to the N :

**Palais des Nations** : *by quai Wilson* FGX :

**Intercontinental**, 7 chemin du Petit-Saconnex, ✉ 1211, ☎ (022) 919 39 39, *Fax (022) 919 38 38*, ≤, 🏛, Fā, ⛱ – ⇅ ▤ TV ☎ 🚗 P – 🎤 25/600. AE ⓓ E VISA JCB. ✗ rest
Meals see ***Les Continents*** below – ***La Pergola :*** **Meals** a la carte 50/92 – ☕ 23 – **285 rm** 420/500, 60 suites.

**Les Continents** - Hotel Intercontinental, 7 chemin du Petit-Saconnex, ✉ 1211, ☎ (022) 919 33 50, *Fax (022) 919 38 38* – ▤ P. AE ⓓ E VISA JCB. ✗
*closed Saturday and Sunday* – **Meals** 55 (lunch)/92 and a la carte 69/121
**Spec.** Gelée de foie gras de canard et artichauts au Sauternes. Ragoût de saumon sauvage aux morilles et asperges vertes, beurre léger aux herbes. Baron de lapin au lard et polenta, sauce au Barolo.

**La Perle du Lac,** 126 r. de Lausanne, ✉ 1202, ☎ (022) 731 79 35, *Fax (022) 731 49 79*, 🏛, « Chalet in a park ≤ lake » – P. AE ⓓ E VISA JCB. ✗
*closed 22 December - 1 February and Monday* – **Meals** 58 (lunch)/120 and a la carte 72/157.

**at Palais des Expositions** : *by quai Wilson* FGX : *5 km* – ✉ *1218 Le Grand-Saconnex* :

**Holiday Inn Crowne Plaza**, 26 voie de Moëns, ☎ (022) 791 00 11, *Fax (022) 798 92 73*, Fā, ≘s, ⛱ – ⇅, ✗ rm, ▤ TV video ☎ 📞 ♿ – 🎤 25/140. AE ⓓ E VISA JCB
**Meals** 35 and a la carte 43/91 – ☕ 25 – **305 rm** 290/410.

**at Chambésy** *5 km* - CT – ✉ *1292 Chambésy* :

**Relais de Chambésy,** 8 pl. de Chambésy, ☎ (022) 758 11 05, *Fax (022) 758 02 30*, 🏛 – AE ⓓ E VISA
*closed Saturday lunch and Sunday* – **Meals** 29 (lunch)/75 and a la carte 42/82.

**at Bellevue** : *by road to Lausanne* FX : *6 km* – ✉ *1293 Bellevue* :

**La Réserve,** 301 rte de Lausanne, ☎ (022) 959 86 88, *Fax (022) 959 85 88*, ≤, 🏛, Park, Fā, ≘s, ⛱, ⛱, ✗, ⚓ – ▤ TV ☎ 🚗 P – 🎤 25/80. AE ⓓ E VISA
**Meals** see ***Tsé Fung*** below – ***Mikado*** - Japanese rest. - *(closed Sunday lunch and Saturday lunch except in summer)* **Meals** 50 (lunch)/95 and a la carte 41/102 – ***La Closerie :*** **Meals** 48/75 and a la carte 65/139 – ☕ 28 – **108 rm** 295/495, 6 suites – ½ P 48.

**Tsé Fung** - Hotel La Réserve, 301 rte de Lausanne, ☎ (022) 959 86 88, *Fax (022) 959 85 88*, 🏛 – ▤ P. AE ⓓ E VISA JCB
**Meals** - Chinese rest. - 50 (lunch)/125 and a la carte 61/110.

### to the E by road to Evian :

**at Cologny** : *by Quai Gustave Ador* GY : *3,5 km* – ✉ *1223 Cologny* :

**Aub. du Lion d'Or** (Byrne/Dupont), 5 pl. Pierre-Gautier, ☎ (022) 736 44 32, *Fax (022) 786 74 62*, ≤, 🏛, « Overlooking the lake and Geneva » – P. AE ⓓ E VISA
*closed January, Saturday and Sunday* – **Meals** 48 (lunch)/140 and a la carte 90/130 – ***Bistro de Cologny :*** **Meals** 39 (lunch) and a la carte 51/82
**Spec.** Salade tiède de homard, grecque de légumes d'été à la coriandre. Blanc de turbot clouté de basilic et tomate confite, supions à l'huile d'olive et piments doux. Pigonneau du Haut Anjou rôti en casserole aux épices, pastilla de légumes.

**at Anières** : *by road to Hermance* : *7 km* – ✉ *1247 Anières* :

**Aub. de Floris** (Legras), 287 rte d'Hermance, ☎ (022) 751 20 20, *Fax (022) 751 22 50*, 🏛, « terrace ≤ lake » – AE E VISA
*closed 9 to 20 April, 20 December - 5 January, Sunday and Monday* – **Meals** 55 (lunch) and a la carte 66/132 – ***Le Café :*** **Meals** 34 and a la carte 41/64
**Spec.** Gaufre de pommes de terre nouvelles et tartare de rouget. Broccolletini de pintade à la sauge, jus de Marsala. Dacquois à la framboise, chiboust à la vanille

### to the E by road to Annemasse :

**at Thônex** : *by rte de Chêne* GZ : *5 km* – ✉ *1226 Thônex* :

**Le Cigalon** (Bessire), 39 rte d'Ambilly, at the customs border of Pierre-à-Bochet, ☎ (022) 349 97 33, *Fax (022) 349 97 33*, 🏛 – P. AE E VISA. ✗
*closed 7 to 31 July, 21 February - 1 March, Saturday lunch, Sunday dinner and Monday* – **Meals** 42 (lunch)/95 and a la carte 64/103
**Spec.** Gaspacho aux médaillons de homard (June - September). Foie gras poêlé au sucre de palme et vinaigre de coco (autumn - winter). Loup de mer rôti en écailles.

### to the S :

**at Vessy** : *by road to Veyrier : 4 km – ✉ 1234 Vessy :*

XX **Alain Lavergnat,** 130 rte de Veyrier, ✆ (022) 784 26 26, *Fax (022) 784 13 34,* – P. AE E VISA
*closed 25 July - 10 August, 21 December - 5 January, 10 to 20 March, Monday from September to June, Saturday from July to August and Sunday* – **Meals** 48 (lunch)/90 and a la carte 76/106.

**at Carouge** : *by Av. Henri-Dunant* FZ *: 3 km – ✉ 1227 Carouge :*

XXX **Aub. de Pinchat** with rm, 33 chemin de Pinchat, ✆ (022) 342 30 77, *Fax (022) 300 22 19,* – TV ☎ P. AE E VISA
*closed 5 to 13 April, 30 August - 13 September, 21 December - 5 January, Sunday and Monday* – **Meals** 45 (lunch)/94 and a la carte 77/124 – **5 rm** 120/145.

XX **L'Olivier de Provence,** 13 r. Jacques-Dalphin, ✆ (022) 342 04 50, *Fax (022) 342 88 80,* – AE O E VISA
*closed 31 July - 17 August, 1 to 11 January, Saturday lunch, Sunday and Bank Holidays* – **Meals** 41 (lunch)/98 and a la carte 60/106.

**at Petit-Lancy** : *by Av. Henri-Dunant* FZ *: 3 km – ✉ 1213 Petit-Lancy :*

**Host. de la Vendée,** 28 chemin de la Vendée, ✆ (022) 792 04 11, *Fax (022) 792 05 46,* , Winter garden – TV ☎ – 40. AE O E VISA
*closed Easter and 24 December - 5 January* – **Meals** *(closed Saturday lunch and Sunday)* 50 (lunch)/120 and a la carte 76/124 – ***Bistro*** *(closed Saturday and Sunday)* **Meals** 36 and a la carte 46/86 – **33 rm** 155/265
**Spec.** Rouget barbet aux fèves, jus de volaille aux miettes de truffes (spring). Filet de perche du lac "Pointe à la bise", mesclun en vinaigrette aux appétits (summer). Douceur des îles au rhum, sauce anglaise, sorbet noix de coco (winter).

**at Lully** *SW : 8 km by road to Bernex – ✉ 1233 Bernex :*

XX **La Colombière** (Lonati), 122 rte de Soral, ✆ (022) 757 10 27, *Fax (022) 757 65 49,* – P. AE O E VISA
*closed 22 August - 22 September, 20 December - 11 January, Saturday and Sunday* – **Meals** (booking essential) 42 (lunch)/82 and a la carte 67/99
**Spec.** Ravioles de poireau et truffe noire "in brodo". Poêlée de gambas, nouilles à l'encre et févettes au basilic (summer). Filet de canette poché au thym, bouillon de laurier, chou et foie gras.

### to the W :

**at Peney-Dessus** : *by road to Satigny and private lane : 10 km – ✉ 1242 Satigny :*

XXX **Domaine de Châteauvieux** (Chevrier) with rm, ✆ (022) 753 15 11, *Fax (022) 753 19 24,* <, , « Beautiful country inn, in a former farm » – TV ☎ P. AE E VISA
*closed 2 to 17 August, 21 December - 6 January* – **Meals** *(closed Sunday and Monday)* 65 (lunch)/165 and a la carte 124/178 – **19 rm** 155/235
**Spec.** Mignon de porcelet cuit en croûte de pain au lard séché et aux girolles (May - September). Tronçon de turbot grillé à l'os, petites ravioles de tourteau à la coriandre (April- August). Gibier à plumes (October - November).

**at Cointrin** : *by road to Lyons : 4 km – ✉ 1216 Cointrin :*

**Mövenpick Genève** M, 20 rte Pré-Bois, ✉ 1215 Geneva, ✆ (022) 798 75 75, *Fax (022) 791 02 84* – rm, TV ☎ P – 25/400. AE O E VISA JCB
***La Brasserie*** : **Meals** a la carte 43/81 – ***Japanese rest.*** *(closed 26 July - 16 August, Saturday lunch, Monday lunch and Sunday)* **Meals** 27 (lunch)/98 and a la carte 47/88 – 24 – **336 rm** 275/395, 4 suites.

**Penta,** 75 av. Louis-Casaï, ✆ (022) 798 47 00, *Fax (022) 798 77 58,* – rm, rm, TV ☎ P – 25/700. AE O E VISA JCB. rest
***La Récolte*** : **Meals** 29 and a la carte 37/89 – 26 – **302 rm** 190/410, 6 suites.

XX **Canonica,** 2nd floor at the airport, ✆ (022) 717 76 76, *Fax (022) 798 77 68,* <, Restaurants arranged around an aircraft cabin – AE O E VISA
***Plein Ciel*** *(closed Sunday except lunch in winter and Saturday)* **Meals** 47/55 and a la carte 59/109 – ***L'Avion*** (Brasserie) **Meals** 28/36 and a la carte 32/77, children 14.

**Vufflens-le-Château** *1134 Vaud* 427 ⑪, 217 ② *– pop. 554 – alt. 471.*

*Berne 118 – Geneva 53 – Lausanne 14 – Morges 3 – Pontarlier 72 – Yverdon-les-Bains 41.*

XXXX ✿✿ **L'Ermitage** (Ravet) with rm, (021) 802 21 91, *Fax (021) 802 22 40*, « Beautiful residence in a garden, pond » – TV ☎ P. VISA
*closed 25 July - 18 August, 20 December - 13 January, Sunday and Monday* – **Meals** 125/185 and a la carte 145/192 – **9 rm** 300/400
**Spec.** Méli-mélo de homard breton et noisettes de ris de veau. Tronçon de turbot rôti à la broche. Canard de Barbarie doré à la broche et confit au jus de pamplemousse et gentiane.

**Crissier** *1023 Vaud* 427 ⑪ 217 ③ *– pop. 5 245 – alt. 470.*

*Berne 111 – Lausanne 6 – Montreux 40 – Nyon 50 – Pontarlier 64.*

XXXX ✿✿✿ **Girardet** (Rochat), 1 r. d'Yverdon, (021) 634 05 05, *Fax (021) 634 24 64*, « Elegant decor » – AE E VISA
*closed 25 July - 18 August, 24 December - 9 January, Sunday and Monday* – **Meals** 185/200 and a la carte 115/270
**Spec.** Chartreuse de pointes d'asperges vertes et morilles à la fricassée de grenouilles (spring). Omble chevalier du lac Léman en court bouillon, beurre battu au cerfeuil (summer). Conversation tiède de Boskoop aux amandes grillées (autumn).

**Brent** *1817 Vaud* 217 ⑭ *– alt. 569.*

*Berne 85 – Geneva 89 – Lausanne 25 – Martigny 47 – Montreux 5.*

XXX ✿✿✿ **Le Pont de Brent** (Rabaey), (021) 964 52 30, *Fax (021) 964 55 30*, « Elegant decor » – P. E VISA
*closed 19 July - 3 August, 21 December - 7 January, Sunday and Monday* – **Meals** 60 (lunch)/175 and a la carte 92/162
**Spec.** Lasagne de langoustines et pétoncles au basilic. Turbot aux coques et thym citron. Evantail aux cerises, glace au lait d'amandes.

---

**ZÜRICH** *8000 Zürich* 427 ⑥, 216 ⑱ *– pop. 345 235 – alt. 409.*

See : *The Quays★★ : ≤★ FZ; Mythenquai : ≤★ CX – Fraumünster cloisters★ (Alter Kreuzgang des Fraumünsters), windows★ EZ – Church of SS. Felix and Regula★ – Cathedral★ (Grossmünster) – Fine Arts Museum★★ (Kunsthaus) FZ – Zoological Gardens★ (Zoo Dolder) – Bührle Collection★★ (Sammlung Bührle).*

Museums : *Swiss National Museum★★ (Schweizerisches Landesmuseum) EY – Rietberg Museum★★ CX* **M²**.

Envir : *Uetliberg★★ SW : by rail – Albis Pass Road★ SW by the Bederstrasse – Former Abbey of Kappel★ SW : 22 km – Eglisau : site★ N : 27 km.*

Excursions : *Boat Trips, Information : Zürichsee-Schiffahrtsgesellschaft, Bürkliplatz 10, (01) 482 10 33.*

*9 Dolder (April-15 Nov.), (01) 261 50 45, Fax (01) 261 53 02 ; 18 at Zumikon, ✉ 8126 (April-Oct.), (01) 918 00 50, Fax (01) 918 00 37, SE : 9 km ; 18 at Hittnau, ✉ 8335 (April-Nov.), (01) 950 24 42, Fax (01) 951 01 66 E : 33 km ; 18 at Breitenloo, ✉ 8309 Nürensdorf (April-Oct.), (01) 836 40 80, Fax (01) 837 10 85 N : 22 km.*

*Zürich-Kloten, (01) 816 22 11.*

*Tourist Office, Im Hauptbahnhof, (01) 215 40 00, Fax (01) 215 40 44 – T.C.S., Alfred Escher-Str. 38, (01) 286 86 86, Fax (01) 286 86 87 – A.C.S., Forchstr. 95, (01) 422 15 00, Fax (01) 422 15 37.*

*Berne 125 – Basle 109 – Geneva 278 – Innsbruck 288 – Milan 304.*

Plans on following pages

**On the right bank of river Limmat (University, Fine Arts Museum) :**

**Dolder Grand Hotel**, Kurhausstr. 65, ✉ 8032, (01) 269 30 00, *Fax (01) 269 30 01*, Park, « Overlooking Zurich lake, town and mountains », – , rest, TV ☎ – 25/120. AE E VISA JCB. rest by Gloriastrasse DV
***La Rotonde :*** **Meals** 80 and a la carte 60/138 – **173 rm** 390/580, 11 suites.

**Zürich Marriott,** Neumühlequai 42, ✉ 8001, (01) 360 70 70, *Fax (01) 360 77 77*, ≤, – , rm, TV video ☎ – 25/250. AE E VISA JCB. rest EY c
***White Elephant*** - Thaï rest. - *(closed 10 to 29 August, 23 December - 6 January and Sunday)* **Meals** 39 (lunch)/65 and a la carte 51/88 – ***La Brasserie :*** **Meals** 34 (lunch) and a la carte 43/94 – 29 – **251 rm** 360/390, 9 suites.

**Eden au Lac,** Utoquai 45, 8023, (01) 266 25 25, *Fax (01) 266 25 00*, – . rest DX a
**Meals** 105 and a la carte 62/129 – **56 rm** 320/610.

**Dolder Waldhaus**, Kurhausstr. 20, 8032, (01) 269 10 00, *Fax (01) 269 10 01*, Zürich and lake, , , , , – , rest, – 35. by Gloriastrasse DV
**Meals** 65 and a la carte 42/93, children 16 – 16 – **67 rm** 220/440.

**Sofitel,** Stampfenbachstr. 60, 8035, (01) 360 60 60, *Fax (01) 360 60 61* – , rm, – 25/70. . rest FY b
***Diff :*** **Meals** 58 (lunch)/98 and a la carte 71/147 – 31 – **168 rm** 300/400.

**Central Plaza**, Central 1, 8001, (01) 251 55 55, *Fax (01) 251 85 35* – video – 35. FY z
***Cascade :*** **Meals** a la carte 50/82 – 24 – **94 rm** 285/350, 6 suites.

**Florhof**, Florhofgasse 4, 8001, (01) 261 44 70, *Fax (01) 261 46 11*, , « Tasteful installation » – , rm, . FZ k
**Meals** *(closed 20 December - 15 January, Saturday, Sunday and Bank Holidays)* 45 (lunch)/72 and a la carte 43/101 – **33 rm** 225/340.

**Europe** without rest, Dufourstr. 4, 8008, (01) 261 10 30, *Fax (01) 251 03 67* – , , . FZ u
15 – **40 rm** 160/280.

**Opera** without rest, Dufourstr. 5, 8008, (01) 251 90 90, *Fax (01) 251 90 01* – video . FZ b
*closed 22 December - 5 January* – **66 rm** 205/320.

**Ambassador,** Falkenstr. 6, 8008, (01) 261 76 00, *Fax (01) 251 23 94* – video . FZ a
**Meals** a la carte 43/117 – **46 rm** 205/340.

**Krone Unterstrass,** Schaffhauserstr. 1, 8006, (01) 360 56 56, *Fax (01)360 56 00* – , rm, – 25/90. CV b
***Grill :*** **Meals** a la carte 41/77 – ***Wirtschaft :*** **Meals** a la carte 36/67 – **57 rm** 145/215.

**Wellenberg** without rest, Niederdorfstr. 10, 8001, (01) 262 43 00, *Fax (01) 251 31 30* – . FZ s
**45 rm** 240/330.

**Helmhaus** without rest, Schifflände 30, 8001, (01) 251 88 10, *Fax (01) 251 04 30* – . FZ v
**25 rm** 210/315.

**Rütli** without rest, Zähringerstr. 43, 8001, (01) 251 54 26, *Fax (01) 261 21 53* – . FY a
**62 rm** 180/260.

**Seegarten,** Seegartenstr. 14, 8008, (01) 383 37 37, *Fax (01) 383 37 38*, – video . DX b
***Latino*** - Italian rest. - *(closed lunch Saturday and Sunday)* **Meals** a la carte 43/78 – **28 rm** 163/279.

**Rex**, Weinbergstr. 92, 8006, (01) 360 25 25, *Fax (01) 360 25 52*, – . DV a
***Blauer Apfel*** *(closed Saturday lunch and Sunday)* **Meals** a la carte 37/76 – **37 rm** 110/190.

**Zunfthaus zur Schmiden,** Marktgasse 20, 8001, (01) 251 52 87, *Fax (01) 261 12 67*, « 15C blacksmith's guild house » – . FZ f
*closed Easter, Pentecost, mid July - mid August and Christmas* – **Meals** a la carte 67/113.

**Kronenhalle,** Rämistr. 4, 8001, (01) 251 66 69, *Fax (01) 251 66 81*, « Collection of exceptional works of art » – . FZ t
**Meals** a la carte 52/125.

**Haus zum Rüden,** Limmatquai 42 (1st floor), 8001, (01) 261 95 66, *Fax (01) 261 18 04*, « 13C guild house » – . FZ c
*closed Saturday and Sunday* – **Meals** 52 (lunch)/93 and a la carte 70/111.

**Zunfthaus zur Zimmerleuten,** Limmatquai 40 (1st floor), 8001, (01) 252 08 34, *Fax (01) 252 08 48*, « 18C guild house » – FZ z
*closed 19 July - 16 August, Sunday and Bank Holidays* – **Meals** a la carte 42/101.

**Conti-da Bianca,** Dufourstr. 1, 8008, (01) 251 06 66, *Fax (01) 251 06 86* – FZ y
*closed mid July - mid August, Saturday lunch and Sunday* – **Meals** – Italian rest. - a la carte 47/104.

# ZÜRICH

| Street | Grid | No. |
|---|---|---|
| Bahnhofstrasse | EYZ | |
| Bellevueplatz | FZ | |
| Limmatquai | FYZ | |
| Löwenstrasse | EY | |
| Paradeplatz | EZ | |
| Poststrasse | EZ | 58 |
| Rennweg | EYZ | 63 |
| Storchengasse | EZ | 85 |
| Strehlgasse | EZ | 87 |
| Uraniastrasse | EYZ | |
| Allmendstrasse | CX | 6 |
| Augustinergasse | EZ | 9 |
| Bärengasse | EZ | 10 |
| Beethovenstrasse | EZ | 12 |
| Birmensdorferstrasse | CX | 15 |
| Claridenstrasse | EZ | 18 |
| Clausiusstrasse | FY | 19 |
| Culmannstrasse | FY | 21 |
| Dufourstrasse | DX | 24 |
| Feldstrasse | CV | 27 |
| Fraumünsterstrasse | EZ | 28 |
| Freiestrasse | DVX | 30 |
| Gablerstrasse | CX | 31 |
| General Wille-Strasse | CX | 33 |
| Hafnerstrasse | EY | 36 |
| Kantonsschulstrasse | FZ | 39 |
| Konradstrasse | EY | 40 |
| Kreuzstrasse | DX | 42 |
| Manessestrasse | CX | 45 |
| Marktgasse | FZ | 46 |
| Münsterhof | EZ | 48 |
| Museumstrasse | EY | 49 |
| Nelkenstrasse | FY | 52 |
| Neumarkt | FZ | 54 |
| Nordstrasse | DV | 55 |
| Rathausbrücke | EFZ | 60 |
| Rindermarkt | FZ | 64 |
| Schimmelstrasse | CX | 69 |
| Seebahnstrasse | CX | 72 |
| Selnaustrasse | CX | 75 |
| Sihlhölzlistrasse | CX | 76 |
| Stadelhoferstrasse | FZ | 78 |
| Stampfenbachplatz | FY | 79 |
| Stampfenbachstrasse | EFY | 81 |
| Stauffacherplatz | CX | 82 |
| Stauffacherstrasse | CVX | 84 |
| Sumatrastrasse | FY | 88 |
| Talacker | EZ | 90 |
| Tannenstrasse | FY | 91 |
| Theaterstrasse | FZ | 93 |
| Toblerstrasse | DV | 96 |
| Tunnelstrasse | CX | 97 |
| Usteristrasse | EY | 100 |
| Waffenplatzstrasse | CX | 102 |
| Weinbergfussweg | FY | 103 |
| Zollikerstrasse | DX | 108 |

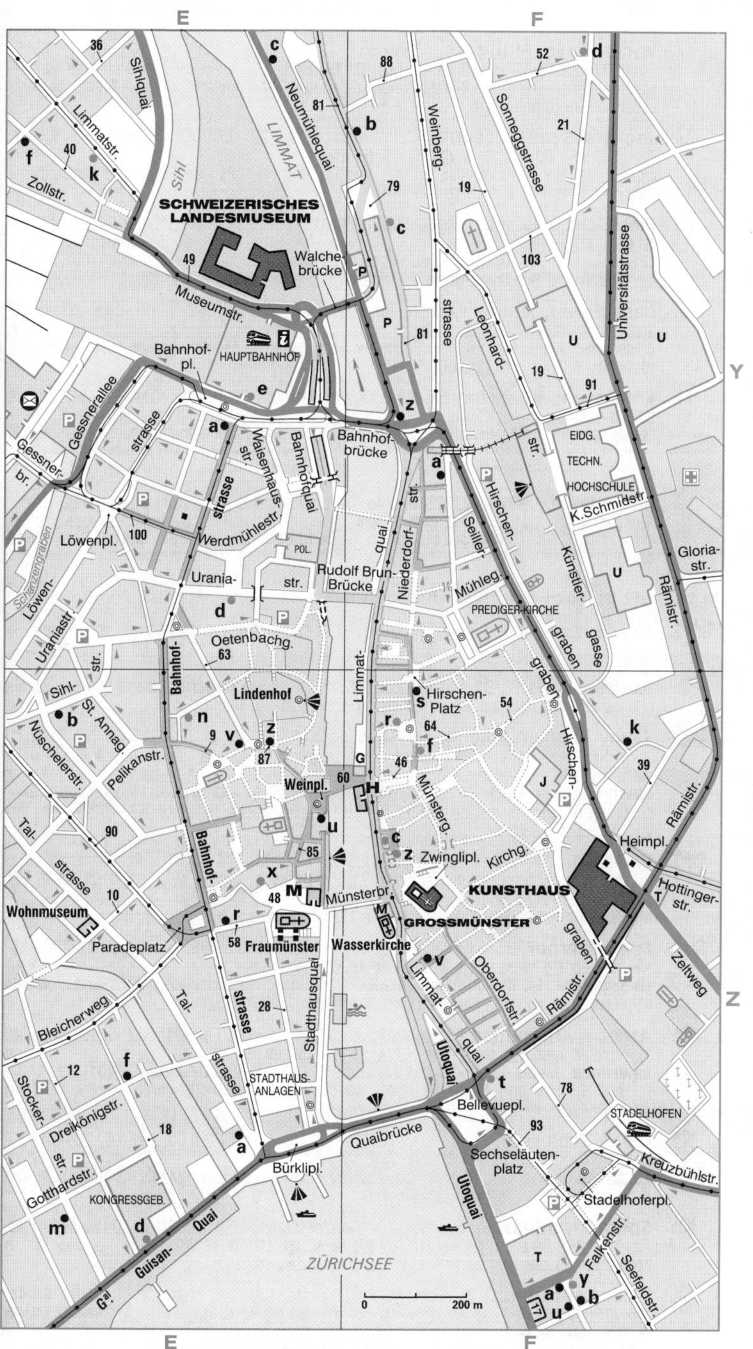

E
F
Y
Z
SCHWEIZERISCHES LANDESMUSEUM
HAUPTBAHNHOF
Bahnhof-pl.
Walche-brücke
Bahnhof-brücke
Rudolf Brun-Brücke
Lindenhof
Weinpl.
Münsterbr.
Fraumünster
Wasserkirche
GROSSMÜNSTER
KUNSTHAUS
Zwinglipl.
Hirschen-Platz
PREDIGER-KIRCHE
EIDG. TECHN. HOCHSCHULE
Wohnmuseum
Paradeplatz
STADTHAUS-ANLAGEN
Bürklipl.
Quaibrücke
Bellevuepl.
Sechseläuten-platz
STADELHOFEN
Stadelhoferpl.
KONGRESSGEB.
ZÜRICHSEE
LIMMAT
Sihl
Sihlquai
Limmatstr.
Zollstr.
Museumstr.
Neumühlequai
Weinberg-strasse
Sonneggstrasse
Leonhard-str.
Universitätstrasse
Gessnerallee
Gessner-br.
Löwenpl.
Werdmühlestr.
Waisenhaus-str.
Bahnhofquai
Limmat-quai
Niederdorf-str.
Seiler-graben
Hirschen-graben
Künstler-gasse
K. Schmidstr.
Gloria-str.
Rämistr.
Mühleg.
Urania-str.
Löwen-str.
Uraniastr.
Schanzengraben
Oetenbachg.
Sihl-str.
St. Annag.
Nüschelerstr.
Pelikanstr.
Bahnhof-strasse
Münsterg.
Kirchg.
Heimpl.
Hottinger-str.
Zeltweg
Tal-strasse
Bleicherweg
Stadthausquai
Oberdorfstr.
Utoquai
Stocker-str.
Dreikönigstr.
Gotthardstr.
Gal Guisan-Quai
Kreuzbühlstr.
Falkenstr.
Seefeldstr.
POL.
0
200 m

XX **Wirtschaft Flühgass,** Zollikerstr. 214, ✉ 8008, ✆ (01) 381 12 15, *Fax (01) 422 75 32,* « 16C inn » – P. AE E VISA by Zollikerstrasse DX
*closed 12 July - 9 August, 24 December - 3 January, Saturday and Sunday* – **Meals** (booking essential) 95 (dinner) and a la carte 52/112.

XX **Jacky's Stapferstube,** Culmannstr. 45, ✉ 8006, ✆ (01) 361 37 48, *Fax (01) 364 00 60,* – P. AE O E VISA FY d
*closed mid July - mid August, Sunday and Monday* – **Meals** - veal and beef specialities - (booking essential) a la carte 72/144.

XX **Riesbächli,** Zollikerstr. 157, ✉ 8008, ✆ (01) 422 23 24, *Fax (01) 422 34 35* – AE O E VISA by Zollikerstrasse DX
*closed 27 July - 10 August, 23 December - 4 January, Saturday except dinner from November-March and Sunday* – **Meals** 50 (lunch)/135 and a la carte 75/128.

XX **Casa Ferlin,** Stampfenbachstr. 38, ✉ 8006, ✆ (01) 362 35 09 – AE O E VISA FY c
*closed mid July - mid August, Saturday and Sunday* – **Meals** – Italian rest. - (booking essential) 48 and a la carte 66/124.

XX **Königstuhl,** Stüssihofstatt 3, ✉ 8001, ✆ (01) 261 76 18, *Fax (01) 262 71 23,* – AE O E VISA FZ r
**Meals** (1st floor) *(closed mid July - mid August, Saturday lunch and Sunday)* 39 (lunch)/65 and a la carte 51/122 – ***Bistro*** *(closed Saturday lunch and Sunday)* **Meals** a la carte 42/84.

X **Blaue Ente,** Seefeldstr. 223 (Mühle Tiefenbrunnen), ✉ 8008, ✆ (01) 422 77 06, *Fax (01) 422 77 41,* – AE O E VISA by Zollikerstrasse DX
*closed 13 July - 5 August and 24 December - 5 January* – **Meals** a la carte 44/89.

## On the left bank of the river Limmat *(Main railway station, Business centre) :*

**Baur au Lac,** Talstr. 1, ✉ 8022, ✆ (01) 220 50 20, *Fax (01) 220 50 44,* , « Lakeside setting and garden », – – 25/60. AE O E VISA JCB. EZ a
***Pavillon*** : **Meals** 68/84 and a la carte 57/131 – ***rive gauche*** *(closed Sunday)* **Meals** a la carte 52/120 – 25 – **107 rm** 430/720, 18 suites.

**Savoy Baur en Ville** M, am Paradeplatz, ✉ 8022, ✆ (01) 215 25 25, *Fax (01) 215 25 00,* « Elegant modern decor » – – 25/70. AE O E VISA JCB. EZ r
***Savoy*** (1st floor) **Meals** 64 (lunch) and a la carte 67/134 – ***Orsini*** (am Münsterhof - Italian rest. - *(booking essential)* **Meals** 54 (lunch)/90 and a la carte 62/132 – **104 rm** 430/630, 8 suites.

**Widder** M, Rennweg 7, ✆ (01) 224 25 26, *Fax (01) 224 24 24,* « Restored old town houses with contemporary interiors » – – 25/170. AE O E VISA JCB. rest EZ v
**Meals** 58 (lunch)/85 and a la carte 58/115 – **42 rm** 360/630, 7 suites.

**Schweizerhof,** Bahnhofplatz 7, ✉ 8001, ✆ (01) 218 88 88, *Fax (01) 218 81 81* – , rm, – 40. AE O E VISA JCB. EY a
***La Soupière*** (1st floor) *(closed 26 July - 10 August, Saturday lunch and Sunday)* **Meals** 65 (lunch)/91 and a la carte 71/122 – **115 rm** 370/550.

**Ascot** M, Tessinerplatz 9, ✉ 8002, ✆ (01) 201 18 00, *Fax (01) 202 72 10,* – , rm, rest, – 25/50. AE O E VISA JCB CX a
***Lawrence*** : **Meals** 48 (lunch) and a la carte 55/89 – ***Fujiya of Japan*** ✆ (01) 201 11 55 *(closed Sunday and Monday)* **Meals** 48 (lunch)/85 and a la carte 55/89 – **73 rm** 220/420.

**Neues Schloss** M, Stockerstr. 17, ✉ 8022, ✆ (01) 286 94 00, *Fax (01) 286 94 45* – video . AE O E VISA JCB. rest EZ m
***Le Jardin*** *(Sunday and Bank Holidays dinner only for residents)* **Meals** 48 (lunch)/89 and a la carte 51/99 – **58 rm** 250/410.

**Splügenschloss,** Splügenstr. 2 / Genferstrasse, ✉ 8002, ✆ (01) 289 99 99, *Fax (01) 289 99 98* – , rm, P. AE O E VISA JCB CX e
**Meals** 58/69 and a la carte 65/125 – **51 rm** 260/540.

**Inter-Continental Zürich** M, Badenerstr. 420, ✉ 8040, ✆ (01) 404 44 44, *Fax (01) 404 44 40,* , , – , rm, – 25/400. AE O E VISA JCB. rest
**Meals** 43 and a la carte 39/94 – 23 – **365 rm** 255/370.

**Zum Storchen,** Weinplatz 2, ✉ 8001, ℘ (01) 211 55 10, *Fax (01) 211 64 51*, ≤ River Limmat and City, 帘, « Riverside setting » - |‡|, ⇎ rm, TV ☎ ✆ - 🏛 25. AE ⓓ E VISA JCB. ✗ rest EZ u
***Rôtisserie*** : Meals 52 (lunch)/88 and a la carte 64/101 - **73 rm** ☕ 280/550.

**Stoller** M, Badenerstr. 357, ✉ 8040, ℘ (01) 405 47 47, *Fax (01) 405 48 48*, 帘 - |‡|, ⇎ rm, TV ☎ ✆ 🚗 P - 🏛 25. AE ⓓ E VISA JCB by Badenerstrasse CV
Meals 28/42 and a la carte 42/85, children 10 - **79 rm** ☕ 195/320.

**Glärnischhof** M, Claridenstr. 30, ✉ 8022, ℘ (01) 286 22 22, *Fax (01) 286 22 86* - |‡|, ⇎ rm, ▤ rest, TV ☎ ✆ - 🏛 30. AE ⓓ E VISA JCB EZ f
***Le Poisson*** *(closed Saturday and Sunday)* **Meals** 49 (lunch)/95 and a la carte 67/103 - ***Vivace*** : **Meals** a la carte 42/75 - **63 rm** ☕ 240/420.

**Glockenhof,** Sihlstr. 31, ✉ 8023, ℘ (01) 211 56 50, *Fax (01) 211 56 60*, 帘 - |‡|, ⇎ rm, ▤ rest, TV ☎ ♿. AE ⓓ E VISA JCB EZ b
Meals a la carte 44/101 - **106 rm** ☕ 250/350.

**Engimatt,** Engimattstr. 14, ✉ 8002, ℘ (01) 284 16 16, *Fax (01) 201 25 16*, 帘, ✗ - |‡| TV ☎ ✆ 🚗. AE ⓓ E VISA JCB CX d
Meals a la carte 40/107, children 15 - **80 rm** ☕ 160/290.

**Kindli** M, Pfalzgasse 1, ✉ 8001, ℘ (01) 211 59 17, *Fax (01) 211 65 28*, 帘, « English country house style installation » - |‡| TV ☎. AE ⓓ E VISA EZ z
***Opus*** ℘ (01) 211 41 82 *(closed Christmas and Sunday)* **Meals** 38 (lunch) and a la carte 45/95 - **21 rm** ☕ 180/270.

**Montana,** Konradstr. 39, ✉ 8005, ℘ (01) 271 69 00, *Fax (01) 272 30 70*, 帘 - |‡| TV ☎ ♿. AE ⓓ E VISA JCB EY f
***Bistro le Lyonnais*** *(closed Saturday lunch and Sunday)* **Meals** 40 and a la carte 38/86 - **74 rm** ☕ 160/290.

**Sukhothai,** Erlachstr. 46, ✉ 8003, ℘ (01) 462 66 22, *Fax (01) 462 66 54* - ▤. AE E VISA. ✗ CX h
*closed Easter, 13 July - 10 August, Christmas, Saturday except September - May, Sunday and Bank Holidays* - **Meals** - Thai rest. - 139 and a la carte 82/142.

**Accademia Piccoli,** Rotwandstr. 48, ✉ 8004, ℘ (01) 241 62 43 - ▤. AE E VISA. ✗ CV n
*closed Saturday except dinner September - April and Sunday* - **Meals** - Italian rest. - a la carte 66/123.

**Intermezzo** - Kongresshaus Zürich, Gotthardstr. 5, ✉ 8022, ℘ (01) 206 36 36, *Fax (01) 206 36 59* - ▤. AE ⓓ E VISA. ✗ EZ d
*closed 11 July - 9 August, Saturday and Sunday* - **Meals** 48 and a la carte 55/86.

**Zunfthaus zur Waag,** Münsterhof 8, ✉ 8001, ℘ (01) 211 07 30, *Fax (01) 212 01 69*, Linen weaver's and hatter's guildhall - AE ⓓ E VISA EZ x
**Meals** a la carte 61/108.

**Sala of Tokyo,** Limmatstr. 29, ✉ 8005, ℘ (01) 271 52 90, *Fax (01) 271 78 07*, 帘 - AE ⓓ E VISA JCB EY k
*closed 19 July - 3 August, 21 December - 5 January, Sunday and Monday* - **Meals** - Japanese rest. - 58/110 and a la carte 48/108.

**da Bernasconi,** Lavaterstr. 87, ✉ 8002, ℘ (01) 201 16 13, *Fax (01) 201 16 49*, 帘 - AE ⓓ E VISA CX b
**Meals** - Italian rest. - a la carte 48/95.

**Il Giglio,** Weberstr. 14, ✉ 8004, ℘ (01) 242 85 97, *Fax (01) 291 01 83* - AE ⓓ E VISA CX c
*closed mid July - mid August, Saturday lunch and Sunday* - **Meals** - Italian rest. - 38 (lunch) and a la carte 43/95.

**Brasserie Lipp,** Uraniastr. 9, ✉ 8001, ℘ (01) 211 11 55, *Fax (01) 212 17 26*, 帘 - ▤. AE ⓓ E VISA EY d
*closed Sunday and Bank Holidays from July to August* - **Meals** a la carte 38/87.

**L'Hexagone,** Kuttelgasse 15, ✉ 8001, ℘ (01) 211 94 11, *Fax (01) 212 70 38*, 帘 - AE E VISA EZ n
*closed 27 July - 9 August, 24 December - 5 January, Saturday and Sunday* - **Meals** *(lunch only)* 35.

**at Zürich-Oerlikon** : *N : by Universitätstrasse* DV *: 5 km* - ✉ *8050 Zürich-Oerlikon* :

**Swissôtel Zürich** M, Am Marktplatz, ℘ (01) 311 43 41, *Fax (01) 312 44 68*, ≤, 帘, ≘s, 🏊 - |‡|, ⇎ rm, ▤ rm, TV video ☎ ♿ 🚗 - 🏛 25/500. AE ⓓ E VISA JCB
***Szenario*** : **Meals** a la carte 44/99 - ☕ 20 - **336 rm** 260/380, 11 suites.

**at Glattbrugg** : *N : by Universitätstrasse* DV : *8 km – ✉ 8152 Glattbrugg :*

**Renaissance Zurich** M, Talackerstr. 1, ✆ (01) 810 85 00, *Fax (01) 810 87 55*, – rm, – 25/300. AE VISA JCB. rest
***Asian Place*** - Asian rest. - *(closed lunch Saturday and Sunday)* **Meals** 83 and a la carte 44/135 – ***Brasserie La Noblesse*** *(closed mid July - mid August, Saturday and Sunday)* **Meals** 43 (lunch) and a la carte 48/96, children 9 – 28 – **196 rm** 304/344, 8 suites.

**Hilton,** Hohenbühlstr. 10, ✆ (01) 810 31 31, *Fax (01) 810 93 66*, – rm, – 25/280. AE VISA
***Harvest Grill*** *(closed July - August, lunch Saturday and Sunday)* **Meals** 47 (lunch)/79 and a la carte 62/118 – ***Taverne*** *(closed 2 weeks in December - January, Saturday - Sunday except dinner from June - September)* **Meals** a la carte 33/86, children 15 – ***Market Place :*** **Meals** a la carte 42/84 – 29 – **270 rm** 310/455, 11 suites.

**Mövenpick** M, Walter Mittelholzerstr. 8, ✆ (01) 808 88 88, *Fax (01) 808 88 77* – rm, – 25/220. AE VISA JCB
***Appenzeller Stube*** *(closed 12 July - 9 August and Saturday lunch)* **Meals** a la carte 46/100 – ***Mövenpick Rest. :*** **Meals** a la carte 30/70 – ***Dim Sum*** - Chinese rest. - *(closed 12 July - 2 August, lunch Saturday and Sunday)* **Meals** 58 and a la carte 35/96 – 23 – **335 rm** 250/350.

**Novotel Zürich Airport,** Talackerstr. 21, ✆ (01) 810 31 11, *Fax (01) 810 81 85*, – rm, – 25/150. AE VISA
**Meals** a la carte 39/83, children 16 – 19 – **257 rm** 182/207.

**Airport,** Oberhauserstr. 30, ✆ (01) 810 44 44, *Fax (01) 810 97 08* – . AE VISA JCB. rest
***Edo Garden :*** **Meals** 60/70 and a la carte 36/89 – ***Fujiya of Japan*** *(closed lunch Saturday and Sunday)* **Meals** 48 and a la carte 55/96 – **44 rm** 180/235 – ½ P 35.

**Bruno's Rest.,** Europastr. 2, ✆ (01) 811 03 01, *Fax (01) 811 03 21*, Elegant modern decor – . AE VISA.
*closed 27 July - 10 August, 24 December - 4 January and Sunday* – **Meals** 59 (lunch)/98 and a la carte 53/105, children 20.

**at Nürensdorf** : *NE by Universitätstrasse and road to Bassersdorf : 19 km – ✉ 8309 Nürensdorf :*

**Zum Bären** with rm, Alte Winterthurerstr. 45, ✆ (01) 836 42 12, *Fax (01) 836 42 17*, – . AE VISA
*closed 20 July - 4 August, 21 December - 3 January, Sunday and Monday* – **Meals** 43 (lunch)/98 and a la carte 62/106 – ***Beizli :*** **Meals** a la carte 43/76 – **14 rm** 150/215
**Spec.** Hummermousse mit asiatischem Garnelen-Gemüsesalat und frischem Koriander. Filet vom Sommerreh im Cornflakesmantel an Portweinsauce. Gebratenes Kalbsfilet mit einer Kruste von getrockneten Tomaten an Olivenjus.

**at Kloten** : *N : by Universitätstrasse* DV : *12 km – ✉ 8302 Kloten :*

**Fly Away** M, Marktgasse 19, ✆ (01) 813 66 13, *Fax (01) 813 51 25*, – rm, . AE VISA
**Meals** - Italian rest. - a la carte 32/72 – 14 – **42 rm** 145/200.

**Top-Air,** at the airport (Terminal A), ✆ (01) 816 60 60, *Fax (01) 816 41 91*, ≤ – . AE VISA JCB
**Meals** a la carte 41/103, children 19.

**at Küsnacht** : *SE : by Bellerivestrasse* DX : *8 km – ✉ 8700 Küsnacht :*

**Ermitage am See** M with rm, Seestr. 80, ✆ (01) 910 52 22, *Fax (01) 910 52 44*, ≤ Zurich lake, , « Lakeside setting, terrace and garden », , – . AE VISA. rest
**Meals** 62 (lunch)/144 and a la carte 80/136 – 17 – **22 rm** 160/340, 4 suites
**Spec.** Salade de roquette aux petits ravioli de tomate "Salsa Verde" et dentelle niçoise. Saint-Pierre rôti à la peau au romarin, fenouil fondant aux tomates séchées. Pyramide croustillante aux fruits rouges, coulis et glace pistache (June - September).

**Petermann's Kunststuben,** Seestr. 160, ✆ (01) 910 07 15, *Fax (01) 910 04 95*, – . AE VISA
*closed 24 August - 12 September, 10 to 24 February, Sunday and Monday* – **Meals** 78 (lunch)/185 and a la carte 86/178
**Spec.** Truffe noire du Périgord sur chou Marcellin (January - March). Coquelet aux écrevisses (May - August). Selle de chevreuil des Grisons à la goutte de sang (September - December).

**at Uetikon am See** : *SE by Bellerivestrasse : 18 km – ✉ 8707 Uetikon am See :*

XX **Wirtschaft zum Wiesengrund** (Hussong), Kleindorfstr. 61, ✆ (01) 920 63 60,
✿✿ *Fax (01) 921 17 09,* – P. AE E VISA.
*closed 26 July - 18 August, 25 January - 8 February, Sunday and Monday* – **Meals** 48 (lunch)/122 and a la carte 86/133
**Spec.** Spargelchartreuse mit Rouget (spring). Praliné von Langustinen (summer). Ganze Ente gefüllt mit Zitronen (winter).

**at Unterengstringen** : *NW : by Sihlquai* CV *: 10 km – ✉ 8103 Unterengstringen :*

XXX **Witschi's,** Zürcherstr. 55, ✆ (01) 750 44 60, *Fax (01) 750 19 68,* , « Elegant modern
✿ installation » – P. AE D E VISA JCB
*closed 26 July - 3 August, 21 December - 5 January, Sunday and Monday* – **Meals** 69 (lunch)/165 and a la carte 99/154
**Spec.** Crêpe Parmentière au caviar (winter - spring). Homard mi-cuit au carpaccio de fenouil à l'huile vierge (spring - summer). Canette de Challans cuite rosée au confit de cerises et gingembre (summer - autumn).

# *United Kingdom*

LONDON – BIRMINGHAM – EDINBURGH
GLASGOW – LEEDS – LIVERPOOL
MANCHESTER

The town plans in the Great Britain Section of this Guide are based upon the Ordnance Survey of Great Britain with the permission of the Controller of Her Majesty's Stationery Office.

# PRACTICAL INFORMATION

## LOCAL CURRENCY

**Pound Sterling:** *1 GBP = 1,66 US $ (Jan. 98).*

## TOURIST INFORMATION

*Tourist information offices exist in each city included in the Guide. The telephone number and address is given in each text under* ℹ

## FOREIGN EXCHANGE

*Banks are usually open between 9.00am and 4.3pm on weekdays only and some open on Saturdays. Most large hotels have exchange facilities. Heathrow and Gatwick Airports have 24-hour banking facilities.*

## SHOPPING

**In London:** *Oxford St./Regent St. (department stores, exclusive shops) Bond St. (exclusive shops, antiques)*

*Knightsbridge area (department stores, exclusive shops, boutiques)*

*For other towns see the index of street names; those printed in red are where the principal shops are found.*

## THEATRE BOOKINGS IN LONDON

*Your hotel porter will be able to make your arrangements or direct you to Theatre Booking Agents.*

*In addition there is a kiosk in Leicester Square selling tickets for the same day's performances at half price plus a booking fee. It is open 12 noon-6.30pm.*

## CAR HIRE

*The international car hire companies have branches in each major city. Your hotel porter should be able to give details and help you with your arrangements.*

## TIPPING

*Many hotels and restaurants include a service charge but where this is not the case an amount equivalent to between 10 and 15 per cent of the bill is customary. Additionally doormen, baggage porters and cloakroom attendants are generally given a gratuity.*

*Taxi drivers are customarily tipped between 10 and 15 per cent of the amount shown on the meter in addition to the fare.*

## SPEED LIMITS

*The maximum permitted speed on motorways and dual carriageways is 70 mph (113 km/h.) and 60 mph (97 km/h.) on other roads except where a lower speed limit is indicated.*

## SEAT BELTS

*The wearing of seat belts in the United Kingdom is compulsory for drivers, front seat passengers and rear seat passengers where seat belts are fitted. It is illegal for front seat passengers to carry children on their lap.*

## ANIMALS

*It is forbidden to bring domestic animals (dogs, cats...) into the United Kingdom.*

# LONDON

404 *folds* (42) *to* (44) *- pop. 6 679 699*



*British Travel Centre, 12 Regent St. Piccadilly Circus, SW1Y 4 PQ, ☎ (0171) 971 0026. Victoria Station Forecourt, SW1, ☎ (0171) 730 3488.*

✈ *Heathrow,* ☎ *(0181) 759 4321 –* **Terminal** *: Airbus (A1) from Victoria, Airbus (A2) from Paddington – Underground (Piccadilly line) frequent service daily.*

✈ *Gatwick,* ☎ *(01293) 535353, and* ☎ *(0181) 763 2020, by A 23 and M 23 –* **Terminal** *: Coach service from Victoria Coach Station (Flightline 777, hourly service) – Railink (Gatwick Express) from Victoria (24 h service).*

✈ *London City Airport,* ☎ *(0171) 474 5555.*

✈ *Stansted, at Bishop's Stortford,* ☎ *(01279) 680500, Fax 66 20 66, NE : 34 m. off M 11 and A 120.*

**British Airways, Victoria Air Terminal** *: 115 Buckingham Palace Rd., SW1,* ☎ *(0171) 834 9411, Fax (0171) 828 7142, p. 16.*

# Sights

## HISTORIC BUILDINGS AND MONUMENTS

*Palace of Westminster*★★★ p. 10 LY – *Tower of London*★★★ p. 11 PVX – *Banqueting House*★★ p. 10 LX – *Buckingham Palace*★★ p. 16 BVX – *Kensington Palace*★★ p. 8 FX – *Lincoln's Inn*★★ p. 17 EV – *Lloyds Building*★★ p. 7 PV – *Royal Hospital Chelsea*★★ p. 15 FU – *St. James's Palace*★★ p. 13 EP – *Somerset House*★★ p. 17 EXY – *South Bank Arts Centre*★★ p. 10 MX – *Spencer House*★★ p. 13 DP – *The Temple*★★ p. 6 MV – *Tower Bridge*★★ p. 11 PX – *London Bridge*★ p. 11 PVX – *Albert Memorial*★ p. 14 CQ – *Apsley House*★ p. 12 BP – *George Inn*★, *Southwark* p. 11 PX – *Guildhall*★ p. 7 OU – *International Shakespeare Globe Centre*★ p. 11 OX **T** – *Dr Johnson's House*★ p. 6 NUV **A** – *Leighton House*★ p. 8 EY – *The Monument*★ (✻★) p. 7 PV **G** – *Royal Albert Hall*★ p. 14 CQ – *Royal Opera Arcade*★ p. 13 FGN – *Staple Inn*★ p. 6 MU **Y** – *Theatre Royal*★ *(Haymarket)* p. 13 GM – *Westminster Bridge*★ p. 10 LY.

## CHURCHES

The City Churches – *St. Paul's Cathedral*★★★ *(Dome* ⩽★★★*)* p. 7 NOV – *St. Bartholomew the Great*★★ p. 7 OU **K** – *St. Mary-at-Hill*★★ p. 7 PV **B** – *Temple Church*★★ p. 6 MV – *All Hallows-by-the-Tower (font cover*★★, *brasses*★*)* p. 7 PV **Y** – *St. Bride*★ *(steeple*★★*)* p. 7 NV **J** – *St. Giles Cripplegate*★ p. 7 OU **N** – *St. Helen Bishopsgate*★ *(monuments*★★*)* p. 7 PUV **R** – *St. James Garlickhythe (tower and spire*★, *sword rests*★*)* p. 7 OV **R** – *St. Margaret Lothbury*★ p. 7 PU **S** – *St. Margaret Pattens (spire*★, *woodwork*★*)* p. 7 PV **N** – *St. Mary Abchurch*★ p. 7 PV **X** – *St. Mary-le-Bow (tower and steeple*★★*)* p. 7 OV **G** – *St. Michael Paternoster Royal (tower and spire*★*)* p. 7 OV **D** – *St. Olave*★ p. 7 PV **S**.

Other Churches – *Westminster Abbey*★★★ p. 10 LY – *Southwark Cathedral*★★ p. 11 PX – *Queen's Chapel*★ p. 13 EP – *St. Clement Danes*★ p. 17 EX – *St. James's*★ p. 13 EM – *St. Margaret's*★ p. 10 LY **A** – *St. Martin in-the-Fields*★ p. 17 DY – *St. Paul's*★ *(Covent Garden)* p. 17 DX – *Westminster Roman Catholic Cathedral*★ p. 10 KY **B**.

## STREETS – SQUARES – PARKS

*The City*★★★ p. 7 NV – *Regent's Park*★★★ *(Terraces*★★, *Zoo*★★*)* p. 5 HIST – *Belgrave Square*★★ p. 16 AVX – *Burlington Arcade*★★ p. 13 DM – *Covent Garden*★★ *(The Piazza*★★*)* p. 17 DX – *Hyde Park*★★ pp. 8 and 9 GHVX – *The Mall*★★ p. 13 FP – *St. James's Park*★★ p. 10 KXY – *Trafalgar Square*★★ p. 17 DY – *Whitehall*★★ *(Horse Guards*★*)* p. 10 LX – *Barbican*★ p. 7 OU – *Bloomsbury*★ p. 6 LMU – *Bond Street*★ pp. 12-13 CK-DM – *Cheyne Walk*★ p. 9 GHZ – *Jermyn Street*★ p. 13 EN – *Leicester Square*★ p. 13 GM – *Neal's Yard*★ p. 17 DV – *Piccadilly Arcade*★ p. 13 DEN – *Piccadilly Circus*★ p. 13 FM – *Queen Anne's Gate*★ p. 10 KY – *Regent Street*★ p. 13 EM – *St. James's Square*★ p. 13 FN – *St. James's Street*★ p. 13 EN – *Shepherd Market*★ p. 12 CN – *Soho*★ p. 13 – *Strand*★ p. 17 DY – *Victoria Embankment gardens*★ p. 17 DEXY – *Waterloo Place*★ p. 13 FN

## MUSEUMS

*British Museum*★★★ p. 6 LU – *National Gallery*★★★ p. 13 GM – *Science Museum*★★★ p. 14 CR – *Tate Gallery*★★★ p. 10 LZ – *Victoria and Albert Museum*★★★ p. 15 DR – *Wallace Collection*★★★ p. 12 AH – *Courtauld Institute of Art*★★ *(Somerset House)* p. 17 EXY – *Museum of London*★★ p. 7 OU **M** – *National Portrait Gallery*★★ p. 13 GM – *Natural History Museum*★★ p. 14 CS – *Sir John Soane's Museum*★★ p. 6 MU **M** – *Imperial War Museum*★ p. 10 NY – *London Transport Museum*★ p. 17 DX – *Madame Tussaud's*★ p. 5 IU **M** – *Planetarium*★ p. 5 IU **M** – *Wellington Museum*★ *(Apsley House)* p. 12 BP

# Alphabetical list of areas included

# LONDON CENTRE

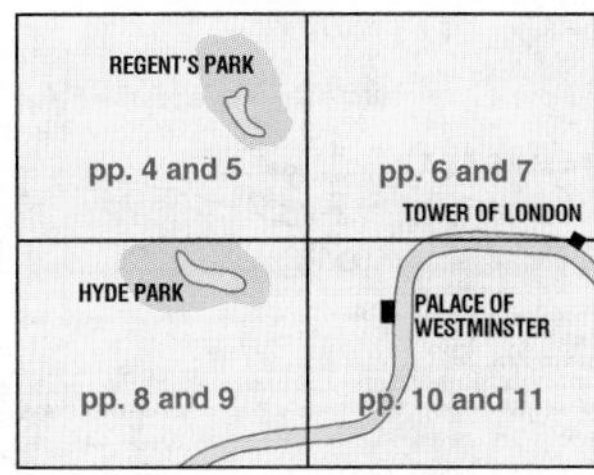


## STREET INDEX TO LONDON CENTRE TOWN PLANS

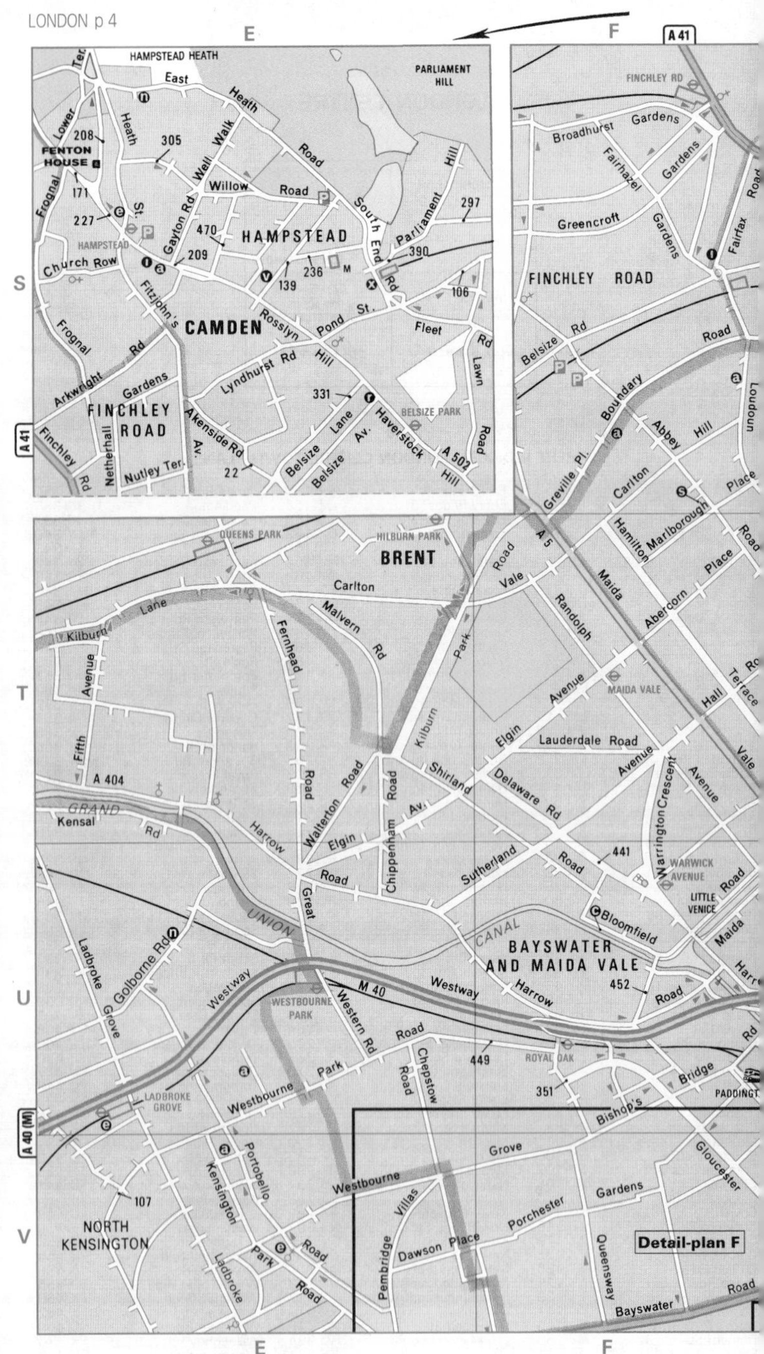
E
F
A 41
HAMPSTEAD HEATH
PARLIAMENT HILL
East Heath Road
Lower Ter.
Heath St.
Well Walk
Willow Road
South End Rd
Parliament Hill
FENTON HOUSE
Frognal
HAMPSTEAD
Gayton Rd
Church Row
Fitzjohn's Av.
CAMDEN
Rosslyn Hill
Pond St.
Fleet Rd
Lawn Road
Frognal
Arkwright Rd
Lyndhurst Rd
FINCHLEY ROAD
Gardens
Netherhall Gardens
Nutley Ter.
Akenside Rd
Belsize Lane
Belsize Av.
Haverstock Hill
A 502
BELSIZE PARK
Finchley Rd
FINCHLEY RD
Broadhurst Gardens
Fairhazel Gardens
Greencroft Gardens
Fairfax Road
Belsize Rd
Boundary Road
Abbey Road
Hill
Loudoun
Greville Pl.
Carlton Hill
Hamilton Place
Marlborough Place
Road
S
T
U
V
QUEENS PARK
KILBURN PARK
BRENT
Carlton Vale
Road
A 5
Maida Vale
Randolph
Abercorn Place
Malvern Rd
Kilburn Lane
Kilburn Park
Fernhead Road
Fifth Avenue
Elgin Avenue
MAIDA VALE
Hall
Terrace
Lauderdale Road
Avenue
Warrington Crescent
Avenue
Shirland Road
Delaware Rd
A 404
GRAND UNION CANAL
Kensal Rd
Harrow Road
Walterton Road
Chippenham Road
Elgin Av.
Sutherland Avenue
Road
Great Western Rd
WARWICK AVENUE
LITTLE VENICE
Bloomfield Road
Maida
Ladbroke Grove
Golborne Rd
Westway
M 40
Westway
BAYSWATER AND MAIDA VALE
Harrow Road
WESTBOURNE PARK
Westbourne Park Road
Chepstow Road
ROYAL OAK
Bishop's Bridge
Rd
PADDINGT
LADBROKE GROVE
A 40 (M)
Kensington Park Road
Portobello Road
Ladbroke
NORTH KENSINGTON
Westbourne Grove
Pembridge Villas
Dawson Place
Porchester Gardens
Queensway
Gloucester
Bayswater Road
Detail-plan F
208
305
171
227
470
297
390
209
236
M
139
106
331
22
441
452
449
351
107

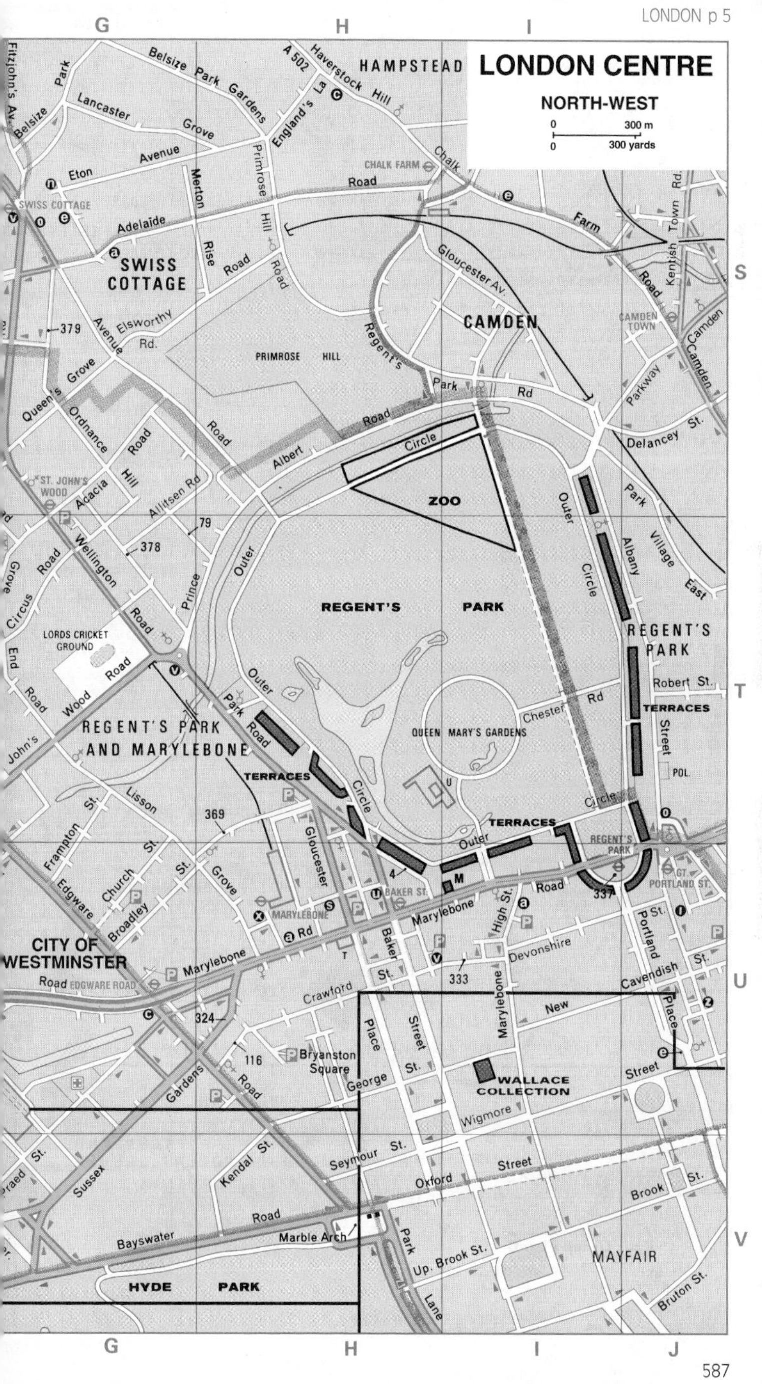
LONDON CENTRE
NORTH-WEST
0 300 m
0 300 yards
HAMPSTEAD
SWISS COTTAGE
CAMDEN
PRIMROSE HILL
ZOO
REGENT'S PARK
QUEEN MARY'S GARDENS
REGENT'S PARK AND MARYLEBONE
TERRACES
LORDS CRICKET GROUND
CITY OF WESTMINSTER
WALLACE COLLECTION
MAYFAIR
HYDE PARK
Marble Arch
CHALK FARM
SWISS COTTAGE
ST. JOHN'S WOOD
CAMDEN TOWN
REGENT'S PARK
GT. PORTLAND ST.
BAKER ST.
MARYLEBONE
EDGWARE ROAD
Oxford Street
Baker St.
Marylebone Road
Bayswater Road
Park Lane
Edgware Road
Prince Albert Road
Outer Circle
Wellington Road
Portland Place
Wigmore Street
Seymour St.
Up. Brook St.
Brook St.
Bruton St.
Bryanston Square

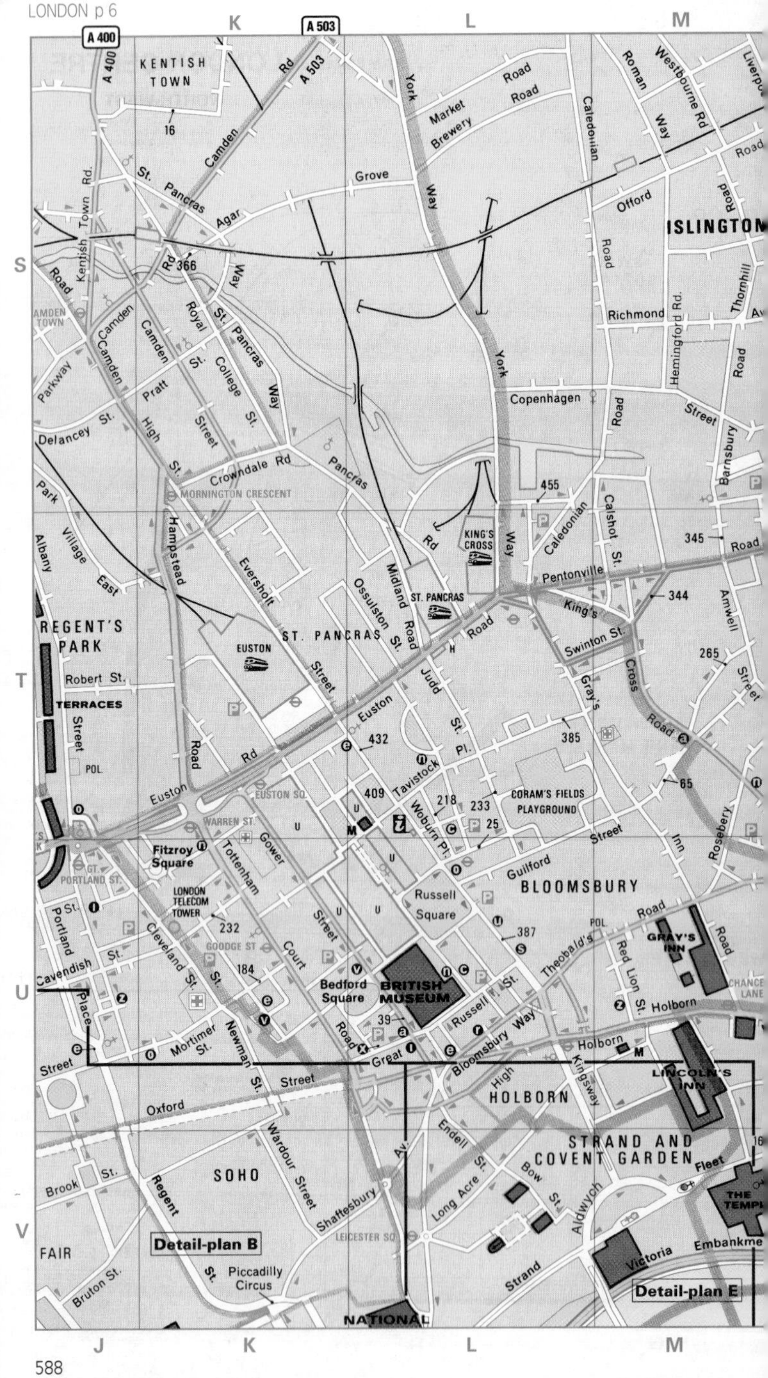

A 400
A 503
KENTISH TOWN
ISLINGTON
REGENT'S PARK
TERRACES
ST. PANCRAS
EUSTON
KING'S CROSS
BLOOMSBURY
BRITISH MUSEUM
HOLBORN
SOHO
STRAND AND COVENT GARDEN
GRAY'S INN
LINCOLN'S INN
CORAM'S FIELDS PLAYGROUND
LONDON TELECOM TOWER
Fitzroy Square
Russell Square
Bedford Square
Piccadilly Circus
MORNINGTON CRESCENT
EUSTON SQ.
WARREN ST.
GT. PORTLAND ST.
GOODGE ST.
LEICESTER SQ.
CHANCERY LANE
NATIONAL
THE TEMPLE
Detail-plan B
Detail-plan E

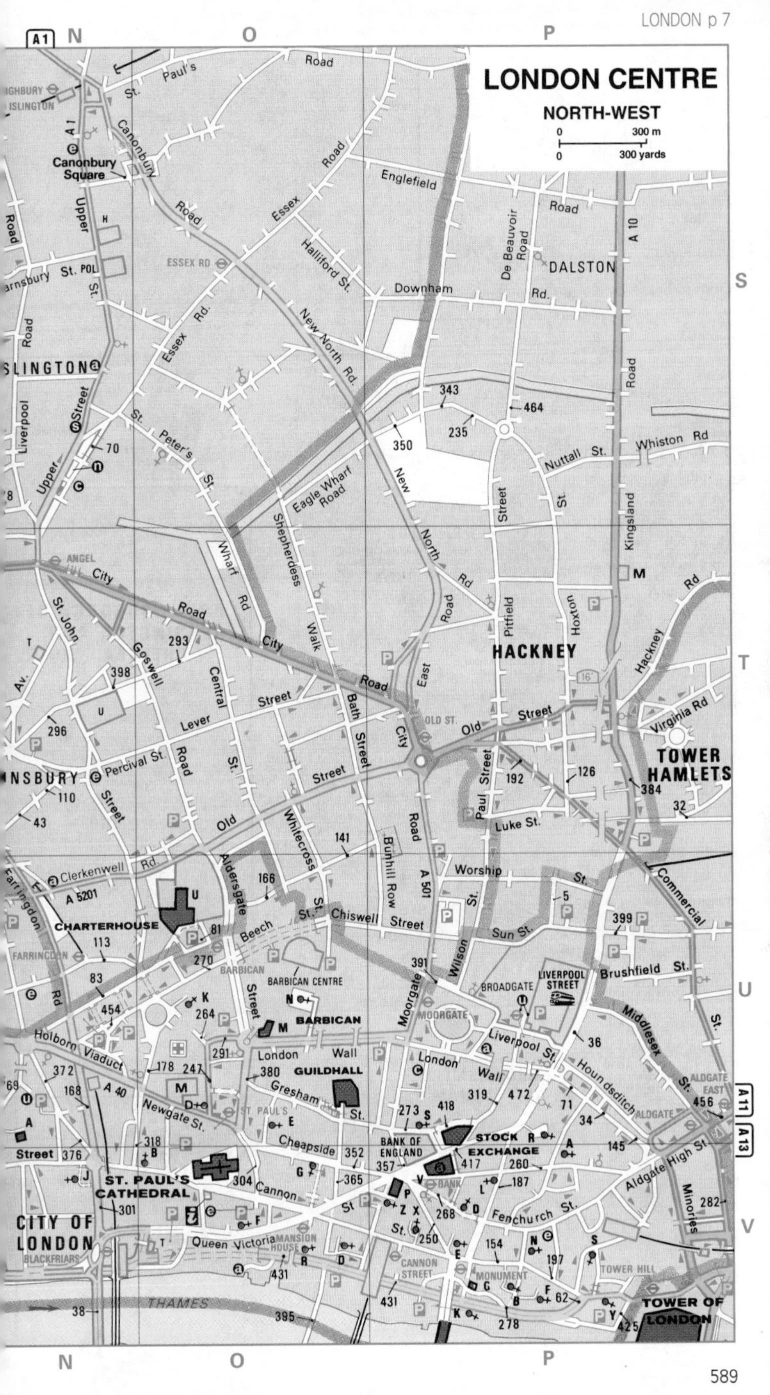
LONDON CENTRE
NORTH-WEST
0 300 m
0 300 yards
N
O
P
S
T
U
V
Canonbury Square
Essex Road
Englefield Road
De Beauvoir Road
DALSTON
Downham Rd.
Halliford St.
ESSEX RD
Essex Rd.
New North Rd.
ISLINGTON
St. Peter's St.
Eagle Wharf Road
Shepherdess Walk
Nuttall St.
Whiston Rd
Kingsland Road
ANGEL
City Road
Wharf Rd
Goswell
Central St.
Lever Street
Bath Street
East Road
Pitfield Street
Hoxton St.
HACKNEY
Hackney Rd
Virginia Rd
TOWER HAMLETS
OLD ST.
Old Street
Percival St.
FINSBURY
Luke St.
Whitecross St.
Bunhill Row
Worship St.
Commercial
Clerkenwell Rd.
Farringdon Rd
CHARTERHOUSE
Aldersgate Street
Beech St.
Chiswell Street
Sun St.
Wilson St.
Moorgate
BARBICAN
BARBICAN CENTRE
BROADGATE
LIVERPOOL STREET
Brushfield St.
Middlesex St.
Holborn Viaduct
London Wall
GUILDHALL
Liverpool St.
Houndsditch
Gresham St.
Newgate St.
ST. PAUL'S
Cheapside
BANK OF ENGLAND
STOCK EXCHANGE
ALDGATE EAST
ALDGATE
Aldgate High St.
Minories
ST. PAUL'S CATHEDRAL
Cannon St
Fenchurch St.
CITY OF LONDON
BLACKFRIARS
Queen Victoria
MANSION HOUSE
CANNON STREET
MONUMENT
TOWER HILL
THAMES
TOWER OF LONDON
A1
A 10
A 501
A 5201
A 40
A11
A13

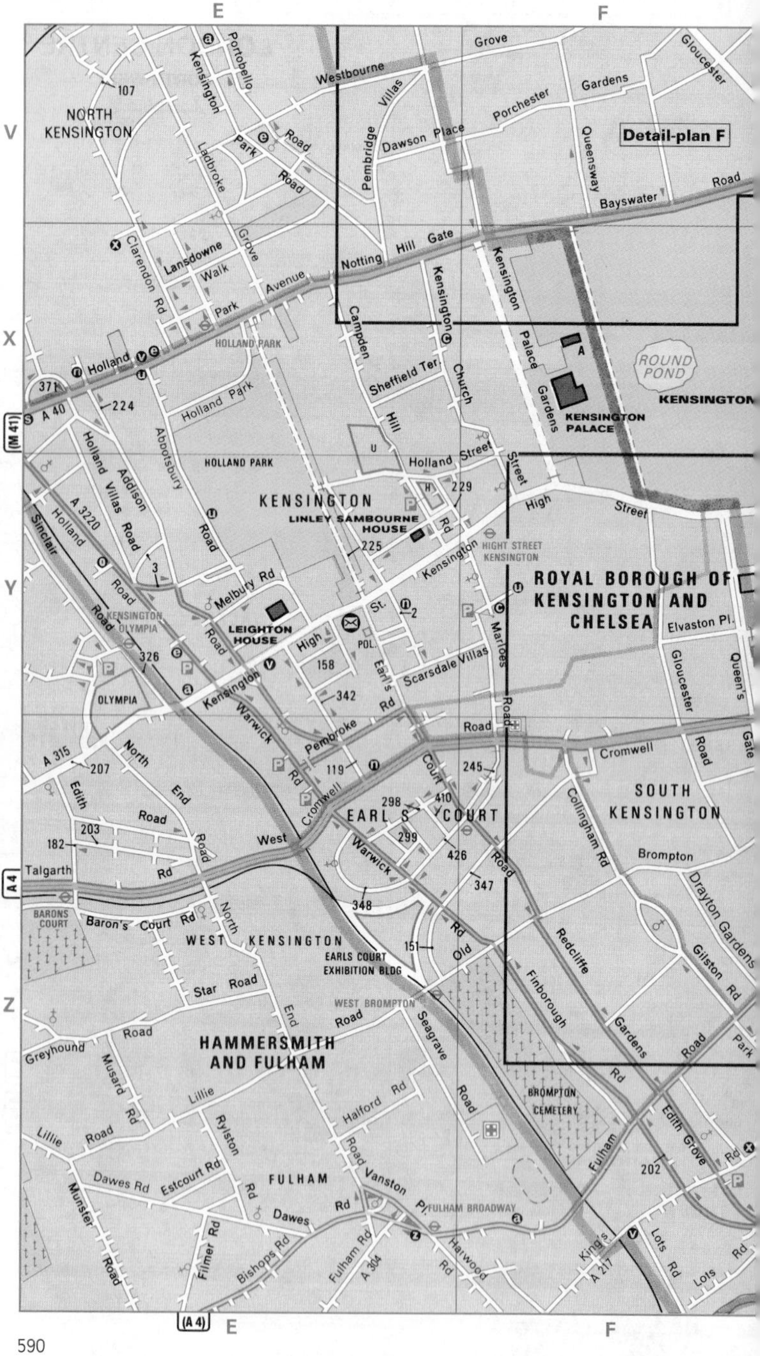

E
F

Grove
Gloucester
Westbourne
Gardens
Portobello
Kensington
107
Villas
Porchester
NORTH KENSINGTON
Park
Road
Dawson Place
Queensway
Detail-plan F
Pembridge
Ladbroke
Road
Road
Bayswater
V
Lansdowne
Clarendon Rd
Walk
Grove
Notting Hill Gate
Kensington
Kensington
Park
Avenue
Campden
HOLLAND PARK
X
Holland
A
ROUND POND
371
224
Sheffield Ter.
Church
Palace
Holland Park
Gardens
KENSINGTON
A 40
KENSINGTON PALACE
(M 41)
Abbotsbury
Hill
Holland
Addison
HOLLAND PARK
U
Holland Street
Villas
Street
229
KENSINGTON
High
Street
A 3220
Road
Rd
LINLEY SAMBOURNE HOUSE
Holland
Road
225
Sinclair
Kensington
HIGHT STREET KENSINGTON
3
ROYAL BOROUGH OF KENSINGTON AND CHELSEA
Y
Road
Melbury Rd
St.
2
Road
KENSINGTON OLYMPIA
Elvaston Pl.
LEIGHTON HOUSE
POL.
Marloes
Road
High
326
158
Scarsdale Villas
Gloucester
Queen's
Kensington
Earl's
OLYMPIA
342
Rd
Warwick
Road
Pembroke
Road
Gate
A 315
North
Cromwell
207
Road
Rd
119
245
Edith
End
Court
298
410
SOUTH KENSINGTON
Cromwell
Road
EARL S COURT
203
299
Collingham Rd
182
West
Road
426
Brompton
Warwick
Talgarth
Rd
Road
347
A 4
Drayton Gardens
348
BARONS COURT
North
Rd
Baron's Court Rd
Gilston Rd
WEST KENSINGTON
151
Redcliffe
Old
EARLS COURT EXHIBITION BLDG
Finborough
Star Road
Z
WEST BROMPTON
End
Road
Seagrave
Gardens
Road
Park
Road
HAMMERSMITH AND FULHAM
Rd
Greyhound
Musard
Rd
Lillie
Halford Rd
Road
BROMPTON CEMETERY
Rylston
Lillie Road
Road
Fulham
Edith Grove
Rd
Dawes Rd
Estcourt Rd
Rd
FULHAM
Vanston
202
Munster
Pl.
FULHAM BROADWAY
Dawes
Rd
Filmer Rd
Lots
Road
Bishops Rd
Fulham Rd
Harwood
King's
Rd
A 304
Rd
A 217
Rd
Lots
(A 4)
E
F

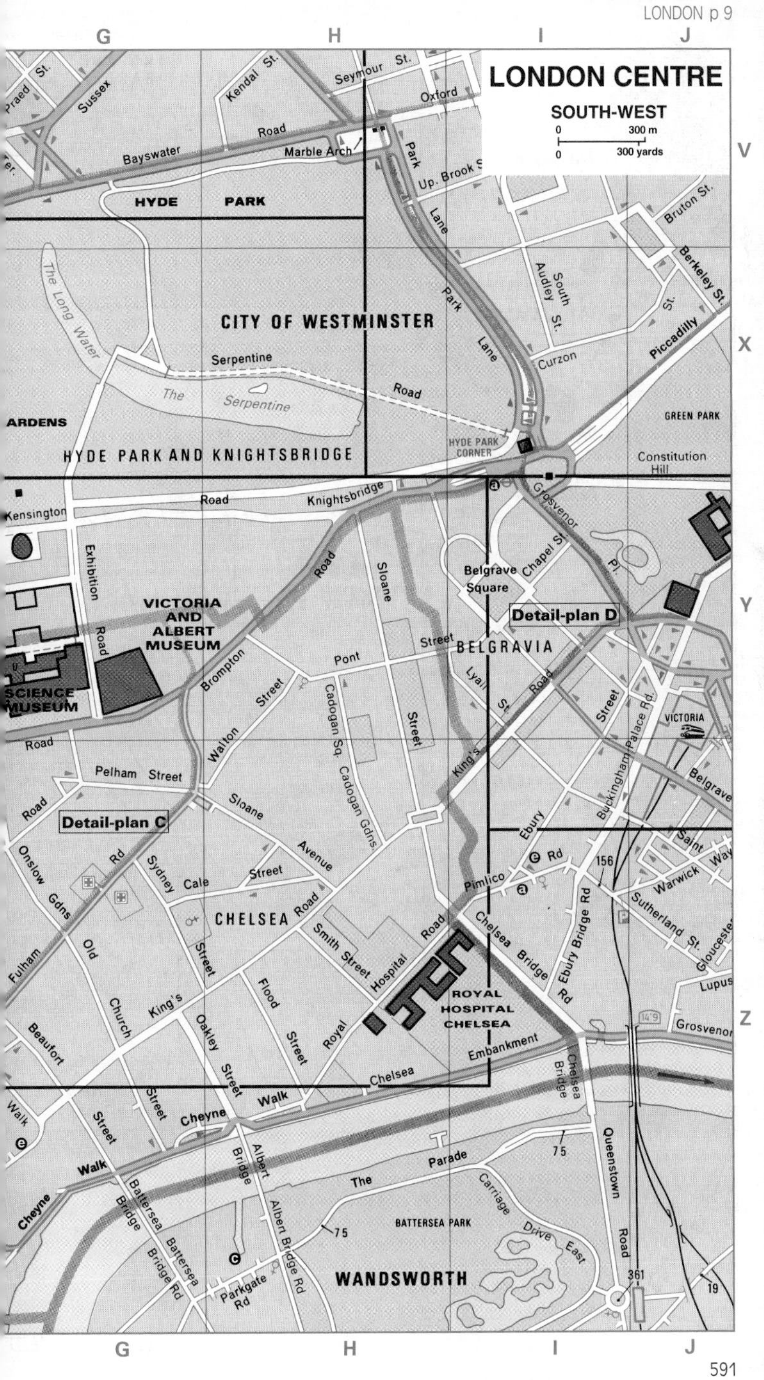
LONDON CENTRE
SOUTH-WEST
0 300 m
0 300 yards
HYDE PARK
CITY OF WESTMINSTER
HYDE PARK AND KNIGHTSBRIDGE
The Long Water
The Serpentine
Serpentine Road
HYDE PARK CORNER
GREEN PARK
Constitution Hill
Marble Arch
Bayswater Road
Oxford St.
Seymour St.
Kendal St.
Sussex
Praed St.
Park Lane
Up. Brook St.
South Audley St.
Curzon St.
Piccadilly
Berkeley St.
Bruton St.
ARDENS
Kensington Road
Knightsbridge
Grosvenor Pl.
Belgrave Square
Chapel St.
Detail-plan D
BELGRAVIA
VICTORIA
Exhibition Road
VICTORIA AND ALBERT MUSEUM
SCIENCE MUSEUM
Brompton Road
Sloane Street
Pont Street
Lyall St.
King's Road
Walton Street
Cadogan Sq.
Cadogan Gdns.
Pelham Street
Sloane Avenue
Detail-plan C
Onslow Gdns
Fulham Rd
Sydney Street
Cale Street
CHELSEA
Smith Street
Royal Hospital Road
ROYAL HOSPITAL CHELSEA
Chelsea Bridge Rd
Ebury Bridge Rd
Ebury St.
Pimlico Rd
Buckingham Palace Rd.
Belgrave
Saint
Warwick Way
Sutherland St.
Gloucester
Lupus
Grosvenor
Old Church Street
Beaufort Street
Oakley Street
Flood Street
Chelsea Embankment
Cheyne Walk
Chelsea Bridge
Albert Bridge
Battersea Bridge
Battersea Bridge Rd
Albert Bridge Rd
Parkgate Rd
The Parade
Carriage Drive East
Queenstown Road
BATTERSEA PARK
WANDSWORTH
Walk
156
149
75
361
19
G H I J
V X Y Z

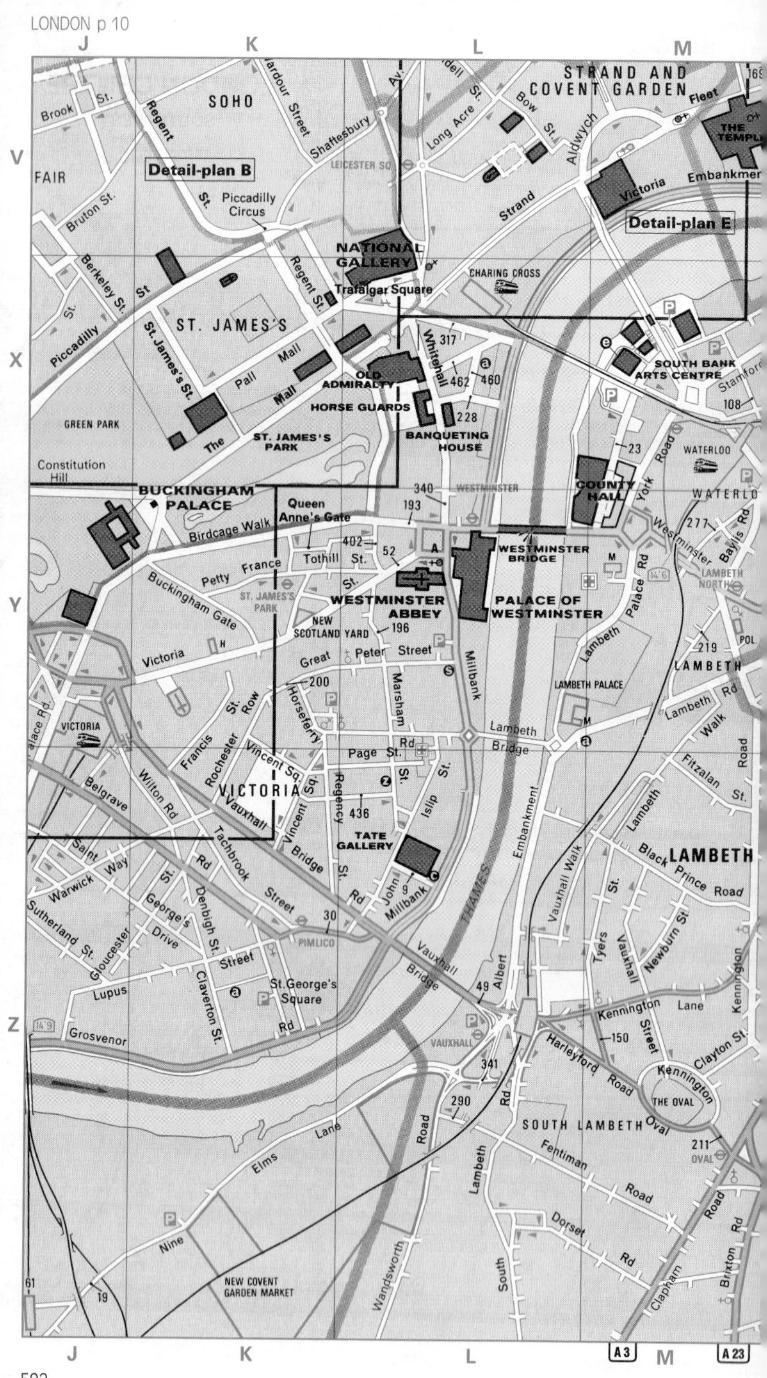
J
K
L
M
V
X
Y
Z
SOHO
STRAND AND COVENT GARDEN
Detail-plan B
Detail-plan E
Piccadilly Circus
NATIONAL GALLERY
Trafalgar Square
CHARING CROSS
ST. JAMES'S
OLD ADMIRALTY
HORSE GUARDS
BANQUETING HOUSE
GREEN PARK
ST. JAMES'S PARK
Constitution Hill
BUCKINGHAM PALACE
SOUTH BANK ARTS CENTRE
WATERLOO
COUNTY HALL
WESTMINSTER
WESTMINSTER BRIDGE
WESTMINSTER ABBEY
PALACE OF WESTMINSTER
NEW SCOTLAND YARD
LAMBETH PALACE
LAMBETH NORTH
LAMBETH
VICTORIA
TATE GALLERY
PIMLICO
THAMES
VAUXHALL
THE OVAL
OVAL
SOUTH LAMBETH
NEW COVENT GARDEN MARKET
Brook St.
Regent St.
Wardour Street
Shaftesbury Av.
Long Acre
Bow St.
Aldwych
Fleet
THE TEMPLE
LEICESTER SQ
Strand
Victoria Embankment
Bruton St.
Berkeley St.
Piccadilly
St. James's St.
Pall Mall
The Mall
Whitehall
Stamford
York Road
Birdcage Walk
Queen Anne's Gate
Tothill St.
Petty France
Buckingham Gate
Victoria St.
Great Peter Street
Marsham St.
Horseferry Rd
Millbank
Lambeth Bridge
Lambeth Palace Rd
Westminster Bridge Rd
Baylis Rd
Lambeth Rd
Lambeth Walk
Kennington Road
Fitzalan St.
Francis St.
Rochester Row
Vincent Sq.
Page St.
Regency St.
Islip St.
John Islip St.
Vauxhall Bridge Rd
Wilton Rd
Belgrave Rd
Tachbrook Street
Saint George's Drive
Warwick Way
Denbigh St.
Sutherland St.
Gloucester St.
Lupus St.
Claverton St.
St.George's Square
Grosvenor Rd
Vauxhall Bridge
Albert Embankment
Vauxhall Walk
Black Prince Road
Newburn St.
Tyers St.
Vauxhall Street
Kennington Lane
Harleyford Road
Kennington Oval
Clayton St.
Fentiman Road
Dorset Rd
South Lambeth Rd
Wandsworth Road
Elms Lane
Nine Elms
Clapham Road
Brixton Rd
A3
A23

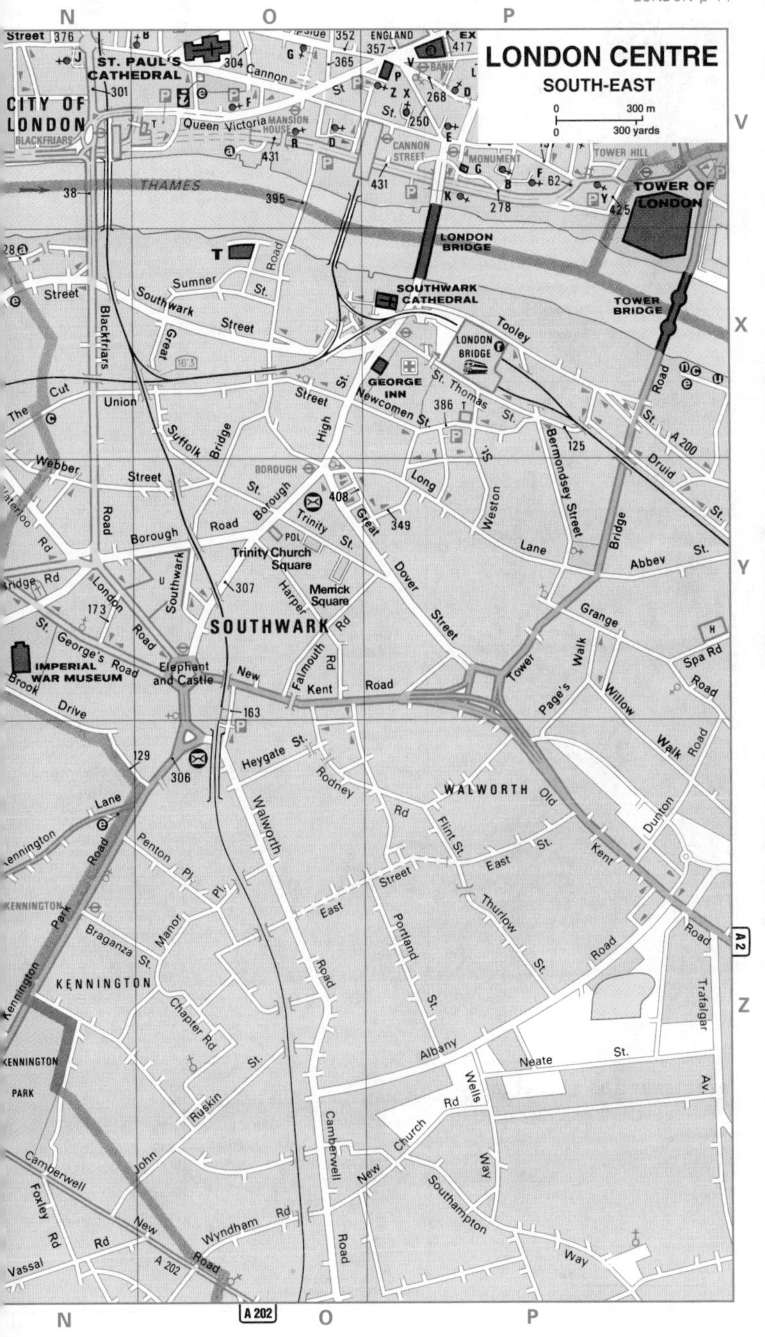
LONDON CENTRE
SOUTH-EAST
0 300 m
0 300 yards
N
O
P
V
X
Y
Z
CITY OF LONDON
ST. PAUL'S CATHEDRAL
THAMES
LONDON BRIDGE
SOUTHWARK CATHEDRAL
TOWER OF LONDON
TOWER BRIDGE
TOWER HILL
MONUMENT
CANNON STREET
MANSION HOUSE
BLACKFRIARS
BANK
GEORGE INN
BOROUGH
Trinity Church Square
Merrick Square
SOUTHWARK
IMPERIAL WAR MUSEUM
Elephant and Castle
WALWORTH
KENNINGTON
KENNINGTON PARK
A 200
A 2
A 202

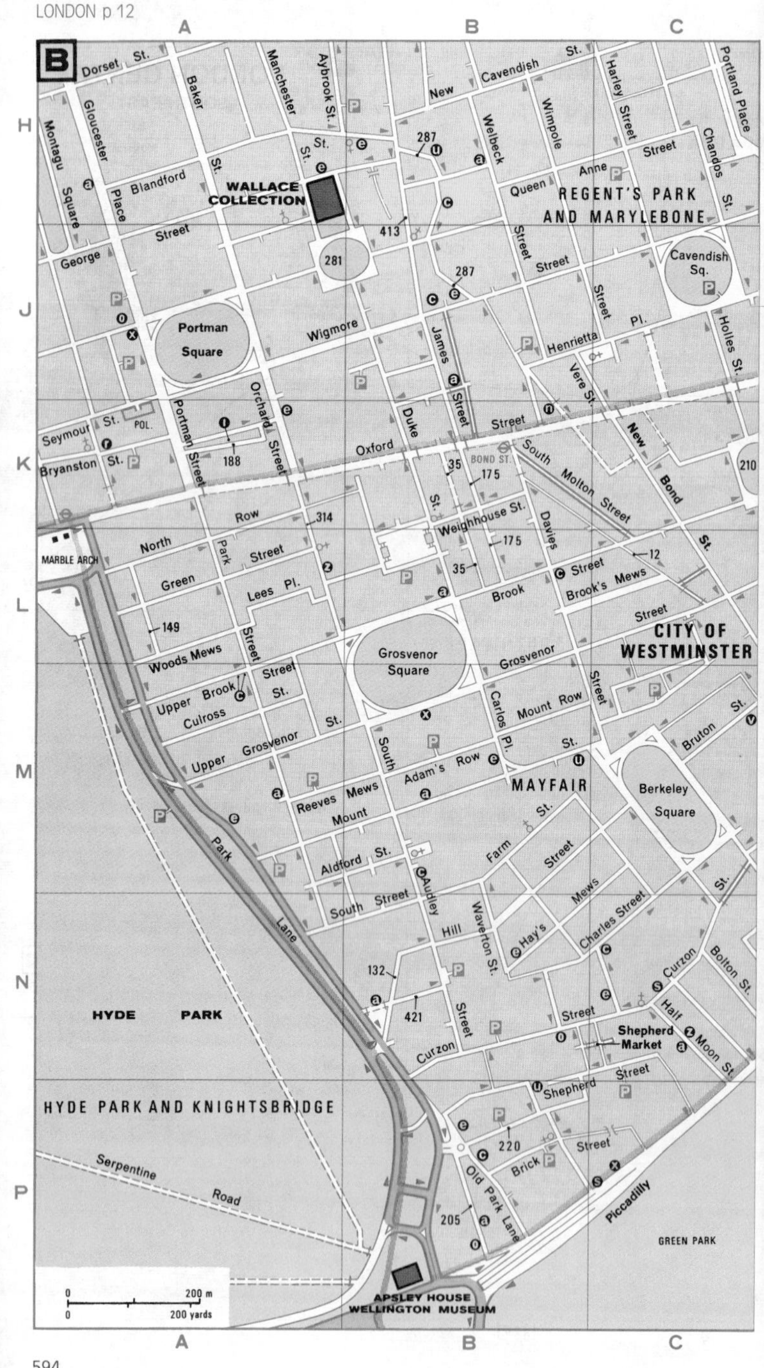
B
A
B
C
H
J
K
L
M
N
P
WALLACE COLLECTION
REGENT'S PARK AND MARYLEBONE
Portman Square
Cavendish Sq.
MARBLE ARCH
Grosvenor Square
CITY OF WESTMINSTER
MAYFAIR
Berkeley Square
HYDE PARK
Shepherd Market
HYDE PARK AND KNIGHTSBRIDGE
Serpentine Road
Piccadilly
GREEN PARK
APSLEY HOUSE WELLINGTON MUSEUM
Oxford Street
Park Lane
Baker St.
Wigmore Street
200 m
200 yards

| Street | Grid | No. |
| --- | --- | --- |
| Arlington Street | DN | 6 |
| Avery Row | CL | 12 |
| Bateman Street | FK | 18 |
| Berwick Street | FK | 26 |
| Binney Street | BL | 35 |
| Carlton Gardens | FP | 74 |
| Deanery Street | BN | 132 |
| Denman Street | FM | 133 |
| Denmark Street | GJ | 134 |
| Duke of York Street | EN | 143 |
| Duke Street ST. JAMES | EN | 146 |
| Dunraven Street | AL | 149 |
| Gerrard Street | GL | 174 |
| Gilbert Street | BL | 175 |
| Glasshouse Street | EM | 179 |
| Granville Place | AK | 188 |
| Great Castle Street | DJ | 189 |
| Greek Street | GK | 198 |
| Hamilton Place | BP | 205 |
| Hanover Square | CK | 210 |
| Hertford Street | BP | 220 |
| Leicester Square | GM | 261 |
| Manchester Square | AJ | 281 |
| Market Place | DJ | 286 |
| Marylebone Lane | BJ | 287 |
| North Audley Street | AK | 314 |
| Old Burlington Street | DM | 322 |
| Old Compton Street | GK | 323 |
| Panton Street | FM | 336 |
| Romilly Street | GL | 368 |
| Thayer Street | BJ | 413 |
| Tilney Street | BN | 421 |
| Warwick Street | EM | 444 |

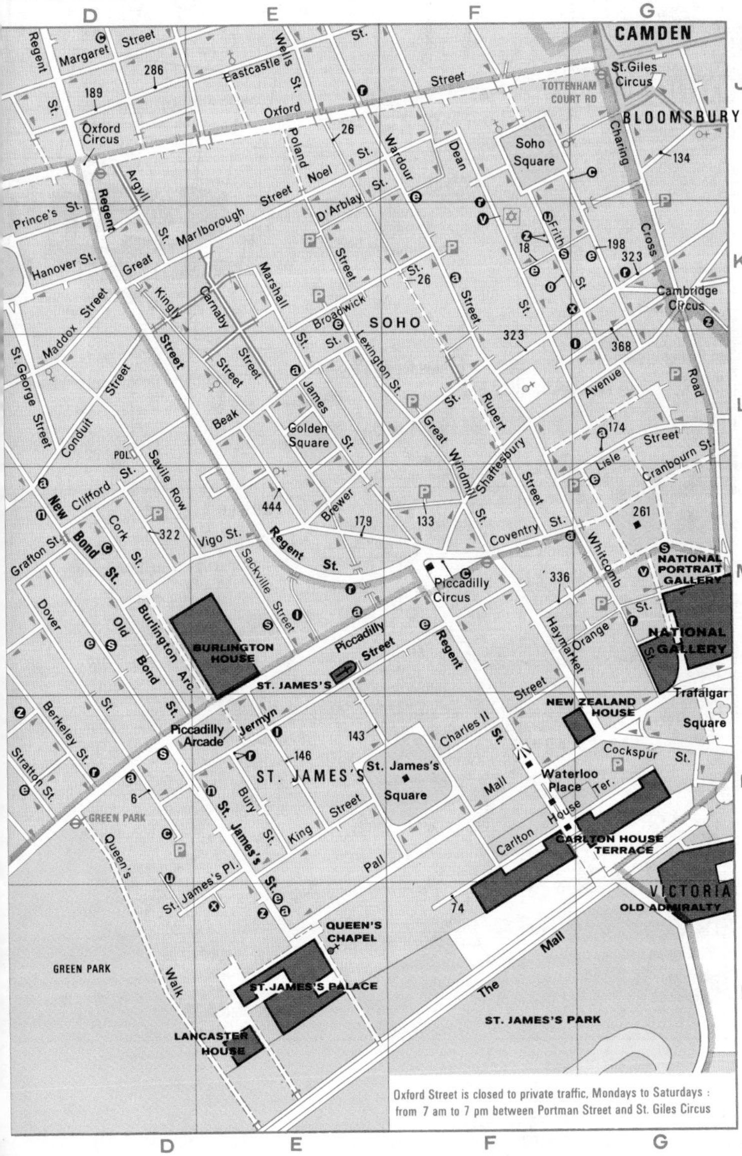

Oxford Street is closed to private traffic, Mondays to Saturdays : from 7 am to 7 pm between Portman Street and St. Giles Circus

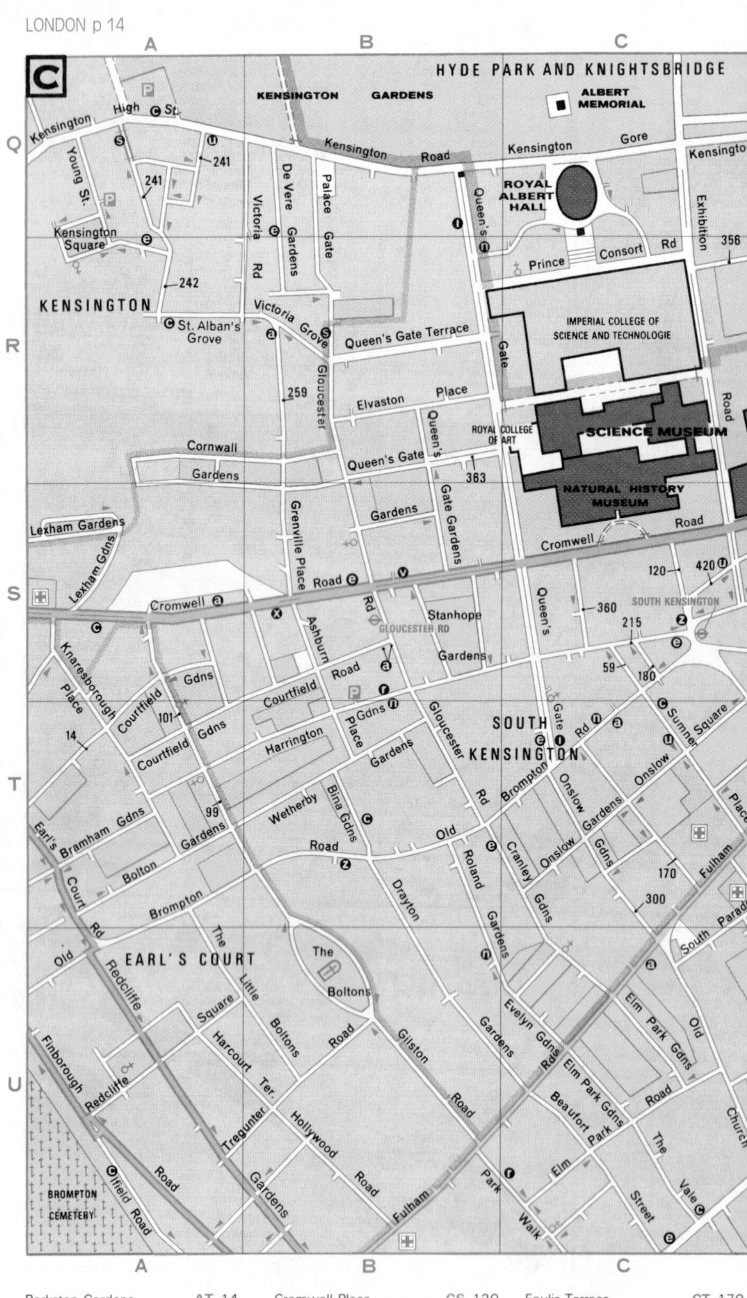
HYDE PARK AND KNIGHTSBRIDGE
KENSINGTON GARDENS
ALBERT MEMORIAL
ROYAL ALBERT HALL
IMPERIAL COLLEGE OF SCIENCE AND TECHNOLOGIE
SCIENCE MUSEUM
NATURAL HISTORY MUSEUM
ROYAL COLLEGE OF ART
KENSINGTON
SOUTH KENSINGTON
EARL'S COURT
BROMPTON CEMETERY
Kensington High St.
Kensington Road
Kensington Gore
Queen's Gate
Cromwell Road
Old Brompton Road
Fulham Road
Gloucester Rd
Earl's Court Rd
Redcliffe Gardens
The Boltons

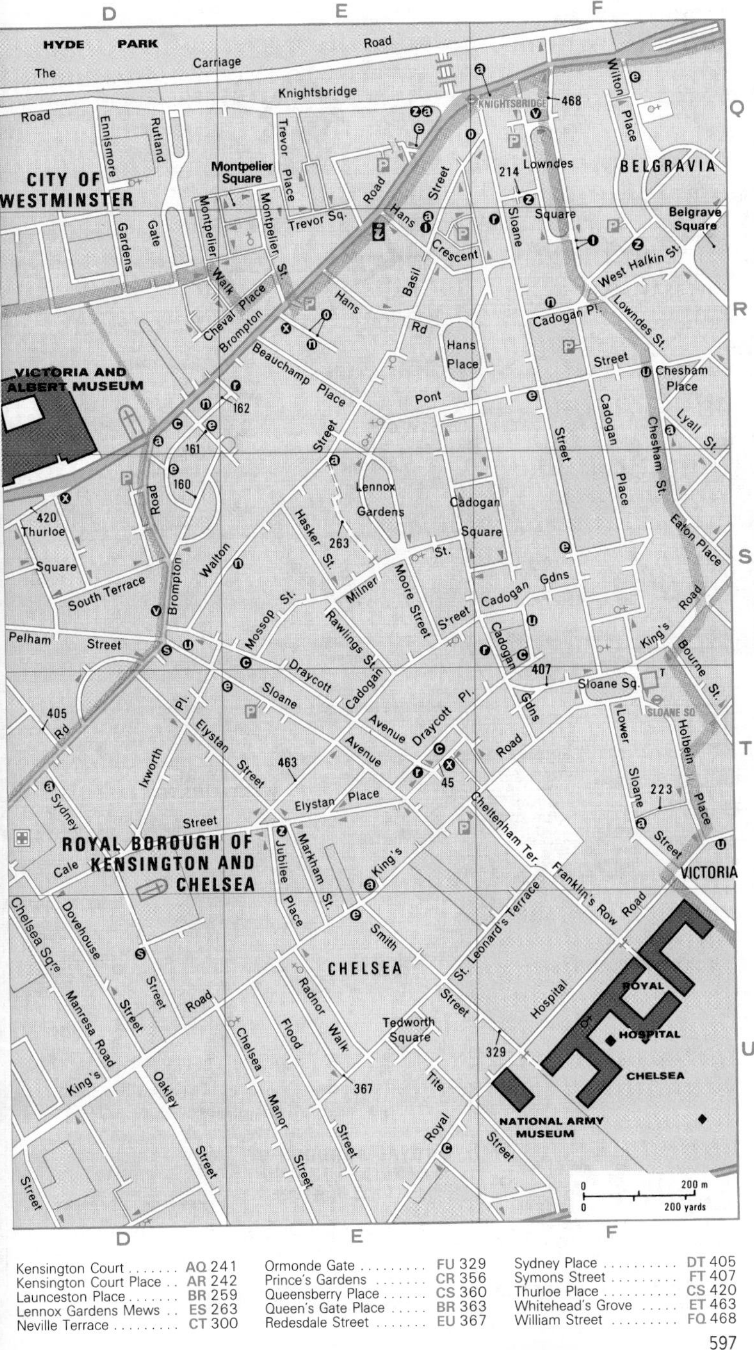
HYDE PARK
The Carriage Road
Knightsbridge
CITY OF WESTMINSTER
BELGRAVIA
VICTORIA AND ALBERT MUSEUM
ROYAL BOROUGH OF KENSINGTON AND CHELSEA
CHELSEA
ROYAL HOSPITAL CHELSEA
NATIONAL ARMY MUSEUM
VICTORIA
200 m
200 yards

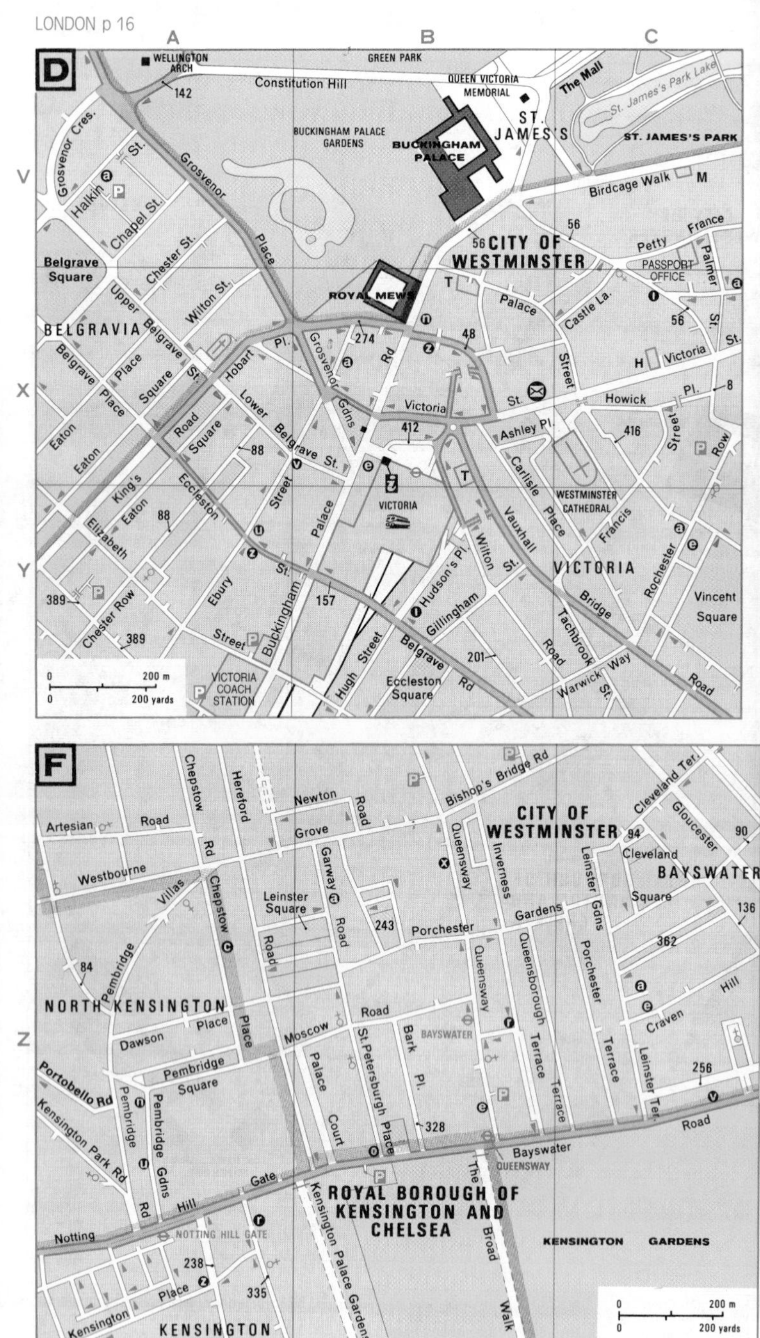

A
B
C
D
WELLINGTON ARCH
GREEN PARK
Constitution Hill
QUEEN VICTORIA MEMORIAL
The Mall
St. James's Park Lake
ST. JAMES'S
ST. JAMES'S PARK
BUCKINGHAM PALACE GARDENS
BUCKINGHAM PALACE
Grosvenor Cres.
Halkin St.
Chapel St.
Grosvenor Place
Birdcage Walk
CITY OF WESTMINSTER
Petty France
PASSPORT OFFICE
Palmer St.
Belgrave Square
Chester St.
Wilton St.
ROYAL MEWS
Palace St.
Castle La.
BELGRAVIA
Upper Belgrave St.
Hobart Pl.
Grosvenor Gdns
Buckingham Palace Rd
Victoria St.
Belgrave Place
Eaton Place
Eaton Square
Lower Belgrave St.
Howick Pl.
Ashley Pl.
Eccleston St.
Elizabeth St.
King's Road
Carlisle Place
WESTMINSTER CATHEDRAL
Francis Street
Rochester Row
VICTORIA
Vauxhall Bridge Road
Wilton Road
Hudson's Pl.
Gillingham St.
Tachbrook St.
Vincent Square
Chester Row
Ebury Street
Buckingham Palace Road
Hugh Street
Belgrave Rd
Eccleston Square
Warwick Way
VICTORIA COACH STATION
0 200 m
0 200 yards
F
Chepstow Rd
Hereford Road
Bishop's Bridge Rd
Newton Road
Artesian Road
Westbourne Grove
Queensway
Inverness Terrace
Leinster Gdns
CITY OF WESTMINSTER
Cleveland Ter.
Gloucester Terrace
Cleveland Square
BAYSWATER
Villas
Chepstow Place
Garway Road
Leinster Square
Porchester Gardens
Pembridge Villas
Queensborough Terrace
Porchester Terrace
Craven Hill
NORTH KENSINGTON
Moscow Road
Dawson Place
St. Petersburgh Place
Bark Pl.
Leinster Ter.
Pembridge Square
Palace Court
Portobello Rd
Pembridge Rd
Pembridge Gdns
Kensington Park Rd
Bayswater Road
QUEENSWAY
Notting Hill Gate
ROYAL BOROUGH OF KENSINGTON AND CHELSEA
The Broad Walk
NOTTING HILL GATE
Kensington Palace Gardens
KENSINGTON GARDENS
Kensington Place
KENSINGTON
V
X
Y
Z

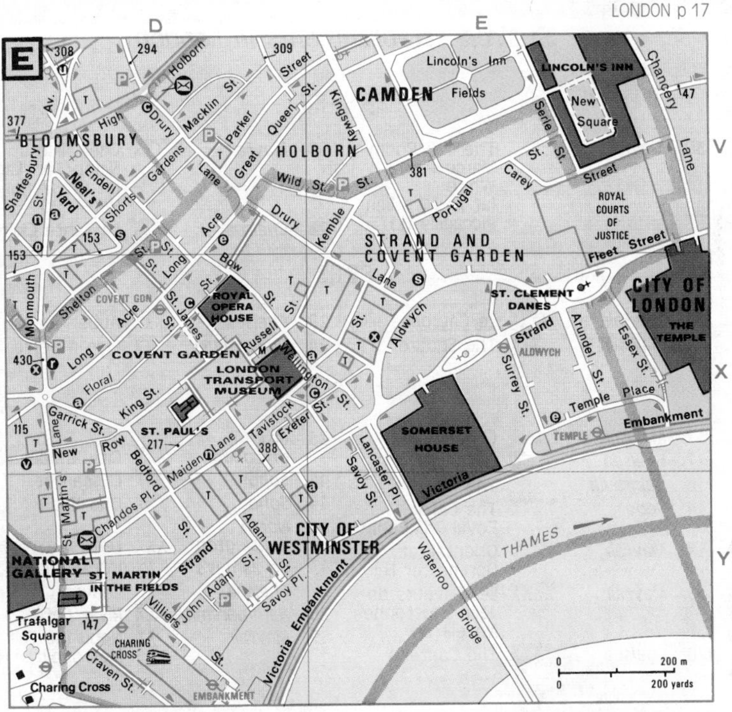

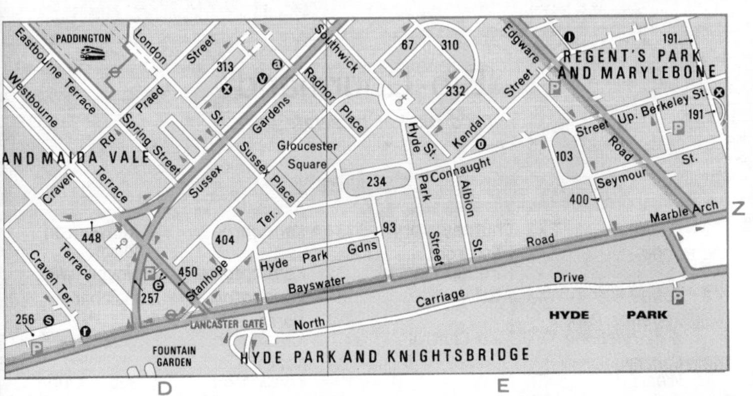
PADDINGTON
REGENT'S PARK AND MARYLEBONE
AND MAIDA VALE
HYDE PARK AND KNIGHTSBRIDGE
Gloucester Square
HYDE PARK
LANCASTER GATE
FOUNTAIN GARDEN
Eastbourne Terrace
Westbourne Terrace
London Street
Praed St.
Spring Street
Sussex Gardens
Sussex Place
Southwick St.
Radnor Place
Hyde Park St.
Kendal St.
Connaught St.
Edgware Road
Up. Berkeley St.
Seymour St.
Marble Arch
Albion St.
Park Street
Bayswater Road
North Carriage Drive
Hyde Park Gdns
Stanhope Ter.
Craven Ter.
Craven Terrace
D
E
Z

## Starred establishments in London

### ✿✿✿

| Page | District | Category | Establishment |
|---|---|---|---|
| 38 | *Mayfair* | XXXXX | The Oak Room Marco Pierre White (at Le Meridien Piccadilly H.) |
| 39 | *Mayfair* | XXXXX | Chez Nico at Ninety Park Lane (at Grosvenor House H.) |
| 28 | *Chelsea* | XXXX | La Tante Claire |

### ✿✿

| Page | District | Category | Establishment |
|---|---|---|---|
| 39 | *Mayfair* | XXXX | Le Gavroche |
| 39 | *Mayfair* | XXX | The Square |
| 28 | *Chelsea* | XXX | Aubergine |
| 24 | *Bloomsbury* | XX | Pied à Terre |

### ✿

| Page | District | Category | Establishment |
|---|---|---|---|
| 37 | *Mayfair* | (hotel) | Connaught |
| 27 | *Chelsea* | (hotel) | Capital |
| 36 | *Belgravia* | (hotel) | The Halkin |
| 44 | *Soho* | XXXX | The Café Royal Grill Room |
| 39 | *Mayfair* | XXXX | Oriental (at Dorchester H.) |
| 39 | *Mayfair* | XXXX | Les Saveurs de Jean-Christophe Novelli W1 |
| 28 | *Chelsea* | XXX | The Canteen |
| 25 | *City of London* | XXX | City Rhodes |
| 44 | *Soho* | XXX | L'Escargot |
| 44 | *Soho* | XXX | Quo Vadis |
| 31 | *North Kensington* | XXX | Leith's |
| 43 | *St. James's* | XX | L'Oranger |
| 29 | *Chelsea* | XX | Chavot |
| 26 | *Hammersmith* | XX | River Café |
| 39 | *Mayfair* | XX | Nobu (at The Metropolitan H.) |

# "Bib Gourmand"

*Good food at moderate prices*

## Meals

| Page | District | Category | Establishment |
|---|---|---|---|
| 29 | *Chelsea* | XXX | Chutney Mary |
| 44 | *Soho* | XXX | L'Escargot (Ground Floor) |
| 44 | *Soho* | XX | Atelier |
| 42 | *Regent's Park & Marylebone* | XX | Nico Central |
| 34 | *Canary Wharf* | XX | MPW |
| 34 | *Whitechapel* | XX | Café Spice Namaste |
| 46 | *Victoria* | XX | Simply Nico |
| 35 | *Wandswolth* | XX | Chez Bruce |
| 31 | *Kensington* | X | Kensington Place |
| 31 | *Kensington* | X | Novelli W8 |
| 31 | *Kensington* | X | Malabar |
| 31 | *North Kensington* | X | Woz |
| 31 | *North Kensington* | X | Sugar Club |
| 31 | *North Kensington* | X | Alastair Little Lancaster Road |
| 36 | *Bayswater & Maida Vale* | X | L'Accento |
| 34 | *Bermondsey* | X | Blue Print Café |

# Restaurants classified according to type

## Seafood

| | | | |
|---|---|---|---|
| 39 | *Mayfair* | XXX | Scotts |
| 40 | *Mayfair* | XX | Bentley's |
| 33 | *South Kensington* | XX | Downstairs at One Ninety |
| 36 | *Bayswater & Maida Vale* | XX | Jason's |
| 29 | *Chelsea* | XX | Poissonnerie de l'Avenue |
| 45 | *Strand & Covent Garden* | XX | Sheekey's |

## Chinese

| | | | |
|---|---|---|---|
| 39 | *Mayfair* | XXXX | ✿ Oriental (at Dorchester H.) |
| 37 | *Hyde Park & Knightsbridge* | XXX | Mr Chow |
| 37 | *Hyde Park & Knightsbridge* | XXX | Pearl of Knightsbridge |
| 39 | *Mayfair* | XXX | Princess Garden |
| 28 | *Chelsea* | XXX | L'Oriental (at La Belle Epoque) |
| 45 | *Strand & Covent Garden* | XXX | West ZENders |
| 29 | *Chelsea* | XX | Good Earth |
| 47 | *Victoria* | XX | Hunan |
| 25 | *City of London* | XX | Imperial City |
| 47 | *Victoria* | XX | Ken Lo's Memories of China |
| 31 | *Kensington* | XX | Ken Lo's Memories of China |
| 26 | *Fulham* | XX | Mao Tai |
| 36 | *Bayswater & Maida Vale* | XX | Poons |
| 29 | *Chelsea* | XX | Red of Knightsbridge |
| 36 | *Bayswater & Maida Vale* | XX | Royal China |
| 35 | *Putney* | XX | Royal China |
| 24 | *Hampstead* | XX | Vegetarian Cottage |
| 24 | *Hampstead* | XX | ZeNW3 |
| 45 | *Soho* | X | Fung Shing |
| 45 | *Soho* | X | Poons |

## English

| | | | |
|---|---|---|---|
| 39 | *Mayfair* | XXX | Grill Room (at Dorchester H.) |
| 46 | *Victoria* | XXX | Shepherd's |
| 29 | *Chelsea* | XX | English Garden |
| 45 | *Strand & Covent Garden* | XX | Rules |
| 24 | *Bloomsbury* | X | Alfred |

## French

| | | | |
|---|---|---|---|
| 39 | *Mayfair* | XXXXX | ✿✿✿ Chez Nico at Ninety Park Lane |
| 39 | *Mayfair* | XXXX | ✿✿ (Le) Gavroche |
| 39 | *Mayfair* | XXXX | ✿ (Les) Saveurs de Jean-Christophe Nonelli WI |
| 28 | *Chelsea* | XXXX | ✿✿✿ (La) Tante Claire |
| 46 | *Victoria* | XXX | Auberge de Provence |
| 29 | *Chelsea* | XX | Brasserie St. Quentin |
| 29 | *Chelsea* | XX | ✿ Chavot |
| 31 | *North Kensington* | XX | Chez Moi |
| 29 | *Chelsea* | XX | (La) Ciboulette |
| 31 | *Kensington* | XX | (L') Escargot Doré |
| 45 | *Strand & Covent Garden* | XX | (L') Estaminet |
| 29 | *Chelsea* | XX | Grill St. Quentin |
| 24 | *Bloomsbury* | XX | Mon Plaisir |
| 29 | *Chelsea* | XX | Poissonnerie de l'Avenue |
| 30 | *Kensington* | XX | (La) Pomme d'Amour |
| 25 | *City of London* | XX | (Le) Quai |
| 37 | *Belgravia* | XX | Vong (French Thai) |
| 42 | *Regent's Park & Marylebone* | X | (L') Aventure |
| 45 | *Stand & Covent Garden* | X | Magno's Brasserie |
| 42 | *Regent's Park & Marylebone* | X | (Le) Muscadet |
| 47 | *Victoria* | X | (La) Poule au Pot |

## Hungarian

| | | | |
|---|---|---|---|
| 44 | *Soho* | XX | Gay Hussar |

## Indian & Pakistani

| | | | |
|---|---|---|---|
| 34 | *Bermondsey* | XXX | Bengal Clipper |
| 33 | *South Kensington* | XXX | Bombay Brasserie |
| 29 | *Chelsea* | XXX | Chutney Mary (Anglo-Indian) |
| 33 | *South Kensington* | XX | Café Lazeez |
| 34 | *Whitechapel* | XX | Cafe Spice Namaste |
| 40 | *Mayfair* | XX | Chor Bizarre |
| 33 | *South Kensington* | XX | Delhi Brasserie |
| 42 | *Regent's Park & Marylebone* | XX | Gaylord |
| 44 | *Soho* | XX | Gopal's |
| 33 | *South Kensington* | XX | Khan's of Kensington |
| 24 | *Bloomsbury* | XX | Malabar Junction |
| 33 | *South Kensington* | XX | Memories of India |
| 42 | *Regent's Park & Marylebone* | XX | (La) Porte des Indes |
| 44 | *Soho* | XX | Red Fort |
| 35 | *Wandsworth* | XX | Tabaq |
| 40 | *Mayfair* | XX | Tamarind |
| 26 | *Hammersmith* | XX | Tandoori Nights |
| 29 | *Chelsea* | XX | Vama |
| 35 | *Wandsworth* | X | Bombay Bicycle Club |
| 31 | *Kensington* | X | Malabar |
| 44 | *Soho* | X | Soho Spice |

## Irish

| | | | |
|---|---|---|---|
| 40 | *Mayfair* | XX | Mulligans |

## Italian

| | | | |
|---|---|---|---|
| 36 | *Belgravia* | 🏨 | ✿ (The) Halkin |
| 28 | *Chelsea* | XXX | Grissini |
| 46 | *Victoria* | XXX | (L') Incontro |
| 46 | *Victoria* | XXX | Santini |
| 36 | *Bayswater & Maida Vale* | XX | Al San Vincenzo |
| 42 | *Regent's Park & Marylebone* | XX | Bertorelli's |
| 45 | *Strand & Covent Garden* | XX | Bertorelli's |
| 42 | *Regent's Park & Marylebone* | XX | Caldesi |
| 29 | *Chelsea* | XX | Caraffini |
| 29 | *Chelsea* | XX | Daphne's |
| 34 | *Dulwich* | XX | Luigi's |
| 31 | *North Kensington* | XX | Orsino |
| 31 | *Kensington* | XX | Osteria del Parco |
| 29 | *Chelsea* | XX | Osteria Le Fate |
| 26 | *Hammersmith* | XX | ✿ River Café |
| 29 | *Chelsea* | XX | Toto's |
| 36 | *Belgravia* | XX | Zafferano |
| 36 | *Bayswater & Maida Vale* | X | (L') Accento |
| 36 | *Bayswater & Maida Vale* | X | Assaggi |
| 34 | *Bermondsey* | X | Cantina Del Ponte |
| 31 | *Kensington* | X | Cibo |
| 47 | *Victoria* | X | Olivo |

## Japanese

| | | | |
|---|---|---|---|
| 43 | *St. James's* | XXX | Suntory |
| 25 | *City of London* | XXX | Tatsuso |
| 42 | *Regent's Park & Marylebone* | XX | Asuka |
| 24 | *Hampstead* | XX | Benihana |
| 29 | *Chelsea* | XX | Benihana |
| 40 | *Mayfair* | XX | Benihana |
| 39 | *Mayfair* | XX | ✿ Nobu |
| 43 | *St. James's* | XX | Matsuri |
| 25 | *City of London* | XX | Miyama |
| 40 | *Mayfair* | XX | Shogun |

## Lebanese

37 *Belgravia* XX (Al) Bustan
29 *Chelsea* XX Beit Eddine
31 *Kensington* XX Phoenicia

## Spanish

28 *Chelsea* XXX Albero & Grana

## Thai

26 *Fulham* XX Blue Elephant
29 *Chelsea* XX Busabong Too
35 *Battersea* XX Chada
36 *Bayswater & Maida Vale* XX Nipa
25 *City of London* XX Sri Siam City
33 *South Kensington* XX Tui
37 *Belgravia* XX Vong (French Thai)
44 *Soho* X Sri Siam

## Vegetarian

24 *Hampstead* XX Vegetarian Cottage

## Vietnamese

45 *Soho* X Saigon

*Greater London is divided, for administrative purposes, into 32 boroughs plus the City; these sub-divide naturally into minor areas, usually grouped around former villages or quarters, which often maintain a distinctive character.*

*of Greater London:* ***0171*** *or* ***0181*** *except special cases.*

## LONDON AIRPORTS

**Heathrow** *Middx. W : 17 m. by A 4, M 4* **Underground** *Piccadilly line direct.*

*(0171) 759 4321* – **Terminal** : Airbus (A 1) from Victoria, Airbus (A 2) from Paddington.

*Underground Station Concourse, Heathrow Airport, TW6 2JA (0171) 824 8844.*

**Radisson Edwardian,** 140 Bath Rd, Hayes, UB3 5AW, (0181) 759 6311, *Fax (0181) 759 4559*, rm, – 550.
***Henleys :*** Meals a la carte 34.50/39.00 **st.** 8.00 – ***Brasserie :*** Meals a la carte approx. 20.50 **st.** 8.00 – 14.00 – **442 rm** 157.00/200.00 **s.**, 17 suites.

**Holiday Inn Crowne Plaza Heathrow London,** Stockley Rd, West Drayton, UB7 9NA, (01895) 445555, *Fax (01895) 445122*, rm, – 200.
***Marlowe :*** Meals a la carte 24.75/36.20 **st.** 7.50 – ***Cafe Galleria :*** Meals a la carte 18.15/27.95 **st.** 7.50 – 12.95 – **372 rm** 175.00/185.00 **st.**, 2 suites.

**Sheraton Skyline,** Bath Rd, Hayes, UB3 5BP, (0181) 759 2535, *Fax (0181) 750 9150*, rm, – 500.
***Colony Room :*** Meals *(closed Sunday)* (dinner only) a la carte 26.25/35.75 **st.** 11.50 – ***Le Jardin :*** Meals 18.75 **st.** and a la carte 11.50 – 15.50 – **346 rm** 185.00/224.50 **st.**, 5 suites.

**London Heathrow Hilton,** Terminal 4, TW6 3AF, (0181) 759 7755, *Fax (0181) 759 7579*, rm, – 240.
***Brasserie :*** Meals 20.95/22.75 **st.** and a la carte 12.00 – ***Zen Oriental :*** Meals - Chinese - 25.80/27.50 **t.** and a la carte 14.80 – 14.95 – **390 rm** 185.00 **st.**, 5 suites – SB.

**Forte Crest,** Sipson Rd, West Drayton, UB7 0JU, (0181) 759 2323, *Fax (0181) 897 8659* – rm, – 100.
Meals *(closed Saturday lunch)* (carving rest.) 17.50 **st.** 7.25 – ***Sampans :*** Meals - Chinese - (dinner only) 17.95 **t.** and a la carte 7.95 – ***Tutto :*** Meals *(closed lunch Saturday, Sunday and Bank Holidays)* 10.00 **t.** and a la carte 8.95 – 11.50 – **521 rm** 125.00/135.00 **st.**, 6 suites – SB.

**Excelsior Heathrow,** Bath Rd, West Drayton, UB7 0DU, (0181) 759 6611, *Fax (0181) 759 3421*, rm, – 700.
Meals (carving rest.) 17.95 **st.** and dinner a la carte 5.75 – ***Wheeler's :*** Meals - Seafood - *(closed lunch Saturday and Sunday and Bank Holidays)* a la carte 21.00/37.00 **st.** 6.75 – 12.50 – **817 rm** 125.00/130.00 **st.**, 10 suites – SB.

**Ramada H. Heathrow,** Bath Rd, TW6 2AQ, (0181) 897 6363, *Fax (0181) 897 1113*, rm, – 550.
Meals 17.50/20.50 **st.** and a la carte 6.00 – 11.25 – **634 rm** 150.00 **st.**, 6 suites.

**Sheraton Heathrow,** Colnbrook bypass, West Drayton, UB7 0HJ, (0181) 759 2424, *Fax (0181) 759 2091* – rm, – 60.
Meals a la carte 15.45/28.70 **st.** 9.50 – 13.50 – **427 rm** 170.00/180.00 **st.**, 4 suites.

**Forte Posthouse Heathrow,** Bath Rd, Hayes, UB3 5AJ, (0181) 759 2552, *Fax (0181) 564 9265* – rm, – 45.
Meals a la carte 14.25/25.65 **st.** 7.25 – 10.95 – **186 rm** 109.00 **st.** – SB.

**Gatwick** *W. Sussex S : 28 m. by A 23 and M 23* - **Train** *from Victoria : Gatwick Express* 404 T 30 – *Crawley.*

*(01293) 535353.*

*International Arrivals Concourse, South Terminal, RH6 0NP (01293) 560108.*

**London Gatwick Airport Hilton,** South Terminal, RH6 0LL, (01293) 518080, *Fax (01293) 528980*, rm, – 500.
Meals 22.95/25.95 **st.** and a la carte – 12.95 – **547 rm** 187.00/217.00 **st.**, 3 suites.

**Ramada H. Gatwick,** Povey Cross Rd, RH6 0BE, (01293) 820169, *Fax (01293) 820259*, *squash* – rm, – 180.
Meals *(closed lunch Saturday and Sunday)* 16.50/17.50 **st.** and a la carte – 11.00 – **250 rm** 85.00 **st.**, 5 suites.

**Le Meridien London Gatwick,** Gatwick Airport (North Terminal), RH6 0PH, (01293) 567070, *Fax (01293) 567739*, rm, – 350. VISA JCB
***New Fortune :*** Meals - Chinese - 25.00 **t.** and a la carte – ***Brasserie :*** Meals *(closed Sunday lunch)* 14.95/18.95 **t.** and dinner a la carte 6.95 – 10.95 – **468 rm** 159.00 **st.**, 6 suites – SB.

**Forte Posthouse Gatwick,** Povey Cross Rd, RH6 0BA, (01293) 771621, *Fax (01293) 771054* – rm, rest, – 120. VISA JCB
Meals 16.95/14.95 **st.** and a la carte 7.50 – 9.95 – **210 rm** 99.00 **st.** – SB.

---

**CAMDEN** *Except where otherwise stated see pp. 4-7.*

**Bloomsbury** – *NW1/W1/WC1.*
*34-37 Woburn Pl. WC1H 0JR (0171) 580 4599.*

**Holiday Inn Kings Cross,** 1 Kings Cross Rd, WC1X 9HX, (0171) 833 3900, *Fax (0171) 917 6163*, squash – rm, – 220. VISA JCB. MT a
Meals *(closed Sunday lunch)* 17.95 **st.** (dinner) and a la carte 18.00/30.00 **st.** 7.00 – 9.75 – **403 rm** 170.00 **st.**, 2 suites – SB.

**Marlborough,** 9-14 Bloomsbury St., WC1B 3QD, (0171) 636 5601, *Fax (0171) 636 0532* – rm, rest, – 200. VISA. LU i
Meals 17.00 **st.** and a la carte 7.50 – 14.00 – **166 rm** 158.00/196.00 **s.**, 7 suites.

**Russell,** Russell Sq., WC1B 5BE, (0171) 837 6470, *Fax (0171) 837 2857* – rm, rest, – 400. VISA JCB. LU o
***Fitzroy Doll's :*** Meals a la carte approx. 21.00 **st.** 7.50 – ***Virginia Woolf's :*** Meals *(closed Sunday dinner)* a la carte 12.85/19.85 **st.** 6.95 – 10.95 – **327 rm** 130.00/155.00 **st.**, 2 suites – SB.

**Grafton,** 130 Tottenham Court Rd, W1P 9HP, (0171) 388 4131, *Fax (0171) 387 7394* – rm, rest, – 100. VISA. KU n
Meals 17.50 **st.** and a la carte 7.50 – 11.00 – **320 rm** 119.00/162.00 **s.**, 4 suites.

**Mountbatten,** 20 Monmouth St., WC2H 9HD, (0171) 836 4300, *Fax (0171) 240 3540* – rm, rest, – 75. VISA. p. 17 DV o
Meals 19.00 **st.** and a la carte 7.50 – 14.00 – **120 rm** 187.00/226.00 **s.**, 7 suites.

**Montague,** 15 Montague St., WC1B 5BJ, (0171) 637 1001, *Fax (0171) 637 2516*, – rm, rest, – 120. VISA JCB. LU c
Meals *(closed lunch Saturday and Sunday)* a la carte 16.00/25.95 **t.** 11.00 – 11.50 – **102 rm** 120.00/160.00 **s.**, 2 suites.

**Covent Garden,** 10 Monmouth St., WC2H 9HB, (0171) 806 1000, *Fax (0171) 806 1100*, – . VISA. p. 17 DV n
Meals a la carte 16.50/29.15 **t.** – 14.50 – **48 rm** 165.00/245.00 **s.**, 2 suites.

**Kingsley,** Bloomsbury Way, WC1A 2SD, (0171) 242 5881, *Fax (0171) 831 0225* – rm, rest, – 90. VISA JCB. LU r
Meals *(closed lunch Saturday, Sunday and Bank Holidays)* 16.00 **t.** and a la carte 5.30 – 11.25 – **137 rm** 125.00/240.00 **st.**

**Forte Posthouse Bloomsbury,** Coram St., WC1N 1HT, (0171) 837 1200, *Fax (0171) 837 5374* – rm, rest, – 750. VISA JCB. LT c
Meals a la carte 18.00/26.00 **st.** 7.95 – 11.95 – **282 rm** 119.00/129.00 **st.**, 2 suites – SB.

**Kenilworth,** 97 Great Russell St., WC1B 3LB, (0171) 637 3477, *Fax (0171) 631 3133* – rm, rest, – 65. VISA. LU a
Meals 16.95 **st.** and a la carte 7.50 – 11.00 – **187 rm** 123.00/166.00 **s.**

**Blooms** without rest., 7 Montague St., WC1B 5BP, (0171) 323 1717, *Fax (0171) 636 6498* – . VISA JCB. LU n
**27 rm** 110.00/165.00 **st.**

**Bonnington in Bloomsbury,** 92 Southampton Row, WC1B 4BH, (0171) 242 2828, *Fax (0171) 831 9170* – rm, rest, – 250. VISA JCB LU s
Meals *(closed lunch Saturday and Sunday)* 11.50/19.75 **st.** and a la carte 8.20 – **215 rm** 105.00/133.00 **t.**

**Bloomsbury Park,** 126 Southampton Row, WC1B 5AD, ☏ (0171) 430 0434, *Fax (0171) 242 0665* – ⦚, ⇆ rm, TV ☎ – 🏛 25. MC AE ⓓ VISA JCB. ✂ LU u
**Meals** 14.95 **t.** (dinner) and a la carte 13.85/17.95 **t.** 🍷 4.90 – ☕ 10.95 – **95 rm** 101.00/145.00 **st.**

**Pied à Terre,** 34 Charlotte St., W1P 1HJ, ☏ (0171) 636 1178, *Fax (0171) 916 1171* – ▤. MC AE ⓓ VISA JCB KU e
*closed Saturday lunch, Sunday, last 2 weeks August, 2 weeks Christmas and Bank Holidays* – **Meals** 23.00/29.50 **t.** and a la carte 39.50/49.50 **t.** 🍷 10.50
**Spec.** Ballottine of duck confit with foie gras and sauté potato salad. Seared scallops with gazpacho, confit tomatoes and ratatouille. Steamed pigeon breast, fondant potato and choucroute.

**Neal Street,** 26 Neal St., WC2H 9PS, ☏ (0171) 836 8368, *Fax (0171) 497 1361* – MC AE ⓓ VISA JCB p. 17 DV s
*closed Sunday, 1 week Christmas and Bank Holidays* – **Meals** a la carte 26.00/39.00 **t.** 🍷 9.00.

**Malabar Junction,** 107 Great Russell St., WC1B 3NA, ☏ (0171) 580 5230 – ▤. MC AE VISA LU x
*closed 25 and 26 December* – **Meals** - South Indian - 8.50/9.50 **st.** and a la carte.

**Mon Plaisir,** 21 Monmouth St., WC2H 9DD, ☏ (0171) 836 7243, *Fax (0171) 379 0121* – MC AE ⓓ VISA JCB p. 17 DV a
*closed Saturday lunch, Sunday, 1 week Christmas-New Year, Easter and Bank Holidays* – **Meals** - French - 14.95/19.95 **st.** and a la carte 🍷 5.95.

**Bleeding Heart,** Bleeding Heart Yard, EC1N 8SJ, off Greville St., Hatton Garden ☏ (0171) 242 2056, *Fax (0171) 831 1402*, ☂ – MC AE ⓓ VISA NU e
*closed Saturday, Sunday, 10 days Christmas-New Year and Bank Holidays* – **Meals** a la carte 17.85/26.40 **t.** 🍷 4.25.

**Alfred,** 245 Shaftesbury Av., WC2H 8EH, ☏ (0171) 240 2566, *Fax (0171) 497 0672*, ☂ – ▤. MC AE ⓓ VISA p. 17 DV u
*closed Saturday lunch, Sunday, Christmas and Bank Holidays* – **Meals** - English - 12.95/15.95 **t.** and a la carte 🍷 6.95.

**Museum Street Cafe,** 47 Museum St., WC1A 1LY, ☏ (0171) 405 3211, *Fax (0171) 405 3211* – ⇆. MC AE VISA LU e
*closed Monday dinner, Saturday, Sunday, 1 week spring, 2 weeks summer and 1 week Christmas* – **Meals** 17.50/23.50 **t.** and a la carte.

## Euston – ✉ *WC1.*

**Euston Plaza,** 17/18 Upper Woburn Pl., WC1H 0HT, ☏ (0171) 383 4105, *Fax (0171) 383 4106*, Lō, ≘s – ⦚, ⇆ rm, ▤ TV ☎ ♿ – 🏛 150. MC AE ⓓ VISA JCB. ✂ KLT e
***Three Crowns :*** **Meals** 18.95 **t.** and dinner a la carte 🍷 6.50 – ***Terrace :*** **Meals** *(closed Saturday and Sunday)* 13.00 **t.** (dinner) and a la carte 11.00/17.95 **t.** 🍷 6.50 – ☕ 12.00 – **150 rm** 141.00/190.00 **st.** – SB.

## Hampstead – ✉ *NW3.*

*Winnington Rd, Hampstead* ☏ *455 0203.*

**Swiss Cottage** without rest., 4 Adamson Rd, NW3 3HP, ☏ (0171) 722 2281, *Fax (0171) 483 4588*, « Antique furniture » – ⦚ TV ☎ – 🏛 50. MC AE ⓓ VISA. ✂ GS n
**58 rm** ☕ 75.00/140.00 **st.**, 5 suites.

**Forte Posthouse Hampstead,** 215 Haverstock Hill, NW3 4RB, ☏ (0171) 794 8121, *Fax (0171) 435 5586* – ⦚, ⇆ rm, ▤ rest, TV ☎ Ⓟ – 🏛 30. MC AE ⓓ VISA JCB ES r
**Meals** (bar lunch Monday to Saturday)/dinner a la carte 14.55/25.65 **t.** 🍷 7.25 – ☕ 10.95 – **140 rm** 99.00 **st.** – SB.

**Byron's,** 3a Downshire Hill, NW3 1NR, ☏ (0171) 435 3544, *Fax (0171) 431 3544* – MC AE VISA ES v
*closed 25 and 26 December* – **Meals** a la carte 19.75/36.95 **t.** 🍷 7.50.

**Benihana,** 100 Avenue Rd, NW3 3HF, ☏ (0171) 586 9508, *Fax (0171) 586 6740* – ▤. MC AE ⓓ VISA JCB GS o
*closed 25 December* – **Meals** - Japanese (Teppan-Yaki) - 10.00/14.00 **st.** and a la carte.

**ZeNW3,** 83-84 Hampstead High St., NW3 1RE, ☏ (0171) 794 7863, *Fax (0171) 794 6956* – ▤. MC AE ⓓ VISA JCB ES a
*closed Christmas* – **Meals** - Chinese - 12.50/27.00 **t.** and a la carte.

Vegetarian Cottage, 91 Haverstock Hill, NW3 4RL, ☏ (0171) 586 1257 – ▤ HS c
**Meals** - Chinese Vegetarian rest.

**Holborn** - ✉ *WC2.*

**Drury Lane Moat House,** 10 Drury Lane, High Holborn, WC2B 5RE, ✆ (0171) 208 9988, *Fax (0171) 831 1548,* - rm, - 60. AE VISA JCB p. 17 DV c
Meals 15.50/16.75 **t.** and a la carte 6.95 - 10.75 - **163 rm** 145.00/175.00 **st.** - SB.

**Regent's Park** - ✉ *NW1.*

**White House,** Albany St., NW1 3UP, ✆ (0171) 387 1200, *Fax (0171) 388 0091,* - rm, rest, - 110. AE VISA JCB. JT o
***The Restaurant :*** Meals a la carte 25.75/68.95 **t.** 7.25 - ***Garden Cafe :*** Meals *(closed Sunday)* a la carte 16.10/28.20 **t.** 7.25 - 12.95 - **582 rm** 145.00/152.00 **st.**, 2 suites.

**Odette's,** 130 Regent's Park Rd, NW1 8XL, ✆ (0171) 586 5486, *Fax (0171) 586 2575* - AE VISA HS i
*closed Saturday lunch, Sunday, 10 days Christmas and Bank Holidays* - **Meals** 10.00 **t.** (lunch) and a la carte 23.75/28.25 **t.** 5.50.

**Swiss Cottage** - ✉ *NW3.*

**Regents Park Marriott,** 128 King Henry's Rd, NW3 3ST, ✆ (0171) 722 7711, *Fax (0171) 586 5822,* - rm, - 400. AE VISA JCB. GS a
Meals 18.95 **t.** and a la carte - 12.95 - **298 rm** 180.00/190.00 **s.**, 5 suites - SB.

**Peter's Chateaubriand,** 65 Fairfax Rd, NW6 4EE, ✆ (0171) 624 5804 - . AE VISA JCB FS i
*closed Saturday lunch, 26 December and 1 January* - **Meals** 14.95 **t.** and a la carte.

**Bradley's,** 25 Winchester Rd, NW3 3NR, ✆ (0171) 722 3457 - . AE VISA GS e
*closed Saturday lunch, 1 week Christmas and Bank Holidays* - **Meals** 15.00 **t.** (lunch) and a la carte 21.90/26.90 **t.** 10.00.

---

**CITY OF LONDON** *Except where otherwise stated* *see p. 7.*

**Tatsuso,** 32 Broadgate Circle, EC2M 2QS, ✆ (0171) 638 5863, *Fax (0171) 638 5864* - . AE VISA JCB PU u
*closed Saturday, Sunday, late December and Bank Holidays* - **Meals** - Japanese - (booking essential) 50.00 **t.** and a la carte.

**Gladwins,** Minister Court, Mark Lane, EC3R 7AA, ✆ (0171) 444 0004, *Fax (0171) 444 0001* - . AE VISA PV e
*closed Saturday, Sunday and Bank Holidays* - **Meals** (lunch only) 32.50 **t.**

**City Rhodes,** 1 New Street Sq., EC4A 3BF, ✆ (0171) 583 1313, *Fax (0171) 353 1662* - . AE VISA NU u
*closed Saturday, Sunday and Bank Holidays* - **Meals** a la carte 22.55/34.30 **t.** 13.95
**Spec.** Escalope of salmon, black treacle, juniper and sherry dressing. Steak and "kidney pie". "Jaffa Cake" pudding.

**Brasserie Rocque,** 37 Broadgate Circle, EC2M 2QS, ✆ (0171) 638 7919, *Fax (0171) 628 5899,* - . AE VISA PU u
*closed Saturday, Sunday and Bank Holidays* - **Meals** (lunch only) 27.50 **t.** and a la carte 5.00.

**Le Quai,** Riverside Walkway, 1 Broken Wharf, High Timber St., EC4V 3QQ, ✆ (0171) 236 6480, *Fax (0171) 236 6479* - . AE VISA JCB OV a
*closed Saturday, Sunday, 2 weeks Christmas and Bank Holidays* - **Meals** - French - (dinner booking essential) 32.50 **t.**

**Miyama,** 17 Godliman St., EC4V 5BD, ✆ (0171) 489 1937, *Fax (0171) 236 0325* - . AE VISA JCB OV e
*closed Saturday dinner, Sunday and Christmas-New Year* - **Meals** - Japanese - 40.00 **t.** and a la carte 7.50.

**Imperial City,** Royal Exchange, Cornhill, EC3V 3LL, ✆ (0171) 626 3437, *Fax (0171) 338 0125* - . AE VISA PV a
*closed Saturday, Sunday, 25 December and Bank Holidays* - **Meals** - Chinese - 19.95/24.95 **t.** and a la carte.

**Sri Siam City,** 85 London Wall, EC2M 7AD, ✆ (0171) 628 5772, *Fax (0171) 628 3395* - . AE VISA PU a
*closed Saturday, Sunday and Bank Holidays* - **Meals** - Thai - 15.50/24.95 **t.** and a la carte 8.00.

## HAMMERSMITH AND FULHAM *p. 8.*

### Fulham – ✉ *SW6.*

**La Reserve,** 422-428 Fulham Rd, SW6 1DU, ✆ (0171) 385 8561, *Fax (0171) 385 7662* – |♦|, ⇔ rm, TV ☎. MC AE ◑ VISA JCB. ✗ FZ a
*closed 25 and 26 December* – **Meals** a la carte 14.00/21.20 **t.** 5.95 – ☕ 3.50 – **41 rm** 79.00/110.00 **st.** – SB.

**Travel Inn Capital,** 3 Putney Bridge Approach, SW6 3JD, ✆ (0171) 471 8300, *Fax (0171) 471 8315* – |♦|, ⇔ rm, TV ♿. MC AE ◑ VISA
**Meals** (grill rest.) – **154 rm** 49.50 **t.**

**Blue Elephant,** 4-6 Fulham Broadway, SW6 1AA, ✆ (0171) 385 6595, *Fax (0171) 386 7665* – ▤. MC AE ◑ VISA EZ z
*closed Saturday lunch and 24 to 27 December* – **Meals** - Thai - (booking essential) 28.00/34.00 **st.** and a la carte.

**755,** 755 Fulham Rd, SW6 5UU, ✆ (0171) 371 0755, *Fax (0171) 371 0695* – ▤. MC AE VISA
*closed Monday lunch, Sunday dinner, 2 weeks in summer, 1 week Christmas and Bank Holidays* – **Meals** 14.00/22.00 **t.** and a la carte 6.95.

**Mao Tai,** 58 New Kings Rd., Parsons Green, SW6 4UG, ✆ (0171) 731 2520 – ▤. MC AE ◑ VISA
*closed 24 to 26 December* – **Meals** - Chinese (Szechuan) - 19.50 **t.** and a la carte.

### Hammersmith – ✉ *W6/W12/W14.*

**River Café** (Ruth Rogers/Rose Gray), Thames Wharf, Rainville Rd, W6 9HA, ✆ (0171) 381 8824, *Fax (0171) 381 6217*, ⛱ – MC AE VISA
*closed Sunday dinner, 1 week Christmas and Bank Holidays* – **Meals** - Italian - (booking essential) a la carte 33.50/40.00
**Spec.** Crab risotto with tomato, lemon and basil. Roast loin of organic pork with salsa verde. Almond tart.

**Tandoori Nights,** 319-321 King St., W6 9NH, ✆ (0181) 741 4328, *Fax (0181) 741 4328* – ▤. MC AE ◑ VISA JCB
*closed 25 and 26 December* – **Meals** - Indian - a la carte 10.30/20.00 **t.** 6.50.

**Snows on the Green,** 166 Shepherd's Bush Rd, Brook Green, W6 7PB, ✆ (0171) 603 2142, *Fax (0171) 602 7553* – MC AE ◑ VISA
*closed Saturday lunch, Sunday dinner, 1 week Christmas and Bank Holiday Mondays* – **Meals** 15.50 **st.** (lunch) and a la carte 19.00/23.00 **st.**

**The Brackenbury,** 129-131 Brackenbury Rd, W6 0BQ, ✆ (0181) 748 0107, *Fax (0181) 741 0905*, ⛱ – MC AE VISA JCB
*closed Saturday lunch, Sunday dinner and Christmas* – **Meals** a la carte 18.00/20.00 **t.** 9.50.

### Shepherd's Bush – ✉ *W14.*

**Chinon,** 23 Richmond Way, W14 0AS, ✆ (0171) 602 5968, *Fax (0171) 602 4082* – ▤. MC AE VISA
*closed Sunday and 24 to 29 December* – **Meals** (dinner only) 17.50 **t.** and a la carte 7.50.

## ISLINGTON *p. 7.*

### Clerkenwell – ✉ *EC1.*

**Maison Novelli,** 29 Clerkenwell Green, EC1R 0DU, ✆ (0171) 251 6606, *Fax (0171) 490 1083* – MC AE ◑ VISA JCB NU a
*closed Saturday lunch, Sunday, New Year and Bank Holidays* – **Meals** a la carte 25.00/40.00 **t.** 12.60.

**Novelli EC1,** 30 Clerkenwell Green, EC1R 0DU, ✆ (0171) 251 6606 – MC AE ◑ VISA JCB NU a
**Meals** *(closed Saturday lunch, Sunday and Bank Holidays)* a la carte 14.30/22.30 **t.** 10.50.

### Islington – ✉ *N1.*

**Stakis London Islington,** Upper St., N1 0UY, ✆ (0171) 354 7700, *Fax (0171) 354 7711* – ⇔ rm, ▤ TV ☎ ♿ – 🏛 35. MC AE ◑ VISA. ✗ NS s
**Meals** a la carte 19.95/30.45 **t.** 7.00 – ☕ 11.50 – **183 rm** 135.00/210.00 **st.** – SB.

**Frederick's,** Camden Passage, N1 8EG, ✆ (0171) 359 2888, *Fax (0171) 359 5173*, ⛱, 🌳 – ▤. MC AE ◑ VISA NS c
*closed Sunday, 1 week Christmas-New Year and Bank Holidays* – **Meals** a la carte 24.00/30.00 **st.** 7.50.

**Lola's,** 359 Upper St., N1 0PD, ✆ (0171) 359 1932, *Fax (0171) 359 2209* – MC AE ◑ VISA JCB NS n
*closed Sunday dinner* – **Meals** 16.50 **t.** (lunch) and a la carte 19.25/26.50 **t.** 7.75.

## KENSINGTON and CHELSEA *(Royal Borough of).*

**Chelsea** – ✉ *SW1/SW3/SW10 – Except where otherwise stated see pp. 14 and 15.*

**Hyatt Carlton Tower,** 2 Cadogan Pl., SW1X 9PY, ✆ (0171) 235 1234, *Fax (0171) 235 9129,* ≤, , , , , – , rm, ▤ TV ☎ – 250. AE VISA JCB. FR n
***Rib Room*** *(✆ (0171) 824 7053)* **: Meals** 26.50/32.50 **t.** and a la carte 15.00 – (see also ***Grissini*** below) – 16.50 – **191 rm** 265.00/320.00, 29 suites.

**Conrad International London,** Chelsea Harbour, SW10 0XG, ✆ (0171) 823 3000, *Fax (0171) 351 6525,* ≤, , , – , rm, ▤ TV ☎ – 180. AE VISA JCB
***The Brasserie* : Meals** 22.50 (dinner) and a la carte 19.50/34.00 16.00 – 17.00, **159 suites** 250.00/280.00.

**Sheraton Park Tower,** 101 Knightsbridge, SW1X 7RN, ✆ (0171) 235 8050, *Fax (0171) 235 8231,* ≤ – , rm, ▤ TV ☎ – 60. AE VISA JCB. FQ v
***101 Knightsbridge*** *(✆ (0171) 235 6067)* **: Meals** 23.50/34.00 **t.** and a la carte 15.50 – 17.00 – **267 rm** 262.00/378.00 **s.**, 22 suites – SB.

**Capital,** 22-24 Basil St., SW3 1AT, ✆ (0171) 589 5171, *Fax (0171) 225 0011* – ▤ TV ☎ – 25. AE VISA. ER a
**Meals** (booking essential) 28.00/55.00 **t.** and a la carte 50.50/55.50 **t.** 9.00 – 17.50 – **48 rm** 167.00/310.00 **s.**
**Spec.** Asparagus tuile with a sauternes, truffle and lime sabayon. Braised duckling in orange, fennel, cinnamon and honey with flat beans. Assiette of vanilla.

**Durley House,** 115 Sloane St., SW1X 9PJ, ✆ (0171) 235 5537, *Fax (0171) 259 6977,* « Georgian town house », , – TV ☎. AE VISA. FS e
**Meals** (room service only) a la carte 18.00/25.50 **t.** 9.95 – 14.50, **11 suites** 220.00/395.00 **s.**

**Cadogan,** 75 Sloane St., SW1X 9SG, ✆ (0171) 235 7141, *Fax (0171) 245 0994,* , – , rm, ▤ rest, TV ☎ – 40. AE VISA. FR e
**Meals** *(closed Saturday lunch)* 17.90/25.50 **t.** and a la carte 6.75 – 14.50 – **61 rm** 140.00/215.00 **st.**, 4 suites – SB.

**Cliveden Town House,** 24-26 Cadogan Gdns., SW3 2RP, ✆ (0171) 730 6466, *Fax (0171) 730 0236,* – , ▤ rm, TV ☎. AE VISA FS c
**Meals** (room service only) – 17.50 – **31 rm** 120.00/250.00 **s.**, 4 suites.

**Franklin,** 28 Egerton Gdns., SW3 2DB, ✆ (0171) 584 5533, *Fax (0171) 584 5449,* « Tastefully furnished Victorian town house », – ▤ TV ☎. AE VISA. DS e
**Meals** (room service only) a la carte 20.00/28.00 **st.** 8.00 – 14.00 – **46 rm** 140.00/275.00 **s.**, 1 suite.

**Basil Street,** 8 Basil St., SW3 1AH, ✆ (0171) 581 3311, *Fax (0171) 581 3693* – TV ☎ – 55. AE VISA JCB. FQ o
**Meals** (carving lunch Saturday) 11.00/19.50 **t.** and a la carte 7.50 – 13.50 – **93 rm** 115.00/170.00 **s.**

**Chelsea,** 17-25 Sloane St., SW1X 9NU, ✆ (0171) 235 4377, *Fax (0171) 235 3705* – , rm, ▤ TV ☎ – 100. AE VISA JCB. FR r
***The Restaurant* : Meals** *(closed Sunday dinner)* 19.50 **t.** (lunch) and a la carte 19.50/32.00 **t.** – 13.75 – **219 rm** 180.00/230.00 **s.**, 5 suites.

**Sydney House,** 9-11 Sydney St., SW3 6PU, ✆ (0171) 376 7711, *Fax (0171) 376 4233,* « Tastefully furnished Victorian town house » – TV ☎. AE VISA DT a
**Meals** (room service only) – 14.10 – **21 rm** 150.00/200.00 **s.**

**Egerton House,** 17-19 Egerton Terr., SW3 2BX, ✆ (0171) 589 2412, *Fax (0171) 584 6540,* « Tastefully furnished Victorian town house » – ▤ TV ☎. AE VISA. DR e
**Meals** (room service only) a la carte 17.50/29.00 **t.** 10.00 – 14.00 – **29 rm** 140.00/210.00.

**Sloane,** 29 Draycott Pl., SW3 2SH, ✆ (0171) 581 5757, *Fax (0171) 584 1348,* « Victorian town house, antiques » – ▤ TV ☎. AE VISA JCB. ET c
**Meals** (room service only) – 12.00 – **12 rm** 130.00/225.00 **s.**

**Eleven Cadogan Gardens,** 11 Cadogan Gdns., SW3 2RJ, ✆ (0171) 730 7000, *Fax (0171) 730 5217,* – TV ☎. AE VISA JCB. FS u
**Meals** (room service only) a la carte 15.00/20.00 7.05 – 11.75 – **55 rm** 138.65/220.90 **t.**, 5 suites.

**The London Outpost of the Carnegie Club** without rest., 69 Cadogan Gdns., SW3 2RB, ✆ (0171) 589 7333, *Fax (0171) 581 4958,* – ▤ TV ☎. AE VISA. FS r
14.75 – **11 rm** 150.00/235.00.

**Beaufort** without rest., 33 Beaufort Gdns., SW3 1PP, (0171) 584 5252, *Fax (0171) 589 2834*, « English floral watercolour collection » – . ER n
**28 rm** 130.00/240.00 **s.**

**Parkes** without rest., 41 Beaufort Gdns., SW3 1PW, (0171) 581 9944, *Fax (0171) 581 1999* – . ER x
**18 rm** 115.00/180.00 **s.**, 15 suites 210.00/265.00 **s.**

**Claverley** without rest., 13-14 Beaufort Gdns., SW3 1PS, (0171) 589 8541, *Fax (0171) 584 3410* – . ER o
**29 rm** 60.00/215.00 **t.**

**Knightsbridge,** 12 Beaufort Gdns., SW3 1PT, (0171) 589 9271, *Fax (0171) 823 9692*, – . ER o
**Meals** (room service only) – **44 rm** 90.00/135.00 **st.**, 6 suites.

**L'Hotel,** 28 Basil St., SW3 1AT, (0171) 589 6286, *Fax (0171) 225 0011* – . ER i
***Le Metro* : Meals** 15.00 **t.** and a la carte – **12 rm** 144.50/169.00 **s.**

**La Tante Claire** (Koffmann), 68-69 Royal Hospital Rd, SW3 4HP, (0171) 352 6045, *Fax (0171) 352 3257* – . EU c
*closed Saturday, Sunday, 10 days Easter, 3 weeks August, 10 days Christmas and Bank Holidays* – **Meals** - French - (booking essential) 28.00 **st.** (lunch) and a la carte 54.00/64.00 **st.** 14.00
**Spec.** Coquilles St. Jacques à la planche, sauce encre. Pied de cochon aux morilles, pomme purée. Croustade de pommes à la fleur d'oranger.

**Aubergine** (Ramsay), 11 Park Walk, SW10 0AJ, (0171) 352 3449, *Fax (0171) 351 1770* – . CU r
*closed Saturday lunch, Sunday, 2 weeks August, 2 weeks Christmas and Bank Holidays* – **Meals** (booking essential) 24.00/45.00-55.00 **t.** 15.00
**Spec.** Tartare of scallops with crème fraîche and caviar in a basil consommé. Braised turbot with a herb and lettuce tortellini and a sea urchin sauce. Tart Tatin of pineapple caramelised with vanilla.

**The Canteen,** Harbour Yard, Chelsea Harbour, SW10 0XD, (0171) 351 7330, *Fax (0171) 351 6189* – .
*closed Saturday lunch, Sunday dinner and Bank Holidays* – **Meals** 19.50 **t.** (lunch) and a la carte 24.95/27.40 **t.** 7.50
**Spec.** Warm salad of sea scallops, apple and cashew nuts. Seared Cajun tuna with a salad of couscous, peppers and olives. Crêpe Suzette soufflé.

**Bibendum,** Michelin House, 81 Fulham Rd, SW3 6RD, (0171) 581 5817, *Fax (0171) 823 7925* – . DS s
*closed 25-26 December and 1 January* – **Meals** 28.00 **t.** (lunch) and dinner a la carte 39.00/50.00 **t.**

**Fifth Floor** (at Harvey Nichols), Knightsbridge, SW1X 7RJ, (0171) 235 5250, *Fax (0171) 823 2207* – . FQ a
*closed dinner Sunday and Bank Holidays and 25 December* – **Meals** 22.50 **t.** (lunch) and dinner a la carte 24.75/41.50 **t.** 7.50.

**La Belle Epoque,** 151 Draycott Av., SW3 3AL, (0171) 460 5000, *Fax (0171) 460 5001* – . ES c
*closed 25 and 26 December* – ***La Salle* : Meals** a la carte 21.25/34.00 **st.** 9.00 – (see also ***L'Oriental*** below).
**La Brasserie** (*(0171) 460 5105*) **: Meals** *(closed 25 and 26 December)* a la carte 17.00/24.50 **st.**

**L'Oriental** (at La Belle Epoque), 151 Draycott Av., SW3 3AL, (0171) 460 5010, *Fax (0171) 460 5001* – . ES c
*closed Sunday and 25-26 December* – **Meals** - Eastern specialities - (dinner only) a la carte 32.00/45.50 **st.**

**Grissini** (at Hyatt Carlton Tower H.), Cadogan Pl., SW1X 9PY, (0171) 858 7171, *Fax (0171) 235 9129* – . FR n
*closed Saturday lunch* – **Meals** - Italian - 19.00 **t.** (lunch) and a la carte 22.00/39.00 **t.** 9.00.

**Albero & Grana,** Chelsea Cloisters, 89 Sloane Av., SW3 3DX, (0171) 225 1048, *Fax (0171) 581 3259* – . ET e
**Meals** - Spanish - (dinner only and Saturday lunch) a la carte approx. 40.00 **t.**

**Turner's,** 87-89 Walton St., SW3 2HP, (0171) 584 6711, *Fax (0171) 584 4441* – . ES n
*closed Saturday lunch and Bank Holidays* – **Meals** 15.00/29.50 **t.** and a la carte 9.50.

XXX **Chutney Mary,** 535 King's Rd, SW10 0SZ, (0171) 351 3113, *Fax (0171) 351 7694* – ▤. MC AE Ⓓ VISA JCB p. 8 FZ v
*closed 25 December dinner and 26 December* – **Meals** - Anglo-Indian - 14.50 **t.** (lunch) and dinner a la carte 23.90/28.05 **t.** 8.75.

XX **Chavot** (Chavot), 257-259 Fulham Rd, SW3 6HY, (0171) 351 7823, *Fax (0171) 376 4971* – MC AE VISA CU a
✿ *closed Saturday lunch and Sunday* – **Meals** - French - 22.50 **t.** (lunch) and a la carte 32.00/40.50 **t.**
**Spec.** Roasted scallops with mustard oil and horseradish potatoes. Venison cutlet with braised cabbage. Citrus terrine with chocolate samosa.

XX **Bluebird,** 350 King's Rd, SW3 5UU, (0171) 559 1000, *Fax (0171) 559 1111* – ▤. MC AE Ⓓ VISA CU e
*closed 25-26 December and lunch 1 January* – **Meals** 15.75 **t.** (lunch) and a la carte 17.00/44.50 **t.**

XX **English Garden,** 10 Lincoln St., SW3 2TS, (0171) 584 7272, *Fax (0171) 581 2848* – ▤. MC AE Ⓓ VISA JCB ET x
**Meals** - English - 16.50 **t.** (lunch) and a la carte 27.00/30.75 **t.** 5.50.

XX **Benihana,** 77 King's Rd, SW3 4NX, (0171) 376 7799, *Fax (0171) 376 7377* – ▤. MC AE Ⓓ VISA JCB EU e
**Meals** - Japanese (Teppan-Yaki) - 10.00/14.00 and a la carte.

XX **La Ciboulette,** 138a King's Rd, SW3 4XB, (0171) 823 7444, *Fax (0171) 823 7457* – ▤. MC AE VISA JCB ET a
*closed Sunday dinner and Bank Holidays* – **Meals** - French - 13.50/18.50 **t.** and a la carte 8.75.

XX **Brasserie St. Quentin,** 243 Brompton Rd, SW3 2EP, (0171) 589 8005, *Fax (0171) 584 6064* – ▤. MC AE Ⓓ VISA JCB DR a
**Meals** - French - a la carte 22.80/38.40 **t.** 6.90.

XX **Poissonnerie de l'Avenue,** 82 Sloane Av., SW3 3DZ, (0171) 589 2457, *Fax (0171) 581 3360* – ▤. MC AE Ⓓ VISA JCB DS u
*closed Sunday, 25-26 December and Bank Holidays* – **Meals** - French Seafood - 18.50 **t.** (lunch) and a la carte 26.00/34.50 **t.** 6.50.

XX **Daphne's,** 112 Draycott Av., SW3 3AE, (0171) 589 4257, *Fax (0171) 581 2232* – ▤. MC AE Ⓓ VISA DS a
*closed 1 week Christmas* – **Meals** - Italian - a la carte 24.50/30.00 8.50.

XX **Vama,** 438 King's Rd, SW10 0LJ, (0171) 351 4118, *Fax (0171) 565 8501* – MC AE Ⓓ VISA p. 9 GZ e
**Meals** - Indian - 9.95 **t.** (lunch) and a la carte 20.50/24.75 **t.** 4.75.

XX **The Collection,** 264 Brompton Rd, SW3 2AS, (0171) 225 1212, *Fax (0171) 225 1050* – ▤. MC AE Ⓓ VISA DS v
*closed Sunday, 25 December and 1 January* – **Meals** a la carte 18.00/31.50 **t.**

XX **Caraffini,** 61-63 Lower Sloane St., SW1W 8DH, (0171) 259 0235 – ▤. MC AE VISA FT a
*closed Sunday and Bank Holidays* – **Meals** - Italian - a la carte 19.40/27.40 **t.** 7.75.

XX **Osteria Le Fate,** 5 Draycott Av., SW3, (0171) 591 0071 – MC VISA ET r
*closed Sunday* – **Meals** - Italian - 18.00/28.00 **st.** and a la carte.

XX **Grill St. Quentin,** 3 Yeoman's Row, SW3 2AL, (0171) 581 8377, *Fax (0171) 584 6064* – ▤. MC AE Ⓓ VISA JCB ER r
**Meals** - French - a la carte 19.00/25.90 **t.** 6.90.

XX **Busabong Too,** 1a Langton St., SW10 0JL, (0171) 352 7414, *Fax (0171) 352 7414* – ▤. MC AE Ⓓ VISA JCB p. 8 FZ x
*closed 24 and 25 December* – **Meals** - Thai - (dinner only) 22.25 **t.** and a la carte.

XX **Toto's,** Walton House, Walton St., SW3 2JH, (0171) 589 0075, *Fax (0171) 581 9668* – ▤. MC AE Ⓓ VISA JCB ES a
*closed 25 to 27 December* – **Meals** - Italian - 19.50/30.00 **st.** and a la carte 7.00.

XX **Red of Knightsbridge,** 8 Egerton Garden Mews, SW3 2EH, (0171) 584 7007 – **Meals** - Chinese - 10.00/15.00 **t.** and a la carte. DR n

XX **Good Earth,** 233 Brompton Rd, SW3 2EP, (0171) 584 3658, *Fax (0171) 823 8769* – ▤. MC AE Ⓓ VISA JCB DR c
*closed 24 to 27 December* – **Meals** - Chinese - 10.95/18.50 **t.** and a la carte 8.00.

XX **Dan's,** 119 Sydney St., SW3 6NR, (0171) 352 2718, *Fax (0171) 352 3265* – MC AE VISA JCB DU s
*closed Sunday dinner and 24 December-2 January* – **Meals** a la carte 23.25/29.25 **t.**

XX **Beit Eddine,** 8 Harriet St., SW1X 9JW, (0171) 235 3969, *Fax (0171) 245 6335* – MC AE Ⓓ VISA FQ z
**Meals** - Lebanese - a la carte approx. 20.00 **t.** 7.50.

**Kensington** - SW7/W8/W11/W14 - *Except where otherwise stated see* pp. 8-11.

**Royal Garden,** 2-24 Kensington High St., W8 4PT, (0171) 937 8000, *Fax (0171) 938 4532*, ←, Ls, ≘s - |‡|, ⇔ rm, ▤ TV ☎ ♿ P - 🏛 600. MC AE ⓓ VISA JCB. ✗ p. 14 AQ c
***The Tenth*** *((0171) 361 1910)* **: Meals** *(closed Saturday lunch and Sunday)* 19.50 **t.** (lunch) and a la carte 20.70/38.75 **t.** 🍷 10.50 - ***Park Terrace*** **: Meals** 18.25 (lunch) and a la carte 17.00/31.00 **t.** 🍷 10.50 - ☕ 16.50 - **385 rm** 175.00/215.00, 15 suites.

**Copthorne Tara,** Scarsdale Pl., W8 5SR, (0171) 937 7211, *Fax (0171) 937 7100* - |‡|, ⇔ rm, ▤ TV ☎ ♿ P - 🏛 500. MC AE ⓓ VISA JCB. ✗ FY u
***Brasserie*** **: Meals** 18.00 **st.** and a la carte 🍷 6.50 - ***Jerome K. Jerome*** **: Meals** *(closed Sunday)* (dinner only) a la carte 22.20/32.30 **st.** 🍷 6.50 - ☕ 13.00 - **815 rm** 170.00/210.00 **st.**, 10 suites.

**Halcyon,** 81 Holland Park, W11 3RZ, (0171) 727 7288, *Fax (0171) 229 8516* - |‡| ▤ TV ☎. MC AE ⓓ VISA. ✗ EX u
Meals - (see ***The Room*** below) - ☕ 14.00 - **40 rm** 170.00/260.00 **st.**, 3 suites.

**The Milestone,** 1-2 Kensington Court, W8 5DL, (0171) 917 1000, *Fax (0171) 917 1010*, Ls, ≘s - |‡| ▤ TV ☎. MC AE ⓓ VISA. ✗ p. 14 AQ u
**Meals** *(closed Saturday, Sunday and Bank Holidays)* 18.00/26.00 **t.** and a la carte 🍷 12.00 - ☕ 15.00 - **48 rm** 220.00/270.00 **st.**, 5 suites.

**London Kensington Hilton,** 179-199 Holland Park Av., W11 4UL, (0171) 603 3355, *Fax (0171) 602 9397* - |‡|, ⇔ rm, ▤ TV ☎ ♿ P - 🏛 300. MC AE ⓓ VISA JCB. ✗ EX s
Meals 20.00 **st.** (dinner) and a la carte 15.00/30.00 **st.** 🍷 9.50 - ***Hiroko*** **: Meals** - Japanese - 15.00/32.00 **st.** and a la carte 🍷 7.00 - ☕ 14.50 - **603 rm** 170.00/250.00 **st.** - SB.

**Kensington Park Thistle,** 16-32 De Vere Gdns., W8 5AG, (0171) 937 8080, *Fax (0171) 937 7616* - |‡|, ⇔ rm, ▤ rest, TV ☎ ♿ - 🏛 120. MC AE ⓓ VISA. ✗
***Moniques Brasserie*** **: Meals** 15.75 **t.** and a la carte 🍷 6.00 - ***Cairngorm Grill*** **: Meals** *(closed Sunday, Monday, August and Bank Holidays)* (dinner only) 21.00 **t.** and a la carte 🍷 8.50 - ☕ 13.50 - **346 rm** 139.00/200.00 **st.**, 6 suites - SB. p. 14 BQ e

Hilton National London Olympia, 380 Kensington High St., W14 8NL, (0171) 603 3333, *Fax (0171) 603 4846*, Ls, ≘s - |‡|, ⇔ rm, ▤ rest, TV ☎ P - 🏛 450
**395 rm**, 10 suites. EY a

**Forte Posthouse Kensington,** Wrights Lane, W8 5SP, (0171) 937 8170, *Fax (0171) 937 8289*, Ls, ≘s, 🏊, 🎾, *squash* - |‡|, ⇔ rm, ▤ rest, TV ☎ P - 🏛 180. MC AE ⓓ VISA JCB. ✗ FY c
Meals 16.95 **t.** and a la carte 🍷 7.50 - ☕ 11.00 - **547 rm** 129.00 **t.**

**Comfort Inn Kensington,** 22-32 West Cromwell Rd, SW5 9QJ, (0171) 373 3300, *Fax (0171) 835 2040* - |‡|, ⇔ rm, ▤ TV ☎ - 🏛 80. MC AE ⓓ VISA JCB. ✗
Meals (bar lunch)/dinner a la carte 9.00/18.00 **st.** 🍷 6.00 - ☕ 8.95 - **125 rm** 85.00/99.00 **st.** EZ n

**Holland Court** without rest., 31-33 Holland Rd, W14 8HJ, (0171) 371 1133, *Fax (0171) 602 9114*, 🌳 - |‡| TV ☎. MC AE ⓓ VISA JCB. ✗ EY e
**22 rm** ☕ 75.00/105.00.

**The Room** (at Halcyon H.), 129 Holland Park Av., W11 3UT, (0171) 221 5411, *Fax (0171) 229 8516*, 🏠 - ▤. MC AE ⓓ VISA EX u
*closed Saturday lunch, 25 to lunch 31 December and Bank Holidays* - **Meals** 26.00/37.00 **t.** and a la carte 26.00/45.00 🍷 7.00.

**Clarke's,** 124 Kensington Church St., W8 4BH, (0171) 221 9225, *Fax (0171) 229 4564* - ▤. MC AE VISA EX c
*closed Saturday, Sunday, 2 weeks August and Christmas* - **Meals** 29.00/40.00 **st.** 🍷 8.50.

**Launceston Place,** 1a Launceston Pl., W8 5RL, (0171) 937 6912, *Fax (0171) 938 2412* - ▤. MC AE VISA JCB p. 14 BR a
*closed Saturday lunch, Sunday dinner, Easter, 25 December, 1 January and Bank Holidays* - **Meals** 17.50 **t.** and a la carte 🍷 6.00.

**Belvedere in Holland Park,** Holland House, off Abbotsbury Rd, W8 6LU, (0171) 602 1238, *Fax (0171) 610 4382*, 🏠, « 19C orangery in park » - ▤. MC AE ⓓ VISA JCB EY u
*closed Sunday dinner, 25 December and 1 January* - **Meals** a la carte 17.00/26.00 **t.** 🍷 8.00.

**Arcadia,** Kensington Court, 35 Kensington High St., W8 5EB, (0171) 937 4294, *Fax (0171) 937 4393* - ▤. MC AE ⓓ VISA p. 14 AQ s
*closed Saturday lunch, 24 to 26 December and 1 January* - **Meals** 15.95 **t.** (lunch) and dinner a la carte 17.70/23.00 **t.** 🍷 6.75.

**La Pomme d'Amour,** 128 Holland Park Av., W11 4UE, (0171) 229 8532, *Fax (0171) 221 4096* - ▤. MC AE ⓓ VISA EX e
*closed Saturday lunch, Sunday and Bank Holidays* - **Meals** - French - 14.20/18.30 **t.** and a la carte 🍷 5.00.

XX **L'Escargot Doré,** 2-4 Thackeray St., W8 5ET, (0171) 937 8508, *Fax (0171) 937 8508* – . MC AE VISA JCB p. 14 AQR e
*closed Saturday lunch, Sunday last 2 weeks August, 1 week Christmas and Bank Holidays* – **Meals** 16.00 **t.** and a la carte 5.80.

XX **Osteria del Parco,** 148 Holland Park Av., W11 4UE, (0171) 221 6090, *Fax (0171) 221 4096* – . MC AE VISA EX v
*closed 25 December* – **Meals** - Italian - a la carte 13.50/19.70 **t.** 4.50.

XX **Ken Lo's Memories of China,** 353 Kensington High St., W8 6NW, (0171) 603 6951, *Fax (0171) 603 0848* – . MC AE VISA JCB EY v
*closed Sunday lunch, 24 December-2 January and Bank Holidays* – **Meals** - Chinese - (booking essential) 17.50/25.50 **t.** and a la carte 11.00.

XX **Phoenicia,** 11-13 Abingdon Rd, W8 6AH, (0171) 937 0120, *Fax (0171) 937 7668* – . MC AE VISA JCB EY n
*closed 25 and 26 December* – **Meals** - Lebanese - (buffet lunch) a la carte 15.00/22.85 **t.** 5.80.

X **Kensington Place,** 201 Kensington Church St., W8 7LX, (0171) 727 3184, *Fax (0171) 229 2025* – . MC AE VISA JCB p. 16 AZ z
*closed 25-26 December and 1 January* – **Meals** (booking essential) 14.50 **t.** (lunch) and a la carte 21.00/36.00 **t.** 5.75.

X **Novelli W8,** 122 Palace Gardens Terr., W8 4RT, (0171) 229 4024, *Fax (0171) 243 1826*, – MC AE VISA JCB p. 16 AZ r
*closed Sunday, Christmas and New Year* – **Meals** (booking essential) 14.50 **t.** (lunch) and a la carte 20.20/29.70 **t.** 11.00.

X **Cibo,** 3 Russell Gdns., W14 8EZ, (0171) 371 6271, *Fax (0171) 602 1371* – MC AE VISA JCB EY o
*closed Saturday lunch, Sunday dinner and 23 to 29 December* – **Meals** - Italian - 16.75 **t.** (lunch) and a la carte 19.95/33.75 **t.**

X **Malabar,** 27 Uxbridge St., W8 7TQ, (0171) 727 8800 – MC VISA p. 16 AZ e
*closed last week August and 4 days Christmas* – **Meals** - Indian - (booking essential) (buffet lunch Sunday) 15.75 **st.** and a la carte 14.95/28.30 **st.** 4.75.

## North Kensington – W2/W10/W11 – *Except where otherwise stated see pp. 4-7.*

**Pembridge Court,** 34 Pembridge Gdns., W2 4DX, (0171) 229 9977, *Fax (0171) 727 4982*, « Collection of antique clothing » – , rest, TV . MC AE VISA
**Meals** (residents only) (restricted menu) (dinner only) a la carte approx. 19.00 **st.** 4.95 – **20 rm** 110.00/175.00 **st.** p. 16 AZ n

**Abbey Court** without rest., 20 Pembridge Gdns., W2 4DU, (0171) 221 7518, *Fax (0171) 792 0858*, « Tastefully furnished Victorian town house » – TV . MC AE VISA JCB. p. 16 AZ u
**22 rm** 88.00/145.00 **t.**

XXX **Leith's,** 92 Kensington Park Rd, W11 2PN, (0171) 229 4481, *Fax (0171) 221 1246* – . MC AE VISA JCB EV e
*closed lunch Saturday and Monday, Sunday, 2 weeks August, 2 weeks Christmas-New Year and Bank Holidays except Good Friday* – **Meals** 19.50/35.00 **t.** and dinner a la carte 33.00/43.75 **t.** 8.25
**Spec.** Roast scallops with spiced lemon couscous, artichokes and a light curry butter. Wild salmon with oxtail consommé, lentil and mushroom dumplings. Braised squab pigeon with pancetta and greens, celeriac fondant.

XX **Chez Moi,** 1 Addison Av., Holland Park, W11 4QS, (0171) 603 8267, *Fax (0171) 603 3898* – . MC AE VISA p. 8 EX n
*closed Saturday lunch, Sunday and Bank Holidays* – **Meals** - French - 15.00 **t.** (lunch) and a la carte 22.25/31.75 **t.** 5.50.

XX **Orsino,** 119 Portland Rd, W11 4LN, (0171) 221 3299, *Fax (0171) 229 9414* – . MC AE VISA p. 8 EX x
*closed 24 and 25 December* – **Meals** - Italian - (booking essential) 15.50 **t.** (lunch) and a la carte 17.00/28.00 **t.** 5.50.

X **Woz,** 46 Golborne Rd, W10 5PR, (0181) 968 2200, *Fax (0181) 968 0550* – MC AE VISA JCB EU n
*closed Monday lunch, Sunday dinner, 1 week April, 2 weeks August and 1 week Christmas* – **Meals** 12.95/22.95 **t.** and lunch a la carte 14.45/20.20 **t.**

X **Sugar Club,** 33a All Saints Rd, W11 1HE, (0171) 221 3844, *Fax (0171) 229 2759*, – . MC AE VISA EU a
*closed 1 week Christmas and August Bank Holiday* – **Meals** 15.50 **t.** (lunch) and a la carte 19.60/29.40 **t.**

X **Alastair Little Lancaster Road,** 136a Lancaster Rd, W11 1QU, (0171) 243 2220 – MC AE VISA EU e
*closed Sunday and Bank Holidays* – **Meals** 19.00/25.00 **t.**

## South Kensington - SW5/SW7/W8 - pp. 14 and 15.

**Gloucester,** 4-18 Harrington Gdns., SW7 4LH, (0171) 373 6030, *Fax (0171) 373 0409*, – , rm, – 650. BS r
**Meals** 9.95 **t.** (lunch) and a la carte 16.00/22.50 **t.** 12.00 – 14.50 – **542 rm** 185.00/205.00 **st.**, 6 suites.

**Pelham,** 15 Cromwell Pl., SW7 2LA, (0171) 589 8288, *Fax (0171) 584 8444*, « Tastefully furnished Victorian town house » – . CS z
***Kemps :*** **Meals** *(closed Saturday)* 12.95/15.95 **t.** and a la carte 16.95/22.20 **t.** – 13.25 – **38 rm** 140.00/215.00 **s.**, 3 suites.

**Blakes,** 33 Roland Gdns., SW7 3PF, (0171) 370 6701, *Fax (0171) 373 0442*, « Antique oriental furnishings » – , rest, . BU n
**Meals** a la carte 30.25/61.25 **st.** 11.00 – 17.00 – **46 rm** 150.00/340.00 **st.**, 5 suites.

**Harrington Hall,** 5-25 Harrington Gdns., SW7 4JW, (0171) 396 9696, *Fax (0171) 396 9090*, , – , rm, – 250.
***Wetherby's :*** **Meals** 19.75 **st.** and a la carte 7.50 – 13.50 – **200 rm** 160.00/175.00 **st.** BT n

**Bailey's,** 140 Gloucester Rd, SW7 4QH, (0171) 373 6000, *Fax (0171) 370 3760* – , rm, – 440. BS a
***Olives :*** **Meals** (dinner only) a la carte 15.75/18.75 **t.** 8.50 – 12.50 – **212 rm** 99.90/293.75 **t.**

**Rembrandt,** 11 Thurloe Pl., SW7 2RS, (0171) 589 8100, *Fax (0171) 225 3363*, , , – , rm, rest, – 250. DS x
**Meals** 16.95 **st.** and a la carte – 10.75 – **195 rm** 150.00/200.00 **st.**

**Regency,** 100 Queen's Gate, SW7 5AG, (0171) 370 4595, *Fax (0171) 370 5555*, , – , rm, rest, – 100. CT e
**Meals** *(closed lunch Saturday and Sunday)* (carving lunch) 21.00 **st.** and a la carte 6.00 – 12.00 – **192 rm** 139.00 **s.**, 6 suites – SB.

**Swallow International,** Cromwell Rd, SW5 0TH, (0171) 973 1000, *Fax (0171) 244 8194*, , , – , rm, – 200.
***Blayneys :*** **Meals** (dinner only) a la carte 30.25/39.50 **st.** – 12.75 – **417 rm** 120.00/155.00 **st.**, 2 suites – SB. AS c

**Holiday Inn Kensington,** 100 Cromwell Rd, SW7 4ER, (0171) 373 2222, *Fax (0171) 373 0559*, , , – , rm, – 130. BS e
**Meals** *(closed lunch Saturday and Sunday)* a la carte 20.50/28.65 **t.** 7.50 – 11.95 – **143 rm** 164.00/184.00 **st.**, 19 suites.

**Jury's Kensington,** 109-113 Queen's Gate, SW7 5LR, (0171) 589 6300, *Fax (0171) 581 1492* – , rm, – 80. CT i
*closed 25 to 28 December* – **Meals** 15.00/20.00 **st.** and a la carte – 11.95 – **172 rm** 145.00/250.00 **st.**

**Vanderbilt,** 68-86 Cromwell Rd, SW7 5BT, (0171) 589 2424, *Fax (0171) 225 2293* – , rm, rest, – 120. BS v
**Meals** 17.50 **st.** and a la carte 7.50 – 11.00 – **223 rm** 115.00/140.00 **s.**

**Forum,** 97 Cromwell Rd, SW7 4DN, (0171) 370 5757, *Fax (0171) 373 1448*, , – , rm, rest, – 400. BS x
**Meals** 18.00 **st.** (dinner) and a la carte 13.45/23.50 **st.** 7.00 – 12.25 – **906 rm** 160.00/180.00 **st.**, 4 suites.

**Gore,** 189 Queen's Gate, SW7 5EX, (0171) 584 6601, *Fax (0171) 589 8127*, « Attractive decor » – , rm, . BR n
*closed 25 and 26 December* – ***Bistrot 190 :*** **Meals** (only members and residents may book) a la carte 16.90/28.20 **t.** – (see also ***Downstairs at One Ninety*** below) – 9.00 – **54 rm** 125.00/280.00 **st.**

**John Howard,** 4 Queen's Gate, SW7 5EH, (0171) 581 3011, *Fax (0171) 589 8403* – . BQ i
**Meals** *(closed Sunday)* (dinner only) 20.00 **t.** and a la carte 6.50 – 11.50 – **43 rm** 89.00/119.00 **st.**, 9 suites.

**Cranley,** 10-12 Bina Gdns., SW5 0LA, (0171) 373 0123, *Fax (0171) 373 9497*, « Antiques » – . BT c
**Meals** (room service only) 7.50 – 12.95 – **33 rm** 140.00/160.00 **st.**, 4 suites.

**Number Sixteen** without rest., 16 Sumner Pl., SW7 3EG, (0171) 589 5232, *Fax (0171) 584 8615*, « Attractively furnished Victorian town houses », – . CT c
8.00 – **36 rm** 80.00/190.00 **st.**

**Cranley Gardens** without rest., 8 Cranley Gdns., SW7 3DB, (0171) 373 3232, *Fax (0171) 373 7944* – . BT e
5.50 – **85 rm** 75.00/105.00 **st.**

**Five Sumner Place** without rest., 5 Sumner Pl., SW7 3EE, (0171) 584 7586, *Fax (0171) 823 9962* – . CT u
**13 rm** 88.00/139.00 **st.**

**Aster House** without rest., 3 Sumner Pl., SW7 3EE, (0171) 581 5888, *Fax (0171) 584 4925*, – . CT u
**12 rm** 80.00/145.00 **st.**

**Bombay Brasserie,** Courtfield Rd, SW7 4UH, (0171) 370 4040, *Fax (0171) 835 1669*, « Raj-style decor, conservatory » – . BS a
*closed 25 and 26 December* – **Meals** - Indian - (buffet lunch) 15.95 **t.** (lunch) and dinner a la carte 23.25/29.10 **t.** 7.25.

**Hilaire,** 68 Old Brompton Rd, SW7 3LQ, (0171) 584 8993, *Fax (0171) 581 2949* – . CT n
*closed Saturday lunch, Sunday and Bank Holidays* – **Meals** (booking essential) 23.00/34.50 **t.** 10.50.

**Shaw's,** 119 Old Brompton Rd, SW7 3RN, (0171) 373 7774, *Fax (0171) 370 5102* – . BT v
*closed Saturday lunch, Sunday, Easter, 1 week August and 1 week Christmas-New Year* – **Meals** 18.50/32.95 **t.** 9.00.

**Downstairs at One Ninety** (at Gore H.), 190 Queen's Gate, SW7 5EU, (0171) 581 5666, *Fax (0171) 581 8172* – . BR n
*closed Saturday lunch, Sunday and Christmas* – **Meals** - Seafood - (booking essential) 22.50 **t.** (lunch) and a la carte 28.25/50.25 **t.**

**Café Lazeez,** 93-95 Old Brompton Rd, SW7 3LD, (0171) 581 9993, *Fax (0171) 581 8200* – . CT a
***Restaurant :*** **Meals** - North Indian - a la carte 17.95/25.55 **t.**
**Cafe : Meals** a la carte 17.95/25.55 **t.**

**Tui,** 19 Exhibition Rd, SW7 2HE, (0171) 584 8359 – CS u
*closed 5 days at Christmas and Bank Holiday Mondays* – **Meals** - Thai - 10.00 **st.** (lunch) and a la carte 16.60/26.65 **t.** 4.75.

**Delhi Brasserie,** 134 Cromwell Rd, SW7 4HA, (0171) 370 7617, *Fax (0171) 244 8639* – . AS a
*closed 25 and 26 December* – **Meals** - Indian - 6.95/14.95 **t.** and a la carte.

**Khan's of Kensington,** 3 Harrington Rd, SW7 3ES, (0171) 581 2900, *Fax (0171) 581 2900* – . CS e
*closed 25 and 26 December* – **Meals** - Indian - 7.95/16.50 **t.** and a la carte.

**Memories of India,** 18 Gloucester Rd, SW7 4RB, (0171) 589 6450, *Fax (0171) 584 4438* – . BR s
*closed 25 December* – **Meals** - Indian - 7.95/15.50 **t.** and a la carte.

## LAMBETH *pp. 10 and 11.*

### Lambeth – *SE1.*

**Novotel London Waterloo,** 113 Lambeth Rd, SE1 7LS, (0171) 793 1010, *Fax (0171) 793 0202*, – , rm, – 40. . LYZ a
**Meals** 14.50 **st.** and a la carte 5.55 – 11.00 – **185 rm** 112.00/132.00 **st.**, 2 suites.

### Waterloo – *SE1.*

**People's Palace,** Level 3, The Royal Festival Hall, SE1 8XX, (0171) 928 9999, *Fax (0171) 928 2355*, Victoria Embankment and River Thames – . p. 26 MX e
**Meals** 14.50/16.50 **t.** and a la carte.

**RSJ,** 13a Coin St., SE1 8YQ, (0171) 928 4554 – . NX e
*closed Saturday lunch, Sunday and Bank Holidays* – **Meals** 15.95 **st.** and a la carte 5.95.

## MERTON

### Wimbledon – *SW19.*

**Cannizaro House**, West Side, Wimbledon Common, SW19 4UE, (0181) 879 1464, *Fax (0181) 879 7338*, , « 18C country house in Cannizaro Park », – , rm, – 60. .
**Meals** 25.75 **t.** and a la carte 10.50 – 13.50 – **44 rm** 150.00/249.00 **t.**, 2 suites – SB.

## SOUTHWARK p. 11.

### Bermondsey – ✉ SE1.

XXX **Le Pont de la Tour,** 36d Shad Thames, Butlers Wharf, SE1 2YE, ☎ (0171) 403 8403, *Fax (0171) 403 0267,* ≤, 🏠, « Riverside setting » – ▤. MC AE ① VISA PX c
*closed Saturday lunch* – **Meals** 27.50 **t.** (lunch) and dinner a la carte 31.50/38.50 **t.**

XXX **Bengal Clipper,** Cardamom Building, Shad Thames, Butlers Wharf, SE1 2YR, ☎ (0171) 357 9001, *Fax (0171) 357 9002* – ▤. MC AE ① VISA JCB PX e
*closed 25 and 26 December* – **Meals** - Indian - a la carte 13.85/28.35 **t.**

X **Blue Print Café,** Design Museum, Shad Thames, Butlers Wharf, SE1 2YD, ☎ (0171) 378 7031, *Fax (0171) 378 6540,* 🏠, « Riverside setting, ≤ Tower Bridge » – MC AE ① VISA PX u
*closed Sunday dinner* – **Meals** a la carte approx. 23.55 **t.**

X **Butlers Wharf Chop House,** 36e Shad Thames, Butlers Wharf, SE1 2YE, ☎ (0171) 403 3403, *Fax (0171) 403 3414,* « Riverside setting, ≤ Tower Bridge » – MC AE ① VISA PX n
*closed Saturday lunch and Sunday dinner* – **Meals** 22.75 **t.** (lunch) and dinner a la carte 24.50/31.75 **t.**

X **Cantina Del Ponte,** 36c Shad Thames, Butlers Wharf, SE1 2YE, ☎ (0171) 403 5403, *Fax (0171) 403 0267,* ≤, 🏠, « Riverside setting » – MC AE ① VISA PX c
**Meals** - Italian-Mediterranean - a la carte 10.50/25.25 **t.**

X **Café dell'Ugo,** 56-58 Tooley St., SE1 2SZ, ☎ (0171) 407 6001, *Fax (0171) 357 8806* – ▤. MC AE ① VISA PX r
*closed Saturday lunch, Sunday and Bank Holidays* – **Meals** 15.00 **t.** (dinner) and a la carte 17.45/26.75 **t.**

### Dulwich – ✉ SE19.

XX **Belair House,** Gallery Rd, Dulwich Village, SE21 7AB, ☎ (0181) 299 9788, *Fax (0181) 299 6793,* 🏠, « Georgian summer house », 🌳 – P. MC AE ① VISA JCB
*closed Monday* – **Meals** 19.95 **t.** (lunch) and a la carte 23.40/50.45 **t.** 🍷 10.00.

XX **Luigi's,** 129 Gipsy Hill, SE19 1QS, ☎ (0181) 670 1843 – ▤. MC AE ① VISA JCB
*closed Sunday* – **Meals** - Italian - a la carte 16.20/24.15 **t.** 🍷 4.90.

### Rotherhithe – ✉ SE16.

**Holiday Inn at Nelson Dock,** 265 Rotherhithe St., Nelson Dock, SE16 1EJ, ☎ (0171) 231 1001, *Fax (0171) 231 0599,* ≤, 🏠, « Riverside setting », Fō, ≘s, 🏊, 🎾 – |$|, ⇔ rm, ▤ rest, TV ☎ & P – 🏛 350. MC AE ① VISA JCB. ✂
*closed 22 to 28 December* – **Meals** 21.50 **st.** and dinner a la carte 🍷 7.50 – ☕ 10.50 – **362 rm** 115.00/135.00 **st.,** 4 suites.

### Southwark – ✉ SE1.

XXX **Oxo Tower** (8th floor), Oxo Tower Wharf, Barge House St., SE1 9PH, ☎ (0171) 803 3888, *Fax (0171) 803 3838,* ≤ London skyline and River Thames, 🏠 – |$| ▤. MC AE ① VISA JCB NX a
*closed Saturday lunch, 25-26 December and 1 January* – **Meals** 24.50 **st.** (lunch) and dinner a la carte 26.50/36.50 **t.** 🍷 10.00.

X **Brasserie** : **Meals** *(closed 23 to 26 December and 1 January)* a la carte 19.50/26.00 **t.**

## TOWER HAMLETS.

### Canary Wharf – ✉ E14.

XX **MPW,** Second Floor, Cabot Place East, E14 4QT, ☎ (0171) 513 0513, *Fax (0171) 513 0551* – ▤. MC AE ① VISA
*closed Saturday, Sunday, 25-26 December and 1 January* – **Meals** a la carte 18.50/31.45 **t.** 🍷 9.00.

### Whitechapel – ✉ E1.

XX **Cafe Spice Namaste,** 16 Prescot St., E1 8AZ, ☎ (0171) 488 9242, *Fax (0171) 488 9339* – ▤. MC AE ① VISA JCB
*closed Saturday lunch, Sunday, 1 week Christmas and Bank Holiday Mondays* – **Meals** - Indian - a la carte 18.70/32.55 **t.** 🍷 6.50.

## WANDSWORTH *p. 9.*

### Battersea - ✉ *SW8/SW11.*

XX **Ransome's Dock,** 35-37 Parkgate Rd, SW11 4NP, ✆ (0171) 223 1611, *Fax (0171) 924 2614,* – MC AE ⓓ VISA HZ c
*closed Sunday dinner and 1 week Christmas* – **Meals** a la carte 19.50/27.75 **t.** (lunch) and a la carte 17.75/27.00 **t.** 6.25.

XX **Chada,** 208-210 Battersea Park Rd, SW11 4ND, ✆ (0171) 622 2209, *Fax (0171) 924 2178* – ▤. MC AE ⓓ VISA JCB
*closed Saturday lunch and Bank Holidays* – **Meals** - Thai - a la carte 12.40/25.15 **st.**

### Putney - ✉ *SW15.*

XX **Putney Bridge,** Lower Richmond Rd, SW15 1LB, ✆ (0181) 780 1811, *Fax (0181) 780 1211,* ≤, « Riverside setting » – MC VISA
**Meals** 17.50 **t.** (lunch) and a la carte 18.00/31.50 **t.** 9.00.

XX Royal China, 3 Chelverton Rd, SW15 1RN, ✆ (0181) 788 0907 – ▤
**Meals** - Chinese rest.

XX **The Phoenix,** Pentlow St., SW15 1LY, ✆ (0181) 780 3131, *Fax (0181) 780 1114* – ▤. MC AE VISA
*closed 25-26 December and Bank Holidays* – **Meals** 12.50 **t.** (lunch) and a la carte 15.20/22.75 **t.** 4.75.

### Wandsworth - ✉ *SW12/SW17/SW18.*

XX **Chez Bruce,** 2 Bellevue Rd, SW17 7EG, ✆ (0181) 672 0114, *Fax (0181) 767 6648* – ▤. MC AE ⓓ VISA
*closed Sunday dinner, 1 week Christmas and Bank Holidays* – **Meals** 18.00/25.00 **t.**

XX **Tabaq,** 47 Balham Hill, SW12 9DR, ✆ (0181) 673 7820, *Fax (0181) 673 2701* – ▤. MC AE ⓓ VISA JCB
*closed Sunday and 25 December* – **Meals** - Indian - a la carte 14.45/24.50 **t.** 4.75.

X **Bombay Bicycle Club,** 95 Nightingale Lane, SW12 8NX, ✆ (0181) 673 6217, *Fax (0181) 673 9100* – MC AE ⓓ VISA
*closed Sunday, Easter and 25 December* – **Meals** - Indian - (dinner only) a la carte 16.00/21.50 **t.** 8.00.

## WESTMINSTER (City of)

### Bayswater and Maida Vale - ✉ *W2/W9 – Except where otherwise stated see pp. 16 and 17.*

**Royal Lancaster,** Lancaster Terr., W2 2TY, ✆ (0171) 262 6737, *Fax (0171) 724 3191,* ≤ – |‡|, ⇆ rm, ▤ TV ☎ P – 1400. MC AE ⓓ VISA JCB. ✂ DZ e
***Park :*** **Meals** *(closed Saturday lunch and Sunday dinner)* 23.50 **st.** and a la carte 11.00 – ***Pavement Cafe :*** **Meals** a la carte 13.70/17.20 **st.** 10.00 – (see also ***Nipa*** below) – 14.50 – **398 rm** 210.00/230.00 **st.**, 20 suites.

**Stakis London Metropole,** Edgware Rd, W2 1JU, ✆ (0171) 402 4141, *Fax (0171) 724 8866,* ≤, Ls, ≘s, ▢ – |‡|, ⇆ rm, ▤ TV ☎ – 1200. MC AE ⓓ VISA JCB. ✂ p. 5 GU c
**Meals** (buffet rest.) 20.50/30.50 **t.** and a la carte – (see also ***Aspects*** below) 8.00 – 17.95 – **721 rm** 150.00/200.00 **st.**, 26 suites – SB.

**The Hempel** ✂, Hempel Garden Sq., 31-35 Craven Hill Gdns., W2 3EA, ✆ (0171) 298 9000, *Fax (0171) 402 4666,* « Minimalist », – |‡| ▤ TV ☎ ♿ P – 40. MC AE ⓓ VISA. ✂ CZ a
***I-Thai :*** **Meals** - Thai-Italian - a la carte 27.00/40.00 **t.** – 17.00 – **41 rm** 220.00/255.00 **s.**, 6 suites.

**Whites,** Bayswater Rd, 90-92 Lancaster Gate, W2 3NR, ✆ (0171) 262 2711, *Fax (0171) 262 2147* – |‡|, ⇆ rm, ▤ TV ☎ P – 30. MC AE ⓓ VISA JCB. ✂ CZ v
**Meals** *(closed Saturday lunch)* 17.50/20.50 **t.** and a la carte 7.90 – 12.50 – **52 rm** 167.00/247.00 **st.**, 2 suites – SB.

**Jarvis London Embassy,** 150 Bayswater Rd, W2 4RT, ✆ (0171) 229 1212, *Fax (0171) 229 2623* – |‡|, ⇆ rm, ▤ rest, TV ☎ P – 100. MC AE ⓓ VISA BZ o
**Meals** (carving rest.) 14.95 **st.** and a la carte 6.50 – 9.50 – **193 rm** 115.00/135.00 **st.**, 1 suite – SB.

**Plaza on Hyde Park,** 1-7 Lancaster Gate, W2 3LG, ✆ (0171) 262 5022, *Fax (0171) 724 8666* – |‡|, ⇆ rm, TV ☎ – 30. MC AE ⓓ VISA JCB. ✂ DZ r
**Meals** a la carte 14.40/25.65 **st.** 6.70 – 10.95 – **402 rm** 125.00/140.00 **st.**

**Stakis London Coburg,** 129 Bayswater Rd, W2 4RJ, (0171) 221 2217, *Fax (0171) 229 0557* – rm, rest, – 100. BZ c
Meals 15.95 **st.** and a la carte – 9.95 – **128 rm** 125.00/150.00 **st.**, 1 suite – SB.

**Hyde Park Towers,** 41-51 Inverness Terr., W2 3JN, (0171) 221 8484, *Fax (0171) 792 3201* – rest, – 45. BZ r
Meals 10.95/13.95 **t.** 5.50 – 7.50 – **114 rm** 110.00/150.00 **t.** – SB.

**Mornington** without rest., 12 Lancaster Gate, W2 3LG, (0171) 262 7361, *Fax (0171) 706 1028* – DZ s
**66 rm** 99.00/140.00.

**Aspects** (at Stakis London Metropole H.), Edgware Rd, W2 1JU, (0171) 402 4141, *Fax (0171) 724 8866*, ≤ London – . p. 5 GU c
*closed Sunday* – **Meals** 20.50/30.50 **t.** and a la carte 8.00.

**Nipa** (at Royal Lancaster H.), Lancaster Terr., W2 2TY, (0171) 262 6737, *Fax (0171) 724 3191* – . DZ e
*closed Saturday lunch and Sunday* – **Meals** - Thai - 23.00 **st.** and a la carte 10.00.

**Poons,** Unit 205, Whiteleys, Queensway, W2 4YN, (0171) 792 2884 – . BZ x
*closed 25 and 26 December* – **Meals** - Chinese - 15.00/25.00 **t.** and a la carte.

**Al San Vincenzo,** 30 Connaught St., W2 2AE, (0171) 262 9623 – EZ o
*closed Saturday lunch and Sunday* – **Meals** - Italian - (booking essential) a la carte 22.00/34.50 **t.** 7.50.

**Jason's,** Blomfield Rd, Little Venice, W9 2PD, (0171) 286 6752, *Fax (0171) 266 4332*, « Canalside setting » – p. 4 FU c
*closed Sunday dinner* – **Meals** - Seafood - 14.95/18.95 **t.** and a la carte.

**Royal China,** 13 Queensway, W2 4QJ, (0171) 221 2535 – .
*closed 25 December* – **Meals** - Chinese - 22.00 **t.** (dinner) and a la carte. BZ e

**Assaggi,** 39 Chepstow Pl., W2 4TS, (0171) 792 5501 – AZ c
*closed Sunday dinner, Monday, Christmas, New Year and Bank Holidays* – **Meals** - Italian - a la carte 21.75/31.75 **t.**

**L'Accento,** 16 Garway Rd, W2 4NH, (0171) 243 2201, *Fax (0171) 243 2201* – BZ a
Meals - Italian - 15.25 **t.** and a la carte 18.75/23.25 **t.**

## Belgravia – SW1 – *Except where otherwise stated see* pp. 14 and 15.

**The Lanesborough,** 1 Lanesborough Pl., SW1X 7TA, (0171) 259 5599, *Fax (0171) 259 5606*, – rm, – 90.
***The Conservatory*** : Meals 24.50/31.50 **st.** and a la carte 13.50 – 17.00 – **86 rm** 205.00/395.00 **s.**, 9 suites. p. 9 IY a

**The Berkeley,** Wilton Pl., SW1X 7RL, (0171) 235 6000, *Fax (0171) 235 4330*, – rm, – 220. FQ e
***Restaurant*** : Meals 26.50/33.00 **st.** and a la carte 10.00 – (see also ***Vong*** below) – 18.50 – **130 rm** 265.00/320.00 **s.**, 26 suites.

**The Halkin,** 5 Halkin St., SW1X 7DJ, (0171) 333 1000, *Fax (0171) 333 1100*, « Contemporary interior design » – rm, – 25. p. 16 AV a
***Stefano Cavallini Restaurant at The Halkin*** : Meals - Italian - *(closed lunch Saturday and Sunday, Easter and 25 December)* (booking essential) 25.00 **st.** (lunch) and a la carte 40.00/53.00 **st.** 9.50 – 14.25 – **36 rm** 255.00/330.00 **s.**, 5 suites – SB
**Spec.** Duck ravioli with savoy cabbage and foie gras. Lobster and pigeon with pea ravioli. Risotto of fried herbs and onions.

**Sheraton Belgravia,** 20 Chesham Pl., SW1X 8HQ, (0171) 235 6040, *Fax (0171) 259 6243* – rm, – 50.
***Chesham's*** : Meals a la carte 26.00/32.00 **st.** 6.00 – 15.00 – **82 rm** 210.00/310.00 **s.**, 7 suites. FR u

**Lowndes,** 21 Lowndes St., SW1X 9ES, (0171) 823 1234, *Fax (0171) 235 1154*, – rm, – 25. FR i
***Brasserie 21*** : Meals 17.00 **t.** and a la carte 9.50 – 13.50 – **77 rm** 235.00/255.00 **s.**, 1 suite.

**Diplomat** without rest., 2 Chesham St., SW1X 8DT, (0171) 235 1544, *Fax (0171) 259 6153* – FR a
**26 rm** 85.00/150.00 **t.**

**Zafferano,** 15 Lowndes St., SW1X 9EY, (0171) 235 5800, *Fax (0171) 235 1971* – . FR i
*closed Sunday, 2 weeks August and Bank Holidays* – **Meals** - Italian - 21.50/25.50 **t.** and a la carte 9.50.

XX **Vong** (at The Berkeley H.), Wilton Pl., SW1X 7RL, (0171) 235 1010, *Fax (0171) 235 1011* – MC AE VISA JCB FQ e
*closed Sunday lunch and 25 December* – **Meals** - French-Thai - 22.00 **t.** (lunch) and a la carte 23.75/39.00 **t.**

XX **Al Bustan,** 27 Motcomb St., SW1X 8JU, (0171) 235 8277, *Fax (0171) 235 1668* – . MC AE VISA FR z
*closed 23 December-4 January* – **Meals** - Lebanese - 13.00 **t.** (lunch) and a la carte 19.50/22.25 **t.** 10.00.

## Hyde Park and Knightsbridge – SW1/SW7 – *pp. 14 and 15.*

**Mandarin Oriental Hyde Park,** 66 Knightsbridge, SW1X 7LA, (0171) 235 2000, *Fax (0171) 235 4552,* – , rm, – 250. MC AE VISA. FQ x
***Restaurant On The Park*** **: Meals** a la carte 21.95/43.95 **t.** 14.00 – 16.50 – **166 rm** 240.00/260.00 **s.**, 19 suites.

**Knightsbridge Green** without rest., 159 Knightsbridge, SW1X 7PD, (0171) 584 6274, *Fax (0171) 225 1635* – . MC AE VISA. EQ z
*closed 24 to 26 December* – 9.50 – **15 rm** 90.00/130.00 **st.**, 12 suites 150.00 **st.**

XXX **Pearl of Knightsbridge,** 22 Brompton Rd, SW1X 7QN, (0171) 225 3888, *Fax (0171) 225 0252* – . MC AE VISA JCB EQ e
*closed 25 and 26 December* – **Meals** - Chinese - 10.80/22.80 **t.** and a la carte.

XXX **Mr. Chow,** 151 Knightsbridge, SW1X 7PA, (0171) 589 7347, *Fax (0171) 584 5780* – . MC AE VISA JCB EQ a
*closed 24 to 26 December* – **Meals** - Chinese - a la carte 30.00/35.00 **t.**

## Mayfair – W1 – *pp. 12 and 13.*

**Dorchester,** Park Lane, W1A 2HJ, (0171) 629 8888, *Fax (0171) 409 0114,* , – , rm, – 550. MC AE VISA JCB. BN a
**Meals** – (see ***Oriental*** and ***Grill Room*** below) – 18.50 – **197 rm** 240.00/300.00 **s.**, 47 suites.

**Claridge's,** Brook St., W1A 2JQ, (0171) 629 8860, *Fax (0171) 499 2210,* – , rm, – 200. MC AE VISA JCB. BL c
***Restaurant*** **: Meals** 29.00/38.00 **st.** and a la carte 29.00/45.00 **st.** 10.50 – ***Causerie*** **:** **Meals** *(closed Saturday and Sunday)* a la carte 30.00/36.00 **st.** 10.50 – 18.00 – **138 rm** 255.00/365.00 **s.**, 60 suites – SB.

**Four Seasons,** Hamilton Pl., Park Lane, W1A 1AZ, (0171) 499 0888, *Fax (0171) 493 1895,* – , rm, – 500. MC AE VISA JCB. BP a
***Lanes*** **: Meals** 32.00 **st.** (lunch) and a la carte 26.00/45.00 **st.** 8.00 – (see also ***Four Seasons*** below) – 17.75 – **201 rm** 250.00/305.00 **s.**, 26 suites.

**Le Meridien Piccadilly,** 21 Piccadilly, W1V 0BH, (0171) 734 8000, *Fax (0171) 437 3574,* , , , *squash* – , rm, – 250. MC AE VISA JCB. EM a
***Terrace Garden*** **: Meals** 19.95 **t.** and a la carte 12.00 – (see also ***The Oak Room Marco Pierre White*** below) – 16.50 – **248 rm** 275.00/335.00, 18 suites.

**Grosvenor House,** Park Lane, W1A 3AA, (0171) 499 6363, *Fax (0171) 493 3341,* , , – , rm, – 1500. MC AE VISA JCB. AM a
***Café Nico*** **: Meals** 29.50 **st.** – ***Pasta Vino*** **: Meals** - Italian - *(closed Saturday and Sunday)* a la carte 32.50/40.75 **t.** – (see also ***Chez Nico at Ninety Park Lane*** below) – 19.50 – **382 rm** 210.00/345.00, 72 suites.

**London Hilton on Park Lane,** 22 Park Lane, W1Y 4BE, (0171) 493 8000, *Fax (0171) 493 4957,* « Panoramic of London », – , rm, – 1000. MC AE VISA JCB. BP e
***Trader Vics*** ( *(0171) 208 4113)* **: Meals** (dinner only) a la carte 19.00/54.50 **t.** 9.00 – ***Park Brasserie*** **: Meals** 25.50 **t.** and a la carte 9.75 – (see also ***Windows*** below) – 17.00 – **394 rm** 340.00, 52 suites.

**Connaught,** Carlos Pl., W1Y 6AL, (0171) 499 7070, *Fax (0171) 495 3262* – . MC AE VISA. BM e
***The Restaurant*** **: Meals** (booking essential) 25.00/55.00 **t.** and a la carte 28.10/56.60 **t.** 12.00 – ***Grill Room*** **: Meals** *(closed Saturday lunch)* (booking essential) 25.00/35.00 **t.** and a la carte 25.10/56.60 **t.** 12.00 – **66 rm** 225.00/340.00 **s.**, 24 suites
**Spec.** Sole "Jubilée". Prélude gourmande Connaught. Sherry trifle "Wally Ladd".

**47 Park Street,** 47 Park St., W1Y 4EB, (0171) 491 7282, *Fax (0171) 491 7281* – . MC AE VISA JCB. AM c
**Meals** (room service) – (see also ***Le Gavroche*** below) – 19.00, **52 suites** 255.00/500.00 **s.**

**Brown's,** Albemarle St., W1X 4BP, (0171) 493 6020, *Fax (0171) 493 9381* – – 70. VISA JCB. DM e
Meals *(closed lunch Saturday, Sunday and Bank Holidays)* 24.00/29.00 **st.** and a la carte 11.00 – 17.50 – **112 rm** 240.00/268.00, 6 suites – SB.

**Park Lane,** Piccadilly, W1Y 8BX, (0171) 499 6321, *Fax (0171) 499 1965* – , rm, – 300. VISA JCB CP x
***Brasserie on the Park*** *( (0171) 290 7364)* **: Meals** 15.95 **st.** and a la carte 8.25 – (see also ***Bracewells*** below) – 17.00 – **286 rm** 220.50/263.00 **s.**, 20 suites.

**Britannia,** Grosvenor Sq., W1A 3AN, (0171) 629 9400, *Fax (0171) 629 7736*, – , rm, – 100. VISA JCB. BM x
***Adams*** **: Meals** *(closed Saturday and Sunday)* 26.00 **t.** and a la carte 13.50 – (see also ***Shogun*** below) – 13.95 – **306 rm** 205.00/295.00 **s.**, 12 suites.

**May Fair Inter-Continental,** Stratton St., W1A 2AN, (0171) 629 7777, *Fax (0171) 629 1459*, , , – , rm, – 290. VISA JCB. DN z
***May Fair Café*** *( (0171) 915 2842)* **: Meals** a la carte 18.00/34.00 **t.** – (see also ***Opus 70*** below) – 16.00 – **262 rm** 269.00/299.00 **st.**, 12 suites.

**Inter-Continental,** 1 Hamilton Pl., Hyde Park Corner, W1V 0QY, (0171) 409 3131, *Fax (0171) 493 3476*, , – , rm, – 1000. VISA JCB. BP o
Meals 22.00/26.00 **t.** and a la carte 9.75 – (see also ***Le Soufflé*** below) – 18.30 – **410 rm** 265.00 **s.**, 48 suites.

**Athenaeum,** 116 Piccadilly, W1V 0BJ, (0171) 499 3464, *Fax (0171) 493 1860*, , – , rm, – 55. VISA JCB. CP s
***Bulloch's at 116*** **: Meals** *(closed lunch Saturday and Sunday)* a la carte 30.40/34.40 **t.** 9.50 – 16.50 – **121 rm** 225.00/295.00 **s.**, 35 suites.

**The Metropolitan,** Old Park Lane, W1Y 4LB, (0171) 447 1000, *Fax (0171) 447 1100*, ≤, « Contemporary interior design », – , rm, . VISA JCB.
Meals (residents and members only) (light lunch)/dinner a la carte 19.50/28.00 **t.** – (see also ***Nobu*** below) – 15.00 – **152 rm** 195.00/275.00 **s.**, 3 suites. BP c

**Westbury,** Bond St., W1A 4UH, (0171) 629 7755, *Fax (0171) 495 1163* – , rm, – 110. VISA DM a
***La Mediterranée*** *(closed Saturday and Sunday lunch)* a la carte approx. 28.50 **t.** 15.50 – 14.75 – **231 rm** 180.00/230.00 **s.**, 13 suites.

**London Marriott Grosvenor Square,** Duke St., Grosvenor Sq., W1A 4AW, (0171) 493 1232, *Fax (0171) 491 3201*, – , rm, – 600. VISA JCB. BL a
***Diplomat*** **: Meals** *(closed Saturday lunch)* 19.50 **t.** (lunch) and a la carte 17.75/27.75 **t.** 12.75 – 12.95 – **210 rm** 235.00 **s.**, 11 suites – SB.

**Chesterfield,** 35 Charles St., W1X 8LX, (0171) 491 2622, *Fax (0171) 491 4793* – , rm, rest, – 110. VISA. CN c
***Butlers*** **: Meals** *(closed Saturday lunch)* 8.95/15.95 **st.** and a la carte 11.00 – 16.00 – **106 rm** 145.00/210.00 **s.**, 4 suites.

**Washington,** 5-7 Curzon St., W1Y 8DT, (0171) 499 7000, *Fax (0171) 495 6172* – , rm, – 80. VISA JCB CN s
Meals a la carte 14.00/20.00 **st.** – 13.95 – **169 rm** 160.00/205.00 **s.**, 4 suites – SB.

**Holiday Inn Mayfair,** 3 Berkeley St., W1X 6NE, (0171) 493 8282, *Fax (0171) 629 2827* – , rm, – 60. VISA JCB.
Meals *(closed Saturday lunch)* 22.00 **t.** and a la carte 8.00 – 12.95 – **181 rm** 160.00/210.00 **st.**, 4 suites. DN r

**Flemings,** 7-12 Half Moon St., W1Y 7RA, (0171) 499 2964, *Fax (0171) 629 4063* – , rest, – 50. VISA JCB. CN z
Meals 9.95/23.50 **st.** and a la carte 9.00 – 11.50 – **120 rm** 130.00/175.00, 10 suites.

**Green Park,** Half Moon St., W1Y 8BP, (0171) 629 7522, *Fax (0171) 491 8971* – , rm, rest, – 70. VISA JCB. CN a
Meals *(closed lunch Saturday, Sunday and Bank Holidays)* a la carte 17.95/31.20 **st.** 6.75 – 10.95 – **160 rm** 135.00/182.00 **st.**, 1 suite.

**London Mews Hilton,** 2 Stanhope Row, W1Y 7HE, (0171) 493 7222, *Fax (0171) 629 9423* – , rm, – 50. VISA JCB.
Meals (dinner only) 19.00 **st.** and a la carte 9.45 – 15.00 – **71 rm** 180.00/216.00 **st.**, 1 suite – SB. BP u

**The Oak Room Marco Pierre White** (at Le Meridien Piccadilly H.), 21 Piccadilly, W1V OBH, (0171) 437 0202 – . VISA EM a
*closed Saturday lunch, Sunday, last 2 weeks August and 2 weeks Christmas-New Year* – **Meals** (booking essential) 29.50/75.00 **t.** 15.00
**Spec.** Foie gras en surprise. Contre-filet "Molly Parkin". Caramelised pineapple with vanilla.

XXXXX ✿✿✿ **Chez Nico at Ninety Park Lane** (Ladenis) (at Grosvenor House H.), Park Lane, W1A 3AA, ✆ (0171) 409 1290, *Fax (0171) 355 4877* – ▤. MC AE ① VISA AM e
*closed Saturday lunch, Sunday, 4 days at Easter, 10 days at Christmas and Bank Holiday Mondays* – **Meals** - French - (booking essential) 32.00/62.00 **t.**
**Spec.** Langoustine ravioli with lobster sauce. Escalope of sea bass with a basil coulis. Glazed lemon tart with raspberry coulis.

XXXX ✿✿ **Le Gavroche** (Roux), 43 Upper Brook St., W1Y 1PF, ✆ (0171) 408 0881, *Fax (0171) 409 0939* – ▤. MC AE ① VISA JCB AM c
*closed Saturday, Sunday, Christmas-New Year and Bank Holidays* – **Meals** - French - (booking essential) 40.00 **st.** (lunch) and a la carte 60.00/94.20 **st.** 🍾 15.00
**Spec.** Terrine de foie gras et confit de canard aux fruits secs et épices. Gibiers suivant la chasse. Bar en papillote farci au fenouil.

XXXX ✿ **Oriental** (at Dorchester H.), Park Lane, W1A 2HJ, ✆ (0171) 317 6328, *Fax (0171) 409 0114* – ▤. MC AE ① VISA JCB BN a
*closed Saturday lunch, Sunday and August* – **Meals** - Chinese (Canton) - 25.50/37.00 **st.** and a la carte 30.00/63.50 **st.** 🍾 14.00
**Spec.** Fried prawns with cashew nuts in a lemon sauce. Stir fried beef with lemon grass and black pepper. Deep fried mixed seafood wrapped in rice paper with mango.

XXXX **Four Seasons** (at Four Seasons H.), Hamilton Pl., Park Lane, W1A 1AZ, ✆ (0171) 499 0888, *Fax (0171) 493 1895* – |♦| ▤ 🚗. MC AE ① VISA JCB BP a
**Meals** a la carte 26.00/48.00 **st.** 🍾 19.00.

XXXX **Windows** (at London Hilton on Park Lane), 22 Park Lane, W1Y 4BE, ✆ (0171) 208 4020, « Panoramic ⋞ of London » – ▤. MC AE ① VISA JCB BP e
*closed Saturday lunch and Sunday dinner* – **Meals** 33.95/33.50 **t.** and dinner a la carte 🍾 13.00.

XXXX ✿ **Les Saveurs de Jean - Christophe Novelli W1,** 37a Curzon St., W1Y 7AF, ✆ (0171) 491 8919, *Fax (0171) 491 3658* – ▤. MC AE VISA JCB BN o
*closed Saturday lunch and Sunday* – **Meals** - French - 28.00/35.00 **t.** and a la carte 22.00/46.50 **t.** 🍾 14.00
**Spec.** Cured trout tartare with croque of cucumber, soft quail egg and caviar. Roast sea bass with sun dried tomatoes, pickled aubergine and picholine olives. Hot and cold, dark and white chocolate plate ; "Liz McGrath".

XXX ✿✿ **The Square,** 6-10 Bruton St., W1X 7AG, ✆ (0171) 495 7100, *Fax (0171) 495 7150* – ▤. MC AE ① VISA CM v
*closed lunch Saturday and Sunday and 1 week Christmas* – **Meals** 45.00 **t.** (dinner) and lunch a la carte 29.50/35.50 **t.** 🍾 11.50
**Spec.** Steamed cod with leeks, oysters and caviar. Cappuccino of shellfish with cannelloni of lobster. Saddle of lamb with a herb crust, purée of shallots and rosemary.

XXX **Grill Room** (at Dorchester H.), Park Lane, W1A 2HJ, ✆ (0171) 317 6336, *Fax (0171) 409 0114* – ▤. MC AE ① VISA JCB BN a
**Meals** - English - 28.00/37.00 **st.** and a la carte 34.00/56.00 **st.** 🍾 14.00.

XXX **Goode's at Thomas Goode,** 19 South Audley St., W1Y 6BN, ✆ (0171) 409 7242, *Fax (0171) 629 4230* – ▤. MC AE ① VISA BM c
*closed Saturday, Sunday, first 3 weeks August, 1 week Christmas and Bank Holidays* – **Meals** (lunch only) 37.50 **t.** 🍾 15.20.

XXX **Le Soufflé** (at Inter-Continental H.), 1 Hamilton Pl., Hyde Park Corner, W1V 0QY, ✆ (0171) 409 3131, *Fax (0171) 409 7460* – ▤ 🚗. MC AE ① VISA JCB BP o
*closed Saturday lunch, Sunday dinner, Monday, 3 weeks January and Bank Holidays* – **Meals** 29.50/45.00 **t.** and a la carte 🍾 10.00.

XXX **Bracewells** (at Park Lane H.), Piccadilly, W1Y 8BX, ✆ (0171) 753 6725, *Fax (0171) 499 1965* – Ⓟ. MC AE ① VISA JCB CP x
*closed Saturday lunch, Sunday, August and Bank Holidays* – **Meals** 26.50 **t.** (lunch) and a la carte 33.95/43.95 **t.** 🍾 9.00.

XXX **Princess Garden,** 8-10 North Audley St., W1Y 1WF, ✆ (0171) 493 3223, *Fax (0171) 629 3130* – ▤. MC AE ① VISA JCB AL z
*closed 4 days Christmas* – **Meals** - Chinese (Peking, Szechuan) - 30.00 **t.** (dinner) and a la carte 29.00/45.00 **t.** 🍾 9.50.

XXX **Opus 70** (at May Fair Inter-Continental H.), Stratton St., W1A 2AN, ✆ (0171) 915 2842, *Fax (0171) 629 1459* – ▤. MC AE ① VISA JCB DN z
*closed Saturday lunch* – **Meals** a la carte 20.00/40.50 **t.**

XXX **Scotts,** 20 Mount St., W1Y 6HE, ✆ (0171) 629 5248, *Fax (0171) 499 8246* – ▤. MC AE ① VISA JCB – **Meals** - Seafood - a la carte 21.70/41.00 **t.** 🍾 7.00. BM a

XX ✿ **Nobu** (at The Metropolitan H.), 19 Old Park Lane, W1Y 4LB, ✆ (0171) 447 4747, *Fax (0171) 447 4749*, ⋞ – ▤. MC AE ① VISA JCB BP c
*closed lunch Saturday and Sunday* – **Meals** - New style Japanese with South American influences - 40.00/50.00 **t.** and a la carte 60.00/100.00 **t.** 🍾 8.50
**Spec.** Lobster ceviche. Black cod with miso. Snow crab with spicy cream sauce.

XX **L'Odéon,** 65 Regent St., W1R 7HH, ☎ (0171) 287 1400, *Fax (0171) 287 1300* – ▤. MC AE ⓓ VISA JCB — EM r
*closed Saturday lunch, 25-26 December, 1 January and Bank Holidays* – **Meals** 17.50 **t.** and a la carte 8.90.

XX **Tamarind,** 20 Queen St., W1X 7PJ, ☎ (0171) 629 3561, *Fax (0171) 499 5034* – MC AE ⓓ VISA — CN e
*closed Saturday lunch, 25 December and 1 January* – **Meals** - Indian - 16.50 **t.** (lunch) and a la carte 27.00/38.50 **t.** 6.75.

XX **Greenhouse,** 27a Hay's Mews, W1X 7RJ, ☎ (0171) 499 3331, *Fax (0171) 499 5368* – ▤. MC AE ⓓ VISA — BN e
*closed Saturday lunch and 25 December* – **Meals** a la carte 30.40/35.00 **t.** 6.00.

XX **Bentley's,** 11-15 Swallow St., W1R 7HD, ☎ (0171) 734 4756, *Fax (0171) 287 2972* – ▤. MC AE ⓓ VISA JCB — EM i
*closed Sunday, 25-26 December and 1 January* – **Meals** - Seafood - a la carte 25.50/40.25 **t.** 11.00.

XX **Nicole's,** 158 New Bond St., W1V 9PA, ☎ (0171) 499 8408, *Fax (0171) 409 0381* – ▤. MC AE ⓓ VISA JCB — DM n
*closed Saturday dinner, Sunday and Bank Holidays* – **Meals** a la carte 25.50/28.50 **t.**

XX Langan's Brasserie, Stratton St., W1X 5FD, ☎ (0171) 491 8822 ▤ — DN e

XX **Marquis,** 121A Mount St., W1Y 5HB, ☎ (0171) 499 1256, *Fax (0171) 493 4460* – MC AE ⓓ VISA JCB — BM u
*closed Saturday lunch, Sunday, 21 August-1 September, 23 December-4 January and Bank Holidays* – **Meals** 19.50 **t.** and a la carte 6.10.

XX **Chor Bizarre,** 16 Albemarle St., W1X 3HA, ☎ (0171) 629 9802, *Fax (0171) 493 7756*, « Authentic Indian decor and furnishings » – MC AE ⓓ VISA JCB — DM s
*closed Sunday, 24 to 26 December and 1 January* – **Meals** - Indian - 12.95/31.00 **t.** and a la carte.

XX **Benihana,** 37 Sackville St., Piccadilly, W1X 2DQ, ☎ (0171) 494 2525, *Fax (0171) 494 1456* – ▤. MC AE ⓓ VISA JCB — EM s
**Meals** - Japanese (Teppan-Yaki) - 10.00/14.00 **st.** and a la carte.

XX **Mulligans,** 13-14 Cork St., W1X 1PF, ☎ (0171) 409 1370, *Fax (0171) 409 2732* – MC AE ⓓ VISA — DM c
*closed Sunday, 1 week Christmas-New Year and Bank Holidays* – **Meals** - Irish - a la carte 19.95/28.85 **t.**

XX **Shogun** (at Britannia H.), Adams Row, W1Y 5DE, ☎ (0171) 493 1255 – ▤. MC AE ⓓ VISA JCB — BM x
*closed Monday* – **Meals** - Japanese - (dinner only) a la carte 22.00/36.00 **st.**

## Regent's Park and Marylebone – ✉ *NW1/NW6/NW8/W1 – Except where otherwise stated see* *pp. 12 and 13.*

*Basement Services Arcade, Selfridges Store, Oxford St., W1* ☎ *(0171) 824 8844.*

**Landmark London,** 222 Marylebone Rd, NW1 6JQ, ☎ (0171) 631 8000, *Fax (0171) 631 8080*, « Victorian Gothic architecture, atrium and winter garden », – 350. MC AE ⓓ VISA JCB. — p. 5 HU a
***The Dining Room :*** **Meals** *(closed Saturday lunch and Sunday dinner)* 24.00/34.00 **st.** and a la carte 8.50 – 18.00 – **288 rm** 245.00/310.00 **s.**, 9 suites.

**Churchill Inter-Continental,** 30 Portman Sq., W1A 4ZX, ☎ (0171) 486 5800, *Fax (0171) 486 1255*, – 200. MC AE ⓓ VISA JCB. — AJ x
***Clementine's :*** **Meals** *(closed Saturday lunch)* 23.00 **t.** and a la carte 8.00 – 16.50 – **415 rm** 280.00, 33 suites.

**Langham Hilton,** 1 Portland Pl., Regent St., W1N 4JA, ☎ (0171) 636 1000, *Fax (0171) 323 2340*, – 250. MC AE ⓓ VISA JCB. — p. 5 JU e
***Memories :*** **Meals** 24.50/31.00 **st.** and dinner a la carte 16.00 – ***Tsar's :*** **Meals** *(closed Sunday)* a la carte 20.80/34.80 **st.** 16.00 – 17.50 – **359 rm** 250.00 **s.**, 20 suites.

**Selfridge,** Orchard St., W1H 0JS, ☎ (0171) 408 2080, *Fax (0171) 629 8849* – 220. MC AE ⓓ VISA JCB. — AK e
***Fletchers :*** **Meals** *(closed Saturday lunch, Sunday, 3 weeks August and Bank Holidays)* 20.00 **t.** and a la carte 14.00 – ***Orchard :*** **Meals** 10.95 **t.** and a la carte 11.50 – 12.50 – **290 rm** 175.00/225.00 **st.**, 4 suites – SB.

**The Leonard,** 15 Seymour St., W1H 5AA, ☎ (0171) 935 2010, *Fax (0171) 935 6700*, « Attractively furnished Georgian town houses » – 30. MC AE ⓓ VISA. — AK n
**Meals** (room service only) – 13.50 – **6 rm** 160.00/180.00 **s.**, **20 suites** 225.00/375.00 **s.**

**Radisson SAS Portman,** 22 Portman Sq., W1H 9FL, ☎ (0171) 208 6000, *Fax (0171) 208 6001,* – rm, rest, – 350. AE VISA JCB. AJ o
Meals 16.50 **st.** (lunch) and a la carte 22.95/36.00 **st.** 10.00 – 15.50 – **272 rm** 195.00/288.00 **st.**, 7 suites.

**London Regent's Park Hilton,** 18 Lodge Rd, NW8 7JT, ☎ (0171) 722 7722, *Fax (0171) 483 2408* – rm, – 150. AE VISA JCB.
***Minsky's :*** **Meals** 19.50/20.95 **st.** and a la carte 10.50 – ***Kashinoki :*** **Meals** - Japanese - *(closed Monday)* 18.50/32.50 **t.** and a la carte 16.00 – 15.50 – **376 rm** 155.00/175.00 **st.**, 1 suite. p. 5 GT v

**Montcalm,** Great Cumberland Pl., W1A 2LF, ☎ (0171) 402 4288, *Fax (0171) 724 9180* – rm, – 80. AE VISA JCB p. 17 EZ x
**Meals** - (see ***The Crescent*** below) – 15.95 – **110 rm** 175.00/230.00 **s.**, 10 suites.

**Clifton Ford,** 47 Welbeck St., W1M 8DN, ☎ (0171) 486 6600, *Fax (0171) 486 7492* – – 150. AE VISA BH a
**Meals** *(closed lunch Saturday and Sunday)* a la carte approx. 22.00 **t.** 6.50 – 14.50 – **183 rm** 210.00/225.00 **s.**, 2 suites.

**Berners,** 10 Berners St., W1A 3BE, ☎ (0171) 666 2000, *Fax (0171) 666 2001* – rm, rest, – 150. AE VISA JCB. EJ r
**Meals** 16.95 **t.** (lunch) and a la carte 20.65/33.70 **t.** 7.50 – 14.95 – **214 rm** 150.00/185.00 **st.**, 3 suites.

**Marble Arch Marriott,** 134 George St., W1H 6DN, ☎ (0171) 723 1277, *Fax (0171) 402 0666,* – rm, – 150. AE VISA JCB. p. 17 EZ i
**Meals** 16.00/20.00 **st.** and a la carte 6.50 – 12.95 – **240 rm** 190.00/210.00 **s.** – SB.

**Berkshire,** 350 Oxford St., W1N 0BY, ☎ (0171) 629 7474, *Fax (0171) 629 8156* – rm, – 40. AE VISA JCB. BK n
**Meals** 19.00 **st.** and a la carte 7.50 – 14.00 – **145 rm** 187.00/226.00 **s.**, 2 suites.

**Forte Posthouse Regent's Park,** Carburton St., W1P 8EE, ☎ (0171) 388 2300, *Fax (0171) 387 2806* – rm, rest, – 320. AE VISA JCB.
**Meals** *(closed lunch Saturday and Sunday)* 16.95 **st.** (dinner) and a la carte 18.80/28.75 **st.** 6.95 – 10.95 – **322 rm** 129.00/149.00 **st.**, 3 suites – SB. p. 5 JU i

**Saint Georges,** Langham Pl., W1N 8QS, ☎ (0171) 580 0111, *Fax (0171) 436 7997,* – rm, – 25. AE VISA JCB. p. 5 JU a
**Meals** a la carte 19.00/26.50 **st.** 7.00 – 12.95 – **83 rm** 145.00/155.00 **st.**, 3 suites – SB.

**Dorset Square,** 39-40 Dorset Sq., NW1 6QN, ☎ (0171) 723 7874, *Fax (0171) 724 3328,* « Attractively furnished Regency town houses », – . AE VISA.
***The Potting Shed :*** **Meals** *(closed Sunday lunch and Saturday)* 14.95 **t.** and a la carte – 12.50 – **37 rm** 98.00/180.00 **s.** p. 5 HU s

**Durrants,** 26-32 George St., W1H 6BJ, ☎ (0171) 935 8131, *Fax (0171) 487 3510,* « Converted Georgian houses with Regency façade » – rest, – 100. AE VISA. AH e
**Meals** 19.50 **t.** and a la carte 8.00 – 10.75 – **89 rm** 95.00/140.00 **st.**, 3 suites.

Rathbone without rest., Rathbone St., W1P 2LB, ☎ (0171) 636 2001, *Fax (0171) 636 3882* – p. 6 KU x
**72 rm.**

**Savoy Court,** Granville Pl., W1H 0EH, ☎ (0171) 408 0130, *Fax (0171) 493 2070* – rest, . AE VISA JCB. AK i
**Meals** 12.00 **st.** (dinner) and a la carte 14.50/20.50 **st.** 6.50 – 11.00 – **95 rm** 111.00/145.00 **s.**

**Langham Court,** 31-35 Langham St., W1N 5RE, ☎ (0171) 436 6622, *Fax (0171) 436 2303* – – 80. AE VISA JCB. p. 5 JU z
**Meals** 19.75 **st.** and a la carte – 11.50 – **56 rm** 129.00/145.00 **st.** – SB.

**Stakis London Harewood,** Harewood Row, NW1 6SE, ☎ (0171) 262 2707, *Fax (0171) 262 2975* – rm, rest, . AE VISA. p. 5 HU x
**Meals** (dinner only) 15.00 **st.** and a la carte 7.50 – 10.50 – **92 rm** 98.00/135.00 **st.** – SB.

**Orrery,** 55 Marylebone High St., W1M 3AE, ☎ (0171) 616 8000, *Fax (0171) 616 8080,* « Converted 19C stables, contemporary interior » – . AE VISA
*closed 25 December and 1 January* – **Meals** (booking essential) 23.50 **t.** (lunch) and dinner a la carte 26.00/41.50 **t.** 13.00. p. 5 IU a

**Interlude,** 5 Charlotte St., W1P 1HD, ☎ (0171) 637 0222, *Fax (0171) 637 0224* – . AE VISA JCB p. 6 KU r
*closed Saturday lunch, Sunday, 2 weeks August, 1 week Christmas-New Year and Bank Holidays* – **Meals** 22.50 **t.** (lunch) and a la carte 25.00/47.00 **t.**

XXX **The Crescent** (at Montcalm H.), Great Cumberland Pl., W1A 2LF, ☎ (0171) 402 4288, *Fax (0171) 724 9180* – ▤. MC AE ⓓ VISA JCB p. 17 EZ x
*closed Saturday lunch and Sunday* – **Meals** 18.00 **t.**

XX **Nico Central,** 35 Great Portland St., W1N 5DD, ☎ (0171) 436 8846, *Fax (0171) 436 3455* – ▤. MC AE ⓓ VISA JCB DJ c
*closed Saturday lunch, Sunday and 23 December-1 January* – **Meals** 25.00/27.00 **st.** ≬ 8.00.

XX **Oceana,** Jason Court, 76 Wigmore St., W1H 9DQ, ☎ (0171) 224 2992, *Fax (0171) 486 1216* – ▤. MC AE ⓓ VISA JCB BJ c
*closed Saturday lunch, Sunday and Bank Holidays* – **Meals** a la carte 15.50/26.50 **t.** ≬ 8.00.

XX **La Porte des Indes,** 32 Bryanston St., W1H 7AE, ☎ (0171) 224 0055, *Fax (0171) 224 1144* – ▤. MC AE ⓓ VISA AK r
*closed Saturday lunch and 25-26 December* – **Meals** - Indian - 20.00/31.00 **t.** and a la carte ≬ 4.75.

XX **Caldesi,** 15-17 Marylebone Lane, W1M 5FE, ☎ (0171) 935 9226, *Fax (0171) 929 0924* – ▤. MC AE ⓓ VISA JCB BJ e
*closed Saturday lunch, Sunday and Bank Holidays* – **Meals** - Italian - 15.00 **t.** and a la carte ≬ 7.00.

XX Bertorelli's, 19-23 Charlotte St., W1P 1HP, ☎ (0171) 636 4174, *Fax (0171) 467 8902* – ▤ p. 6 KU v
**Meals** - Italian rest.

XX **Stephen Bull,** 5-7 Blandford St., W1H 3AA, ☎ (0171) 486 9696, *Fax (0171) 490 3128* – ▤. MC AE VISA BH e
*closed Saturday lunch, Sunday, 24 December-2 January and Bank Holidays* – **Meals** a la carte 22.75/32.00 **t.** ≬ 10.50.

XX **Asuka,** Berkeley Arcade, 209a Baker St., NW1 6AB, ☎ (0171) 486 5026, *Fax (0171) 224 1741* – MC AE VISA JCB p. 5 HU u
*closed Saturday lunch, Sunday and Bank Holidays* – **Meals** - Japanese - 13.50/23.90 **t.** and a la carte ≬ 9.70.

XX **Gaylord,** 79-81 Mortimer St., W1N 7TB, ☎ (0171) 580 3615, *Fax (0171) 636 0860* – ▤. MC AE ⓓ VISA JCB p. 6 KU o
**Meals** - Indian - 16.95 **t.** and a la carte.

X **Justin de Blank,** 120-122 Marylebone Lane, W1M 5FZ, ☎ (0171) 486 5250, *Fax (0171) 935 4046* – MC AE VISA BH u
*closed Saturday, Sunday, Christmas, New Year and Bank Holidays* – **Meals** a la carte 14.45/19.95 **t.**

X **The Blenheim,** 21 Loudoun Rd, NW8 0NB, ☎ (0171) 625 1222, *Fax (0171) 328 1593,* 🏞 – MC AE ⓓ VISA p. 4 FS a
*closed 24-25 December and 1 January* – **Meals** a la carte 18.15/21.15 **t.**

X **L'Aventure,** 3 Blenheim Terr., NW8 0EH, ☎ (0171) 624 6232, *Fax (0171) 625 5548* – MC AE VISA p. 4 FS s
*closed Saturday lunch, 4 days Easter and first 2 weeks January* – **Meals** - French - 18.50/26.50 **t.** ≬ 7.50.

X **Union Café,** 96 Marylebone Lane, W1M 5FP, ☎ (0171) 486 4860 – MC VISA JCB BH c
*closed Sunday, Christmas-New Year and Bank Holidays* – **Meals** a la carte 17.00/24.00 **t.**

X **Zoe,** 3-5 Barrett St., St. Christopher's Pl., W1M 5HH, ☎ (0171) 224 1122, *Fax (0171) 935 5444* – ▤. MC AE ⓓ VISA BJ a
*closed Sunday and Bank Holidays* – **Meals** 12.50 **t.** and a la carte.

X **Le Muscadet,** 25 Paddington St., W1M 3RF, ☎ (0171) 935 2883, *Fax (0171) 935 2883* – ▤. MC VISA JCB p. 5 HU v
*closed Saturday lunch, Sunday, Easter, last 3 weeks August and 25-31 December* – **Meals** - French - 19.50 **t.** and a la carte ≬ 10.00.

## St. James's – ✉ *W1/SW1/WC2* – *pp. 12 and 13.*

**Ritz,** 150 Piccadilly, W1V 9DG, ☎ (0171) 493 8181, *Fax (0171) 493 2687,* 🏞 – |‡|, ⇜ rm, ▤ TV ☎ – 🏛 50. MC AE ⓓ VISA JCB. ✻ DN a
***Italian Garden*** : **Meals** (summer only) 29.00/38.50 **st.** and a la carte – (see also ***The Restaurant*** below) – ☕ 19.50 – **116 rm** 225.00/325.00 **s.**, 14 suites – SB.

**Dukes** 🌿, 35 St. James's Pl., SW1A 1NY, ☎ (0171) 491 4840, *Fax (0171) 493 1264* – |‡| ▤ TV ☎ – 🏛 50. MC AE ⓓ VISA JCB. ✻ EP x
**Meals** *(closed Saturday lunch)* (residents only) a la carte 24.45/33.95 ≬ 7.00 – ☕ 14.00 – **73 rm** 165.00/215.00 **s.**, 8 suites.

**Stafford** 🌿, 16-18 St. James's Pl., SW1A 1NJ, ☎ (0171) 493 0111, *Fax (0171) 493 7121* – |‡| ▤ TV ☎ – 🏛 35. MC AE ⓓ VISA JCB. ✻ DN u
**Meals** *(closed Saturday lunch)* 23.50/26.25 **st.** and a la carte ≬ 8.50 – ☕ 15.50 – **75 rm** 190.00/245.00, 5 suites.

**22 Jermyn Street,** 22 Jermyn St., SW1Y 6HL, ☎ (0171) 734 2353, *Fax (0171) 734 0750* – 🛗 📺 ☎. MC AE 🔘 VISA JCB. ✈ FM e
Meals (room service only) – ☕ 16.50 – **5 rm** 195.00 **s.**, **13 suites** 250.00/285.00 **s.**

**Cavendish,** 81 Jermyn St., SW1Y 6JF, ☎ (0171) 930 2111, *Fax (0171) 839 2125* – 🛗, ⇔ rm, ▤ rest, 📺 ☎ 🚗 – 🏛 80. MC AE 🔘 VISA JCB. ✈ EN i
Meals *(closed Saturday lunch)* 19.50 **st.** (lunch) and dinner a la carte approx. 24.50 **st.** 🍷 8.95 – ☕ 13.50 – **253 rm** 150.00/170.00 **s.**, 2 suites – SB.

**Pastoria,** 3-6 St. Martin's St., off Leicester Sq., WC2H 7HL, ☎ (0171) 930 8641, *Fax (0171) 925 0551* – 🛗, ⇔ rm, ▤ rest, 📺 ☎ – 🏛 60. MC AE 🔘 VISA. ✈ GM v
Meals a la carte 16.00/23.00 **st.** 🍷 7.50 – ☕ 11.00 – **58 rm** 140.00/191.00 **s.**

**Royal Trafalgar Thistle,** Whitcomb St., WC2H 7HG, ☎ (0171) 930 4477, *Fax (0171) 925 2149* – 🛗, ⇔ rm, 📺 ☎. MC AE 🔘 VISA JCB. ✈ GM r
Meals 13.50/17.50 **st.** and a la carte 🍷 5.75 – ☕ 13.50 – **108 rm** 127.00/165.00 **st.** – SB.

**Hospitality Inn Piccadilly** without rest., 39 Coventry St., W1V 8EL, ☎ (0171) 930 4033, *Fax (0171) 925 2586* – 🛗 ⇔ 📺 ☎. MC AE VISA JCB. ✈
☕ 12.50 – **91 rm** 137.00/170.00 **st.** FGM a

**The Restaurant** (at Ritz H.), 150 Piccadilly, W1V 9DG, ☎ (0171) 493 8181, *Fax (0171) 493 2687*, 🌳, « Elegant restaurant in Louis XVI style » – ▤. MC AE 🔘 VISA JCB DN a
Meals (dancing Friday and Saturday evenings) 29.00/38.50 **st.** and a la carte 42.50/93.50 **st.**

**Quaglino's,** 16 Bury St., SW1Y 6AL, ☎ (0171) 930 6767, *Fax (0171) 839 2866* – ▤. MC AE 🔘 VISA EN r
Meals (booking essential) 14.50 (lunch) and a la carte 19.50/50.50 🍷 10.50.

**Suntory,** 72-73 St. James's St., SW1A 1PH, ☎ (0171) 409 0201, *Fax (0171) 499 0208* – ▤. MC AE 🔘 VISA JCB EP z
*closed Sunday, Easter, 25-26 December, 1 January and Bank Holidays* – **Meals** - Japanese - 15.00/49.80 **st.** and a la carte 🍷 12.00.

**33,** 33 St. James's St., SW1A 1HD, ☎ (0171) 930 4272, *Fax (0171) 930 7618* – ▤. MC AE 🔘 VISA EN n
*closed Saturday lunch, Sunday, Christmas and Bank Holidays* – **Meals** a la carte 22.90/43.95 **st.** 🍷 16.00.

**L'Oranger,** 5 St. James's St., SW1A 1EF, ☎ (0171) 839 3774, *Fax (0171) 839 4330*, 🌳 – ▤. MC AE 🔘 VISA JCB EP a
*closed Sunday lunch and 1 week Christmas* – **Meals** 22.00/29.50 **t.** 🍷 8.00
**Spec.** Marinated tuna in crushed black pepper with white radish and green salad. Roasted sea bass with confit of peppers and aubergine crisps. Loin of pork and Toulouse sausage with piquant mustard grain sauce.

**Criterion Brasserie Marco Pierre White,** 224 Piccadilly, W1V 9LB, ☎ (0171) 930 0488, *Fax (0171) 930 8190*, « 19C Neo-Byzantine decor » – MC AE VISA
*closed 24-25 December and 1 January* – **Meals** 17.95 **t.** (lunch) and a la carte 24.75/32.95 **t.** 🍷 14.00. FM c

**Le Caprice,** Arlington House, Arlington St., SW1A 1RT, ☎ (0171) 629 2239, *Fax (0171) 493 9040* – ▤. MC AE 🔘 VISA DN c
*closed dinner 24 to 26 December, 1 January and August Bank Holiday* – **Meals** a la carte 25.00/44.75 **t.** 🍷 8.50.

**Cave** (at Caviar House), 161 Piccadilly, W1V 9DF, ☎ (0171) 409 0445, *Fax (0171) 493 1667* – ▤. MC AE 🔘 VISA DN s
*closed Sunday, 25-26 December and 1 January* – **Meals** 25.25 **t.** (lunch) and dinner a la carte 31.75/36.75 **t.** 🍷 10.75.

**The Avenue,** 7-9 St. James's St., SW1A 1EE, ☎ (0171) 321 2111, *Fax (0171) 321 2500* – ▤. MC AE 🔘 VISA EP e
Meals 19.50 **t.** (lunch) and dinner a la carte 18.85/31.20 **t.**

**Matsuri,** 15 Bury St., SW1Y 6AL, ☎ (0171) 839 1101, *Fax (0171) 930 7010* – ▤. MC AE 🔘 VISA JCB EN r
*closed Sunday, 25 December and Bank Holidays* – **Meals** - Japanese (Teppan-Yaki, Sushi) - 20.00/35.00 **t.** and a la carte 🍷 9.50.

## Soho – ✉ *W1/WC2* – *pp. 12 and 13.*

**Hampshire,** Leicester Sq., WC2H 7LH, ☎ (0171) 839 9399, *Fax (0171) 930 8122* – 🛗, ⇔ rm, ▤ 📺 ☎ – 🏛 80. MC AE 🔘 VISA. ✈ GM s
Meals 18.00 **st.** and a la carte 🍷 8.00 – ☕ 14.00 – **119 rm** 243.00/298.00 **s.**, 5 suites.

**Hazlitt's** without rest., 6 Frith St., W1V 5TZ, ☎ (0171) 434 1771, *Fax (0171) 439 1524*, « Early 18C town houses » – 📺 ☎. MC AE 🔘 VISA JCB. ✈ FK u
*closed 24 to 26 December* – **22 rm** 115.00/148.00 **s.**, 1 suite.

XXXX **The Café Royal Grill Room,** 68 Regent St., W1R 6EL, ☏ (0171) 437 1177, « Rococo decoration » – ▤. MC AE ⓓ VISA EM e
closed Saturday lunch and Sunday – **Meals** 22.50 **t.** (lunch) and a la carte 35.00/45.00 **t.** 🍷 10.15
**Spec.** Aspic of oyster Moscovite. Noisettes of lamb Edouard VII. Marjolaine.

XXX **Richard Corrigan at Lindsay House,** 21 Romilly St., W1V 5TG, ☏ (0171) 439 0450, *Fax (0171) 439 7849* – ▤. MC ⓓ VISA GL i
*closed Saturday lunch, Sunday and 25-26 December* – **Meals** a la carte 24.00/40.00 **t.** 🍷 7.00.

XXX **L'Escargot,** 48 Greek St., W1V 5LQ, ☏ (0171) 437 2679, *Fax (0171) 437 0790* – ▤. MC AE ⓓ VISA JCB GK e
***Ground Floor*** **:** **Meals** *(closed Saturday lunch, Sunday, 25-26 December and 1 January)* 17.50/23.45 **t.** and a la carte 23.45/29.45 **t.** 🍷 9.50 – ***First Floor*** **: Meals** *(closed Saturday lunch, Sunday, Monday and August)* 23.50/38.00 **t.** 🍷 9.50
**Spec.** Carpaccio of beef, parmesan crackling and herb dressing. Breast of duck with Anna potatoes and carrot, red wine jus. Ginger brûlée with a warm rhubarb compote.

XXX **Quo Vadis,** 26-29 Dean St., W1A 6LL, ☏ (0171) 437 9585, *Fax (0171) 434 9972* – ▤. MC AE VISA FK v
*closed lunch Saturday and Sunday* – **Meals** 17.95 **t.** (lunch) and a la carte 24.50/43.00 **t.** 🍷 9.00
**Spec.** Grilled scallops, gros sel, citrus fruits and beurre orange. Escalope of calf's liver with bacon and sage, pomme purée and sauce diable. Marquise of bitter chocolate with caramel sauce.

XX **Red Fort,** 77 Dean St., W1V 5HA, ☏ (0171) 437 2115, *Fax (0171) 434 0721* – ▤. MC AE ⓓ VISA FJK r
**Meals** - Indian - (buffet lunch) 12.50/25.00 **t.** and a la carte 🍷 7.50.

XX **Mezzo,** Lower ground floor, 100 Wardour St., W1V 3LE, ☏ (0171) 314 4000, *Fax (0171) 314 4040* – ▤. MC AE ⓓ VISA FK a
*closed lunch Saturday and 1 January and 25-26 December* – **Meals** 15.50 **t.** (lunch) and a la carte 21.00/35.50 **t.**

XX **Soho Soho,** (first floor), 11-13 Frith St., W1V 5TS, ☏ (0171) 494 3491, *Fax (0171) 437 3091*, 🍽 – ▤. MC AE ⓓ VISA JCB FK s
*closed Saturday lunch, Sunday, 25 December and Bank Holidays* – **Meals** 15.50 **t.** (dinner) and a la carte 20.25/30.40 **t.** 🍷 9.00.

XX **Lexington,** 45 Lexington St., W1R 3LG, ☏ (0171) 434 3401, *Fax (0171) 287 2997* – ▤. MC AE ⓓ VISA JCB EK e
*closed Saturday lunch, Sunday and Bank Holidays* – **Meals** a la carte 18.50/23.70 **t.** 🍷 7.50.

XX **Gopal's,** 12 Bateman St., W1V 5TD, ☏ (0171) 434 0840 – ▤. MC AE VISA FK e
*closed 25 and 26 December* – **Meals** - Indian - a la carte 15.95/23.40 **t.**

XX **Gay Hussar,** 2 Greek St., W1V 6NB, ☏ (0171) 437 0973, *Fax (0171) 437 4631* – ▤. MC AE ⓓ VISA GJ c
*closed Sunday and Bank Holidays* – **Meals** - Hungarian - 16.00 **t.** (lunch) and a la carte 19.25/24.95 **t.** 🍷 6.50.

XX **Atelier,** 41 Beak St., W1R 3LE, ☏ (0171) 287 2057, *Fax (0171) 287 1767* – MC AE ⓓ VISA EL a
*closed Saturday lunch, Sunday, 1 week Christmas and Bank Holidays* – **Meals** 19.50 **t.** and a la carte 25.75/28.00 **t.** 🍷 8.25.

X **dell 'Ugo,** 56 Frith St., W1V 5TA, ☏ (0171) 734 8300, *Fax (0171) 734 8784* – MC AE ⓓ VISA FK z
*closed Saturday lunch, Sunday and Bank Holidays* – **Meals** 12.50 **t.** (lunch) and a la carte 16.95/25.90 **t.**

X **Soho Spice,** 124-126 Wardour St., W1V 3LA, ☏ (0171) 434 0808, *Fax (0171) 434 0799* – MC AE ⓓ VISA FJ e
*closed Sunday* – **Meals** - Indian - 14.95 **t.** and a la carte.

X **Sri Siam,** 16 Old Compton St., W1V 5PE, ☏ (0171) 434 3544, *Fax (0171) 287 1311* – ▤. MC AE ⓓ VISA GK r
*closed Sunday lunch, 25-26 December and 1 January* – **Meals** - Thai - 11.50/16.80 **t.** and a la carte 🍷 8.00.

X **Alastair Little,** 49 Frith St., W1V 5TE, ☏ (0171) 734 5183 – MC AE VISA JCB
*closed Saturday lunch, Sunday and Bank Holidays* – **Meals** (booking essential) 25.00/30.00 **t.** 🍷 14.50. FK o

X **Bistrot Soho,** 64 Frith St., W1V 5TA, ☏ (0171) 734 4545, *Fax (0171) 287 1027* – ▤. MC AE ⓓ VISA FK z
*closed Sunday, 25-26 December and 1 January* – **Meals** 16.50 (lunch) and a la carte 18.00/31.25 🍷 8.75.

X **Poons,** 4 Leicester St., Leicester Sq., WC2H 7BL, ✆ (0171) 437 1528 – ▤. MC AE VISA JCB GM e
*closed 24 to 26 December* – **Meals** - Chinese - a la carte 9.50/13.60 **t.**

X **Fung Shing,** 15 Lisle St., WC2H 7BE, ✆ (0171) 734 0284, *Fax (0171) 734 0284* – ▤. MC AE ⓓ VISA GL a
*closed 24 to 26 December* – **Meals** - Chinese (Canton) - 15.00 **t.** and a la carte ₰ 5.00.

X **Saigon,** 45 Frith St., W1V 5TE, ✆ (0171) 437 7109, *Fax (0171) 734 1668* – ▤. MC AE ⓓ VISA FGK x
*closed Sunday, Easter, Christmas and Bank Holidays* – **Meals** - Vietnamese - a la carte 13.10/16.50.

## Strand and Covent Garden – ✉ *WC2* – *p. 17.*

**The Savoy,** Strand, WC2R 0EU, ✆ (0171) 836 4343, *Fax (0171) 240 6040*, ₺, ≘s, ▣ – |♦|, ⇐ rm, ▤ TV ☎ ⇔ – 🏃 500. MC AE ⓓ VISA JCB. ✂ DEY a
***Grill*** : **Meals** *(closed Saturday lunch, Sunday and August)* 29.75 **t.** (dinner) and a la carte 35.00/50.50 **st.** ₰ 9.95 – ***River*** : **Meals** 28.50/37.50 **st.** and a la carte 43.50/55.00 **st.** ₰ 9.95 – ☐ 17.50 – **154 rm** 240.00/365.00 **s.**, 48 suites – SB.

**Le Meridien Waldorf,** Aldwych, WC2B 4DD, ✆ (0171) 836 2400, *Fax (0171) 836 7244* – |♦|, ⇐ rm, ▤ rm, TV ☎ – 🏃 450. MC AE ⓓ VISA JCB. ✂ EX x
**Meals** a la carte 20.40/31.45 **t.** ₰ 12.00 – ☐ 15.00 – **286 rm** 210.00/280.00 **s.**, 6 suites – SB.

**The Howard,** Temple Pl., WC2R 2PR, ✆ (0171) 836 3555, *Fax (0171) 379 4547*, ⩽ – |♦|, ⇐ rm, ▤ TV ☎ ⇔ – 🏃 100. MC AE ⓓ VISA JCB. ✂ EX e
**Meals** 28.50 **st.** and a la carte – ☐ 18.00 – **133 rm** 200.00/260.00 **st.**, 2 suites.

XXX **Ivy,** 1 West St., WC2H 9NE, ✆ (0171) 836 4751, *Fax (0171) 497 3644* – ▤. MC AE ⓓ VISA p. 13 GK z
*closed dinner 24 to 26 December, 1 January and August Bank Holiday* – **Meals** a la carte 25.00/44.25 **t.** ₰ 9.50.

XXX **WestZENders,** 4a Upper St. Martin's Lane, WC2H 9EA, ✆ (0171) 497 0376, *Fax (0171) 497 0378* – ▤. MC AE ⓓ VISA JCB DX x
*closed 25 and 26 December* – **Meals** - Chinese - 19.80 **t.** (dinner) and a la carte 17.30/32.50 **t.**

XX **Rules,** 35 Maiden Lane, WC2E 7LB, ✆ (0171) 836 5314, *Fax (0171) 497 1081*, « London's oldest restaurant with collection of antique cartoons, drawings and paintings » – MC AE ⓓ VISA DX n
*closed 4 days Christmas* – **Meals** - English - a la carte 25.45/29.15 **t.** ₰ 5.95.

XX **Bank,** 1 Kingsway, Aldwych, ✆ (0171) 379 9797, *Fax (0171) 379 9014* – MC AE ⓓ VISA
*closed 25-26 December and Bank Holidays* – **Meals** 16.50 **t.** (lunch) and a la carte 16.00/29.00 **t.** EX s

XX **Christopher's,** 18 Wellington St., WC2E 7DD, ✆ (0171) 240 4222, *Fax (0171) 240 3357* – ▤. MC AE ⓓ VISA JCB EX z
*closed Sunday, 25-26 December and Bank Holidays* – **Meals** a la carte 22.00/33.50 **t.** ₰ 9.00.

XX **L'Estaminet,** 14 Garrick St., off Floral St., WC2 9BJ, ✆ (0171) 379 1432 – MC AE VISA JCB
*closed Sunday, Easter, 25 December and Bank Holidays* – **Meals** - French - a la carte 18.95/28.20 **t.** ₰ 7.00. DX a

XX **Sheekey's,** 28-32 St. Martin's Court, WC2N 4AL, ✆ (0171) 240 2565, *Fax (0171) 240 8114* – ▤. MC AE ⓓ VISA DX v
*closed Sunday, Easter, 25 December and Bank Holidays* – **Meals** - Seafood - 14.75/17.95 **t.** and a la carte.

XX **Bertorelli's,** 44a Floral St., WC2E 9DA, ✆ (0171) 836 3969, *Fax (0171) 836 1868* – ▤. MC AE ⓓ VISA JCB DX c
*closed Sunday and 25 December* – **Meals** - Italian - a la carte approx. 23.50 **t.** ₰ 7.50.

X **Stephen Bull St. Martin's Lane,** 12 Upper St. Martin's Lane, WC2 H9DL, ✆ (0171) 379 7811 – ▤. MC AE VISA DX r
*closed Saturday lunch, Sunday, 1 week Christmas-New Year and Bank Holidays* – **Meals** a la carte 22.95/27.95 **t.** ₰ 8.25.

X **Le Café du Jardin,** 28 Wellington St., WC2E 7BD, ✆ (0171) 836 8769, *Fax (0171) 836 4123* – ▤. MC AE ⓓ VISA EX a
**Meals** 13.50 **t.** and a la carte ₰ 7.00.

X **Magno's Brasserie,** 65a Long Acre, WC2E 9JH, ✆ (0171) 836 6077, *Fax (0171) 379 6184* – ▤. MC AE ⓓ VISA JCB DV e
**Meals** - French - 16.95 **t.** and a la carte ₰ 7.95.

X **Joe Allen,** 13 Exeter St., WC2E 7DT, ✆ (0171) 836 0651, *Fax (0171) 497 2148* – ▤. MC AE VISA EX c
*closed 24 and 25 December* – **Meals** 13.00 **t.** (lunch) and a la carte 19.00/28.00 **t.** ₰ 5.50.

**Victoria** - ✉ *SW1 - Except where otherwise stated see* *p. 16.*
*Victoria Station Forecourt, SW1V 1JU ☎ (0171) 824 8844.*

**St. James Court,** 45 Buckingham Gate, SW1E 6AF, ☎ (0171) 834 6655, *Fax (0171) 630 7587,* – rm, 180. VISA JCB. *Café Mediterranée* : Meals 15.00 **t.** (lunch) and a la carte 21.95/28.50 **t.** 8.50 – ***Inn of Happiness*** : Meals - Chinese - *(closed Saturday lunch)* 15.50/18.50 **t.** and a la carte 8.50 – (see also ***Auberge de Provence*** below) – 15.00 – **372 rm** 120.00/185.00 **s.**, 18 suites. CX i

**Royal Horseguards Thistle,** 2 Whitehall Court, SW1A 2EJ, ☎ (0171) 839 3400, *Fax (0171) 925 2263* – rm, 180. VISA JCB. Meals 22.50 **t.** and a la carte 6.95 – 13.50 – **278 rm** 179.00/275.00 **st.**, 3 suites. p. 10 LX a

**Stakis London St. Ermin's,** Caxton St., SW1H 0QW, ☎ (0171) 222 7888, *Fax (0171) 222 6914* – rm, rest, 250. VISA JCB. ***Cloisters*** : Meals *(closed lunch Saturday and Sunday)* 17.95/19.95 **st.** and a la carte – ***Caxton Grill*** : Meals *(closed Saturday lunch, Sunday and Bank Holidays)* a la carte 25.50/38.40 **st.** – 11.95 – **288 rm** 140.00/185.00 **st.**, 2 suites – SB. CX a

**Goring,** 15 Beeston Pl., Grosvenor Gdns., SW1W 0JW, ☎ (0171) 396 9000, *Fax (0171) 834 4393* – rm, 50. VISA. BX a
Meals 27.50/36.00 **st.** 9.00 – 14.50 – **72 rm** 155.00/180.00 **s.**, 4 suites.

**Grosvenor Thistle,** 101 Buckingham Palace Rd, SW1W 0SJ, ☎ (0171) 834 9494, *Fax (0171) 630 1978* – rm, 200. VISA JCB. BX e
Meals (carving rest.) 17.85 **st.** and a la carte 6.75 – 13.50 – **363 rm** 127.00/185.00 **st.**, 3 suites.

**Royal Westminster Thistle,** 49 Buckingham Palace Rd, SW1W 0QT, ☎ (0171) 834 1821, *Fax (0171) 931 7542* – rm, 180. VISA JCB. BX z
Meals 12.95/21.95 **st.** and a la carte 8.00 – 12.50 – **134 rm** 145.00/200.00 **st.** – SB.

**Dolphin Square,** Dolphin Sq., SW1V 3LX, ☎ (0171) 834 3800, *Fax (0171) 798 8735,* squash – rest, 50. VISA. Meals 15.70 **st.** and a la carte 12.20/23.75 **st.** 7.75 – 12.50 – **15 rm** 100.00/180.00 **st.**, **137 suites** 115.00/180.00 **st.** p. 10 KZ a

**Rubens,** 39-41 Buckingham Palace Rd, SW1W 0PS, ☎ (0171) 834 6600, *Fax (0171) 828 5401* – rm, rest, 75. VISA. Meals *(closed lunch Saturday and Sunday)* (carving lunch) 15.95 **st.** and dinner a la carte – 10.95 – **178 rm** 99.00/155.00 **s.**, 1 suite. BX n

Rochester, 69 Vincent Sq., SW1P 2PA, ☎ (0171) 828 6611, *Fax (0171) 233 6724* – rest, 60 CY e
**80 rm.**

**Holiday Inn London Victoria,** 2 Bridge Pl., SW1V 1QA, ☎ (0171) 834 8123, *Fax (0171) 828 1099,* – rm, 180. VISA JCB. BY i
Meals 17.95/25.00 **st.** and dinner a la carte – 11.50 – **212 rm** 150.00/160.00 **st.**

**Auberge de Provence** (at St. James Court H.), 45 Buckingham Gate, SW1E 6AF, ☎ (0171) 821 1899, *Fax (0171) 630 7587* – VISA JCB CX i
Meals - French - a la carte 24.65/30.75 **t.** 8.00.

**L'Incontro,** 87 Pimlico Rd, SW1W 8PH, ☎ (0171) 730 6327, *Fax (0171) 730 5062* – VISA JCB p. 15 FT u
*closed lunch Saturday and Sunday and 25-26 December* – **Meals** - Italian - 20.50 **t.** (lunch) and a la carte 27.50/51.50 **t.** 11.50.

**Santini,** 29 Ebury St., SW1W 0NZ, ☎ (0171) 730 4094, *Fax (0171) 730 0544* – VISA JCB ABX v
*closed lunch Saturday and Sunday and 25-26 December* – **Meals** - Italian - 19.75 **t.** (lunch) and a la carte 25.00/51.75 **t.** 11.00.

**Shepherd's,** Marsham Court, Marsham St., SW1P 4LA, ☎ (0171) 834 9552, *Fax (0171) 233 6047* – VISA p. 10 LZ z
*closed Saturday, Sunday and Bank Holidays* – **Meals** - English - (booking essential) 23.95 **t.** 5.50.

**Simply Nico,** 48a Rochester Row, SW1P 1JU, ☎ (0171) 630 8061 – VISA JCB CY a
*closed Saturday lunch, Sunday, 10 days Christmas, Easter and Bank Holidays* – Meals (booking essential) 25.00/27.00 **st.** 10.00.

**The Atrium,** 4 Millbank, SW1P 3JA, ☎ (0171) 233 0032, *Fax (0171) 233 0010* – VISA p. 10 LY s
*closed Saturday, Sunday, 25 December and 1 January* – **Meals** a la carte 20.50/25.95 **t.**

**Ken Lo's Memories of China,** 67-69 Ebury St., SW1W 0NZ, (0171) 730 7734, *Fax (0171) 730 2992* – ▤. MC AE ⓓ VISA JCB AY u
*closed Sunday lunch, 24 December-1 January and Bank Holidays* – **Meals** - Chinese - 20.50/24.50 **t.** and a la carte.

**Hunan,** 51 Pimlico Rd, SW1W 8NE, (0171) 730 5712, *Fax (0171) 730 8265* – MC AE VISA p. 9 IZ a
*closed Sunday lunch, 25-26 December and Bank Holidays* – **Meals** - Chinese (Hunan) - a la carte 11.40/48.80.

**Tate Gallery,** Tate Gallery, Millbank, SW1P 4RG, (0171) 887 8877, *Fax (0171) 887 8007,* « Rex Whistler murals » – ▤. MC AE VISA JCB p. 10 LZ c
*closed Sunday and 24 to 26 December* – **Meals** (booking essential) (lunch only) 25.00 **t.** and a la carte.

**Olivo,** 21 Eccleston St., SW1W 9LX, (0171) 730 2505, *Fax (0171) 824 8190* – ▤. MC AE VISA AY z
*closed lunch Saturday and Sunday and Bank Holidays* – **Meals** - Italian - 16.00 **t.** (lunch) and dinner a la carte 22.50/29.00 **t.** 8.00.

**La Poule au Pot,** 231 Ebury St., SW1W 8UT, (0171) 730 7763, *Fax (0171) 259 9651,* – ▤. MC AE ⓓ VISA JCB p. 9 IZ e
**Meals** - French - 13.95 **t.** (lunch) and a la carte 24.85/36.60 **t.** 5.50.

**Bray-on-Thames** *Berks. W : 34 m. by M 4 (junction 8-9) and A 308* 404 R 29 – *pop. 8 121* – ✉ *Maidenhead.*

**Waterside Inn** (Roux) with rm, Ferry Rd, SL6 2AT, (01628) 620691, *Fax (01628) 784710,* « Thames-side setting » –, ▤ rest, TV ☎ P. MC AE ⓓ VISA JCB.
*closed 26 December-30 January* – **Meals** - French - *(closed Tuesday lunch, Sunday dinner from mid October-mid April, Monday and Bank Holidays)* 30.50-45.50/69.50 **st.** and a la carte 59.80/88.50 **st.** 9.50 – **8 rm** 140.00/170.00 **st.**, 1 suite
**Spec.** Tronçonnettes de homard poêlées minute au Porto blanc. Filets de lapereau grillés aux marrons glacés. Soufflé chaud aux framboises.

**Reading** *Berks. at Shinfield W : 43 m. by M 4 and A 329 on A 327* 403 404 Q 29 – *pop. 213 474.*
*Town Hall, Blagrave St., RG1 1QH (0118) 956 6226.*

**L'Ortolan** (Burton-Race), The Old Vicarage, Church Lane, RG2 9BY, (01189) 883783, *Fax (01189) 885391,* – P. MC AE ⓓ VISA
*closed Sunday dinner and Monday* – **Meals** - French - 19.90/39.50 **t.** and a la carte 64.50/82.00 **t.** 11.00
**Spec.** Papillote de saumon et petits pois à la française. Pigeon sauvage rôti et sa garniture hivernale. Tarte soufflée au chocolat amer et sa glace au chocolat blanc.

**Oxford** *Oxon. at Great Milton NW : 49 m. by M 40 (junction 7) and A 329* 403 404 Q 28 – *pop. 118 795* – ✉ *Great Milton.*
*The Old School, Gloucester Green, OX1 2DA (01865) 726871.*

**Le Manoir aux Quat' Saisons** (Blanc), Church Rd, OX44 7PD, (01844) 278881, *Fax (01844) 278847,* «, « Part 15C and 16C manor house, gardens », park, – rest, ▤ rest, TV ☎ P – 35. MC AE ⓓ VISA JCB.
*closed 5 to 19 January* – **Meals** - French - 32.00 **t.** (lunch Monday to Saturday) and a la carte 63.00/78.00 **t.** – 13.50 – **16 rm** 195.00/295.00 **t.**, 3 suites – SB
**Spec.** Aiguillette de saumon sauvage en gelée, sauce aigre doux au caviar. Assiette d'agneau de lait et jus de cuisson. Soufflé à la pistache et sorbet cacao amer.

---

**BIRMINGHAM** *W. Mids.* 403 404 O 26 **Great Britain G.** – *pop. 965 928.*
**See :** *City★ – Museum and Art Gallery★★* JZ **M²** – *Barber Institute of Fine Arts★★ (at Birmingham University)* EX – *Cathedral of St. Philip (stained glass portrayals★)* KYZ.
**Envir. :** *Aston Hall★★* FV **M**.
**Exc. :** *Black Country Museum★, Dudley, NW : 10 m. by A 456 and A 4123.*
*Edgbaston, Church Rd (0121) 454 1736* FX – *Hilltop, Park Lane, Handsworth (0121) 554 4463* – *Hatchford Brook, Coventry Rd, Sheldon (0121) 743 9821* HX – *Brand Hall, Heron Rd, Oldbury, Warley (0121) 552 2195* – *Harborne Church Farm, Vicarage Rd, Harborne (0121) 427 1204* EX.
*Birmingham International Airport : (0121) 767 5511, E : 6 ½ m. by A 45.*
*Convention & Visitor Bureau, 2 City Arcade, B2 4TX (0121) 643 2514, Fax (0121) 616 1038 – Convention & Visitor Bureau, National Exhibition Centre, B40 1NT (0121) 780 4321 – Birmingham Airport, Information Desk, B26 3QJ, (0121) 767 7145/7146.*
*London 122 – Bristol 91 – Liverpool 103 – Manchester 86 – Nottingham 50.*

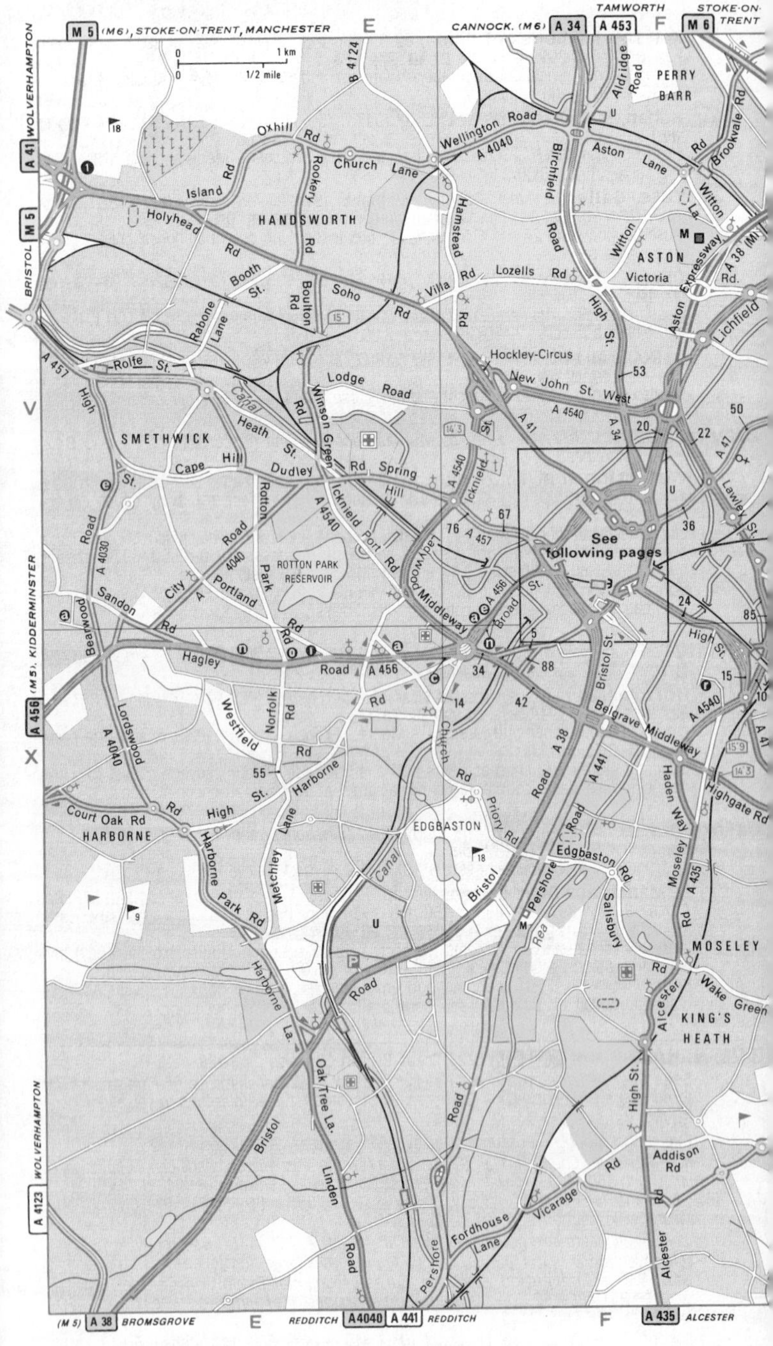

M 5 (M6), STOKE-ON-TRENT, MANCHESTER
CANNOCK. (M6) A 34
A 453 TAMWORTH
M 6 STOKE-ON-TRENT
A 41 WOLVERHAMPTON
M 5 BRISTOL
A 456 (M5), KIDDERMINSTER
A 4123 WOLVERHAMPTON
(M 5) A 38 BROMSGROVE
REDDITCH A4040
A 441 REDDITCH
A 435 ALCESTER
E
F
V
X
HANDSWORTH
PERRY BARR
ASTON
SMETHWICK
ROTTON PARK RESERVOIR
EDGBASTON
HARBORNE
MOSELEY
KING'S HEATH
See following pages
Hockley-Circus

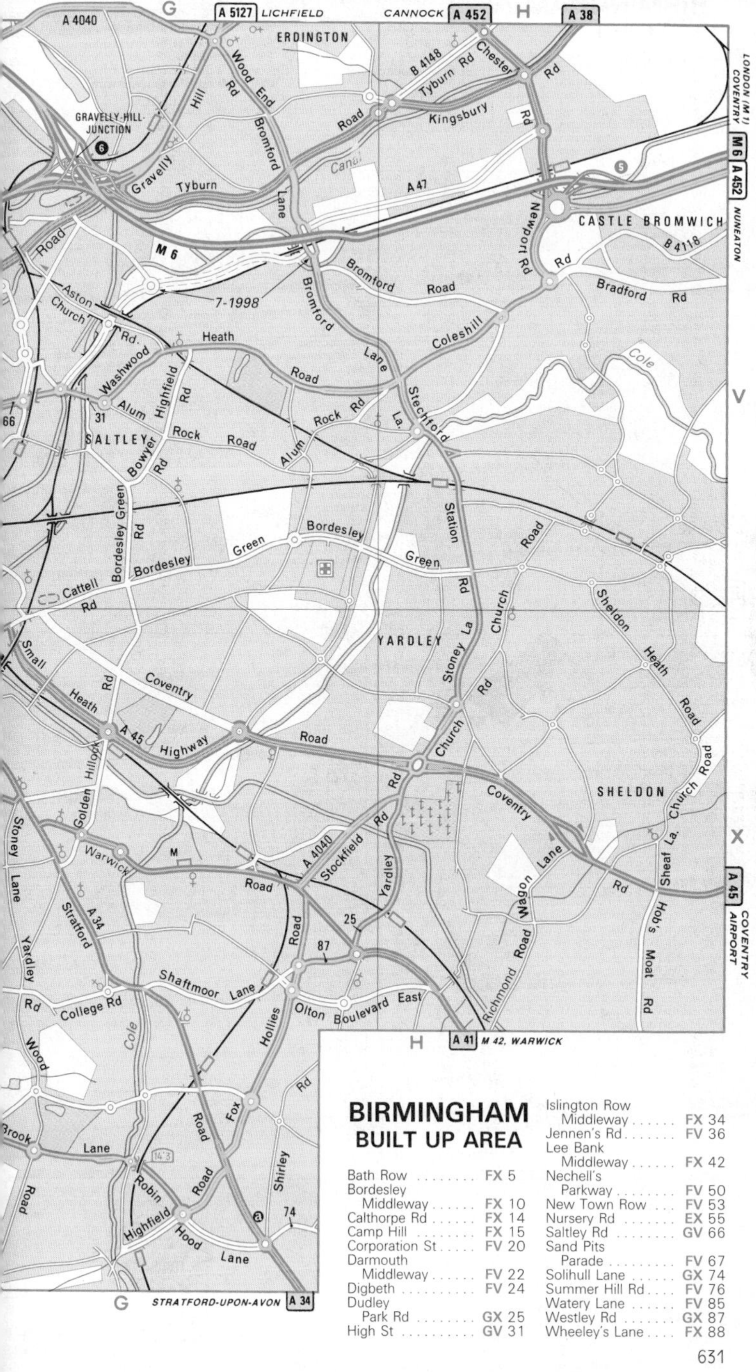


## BIRMINGHAM BUILT UP AREA

| | |
|---|---|
| Bath Row | FX 5 |
| Bordesley Middleway | FX 10 |
| Calthorpe Rd | FX 14 |
| Camp Hill | FX 15 |
| Corporation St | FV 20 |
| Darmouth Middleway | FV 22 |
| Digbeth | FV 24 |
| Dudley Park Rd | GX 25 |
| High St | GV 31 |
| Islington Row Middleway | FX 34 |
| Jennen's Rd | FV 36 |
| Lee Bank Middleway | FX 42 |
| Nechell's Parkway | FV 50 |
| New Town Row | FV 53 |
| Nursery Rd | EX 55 |
| Saltley Rd | GV 66 |
| Sand Pits Parade | FV 67 |
| Solihull Lane | GX 74 |
| Summer Hill Rd | FV 76 |
| Watery Lane | FV 85 |
| Westley Rd | GX 87 |
| Wheeley's Lane | FX 88 |

# BIRMINGHAM
## CENTRE

| | | |
|---|---|---|
| Albert St. | KZ | 2 |
| Bull St. | KY | 13 |
| Dale End | KZ | 21 |
| Hall St. | JY | 29 |
| Holloway Circus | JZ | 32 |
| James Watt Queensway | KY | 35 |
| Jennen's Rd | KY | 36 |
| Lancaster Circus | KY | 39 |
| Lancaster St. | KY | 41 |
| Masshouse Circus | KY | 43 |
| Moor St. Queensway | KZ | 46 |
| Navigation St. | JZ | 49 |
| Newton St. | KY | 52 |
| Paradise Circus | JZ | 56 |
| Priory Queensway | KY | 57 |
| St. Chads Circus | JKY | 62 |
| St. Chads Ringway | KY | 63 |
| St. Martin's Circus | KZ | 64 |
| Shadwell St. | KY | 70 |
| Smallbrook Queensway | KZ | 71 |
| Snow Hill Queensway | KY | 73 |
| Summer Row | JY | 77 |
| Temple Row | KZ | 80 |
| Waterloo St. | JZ | 84 |

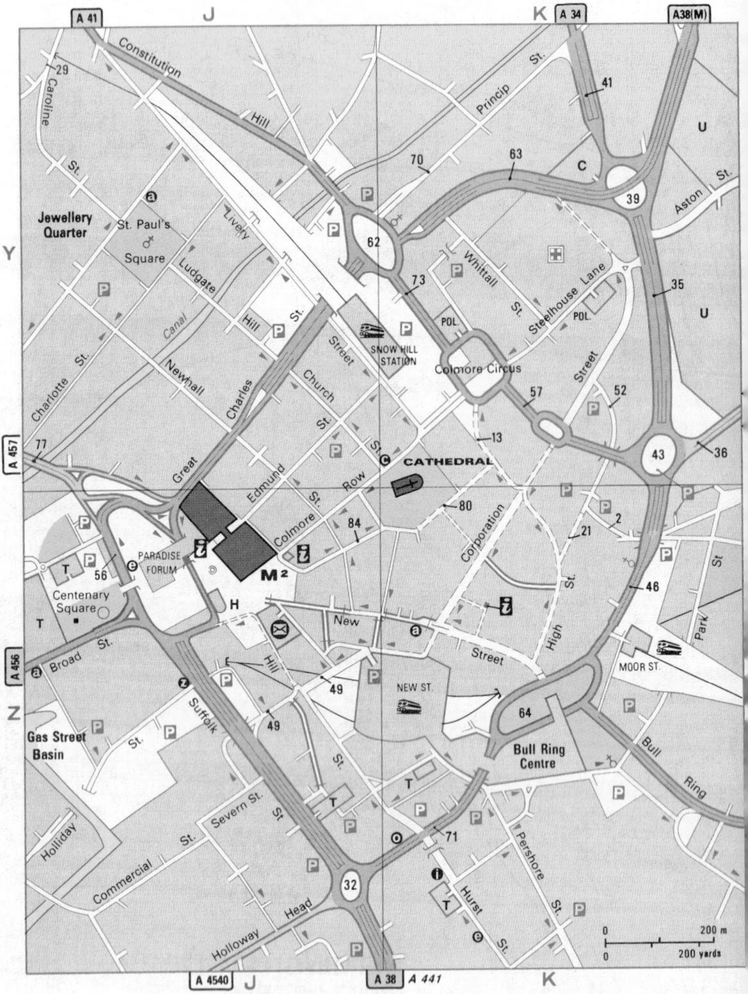


GREEN TOURIST GUIDES

Picturesque scenery, buildings
Attractive route
Touring programmes
Plans of towns and buildings.

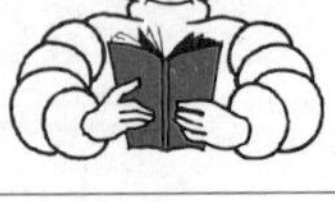

## STREET INDEX TO BIRMINGHAM TOWN PLANS

| Street | Grid | No. |
|---|---|---|
| Bull Ring Centre | KZ | |
| Corporation St. | KYZ | |
| New St. | JKZ | |
| Paradise Forum Shopping Centre | JZ | |
| Addison Rd | FX | |
| Albert St. | KZ | 2 |
| Alcester Rd | FX | |
| Aldridge Rd | FV | |
| Alum Rock Rd | GV | |
| Aston Church Rd | GV | |
| Aston Expressway | FV | |
| Aston Lane | FV | |
| Aston St. | KY | |
| Bath Row | FX | 5 |
| Bearwood Rd | EV | |
| Belgrave Middleway | FX | |
| Birchfield Rd | FV | |
| Booth St. | EV | |
| Bordesley Green | GV | |
| Bordesley Green Rd | GV | |
| Bordesley Middleway | FX | 10 |
| Boulton Rd | EV | |
| Bowyer Rd | GV | |
| Bradford Rd | HV | |
| Bristol Rd | EX | |
| Bristol St. | FX | |
| Broad St. | FV | |
| Bromford Lane | GV | |
| Bromford Rd | HV | |
| Brook Lane | GX | |
| Brookvale Rd | FV | |
| Bull Ring | KZ | |
| Bull Ring Centre | KZ | |
| Bull St. | KY | 13 |
| Calthorpe Rd | FX | 14 |
| Camp Hill | FX | 15 |
| Cape Hill | EV | |
| Caroline St. | JY | |
| Cattell Rd | GV | |
| Centenary Square | JZ | |
| Charlotte St. | JY | |
| Chester Rd | HV | |
| Church Lane | EV | |
| Church Rd EDGBASTON | FX | |
| Church Rd SHELDON | HX | |
| Church Rd YARDLEY | HX | |
| Church St. | JY | |
| City Rd | EV | |
| Coleshill Rd | HV | |
| College Rd | GX | |
| Colmore Circus | KY | |
| Colmore Row | JZ | |
| Commercial St. | JZ | |
| Constitution Hill | JY | |
| Corporation St. | FV | 20 |
| Court Oak Rd | EX | |
| Coventry Rd | GX | |
| Dale End | KZ | 21 |
| Darmouth Middleway | FV | 22 |
| Digbeth | FV | 24 |
| Dudley Park Rd | GX | 25 |
| Dudley Rd | EV | |
| Edgbaston Rd | FX | |
| Edmund St. | JYZ | |
| Fordhouse Lane | FX | |
| Fox Hollies Rd | GX | |
| Golden Hillock Rd | GX | |
| Gravelly Hill | GV | |
| Gravelly Hill Junction | GV | |
| Great Charles St. | JY | |
| Hadden Way | FX | |
| Hagley Rd | EX | |
| Hall St. | JY | 29 |
| Hampstead Rd | FV | |
| Harborne Lane | EX | |
| Harborne Park Rd | EX | |
| Harborne Rd | EX | |
| Heath St. | EV | |
| Highfield Rd | GX | |
| Highfield Rd SALTLEY | GV | |
| Highgate Rd | FX | |
| High St. | KZ | |
| High St. ASTON | FV | |
| High St. BORDESLEY | FX | |
| High St. HARBORNE | EX | |
| High St. KING'S HEATH | FX | |
| High St. SALTLEY | GV | 31 |
| High St. SMETHWICK | EV | |
| Hill St. | JZ | |
| Hob's Moat Rd | HX | |
| Hockley Circus | FV | |
| Hockley Hill | JY | |
| Holliday St. | JZ | |
| Holloway Circus | JZ | 32 |
| Holloway Head | JZ | |
| Holyhead Rd | EV | |
| Hurst St. | KZ | |
| Icknield Port Rd | EV | |
| Icknield St. | FV | |
| Island Rd | EV | |
| Islington Row Middleway | FX | 34 |
| James Watt Queensay | KY | 35 |
| Jennen's Rd | FV | 36 |
| Kingsbury Rd | HV | |
| Ladywood Middleway | EV | |
| Lancaster Circus | KY | 39 |
| Lancaster St. | KY | 41 |
| Lawley St. | FV | |
| Lee Bank Middleway | FX | 42 |
| Lichfield Rd | FV | |
| Linden Rd | EX | |
| Livery St. | JY | |
| Lodge Rd | EV | |
| Lordswood Rd | EX | |
| Lozells Rd | FV | |
| Ludgate Hill | JY | |
| Masshouse Circus | KY | 43 |
| Metchley Lane | EX | |
| Moor St. Queensway | KZ | 46 |
| Moseley Rd | FX | |
| Navigation St. | JZ | 49 |
| Nechell's Parkway | FV | 50 |
| Newhall St. | JY | |
| New John St. West | FV | |
| Newport Rd | HV | |
| New St. | JZ | |
| Newton St. | KY | 52 |
| New Town Row | FV | 53 |
| Norfolk Rd | EX | |
| Nursery Rd | EX | 55 |
| Oak Tree Lane | EX | |
| Olton Bd East | GX | |
| Oxhill Rd | EV | |
| Paradise Circus | JZ | 56 |
| Park St. | KZ | |
| Pershore Rd | FX | |
| Pershore St. | KZ | |
| Portland Rd | EV | |
| Princip St. | KY | |
| Priory Queensway | KY | 57 |
| Priory Rd | FX | |
| Rabone Lane | EV | |
| Richmond Rd | HX | |
| Robin Hood Lane | GX | |
| Rolfe St. | EV | |
| Rookery Rd | EV | |
| Rotton Park Rd | EV | |
| St. Chads Circus | JY | 62 |
| St. Chads Ringway | KY | 63 |
| St. Martin's Circus | KZ | 64 |
| St. Paul's Square | JY | |
| Salisbury Rd | FX | |
| Saltley Rd | GV | 66 |
| Sandon Rd | EV | |
| Sand Pits Parade | FV | 67 |
| Severn St. | JZ | |
| Shadwell St. | KY | 70 |
| Shaftmoor Lane | GX | |
| Sheaf Lane | HX | |
| Sheldon Heath Rd | HX | |
| Shirley Rd | GX | |
| Smallbrook Queensway | KZ | 71 |
| Small Heath Highway | GX | |
| Snow Hill Queensway | KY | 73 |
| Soho Rd | EV | |
| Solihull Lane | GX | 74 |
| Spring Hill | EV | |
| Station Rd | HV | |
| Stechford Lane | HV | |
| Steelhouse Lane | KY | |
| Stockfield Rd | GX | |
| Stoney La MOSELEY | GX | |
| Stoney La SHELDON | HX | |
| Stratford Rd | GX | |
| Suffolk St. | JZ | |
| Summer Hill Rd | FV | 76 |
| Summer Row | JY | 77 |
| Temple Row | KZ | 80 |
| Tyburn Rd | GV | |
| Vicarage Rd | FX | |
| Victoria Rd | FV | |
| Villa Rd | FV | |
| Wagon Lane | HX | |
| Wake Green Rd | FX | |
| Warwick Rd | GX | |
| Washwood Heath Rd | GV | |
| Waterloo St. | JZ | 84 |
| Watery Lane | FX | 85 |
| Wellington Rd | FV | |
| Westfield Rd | EX | |
| Westley Rd | GX | 87 |
| Wheeley's Lane | FX | 88 |
| Whittal St. | KY | |
| Winson Green Rd | EV | |
| Witton Lane | FV | |
| Witton Rd | FV | |
| Wood End Rd | GV | |
| Yardley Rd | HX | |
| Yardley Wood Rd | GX | |

Pleasant hotels and restaurants
are shown in the Guide by a red sign.
Please send us the names
of any where you have enjoyed your stay.
Your **Michelin Guide** will be even better.

**Hyatt Regency,** 2 Bridge St., B1 2JZ, ✆ (0121) 643 1234, *Fax (0121) 616 2323*, ≤, Ⓛ, ⌂s, ◻ – |♦|, ⇹ rm, ▤ ◻ ☎ ⇔ – 🏫 250. ⓒ AE ⓓ VISA. ✂ JZ a
Meals – (see ***Number 282*** below) – ☕ 12.00 – **308 rm** 155.00/180.00 **st.**, 11 suites.

**Swallow,** 12 Hagley Rd, B16 8SJ, ✆ (0121) 452 1144, *Fax (0121) 456 3442*, Ⓛ, ◻ – |♦|, ⇹ rm, ▤ ◻ ☎ ♿ Ⓟ – 🏫 25. ⓒ AE ⓓ VISA FX c
***Langtrys :*** Meals *(closed Sunday)* a la carte 24.15/30.00 **t.** 🍷 8.50 – (see also ***Sir Edward Elgar's*** below) – **94 rm** ☕ 150.00/190.00 **st.**, 4 suites – SB.

**Holiday Inn Crowne Plaza,** Central Sq., Holliday St., B1 1HH, ✆ (0121) 631 2000, *Fax (0121) 643 9018*, Ⓛ, ⌂s, ◻ – |♦|, ⇹ rm, ▤ ◻ ☎ ♿ Ⓟ – 🏫 150. ⓒ AE ⓓ VISA JCB. ✂ JZ z
Meals *(closed Saturday lunch)* (carving lunch) 15.95/19.50 **st.** and dinner a la carte 🍷 9.00 – ☕ 11.95 – **281 rm** 135.00/145.00 **st.**, 3 suites – SB.

**Copthorne,** Paradise Circus, B3 3HJ, ✆ (0121) 200 2727, *Fax (0121) 200 1197*, Ⓛ, ⌂s, ◻ – |♦|, ⇹ rm, ▤ rest, ◻ ☎ ♿ Ⓟ – 🏫 180. ⓒ AE ⓓ VISA. ✂ JZ e
Meals 21.95 **st.** (dinner) and a la carte 13.85/25.70 **st.** – ☕ 11.75 – **209 rm** 120.00/150.00 **st.**, 3 suites – SB.

**Jonathan's,** 16-24 Wolverhampton Rd, Oldbury, B68 0LH, W : 4 m. by A 456 ✆ (0121) 429 3757, *Fax (0121) 434 3107*, « Authentic Victorian furnishings and memorabilia » – ⇹ rest, ◻ ☎ Ⓟ. ⓒ AE ⓓ VISA
Meals - English - (closed Sunday dinner) 15.90 **t.** and a la carte 🍷 6.75 – **21 rm** ☕ 75.00/85.00 **st.**, 11 suites 125.00 **st.** – SB.

**The Burlington,** 6 Burlington Arcade, 126 New St., B2 4JQ, ✆ (0121) 643 9191, *Fax (0121) 643 5075*, Ⓛ, ⌂s – |♦|, ⇹ rm, ▤ rest, ◻ ☎ – 🏫 450. ⓒ AE ⓓ VISA
*closed 25 December* – ***Berlioz :*** Meals *(closed lunch Saturday and Sunday)* 17.95 **st.** and a la carte 🍷 6.50 – ☕ 10.95 – **107 rm** 105.00/115.00 **st.**, 5 suites – SB. KY a

**Grand,** Colmore Row, B3 2DA, ✆ (0121) 607 9988, *Fax (0121) 233 1465* – |♦|, ⇹ rm, ▤ rest, ◻ ☎ – 🏫 500. ⓒ AE ⓓ VISA JCB JKY c
Meals 12.00/14.50 **st.** and a la carte. 🍷 8.00 – ☕ 10.50 – **170 rm** 110.00/135.00 **st.**, 2 suites – SB.

**Plough and Harrow,** 135 Hagley Rd, Edgbaston, B16 8LS, ✆ (0121) 454 4111, *Fax (0121) 454 1868*, 🌳 – |♦| ⇹ ◻ ☎ Ⓟ – 🏫 70. ⓒ AE ⓓ VISA JCB. ✂
Meals *(closed Saturday lunch)* a la carte 18.40/26.70 **st.** 🍷 6.45 – ☕ 9.25 – **42 rm** 85.00/100.00 **st.**, 2 suites – SB. EX a

**Forte Posthouse Birmingham City,** Smallbrook, Queensway, B5 4EW, ✆ (0121) 643 8171, *Fax (0121) 631 2528*, Ⓛ, ⌂s, ◻, squash – |♦|, ⇹ rm, ▤ ◻ ☎ Ⓟ – 🏫 630. ⓒ AE ⓓ VISA JCB KZ o
Meals 12.95/16.25 **t.** and a la carte 🍷 8.85 – ☕ 9.95 – **252 rm** 94.00 **st.**, 1 suite – SB.

**Strathallan Thistle,** 225 Hagley Rd, Edgbaston, B16 9RY, ✆ (0121) 455 9777, *Fax (0121) 454 9432* – |♦|, ⇹ rm, ▤ rest, ◻ ☎ Ⓟ – 🏫 170. ⓒ AE ⓓ VISA JCB. ✂
Meals *(closed Saturday lunch)* 17.25 **st.** (dinner) and a la carte 15.50/27.45 **st.** 🍷 5.85 – ☕ 10.50 – **148 rm** 97.00/131.00 **st.**, 3 suites – SB. EX i

**Apollo,** 243 Hagley Rd, Edgbaston, B16 9RA, ✆ (0121) 455 0271, *Fax (0121) 456 2394* – |♦|, ⇹ rm, ▤ rest, ◻ ☎ Ⓟ – 🏫 150. ⓒ AE ⓓ VISA JCB EX o
Meals *(closed Saturday lunch)* (carving lunch) 12.95/14.95 **st.** and a la carte 🍷 5.50 – ☕ 9.50 – **124 rm** 75.00/105.00 **st.**, 2 suites – SB.

**Quality Norfolk,** 267 Hagley Rd, B16 9NA, ✆ (0121) 454 8071, *Fax (0121) 455 6149* – |♦|, ⇹ rm, ▤ rest, ◻ ☎ Ⓟ – 🏫 100. ⓒ AE ⓓ VISA p. 4 EX n
Meals *(closed Sunday lunch)* (carving rest.) 8.50/15.00 **st.** and dinner a la carte 🍷 6.00 – **166 rm** ☕ 59.50/69.50 **st.** – SB.

**Novotel,** 70 Broad St., B1 2HT, ✆ (0121) 643 2000, *Fax (0121) 643 9796*, Ⓛ, ⌂s – |♦|, ⇹ rm, ▤ rest, ◻ ☎ ♿ Ⓟ – 🏫 250. ⓒ AE ⓓ VISA. ✂ FV e
Meals 15.00 **st.** and a la carte 🍷 5.75 – ☕ 8.95 – **148 rm** 79.00/85.00 **st.**

**Chamberlain,** Alcester St., B12 0PJ, ✆ (0121) 606 9000, *Fax (0121) 606 9001* – |♦| ⇹, ▤ rest, ◻ ☎ ⇔ – 🏫 400. ⓒ AE ⓓ VISA JCB. ✂ p. 4 FX r
Meals *(closed Saturday lunch)* (carving rest.) 6.00/10.00 **st.** – **250 rm** ☕ 35.00/80.00 **st.**

**Sir Edward Elgar's** (at Swallow H.), 12 Hagley Rd, B16 8SJ, ✆ (0121) 452 1144, *Fax (0121) 456 3442* – ▤ Ⓟ. ⓒ AE ⓓ VISA FX c
*closed Saturday lunch* – **Meals** 21.50/27.00 **t.** and a la carte 🍷 8.50.

**Leftbank,** 79 Broad St., B15 1QA, ✆ (0121) 643 4464, *Fax (0121) 643 4464* – ⓒ AE ⓓ VISA JCB FV a
*closed Saturday lunch, Sunday, 25 December-10 January and Bank Holidays* – **Meals** 14.50 **t.** (lunch) and dinner a la carte 20.30/30.50 **t.** 🍷 6.50.

**Number 282** (at Hyatt Regency H.), 2 Bridge St., B1 2JZ, ✆ (0121) 643 1234, *Fax (0121) 616 2323* – ▤ ⇔. ⓒ AE ⓓ VISA JZ a
*closed Saturday* – **Meals** 16.00/17.00 **st.**

**Shimla Pinks,** 214 Broad St., B15 1AY, (0121) 633 0366, *Fax (0121) 633 0366* – . MC AE D VISA FX n
*closed lunch Saturday and Sunday, 25 December and 1 January* – **Meals** - Indian - 6.95/19.95 **t.** and a la carte 6.95.

**Henry's,** 27 St. Paul's Sq., B3 1RB, (0121) 200 1136, *Fax (0121) 200 1190* – . MC AE D VISA JY a
**Meals** - Chinese (Canton) - 15.00 **t.** and a la carte 7.00.

**Dynasty,** 93-103 Hurst St., B5 4TE, (0121) 622 1410, *Fax (0121) 622 1410* – MC AE D VISA JCB KZ e
*closed Christmas and Bank Holidays* – **Meals** - Chinese - (lunch by arrangement)/dinner a la carte 14.00/24.00 **t.**

**Maharaja,** 23-25 Hurst St., B5 4AS, (0121) 622 2641, *Fax (0121) 662 4021* – . MC AE D VISA KZ i
*closed Sunday and Bank Holidays* – **Meals** - North Indian - a la carte 9.00/11.85 **t.** 6.25.

**Franzl's,** 151 Milcote Rd, Bearwood, Smethwick, B67 5BN, (0121) 429 7920, *Fax (0121) 429 1615* – MC AE D VISA JCB EV a
*closed Sunday, Monday and August* – **Meals** - Austrian - (dinner only) 13.45/19.45 **t.** 5.15.

**at Hall Green** *SE : 5 ¾ m. by A 41 on A 34 – Birmingham :*

**Robin Hood,** Stratford Rd, B28 9ES, (0121) 745 9900, *Fax (0121) 733 1075* – . MC AE VISA GX a
*closed 1 week Christmas* – **Meals** (grill rest.) a la carte approx. 12.20 **st.** 4.95 – **30 rm** 70.00/85.00 **st.** – SB.

**at Birmingham Airport** *SE : 9 m. by A 45 –* HX *– Birmingham :*

**Novotel,** Passenger Terminal, B26 3QL, (0121) 782 7000, *Fax (0121) 782 0445* – , rm, rest, – 35. MC AE D VISA
*closed 25 December* – **Meals** 8.00/16.00 **st.** and a la carte 5.55 – 8.75 – **195 rm** 88.00 **st.** – SB.

**Forte Posthouse Birmingham Airport,** Coventry Rd, B26 3QW, on A 45 (0121) 782 8141, *Fax (0121) 782 2476* – rm, – 130. MC AE D VISA JCB
**Meals** a la carte 18.10/25.40 **st.** – 9.95 – **136 rm** 79.00 **st.** – SB.

**at National Exhibition Centre** *SE : 9 ½ m. on A 45 –* HX *– Birmingham :*

**Birmingham Metropole,** Bickenhill, B40 1PP, (0121) 780 4242, *Fax (0121) 780 3923,* , , – , rm, – 2000. MC AE D VISA
*closed 25 and 26 December* – **Meals** (carving rest.) 24.75 **t.** and a la carte 12.00 – ***Primavera :*** **Meals** - Italian - *(closed Saturday lunch and Sunday)* a la carte 18.60/40.55 **t.** 8.50 – **787 rm** 187.00/235.00 **t.**, 15 suites – SB.

**Arden,** Coventry Rd, B92 0EH, (01675) 443221, *Fax (01675) 443221,* , , – , rm, – 170. MC AE D VISA.
**Meals** (bar lunch Saturday) 15.00 **st.** and a la carte 6.35 – 9.00 – **146 rm** 79.00/129.00 **st.**

**at Northfield** *SW : 6 m. by A 38 –* EX *– Birmingham :*

**Norwood,** 87-89 Bunbury Rd, B31 2ET, *via Church rd* (0121) 411 2202, *Fax (0121) 411 2202,* – . MC AE D VISA JCB
*closed 24 to 26 December* – **Meals** *(closed Friday to Sunday)* (dinner only) 16.50 **st.** 4.50 – **18 rm** 69.00/74.00 **st.**

**at Kings Norton** *SW : 7 m. on A 441 –* EX *– Birmingham :*

**Mill House,** 180 Lifford Lane, B30 3NT, (0121) 459 5800, *Fax (0121) 459 8553,* – . MC AE D VISA JCB.
*closed 1 to 16 January* – **Meals** – (see ***Lombard Room*** below) – **8 rm** 95.00/105.00 **t.**, 1 suite – SB.

**Lombard Room,** 180 Lifford Lane, B30 3NT, (0121) 459 5800, *Fax (0121) 459 8553,* , – . MC AE D VISA JCB
*closed lunch Monday and Saturday, Sunday dinner, 1-16 January and Bank Holidays* – **Meals** 16.85/23.50 **t.**

**at Great Barr** *NW : 6 m. on A 34 –* FV *– Birmingham :*

**Forte Posthouse Birmingham,** Chapel Lane, B43 7BG, (0121) 357 7444, *Fax (0121) 357 7503,* , , – rm, – 120. MC AE D VISA
**Meals** a la carte 19.00/26.00 7.00 – 9.95 – **192 rm** 89.00 **st.** – SB.

**at West Bromwich** *NW : 6 m. on A 41 – EV – ✉ Birmingham :*

**Moat House Birmingham,** Birmingham Rd, B70 6RS, ✆ (0121) 609 9988, *Fax (0121) 525 7403,* – , rm, rest, – 180. VISA
**Meals** 13.95 **st.** and a la carte – 8.50 – **168 rm** 99.00/114.00 **st.** – SB.

---

**BATH** *Bath & North East Somerset* 403 404 M 29 – *pop. 85 202.*

*Abbey Chambers, Abbey Churchyard, BA1 1LY ✆ (01225) 477101.*
*London 119 – Birmingham 98.*

**Lettonie** (Blunos) with rm, 35 Kelston Rd, BA1 3QH, ✆ (01225) 446676, *Fax (01225) 447541,* ←, – rest, . VISA
*closed Sunday, Monday, 2 weeks August and 2 weeks Christmas* – **Meals** 21.95/38.50 **t.** 15.00 – **5 rm** 75.00/135.00 **t.**
**Spec.** Borsch terrine with shredded beef, piragi and soured cream. Calves sweetbreads with ham and chicken mousse, lemon cream sauce. Apple and vanilla parfait with an apple sorbet.

---

**EDINBURGH** *Edinburgh City* 401 K 16 **Scotland G.** – *pop. 418 914.*

**See :** *City★★★ Edinburgh International Festival★★★ (August) – National Gallery of Scotland★★* DY **M**[4] *– Royal Botanic Garden★★★ – The Castle★★ AC* DYZ *: Site★★★ – Palace Block (Honours of Scotland★★★) – St. Margaret's Chapel (※★★★) – Great Hall (Hammerbeam Roof★★) – ←★★ from Argyle and Mill's Mount* DZ *– Abbey and Palace of Holyroodhouse★★ AC (Plasterwork Ceilings★★★, ※★★ from Arthur's Seat) – Royal Mile★★ : St. Giles' Cathedral★★ (Crown Spire★★★)* EYZ *– Gladstone's Land★ AC* EYZ **A** *– Canongate Talbooth★* EY **B** *– New Town★★ (Charlotte Square★★★* CY **14** *– Royal Museum of Scotland★★* EZ **M**[2] *– The Georgian House ★ AC* CY **D** *– Scottish National Portrait Gallery★* EY **M**[3] *– Dundas House★* EY **E***) – Scottish National Gallery of Modern Art★ – Victoria Street★* EZ **84** *Scott Monument★ (←★) AC* EY **F** *– Craigmillar Castle★ AC – Calton Hill (※★★★ AC from Nelson's Monument)* EY.

**Envir. :** *Edinburgh Zoo★★ AC – Hill End Ski Centre (※★★) AC , S : 5 ½ m. by A 702 – The Royal Observatory (West Tower ←★) AC – Ingleston, Scottish Agricultural Museum★, W : 6 ½m. by A 8.*

**Exc. :** *Rosslyn Chapel★★ AC (Apprentice Pillar★★★) S : 7 ½ m. by A 701 and B 7006 – Forth Bridges★★, NW : 9 ½ m. by A 90 – Hopetoun House★★ AC , NW : 11 ½ m. by A 90 and A 904 – Dalmeny★ (Dalmeny House★ AC , St. Cuthbert's Church★ - Norman South Doorway★★) NW : 7 m. by A 90 – Crichton Castle (Italianate courtyard range★) AC, SE : 10 m. by A 7 and B 6372.*

*18, 18 Braid Hills, Braid Hills Rd ✆ (0131) 447 6666 – 18 Craigmillar Park, 1 Observatory Rd ✆ (0131) 667 2837 – 18 Carrick Knowe, Glendevon Park ✆ (0131) 337 1096 – 18 Duddingston Road West ✆ (0131) 661 1005 – 18 Silverknowes, Parkway ✆ (0131) 336 3843 – 18 Liberton, 297 Gilmerton Rd ✆ (0131) 664 3009 18, 18 Dalmahoy Hotel C.C., Kirknewton ✆ (0131) 333 4105/1845 – 9 Portobello, Stanley St. ✆ (0131) 669 4361.*

*Edinburgh Airport : ✆ (0131) 333 1000, W : 6 m. by A 8* – **Terminal :** *Waverley Bridge.*

*Edinburgh & Scotland Information Centre, 3 Princes St., EH2 2QP ✆ (0131) 557 1700 – Edinburgh Airport, Tourist Information Desk ✆ (0131) 333 2167.*
*Glasgow 46 – Newcastle upon Tyne 105.*

Plan opposite

**Balmoral,** Princes St., EH2 2EQ, ✆ (0131) 556 2414, *Fax (0131) 557 3747,* , , – , rm, – 350. VISA JCB. EY n
***Hadrian's* :** **Meals** a la carte 28.75/41.00 **st.** 7.25 – (see also ***Number One*** below) – 15.00 – **165 rm** 170.00/205.00 **st.**, 21 suites – SB.

**Caledonian,** Princes St., EH1 2AB, ✆ (0131) 459 9988, *Fax (0131) 225 6632* – , rm, rest, – 300. VISA. CY n
***Carriages* :** **Meals** *(closed Saturday lunch)* a la carte 19.40/27.85 **st.** 6.95 – (see also ***Pompadour*** below) – 14.95 – **223 rm** 147.00/275.00 **t.**, 11 suites – SB.

**Sheraton Grand,** 1 Festival Sq., EH3 9SR, ✆ (0131) 229 9131, *Fax (0131) 229 6254,* , , – , rm, – 500. VISA JCB. CDZ v
***Terrace* :** **Meals** 20.50 **t.** and a la carte – (see also ***Grill Room*** below) – 14.00 – **244 rm** 180.00/220.00 **st.**, 17 suites.

**George Inter-Continental,** 19-21 George St., EH2 2PB, ✆ (0131) 225 1251, *Fax (0131) 226 5644* – , rm, – 200. VISA. DY z
***Le Chambertin* :** **Meals** *(closed Saturday lunch and Sunday)* 23.50/26.00 **t.** – ***Carvers*** *(✆ (0131) 459 2305)* **: Meals** 17.95 **t.** and a la carte 7.50 – 11.85 – **193 rm** 145.00/200.00 **st.**, 2 suites – SB.

# EDINBURGH

| Street | Grid | No. |
|---|---|---|
| Castle Street | DY | |
| Frederick Street | DY | |
| George Street | DY | |
| Hanover Street | DY | |
| High Street | EYZ | 37 |
| Lawnmarket | EYZ | 46 |
| Princes Street | DY | |
| St. James Centre | EY | |
| Waverley Market | EY | |
| Bernard Terrace | EZ | 3 |
| Bread Street | DZ | 6 |
| Bristo Place | EZ | 7 |
| Candlemaker Row | EZ | 9 |
| Castlehill | DZ | 10 |
| Chambers Street | EZ | 12 |
| Chapel Street | EZ | 13 |
| Charlotte Square | CY | 14 |
| Deanhaugh Street | CY | 23 |
| Douglas Gardens | CY | 25 |
| Drummond Street | EZ | 27 |
| Forrest Road | EZ | 31 |
| Gardner's Crescent | CZ | 32 |
| George IV Bridge | EZ | 33 |
| Gassmarket | DZ | 35 |
| Home Street | DZ | 38 |
| Hope Street | CY | 39 |
| Johnston Terrace | DZ | 42 |
| King's Bridge | DZ | 44 |
| King's Stables Road | DZ | 45 |
| Leith Street | EY | 47 |
| Leven Street | DZ | 48 |
| Lothian Street | EZ | 51 |
| Mound (The) | DY | 55 |
| North Bridge | EY | 61 |
| North St. Andrew Street | EY | 66 |
| Raeburn Place | CY | 69 |
| Randolph Crescent | CY | 71 |
| St. Andrew Square | EY | 73 |
| St. Mary's Street | EY | 75 |
| Shandwick Place | CYZ | 77 |
| South Charlotte Street | DY | 78 |
| South St. David Street | DEY | 79 |
| Spittal Street | DZ | 83 |
| Victoria Street | EZ | 84 |
| Waterloo Place | EY | 87 |
| Waverley Bridge | EY | 89 |
| West Maitland Street | CZ | 92 |

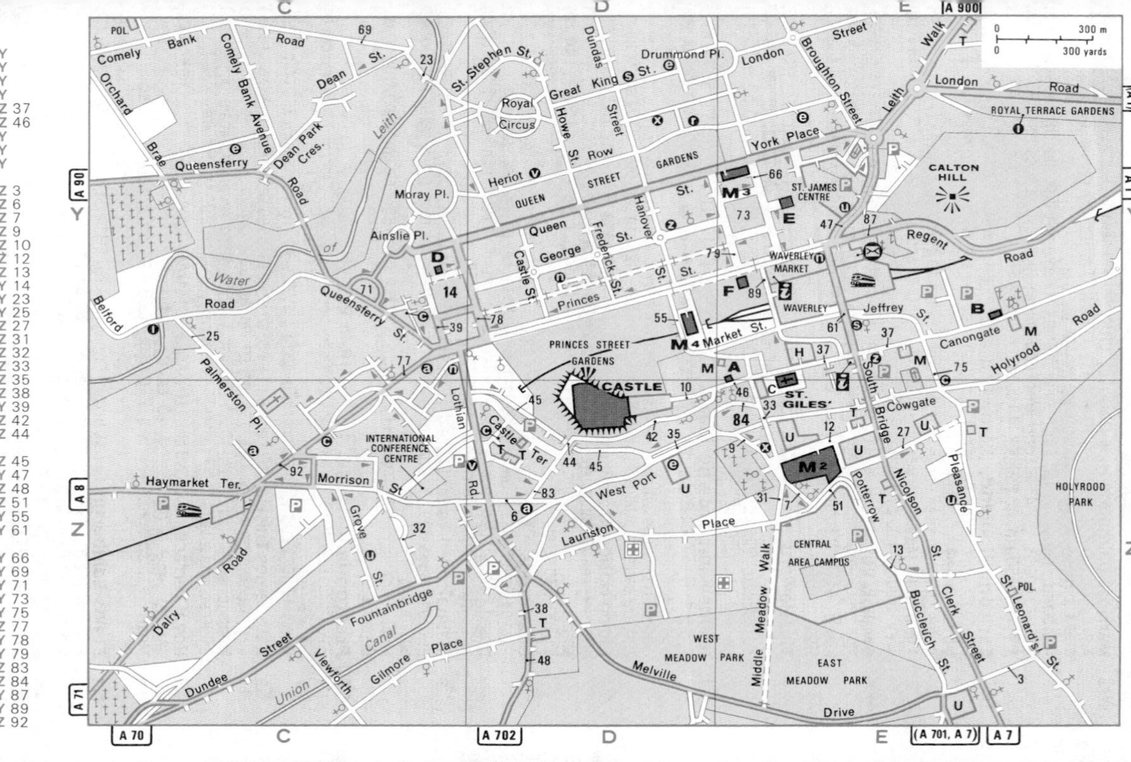

**Marriott Dalmahoy H. & Country Club**, Kirknewton, EH27 8EB, SW : 7 m. on A 71 (0131) 333 1845, *Fax (0131) 333 1433*, ≤, park, squash – rm, – 400. AE VISA JCB.
***Pentland*** : Meals *(closed lunch Saturday and Sunday)* 15.00 **st.** (lunch) and a la carte 21.50/27.00 **st.** 7.45 – ***Long Weekend*** : Meals (grill rest.) a la carte 10.75/19.25 **st.** 7.45 – **150 rm** 130.00/140.00 **st.**, 1 suite – SB.

**Carlton Highland,** North Bridge St., EH1 1SD, (0131) 556 7277, *Fax (0131) 556 2691*, squash – rm, rest. – 280. AE VISA EY s
***Quills*** : Meals *(closed Saturday lunch and Sunday)* 10.45/17.50 **t.** and a la carte 5.95 – ***Eureka*** : Meals (carving rest.) 10.45/17.50 **t.** and a la carte 5.95 – **193 rm** 119.00/204.00 **t.**, 4 suites – SB.

**Swallow Royal Scot,** 111 Glasgow Rd, EH12 8NF, W : 4 ½ m. on A 8 (0131) 334 9191, *Fax (0131) 316 4507*, – rm, – 300. AE VISA
Meals 16.00/22.50 **st.** and a la carte 7.50 – **255 rm** 110.00/145.00 **st.**, 4 suites – SB.

**The Howard,** 34 Great King St., EH3 6QH, (0131) 557 3500, *Fax (0131) 557 6515*, « Georgian town houses » – rest., rest. – 40. AE VISA.
***36*** : Meals *(closed Saturday lunch)* a la carte 17.65/29.70 **st.** 11.50 – **15 rm** 110.00/275.00 **st.** DY s

**Holiday Inn Crowne Plaza,** 80 High St., EH1 1TH, (0131) 557 9797, *Fax (0131) 557 9789*, – rm, – 200. AE VISA JCB. EY z
*closed 25 to 28 December* – Meals *(closed Saturday lunch and Sunday)* 16.50 **st.** (dinner) and a la carte 11.50/29.50 **st.** 8.00 – 13.50 – **229 rm** 165.00/190.00 **st.**, 9 suites.

**Hilton National,** 69 Belford Rd, EH4 3DG, (0131) 332 2545, *Fax (0131) 332 3805* – rm, – 130. AE VISA JCB. CY i
Meals (bar lunch)/dinner 17.50 **t.** and a la carte 6.30 – 11.50 – **144 rm** 115.00/250.00 **st.**

**Channings,** South Learmonth Gdns., EH4 1EZ, (0131) 315 2226, *Fax (0131) 332 9631*, – 35. AE VISA JCB. CY e
*closed 24 to 28 December* – Meals *(closed lunch Saturday and Sunday)* 9.95/21.00 **t.** and a la carte 5.75 – **48 rm** 105.00/220.00 **t.** – SB.

**Malmaison,** 1 Tower Pl., Leith, EH6 7DB, NE : 2 m. by A 900 (0131) 555 6868, *Fax (0131) 555 6999*, « Contemporary interior » – rest., – 100. AE VISA
Meals - Brasserie - 13.00 **st.** and a la carte 6.00 – 10.50 – **54 rm** 90.00/100.00 **st.**, 6 suites.

**Prestonfield House**, Priestfield Rd, EH16 5UT, (0131) 668 3346, *Fax (0131) 668 3976*, ≤, « Part 17C country house », – rm, . AE VISA JCB
Meals 17.00/28.00 **t.** and dinner a la carte 7.00 – **31 rm** 185.00/295.00 **t.** – SB.

**King James Thistle,** 107 Leith St., EH1 3SW, (0131) 556 0111, *Fax (0131) 557 5333* – rm, – 250. AE VISA JCB. EY u
Meals *(closed Sunday lunch)* 10.20/15.20 **st.** 7.50 – ***Saint Jacques*** : Meals (dinner only) 21.50 **st.** and a la carte – 10.75 – **138 rm** 115.00/162.00 **st.**, 5 suites – SB.

**Royal Terrace,** 18 Royal Terr., EH7 5AQ, (0131) 557 3222, *Fax (0131) 557 5334*, – 80. AE VISA. EY i
Meals 17.90 **st.** and a la carte 7.50 – 10.50 – **93 rm** 120.00/180.00 **st.**, 1 suite – SB.

**Stakis Edinburgh Grosvenor,** Grosvenor St., EH12 5EF, (0131) 226 6001, *Fax (0131) 220 2387* – – 500. AE VISA CZ a
Meals *(closed Sunday lunch)* 11.00/20.00 **t.** and a la carte 8.00 – 9.50 – **186 rm** 108.00/135.00 **t.**, 1 suite – SB.

**Point,** 34 Bread St., EH3 9AF, (0131) 221 9919, *Fax (0131) 221 9929* – . AE VISA. DZ a
*closed 25 and 26 December* – Meals *(closed Sunday lunch)* 7.90/10.80 **t.** 6.00 – 8.00 – **94 rm** 80.00/145.00 **st.** – SB.

**Edinburgh Capital Moat House,** Clermiston Rd, EH12 6UG, (0131) 535 9988, *Fax (0131) 334 9712*, – – 300. AE VISA.
Meals 16.50 **t.** 6.00 – 10.50 – **111 rm** 89.00/155.00 **t.** – SB. by A 8 CZ

**Holiday Inn Garden Court,** 107 Queensferry Rd, EH4 3HL, (0131) 332 2442, *Fax (0131) 332 3408*, ≤, – rm, rest. – 60. AE VISA JCB by A 90 CY
Meals 10.95/14.95 **st.** and a la carte 5.05 – 9.45 – **118 rm** 89.50/140.00 **st.**, 1 suite – SB.

**Forte Posthouse Edinburgh,** Corstorphine Rd, EH12 6UA, W : 3 m. on A 8 ☎ (0131) 334 0390, *Fax (0131) 334 9237* – |‡|, ⇔ rm, ≡ rest, TV ☎ P – 🧑‍🏫 120. MC AE O VISA JCB. ✻
**Meals** a la carte 14.00/21.00 **t.** – ☕ 9.95 – **204 rm** 79.00/99.00 **st.** – SB.

**Jarvis Ellersly House,** 4 Ellersly Rd, EH12 6HZ, ☎ (0131) 337 6888, *Fax (0131) 313 2543,* ⚘ – |‡|, ⇔ rm, TV ☎ P – 🧑‍🏫 70. MC AE O VISA
**Meals** (Saturday lunch by arrangement) 10.95/14.95 **t.** and dinner a la carte 🍷 7.00 – ☕ 8.50 – **57 rm** 109.00/135.00 **t.** – SB. by A 8 CZ

**Apex International,** 31-35 Grassmarket, EH1 2HS, ☎ (0131) 300 3456, *Fax (0131) 220 5345* – |‡|, ⇔ rm, ≡ rest, TV ☎ P. MC AE O VISA. ✻ DZ e
**Meals** (carving rest.) (bar lunch)/dinner 14.50 **st.** and a la carte 🍷 6.50 – ☕ 6.95 – **99 rm** 74.95 **st.** – SB.

**Maitland** without rest., 25a Shandwick Pl., EH2 4RG, ☎ (0131) 229 1467, *Fax (0131) 229 7549* – |‡| ⇔ TV ☎. MC AE O VISA JCB. ✻ CY a
**65 rm** ☕ 69.50/130.00 **st.**

**Drummond House** without rest., 17 Drummond Pl., EH3 6PL, ☎ (0131) 557 9189, *Fax (0131) 557 9189,* « Georgian town house » – ⇔. MC VISA. ✻ DY e
*closed Christmas* – **4 rm** ☕ 60.00/90.00 **st.**

**17 Abercromby Place,** 17 Abercromby Pl., EH3 6LB, ☎ (0131) 557 8036, *Fax (0131) 558 3453,* « Georgian town house » – ⇔ TV ☎ P. MC VISA. ✻ DY r
**Meals** (by arrangement) 25.00 – **6 rm** ☕ 45.00/90.00 **t.**

**Sibbet House** without rest., 26 Northumberland St., EH3 6LS, ☎ (0131) 556 1078, *Fax (0131) 557 9445,* « Georgian town house » – ⇔ TV ☎. MC VISA. ✻ DY x
**5 rm** ☕ 75.00/120.00 **s.**, 1 suite.

**27 Heriot Row** without rest., 27 Heriot Row, EH3 6EN, ☎ (0131) 225 9474, *Fax (0131) 220 1699,* « Georgian town house », ⚘ – ⇔ TV ☎. MC VISA. ✻ DY v
**3 rm** ☕ 50.00/90.00.

XXXX **Number One** (at Balmoral H.), 1 Princes St., EH2 2EQ, ☎ (0131) 556 6727, *Fax (0131) 557 3747* – ≡. MC AE O VISA JCB EY n
*closed lunch Saturday and Sunday* – **Meals** 16.95/21.50 **st.** and a la carte 🍷 7.25.

XXXX **Pompadour** (at Caledonian H.), Princes St., EH1 2AB, ☎ (0131) 459 9988, *Fax (0131) 225 6632* – P. MC AE O VISA CY n
*closed Sunday and Monday* – **Meals** (dinner only) a la carte 35.95/49.90 🍷 9.95.

XXX **Grill Room** (at Sheraton Grand H.), 1 Festival Sq., EH3 9SR, ☎ (0131) 229 9131, *Fax (0131) 229 6254* – ≡ P. MC AE O VISA JCB CDZ v
*closed Saturday lunch and Sunday* – **Meals** 25.50/34.00 **t.** and a la carte 🍷 13.00.

XX **Haldanes,** 39A Albany St., EH1 3QY, ☎ (0131) 556 8407, ⛱ – MC AE VISA EY e
*closed Saturday and Sunday lunch* – **Meals** 13.95 **st.** (lunch) and dinner a la carte approx. 30.00 **st.** 🍷 6.50.

XX **Kelly's,** 46 West Richmond St., EH8 9DZ, ☎ (0131) 668 3847 – ⇔. MC VISA EZ u
*closed Sunday to Tuesday, 25-26 December and 1 January* – **Meals** 25.00 **t.** (dinner) and lunch a la carte 12.50/17.50 **t.** 🍷 7.70.

XX **L'Auberge,** 56 St. Mary's St., EH1 1SX, ☎ (0131) 556 5888, *Fax (0131) 556 2588* – ≡. MC AE O VISA JCB EYZ c
*closed Monday, 25 December and 1-2 January* – **Meals** - French - 13.50/26.50 **t.** and a la carte 🍷 6.50.

XX **Martins,** 70 Rose St., North Lane, EH2 3DX, ☎ (0131) 225 3106 – ⇔. MC AE O VISA JCB DY n
*closed Saturday lunch, Sunday, Monday, 1 week in spring, 1 week in autumn, and 24 December-19 January* – **Meals** (booking essential) a la carte 19.10/36.50 **t.** 🍷 5.90.

XX **(fitz)Henry,** 19 Shore Pl., Leith, EH6 6SW, ☎ (0131) 555 6625, *Fax (0131) 228 2998,* « Part 17C warehouse » – MC AE VISA by A 900 EY
*closed Sunday, 25-26 December and 1-2 January* – **Meals** 13.50/22.00 **t.** 🍷 7.25.

XX **Raffaelli,** 10 Randolph Pl., EH3 7TA, ☎ (0131) 225 6060, *Fax (0131) 225 8830* – MC AE O VISA CY c
*closed Saturday lunch, Sunday, 25-26 December, 1-2 January and Bank Holiday Monday* – **Meals** - Italian - a la carte 16.60/32.40 **t.** 🍷 5.90.

XX **Indian Cavalry Club,** 3 Atholl Pl., EH3 8HP, ☎ (0131) 228 3282, *Fax (0131) 225 1911* – MC AE O VISA CZ c
**Meals** - Indian - 6.95 **t.** (lunch) and a la carte 9.55/17.85 **t.**

XX **Vintners Room,** The Vaults, 87 Giles St., Leith, EH6 6BZ, ☎ (0131) 554 6767, *Fax (0131) 467 7130* – ⇔. MC AE VISA by A 900 EY
*closed Sunday and 2 weeks Christmas-New Year* – **Meals** a la carte 13.00/28.25 **t.** 🍷 5.00.

**Yumi,** 2 West Coates, EH12 5JQ, ☎ (0131) 337 2173, *Fax (0131) 337 2818* – P. MC VISA JCB
*closed Sunday and 2 weeks Christmas-New Year* – **Meals** - Japanese - (dinner only) 36.00 **t.** 5.00.

**Denzler's 121,** 121 Constitution St., EH6 7AE, ☎ (0131) 554 3268, *Fax (0131) 467 7239* – MC AE DC VISA JCB on A 900 EY
*closed Saturday lunch, Sunday, Monday and 2 weeks late July* – **Meals** 10.40/17.95 **st.** and a la carte 5.50.

**Merchants,** 17 Merchant St., EH1 2QD, off Candlemaker Row, (under bridge) ☎ (0131) 225 4009, *Fax (0131) 557 9318* – MC AE DC VISA JCB EZ x
*closed Sunday and 26 December* – **Meals** (booking essential) 10.50/17.50 **t.** and a la carte 5.50.

**Atrium,** 10 Cambridge St., EH1 2ED, ☎ (0131) 228 8882, *Fax (0131) 228 8808* – MC AE VISA DZ c
*closed Saturday lunch, Sunday and 1 week Christmas-New Year* – **Meals** a la carte 18.50/27.00 **t.** 8.50.

**at Bonnyrigg** *(Midlothian) SE : 8 m. by A 7 on A 6094* – EZ – ✉ *Edinburgh* :

**Dalhousie Castle,** EH19 3JB, *SE : 1 ¼ m. on B 704* ☎ (01875) 820153, *Fax (01875) 821936*, ←, « Part 13C and 15C castle with Victorian additions », – TV ☎ P – 120. MC AE DC VISA JCB.
*closed 3 weeks January* – **Meals** 25.00 **st.** (dinner) and lunch a la carte 13.45/18.05 **st.** 7.75 – **28 rm** 90.00/210.00 **st.** – SB.

**at Edinburgh International Airport** *W : 7 ½ m. by A 8* – CZ – ✉ *Edinburgh* :

**Stakis Edinburgh Airport,** , EH28 8LL, ☎ (0131) 519 4400, *Fax (0131) 519 4422* – rm, rest, TV ☎ P – 220. MC AE DC VISA.
**Meals** (grill rest.) 7.25/15.00 **t.** and a la carte 5.00 – 9.75 – **134 rm** 120.00/135.00 **st.** – SB.

**at Ingliston** *W : 7 ¾ m. on A 8* – CZ – ✉ *Edinburgh* :

**Norton House**, EH28 8LX, *on A 8* ☎ (0131) 333 1275, *Fax (0131) 333 5305*, ←, – rm, TV ☎ P – 300. MC AE DC VISA.
**Meals** *(closed Saturday lunch)* 25.50 **t.** (dinner) and a la carte 23.25/35.40 **t.** 7.50 – **46 rm** 115.00/145.00 **t.**, 1 suite – SB.

Price — For full details of the prices quoted in this Guide, consult the introduction.

**GLASGOW** *Glasgow City* 401 402 H 16 **Scotland G.** – *pop. 662 853.*

**See** : *City*★★★ – *Cathedral*★★★ (←★) DZ – *The Burrell Collection*★★★ – *Hunterian Art Gallery*★★ *(Whistler Collection*★★★ – *Mackintosh Wing*★★★ *AC )* CY **M**4 – *Museum of Transport*★★ *(Scottish Built Cars*★★★, *The Clyde Room of Ship Models*★★★*)* – *Art Gallery and Museum Kelvingrove*★★ CY – *Pollok House*★ *(The Paintings*★★*)* – *Tolbooth Steeple*★ DZ **A** – *Hunterian Museum (Coin and Medal Collection*★*)* CY **M**1 – *City Chambers*★ DZ **C** – *Glasgow School of Art*★ *AC* CY **B** – *Necropolis (*←★ *of Cathedral)* DYZ.

**Envir.** : *Paisley Museum and Art Gallery (paisley Shawl Section*★*), W : 4 m. by M 8.*

**Exc.** : *The Trossachs*★★★, *N : 31 m. by A 879, A 81 and A 821* – *Loch Lomond*★★, *NW : 19 m. by A 82.*

*18 Littlehill, Auchinairn Rd ☎ (0141) 772 1916 – 18 Deaconsbank, Rouken Glen Park, Stewarton Rd, Eastwood ☎ (0141) 638 7044 – 18 Linn Park, Simshill Rd ☎ (0141) 637 5871 – 18 Lethamhill, Cumbernauld Rd ☎ (0141) 770 6220 – 9 Alexandra Park, Dennistown ☎ (0141) 556 3991 – 9 King's Park, 150a Croftpark Av., Croftfoot ☎ (0141) 634 1597 – 9 Knightswood, Lincoln Av. ☎ (0141) 959 6358 9 Ruchill, Brassey St. ☎ (0141) 946 7676.*

*Access to Oban by helicopter.*

*Erskine Bridge (toll).*

*Glasgow Airport : ☎ (0141) 887 1111, W : 8 m. by M 8* – **Terminal** : *Coach service from Glasgow Central and Queen Street main line Railway Stations and from Anderston Cross and Buchanan Bus Stations* *Prestwick International Airport : ☎ (01292) 479822* **Terminal** : *Buchanan Bus Station.*

*11 George Sq., G2 1DY ☎ (0141) 204 4400 – Glasgow Airport, Tourist Information Desk, Paisley ☎ (0141) 848 4440.*

*Edinburgh 46 – Manchester 221.*

Plans on following pages

**Glasgow Hilton,** 1 William St., G3 8HT, ☎ (0141) 204 5555, *Fax (0141) 204 5004*, ≤, Fö, ≘s, ⊠ – |‡|, ⇔ rm, ▤ TV ☎ ♿ P – 🏛 1000. MC AE ⓓ VISA JCB. ✂ CZ s
***Minsky's :*** Meals a la carte 15.70/30.20 **st.** 🍷 8.50 – (see also ***Camerons*** below) – ☕ 13.50 – **315 rm** 171.00 **st.**, 4 suites.

**One Devonshire Gardens,** 1 Devonshire Gdns., G12 0UX, ☎ (0141) 339 2001, *Fax (0141) 337 1663*, « Victorian town houses, opulent interior design » – ⇔ rest, TV ☎ – 🏛 50. MC AE ⓓ VISA. ✂ by A 82 CY
Meals *(closed Saturday lunch)* 25.00/40.00 **t.** 🍷 10.00 – ☕ 14.50 – **25 rm** 150.00/210.00 **t.**, 2 suites
**Spec.** Seared spiced scallops with lemon grass couscous. Roasted Bresse pigeon, confit of cabbage and root vegetables, thyme jus. Iced vanilla parfait with roasted strawberries and balsamic vinegar.

**Glasgow Moat House,** Congress Rd, G3 8QT, ☎ (0141) 306 9988, *Fax (0141) 221 2022*, ≤, Fö, ≘s, ⊠ – |‡|, ⇔ rm, ▤ TV ☎ ♿ P – 🏛 800. MC AE ⓓ VISA. ✂ CZ r
***Mariners :*** Meals *(closed Saturday lunch, Sunday and 26 December-13 January)* 16.50 **st.** (lunch) and dinner a la carte – ***Pointhouse :*** Meals 16.95/19.95 **st.** and a la carte – ☕ 10.95 – **267 rm** 132.00/162.00 **st.**, 16 suites.

**Glasgow Marriott,** 500 Argyle St., Anderston, G3 8RR, ☎ (0141) 226 5577, *Fax (0141) 221 7676*, Fö, ≘s, ⊠, squash – |‡|, ⇔ rm, ▤ TV ☎ ♿ P – 🏛 720. MC AE ⓓ VISA JCB. ✂ CZ a
***Terrace :*** Meals *(closed Saturday lunch)* 17.95 **t.** (dinner) and a la carte 16.95/26.15 **t.** 🍷 7.25 – ☕ 10.95 – **296 rm** 94.00/104.00 **st.**, 4 suites.

**Glasgow Thistle,** 36 Cambridge St., G2 3HN, ☎ (0141) 332 3311, *Fax (0141) 332 4050* – |‡|, ⇔ rm, ▤ rest, TV ☎ ♿ P – 🏛 1500. MC AE ⓓ VISA JCB DY z
***Garden Cafe :*** Meals (carving rest.) 13.00/18.50 **st.** and a la carte – ***Prince of Wales :*** Meals *(closed Saturday lunch and Sunday)* 19.00/27.50 **st.** and a la carte – ☕ 13.00 – **299 rm** 99.00/164.00 **st.**, 3 suites – SB.

**Forte Posthouse Glasgow City,** Bothwell St., G2 7EN, ☎ (0141) 248 2656, *Fax (0141) 221 8986*, ≤ – |‡|, ⇔ rm, ▤ TV ☎ P – 🏛 800. MC AE ⓓ VISA JCB CZ z
***The Carvery :*** Meals (dinner only) a la carte approx. 15.75 **t.** – ***Jules Verne :*** Meals *(closed lunch Saturday and Sunday)* 13.20 **st.** 🍷 6.75 – ☕ 10.95 – **246 rm** 79.00 **st.**, 1 suite.

**Devonshire,** 5 Devonshire Gdns., G12 0UX, ☎ (0141) 339 7878, *Fax (0141) 339 3980* – TV ☎ – 🏛 50. MC AE ⓓ VISA. ✂ by A 82 CY
Meals a la carte 22.50/35.00 **st.** 🍷 8.00 – ☕ 12.75 – **14 rm** 115.00/165.00 **st.** – SB.

**Malmaison,** 278 West George St., G2 4LL, ☎ (0141) 572 1000, *Fax (0141) 572 1002*, « Contemporary interior » – |‡| TV ☎. MC AE ⓓ VISA. ✂ CY c
Meals - Brasserie - a la carte 16.95/22.90 **t.** – ☕ 10.50 – **69 rm** 90.00 **st.**, 4 suites.

**Copthorne Glasgow,** George Sq., G2 1DS, ☎ (0141) 332 6711, *Fax (0141) 332 4264* – |‡|, ⇔ rm, TV ☎ – 🏛 100. MC AE ⓓ VISA JCB DZ n
*closed 25 and 26 December* – **Meals** *(closed Saturday and Sunday lunch)* a la carte 24.40/29.90 **t.** 🍷 7.00 – ☕ 11.50 – **135 rm** 118.00/128.00 **st.**, 5 suites.

Stakis Glasgow Grosvenor, Grosvenor Terr., Great Western Rd, G12 0TA, ☎ (0141) 339 8811, *Fax (0141) 334 0710* – |‡|, ⇔ rm, TV ☎ P – 🏛 450 CY s
**94 rm**, 2 suites.

Holiday Inn Garden Court Glasgow, Theatreland, 161 West Nile St., G1 2RL, ☎ (0141) 353 2595, *Fax (0141) 332 7447* – ⇔ rm, TV ☎ – 🏛 80 DY a
**80 rm.**

**County H. Glasgow Kelvin Park Lorne,** 923 Sauchiehall St., G3 7TE, ☎ (0141) 314 9955, *Fax (0141) 337 1659* – |‡|, ⇔ rm, TV ☎ P – 🏛 300. MC AE ⓓ VISA. ✂ CY e
Meals 9.95 **st.** (lunch) and a la carte approx. 17.85 **st.** 🍷 6.50 – ☕ 8.50 – **97 rm** 85.00/105.00 **st.**, 1 suite.

**Swallow Glasgow,** 517 Paisley Road West, G51 1RW, ☎ (0141) 427 3146, *Fax (0141) 427 4059*, Fö, ≘s, ⊠ – |‡|, ⇔ rm, ▤ rest, TV ☎ P – 🏛 350. MC AE ⓓ VISA by A 8 CZ
Meals *(closed Saturday lunch)* (carving lunch) 11.00/17.50 **st.** 🍷 7.50 – **117 rm** ☕ 95.00/135.00 **st.** – SB.

**Stakis Glasgow City,** Hill St., G3 6PR, ☎ (0141) 333 1515, *Fax (0141) 333 1221* – |‡|, ⇔ rm, TV ☎ ♿ – 🏛 35. MC AE ⓓ VISA. ✂ DY c
Meals (grill rest.) (bar lunch)/dinner 12.50 **st.** and a la carte 🍷 7.00 – ☕ 8.95 – **93 rm** 63.00/73.00 **st.**

**Tinto Firs Thistle,** 470 Kilmarnock Rd, G43 2BB, ☎ (0141) 637 2353, *Fax (0141) 633 1340* – ⇔ rm, TV ☎ P – 🏛 200. MC AE ⓓ VISA JCB by A 77 DZ
Meals (bar lunch Monday and Saturday) 12.95/19.95 **st.** and a la carte 🍷 5.95 – ☕ 9.95 – **25 rm** 82.00/102.00 **st.**, 2 suites – SB.

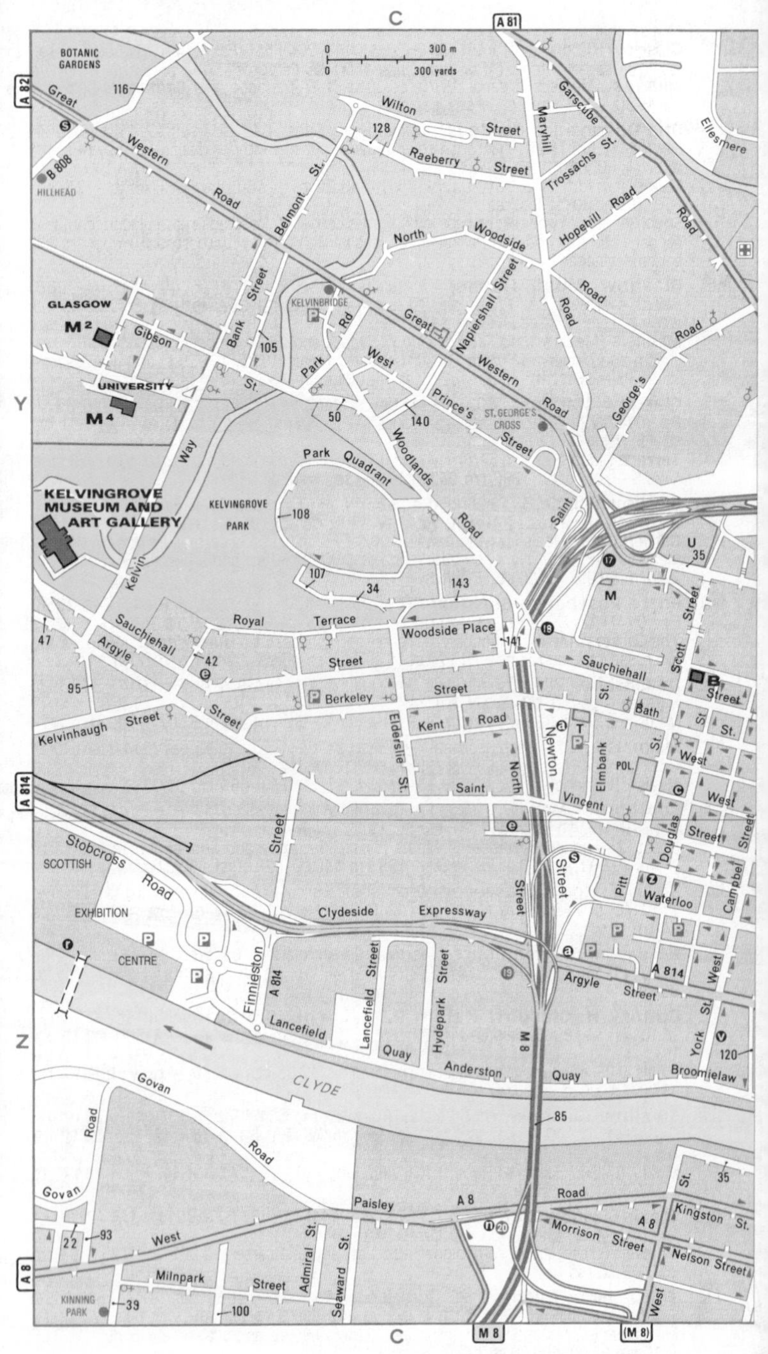
C
A 81
A 82
BOTANIC GARDENS
0 300 m
0 300 yards
Great Western Road
B 808
HILLHEAD
Wilton Street
Raeberry Street
Belmont St.
Maryhill Road
Garscube Road
Trossachs St.
Hopehill Road
Ellesmere
North Woodside Road
Bank Street
Napiershall Street
GLASGOW
M²
Gibson St.
UNIVERSITY
M⁴
KELVINBRIDGE
Park Rd
West Prince's Street
ST. GEORGE'S CROSS
St. George's Road
Y
Kelvin Way
Park Quadrant
Woodlands Road
KELVINGROVE MUSEUM AND ART GALLERY
KELVINGROVE PARK
Saint
Royal Terrace
Woodside Place
Sauchiehall Street
Argyle Street
Berkeley Street
Kent Road
Elderslie St.
Kelvinhaugh Street
North Street
Newton Street
Elmbank St.
POL.
Bath St.
Scott Street
West Regent St.
West George Street
Saint Vincent Street
Douglas St.
Pitt Street
Waterloo Street
Campbell Street
A 814
Stobcross Road
SCOTTISH EXHIBITION CENTRE
Clydeside Expressway
Finnieston Street
Lancefield Street
Lancefield Quay
Hydepark Street
M 8
Argyle Street
West St.
York St.
Broomielaw
Anderston Quay
Z
CLYDE
Govan Road
Paisley Road
A 8
Morrison Street
Kingston St.
Nelson Street
West Street
Milnpark Street
Admiral St.
Seaward St.
KINNING PARK
M 8
(M 8)

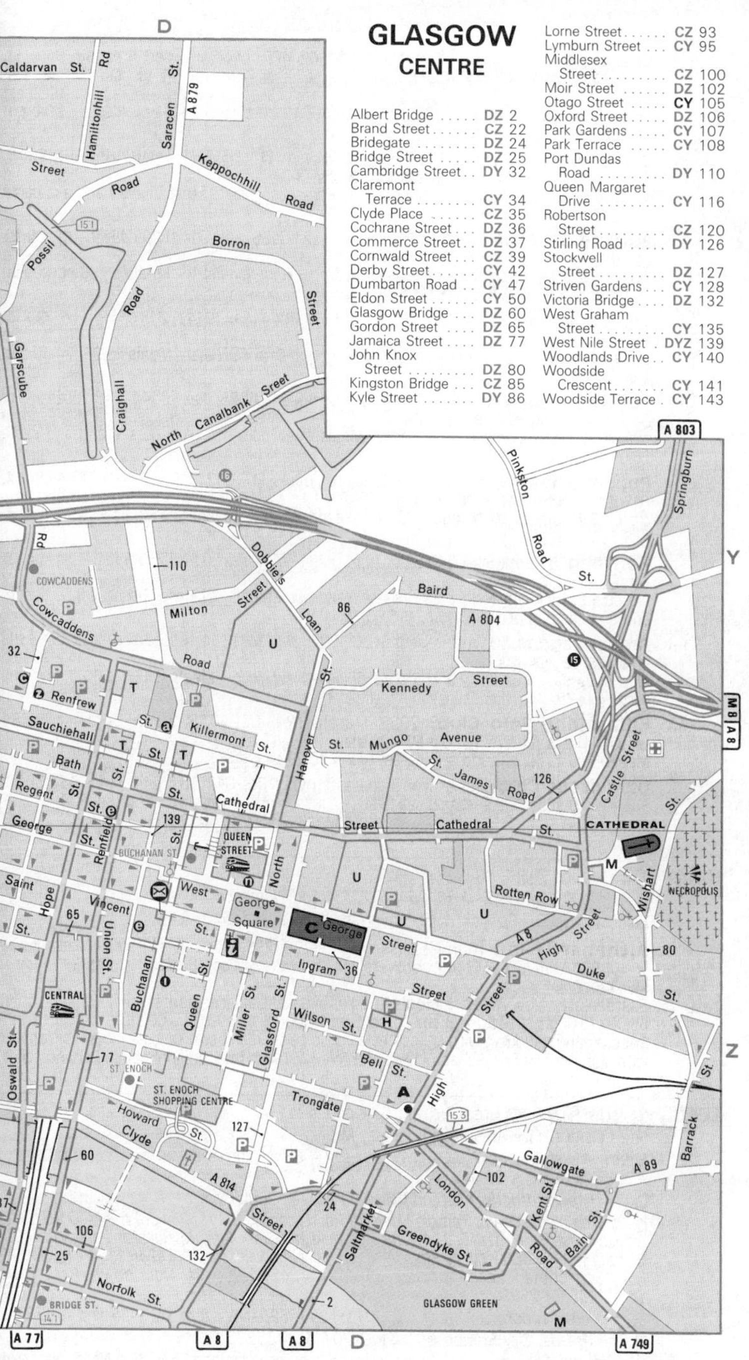

GLASGOW
CENTRE
Albert Bridge ..... DZ 2
Brand Street ...... CZ 22
Bridegate ......... DZ 24
Bridge Street ..... DZ 25
Cambridge Street .. DY 32
Claremont Terrace ........ CY 34
Clyde Place ...... CZ 35
Cochrane Street .... DZ 36
Commerce Street .. DZ 37
Cornwald Street ... CZ 39
Derby Street ...... CY 42
Dumbarton Road .. CY 47
Eldon Street ...... CY 50
Glasgow Bridge ... DZ 60
Gordon Street .... DZ 65
Jamaica Street .... DZ 77
John Knox Street ......... DZ 80
Kingston Bridge ... CZ 85
Kyle Street ....... DY 86
Lorne Street ...... CZ 93
Lymburn Street ... CY 95
Middlesex Street ......... CZ 100
Moir Street ...... DZ 102
Otago Street ..... CY 105
Oxford Street .... DZ 106
Park Gardens ..... CY 107
Park Terrace ..... CY 108
Port Dundas Road ......... DY 110
Queen Margaret Drive ......... CY 116
Robertson Street ......... CZ 120
Stirling Road ..... DY 126
Stockwell Street ......... DZ 127
Striven Gardens ... CY 128
Victoria Bridge .... DZ 132
West Graham Street ......... CY 135
West Nile Street . DYZ 139
Woodlands Drive .. CY 140
Woodside Crescent ....... CY 141
Woodside Terrace . CY 143
D
Y
Z
A 803
A 879
A 804
M 8
A 8
A 77
A 749
A 89
A 814
Saracen St.
Keppochhill Road
Possil Road
Borron Street
Garscube Rd
Craighall Road
North Canalbank Street
Pinkston Road
Springburn
Baird St.
Dobbie's Loan
Milton Street
Cowcaddens Road
COWCADDENS
Kennedy Street
Hanover St.
St. Mungo Avenue
St. James Road
Castle Street
CATHEDRAL
NECROPOLIS
Cathedral Street
Killermont St.
Sauchiehall St.
Renfrew St.
Bath St.
Regent St.
George St.
Saint Vincent St.
West George St.
George Square
QUEEN STREET
BUCHANAN ST.
CENTRAL
Union St.
Buchanan St.
Queen St.
Miller St.
Glassford St.
North
Ingram Street
Wilson St.
Bell St.
Trongate
High Street
Duke St.
Rotten Row
Wishart St.
Barrack St.
Gallowgate
London Road
Kent St.
Bain St.
Greendyke St.
Saltmarket
GLASGOW GREEN
ST. ENOCH
ST. ENOCH SHOPPING CENTRE
Howard St.
Clyde Street
Oswald St.
Norfolk St.
BRIDGE ST.

**Charing Cross Tower,** Elmbank Gdns., G2 4PP, pedestrianised area off Bath St. ✆ (0141) 221 1000, *Fax (0141) 248 1000,* ≤ – |$|, ⇔ rm, TV ☎. MC AE ① VISA. ⚘ CY a
**Meals** (bar lunch)/dinner a la carte 10.40/19.20 **t.** 5.25 – ☐ 6.95 – **281 rm** 44.50/49.50 **st.**

**Camerons** (at Glasgow Hilton H.), 1 William St., G3 8HT, ✆ (0141) 204 5511, *Fax (0141) 204 5004* – ▤ P. MC AE ① VISA JCB CZ s
**Meals** *(closed Saturday lunch, Sunday and Bank Holidays)* 19.50 **st.** (lunch) and a la carte 21.45/39.20 **st.** 8.50.

**Buttery,** 652 Argyle St., G3 8UF, ✆ (0141) 221 8188, *Fax (0141) 204 4639* – P. MC AE ① VISA CZ e
*closed Saturday lunch, Sunday, 25-26 December and 1 January* – **Meals** 15.85 **st.** (lunch) and a la carte 23.05/29.80 **t.** 9.25.

**Yes,** 22 West Nile St., G1 2PW, ✆ (0141) 221 8044, *Fax (0141) 248 9159* – ▤. MC AE ① VISA DZ e
*closed Sunday, 25-26 December, 1-2 January and Bank Holidays* – **Meals** 15.95/24.50 and a la carte.

**Rogano,** 11 Exchange Pl., G1 3AN, ✆ (0141) 248 4055, *Fax (0141) 248 2608,* « Art Deco » – ▤. MC AE ① VISA JCB DZ i
*closed 25 December and 1 January* – **Meals** - Seafood - 16.50 **t.** (lunch) and a la carte 26.00/36.00 **t.** 7.00.

**Puppet Theatre,** 11 Ruthven Lane, off Byres Rd, G12 9BG, ✆ (0141) 339 8444, *Fax (0141) 339 7666* – MC AE VISA on B 808 CY
*closed Saturday lunch, Monday, 25-26 December and 1-2 January* – **Meals** 14.95/24.95 **t.** 6.75.

**Ho Wong,** 82 York St., G2 8LE, ✆ (0141) 221 3550, *Fax (0141) 248 5330* – ▤. MC AE ① VISA CZ v
*closed Sunday lunch and 3 days Chinese New Year* – **Meals** - Chinese (Peking) - 8.50 (lunch) and a la carte approx. 19.00 **t.** 5.95.

**Amber Regent,** 50 West Regent St., G2 2QZ, ✆ (0141) 331 1655, *Fax (0141) 353 3398* – ▤. MC AE ① VISA JCB DY e
*closed Sunday, 1 January and 3 days Chinese New Year* – **Meals** 8.45/24.00 **t.** and a la carte 5.95.

**Killermont Polo Club,** 2022 Maryhill Rd, G20 0AB, NW : 3 m. on A 81 ✆ (0141) 946 5412 – P. MC AE ① VISA
**Meals** 6.95 **t.** (lunch) and a la carte 14.20/20.00 **t.**

**Ubiquitous Chip,** 12 Ashton Lane, off Byres Rd, G12 8SJ, ✆ (0141) 334 5007, *Fax (0141) 337 1302* – MC AE ① VISA by A 808 CY
*closed 25 and 31 December-2 January* – **Meals** 23.60/31.60 **t.** 5.50.

---

**ULLAPOOL** *Highland* 401 E 10 – *pop. 1 231.*
*Argyle St., IV26 2UR ✆ (01854) 612135 (April-November).*
*Edinburgh 215 – Glasgow 225 – Inverness 59 – Aberdeen 168.*

**Altnaharrie Inn** (Gunn Eriksen) ⛴, IV26 2SS, SW : ½ m. by private ferry ✆ (01854) 633230, « Former drovers' inn on banks of Loch Broom, ≤ Ullapool », ⛺ – ⇔. MC VISA. ⚘
*Easter-early November* – **Meals** (booking essential) (residents only) (dinner only) 65.00/75.00 **st.** 7.50 – **8 rm** ☐ (dinner included) 165.00/400.00 **st.**
**Spec.** Young monkfish with thin slices of crisp celeriac and two sauces. "Soup" of lobster with summer truffles. Squab pigeon and foie gras with roasted kohlrabi and chanterelles.

---

**LEEDS** *W. Yorks.* 402 P 22 **Great Britain G.** – *pop. 424 194.*
**See :** *City★ – City Art Gallery★ AC* DZ **M.**
**Envir. :** *Kirkstall Abbey★ AC , NW : 3 m. by A 65 – Templenewsam★ (decorative arts★) AC , E : 5 m. by A 64 and A 63.*
**Exc. :** *Harewood House★★ (The Gallery★) AC , N : 8 m. by A 61.*
*18, 18 Temple Newsam, Temple Newsam Rd, Halton ✆ (0113) 264 5624 – 18 Gotts Park, Armley Ridge Rd ✆ (0113) 234 2019 – 18 Middleton Park, Ring Rd, Beeston Park, Middleton ✆ (0113) 270 9506 – 18, 9 Moor Allerton, Coal Rd, Wike ✆ (0113) 266 1154 – 18 Howley Hall, Scotchman Lane, Morley ✆ (01924) 472432 – 9 Roundhay, Park Lane ✆ (0113) 266 2695.*
*Leeds - Bradford Airport : ✆ (0113) 250 9696, NW : 8 m. by A 65 and A 658.*
*The Arcade, City Station, LS1 1PL ✆ (0113) 242 5242.*
*London 204 – Liverpool 75 – Manchester 43 – Newcastle upon Tyne 95 – Nottingham 74.*

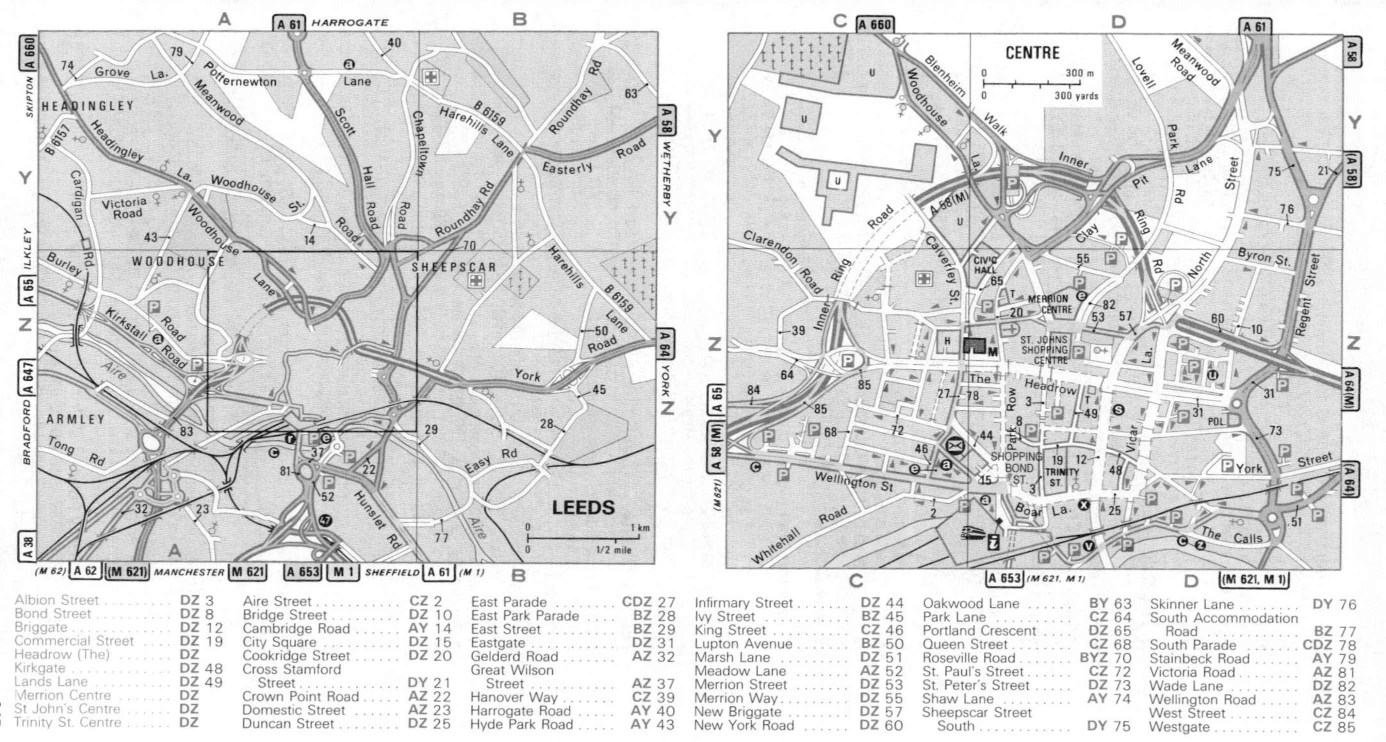


| | | | |
|---|---|---|---|
| Albion Street | DZ 3 | Aire Street | CZ 2 |
| Bond Street | DZ 8 | Bridge Street | DZ 10 |
| Briggate | DZ 12 | Cambridge Road | AY 14 |
| Commercial Street | DZ 19 | City Square | DZ 15 |
| Headrow (The) | DZ | Cookridge Street | DZ 20 |
| Kirkgate | DZ 48 | Cross Stamford Street | DY 21 |
| Lands Lane | DZ 49 | Crown Point Road | AZ 22 |
| Merrion Centre | DZ | Domestic Street | AZ 23 |
| St John's Centre | DZ | Duncan Street | DZ 25 |
| Trinity St. Centre | DZ | | |

| | | | |
|---|---|---|---|
| East Parade | CDZ 27 | Infirmary Street | DZ 44 |
| East Park Parade | BZ 28 | Ivy Street | BZ 45 |
| East Street | BZ 29 | King Street | CZ 46 |
| Eastgate | DZ 31 | Lupton Avenue | BZ 50 |
| Gelderd Road | AZ 32 | Marsh Lane | DZ 51 |
| Great Wilson Street | AZ 37 | Meadow Lane | AZ 52 |
| Hanover Way | CZ 39 | Merrion Street | DZ 53 |
| Harrogate Road | AY 40 | Merrion Way | DZ 55 |
| Hyde Park Road | AY 43 | New Briggate | DZ 57 |
| | | New York Road | DZ 60 |

| | | | |
|---|---|---|---|
| Oakwood Lane | BY 63 | Skinner Lane | DY 76 |
| Park Lane | CZ 64 | South Accommodation Road | BZ 77 |
| Portland Crescent | DZ 65 | South Parade | CDZ 78 |
| Queen Street | CZ 68 | Stainbeck Road | AY 79 |
| Roseville Road | BYZ 70 | Victoria Road | AZ 81 |
| St. Paul's Street | CZ 72 | Wade Lane | DZ 82 |
| St. Peter's Street | DZ 73 | Wellington Road | AZ 83 |
| Shaw Lane | AY 74 | West Street | CZ 84 |
| Sheepscar Street South | DY 75 | Westgate | CZ 85 |

**Oulton Hall,** Rothwell Lane, Oulton, LS26 8HN, SE : 5 ½ m. by A 61 and A 639 ☎ (0113) 282 1000, *Fax (0113) 282 8066*, ≤, squash – rest, – 330.
***Bronte* : Meals** *(closed Saturday lunch)* 14.00/22.50 **st.** and dinner a la carte – **150 rm** 130.00/150.00 **st.**, 2 suites – SB.

**Leeds Marriott,** 4 Trevelyan Sq., Boar Lane, LS1 6ET, ☎ (0113) 236 6366, *Fax (0113) 236 6367*, – rm, – 300.
***Dyson's* (☎ *(0113) 236 6444)* : Meals** *(closed Sunday dinner)* 15.95 **st.** (dinner) and a la carte 16.90/21.90 **t.** 7.50 – 10.95 – **240 rm** 89.00/99.00 **st.**, 4 suites – SB. DZ x

**42 The Calls,** 42 The Calls, LS2 7EW, ☎ (0113) 244 0099, *Fax (0113) 234 4100*, ≤, « Converted riverside grain mill » – rm, – 55.
*closed 5 days Christmas* – **Meals** – (see ***Pool Court at 42*** below) (see also ***Brasserie Forty Four*** below) – 11.50 – **38 rm** 95.00/145.00 **st.**, 3 suites – SB. DZ z

**Holiday Inn Crown Plaza,** Wellington St., LS1 4DL, ☎ (0113) 244 2200, *Fax (0113) 244 0460*, – rm, – 200.
**Meals** 14.95/17.95 **t.** and a la carte 5.95 – 11.95 – **120 rm** 120.00 **st.**, 5 suites – SB. CZ c

**Hilton National Leeds,** Neville St., LS1 4BX, ☎ (0113) 244 2000, *Fax (0113) 243 3577*, – rm, – 400. AZ r
**Meals** 11.95/16.95 **t.** and a la carte 6.50 – 11.95 – **186 rm** 115.00 **st.**, 20 suites.

**Queen's,** City Sq., LS1 1PL, ☎ (0113) 243 1323, *Fax (0113) 242 5154* – rm, – 600. DZ a
**Meals** (carving rest.) 12.50/15.70 **st.** 6.25 – ***Harewood* : Meals** *(closed Saturday lunch)* 10.50/17.50 and a la carte 6.25 – 11.50 – **184 rm** 85.00/95.00 **st.**, 6 suites – SB.

**Village H. and Leisure Club,** Otley Rd, Headingley, LS16 5PR, *NW : 3 ½ m. on A 660* ☎ (0113) 278 1000, *Fax (0113) 278 1111*, heated, *squash* – – 250.
**Meals** (grill rest.) a la carte 9.90/23.40 **t.** 3.90 – **94 rm** 86.00/119.00 **t.**

**Weetwood Hall,** Otley Rd, LS16 5PS, *NW : 4 m. on A 660* ☎ (0113) 230 6000, *Fax (0113) 230 6095*, – rest, – 150.
**Meals** 12.95/15.25 **st.** and dinner a la carte 6.95 – 8.25 – **108 rm** 72.50/120.00 **st.**

**Haley's,** Shire Oak Rd, Headingley, LS6 2DE, *NW : 2 m. off Otley Rd (A 660)* ☎ (0113) 278 4446, *Fax (0113) 275 3342* – – 25.
*closed 26 to 30 December* – **Meals** *(closed Sunday dinner to non-residents)* (dinner only and Sunday lunch June-September)/dinner a la carte 22.25/26.75 **st.** 6.75 – **22 rm** 110.00/150.00 **st.** – SB.

**Merrion Thistle,** Merrion Centre, 17 Wade Lane, LS2 8NH, ☎ (0113) 243 9191, *Fax (0113) 242 3527* – rest, – 80.
**Meals** 14.75 **t.** (dinner) and a la carte 20.45/27.40 **t.** 5.40 – 9.75 – **108 rm** 99.00/120.00 **st.**, 1 suite. DZ e

**Metropole,** King St., LS1 2HQ, ☎ (0113) 245 0841, *Fax (0113) 242 5156* – rm, – 200. CZ e
**Meals** *(closed Sunday lunch and Bank Holidays)* 15.95 **t.** (dinner) and a la carte 16.00/25.00 **st.** 5.25 – 9.95 – **104 rm** 89.00/150.00 **st.**, 1 suite – SB.

**Golden Lion,** 2 Lower Briggate, LS1 4AE, ☎ (0113) 243 6454, *Fax (0113) 242 9327* – rm, – 120. DZ v
**Meals** (bar lunch)/dinner 16.25 **t.** and a la carte 4.65 – **89 rm** 91.00/111.00 – SB.

**Pool Court at 42** (at 42 The Calls H.), 44 The Calls, LS2 7EW, ☎ (0113) 244 4242, *Fax (0113) 234 3332*, « Riverside setting » – DZ z
*closed Saturday lunch, Sunday, 1 week Christmas and Bank Holidays* – **Meals** 17.00/29.50 **t.** 8.95
**Spec.** Chicken and crab boudin with steamed seaweed and lobster velouté. Duckling breast with duck confit and foie gras pie, port wine sauce. Bitter-sweet chocolate "St. Emilion" with crème anglaise.

**Rascasse** (Gueller), Canal Wharf, Water Lane, LS11 5BB, ☎ (0113) 244 6611, *Fax (0113) 244 0736*, ≤, « Converted grain warehouse, canalside setting » – AZ c
*closed Saturday lunch, Sunday, 1 week after Christmas and Bank Holiday Mondays* – **Meals** 17.00/18.00 **t.** and a la carte 21.75/31.25 **t.** 7.00
**Spec.** Marinière of monkfish and calamari, fresh coriander. Papillotes of squab pigeon "Rascasse", essence of ceps. Caramelised lemon tart, raspberry sorbet.

**Leodis,** Victoria Mill, Sovereign St., LS1 4BJ, ☎ (0113) 242 1010, *Fax (0113) 243 0432*, « Converted riverside warehouse » – AZ e
*closed Saturday lunch, Sunday, 25-26 December and 1 January* – **Meals** 13.95 **t.** and a la carte 15.90/25.30 **t.** 6.45.

**Brasserie Forty Four** (at 42 The Calls H.), 44 The Calls, LS2 7EW, ☎ (0113) 234 3232, *Fax (0113) 234 3332* – DZ z
*closed Saturday lunch, Sunday, 1 week Christmas and Bank Holidays* – **Meals** 11.95 **t.** (lunch) and dinner a la carte 17.35/21.90 **t.** 7.70.

XX **Fourth Floor** (at Harvey Nichols), 107-111 Briggate, LS1 6AZ, ✆ (0113) 204 8000, *Fax (0113) 204 8080* – ▤. MC AE ① VISA JCB DZ s
*closed dinner Monday to Wednesday, Sunday, 25-26 December and 1 January* – **Meals** a la carte 16.25/26.50 **t.** ▯ 7.50.

XX **Maxi's,** 6 Bingley St., LS3 1LX, *off Kirkstall Rd* ✆ (0113) 244 0552, *Fax (0113) 234 3902,* « Pagoda, ornate decor » – ▤ Ⓟ. MC AE ① VISA AZ a
**Meals** - Chinese (Canton, Peking) - 17.50 **t.** and a la carte.

XX **Lucky Dragon,** Templar Lane, LS2 7LP, ✆ (0113) 245 0520, *Fax (0113) 245 0520* – ▤. MC AE ① VISA JCB DZ u
*closed 25 December* – **Meals** - Chinese (Cantonese) - 15.50 **t.** ▯ 4.75.

X **The Calls Grill,** Calls Landing, 38 The Calls, LS2 7EW, ✆ (0113) 245 3870, *Fax (0113) 243 9035,* « Converted riverside warehouse » – ▤ Ⓟ. MC AE ① VISA
*closed Sunday lunch* – **Meals** (grill rest.) 11.00 **t.** (dinner) and a la carte 13.10/25.95 **t.** ▯ 6.95. DZ c

X **Sous le nez en ville,** Quebec House, Quebec St., LS1 2HA, ✆ (0113) 244 0108, *Fax (0113) 245 0240* – MC AE VISA CZ a
*closed Sunday, 25-26 December and Bank Holidays* – **Meals** 14.95 **st.** (dinner) and a la carte 17.40/24.15 ▯ 5.75.

**at Seacroft** *NE : 5 ½ m. at junction of A 64 with A 6120* – BZ – ✉ *Leeds :*

Stakis Leeds, Ring Rd, LS14 5QF, ✆ (0113) 273 2323, *Fax (0113) 232 3018* – |‡|, ⇚ rm, TV ☎ Ⓟ – 🏛 250
**100 rm.**

**at Garforth** *E : 6 m. by A 63 at junction with A 642* – BZ – ✉ *Leeds :*

Hilton National, Wakefield Rd, LS25 1LH, ✆ (0113) 286 6556, *Fax (0113) 286 8326,* Fō, ≘s, ▣ – ⇚ rm, ▤ rest, TV ☎ ♿ Ⓟ – 🏛 350
**144 rm.**

XX **Aagrah,** Aberford Rd, LS25 1BA, *on A 642* ✆ (0113) 287 6606 – Ⓟ. MC AE VISA
*closed 25 December* – **Meals** - Indian - (dinner only) a la carte 10.80/16.30 **t.**

**at Pudsey** *W : 5 ¾ m. by A 647* – AZ – ✉ *Leeds :*

XX **Aagrah,** 483 Bradford Rd, LS28 8ED, *on A 647* ✆ (01274) 668818, *Fax (01274) 669803* – Ⓟ. MC AE VISA
*closed 25 December* – **Meals** - Indian - (dinner only) a la carte 10.80/16.30 **t.**

**at Horsforth** *NW : 5 m. by A 65* – AZ – *off A 6120* – ✉ *Leeds :*

X **Paris,** Calverley Bridge, Calverley Lane, Rodley, LS13 1NP, *SW : 1 m. by A 6120* ✆ (0113) 258 1885, *Fax (0113) 239 0651* – ▤ Ⓟ – 🏛 40. MC AE ① VISA
*closed Saturday lunch and 26 December* – **Meals** 11.95 **t.** and a la carte ▯ 6.00.

**at Bramhope** *NW : 8 m. on A 660* – AY – ✉ *Leeds :*

**Forte Posthouse Leeds/Bradford,** Leeds Rd, LS16 9JJ, ✆ (0113) 284 2911, *Fax (0113) 284 3451,* ≤, Fō, ≘s, ▣, ⛱, *park* – |‡|, ⇚ rm, TV ☎ Ⓟ – 🏛 160. MC AE ① VISA
**Meals** a la carte 9.95/24.55 **st.** ▯ 6.95 – ☕ 10.95 – **123 rm** 89.00 **st.**, 1 suite – SB.

**Jarvis Parkway H. and Country Club,** Otley Rd, LS16 8AG, *S : 2 m. on A 660* ✆ (0113) 267 2551, *Fax (0113) 267 4410,* Fō, ≘s, ▣, ⛱, 🎾 – |‡|, ⇚ rm, TV ☎ ♿ Ⓟ – 🏛 300. MC AE ① VISA
**Meals** 13.50/16.80 **t.** and dinner a la carte ▯ 6.00 – ☕ 10.50 – **105 rm** 99.00/109.00 **st.** – SB.

---

**LIVERPOOL** *Mersey.* 402 403 L 23 **Great Britain G.** – *pop. 481 786.*

See : *City★ - Walker Art Gallery★★* DY **M2** – *Liverpool Cathedral★★ (Lady Chapel★)* EZ – *Metropolitan Cathedral of Christ the King★★* EY – *Albert Dock★* CZ *(Merseyside Maritime Museum★ AC* **M1** *- Tate Gallery Liverpool★).*

Exc. : *Speke Hall★ AC , SE : 8 m. by A 561.*

18, 9 *Allerton Municipal, Allerton Rd ✆ (0151) 428 1046* – 18 *Liverpool Municipal, Ingoe Lane, Kirkby ✆ (0151) 546 5435* – 9 *Bowring, Bowring Park, Roby Rd, Huyton ✆ (0151) 489 1901.*

*Mersey Tunnels (toll).*

✈ *Liverpool Airport : ✆ (0151) 486 8877, SE : 6 m. by A 561* – **Terminal :** *Pier Head.*

⛴ *to Isle of Man (Douglas) (Isle of Man Steam Packet Co. Ltd) 1-2 weekly (4 h) – to Northern Ireland (Belfast) (Norse Irish Ferries Ltd) weekly (11 h).*

⛴ *to Birkenhead (Mersey Ferries) – to Wallasey (Mersey Ferries).*

ℹ *Merseyside Welcome Centre, Clayton Square Shopping Centre, L1 1QR ✆ (0151) 709 3631 – Atlantic Pavilion, Albert Dock, L3 4AE ✆ (0151) 708 8854.*

*London 219 – Birmingham 103 – Leeds 75 – Manchester 35.*

# LIVERPOOL
## CENTRE

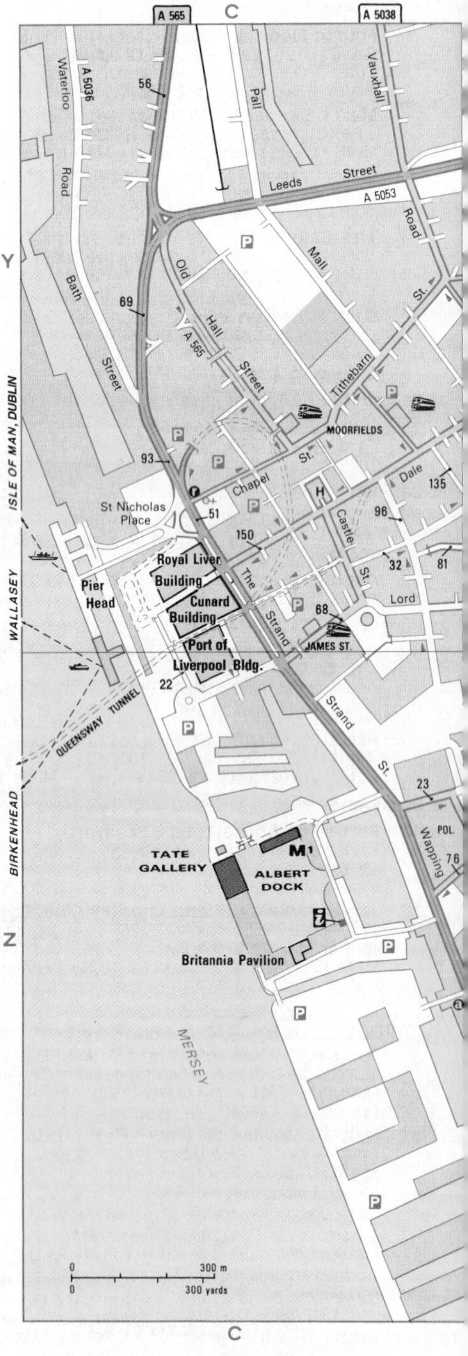

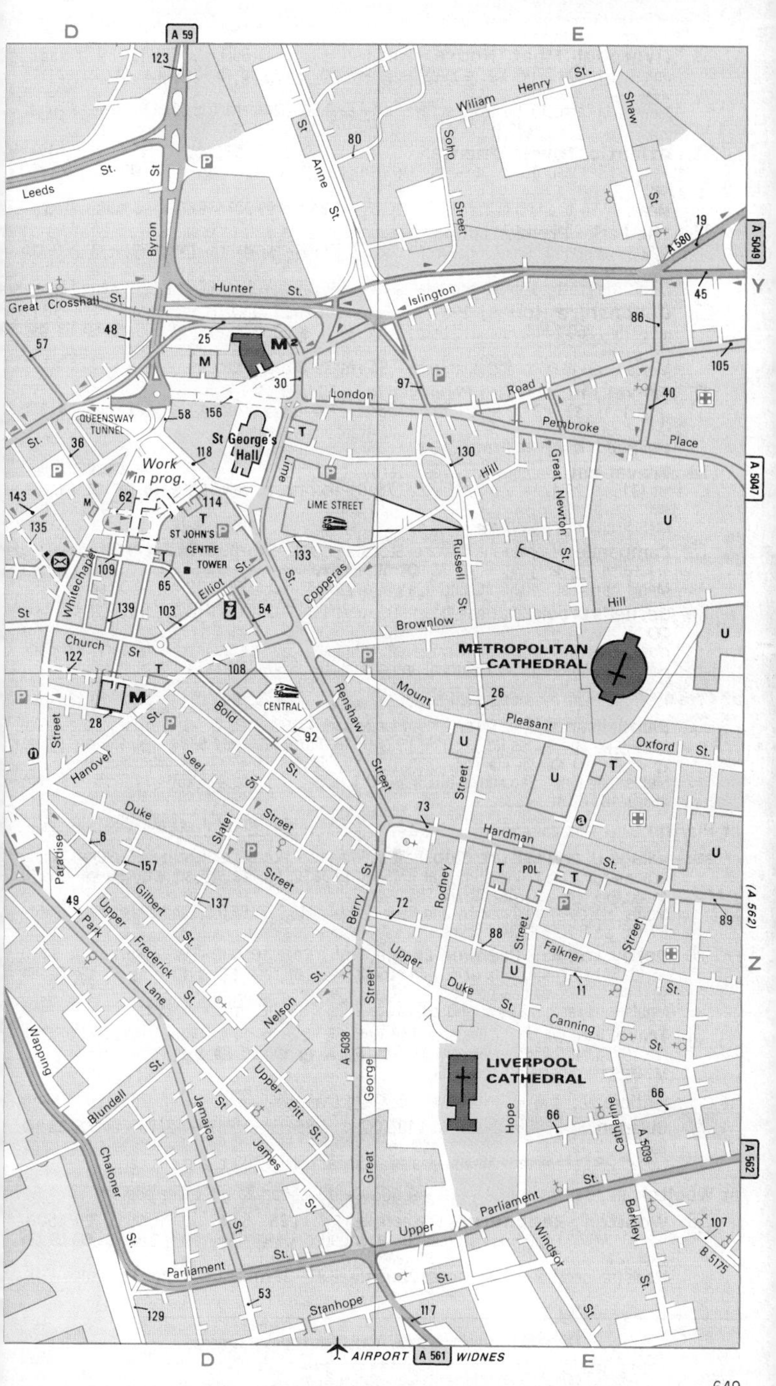

D
A 59
E
St George's Hall
LIME STREET
ST JOHN'S CENTRE TOWER
METROPOLITAN CATHEDRAL
CENTRAL
LIVERPOOL CATHEDRAL
QUEENSWAY TUNNEL
Work in prog.
A 5049
A 5047
A 562
A 5038
A 5039
A 580
B 5175
Y
Z
AIRPORT
A 561
WIDNES

**Liverpool Moat House,** Paradise St., L1 8JD, ℘ (0151) 471 9988, *Fax (0151) 709 2706*, Ⓕ, ≘, ☒ – |♦|, ⇔ rm, ▤ TV ☎ Ⓟ – 🔺 400. MC AE ⓞ VISA JCB DZ n
Meals a la carte 15.95/23.40 **st.** 🌡 5.95 – ☕ 9.50 – **244 rm** 105.00/125.00 **st.**, 7 suites – SB.

**Atlantic Tower Thistle,** 30 Chapel St., L3 9RE, ℘ (0151) 227 4444, *Fax (0151) 236 3973*, ← – |♦|, ⇔ rm, ▤ TV ☎ Ⓟ – 🔺 100. MC AE ⓞ VISA. ✻ CY r
Meals 17.50 **t.** and a la carte – ☕ 10.25 – **223 rm** 99.00/119.00 **st.**, 3 suites – SB.

**The Park - Premier Lodge,** Dunningsbridge Rd, L30 6YN, N : 6 ¾ m. by A 59 on A 5036 ℘ (0151) 525 7555, *Fax (0151) 525 2481* – |♦|, ⇔ rm, TV ☎ Ⓟ – 🔺 200. MC AE ⓞ VISA. ✻
Meals (grill rest.) 6.55 **st.** and a la carte 🌡 3.95 – ☕ 6.95 – **60 rm** 42.25 **st.** – SB.

**Devonshire House,** 293-297 Edge Lane, L7 9LD, E : 2 ¼ m. on A 5047 ℘ (0151) 260 2414, *Fax (0151) 263 2109*, ⚘ – |♦| TV ☎ ♿ Ⓟ – 🔺 300. MC AE ⓞ VISA. ✻
Meals 8.95/16.00 **t.** and a la carte – **54 rm** ☕ 80.00/100.00 **t.**

**Travel Inn,** Northern Perimeter Rd, L30 7PT, N : 6 m. by A 59 on A 5036 ℘ (0151) 531 1497, *Fax (0151) 520 1842* – ⇔ rm, ▤ rest, TV ♿ Ⓟ. MC AE ⓞ VISA. ✻
Meals (grill rest.) – **43 rm** 36.50 **t.**

**Travel Inn,** Queens Dr., West Derby, L13 0DL, E : 4 m. on A 5058 (Ringroad) ℘ (0151) 228 4724, *Fax (0151) 220 7610* – ⇔ rm, ▤ rest, TV ♿ Ⓟ. MC AE ⓞ VISA. ✻ by A 5049 EY
Meals (grill rest.) – **40 rm** 36.50 **t.**

**Campanile,** Wapping and Chaloner St., L3 4AJ, ℘ (0151) 709 8104, *Fax (0151) 709 8725* – ⇔ rm, TV ☎ ♿ Ⓟ – 🔺 30. MC AE ⓞ VISA CZ a
Meals (grill rest.) 10.55 **st.** and a la carte 🌡 5.25 – ☕ 4.50 – **78 rm** 38.00 **st.**

**Becher's Brook,** 29a Hope St., L1 9BQ, ℘ (0151) 707 0005, *Fax (0151) 708 7011* – ⇔. MC AE VISA EZ a
*closed Saturday lunch, Sunday, 2 to 9 August, 25-26 December, 1 January and Bank Holidays* – **Meals** 16.50 **t.** (lunch) and a la carte 23.50/28.00 **t.** 🌡 9.00.

**at Crosby** *N : 5 ½ m. by A 565 – CY :*

**Blundellsands,** The Serpentine, Blundellsands, L23 6YB, W : 1 ¼ m. via College Rd, Mersey Rd and Agnes Rd ℘ (0151) 924 6515, *Fax (0151) 931 5364* – |♦|, ⇔ rm, TV ☎ Ⓟ – 🔺 250. MC AE ⓞ VISA
**Meals** (bar lunch Saturday) 10.25/14.50 **t.** and a la carte 🌡 5.25 – ☕ 7.95 – **37 rm** 45.00/100.00 **st.** – SB.

**at Huyton** *E : 8 ¼ m. by A5047 – EY – and A 5080 on B 5199 – ✉ Liverpool :*

**Village H. and Leisure Club,** Fallows Way, L35 1RZ, SE : 3 ¼ m. by A 5080 off Windy Arbor Rd ℘ (0151) 449 2341, *Fax (0151) 449 3832*, Ⓕ, ≘, ☒, squash – |♦|, ⇔ rm, TV ☎ ♿ Ⓟ – 🔺 250. MC AE ⓞ VISA. ✻
**Meals** *(closed lunch Saturday and Bank Holidays)* 15.95/18.50 **st.** and a la carte 🌡 6.25 – **62 rm** ☕ 84.00/110.00 **st.**

**Derby Lodge - Premier Lodge,** Roby Rd, L36 4HD, SW : 1 m. on A 5080 ℘ (0151) 480 4440, *Fax (0151) 443 0932*, ⚘ – ▤ rest, TV ☎ Ⓟ – 🔺 35. MC AE ⓞ VISA. ✻
**Meals** (grill rest.) 12.95 **t.** and a la carte – ☕ 4.95 – **8 rm** ☕ 44.25 **t.**

**Travel Inn,** Wilson Rd, Tarbock, L36 6AD, SE : 2 ¼ m. on A 5080 ℘ (0151) 480 9614, *Fax (0151) 480 9361* – ⇔ rm, ▤ rest, TV ♿ Ⓟ. MC AE ⓞ VISA. ✻
**Meals** (grill rest.) – **40 rm** 36.50 **t.**

**at Grassendale** *SE : 4 ½ m. on A 561 – EZ – ✉ Liverpool :*

**Gulshan,** 544-548 Aigburth Rd, L19 3QG, *on A 561* ℘ (0151) 427 2273 – ▤. MC AE ⓞ VISA
*closed 25 December* – **Meals** - Indian - (dinner only) 16.00 **t.** and a la carte.

**at Woolton** *SE : 6 m. by A 562 – EZ –, A 5058 and Woolton Rd – ✉ Liverpool :*

**Woolton Redbourne,** Acrefield Rd, L25 5JN, ℘ (0151) 421 1500, *Fax (0151) 421 1501*, « Victorian house, antiques », ⚘ – ⇔ rest, TV ☎ Ⓟ. MC AE ⓞ VISA JCB
**Meals** (residents only) (dinner only) 22.95 **t.** 🌡 6.95 – **25 rm** ☕ 63.00/92.00 **t.**, 1 suite – SB.

Do not use yesterday's maps for today's journey.

**MANCHESTER** *Gtr. Manchester* 402 403 404 N 23 **Great Britain G.** – *pop. 402 889.*

**See** : *City★ – Castlefield Heritage Park★* CZ – *Town Hall★* CZ – *City Art Gallery★* CZ **M²** – *Cathedral★ (Stalls and Canopies★)* CY.

*Heaton Park, Prestwick* ☎ *(0161) 798 0295 – Houldsworth Park, Houldsworth St., Reddish, Stockport* ☎ *(0161) 442 9611 – Chorlton-cum-Hardy, Barlow Hall, Barlow Hall Rd* ☎ *(0161) 881 3139 – William Wroe, Pennybridge Lane, Flixton* ☎ *(0161) 748 8680.*

*Manchester International Airport :* ☎ *(0161) 489 3000, S : 10 m. by A 5103 and M 56* – **Terminal** : *Coach service from Victoria Station.*

*Manchester Visitor Centre, Town Hall Extension, Lloyd St., M60 2LA* ☎ *(0161) 234 3157/8 – Manchester Airport, International Arrivals Hall, Terminal T1, M90 3NY* ☎ *(0161) 436 3344.*

*Manchester Airport, International Arrivals Hall, Terminal 2, M90 4TU* ☎ *(0161) 489 6412.*

*London 202 – Birmingham 86 – Glasgow 221 – Leeds 43 – Liverpool 35 – Nottingham 72.*

**Victoria and Albert,** Water St., M3 4JQ, ☎ (0161) 832 1188, *Fax (0161) 834 2484,* « Converted 19C warehouse, television themed interior », – rm, 300. VISA. by Quay St. CZ
***Cafe Maigret*** **:** **Meals** a la carte 17.50/31.50 **t.** 10.50 – (see also ***Sherlock Holmes*** below) – 10.50 – **152 rm** 149.00 **st.**, 4 suites – SB.

**Holiday Inn Crowne Plaza Midland,** Peter St., M60 2DS, ☎ (0161) 236 3333, *Fax (0161) 932 4100,* *squash* – rm, – 600. VISA JCB. CZ x
***French rest.*** **: Meals** (dinner only) 32.50 **t.** and a la carte – ***Trafford Room*** **: Meals** *(closed Saturday lunch)* (carving rest.) 18.95 **t.** and a la carte – 11.95 – **296 rm** 150.00/170.00 **t.**, 7 suites – SB.

**Ramada,** Blackfriars St., Deansgate, M3 2EQ, ☎ (0161) 835 2555, *Fax (0161) 835 3077* – rm, rest, – 400. VISA JCB. CY v
**Meals** 12.50/19.50 **st.** and a la carte – 10.50 – **195 rm** 128.00 **st.**, 5 suites.

**Palace,** Oxford St., M60 7HA, ☎ (0161) 288 1111, *Fax (0161) 288 2222,* « Victorian Gothic architecture, former Refuge Assurance building » – – 850. VISA CZ s
***Waterhouses*** **: Meals** *(closed lunch Saturday and Sunday)* 14.95/16.95 **t.** and dinner a la carte 5.95 – 10.50 – **169 rm** 109.00/149.00 **st.**, 13 suites – SB.

**Copthorne Manchester,** Clippers Quay, Salford Quays, M5 2XP, ☎ (0161) 873 7321, *Fax (0161) 873 7318,* – rm, rest, – 150. VISA. by A 56 CZ
***Chandlers*** **: Meals** 17.50/19.50 **st.** and a la carte 9.50 – 11.95 – **166 rm** 140.00/175.00 **st.**

**Portland Thistle,** 3-5 Portland St., Piccadilly Gdns., M1 6DP, ☎ (0161) 228 3400, *Fax (0161) 228 6347,* – rm, – 300. VISA CZ a
***Winston's*** **: Meals** 16.45/20.45 **st.** and a la carte 6.95 – 11.25 – **204 rm** 108.00/143.00 **st.**, 1 suite – SB.

**Castlefield,** Liverpool Rd, M3 4JR, ☎ (0161) 832 7073, *Fax (0161) 839 0326,* – rest, – 60. VISA. by Quay St. CZ
*closed 25 and 26 December* – **Meals** (bar lunch)/dinner 14.95 **t.** and a la carte 4.45 – **48 rm** 74.00/80.00 **t.** – SB.

**Campanile,** 55 Ordsall Lane, M5 4RS, *by A 56 off A 57* ☎ (0161) 833 1845, *Fax (0161) 833 1847* – – 60. VISA JCB
**Meals** 10.55 **st.** and a la carte 4.95 – 4.50 – **105 rm** 38.00.

**Comfort Friendly Inn,** Birch St., Hyde Rd, West Gorton, M12 5NT, *SE : 2 ½ m. by A 57* ☎ (0161) 220 8700, *Fax (0161) 220 8848* – – 100. VISA
**Meals** (bar lunch)/dinner 9.75 **st.** and a la carte 4.50 – 5.75 – **90 rm** 38.50 **st.** – SB.

**Travel Inn,** Basin 8, The Quays, Salford Quays, M5 4SQ, ☎ (0161) 872 4026, *Fax (0161) 876 0094* – rm, VISA.
**Meals** (grill rest.) – **52 rm** 36.50 **t.**

**Sherlock Holmes** (at Victoria and Albert H.), Water St., M3 4JQ, ☎ (0161) 832 1188, *Fax (0161) 832 2484* – VISA by Quay St. CZ
**Meals** *(closed Sunday)* 18.00/34.00 **t.** and dinner a la carte 10.95.

**Simply Heathcotes,** Jackson Row, M2 5WB, ☎ (0161) 835 3536, *Fax (0161) 835 3534* – VISA JCB CZ c
*closed 25-26 December, 1 January and Bank Holidays* – **Meals** 11.50/17.50 **t.** and a la carte 21.50/26.50 **t.** 6.50.

**Air,** 40 Chorlton St., M1 3HW, ☎ (0161) 661 1111, *Fax (0161) 661 1112* – VISA CZ e
*closed lunch July and August, Sunday, 25-26 December, 1 January and Easter Sunday* – **Meals** a la carte 21.90/27.40 **t.**

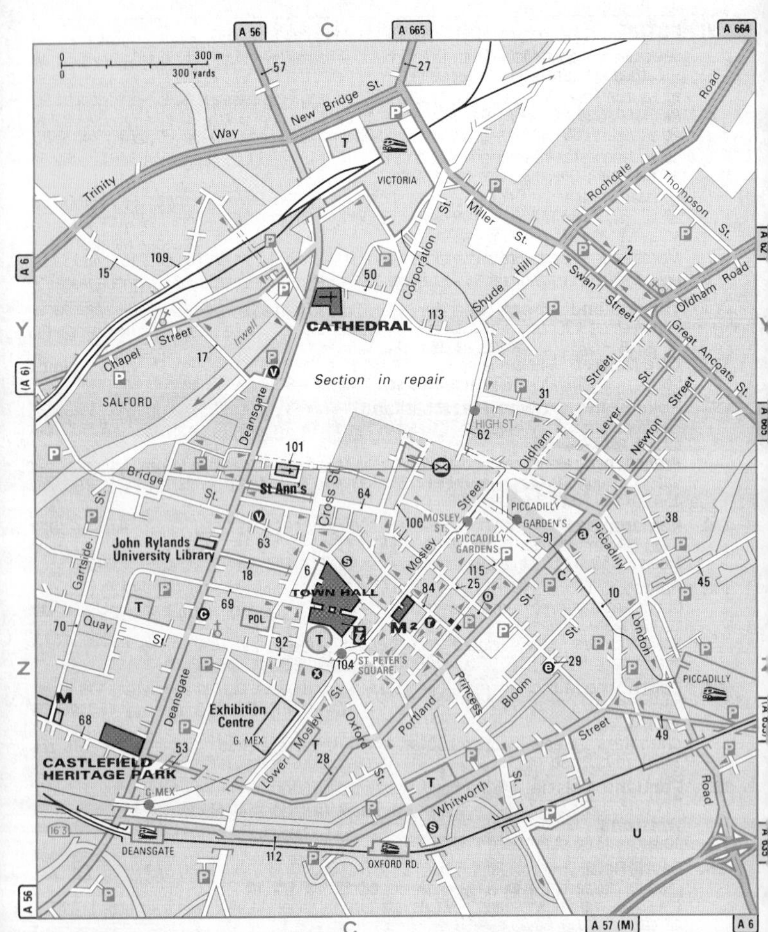


## MANCHESTER CENTRE

Deansgate . . . . . . . . . . . . CYZ
Lower Mosley Street . . . . . CZ
Mosley Street . . . . . . . . . . CZ
Princess Street . . . . . . . . . CZ

Addington Street . . . . . . . . CY 2
Albert Square . . . . . . . . . . CZ 6
Aytoun Street . . . . . . . . . . CZ 10
Blackfriars Road . . . . . . . . CY 15
Blackfriars Street . . . . . . . CY 17
Brazennose Street . . . . . . . CZ 18
Charlotte Street . . . . . . . . CZ 25
Cheetham Hill Road . . . . . . CY 27
Chepstow Street . . . . . . . . CZ 28
Chorlton Street . . . . . . . . . CZ 29
Church Street . . . . . . . . . . CY 31
Dale Street . . . . . . . . . . . . CZ 38
Ducie Street . . . . . . . . . . . CZ 45
Fairfield Street . . . . . . . . . CZ 49
Fennel Street . . . . . . . . . . CY 50
Great Bridgewater Street . . CZ 53
Great Ducie Street . . . . . . . CY 57
High Street . . . . . . . . . . . . CY 62
John Dalton Street . . . . . . . CZ 63
King Street . . . . . . . . . . . . CZ 64
Liverpool Road . . . . . . . . . CZ 68
Lloyd Street . . . . . . . . . . . CZ 69
Lower Byrom St. . . . . . . . . CZ 70
Nicholas Street . . . . . . . . . CZ 84
Parker Street . . . . . . . . . . CZ 91
Peter Street . . . . . . . . . . . CZ 92
St. Ann's Street . . . . . . . . CY 101
St. Peter's Square . . . . . . . CZ 104
Spring Gardens . . . . . . . . . CZ 106
Viaduct Street . . . . . . . . . . CY 109
Whitworth Street West . . . CZ 112
Withy Grove . . . . . . . . . . . CY 113
York Street . . . . . . . . . . . . CZ 115

XX **Brasserie St Pierre,** 57-63 Princess St., M2 4EQ, ☎ (0161) 228 0231, *Fax (0161) 228 0231* – MC AE VISA CZ s
*closed Saturday lunch, Monday dinner, Sunday and 24 December-2 January* – **Meals** 13.95 **t.** and a la carte.

XX **Est, Est, Est,** 5 Ridgefield, M2 6EG, ☎ (0161) 833 9400 – ▤ rest. MC AE O VISA JCB
*closed 25 and 26 December* – **Meals** - Italian - a la carte 10.50/17.50 ♁ 4.80. CZ v

XX **Giulio's Terrazza,** 14 Nicholas St., M1 4EJ, ☎ (0161) 236 4033, *Fax (0161) 228 6501* – ▤. MC AE O VISA JCB – *closed Sunday, 25 December and Bank Holidays* – **Meals** - Italian - 9.50/12.50 **t.** and a la carte ♁ 5.80. CZ r

**Koreana,** Kings House, 40a King St. West, M3 2WY, ☎ (0161) 832 4330, *Fax (0161) 832 2293* – MC AE D VISA CZ z
*closed lunch Saturday and Bank Holidays, Sunday and 1 week Christmas* – **Meals** - Korean - 5.50/13.50 **t.** and a la carte.

**Royal Orchid,** 36 Charlotte St., M1 4FD, ☎ (0161) 236 5183, *Fax (0161) 236 8830* – MC AE D VISA CZ o
*closed lunch Monday and Saturday, Sunday and 25-26 December* – **Meals** - Thai - 8.50 **t.** (lunch) and a la carte 12.25/19.70 **t.** 4.50.

**Market,** 104 High St., M4 1HQ, ☎ (0161) 834 3743, *Fax (0161) 834 3743* – MC AE D VISA JCB CY o
*closed Sunday to Tuesday, 1 week Easter, August and 1 week Christmas* – **Meals** - Bistro - (dinner only) a la carte 16.85/24.35 **t.** 4.95.

**Mash,** 40 Chorlton St., M1 3HW, ☎ (0161) 661 6161, *Fax (0161) 661 6060* – ▤. MC AE VISA CZ e
*closed Easter Sunday, 25-26 December and 1 January* – **Meals** a la carte 13.50/20.50 **t.**

**at Northenden** *S : 5 ¼ m. by A 57 (M) – CZ – and A 5103 – ✉ Manchester :*

**Forte Posthouse Manchester,** Palatine Rd, M22 4FH, ☎ (0161) 998 7090, *Fax (0161) 946 0139* – |‡|, ⇔ rm, TV ☎ P – 150. MC AE D VISA JCB
*closed 24 December-3 January* – **Meals** (bar lunch Saturday and Sunday) a la carte 17.75/26.20 **st.** 7.25 – ☕ 8.95 – **190 rm** 69.00 **st.** – SB.

**at Manchester Airport** *S : 9 m. by Lower Mosley St. – CZ – and A 5103 off M 56 – ✉ Manchester :*

**Manchester Airport Hilton,** Outwood Lane (Terminal One), M90 4WP, ☎ (0161) 435 3000, *Fax (0161) 435 3040*, Fδ, ≘s, ⊠ – |‡|, ⇔ rm, ▤ TV ☎ ♿ P – 300. MC AE D VISA JCB. ✻
**Meals** 18.50 **t.** (lunch) and a la carte 23.20/28.45 **t.** 10.50 – ***Portico* : Meals** *(closed Sunday and Bank Holidays)* (dinner only) 29.00 **t.** 11.50 – ☕ 13.95 – **222 rm** 150.00/210.00 **st.**, 1 suite – SB.

**Forte Posthouse Manchester Airport,** Outwood Lane (Terminal One), M90 3NS, ☎ (0161) 437 5811, *Fax (0161) 436 2340*, Fδ, ≘s, ⊠ – |‡|, ⇔ rm, ▤ TV ☎ P – 75. MC AE D VISA JCB. ✻
**Meals** (bar lunch Monday to Saturday)/dinner 12.95 **t.** and a la carte – ☕ 10.95 – **284 rm** 89.00/129.00 **st.**, 1 suite – SB.

**Etrop Grange,** Thorley Lane, M90 4EG, ☎ (0161) 499 0500, *Fax (0161) 499 0790* – ⇔ rm, TV ☎ ♿ P – 40. MC AE D VISA JCB
**Meals** *(closed Saturday lunch)* 17.50/30.00 **st.** 7.50 – ☕ 10.75 – **37 rm** 110.00/160.00 **st.**, 2 suites – SB.

**Holiday Inn Garden Court,** Outwood Lane (Terminal One), M90 4HL, ☎ (0161) 498 0333, *Fax (0161) 498 0222* – |‡|, ⇔ rm, TV ☎ ♿ P. MC AE D VISA JCB. ✻
**Meals** *(closed lunch Saturday and Sunday)* (bar lunch)/dinner 14.00 **st.** and a la carte – ☕ 5.95 – **163 rm** 57.00 **st.**

**Moss Nook,** Ringway Rd, Moss Nook, M22 5WD, ☎ (0161) 437 4778, *Fax (0161) 498 8089* – P. MC AE D VISA
*closed Saturday lunch, Sunday, Monday and 2 weeks Christmas* – **Meals** 16.95/29.95 **t.** and a la carte 7.00.

**at Worsley** *W : 7 ¼ m. by A 6 – CY –, A 5063, M 602 and M 62 (eastbound) on A 572 – ✉ Manchester :*

**Novotel Manchester West,** Worsley Brow, M28 2YA, at junction 13 of M 62 ☎ (0161) 799 3535, *Fax (0161) 703 8207*, ⛱ heated – |‡|, ⇔ rm, ▤ rest, TV ☎ ♿ P – 220. MC AE D VISA
**Meals** 16.00 **st.** and a la carte 5.35 – ☕ 8.95 – **119 rm** 69.00 **st.**

**Tung Fong,** 2 Worsley Rd, M28 4NL, *on A 572* ☎ (0161) 794 5331, *Fax (0161) 727 9598* – ▤. MC AE VISA
*closed lunch Saturday and Sunday* – **Meals** - Chinese (Peking) - 5.90/15.50 **st.** and a la carte.

**at Pendlebury** *NW : 4 m. by A 6 – CY – on A 666 – ✉ Manchester :*

**Henry Boddington,** 219 Bolton Rd, M27 8TG, ☎ (0161) 736 5143, *Fax (0161) 737 2786* – TV ☎ ♿ P. MC AE D VISA. ✻
**Meals** (grill rest.) 6.55 **t.** and a la carte – ☕ 4.95 – **30 rm** 44.25 **t.**

**at Swinton** *NW : 4 m. by A 6 – CY –, A 580 and A 572 on B 5231 – ✉ Manchester :*

**New Ellesmere - Premier Lodge,** East Lancs Rd, M27 8AA, SW : ½ m. on A 580 ☎ (0161) 728 2791, *Fax (0161) 794 8222* – ⇔ rm, TV ☎ ♿ P. MC AE D VISA. ✻
**Meals** (grill rest.) a la carte 8.55/14.30 **st.** 4.25 – ☕ 4.95 – **27 rm** 44.25 **st.**

# *Calendar of main tradefairs and other international events in 1998*

## *AUSTRIA*

| | | |
|---|---|---|
| ***Vienna*** | *Wiener Festwochen* | *8 May to 14 June* |
| ***Salzburg*** | *Salzburg Festival (Festspiele)* | *4 to 13 April*<br>*24 July to 30 August* |

## *BENELUX*

| | | |
|---|---|---|
| ***Amsterdam*** | *Holland Festival* | *June* |
| ***Bruges*** | *Ascension Day Procession* | *Ascension* |
| ***Brussels*** | *Guild Procession (Ommegang)* | *first Thursday of July and the previous Tuesday* |
| | *Holiday and Leisure Activities International Show* | *Late March 99* |
| | *Belgian Antique Dealers Fair* | *Late Jan. to early Feb. 99* |
| | *Eurantica (Antiques Show)* | *Late March 99* |

## *CZECH REPUBLIC*

| | | |
|---|---|---|
| ***Prague*** | *Prague's Spring International Music Festival* | *3 to 14 May* |

## *DENMARK*

| | | |
|---|---|---|
| ***Copenhagen*** | *International Fashion Fair* | *9 to 11 August* |
| | *Scandinavian Furniture Fair* | *26 to 30 August* |

## *FINLAND*

| | | |
|---|---|---|
| ***Helsinki*** | *International Horse Show* | *15 to 19 April* |
| | *International Fashion Fair* | *21 to 23 August* |
| | *Helsinki Festival* | *21 August to 6 Sept.* |
| | *Helsinki Motor Show* | *11 to 13 December* |

## *FRANCE*

| | | |
|---|---|---|
| ***Paris*** | *Paris Fair* | *29 April to 10 May* |
| | *Mondial Automobile* | *1 to 11 October* |
| ***Cannes*** | *International Film Festival* | *13 to 24 May* |
| ***Lyons*** | *Lyons Fair* | *Late March 99* |
| ***Marseilles*** | *Marseilles Fair* | *25 Sept. to 5 Oct.* |

## *GERMANY*

| | | |
|---|---|---|
| ***Berlin*** | *Berlin Fair (Grüne Woche)* | *16 to 25 January* |
| ***Frankfurt*** | *International Fair* | *14 to 18 February*<br>*29 August to 2 Sept.* |
| | *Frankfurt Book Fair* | *7 to 12 October* |
| ***Hanover*** | *Hanover Fair* | *20 to 25 April* |
| ***Leipzig*** | *International Book Fair* | *26 to 29 March* |
| ***Munich*** | *Beer Festival (Oktoberfest)* | *19 Sept. to 4 Oct.* |

## *GREECE*

| | | |
|---|---|---|
| ***Athens*** | *Athens Festival* | *June to Sept.* |

## *HUNGARY*

| | | |
|---|---|---|
| ***Budapest*** | *Spring Festival (Music, Arts)* | *13 to 29 March* |
| | *Travel 98 (International Tourism Exhibition)* | *26 to 29 March* |
| | *International Jazz Festival* | *4 and 5 July* |
| | *International Fashion Fair* | *30 August to 1 Sept.* |
| | *International Wine Festival* | *8 to 13 Sept.* |
| | *International Motor Exhibition* | *29 Sept. to 4 Oct.* |

## *IRELAND*

| | | |
|---|---|---|
| ***Dublin*** | *Dublin Horse Show* | *first week August* |

## *ITALY*

| | | |
|---|---|---|
| ***Milan*** | *Bit (International Tourism Exchange)* | *25 February to 1 March* |
| | *Fashion Fair (Moda Milano)* | *27 February to 3 March*<br>*2 to 10 October* |
| | *SMAU (International Exhibition of Information and Communication Technology)* | *22 to 26 October* |
| ***Florence*** | *Pitti Bimbo* | *19 to 21 June* |
| | *Fashion Fair (Pitti Immagine Uomo)* | *25 to 28 June* |
| ***Turin*** | *International Car Exhibition* | *24 April to 3 May* |
| | *International Book Fair* | *21 to 25 May* |
| ***Venice*** | *International Film Festival* | *27 August to 6 September* |
| | *The Carnival* | *31 January to 11 February 99* |

## *NORWAY*

| | | |
|---|---|---|
| ***Oslo*** | *Fashion Fair* | *14 to 16 August and*<br>*12 to 14 February 99* |

## *POLAND*

| | | |
|---|---|---|
| **Warsaw** | *International Book Fair* | *14 to 19 May* |
| | *Mozart Festival* | *15 June to 26 July* |
| | *Jazz Jamboree* | *October* |

## *PORTUGAL*

| | | |
|---|---|---|
| **Lisbon** | *Antiques Fair* | *18 to 26 April* |
| | *International Handicraft Exhibition* | *4 to 12 July* |

## *SPAIN*

| | | |
|---|---|---|
| **Madrid** | *Fitur* | *28 Jan. to 1 Feb.* |
| | *International Fashion Week* | *10 to 15 Feb.* |
| | *Feriarte* | *21 to 29 Nov.* |
| **Barcelona** | *Fashion Barcelona* | *31 Jan. to 2 Feb.* |
| | *International Exhibition of the Components and Maintenance Equipment for the Motor Trade* | *17 to 20 April* |
| **Sevilla** | *April Fair* | *28 April to 3 May* |
| **Valencia** | *Fallas* | *15 to 19 March* |
| | *International Fair* | *26 Dec. to 3 Jan. 99* |

## *SWEDEN*

| | | |
|---|---|---|
| **Stockholm** | *Stockholm Water Festival* | *7 to 15 August* |
| | *International Fashion Fair* | *28 to 30 August* |
| | *Stockholm Film Festival* | *6 to 15 Nov.* |
| | *International Boat Show* | *28 Febr. to 8 March 99* |
| | *International Art Fair* | *4 to 8 March 99* |
| **Gothenburg** | *International Horse Show* | *2 to 5 April* |
| | *International Book & Library Fair* | *22 to 25 October* |
| | *International Boat Show* | *30 Jan. to 8 February 99* |

## *SWITZERLAND*

| | | |
|---|---|---|
| **Berne** | *BEA : Exhibition for Handicraft, Agriculture, Trade and Industry* | *25 April to 4 May* |
| **Basle** | *European Watch, Clock and Jewellery Fair* | *22 to 29 April* |
| **Geneva** | *International Exhibition of inventions, new technologies and products* | *27 March to 5 April* |
| | *International Fair for travel, languages and cultures* | *29 April to 3 May* |
| | *International Motor Show* | *4 to 14 March 99* |
| **Zürich** | *Züspa : Zurich Autumn Show for Home and Living, Sport and Fashion* | *24 Sept. to 4 Oct.* |

## *UNITED KINGDOM*

| | | |
|---|---|---|
| *London* | *Fine Art and Antiques Fair* | *4 to 14 June* |
| | *International Film Festival* | *5 to 22 Nov.* |
| | *London International Boat Show* | *8 to 17 January 99* |
| | *London International Bookfair* | *28 to 30 March 99* |
| *Birmingham* | *Classic and Sportscar Show* | *2 to 4 May* |
| | *International Motor Show* | *20 Oct. to 1 November* |
| | *Autotech Trade Show* | *10 to 12 November* |
| | *International Motorcycle Show* | *12 to 22 November* |
| | *National Classic Motor Show* | *28 and 29 November* |
| *Edinburgh* | *Arts Festival* | *9 August to 5 Sept.* |
| | *Book Festival* | *15 to 31 August* |
| | *International Film Festival* | *16 to 30 August* |
| *Leeds* | *International Film Festival* | *2 weeks October* |

# *International Dialling Codes*

*When making an international call do not dial the first "0" of the city codes.*

# *Indicatifs Téléphoniques Internationaux*

*Pour les communications internationales, le zéro (0) initial de l'indicatif interurbain n'est pas à chiffrer.*

| from \ to | A | B | CH | CZ | D | DK | E | FIN | F | GB | GR |
|---|---|---|---|---|---|---|---|---|---|---|---|
| **A Austria** | | 0032 | 0041 | 00420 | 0049 | 0045 | 0034 | 00358 | 0033 | 0044 | 0030 |
| **B Belgium** | 0043 | | 0041 | 00420 | 0049 | 0045 | 0034 | 00358 | 0033 | 0044 | 0030 |
| **CH Switzerland** | 0043 | 0032 | | 00420 | 0049 | 0045 | 0034 | 00358 | 0033 | 0044 | 0030 |
| **CZ Czech Republic** | 0043 | 0032 | 0041 | | 0049 | 0045 | 0034 | 00358 | 0033 | 0044 | 0030 |
| **D Germany** | 0043 | 0032 | 0041 | 00420 | | 0045 | 0034 | 00358 | 0033 | 0044 | 0030 |
| **DK Denmark** | 0043 | 0032 | 0041 | 00420 | 0049 | | 0034 | 00358 | 0033 | 0044 | 0030 |
| **E Spain** | 0043 | 0032 | 0041 | 00420 | 0049 | 0045 | | 00358 | 0033 | 0044 | 0030 |
| **FIN Finland** | 0043 | 0032 | 0041 | 00420 | 0049 | 0045 | 0034 | | 0033 | 0044 | 0030 |
| **F France** | 0043 | 0032 | 0041 | 00420 | 0049 | 0045 | 99034 | 00358 | | 0044 | 0030 |
| **GB United Kingdom** | 0043 | 0032 | 0041 | 00420 | 0049 | 0045 | 0034 | 00358 | 0033 | 44 | 0030 |
| **GR Greece** | 0043 | 0032 | 0041 | 00420 | 0049 | 0045 | 0034 | 00358 | 0033 | 0044 | |
| **H Hungary** | 0043 | 0032 | 0041 | 00420 | 0049 | 0045 | 0034 | 00358 | 0033 | 0044 | 0030 |
| **I Italy** | 0043 | 0032 | 0041 | 00420 | 0049 | 0045 | 0034 | 00358 | 0033 | 0044 | 0030 |
| **IRL Ireland** | 0043 | 0032 | 0041 | 00420 | 0049 | 0045 | 0034 | 00358 | 0033 | 0044 | 0030 |
| **J Japan** | 00143 | 00132 | 00141 | 00142 | 0149 | 00145 | 00134 | 001358 | 00133 | 00130 | 0030 |
| **L Luxembourg** | 0043 | 0032 | 0041 | 00420 | 0049 | 0045 | 0034 | 00358 | 0033 | 0044 | 0030 |
| **N Norway** | 0043 | 0032 | 0041 | 00420 | 0049 | 0045 | 0034 | 00358 | 0033 | 0044 | 0030 |
| **NL Netherlands** | 0043 | 0032 | 0041 | 00420 | 0049 | 0045 | 0034 | 00358 | 0033 | 0044 | 0030 |
| **PL Poland** | 0043 | 0032 | 0041 | 00420 | 0049 | 0045 | 0034 | 00358 | 0033 | 0044 | 0030 |
| **P Portugal** | 0043 | 0032 | 0041 | 00420 | 0049 | 0045 | 0034 | 00358 | 0033 | 0044 | 0030 |
| **RUS Russia** | 81043 | 81032 | 81041 | 6420 | 81049 | 81045 | * | 009358 | 81033 | 81044 | * |
| **S Sweden** | 0043 | 0032 | 0041 | 00420 | 0049 | 0045 | 00934 | 00358 | 0033 | 0044 | 0030 |
| **USA** | 1143 | 01132 | 01141 | 011420 | 01149 | 01145 | 01134 | 01358 | 01133 | 01144 | 01130 |

** Direct dialing not possible**  ** Pas de sélection automatique*

# *Internationale Telefon-Vorwahlnummern*

*Bei Auslandsgesprächen bitte die 0 der Ortsnetzkennzahl nicht mitwählen.*

# 国際電話国別番号

| (H) | (I) | (IRL) | (J) | (L) | (N) | (NL) | (PL) | (P) | (RUS) | (S) | (USA) | |
|---|---|---|---|---|---|---|---|---|---|---|---|---|
| 0036 | 0039 | 00353 | 0081 | 00352 | 0047 | 0031 | 0048 | 00351 | 007 | 0046 | 001 | **Austria A** |
| 0036 | 0039 | 00353 | 0081 | 00352 | 0047 | 0031 | 0048 | 00351 | 007 | 0046 | 001 | **Belgium B** |
| 0036 | 0039 | 00353 | 0081 | 00352 | 0047 | 0031 | 0048 | 00351 | 007 | 0046 | 001 | **Switzerland CH** |
| 0036 | 0039 | 00353 | 0081 | 00352 | 0047 | 0031 | 0048 | 00351 | 007 | 0046 | 001 | **Czech Republic CZ** |
| 0036 | 0039 | 00353 | 0081 | 00352 | 0047 | 0031 | 0048 | 00351 | 007 | 0046 | 001 | **Germany D** |
| 0036 | 0039 | 00353 | 0081 | 00352 | 0047 | 0031 | 0048 | 00351 | 007 | 0046 | 001 | **Denmark DK** |
| 0036 | 0039 | 00353 | 0781 | 00352 | 0047 | 0031 | 0048 | 00351 | 077 | 0046 | 071 | **Spain E** |
| 0036 | 0039 | 00353 | 0081 | 00352 | 0047 | 0031 | 0048 | 00351 | 9907 | 0046 | 001 | **Finland FIN** |
| 0036 | 0039 | 00353 | 0081 | 00352 | 0047 | 0031 | 0048 | 00351 | 007 | 0046 | 001 | **France F** |
| 0036 | 0039 | 00353 | 0081 | 00352 | 0047 | 0031 | 0048 | 00351 | 007 | 0046 | 001 | **United Kingdom GB** |
| 0036 | 0039 | 00353 | 0081 | 00352 | 0047 | 0031 | 0048 | 00351 | 007 | 0046 | 001 | **Greece GR** |
| | 0039 | 00353 | 0081 | 00352 | 0047 | 0031 | 0048 | 00351 | 007 | 0046 | 001 | **Hungary H** |
| 0036 | | 00353 | 0081 | 00352 | 0047 | 0031 | 0048 | 00351 | * | 0046 | 001 | **Italy I** |
| 0036 | 0039 | | 0081 | 00352 | 0047 | 0031 | 0048 | 00351 | 007 | 0046 | 001 | **Ireland IRL** |
| 00136 | 00139 | 001353 | | 01352 | 00147 | 00131 | 00148 | 01351 | * | 01146 | 0011 | **Japan J** |
| 0036 | 0039 | 00353 | 0081 | | 0047 | 0031 | 0048 | 00351 | 007 | 0046 | 001 | **Luxembourg L** |
| 0036 | 0039 | 00353 | 0081 | 00352 | | 0031 | 0048 | 00351 | 007 | 0046 | 001 | **Norway N** |
| 0036 | 0039 | 00353 | 0081 | 00352 | 0047 | | 0048 | 00351 | 007 | 0046 | 001 | **Netherlands NL** |
| 0036 | 0039 | 00353 | 0081 | 00352 | 0047 | 0031 | | 00351 | 007 | 0046 | 001 | **Poland PL** |
| 0036 | 0039 | 00353 | 0081 | 00352 | 0047 | 0031 | 0048 | | 007 | 0046 | 001 | **Portugal P** |
| 636 | * | * | * | * | * | 81031 | 648 | * | | * | * | **Russia RUS** |
| 0036 | 0039 | 00353 | 00981 | 00352 | 0047 | 0031 | 0048 | 00935 | 097 | | 0091 | **Sweden S** |
| 01136 | 01139 | 011353 | 01181 | 011352 | 01147 | 01131 | 01148 | * | 011351 | 01146 | | **USA** |

* *Selezione automatica impossibile*

* *Automatische Vorwahl nicht möglich*

# Notes
# Notizen

# Notes
# Notizen

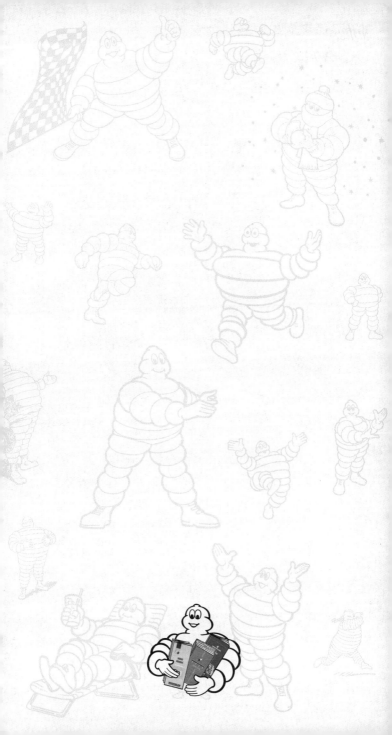

# Notes
# Notizen

*Manufacture française des pneumatiques Michelin*

*Société en commandite par actions au capital de 2 000 000 000 de francs*
*Place des Carmes-Déchaux – 63 Clermont-Ferrand (France)*
*R.C.S. Clermont-Fd B 855 200 507*

**Michelin et Cie, propriétaires-éditeurs, 1998**
*Dépôt légal : mars 98 – ISBN 2.06.070089-2*



*Printed in the EU – 3.1998*
*Photocomposition – Imposition : MAURY Imprimeur S.A., Malesherbes*
*Impression : MAURY Imprimeur S.A., Malesherbes – KAPP LAHURE JOMBART, Evreux*
*Reliure : S.I.R.C., Marigny-le-Châtel*

*Illustrations : Nathalie Benavides, Patricia Haubert, Cécile Imbert/MICHELIN*
*Narratif Systèmes/Genclo p. 62, p. 64, p. 177, p. 281, p. 603*
*Rodolphe Corbel p. 463*